ANIMAL SCIENCE

(Animal Agriculture Series)

ANIMAL SCIENCE

(Animal Agriculture Series)

by

M. E. ENSMINGER, B.S., M.A., PH.D.

Formerly: Assistant Professor in Animal Science
University of Massachusetts

Chairman, Department of Animal Science
Washington State University

Consultant, General Electric Company
Nucleonics Department (Atomic Energy Commission)

Currently: Consultants—Agriservices
Clovis, California

President
Agriservices Foundation

Collaborator
U.S. Department of Agriculture

Distinguished Professor
Wisconsin State University

Sixth Edition

THE INTERSTATE
PRINTERS & PUBLISHERS, INC.
Danville, Illinois

First Edition, 1950
Second Edition, 1951
Third Edition, 1955
Fourth Edition, 1960
Fifth Edition, 1962
Sixth Edition, 1969

Library of Congress
Catalog Card Number
67-15836

Printed in U.S.A.

To the Memory
of my father, the late Jacob Ensminger, who
was my first instructor in animal science
and the best stockman I have ever known,
this book is dedicated.

PREFACE TO THE SIXTH EDITION

Farm animals include beef and dairy cattle, sheep, swine, poultry, and horses. Hence, I have added sections on dairy cattle and poultry to this revision of *Animal Science*, better to serve integrated animal courses and farms.

Also, in this edition, I have attempted to anticipate the country's future food and fiber needs, better to insure that they will be met. We now have over 200,000,000 people in the United States. Population experts say that we shall have 243,400,000 by 1980. We shall also need to feed additional millions of people in the less developed countries. It is predicted that world population will double by the year 2000—that it will total 6 billion by that time.

There will be fewer, but larger, farms. By 1980, it is estimated that there will be fewer than 2 million farms (down from 6,800,000 in 1935; 3,176,000 in 1967) and that they will average over 550 acres in size (up from 350 acres in 1967).

Science and technology will continue to be the great multipliers, making possible increased efficiency of production. In 1966, each farm worker produced enough food and fiber for 33 persons, including himself, plus sufficient exports for 6 persons; by 1975, each farm worker will need to produce enough food and fiber for 43 persons at home, including himself.

Consumers in other countries spend 30 to 60 per cent of their weekly pay check for food, compared to our 18.2 per cent. The average American worker (with earnings of $2.25 per hour) had to toil only 19 minutes to buy 1 pound of beef in 1966; whereas, he had to work 36 minutes in 1929—nearly double the time—to buy 1 pound of beef.

There is every reason to expect that this "food and fiber power" will continue to be generated by American farmers and ranchers. However, in doing so, the business aspects of livestock production will become increasingly important. More capital will be required, and competent management will be in demand. Margins will become smaller, and greater efficiency of production will be essential. Computers will be used extensively. Because of the increasing importance of international trade and communications, we shall gradually change from the U. S. system of weights and measures to the metric system. To facilitate the latter transition, both systems are given in the tabular material in this edition of *Animal Science*.

Of the basic needs of man, none is more important than food and fiber; and the exploding world population accentuates the need for increased production. As long as we eat food and wear clothes, there will always be an agriculture. Indeed, never has there been so much reason to have confidence in, and be optimistic about, the future. The years ahead will be the most rewarding in the history of the livestock industry.

M. E. ENSMINGER

Clovis, California
July, 1969

REFERENCES

The following books are by the same author and publisher as *Animal Science:*

Beef Cattle Science
Sheep and Wool Science
Swine Science
Horses and Horsemanship
The Stockman's Handbook

Each of the books devoted to a specific class of farm animals contains much wider and more complete coverage for the species indicated by name than is possible in *Animal Science*.

The Stockman's Handbook is a modern know-how, show-how book which contains, under one cover, the pertinent things that a stockman needs to know in the daily operation of a farm or ranch. It covers the broad field of animal agriculture, concisely and completely, and, whenever possible, in tabular and outline form.

OTHER SELECTED REFERENCES

Title of Publication	Author(s)	Publisher
Animal Science and Industry	Duane Acker	Prentice-Hall, Englewood Cliffs, N. J., 1964.
Basic Animal Husbandry	J. M. Kays	Prentice-Hall, Englewood Cliffs, N. J., 1958.
Farms & Farmers in an Urban Age	Edward Higbee	The Twentieth Century Fund, New York, N. Y., 1963.
Introduction to Livestock Production	H. H. Cole, *et al.*	W. H. Freeman & Co., San Francisco, Calif., 1966.
Introductory Animal Husbandry	A. L. Anderson	Macmillan Co., New York, N. Y., 1958.
Introductory Animal Science	W. P. Garrigus	J. P. Lippincott Co., Chicago, Ill., 1954.
Livestock and Livestock Products	T. C. Byerly	Prentice-Hall, Englewood Cliffs, N. J., 1964.
Livestock and Poultry Production	C. E. Bundy R. V. Diggins	Prentice-Hall, New York, N. Y., 1954.
Livestock Production	W. H. Peters R. H. Grummer	McGraw-Hill Book Co., New York, N. Y., 1954.
Practical Animal Husbandry	Jack Widmer	Charles Scribner's Sons, New York, N. Y., 1949.
Raising Livestock	W. H. Peters G. P. Deyoe	McGraw-Hill Book Co., New York, N. Y., 1946.
Types and Market Classes of Livestock	H. W. Vaughan	College Book Co., Columbus, Ohio, 1941.

CONTENTS

Chapter   Page

General Sections

   I The Field of Animal Science.. 1
  II Some Principles of Genetics and Animal Breeding............................ 31
 III Feeding Livestock 83
  IV Livestock Buildings and Equipment... 165
   V Animal Health, Disease Prevention, and Parasite Control................. 191
  VI Marketing Livestock 221
 VII Meat and Animal By-products.. 269
VIII Business Aspects of Animal Production... 319

Beef Cattle

  IX The Beef Cattle Industry... 335
   X Types and Breeds of Beef and Dual-Purpose Cattle......................... 361
  XI Establishing the Herd; Selecting and Judging Beef Cattle................ 375
 XII Systems of Beef Production... 391
XIII Breeding Beef Cattle.. 399
 XIV Feeding Beef Cattle.. 423
  XV Marketing and Slaughtering Cattle and Calves................................... 465

Dairy Cattle

  XVI The Dairy Industry... 487
 XVII Breeds of Dairy Cattle... 499
XVIII Establishing the Dairy Herd; Selecting and Judging.......................... 505
  XIX Breeding Dairy Cattle.. 515
   XX Feeding and Management of Dairy Cattle.. 539
  XXI Milk Secretion and Handling... 581
 XXII Marketing Milk and Dairy Products.. 601

Sheep

 XXIII The Sheep and Goat Industry.. 619
  XXIV Types and Breeds of Sheep.. 645
   XXV Establishing the Flock; Selecting and Judging Sheep....................... 661
  XXVI Systems of Sheep Production.. 677
 XXVII Breeding Sheep 683
XXVIII Feeding Sheep 705

Chapter		Page
XXIX	Marketing and Slaughtering Sheep and Lambs	731
XXX	Wool and Mohair	747
XXXI	Goats	779

Swine

XXXII	The Swine Industry	791
XXXIII	Types and Breeds of Swine	805
XXXIV	Establishing the Herd; Selecting and Judging Swine	817
XXXV	Breeding Swine	827
XXXVI	Feeding Swine	851
XXXVII	Marketing and Slaughtering Hogs	887

Poultry

XXXVIII	The Poultry Industry	901
XXXIX	Poultry Breeds and Breeding; Selecting and Culling	919
XL	Poultry Nutrition and Feeding	947
XLI	Poultry Houses and Equipment	985
XLII	Poultry Health, Disease Prevention, and Parasite Control	1003
XLIII	Specialization; Business Management in Poultry Production	1025
XLIV	The Egg	1049
XLV	Marketing Poultry and Eggs	1061

Horses

XLVI	The Horse Industry	1077
XLVII	Types; and Market and Show Classes of Horses	1101
XLVIII	Types and Breeds of Horses	1123
XLIX	Selecting and Judging Horses	1139
L	Breeding Horses	1157
LI	Feeding Horses	1189
	Appendix	1215
	Index	1237

ANIMAL SCIENCE

(Animal Agriculture Series)

CHAPTER I

THE FIELD OF ANIMAL SCIENCE

Contents   Page

The Birth of Animal Science.. 2
Distribution of Animals and Early American Importations................... 4
Transformation of the United States Livestock Industry...................... 4
    United States Animal and Human Population Trends...................... 5
    Animal Products Versus a Cereal Grain Diet.................................. 6
Magnitude of the United States Livestock Industry............................. 9
    Land Area and Number of Farms and Ranches
      Devoted to Animal Production.. 9
    Comparative Cash Income Derived from Different Agricultural Pursuits...... 11
    Number and Value of Livestock on Farms and Ranches................ 14
    Size of the Meat Packing Industry... 15
    Other Organizations Engaged in the Livestock Industry................. 15
The Functions of Animals... 15
    Animals Contribute Food, Clothing, Power, and Recreation.......... 15
    Animals Convert Inedible Feeds into Valuable Products............... 18
    Animals Serve as the Sheet Anchor in Erosion Control................. 20
    Animals Maintain Soil Fertility... 21
    Animals Serve as an Important Companion of Grain Production..... 22
    Animals Make for Desirable Diversification.................................. 22
    Other Functions of Animals... 23
Some Factors to Consider in Establishing the Livestock Enterprise..... 23
    Systems of Farming.. 23
    Leading Livestock States of the United States............................... 24
    Kind of Livestock Adapted to the Region..................................... 24
    Kind of Livestock Adapted to the Farm or Ranch......................... 26
    Requisites of a Successful Stockman.. 26
    Quality of Livestock to Keep... 27
New Animal Frontiers Through Research... 28
Questions for Study and Discussion... 29
Selected References 29

Animal science refers to the total store of knowledge relative to the breeding, feeding, care and management of animals and the marketing and processing of animals and their products, as gained through practical experience and research methods.

Animal agriculture is essential to a well-nourished and happy people. If we would look in the family refrigerator, we would find a lot of animal products—foods derived from beef and dairy cattle, pigs, sheep, and poultry. Behind the livestock, we would see vast expanses of pasture and range land, feed grains, and such by-product feeds as cull potatoes, beet by-products, and surplus citrus fruit—all being utilized as animal feeds. Back of the feeds are the soil resources, spring rains, and the energy of the sun. With calloused hands, the farmer and rancher combine these to produce a tasty platter of meat for the table, cream for the peaches, butter for the biscuit, and cheese for the macaroni—and all are derived from the land via animals. In addition, leather, fats, wool, grease for soap, glands for adrenalin and other essential medical products, glues,

1

gelatins, important organic chemicals, and countless other materials come from animals raised on American farms and ranches. But back of present-day successful animal production has gone years of experience and scientific research—progress in animal breeding; feeding; physiology; disease and parasite control; management; marketing; and processing, storing, and distribution of meat, milk, and eggs. This progress is the result of studies and experiences that have extended from the farms and ranches to the nation's kitchens.

THE BIRTH OF ANIMAL SCIENCE

The field of animal science had its humble beginning with the domestication of animals, for from this remote day forward it was necessary to give attention to their breeding, feeding, and care and management.

Fig. 1-1. Ancient drawing of a bison on a rock, made by Paleolithic (Old Stone Age) man. Even prior to their domestication, man revered animals, according them a conspicuous place in the art of the day. (Courtesy, The Bettmann Archive)

The domestication of animals also marked the first step toward the civilization of the most primitive tribes of men—the transformation from the savage to the civilized way of life. Savage man hunted animals as sources of food and raiment. He lived on what roots, berries, and seeds he could find and on such insects, animals, and fish as he could catch. In addition, he was only too likely to include his fellow man in his hunting and eating.

From very early times, man had domesticated the dog, using him to assist in his hunting and to provide protection by night. Perhaps even more important, the presence of the dog furnished animal companionship, thus filling a deep-rooted want which has always existed in human beings.

Fig. 1-2. Neolithic (New Stone Age) man continued to hunt animals as a source of food and raiment, even though at this remote period many animals had been domesticated. (Photo from a painting by Charles Knight, obtained through the courtesy of the American Museum of Natural History, New York)

Fig. 1-3. Photograph of the painting, *The Sacrifice of Noah*, by Bernardo Cavallino. This shows an animal being served up as an offering to the deities. (Courtesy, National Gallery of Art, Kress Collection)

Gradually, man adopted a more settled mode of life, and with this came the desire to safeguard the food supply for times when hunting was poor and to have the food close at hand. At this stage, seeds were planted near the camp site; roots and grains were stored for winter use; and nearly all of our modern animals were tamed and confined or, as we say, domesticated.

In addition to using domestic animals as a more certain supply of food and clothing, ingenious man soon began to use them for purposes of pack and draft. Also, through selection and controlled matings, he molded animal types better to serve specific needs.

But the contribution of animals extended far beyond their utility value. Man revered animals, giving them a conspicuous place in the art of the day and making them the chief object of worship and myth and the sacrificial offering of many a religious ceremony. From the day of domestication forward, the herding of animals became indicative of the superiority of one tribe over another, and always the great livestock countries of the world have supported the most advanced civilizations and have been the most powerful. Down through the ages, therefore, animals have been man's most useful helpmates—contributing richly to his food, clothing, power, recreation, and inspiration.

DISTRIBUTION OF ANIMALS AND EARLY AMERICAN IMPORTATIONS

Man appeared to follow the migration of animals prior to their domestication in order to keep near his food supply. But with the taming and confinement of animals, man took the initiative in migrating and moved animals with him. It was in this very manner that domestic animals were brought to the Western Hemisphere; for only the llama, alpaca, guinea pig, and turkey were native to the Americas at the time of Columbus' first landing in 1492. Yet, today, the United States possesses the largest and most varied domestic animal population of all countries.

It is generally believed that cattle, pigs, sheep, goats, and horses were first brought to the West Indies by Christopher Columbus on his second voyage in 1493. Cattle, horses, and sheep were brought to Mexico by Cortez in 1519; whereas pigs and horses were first introduced directly into what is now the United States by Hernando DeSoto in 1539.

TRANSFORMATION OF THE UNITED STATES LIVESTOCK INDUSTRY

The domestic animals that were first brought to America by the Spanish explorers were of low efficiency in comparison with those of present standards. Nevertheless, they furnished the sturdy foundation stock that was subsequently improved and developed into a great industry.

As cities grew and animals increased in numbers and pushed inland from the eastern seaboard, there was the development of trailing and marketing, the enlargement of the local slaughterhouse, and eventually the birth of the modern packing industry. Following closely in period of time came the development of railroads, the luxury of rail transportation of animals, and the perfection of artificial refrigeration and the refrigerator car. Such developments marked a new era in animal production. In the meantime, there was the opening of the fertile Ohio valley and the western range.

Fig. 1-4. George Washington at Mount Vernon. The first president possessed a keen interest in animals and contributed immeasurably to their improvement. (From a Currier and Ives lithograph, obtained through the courtesy of The Bettmann Archive)

With this rapid development and expansion of the livestock industry came the demand for improvement in breeding. Progressive breeders, ever awake to their opportunity, proceeded to make large importations of animals from the mother countries—especially from Great Britain, France, and Spain. Thus, through the years, the Texas Longhorns were replaced by the prime bullock; the Arkansas Razorbacks were replaced by improved meat-type swine; and the black, brown, and spotted sheep were replaced by modern mutton and wool-type animals. Hand in hand with improved breeding came improved feeding and management.

United States Animal and Human Population Trends

Despite all the improvements that have been wrought in the husbandry of animals and in the marketing, processing, and distribution of animals and their products, United States animal numbers have failed to keep pace with human population increases. Table 1-1 gives the comparative United States animal and human populations in 1840 and 1968, whereas Figure 1-5 shows their respective population trends during this same period of time.

On January 1, 1968, for every hundred people in this country there were 54 cattle and calves, compared with a peak of 97 in 1888; 11 sheep and lambs, compared with 124 in the peak year of 1867; and 27 hogs, compared with an all-time high of 94 in 1872.

But animal numbers alone do not tell the whole story. Productivity per animal unit has been greatly accelerated. Meat animals now mature more rapidly

TABLE 1—1

UNITED STATES ANIMAL AND HUMAN POPULATION
IN 1840 AND 1968[1]

Human or Animal Population	1840 or as Designated	1968
Human population	17,069,000	200,000,000
All cattle	14,971,000	108,813,000
Milk cows (cows and heifers 2 years old or over kept for milk) 1850	6,385,000	14,662,000
Sheep	19,311,000	22,122,000
Swine	26,301,000	54,263,000
Horses and mules 1966	4,336,000	6,312,000
Poultry (chicken and turkeys) 1880	102,272,000	431,839,000

[1]Sources of data; Human population from *The World Almanac and Book of Facts*; livestock, except horses, from *Livestock and Poultry Inventory*, January 1, USDA, Crop Reporting Board, Release of February 13, 1968; and horses from *Fact Sheet Relative to U.S. Horse Population*, February 15, 1966.

than formerly—the quicker turnover actually meaning more products from a fewer number of animals. Dairy cattle and poultry also produce more milk and eggs, respectively. Also, meat exports have steadily declined. Despite a tremendous human population increase with a much smaller change in meat animal numbers, per capita meat consumption in this country has changed very little. For example, the 1905 per capita red meat consumption totaled 154.4 pounds, whereas in 1966 it was 166.9 pounds.

Further human population increases are inevitable; and, hand in hand with it, science and technology will continue to make for greater efficiency of production. Fewer farms and farm workers will produce more food and fiber. (See Figs. 1-6 and 1-7.)

Perhaps in the future some additional quantities of meats may be imported for the purpose of maintaining a high per capita red meat consumption for the expanding human population. More important, however—inefficient animals must be eliminated. This elimination is inevitable if this nation is to have a long-range meat program that will supply the nutritional requirements of an expanding population on a basis which will be profitable to producers. Also, in the years ahead, increased emphasis will be needed on such things as higher percentage calf, lamb, and pig crops; and on lessening losses due to diseases and parasites.

Animal Products Versus a Cereal Grain Diet

Historically, the people of new and sparsely populated countries have been meat eaters, whereas the people of the older and more densely populated areas have been vegetarians. The latter group has been forced to eliminate considerable animals and to consume plants and grains directly in an effort to avoid famine. Unless the people of America either greatly increase the efficiency of animal production or step up meat imports, it is quite likely that we shall gradually lower the per capita red meat consumption.

Forgetting for a moment the high nutritive values of meats, there can be

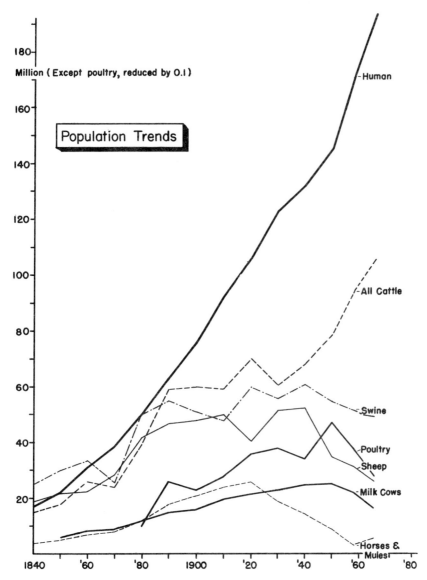

Fig. 1-5. U.S. animal and human population trends. Note that animal numbers have failed to keep pace with human population increases. (Prepared from Census and USDA data; drawing by Steve Allured)

no question that more hunger can be alleviated with a given quantity of grain by completely eliminating animals. When fed grains alone, about 12 to 15 pounds of concentrates must be supplied to livestock in order to produce enough meat and other livestock products to support a man for one day, whereas 2 or 3 pounds of grain (corn, wheat, rice, soybeans, etc.) eaten directly will support a man for a day. Thus, a given quantity of grain eaten directly will feed five to six times more people than it will if it is first fed to livestock and then is eaten indirectly by humans in the form of livestock products. This is caused by the

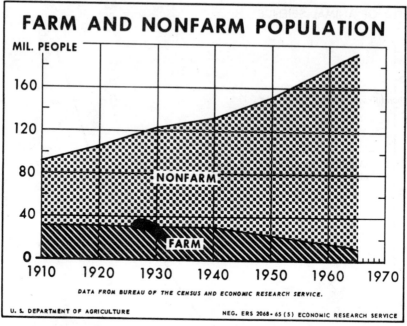

Fig. 1-6. In 1966, the U.S. nonfarm population totaled 184,749,000, whereas the farm population was 11,595,000—of which 5,214,000 persons were classified as farm workers. Exclusive of exports, in 1966, each farm worker produced enough farm products for 33 persons, including himself. (Figures from *Agricultural Statistics,* 1967, USDA, Table 649, p. 526, and Table 651, p. 528)

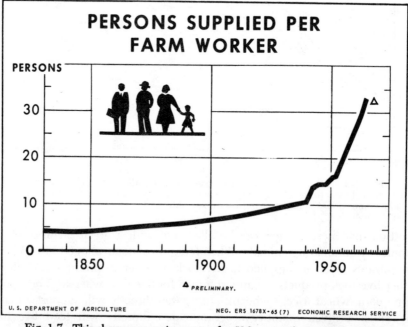

Fig. 1-7. This shows one major reason for U.S. strength. In 1820, each farm worker supplied farm products for 4.12 persons, including himself. In 1966 the figure was 33; and by 1975, it is expected to be 43.

unavoidable nutrient losses in all animal feeding and the fact that no return is received from that portion of the animal's feed which goes for maintenance (which amounts to approximately one-half). This is precisely the reason why the people of the Orient have been forced into becoming vegetarians.

Yet the people of this country will never voluntarily submit to this Oriental way of life. It would not be making the most efficient use of our American resources, particularly the pasture and range areas and inedible concentrates and by-products. Then there is the added problem of erosion control and fertility maintenance which can best be accomplished through livestock farming or ranching. The inclusion of animal products in the diet also makes for greater palatability and ease in providing the necessary nutrients—especially quality proteins, minerals, and vitamins. The latter is important, for a person may be receiving all that he needs in the way of calories and yet be undernourished. For this reason, meat, milk, and eggs are often referred to as protective foods.

Finally, the presence of animals makes for an ever-normal refrigerator rather than an ever-normal granary. When feeds are abundant, animals may be fed more liberally and longer; whereas, when feeds are scarce, more animals can be slaughtered, and they can be slaughtered at lighter weights and with less finish. Where people rely chiefly on a cereal grain diet rather than on animal products—as in the Orient where famines so often stalk across the land—no such flexibility exists.

MAGNITUDE OF THE UNITED STATES LIVESTOCK INDUSTRY

The far-flung livestock business comprises one of the largest industries in the United States. Providing America's meat requires 3.1 million farms and ranches, approximately 4,000 meat packers, and 300,000 meat retail outlets. It requires immense investments in land, herds, processing plants, and vast networks of transportation lines and distribution facilities. In the sections that follow, the magnitude of the livestock industry will be shown through several important criteria.

Land Area and Number of Farms and Ranches Devoted to Animal Production

Animals are the largest users of the nation's land. Figure 1-8 and Table 1-2 show land use, land ownership, and the number of farms and ranches in the United States.

Although land use is not constant, it is noteworthy that 60 per cent of the total land area of the United States is devoted to the production of animal feeds, including 49.4 per cent of the United States lands used for grazing purposes and an additional 10.6 per cent devoted to the production of hay and other forage crops and grain. Both publicly and privately owned lands are used in the production of animal feeds.

Most United States lands are privately owned, but an astounding 526 million acres, or 27.7 per cent—over one acre in four—of all United States

LAND Use, Ownership and Number of Farms and Ranches in the U. S.

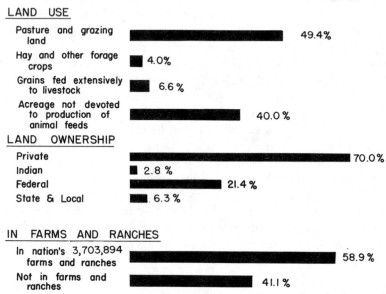

TOTAL LAND AREA OF THE UNITED STATES 1,902 MILLION ACRES

LAND USE

Pasture and grazing land — 49.4%

Hay and other forage crops — 4.0%

Grains fed extensively to livestock — 6.6%

Acreage not devoted to production of animal feeds — 40.0%

LAND OWNERSHIP

Private — 70.0%

Indian — 2.8%

Federal — 21.4%

State & Local — 6.3%

IN FARMS AND RANCHES

In nation's 3,703,894 farms and ranches — 58.9%

Not in farms and ranches — 41.1%

Fig. 1-8. Land use and ownership of the total land area of the United States, excluding Alaska and Hawaii. It is noteworthy (1) that 60 per cent of the total U.S. land area is devoted to the production of animal feeds; and (2) that 27.7 per cent of the total U.S. land area is under public ownership. (Data based on Table 1-2 of this book; drawing by R. F. Johnson)

lands, are under public ownership. The federal government, with 407 million acres, or 21.4 per cent of all United States lands, controls most of the publicly owned lands. State and local governments own an additional 119 million acres. The publicly owned lands are, for the most part, effectively used by private farmers and ranchers for livestock production under a grazing permit system. It is unfortunate, however, that about 47.1 per cent of the federal holdings of the 50 states is located in the 11 western livestock states of Arizona, California, Colorado, Idaho, Montana, Nevada, New Mexico, Oregon, Utah, Washington, and Wyoming (see Fig. 1-9). Also, it is noteworthy that federal lands comprise 47.8 per cent of the total land area of these 11 states; whereas, by contrast, in the state of New York, only 9/10 of 1 per cent of the land is federally controlled. Naturally, the character of the land area rather than state boundaries has been the chief criterion in arriving at what lands shall remain under federal ownership.

Table 1-2 also brings out the fact that 58.9 per cent of the total land area of the United States is operated in the nation's 3,176,000 farms and ranches. The remaining 41.1 per cent of nonfarm and ranch areas consists chiefly of publicly owned lands, cities and towns, and areas not suitable or available for private operations, but much of this area is grazed by animals.

TABLE 1—2

LAND USE, LAND OWNERSHIP, AND NUMBER OF FARMS
AND RANCHES IN THE UNITED STATES,
EXCLUDING ALASKA AND HAWAII[1]

			Area		Percentage of Total
			(million acres)	(million hectares)	(%)
Total land area of the United States			1,902	770	100.0
I Land Use	A. Area devoted to production of animal feeds		1,142	463	60.0
		Pasture and grazing land	939	380	49.4
		Hay and other forage crops[2]	77	31	4.0
		Grains fed extensively to livestock	126	51	6.6
	B. Area not devoted to production of animal feeds (including forests not pastured, urban areas, roads, farmsteads, crop failure and fallow and idle areas)		760	308	40.0
II Land Ownership	A. Private ownership		1,323	536	70.0
	B. Indian land		53	21	2.8
	C. Public ownership		526	213	27.7
		Federal	407	165	21.4
		State and local governments	119	48	6.3
III In Farms and Ranches	A. Land in nation's 3,176,000 farms (1967) and ranches		1,120	454	58.9
	B. Land not in farms and ranches		782	317	41.1

[1]Sources of data: H. H. Wooten, Head, Land Utilization Section, Land and Water Research Branch, Agricultural Research Service, U. S. Department of Agriculture, Washington D. C. *Major Uses of Land in the United States,* USDA Information Bull. No. 168, Jan. 1957.
[2]Acreages harvested in 1959 as reported by the 1959 Agricultural Census. Hay and other forage included all hay, all fodder and forage, silage, peanut vines, velvet beans, etc. Grains fed extensively included corn, oats, barley, sorghum, and mixed grain.

Since pasture and grazing lands are primarily devoted to livestock production, it is important that the stockman be informed as to location, type of cover, and the kind of ownership of the 939 million acres devoted to pasture and grazing land in the United States. Figure 1-10 presents this information. As shown, the two areas known as the western states and the Great Plains, respectively, are the largest and most important grazing territories in the nation. It is to be noted that of the 939 million acres of pasture land, about 696 million acres are grassland pasture and range, 243 million acres are woodland and forest, and arid woodland. Approximately 609 million acres, or only two-thirds of the 939 million acres of pasture and grazing lands, is privately owned. Of the remaining 329 million acres, about 243 million acres are federally owned, with 43 million acres belonging to state and local governments and 43 million acres of Indian land.

Comparative Cash Income Derived from
Different Agricultural Pursuits

The leading sources of farm and ranch income in the United States for 1964 are shown in Figure 1-11 and Table 1-3.

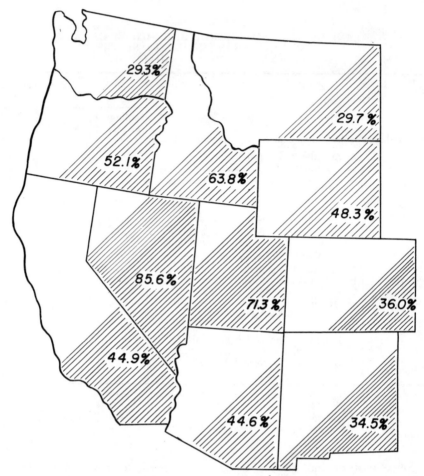

Fig. 1-9. Proportion of all land in each of the 11 western states owned by the U.S. government. This does not include trust properties.

It is noteworthy that livestock and their products accounted for 53.6 per cent of the cash income derived by United States farmers and ranchers, with the sale of livestock for meat purposes exceeding any other single source. Thus, of each $100.00 worth of products sold, animals and their products accounted for $53.60; whereas grains, cotton, vegetables, fruit and nuts, tobacco, etc., brought in $46.40.

As would be expected, the proportions are somewhat changeable from year to year, depending upon the relative value of the various farm products and the amount produced. In addition to the cash income aspects, it is important to remember that the available home supply of animal products greatly improves the diets of farm people.

PASTURE   AND   GRAZING   LAND
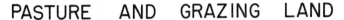

Location of all pasture and grazing land: 939 million acres[1.]

Western states ▨▨▨▨▨▨▨▨▨▨▨ 508 million

Great Plains states▨▨▨▨▨▨ 237 million

Southern states ▨▨▨ 113 million

North Central and ▨▨ 81 million
    Northeastern states

Types of pasture and grazing land: 939   million acres[2.]

Grassland pasture ▨▨▨▨▨▨▨▨▨▨▨▨▨▨ 696 million
and range

Woodland,
forest, and   243 million
arid-woodland,
grazed

Ownership of pasture and grazing land: 939 million acres[3.]

Private land ▨▨▨▨▨▨▨▨▨▨▨▨▨ 609 million

Federal ▨▨▨ 243 million

State and local
    governments ▨ 43 million   *Each symbol = 50 million acres*

Indian land ▨ 43 million

Fig. 1-10. Location, type, and ownership of the 939 million acres devoted to pasture and grazing land in the U.S., excluding Alaska and Hawaii. Communication from H. Thomas Frey, Geographer, Land Resources Branch, Natural Resource Economics Division, USDA.

---

[1] 11 western states; 7 Great Plains states; 12 southern states; 18 north central and northeastern states.

[2] Grassland pasture and range includes all nonforested pasture including 66 million acres of cropland used only for pasture.

[3] Land estimated to have been used for pasture and grazing in 1959. (Source of data: *Major Uses of Land and Water,* Agricultural Economics Report No. 13, USDA.)

(Drawing by Steve Allured)

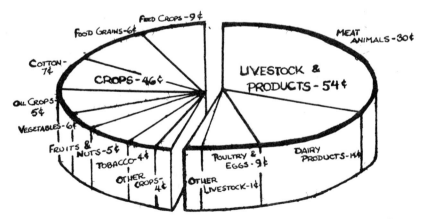

Fig. 1-11. Comparative cash income derived from different agricultural pursuits. (Data obtained from USDA)

TABLE 1—3

COMPARATIVE CASH INCOME OF NATION'S FARMERS
DERIVED FROM DIFFERENT AGRICULTURAL PURSUITS
IN 1964[1]

Leading Sources of Farm and Ranch Income	Per Cent of Cash Income Derived from Sources Indicated
	(%)
Livestock and products:	53.6
Cattle and calves	21.0
Dairy products	13.6
Poultry and eggs	9.0
Hogs	8.1
Sheep, lambs, and wool	1.2
Other livestock and products	.7
Crops:	46.4
Feed crops	9.1
Cotton, cotton seed	6.9
Vegetables	6.2
Food grains	5.9
Oil bearing crops	5.3
Fruit and nuts	4.7
Tobacco	3.8
Other crops	4.5

[1]*Agricultural Statistics, 1965*, USDA, Table 687, p. 480.

Number and Value of Livestock on Farms and Ranches

Table 1-4 gives the numbers and total value of livestock on United States farms and ranches, by classes, in 1968. As will be noted, there were more than

TABLE 1—4

NUMBERS AND VALUE (TOTAL VALUE AND VALUE/HEAD)
OF LIVESTOCK ON UNITED STATES FARMS, BY CLASSES,
JANUARY 1, 1968[1]

Class	Number	Farm Value	
		Value	Total Value
		(dollars/head)	(thousands)
All cattle	108,813,000	$149.00	$16,183,380
Milk cows (cows and heifers 2 yrs. old or over kept for milk)	14,662,000	251.00	3,679,000
Sheep	22,122,000	19.20[2]	425,444
Goats and kids (1959)[3]	3,497,710	8.74	30,577
Swine	54,263,000	29.70	1,610,510
Horses and mules[4]	6,500,000	775.00	5,037,500
Sub-totals of farm animals (deleting cattle kept for milk)	195,195,710		18,219,334
Chickens	424,550,000	1.10	466,598
Turkeys	7,289,000	4.68	34,121
Grand totals (farm animals plus poultry)	627,034,710		18,720,053

[1]*Livestock and Poultry Inventory*, January 1, 1968, USDA, Feb. 13, 1968, pp. 1 and 2.
[2]Stock sheep.
[3]*1959 Census of Agriculture*, Vol. II, General Report, p. 572.
[4]*Fact Sheet Relative to U.S. Horse Population*, Feb. 15, 1966.

195 million head of farm animals with an aggregate value of more than $18 billion. In addition, there were more than 431.8 million turkeys and chickens; and the total value of farm animals and poultry was more than $18.7 billion. Thus, animals represent a huge investment on the part of farmers and ranchers.

Size of the Meat Packing Industry

In total value of products produced, the meat packing industry ranks as one of the big three—so ranking along with the automobile and steel industries. It also regularly provides about one-fourth of the nation's manufactured food products and employs 300,000 workers, or nearly one-sixth of the wage earners engaged in manufacturing foods and kindred products. Meat packing, therefore, is one of the nation's leading industries.

Other Organizations Engaged in the Livestock Industry

In addition to the millions of people and the many facilities engaged in raising livestock and in slaughtering, processing, and distributing the products therefrom, additional personnel and facilities are equally essential in the operation of the far-flung livestock industry. This includes such essential operations as (1) transportation and communication; (2) marketing; (3) commercial feed companies; (4) breed magazines; (5) purebred registry associations; and (6) research, teaching, extension, promotional, and regulatory organizations and officials.

THE FUNCTIONS OF ANIMALS

The average person is aware, at least in part, of the basic utility functions of animals in contributing food, clothing, power, and recreation. Few recognize, however, that—because of their added functions—animals are an integral part of a sound, mature, and permanent agriculture.

Animals Contribute Food, Clothing, Power, and Recreation

The primary utility function of animals is the production of food, clothing, power, and recreation—products upon which man became more and more dependent with each succeeding step in his advancing civilization.

Food.—The development of railroads, the perfection of artificial refrigeration, the growth of livestock markets and packing houses, the improvement and extension of highways, and the invention of the motor truck, all richly enhanced the food supply, especially the quality and quantity of available animal products. Today, nearly half of the total food supply of man is contributed by mammalian, avian, and aquatic life. The list of food products of animal origin includes meat from domestic and wild animals, fowl and eggs from domestic and wild birds, fish of many kinds, and milk from cows, mares, goats, and sheep. Research has given positive proof of the leadership of these animal foods as

TABLE 1—5

ANNUAL PER CAPITA CONSUMPTION
OF SELECTED FOOD PRODUCTS 1965[1]

Product	Per Capita/Year	
	(lbs.)	(kg)
Meats (total red meat)	166.9	75.8
Beef	99.3	45.1
Veal	5.2	2.4
Lamb and mutton	3.7	1.7
Pork (excluding lard)	58.7	26.6
Fish (edible weight)	11.0	5.0
Poultry products		
Eggs, number	308.0	308.0
Chicken (ready-to-cook)	33.3	15.1
Turkey (ready-to-cook)	7.4	3.4
Dairy products		
Cheese	9.4	4.3
Condensed and evaporated milk	10.8	4.9
Fluid milk and cream	302.0	137.1
Ice cream	18.4	8.4
Fats and oils	47.6	21.6
Butter	6.5	3.0
Margarine	9.9	4.5
Lard	6.4	2.9
Shortening	13.9	6.3
Other edible fats and oils	14.2	6.4
Fruits		
Fresh	83.0	37.7
Processed	47.4	21.5
Vegetables (fresh, canned, and frozen)	154.2	70.0
Potatoes and sweet potatoes	115.6	52.5
Sugar (refined)	96.5	43.8

[1]*USDA Report*, NFS-116, Table 5, p. 15, May, 1966. (Courtesy, John C. Pierce, Deputy Director, Livestock Division, Consumer and Marketing Service, USDA.)

rich sources of those nutrients that are so essential for good health and proper nutrition.

In general, the consumption of food products of animal origin is limited by their cost, which in turn is governed by supply and demand. Naturally, the comparative prices of other food products and competition is also a major factor. On the average, consumers spend 4.3 per cent of their total income, or 24.5 per cent of their food budget, for meat.[1] Figure 7-18 shows the trends in per capita consumption of foods by groups. Table 1-5 shows the United States per capita consumption of selected food products.

Although the United States per capita consumption of animal products is higher than in most countries, without doubt, for a considerable number of people, it is still far below the nutritional optimum. For example, the daily dairy products consumption of each man, woman, and child in the United States

[1]*Food from Farmer to Consumer*, Report of the National Commission on Food Marketing, June 1966, Table 2, p. 7.

Fig. 1-12. Animals contribute food. (Courtesy, American Dairy Association, 20 North Wacker Drive, Chicago, Ill.)

merely averages one and one-half glasses of milk, three-fourths ounce of butter (three pats), one-fourth ounce of cheese, plus one dish of ice cream per week. Moreover, except for the cost factor, most people could—with benefit from a health standpoint—consume more meat and eggs than they are now getting. It is believed that a per capita red meat consumption of somewhere between 175 and 180 pounds would be desirable from a nutritional standpoint.

Clothing.—Today, the chief contributions of animal life to clothing for man are in the forms of wool, leather, hair, and furs. In addition to serving as sources of clothing, each of these articles has many additional uses. For example, leather not only provides boots and shoes, jackets and helmets, gloves and mittens, and belts; but it is used in the manufacture of harness, belting, scabbards, holsters, gaskets, and countless other articles.

Power.—In the United States, we commonly think of horses and mules as the only sources of animal power, but in the more isolated sections of this country oxen are so used. Also, in different parts of the world and at different times, buffalo, reindeer, elephants, camels, goats, and dogs have all been brought under man's submission and used as sources of power for different purposes.

With the invention and extension of mechanical power during the nineteenth and twentieth centuries, there has been a steady but marked decline in the use of animals as a source of power. Thus, the use of horses and mules in the United States has decreased—the use of horses reaching a peak in numbers in 1915 and that of mules reaching a peak in 1925.

Fig. 1-13. Animals contribute clothing in the forms of wool, leather, hair, and furs. Picture shows wool clothing. (Courtesy, American Sheep Producers Council, Inc.)

Recreation.—Throughout the ages, animal life has contributed to recreation and sport. It is reasonable to surmise that a certain amount of enjoyment must have accompanied primitive man's hunting and fishing, though in times of scarcity it was a grim business. Today, wild animals and aquatic life contribute richly to man's enjoyment. Domestic animals, notably the horse and the dog, are used extensively in recreation and sport. Also, the animals in the zoo and the circus are a source of recreation for old and young alike. In recent years, many men of wealth have established outstanding purebred herds and flocks as a means of recreation and enjoyment. In brief, no mechanical device made by man has had such wide appeal as animals, for they serve as sources of recreation to people of all walks of life.

Animals Convert Inedible Feeds into Valuable Products

About two-thirds of the feed used by livestock is not suited for human

Fig. 1-14. Animals contribute power. However, with the invention and extension of mechanical power, there has been a steady but marked decline in this function of animals. Picture shows big-team hitches drawing combines in the famous Palouse wheat area of eastern Washington prior to the advent of tractor power. (Photo by Hutchison; print courtesy, Washington State University)

Fig. 1-15. Animals contribute to recreation and sport. Picture of a trail ride. (Courtesy, American Quarter Horse Association, Amarillo, Texas)

consumption. In this category are hay, pasture, coarse forages (such as straws, fodders, etc.); certain grains; such by-products as are obtained from mills, packing houses, etc.; and damaged grains and foods and garbage. These are converted into meat, eggs, milk, and wool.

Such well-known grains as corn, oats, and barley would have only limited value if restricted solely to direct human consumption, but because they can eventually ride to market as animal products, their value is immensely greater. A distinction needs to be made, therefore, between food grains for people and feed grains for livestock. It is also well to remember that farm animals—especially sheep and beef cattle—exist largely on such roughages as pasture, hay, and silage (see Table 1-6).

TABLE 1—6

PERCENTAGE OF FEED FOR DIFFERENT CLASSES OF LIVESTOCK
DERIVED FROM (1) CONCENTRATES AND (2) ROUGHAGES
INCLUDING PASTURE, AVERAGES FOR THE FEEDING
YEARS, 1962, '63, and '64[1]

Class of Animal	Concentrates	Roughages
	(per cent)	(per cent)
Beef cattle	21.2	78.8
Dairy cattle	31.3	68.7
Sheep and goats	10.2	89.8
Swine	95.6	4.4
Horses and mules	22.9	77.1
Poultry	98.2	1.8
All livestock	45.2	54.8

[1]Unpublished data provided by Mr. Earl F. Hodges, Agricultural Economist, Economic Research Service, USDA, Washington, D.C.

Much of the forage utilized in livestock production is produced on land not suited for the raising of bread grains or gardens. Then, too, in addition to the character of the land itself, labor, tools, storage, processing plants, and transportation facilities would be limiting factors in any rapid shift away from utilizing the present inedible feeds by animals.

Animals Serve as the Sheet Anchor in Erosion Control

The spirit of adventure and the desire for freedom caused brave men to enter this country—a country characterized by a deep and fertile soil that supported great forests and broad prairies inhabited only by the Indians and the wild game which they hunted. That same gainful and aggressive spirit caused the pioneer to walk behind the plow for the breaking of the plains and to swing the axe for the cutting of the virgin forest. Within a short time, these fertile areas were to become known as the dairy and industrial area of the East; the Corn Belt of the central United States; the Cotton Belt of the South; and the wheat, alfalfa, fruit, and range country of the West—all supporting a prosperous and contented population.

Although these same fields of these United States have been in cultivation little more than 250 years—for the most part less than 100 years—many of them have already reached a stage of low productivity, due primarily to soil erosion.

The increased use of forage crops, especially grasses and legumes, appears to be the most logical basis for a sound program of soil and moisture conservation. These sod-forming crops "nail the soil in place," preventing both wind and water erosion. Moreover, if properly utilized in livestock production, these forage crops afford adequate remuneration through adding to the weight of stock and returning valuable organic matter and nutrients to the soil.

Fig. 1-16. Animals serve as the sheet anchor in erosion control. Picture shows a seriously eroded condition as the result of careless land use. The increased use of forage crops, especially grasses and legumes, offers the most logical approach to a sound program of soil and moisture conservation. (Courtesy, USDA)

Every citizen of the United States should come to realize that the land, regardless of ownership, is only a gift made by nature—a gift that should be passed on to posterity. Man depends upon the topsoil for the production of food, clothing, and shelter.

Animals Maintain Soil Fertility

It should also be pointed out that cash crops, if removed from the farm, whether they be grains or forages, result in the marketing of soil fertility. Although it is possible to use green-manure crops from the standpoint of the retention of soil fertility, it is usually more practical to attain this end through feeding the grains and forages to animals. On the average general farm, with various classes and ages of animals, probably 80 per cent of the fertilizing value of the feed is excreted in the feces and urine. With proper conservation, therefore, this fertility value may be returned to the soil.

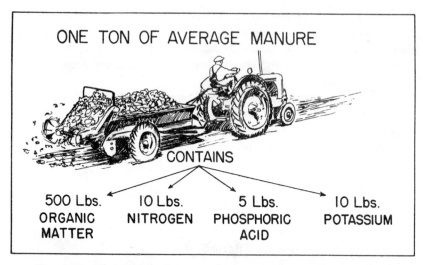

Fig. 1-17. The content of 1 ton of average manure. (Drawing by Steve Allured; courtesy, Washington State University)

Laboratory analyses reveal that a ton of average farm manure contains 500 pounds of organic matter, 10 pounds of nitrogen, 5 pounds of phosphoric acid, and 10 pounds of potassium. It must be remembered, however, that much of the fertilizing value is lost if the manure is not handled properly. Thus, when piled in an unpaved yard and left exposed to the sun, wind, and rain, manure will lose about half of its nitrogen and potash content. Where animals are running in the field, most of the fertilizing value of the manure is conserved. Though manure is more difficult to handle and more expensive under barn or feedlot conditions, most of its fertilizing value can be saved by using plenty of bedding to absorb liquids and by storing the manure in a watertight, weather-protected pit. Since much of the nitrogen value is in the liquids, some farmers provide a cistern and pump outside one end of the pit to handle the liquid manure.

By carefully saving all of the manure produced in livestock farming, the soil may be enriched and crop yields increased.

Animals Serve as an Important Companion of Grain Production

Livestock feeding provides a large and flexible outlet for the year-to-year changes in grain supplies. When there is a large production of grain, more can be fed to livestock, with the animals carried to heavier weights and higher finish. On the other hand, when grain supplies are low, herds and flocks can be maintained by reducing the grain that is fed and by increasing the grasses and roughages. Thus, livestock give stability to grain farming.

Animals Make for Desirable Diversification

Diversification refers to having more than one type of enterprise or source of income. There can be diversification within a specialty. For example, the poultryman might produce and market table eggs, day-old chicks, broilers, capons, etc.

In contrast to "one crop" farming, as applied to either plants or animals, a well-diversified livestock program has the following advantages:

1. It distributes the risks.
2. It establishes a more desirable basis for credit.
3. It makes for better distribution of labor—providing employment throughout the year.
4. It provides for more effective utilization of home-grown feeds.
5. It makes for a more flexible farm program.
6. It allows for the development of superior markets.
7. It affords an opportunity for the application of wider experience and superior managerial ability.

Without attempting to elaborate upon each point, it should be readily apparent that a well-managed diversified livestock program makes for a sound and stable agriculture. Also, over a long period of time, it makes for a more profitable enterprise; for, after all, though the need of the general public for animal products creates a demand for them, farmers would not engage in livestock production without a profit incentive.

Other Functions of Animals

Livestock have other values. Every day millions of people use animal products for their health, enjoyment, amusement, beautification, and general happiness. Livestock are not processed for meat and hides alone. The insulin that keeps the diabetic alive and innumerable other by-products which contribute to the welfare of society are derived from the livestock and meat industry.

SOME FACTORS TO CONSIDER IN ESTABLISHING THE LIVESTOCK ENTERPRISE

It is not intended that this section shall cover all of the multiple factors that should be considered in establishing a livestock enterprise. Rather, it is hoped that thought may be focused on some of the primary factors that should be considered if the venture is to be successful.

Systems of Farming

Three broad systems of farming are practiced in the United States: (1) crop farming, (2) livestock farming, and (3) crop and livestock farming combined. Because considerable variation exists within each classification, some farm management specialists prefer further and more refined divisions. For example, instead of placing crop farming in one category, there are those who list one-crop farms and diversified-crop farms as two separate systems of farming. For purposes of this discussion, however, the three broad classifications will be used, with each system of farming defined as follows:

1. **Crop farming** is that system in which crops are grown that are useful for food, feed, or clothing—with the income derived from the sale of cash crops.

2. **Livestock farming** is that system in which the crops are used chiefly or entirely as a feed for animals—with the income derived from the sale of animals, meat, milk, eggs, and/or wool.

3. **Crop and livestock farming combined** is that system that combines significant amounts of crop and livestock farming—with the income derived both from the sale of cash crops and animals and their by-products.

Leading Livestock States of the United States

It is but natural to find, in a country so large and variable as the United States, that some areas and states are better adapted to livestock production than others. Though the size of land area within each of the 50 states varies considerably and, consequently, is a major factor in determining the total livestock population of each, the cash receipts of livestock and livestock products by states is one of the best available criteria of the general livestock adaptation of the respective states. This information is presented in Table 1-7.

TABLE 1—7

LEADING LIVESTOCK STATES BY RANK BASED ON 1966 CASH
RECEIPTS OF LIVESTOCK AND LIVESTOCK PRODUCTS[1]

State	Cash Receipts of Livestock and Livestock Products
	(in 1,000 dollars)
Iowa	2,573,229
California	1,556,763
Texas	1,385,274
Illinois	1,326,109
Minnesota	1,271,124
Wisconsin	1,218,287
Nebraska	1,138,666
Kansas	976,512
Missouri	918,027
Indiana	799,691
United States total	24,835,165

[1]*Agricultural Statistics, 1967*, USDA, p. 572.

As, over a long period of time, farmers and ranchers do those things which are most profitable to them, there is perhaps considerable logic in assuming that there exists in these leading livestock states a set of conditions making for successful livestock production. This fact is of importance to those who wish to get established in the livestock business in an adapted area.

Kind of Livestock Adapted to the Region

Some regions or areas of the United States possess a combination of feed and economic conditions that make them best adapted to a particular kind or kinds of livestock. Available feeds are determined chiefly by climate, soil, and topography; whereas economic conditions are determined by markets, available labor, transportation facilities, and perishability of product.

Because of a combination of feed and economic conditions, the following kinds of livestock farming predominate in different regions or areas of the United States:

The Dairy Region.—This region includes the densely populated northeastern part of the United States, extending from southern Minnesota north and east. The rainfall and climate of the area are well adapted to the production of pasture, hay, silage crops, and oats—important crops for the dairy ration. In addition, there are excellent and nearby markets for milk, a highly perishable product.

The Corn Belt.—This region refers to the seven Corn Belt states of Iowa, Illinois, Nebraska, Missouri, Kansas, Indiana, and Ohio. The climate, soil, and topography of the area are well suited to the production of corn, the principal crop; and corn is pre-eminently adapted to the finishing of hogs and cattle. Also, the Corn Belt feedlots are in close proximity to the largest livestock markets in the world.

The Cotton Belt.—This region, which derives its name from its predominant crop, is confined to southeastern United States. Corn is the second most important crop of the area, and there is a considerable acreage of peanuts, sweet potatoes, and other crops, part or all of which are fed to animals. More important, from the standpoint of efficient livestock production, year-round pastures are possible in this area. The combination of a mild climate, a variety of crops, and a long grazing season makes the Cotton Belt well adapted to most all types of livestock production. From an economic standpoint, the region has an abundance of comparatively cheap labor, but satisfactory market outlets are in need of further development.

The Western Range.—This region comprises the great ranching area of the United States which lies west of the one hundredth meridian. The extensive grazing areas of this territory are especially suited to the production of lambs and wool and feeder cattle—highly concentrated and nonperishable products that may be economically and successfully transported great distances to market.

Although regional adaptations are important and should always be given careful consideration when selecting the livestock enterprise, it is well to keep in mind that some regions are almost equally well suited to other kinds of livestock than those for which they are most noted. For example, the Corn Belt states are well adapted to and support a considerable number of animals other than hogs and beef cattle—including sheep, dairy cattle, poultry, and horses. Likewise, poultry successfully competes with dairy cattle in northeastern United States, and some of the more isolated grazing areas of the Dairy Belt are best adapted to beef production. Also, some of the irrigated valleys of the Far West are noted for their large cattle and sheep feeding yards—largely because of their cheap and abundant by-product feeds.

Kind of Livestock Adapted to the Farm or Ranch

Under some conditions a hog farmer may have one neighbor who is a cattle feeder, a second who operates a dairy, a third who keeps a sizeable farm flock of sheep, a fourth who produces light horses for recreation and sport, and a fifth whose chief source of income is from poultry. All may be successful and satisfied with their respective livestock enterprises. This indicates, therefore, that several types of livestock farming may be nearly equally well adapted to an area or region. This means that the selection of the dominant type of livestock enterprise should be analyzed from the standpoint of the individual farm or ranch.

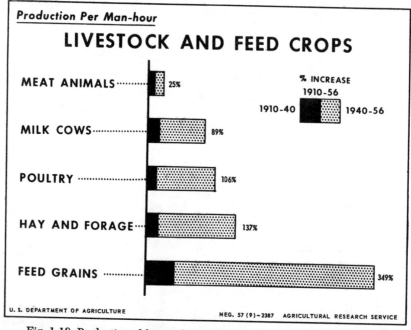

Fig. 1-18. Production of livestock and feed crops per man-hour has increased greatly in recent years (note % increase from 1910-40 vs. 1940-56), due primarily to increased automation. We have practically eliminated the scoop shovel, pitch fork, bucket, and basket. *Automation is a coined word meaning the mechanical handling of materials.*

Usually a combination of several factors suggests the livestock enterprise or enterprises best adapted to a particular farm or ranch. One of these factors is the labor requirement. Table 1-8 may be of assistance in arriving at a decision as to the kind or kinds of livestock best suited to the individual farm or ranch.

Requisites of a Successful Stockman

The first and most important requisite of a successful stockman is that he must possess a great love for animals. This appears to be an inborn trait, for some people never acquire a natural ability to work with animals—no matter how long

TABLE 1—8

ANIMAL LABOR REQUIREMENTS

Animal or Product	Man Hours/Hundredweight Production[1]		No. Head Cared for in 1968 by One Man in the Most Efficient Operations[2]	
	1935-1939	1960-64		
Beef cattle	(hours) 4.2	(hours) 2.7	Cow-calf Feedlot cattle	250 1,500
Milk cows	3.4	1.3	Milk cows	100
Sheep	6.3	4.4	Farm flock ewes Range ewes Feedlot lambs	500 1,000 7,500
Hogs	3.2	2.1	Sows	100
Eggs	1.7/100 eggs	0.6/100 eggs	Laying hens (cage) Laying hens (floor)	40,000[3] 15,000[3]
Broilers	8.5	0.9		75,000
Turkeys	23.7	2.9		40,000

[1]*Food and Fiber for the Future*, report of the National Advisory Commission on Food and Fiber, July, 1967, p. 155, Table 2-c; except for sheep which were estimated by M. E. Ensminger.
[2]Estimates by Dr. M. E. Ensminger.
[3]Does not include time devoted to egg processing.

or how hard they try. When such love for stock exists, animals are more docile and easier to handle, for the caretaker's feelings are relayed to his charges. Also, a great love for animals appears to be essential if the caretaker is to feed them regularly, cheerfully, and with enjoyment, without regard to long hours and Sundays or holidays; if he is to provide clean, dry bedding, despite the fact that a driving storm may make it necessary to repeat the same operation the next day; if he is to serve as nursemaid to newborn or sick animals, though it may mean the loss of sleep and working with cold, numb fingers; and if he is to remain calm and collected, though striking an animal or otherwise giving vent to his feelings might at first appear to be warranted.

Next to having a great love for animals, it is important that the successful stockman have adequate knowledge of the broad field of animal science. In addition, a good stockman must be well versed relative to soils and crops, for in most successful livestock enterprises the feeds are home-grown. In general, this means that the livestock farmer or rancher should be equally as competent as the grain farmer from the standpoint of raising feeds, and, in addition, he must be thoroughly competent in the production and marketing of animals. Successful livestock farming requires great skill.

Finally, experience, industry, and good judgment are very necessary requisites of a successful stockman. These words carry the same connotation in all industries and are self-explanatory.

Quality of Livestock to Keep

Once the kind or kinds of animals has been decided upon, good foundation stock should be selected, and they should receive proper care. A combination of good breeding and husbandry are prerequisites to high and efficient production as indicated by: (1) saving a high percentage of newborn animals, (2) efficient feed utilization, and (3) high production of meat, milk, eggs, and wool. There is much truth in the statement that livestock of superior breeding, properly fed and managed, are the "brand" of the successful farm or ranch.

Though preference should be a major factor in selecting a breed, it should be remembered that there are more differences within breeds than between breeds.

NEW ANIMAL FRONTIERS THROUGH RESEARCH

In the past, stockmen could be successful if they merely bred, fed, and managed their animals. Today, this is not enough. For profit and survival, their operations must be predicated on more and better research followed by prudent application.

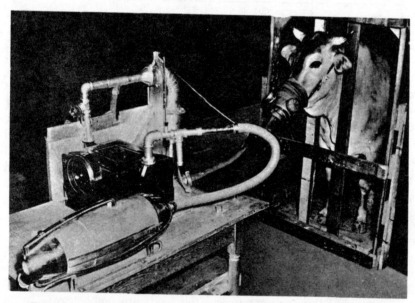

Fig. 1-19. Evaluating heat tolerance by respiratory volume. In the future, environmental control will be an important consideration in livestock buildings. (Courtesy, USDA)

During the 25-year period from 1940 through 1964, production of meat, milk, eggs, wool and mohair per breeding unit (per beef cow, dairy cow, ewe, goat, sow, chicken and turkey, but exclusive of horses and mules) increased by an average of 37 per cent.[2]

---

[2] *Changes in Farm Production and Efficiency,* a summary report, 1965, USDA Stat. Bul. 233, Rev., July 1965, p. 25, Table 11.

Research gave us Mendel's laws of inheritance, an understanding of nutrient requirements, the antibiotics, insecticides, and a host of other discoveries. In brief, it is no exaggeration to say that we are eating better and living healthier and longer as a result of science and technology.

Because we have made so much progress in the past, some people may be of the opinion that all of the worth-while things in the field of animal science have been done. Not so! We need new technology to produce livestock and their products more efficiently, and we need to adjust and adapt the industry to changes in other parts of our economy. We need to increase efficiency of reproduction—to bring reproductive rates and seasons under more precise control, and to reduce losses, both before and after birth; we need to improve feed conversion and lower feed costs; we need to increase growth rates; we need to improve the quality of meat, milk, and fiber produced; and we need new management practices, facilities, and equipment to reduce labor and increase productive efficiency. All these challenges, and more, lie ahead.

QUESTIONS FOR STUDY AND DISCUSSION

1. What is meant by the term "animal agriculture"?
2. Why have the great livestock countries of the world supported the most advanced civilizations and been the most powerful?
3. What was the chief motive in bringing the first animals into the U.S.?
4. What prompted the early improvement of animals in the U.S.?
5. In the future, what practical methods may be used for the purpose of maintaining high per capita red meat, milk, and egg consumption for our expanding population?
6. Why do we not eliminate animals in the U.S. and go on a cereal grain diet?
7. Show the magnitude of the U.S. livestock industry, using all possible criteria.
8. List the functions of animals and discuss the importance of each function.
9. List and discuss the primary factors to consider in establishing the livestock enterprise.
10. If you were to raise livestock, would you produce purebred or commercial animals? Give reasons for your choice.

SELECTED REFERENCES

Title of Publication	Author(s)	Publisher
Basic Animal Husbandry	J. M. Kays	Prentice-Hall, Inc., Englewood Cliffs, N. J., 1958.
Beef Cattle Science	M. E. Ensminger	The Interstate Printers & Publishers, Danville, Ill., 1968.
Horses and Horsemanship	M. E. Ensminger	The Interstate Printers & Publishers, Danville, Ill., 1969.
Introductory Animal Husbandry	A. L. Anderson	The Macmillan Company, New York, N.Y., 1959.
Introductory Animal Science	W. P. Garrigus	J. B. Lippincott Company, Chicago, Ill., 1954.
Livestock and Livestock Products	T. C. Byerly	Prentice-Hall, Inc., Englewood Cliffs, N. J., 1964.
Livestock and Poultry Production	C. E. Bundy R. V. Diggins	Prentice-Hall, Inc., New York, N. Y., 1954.

Titles of Publication	Author(s)	Publisher
Livestock Production	W. H. Peters R. H. Grummer	McGraw-Hill Book Co., New York, N. Y., 1954.
Practical Animal Husbandry	Jack Widmer	Charles Scribner's Sons, New York, N. Y., 1954.
Raising Livestock	W. H. Peters G. P. Deyoe	McGraw-Hill Book Co.; New York, N. Y., 1946.
Sheep and Wool Science	M. E. Ensminger	The Interstate Printers & Publishers, Danville, Ill., 1964.
Swine Science	M. E. Ensminger	The Interstate Printers & Publishers, Danville, Ill., 1969.
Stockman's Handbook, The	M. E. Ensminger	The Interstate Printers & Publishers, Danville, Ill., 1969.
Types and Market Classes of Livestock	H. W. Vaughan	College Book Co., Columbus, Ohio, 1941.
Western Stock Ranching	M. H. Saunderson	The University of Minnesota Press. Minneapolis, Minn., 1950.

Chapter II

SOME PRINCIPLES OF GENETICS AND ANIMAL BREEDING[1]

Contents | Page
Mendel's Contribution to Genetics.. 34
Some Fundamentals of Heredity.. 35
The Gene as the Unit of Heredity.. 35
Mutations 38
Simple Gene Inheritance (Qualitative Traits)................................... 39
Dominant and Recessive Factors.. 40
Incomplete or Partial Dominance.. 44
Multiple Gene Inheritance (Quantitative Traits)............................. 44
Multiple Births 45
Sex Determination... 46
Lethals and Abnormalities of Development....................................... 47
The Relative Importance of Sire and Dam....................................... 49
Prepotency 50
Nicking 50
Family Names... 51
Heredity and Environment.. 52
Systems of Breeding... 55
Purebreeding 55
Inbreeding 56
Closebreeding 57
Linebreeding 58
Outcrossing 60
Grading Up.. 61
Crossbreeding 63
Selection in Livestock Breeding.. 64
Bases of Selection... 64
Selection Based on Type and Individuality................................... 65
Selection Based on Pedigree.. 65
Selection Based on Show-Ring Winnings...................................... 65
Selection Based on Production Testing.. 66
Selection for Several Characters.. 71
Determining Relative Emphasis to Place on Each Character........ 71
Systems of Selection.. 72
Artificial Insemination 74
Advantages of Artificial Insemination.. 75
Limitations of Artificial Insemination.. 76
Some Practical Considerations of Artificial Insemination............ 78
Breed Registry Associations... 78
New Animal Frontiers Through Breeding... 79
Questions for Study and Discussion.. 81
Selected References 81

Selection followed by mating of the best with the best has long been the principal tool through which man has attempted to bring about the improvement of domestic animals. Following the domestication of livestock, man began to

[1] The author gratefully acknowledges the helpful suggestions of the following authority in genetics and animal breeding who reviewed this chapter, and other breeding chapters of *Animal Science:* Dr. E. J. Warwick, Assistant Director, Animal Husbandry Research Division, USDA, Washington. D.C.

choose certain animals for breeding while others were slaughtered and eaten. Until very recent times, the general principle that "like begets like" was the only recognized law of heredity. That the application of this principle over a long period of time has been effective in modifying animal types in the direction of selection is evident from a comparison of present-day types of animals within each class of livestock. Thus, the speed of representatives of the modern Thoroughbred —coupled with their general lithe, angular build, and nervous temperament—is in sharp contrast to the slow, easy gaits and the docility of the Tennessee Walking Horse. Yet there is good and substantial evidence to indicate that both breeds descended from a common ancestry. Because of the diversity of genes carried by the original parent stock, it has been possible, through selection, to evolve with two distinct breeds—one highly adapted to fast running races and the other to a slow, ambling gait. Also, through selection accompanied by planned matings, this same parent stock has been altered into horses especially adept as hunters, jumpers, stock horses, polo mounts, three- and five-gaited park hacks, harness race horses, etc. Through selection and controlled matings, man has also developed the many diverse types and breeds of cattle, sheep, and swine.

There can be little doubt that men like Bakewell, the English patriarch, and other eighteenth-century breeders had made a tremendous contribution in pointing the way toward livestock improvement before Mendel's laws became known to the world in the early part of the twentieth century. Robert Bakewell's use of progeny testing through his ram letting was truly epoch making, and his improvement of Shire horses and Longhorn cattle was equally outstanding. He and other pioneers had certain ideals in mind and, according to their standards, they were able to develop some nearly perfect specimens. These men were intensely practical, never overlooking the utility value or the market requirements. No animal met with their favor unless such favor was earned by meat upon the back, milk in the pail, weight and quality of wool, pounds gained for pounds of feed consumed, draft ability, or some other performance of practical value. Their ultimate goal was that of furnishing better animals for the market or lowering the cost of production. It must be just so with the master breeders of the present and future.

Others took up the challenge of animal improvement where Bakewell and his contemporaries left off, slowly but surely molding animal types. Thus, during the past hundred years, remarkable progress has been made in breeding better meat animals—animals that are more efficient and, at the same time, that produce cuts of meat more nearly meeting the exacting requirements of the consuming public. The Texas Longhorn steer—built for stamina and ability to fight and producing tough, stringy meat—has been replaced by the earlier-maturing, prime bullock. The wild boar and the Arkansas Razorback have been replaced by the modern meat and bacon types of swine; and the black, brown, and multicolored sheep have been replaced by the present-day mutton and wool breeds.

Despite the remarkable progress of the past, much remains to be done. A casual glance at the daily receipts of any public stockyards is convincing evidence of the task ahead. The challenge is primarily that of improving the great masses of animals in order that more of them may approach the too few nearly perfect specimens. Also, in the years ahead, there must be (1) improved reproduction— and this calls for higher percentage young crop, fewer death losses from birth to weaning, earlier weaning ages, and heavier weaning weights (see Table 2-1); (2) increased productivity per animal (see Table 2-2 for current productivity); (3) greater efficiency of production; and (4) improved market products. With the experience of the pioneers to guide us and with our present knowledge of

TABLE 2—1

REPRODUCTION STATISTICS

Class of Animal	Of Those Bred, Per Cent Giving Birth to Young (live and born dead)	Average Death Losses from Birth to Weaning	Average Weaning Age	Average Weaning Weight	
	(%)	(%)	(months)	(lbs.)	(kg)
Cattle..............	86	6[1]	7.3[2]	400[3]	182
Sheep..............	90-94	28[4]	4[5]	70[5]	32
Swine..............	80-85	30-35[6]	1.5-2[5]	30[5]	14
Horses.............	50	6[5]	5-6[7]	350-500[5]	'159-227

[1]*Agricultural Statistics, 1965*, USDA, Table 459, p. 312.
[2]*Problems and Practices of American Cattlemen*, Wash. Agric. Exp. Sta. Bul. 562, 1955, p. 85.
[3]*Beef Cattle Science*, 4th ed., Ch. XIV.
[4]Calculated as follows: *Sheep and Wool Science*, 3rd ed., p. 171, shows 119.6% lamb crop, based on Hansson's data. *Agricultural Statistics, 1965*, USDA, Table 497, p. 337, shows 92 lambs raised/100 ewes one year and over.
[5]Estimate by Dr. M. E. Ensminger.
[6]*Swine Science*, 3rd ed., p. 164.
[7]*Horses and Horsemanship*, 3rd ed., 1963, p. 515.

TABLE 2—2

AVERAGE ANNUAL PRODUCTION PER ANIMAL[1]

Animal	Production	
	(lbs)	(kg)
Beef cow, calf weaned per cow bred[2]..............................	320	145
Milk cows, 1966[3]		
Milk...	8,513	3,870
Butterfat..	314	143
Sheep:		
Lamb weaned[4]..	64	29
Wool (fleece), 1964[5]......................................	8.4	3.8
Sow, pigs weaned[6]...	121.5	55.2
Chicken (hen) eggs, number, 1966[7].....................................	218	218

[1]In this table, in computing pounds of calves, lambs, and pigs weaned, consideration is given to barren animals, and to death losses from birth to weaning. 1964 data for milk cows, wool, and eggs.
[2]Estimate made by M. E. Ensminger. Basis: 86% calf crop, 6% death loss from birth to weaning, and 400 lb. weaning weight (average weaning weight of 400 lbs. from *Beef Cattle Science*, 4th ed., Ch. 14).
[3]*Agricultural Statistics 1967*, USDA, Table 555, p. 445.
[4]Estimate made by M. E. Ensminger. Basis: 92% lamb crop saved (*Agricultural Statistics 1965*, USDA. Table 497, p. 337) and estimating an average weaning weight of 70 pounds.
[5]*Agricultural Statistics 1965*, USDA. Table 510, p. 347.
[6]Estimate made by M. E. Ensminger. Basis: 7.22 pigs farrowed/litter (*Livestock and Meat Statistics*, Supp. for 1964, Stat. Bul. No. 333, Tables 26 and 27, p. 17). 30% death loss from birth to weaning, 30-lb. weaning weight, and 80% of sows bred farrowing.
[7]*Agricultural Statistics 1967*, USDA. Table 621, p. 501.

genetics and physiology of reproduction, progress should now be much more certain and rapid. In the past, animal breeding has been an art. In the future, it is destined to be both an art and a science.

MENDEL'S CONTRIBUTION TO GENETICS

Modern genetics was really founded by Gregor Johann Mendel, a cigar-smoking Austrian monk, who conducted breeding experiments with garden peas from 1857 to 1865, during the time of the U.S. Civil War. In his monastery at Brünn (now Brno, in Czechoslovakia), Mendel applied a powerful curiosity and a clear mind to reveal some of the basic principles of hereditary transmission. In 1866, he published in the proceedings of a local scientific society a report covering 8 years of his studies, but for 34 years his findings went unheralded and ignored. Finally, in 1900, 16 years after Mendel's death, three European biologists independently duplicated his findings, and this led to the dusting off of the original paper published by the monk 34 years earlier.

The essence of Mendelism is that inheritance is by particles or units (called genes), that these genes are present in pairs—one member of each pair having come from each parent—and that each gene maintains its identity generation after generation. Thus, Mendel's work with peas laid the basis for two of the general laws of inheritance: (1) the law of segregation and (2) the inde-

Fig. 2-1. Gregor Johann Mendel (1822-1884) a cigar-smoking Austrian monk, whose breeding experiments with garden peas founded modern genetics. (Courtesy, The Bettmann Archive)

pendent assortment of genes. Later genetic principles have been added; yet all the phenomena of inheritance, based upon the reactions of genes, are generally known under the collective term, Mendelism.

Thus, modern genetics is really unique in that it was founded by an amateur who was not trained in science and who did his work merely as a hobby. During the years since the rediscovery of Mendel's principles (in 1900), many additional genetic principles have been added, but the fundamentals as set forth by Mendel have been proved correct in every detail. It can be said, therefore, that inheritance in both plants and animals follows the biological laws discovered by Mendel.

SOME FUNDAMENTALS OF HEREDITY

The author has no intention of covering all of the diverse field of genetics and animal breeding. Rather, he will present a condensation of the known facts in regard to the field and will briefly summarize their applications to practical operations.

The Gene as the Unit of Heredity

Genes determine all the hereditary characteristics of animals, from the body type to the color of the hair. They are truly the fundamental unit of genetics.

The bodies of all animals are made up of millions or even billions of tiny cells, microscopic in size. Each cell contains a nucleus in which there are a number of pairs of bundles, called chromosomes. In turn, the chromosomes carry pairs of minute particles, called genes, which are the basic hereditary material. The

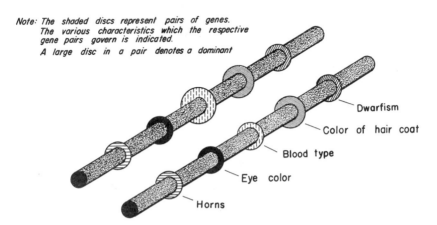

Schematic Drawing of a
Pair of Chromosomes

Note: The shaded discs represent pairs of genes.
The various characteristics which the respective
gene pairs govern is indicated.
A large disc in a pair denotes a dominant

Dwarfism

Color of hair coat

Blood type

Eye color

Horns

Fig. 2-2. A pair of bundles, called chromosomes, carrying minute particles, called genes. The genes determine all the hereditary characteristics of living animals, from length of leg to body size. (Drawing by R. F. Johnson)

nucleus of each body cell of cattle and horses contains 30 pairs of chromosomes[2] or a total of 60, whereas there are perhaps thousands of pairs of genes. These genes determine all the hereditary characteristics of living animals. Thus, inheritance goes by units rather than by the blending of two fluids, as our grandfathers thought.

The modern breeder knows that the job of transmitting qualities from one generation to the next is performed by the germ cells—a sperm from the male and an ovum or egg from the female. All animals, therefore, are the result of the union of two such tiny cells, one from each of its parents. These two germ cells contain all the anatomical, physiological, and psychological characters that the offspring will inherit.

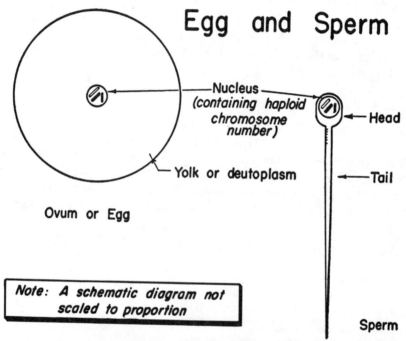

Fig. 2-3. Egg and sperm. The parent germ cells, the egg from the female and the sperm from the male, unite and transmit to the offspring all the characters that it will inherit. (Drawing by R. F. Johnson)

In the body cells of an animal, each of the chromosomes is duplicated; whereas in the formation of the sex cells, the egg and the sperm, a reduction division occurs and only one chromosome and one gene of each pair goes into a sex cell. This means that only half the number of chromosomes and genes present in the body cells of the animal go into each egg and sperm, but each sperm or egg cell

---

[2] Sheep have 54 chromosomes; swine 40; and man 46, not 48 as long believed (the latter discovery was made by Dr. J. H. Tjio, and reported at the First International Congress of Human Genetics, Copenhagen).

has genes for every characteristic of its species. As will be explained later, the particular half that any one germ cell gets is determined by chance. When mating and fertilization occur, the single chromosomes from the germ cell of each parent unite to form new pairs, and the genes are again present in duplicate in the body cells of the embryo.

With all possible combinations in 30 pairs of chromosomes (the specie number in cattle and horses) and the genes that they bear, any sire or dam can transmit over one billion different samples of its own inheritance; and the combination from both parents makes possible one billion times one billion genetically different offspring. It is not strange, therefore, that no two animals within a given breed (except identical twins from a single egg split after fertilization) are exactly alike. We can marvel that the members of a given breed bear as much resemblance to each other as they do.

Even between such closely related individuals as full sisters, it is possible that there will be quite wide differences in size, growth rate, temperament, conformation, and in almost every conceivable character. Admitting that many of these differences may be due to undetected differences in environment, it is still true that in such animals much of the variation is due to hereditary differences. A sire, for example, will sometimes transmit to one offspring much better inheritance than he does to most of his get, simply as the result of chance differences in the genes that go to different sperm at the time of the reduction division. Such difference in inheritance of offspring has been called both the hope and the despair of the livestock breeder.

If an animal gets similar determiners or genes from each parent, it will produce a uniform set of offspring; because any half of its inheritance is just like any other half. For example, regardless of what combination of chromosomes go into a particular germ cell, it will be just like any other egg or sperm from the same individual. Such animals are referred to as being homozygous. Few, if any, of our animals are in this hereditary state at the present time. Instead of being homozygous, they are heterozygous. This explains why there may be such wide variation within the offspring of any given sire or dam. The wise and progressive breeder recognizes this fact, and he insists on the production records of all get rather than that of just a few meritorious individuals.

Variation between the offspring of animals that are not pure or homozygous, to use the technical term, is not to be marveled at, but is rather to be expected. No one would expect to draw exactly 35 sound apples and 15 rotten ones every time he took a random sample of 50 from a barrel containing 70 sound ones and 30 rotten ones, although on the average—if enough samples were drawn—he would expect to get about that proportion of each. Individual drawings would, of course, vary rather widely. Exactly the same situation applies to the relative numbers of "good" and "bad" genes that may be present in different germ cells from the same animal. Because of this situation, the mating of a mare with a fine track record to a stallion that on the average transmits relatively good performance will not always produce a foal of a merit equal to that of its parent. The foal could be markedly poorer than the parents or, happily, it could in some cases be better than either parent. The same situation applies to matings within all species of farm animals.

Selection and close breeding are the tools through which the stockman can obtain sires and dams whose chromosomes and genes contain similar hereditary determiners—animals that are genetically more homozygous.

Mutations

Gene changes are technically known as mutations. *A mutation may be defined as a sudden variation which is later passed on through inheritance and that results from changes in a gene or genes.* Mutations are not only rare, but they are prevailingly harmful. For all practical purposes, therefore, the genes can be thought of as unchanged from one generation to the next. The observed differences between animals are usually due to different combinations of genes being present rather than to mutations. Each gene probably changes only about once in each 100,000 to 1,000,000 animals produced.

Fig. 2-4. Polled Hereford bull Giant 101740AHR 1APHR, the sire that Warren Gammon used most extensively beginning in 1901. The occurrence of the polled characteristic within the horned Hereford breed is an example of a mutation or "sport" of economic importance. Out of this gene change arose the Polled Hereford breed of cattle. (Courtesy, B. O. Gammon, Secretary Emeritus, American Polled Hereford Association)

Once in a great while a mutation occurs in a farm animal, and it produces a visible effect in the animal carrying it. These animals are commonly called "sports." Such "sports" are occasionally of practical value or of value in establishing such things as breed trademarks. The occurrence of the polled characteristic within the horned Hereford and Shorthorn breeds is an example of a mutation or "sport" of economic importance.[3] Out of this has arisen the Polled Hereford and Polled Shorthorn breeds of cattle.

Gene changes can be accelerated by exposure to X rays, radium, mustard gas, and ultraviolet light. Such changes may eventually be observed in the offspring of both people and animals of Japan who were exposed to the atom bombs unleashed in World War II.

Simple Gene Inheritance (Qualitative Traits)[4]

In the simplest type of inheritance, only one pair of genes is involved. Thus, a pair of genes is responsible for the color of hair in Shorthorn cattle. An animal having two genes for red (RR) is actually red in color, whereas an animal having two genes for white (rr) is white in color. On the other hand, a Shorthorn which has one gene for red (R) and one for white (r), is neither red nor white but roan (Rr), which is a mixture of red and white. Thus, red X white matings in Shorthorn cattle usually produce roan offspring. Likewise, white X white matings generally produce white offspring; but it must be remembered that white in Shorthorns is seldom pure, for the face bristles, eyelashes, and ears usually carry red hairs. Roans, having one gene for red and one for white on the paired chromosomes will never breed true and, if mated together, will produce calves in the proportion of one red, two roans, and one white. If one wishes to produce roans, the most certain way is to mate red cows with a white bull or vice versa, for then all the calves will be roan. If a roan animal is bred to a red one, one-half the offspring will be red, whereas the other half will be roan. Likewise, when a roan animal is bred to a white one, approximately an equal number of roan and white calves will be produced.

It should be borne in mind that the various gene combinations, such as referred to previously, occur at random and that the various colors will appear in the offspring in the proportions indicated only when relatively large numbers are concerned. The possible gene combinations, therefore, are governed by the laws of chance, operating in much the same manner as the results obtained from flipping coins. For example, if a penny is flipped often enough, the number of heads and tails will come out about even. However, with the laws of chance in operation, it is possible that out of any four tosses one might get all heads, all tails, or even three to one. In exactly the same manner, a Shorthorn breeder may be highly elated in obtaining four red calves from a roan X roan mating only to be greatly depressed when the next four calves from the same matings are white in color.

In addition to color of hair, other examples of simple gene inheritance in

---

[3] The horned gene mutates to the polled gene at a fairly high frequency, apparently at the rate of about 1 in 20,000.

[4] The Shorthorn color situation given in this section does not always occur as expected because of modifying factors with small effects. Apparently, the white color of Shorthorns is seldom pure. Moreover, there exists the spotted red and white Shorthorn, which is presumably of a different genetic combination, possibly somewhat similar to spotted Ayrshires and Holstein-Friesians.

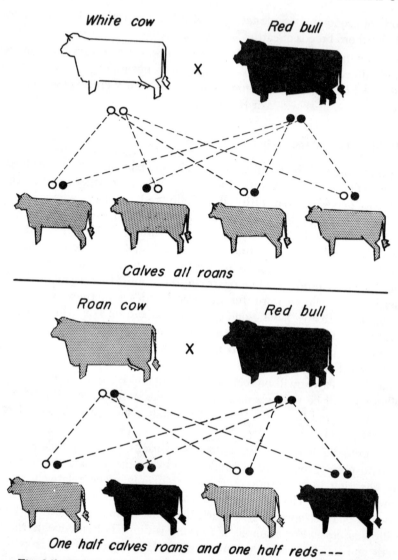

Fig. 2-5. Diagrammatic illustration of the inheritance of color in Shorthorn cattle. Red X white matings in Shorthorn catttle usually produce roan offspring; whereas roan X red matings produce one-half red offspring and one-half roan offspring. (Drawings by R. F. Johnson)

animals (sometimes referred to as qualitative traits) include the presence or absence of horns, type of blood, and lethals.

DOMINANT AND RECESSIVE FACTORS

In the example of Shorthorn colors, each gene of the pair (R and r) produced a visible effect, whether paired as identical genes (two reds or two whites) or as two different genes (red and white). This is not true of all genes; some of them have the ability to prevent or mask the expression of others, with the result that the genetic make-up of such animals cannot be recognized with perfect accuracy. This ability to cover up or mask the presence of one member of a set of genes is called dominance. The gene which masks the one is the dominant gene; the one which is masked is the recessive gene.

In cattle, the polled character is dominant to the horned character. Thus, if a *pure polled* bull is used on horned cows (or vice versa), the resulting progeny are not midway between the two parents but are of polled character.[5] It must be remembered, however, that not all hornless animals are pure for the polled character; many of them carry a factor for horns in the hidden or recessive condition. In genetic terminology, animals that are pure for a certain character —for example, the polled characteristic—are termed *homozygous*, whereas those that have one dominant and one recessive factor are termed *heterozygous*. A simple breeding test can be used in order to determine whether a polled bull is homozygous or heterozygous, but it is impossible to determine such purity or impurity through inspection. The breeding test consists of mating the polled sire with a number of horned females. If the bull is pure or homozygous for the polled character, all of the calves will be polled; if he is impure or heterozygous, only half of the resulting offspring will, on the average, be polled and half will have horns like the horned parents. Many breeders of Polled Herefords or Polled Shorthorns test their herd sires in this manner, mating the prospective sire to several horned animals.

It is clear, therefore, that a dominant character will cover up a recessive. Hence an animal's breeding performance cannot be recognized by its phenotype (how it looks), a fact which is of great significance in practical breeding.

Another example of dominance is that of the white face of Hereford cattle— the white face being dominant over the type of coloration in which the head and body are of the same color. Undoubtedly, this condition of dominance, which constitutes a trademark of the breed, has been of importance from a promotional standpoint.

As can be readily understood, dominance often makes the task of identifying and discarding all animals carrying an undesirable recessive factor a difficult one. Recessive genes can be passed on from generation to generation, appearing only when two animals, both of which carry a recessive factor, happen to mate. Even then, only one out of four offspring produced will, on the average, be homozygous for the recessive factor and show it.

---

[5] It is noteworthy, however, that when a homozygous polled animal is crossed with a homozygous horned animal, some "scurs" or small loosely attached horns usually appear. There are conflicting reports and opinions concerning the inheritance of scurs, with the following theories prevailing:

1. That the gene for scurs is recessive and independent of the major genes for horns. According to this theory, scurs appear only in individuals homozygous for the scurred gene (sc sc).
2. That scurs are a sex-influenced character. According to this theory, scurs will occur in males either homozygous (Sc Sc) or heterozygous (Sc sc) for the character, but only in females homozygous (Sc Sc) for the character; in other words, it acts as a dominant in polled males and a recessive in polled females.
3. That the major gene (P) for polled condition is only partially dominant, with heterozygous individuals (Pp) tending to be scurred, especially in bulls.

Horns prevent the expression of any genes an animal may have for scurs, and, thus, complicate studies designed to determine the exact mode of inheritance of scurs.

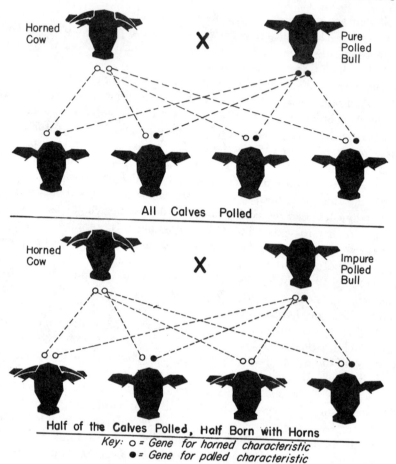

Fig. 2-6. Diagrammatic illustration of the inheritance of horns in cattle. If a bull that is pure or homozygous for the polled character is mated with a number of horned females, all of the calves will be polled; if a bull that is impure or heterozygous for the polled character is mated with a number of horned females, only half of the calves will, on the average, be polled. (Drawing by R. F. Johnson)

In cattle, the red color in the Angus breed is an example of such an undesirable recessive factor. Black polled cattle have been known in Scotland since 1523; and since the days of Hugh Watson, William McCombie, and George McPherson Grant, black has been the accepted color of the breed. Yet, down through the years, a recessive factor for red coat color has persisted in the breed. For this reason, a red calf occasionally and unexpectedly shows up in a purebred Angus herd (about one red calf appears in every 200 to 500 Angus calves dropped[6]). This occasional appearance of a red calf in the Angus breed does not signify any impurity of breeding but merely the outcropping of a long hidden re-

[6] In order to obtain one red calf out of 200, one parent out of every 7 must be a carrier of the red gene. Actually, to get 1/196 red calves, there must be 1/14 b reproductive cells in both males and females because $1/14 \times 1/14 = 1/196$. Thus 1/7 of the parents must be Bb while 6/7 are BB.

cessive gene. When a red calf does appear, one can be very certain that both the sire and dam contributed equally to the condition and that each of them carries the recessive gene for red color. This fact should be given consideration in the culling program.

As the factor for red is recessive, the red animals are pure for color. The mating of two red animals, therefore, will always produce red calves.[7]

Other examples of undesirable recessives are red color in Holstein cattle and dwarfism in cattle.

Fig. 2-7. Two purebred calves of the same breed. The white (albino) calf is the result of undesirable recessive factors that were carried by both the sire and dam. Recessive genes can be passed on for many generations without their presence becoming evident until such time as two animals are mated both of which carry the same recessive factors. (Courtesy, Washington State University)

Assuming that a hereditary defect or abnormality has occurred in a herd or flock and that it is recessive in nature, the breeding program to be followed to prevent or minimize the possibility of its future occurrence will depend somewhat on the type of herd or flock involved—especially on whether it is a commercial or purebred herd. In an ordinary commercial herd, the breeder can usually guard against further reappearance of the undesirable recessive by simply using an outcross (unrelated) sire within the same breed or by crossbreeding with a sire from another breed. With this system, the breeder is fully aware of the recessive being present, but he has taken action to keep it from showing up.

On the other hand, if such an undesirable recessive appears in a purebred herd or flock, the action should be more drastic. A reputable purebred breeder has an obligation not only to himself but to his customers among both the purebred and commercial herds. Purebred animals must be purged of undesirable genes and lethals. This can be done by:

1. Eliminating those sires and dams that are known to have transmitted the undesirable recessive character.

---

[7] A separate U.S. breed registry association for these Red Angus cattle was organized in 1954. To these breeders, the recessive gene for red is desirable.

2. Eliminating both the abnormal and normal offspring produced by these sires and dams (approximately half of the normal animals will carry the undesirable character in the recessive condition).

3. By, in some instances, breeding a prospective herd sire to a number of females known to carry the factor for the undesirable recessive, thus making sure that the new sire is free from the recessive.

Such action in a purebred herd is expensive, and it calls for considerable courage. Yet it is the only way in which the purebred livestock of the country can be freed from such undesirable genes.

INCOMPLETE OR PARTIAL DOMINANCE

The results of crossing polled with horned cattle are clear-cut because the polled character is completely dominant over its allele (horned). If, however, a cross is made between a red and a white Shorthorn, the result is a roan (mixture of red and white hairs) color pattern. In the latter cross, the action of a gene is such that it does not cover the allele, which is known as incomplete dominance; or, stated differently, the roan color is the result of the action of a pair of genes (joint action) neither of which is dominant. This explains the futility of efforts to develop Shorthorns pure for roan.

The preceding discussion also indicates that there are varying degrees of dominance—from complete dominance to an entire lack of dominance. In the vast majority of cases, however, dominance is neither complete nor absent, but incomplete or partial. Also, it is now known that dominance is not the result of single-factor pairs but that the degree of dominance depends upon the animal's whole genetic makeup together with the environment to which it is exposed, and the various interactions between the genetic complex (genotype) and the environment.

Multiple Gene Inheritance (Quantitative Traits)

Relatively few characters of economic importance in farm animals are inherited in as simple a manner as the coat color or polled condition described. Commercially important characters—such as meat production, milk and butterfat production, egg production, and wool production—are due to many genes; thus, they are called multiple-factor characters or multiple-gene characters. Because such characters show all manner of gradation—from high to low production, for example—they are sometimes referred to as quantitative traits.

In quantitative inheritance, the extremes (either good or bad) tend to swing back to the average. Thus, the offspring of a grand champion bull and a grand champion cow are not apt to be as good as either parent. Likewise, and happily so, the progeny of two very mediocre parents will likely be superior to either parent.

Estimates of the number of pairs of genes affecting each economically important characteristic vary greatly, but the majority of geneticists agree that for most such characters 10 or more pairs of genes are involved. Growth rate in cattle, therefore, is affected by: (1) the animal's appetite; (2) feed consumption; (3) feed utilization—that is, the proportion of the feed eaten that is absorbed into the blood stream; (4) feed assimilation—the use to which the nutrients are put after absorption; and (5) feed conversion—whether used for muscle, fat, or bone formation. This should indicate clearly enough that such an economic characteristic as growth rate is controlled by many genes and that it is difficult to determine the mode of inheritance of such characters.

Multiple Births

From Table 2-3 it is obvious that there are wide specie differences in multiple births; the ewe being the most prolific and the beef cow the least. Of course, it is well known that the sow is more prolific than any of these animals, being exceeded only by the hen.

TABLE 2—3

FREQUENCY OF MULTIPLE BIRTHS

Species	Twins		Triplets		Quadruplets	
(all breeds)	(% of twin births)	(no. of twin births in each 1,000 births)	(% of triplet births)	(ratio of triplet births)	(% of quad-ruplet births)	(ratio of quad-ruplet births)
Beef cattle	0.5	5				
Dairy cattle	2.0	20	.03	4 in 14,111 (in Brown Swiss)	.01	1 in 14,111 (in Brown Swiss)
Sheep	20-60	200-600	1-2	10-20/1,000	.02-.10	2-10/10,000
Horses	1.5	15				

The tendency to produce twins is inherited to some extent; thus, more twins are produced in some breeds and in some families than in others. But factors other than heredity play a major part in determining whether any particular birth shall be a twin birth.

Most sheepmen have long considered twinning desirable, but they frown upon triplets because size of lamb and survival rate are greatly reduced in such births.

Most cattlemen prefer single births to twins due to (1) the high incidence of freemartins (sterile heifers) in twins of opposite sexes, (2) the increased mortality rate of the calves, and (3) the tendency of cows that have produced twins to have a lowered conception rate following twinning.

In horses, single births are clearly best; twin foals are seldom successfully raised, the death of one or both foals being common.

Twins may be either fraternal (dizygotic) or identical (monozygotic). Fraternal twins are produced from two separate ova that were fertilized by different sperm. Identical twins result when a single fertilized egg divides, very early in its embryology, into two separate individuals.

In humans, nearly half of the like-sexed twins are identical, whereas in cattle only 5 to 12 per cent of such births are identical. Such twins are always of the same sex, a pair of males or a pair of females, and alike genetically—

their chromosomes and genes are alike; they are 100 per cent related. When identical twins are not entirely separated, they are known as Siamese twins.

Genetically, fraternal twins are no more alike than full brothers and sisters born at different times; they are only 50 per cent related. They usually resemble each other more, however, because they were subjected to the same intrauterine environment before birth and generally they are reared under much the same environment. Also, fraternal twins may be of different sexes.

Sex Determination

On the average, and when considering a large population, approximately equal numbers of males and females are born in all common species of animals. To be sure, many notable exceptions can be found in individual herds. The history of the Washington State University Angus herd, for example, reads like a story book. The entire herd was built up from one foundation female purchased in 1910. She produced seven daughters. In turn, her first daughter produced six females. Most remarkable yet and extremely fortunate from the standpoint of building up the cow herd, it was four years before any bull calves were dropped in the herd.

Such unusual examples often erroneously lead the stockman to think that something peculiar to the treatment or management of a particular herd resulted in a preponderance of males or females, as the case may be. In brief, through such examples, the breeder may get the impression that variation in the sex ratio is not random but that it is under the control of some unknown and mysterious influence. Under such conditions, it can be readily understood why the field of sex control is a fertile one for fraudulent operators. Certainly, any fool-proof method of controlling sex would have tremendous commercial possibilities. For example, cattlemen wishing to build up a herd could then secure a high percentage of heifer calves. On the other hand, the commercial cattleman would then elect to produce only enough heifers for replacement purposes. From an economic standpoint, he would want a preponderance of bull calves for the reason that commercial steers sell for a higher price than do commercial heifers. Unfortunately, no such method of sex control is known.

The most widely accepted theory of sex determination at the present time is that sex is determined by the chromosomal make-up of the individual. One particular pair of the chromosomes is called the sex chromosomes. In farm animals, the female has a pair of similar chromosomes (usually called X chromosomes), whereas the male has a pair of unlike sex chromosomes (usually called X and Y chromosomes). In the bird, this condition is reversed, the females having the unlike pair and the male having the like pair.

The pairs of sex chromosomes separate out when the germ cells are formed. Thus, each of the ova or eggs produced by the cow contains the X chromosome; whereas the sperm of the bull are of two types, one half containing the X chromosome and the other half the Y chromosome. Since, on the average, the eggs and sperm unite at random, it can be understood that half of the progeny

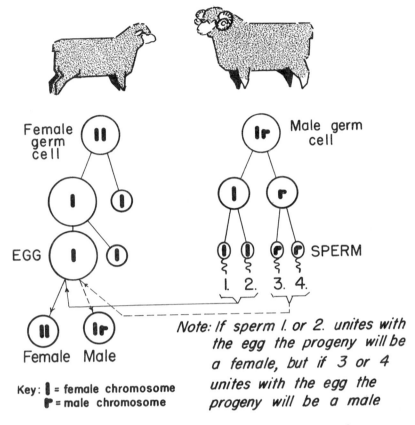

Female germ cell

Male germ cell

EGG

SPERM

1. 2. 3. 4.

Female Male

Note: If sperm 1. or 2. unites with the egg the progeny will be a female, but if 3 or 4 unites with the egg the progeny will be a male

Key: ▮ = female chromosome
     ▮ = male chromosome

Fig. 2-8. Diagrammatic illustration of the mechanism of sex determination in farm animals, showing how sex is determined by the chromosomal make-up of the individual. The female has a pair of like sex chromosomes, whereas the male has a pair of unlike sex chromosomes. Thus, if an egg and sperm of like sex chromosomal make-up unite, the offspring will be a female; whereas if an egg and sperm of unlike sex chromosomal make-up unite, the offspring will be a male. (Drawing by R. F. Johnson)

will contain the chromosomal make-up XX (females)[8] with the other half XY (males).[8]

Lethals and Abnormalities of Development

Lethals may be defined as congenital abnormalities which result in the death of an animal, either at birth or later in life. Other defects occur which are not sufficiently severe to cause death but which do impair the usefulness of the affected animals.

Many such abnormal animals are born on the nation's farms and ranches each year. Unfortunately, the purebred breeder, whose chief business is that of

[8]The scientists' symbols for the male and female, respectively, are: ♂ (the sacred shield and spear of Mars, the Roman god of war) and ♀ (the looking glass of Venus, the Roman goddess of love and beauty).

selling breeding stock, is likely to "keep mum" about the appearance of any defective animals in his herd because of the justifiable fear that it may hurt his sales. With the commercial producer, however, the appearance of such lethals as bulldog calves is simply so much economic loss, with the result that he generally, openly and without embarrassment, admits the presence of the abnormality and seeks correction.

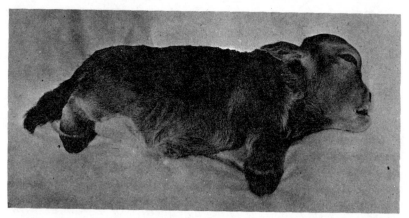

Fig. 2-9. A "bulldog" calf, a lethal condition that is the result of homozygous recessive genes. The animal was born alive and lived about an hour. (Courtesy, Prof. Graydon W. Brandt, The Clemson Agricultural College)

The embryological development—the development of the young from the time that the egg and the sperm unite until the animal is born—is very complicated. Thus, the oddity probably is that so many of the offspring develop normally rather than that a few develop abnormally.

Many such abnormalities (commonly known as monstrosities or freaks) are hereditary, being caused by certain "bad" genes. Moreover, the bulk of such lethals are recessive and may, therefore, remain hidden for many generations. The prevention of such genetic abnormalities requires that the germ plasm be purged of the "bad" genes. This means that, where recessive lethals are involved, the stockman must be aware of the fact that both parents carry the gene. For the total removal of the lethals, test matings and rigid selection must be practiced. The best test mating to use for a given sire consists of mating him to some of his own daughters.

In addition to hereditary abnormalities, there are certain abnormalities that may be due to nutritional deficiencies, or to "accidents of development"—the latter including those which appear to occur sporadically and for which there is no well-defined reason. When only a few defective individuals occur within a particular herd, it is often impossible to determine whether their occurrence is due to: (1) defective heredity, (2) defective nutrition, or (3) merely to accidents of development. If the same abnormality occurs in any appreciable number of animals, however, it is probably either hereditary or nutritional. In any event, the diagnosis of the condition is not always a simple matter.

The following conditions would tend to indicate a hereditary defect:

1. If the defect had previously been reported as hereditary in the same breed of livestock.

2. If it occurred more frequently within certain families or when there had been inbreeding.

3. If it occurred in more than one season and when different rations had been fed.

The following conditions might be accepted as indications that the abnormality was due to a nutritional deficiency:

1. If it had previously been reliably reported to be due to a nutritional deficiency.

2. If it appeared to be restricted to a certain area.

3. If it occurred when the ration of the mother was known to be deficient.

4. If it disappeared when an improved ration was fed.

If there is suspicion that the ration is defective, it should be improved, not only from the standpoint of preventing such deformities, but from the standpoint of good and efficient management.

If there is good and sufficient evidence that the abnormal condition is hereditary, the steps to be followed in purging the herd of the undesirable gene are identical to those for ridding the herd of any other undesirable recessive factor. An inbreeding program, of course, is the most effective way in which to expose hereditary lethals in order that purging may follow.

The Relative Importance of Sire and Dam

As a sire can have so many more offspring during a given season or a lifetime than a dam, he is from a hereditary standpoint a more important individual than any one female so far as the whole herd is concerned, although both the sire and the dam are of equal importance so far as concerns any one offspring. Because of their wider use, therefore, sires are usually culled more rigidly than females, and the breeder can well afford to pay more for an outstanding sire than for an equally outstanding female.

Experienced stockmen have long felt that daughters often more closely resemble their sires, whereas the sons resemble their dams. Some sires and dams, therefore, enjoy a reputation based almost exclusively on the merit of their sons, whereas others owe their prestige to their daughters. Although this situation is likely to be exaggerated, any such phenomenon that may exist is due to sex-linked inheritance which may be explained as follows: The genes that determine sex are carried on one of the chromosomes. The other genes that are located on the same chromosome will be linked or associated with sex and will be transmitted to the next generation in combination with sex. Thus, because of sex linkage, there are more color-blind men than color-blind women. In poultry breeding, the sex-linked factor may be used in a practical way for the purpose of distinguishing the pullets from the cockerels early in life, through the process known as "sexing" the chicks. When a black cock is crossed with barred hens, all the cocks come barred and all the hens come black. It should be emphasized, however, that under most conditions, it appears that the influence of the sire and dam on any one offspring is about equal. Most breeders, therefore, will do well to seek excellence in both sexes of breeding animals.

Prepotency

Prepotency refers to the ability of the animal, either male or female, to stamp its own characteristics on its offspring. The offspring of a prepotent bull, for example, resemble both their sire and each other more closely than usual. The only conclusive and final test of prepotency consists of the inspection of the get.

From a genetic standpoint, there are two requisites that an animal must possess in order to be prepotent: (1) dominance and (2) homozygosity. Every offspring that receives a dominant gene or genes will show the effect of that gene or genes in the particular character or characters which result therefrom. Moreover, a perfectly homozygous animal would transmit the same kind of genes to all of its offspring. Although entirely homozygous animals probably never exist, it is realized that a system of inbreeding is the only way to produce animals that are as nearly homozygous as possible.

It should be emphasized that it is impossible to determine just how important prepotency may be in animal breeding, although many sires of the past have enjoyed a reputation of being extremely prepotent. Perhaps these animals were prepotent, but there is also the possibility that their reputation for producing outstanding animals may have rested upon the fact that they were mated to some of the best females of the breed.

In summary, it may be said that if a given sire or dam possesses a great number of genes that are completely dominant for desirable type and performance and if the animal is relatively homozygous, the offspring will closely resemble the parent and resemble each other, or be uniform. Fortunate, indeed, is the breeder who possesses such an animal.

Nicking

If the offspring of certain matings are especially outstanding and in general better than their parents, breeders are prone to say that the animals nicked well. For example, a cow may produce outstanding calves to the service of a certain bull, but when mated to another bull of apparent equal merit as a sire, the offspring may be disappointing. Or sometimes the mating of a rather average bull to an equally average cow will result in the production of a most outstanding individual both from the standpoint of type and performance.

So-called successful nicking is due, genetically speaking, to the fact that the right combination of genes for good characters are contributed by each parent, although each of the parents within itself may be lacking in certain genes necessary for excellence. In other words, the animals nicked well because their respective combinations of good genes were such as to complement each other.

Fig. 2-10. Anxiety 4th 9904, whose sons were alleged to nick exceedingly well on the daughters of North Pole in the Gudgell and Simpson herd of Hereford cattle. (Courtesy, *The American Hereford Journal*)

The history of animal breeding includes records of several supposedly favorable nicks, one of the most famous of which was the favorable result secured from crossing sons of Anxiety 4th with daughters of North Pole in the Gudgell and Simpson herd of Hereford cattle. At this late date, it is impossible to determine whether these Anxiety 4th-North Pole matings were successful because of nicking or whether the good results should be more rightfully attributed to the fact that the sons of Anxiety 4th were great breeding bulls and that they merely happened to be mated, for the most part, with daughters of North Pole because the available females in the Gudgell and Simpson herd were of this particular breeding.

Because of the very nature of successful nicks, outstanding animals arising therefrom must be carefully scrutinized from a breeding standpoint, because, with their heterozygous origin, it is quite unlikely that they will breed true.

Family Names

In cattle, depending upon the breed, family names are traced through either the males or females. In Angus and Shorthorn cattle, the family names had their origin with certain great foundation females, whereas in Herefords the family names trace through the sires. Similar family names exist in horses, but in both hogs and sheep less importance is attached to them.

Unfortunately, the value of family names is generally grossly exaggerated. Obviously, if the foundation male or female, as the case may be, is very many generations removed, the genetic superiority of this head of a family is halved so many times by subsequent matings that there is little reason to think that one family is superior to another. The situation is often further distorted by breeders placing a premium on family names of which there are few members, little realizing that, in at least some cases, there may be unfortunate reasons for the scarcity in numbers.

Such family names have about as much significance as human family names. Who would be so foolish as to think that the Joneses as a group are alike and different from the Smiths? Perhaps, if the truth were known, there have been many individuals with each of these family names who have been of no particular credit to the clan, and the same applies to all other family names.

Family names lend themselves readily to speculation. Because of this, the history of livestock breeding has often been blighted by instances of unwise pedigree selection on the basis of not too meaningful family names. The most classical example of a situation of this type occurred with the Duchess family of Shorthorn cattle, founded by the noted pioneer English Shorthorn breeder, Thomas Bates. Bates, and more especially those later breeders who emulated him, followed preferences in bloodlines within increasingly narrow limits, until ultimately they were breeding cattle solely according to fashionable pedigrees, using good, bad, and indifferent animals. Fad and fancy in pedigrees dominated the situation, and the fundamental importance of good individuality as the basis of selecting animals for breeding purposes was for the time largely ignored. The sole desire of these breeders was to concentrate the Duchess blood. The climax of the "Duchess boom" (or "Bates boom") came in September, 1873, when the New York Mills herd was sold at auction with English and American breeders competing for the offering. At this memorable event, 109 head of Duchess-bred cattle averaged $3,504 per head, with the seven-year-old 8th Duchess of Geneva selling at the world's record price of $40,600.

As with most booms, the New York Mills sale was followed by a rather critical reaction, and eventually the bottom dropped out of values. Even more tragic, the owners of Duchess Shorthorns suddenly came to a realization that indiscriminate inbreeding and a lack of selection had put the family name in disrepute. As a result, the strain became virtually extinct a few years later.

On the other hand, certain linebred families—linebred to a foundation sire or dam so that the family is kept highly related to it—do have genetic significance. Moreover, if the programs involved have been accompanied by rigid culling, many good individuals may have evolved, and the family name may be in good repute. The Anxiety 4th family of Hereford cattle is probably the best-known family of this kind in meat animals. Even so, there is real danger in assuming that an "airtight" or "straight-bred" Anxiety 4th pedigree is within itself meritorious and that this family is superior to that of any other family in Hereford cattle.

Heredity and Environment

A massive purebred bull, standing belly deep in straw and with a manger full of feed before him, is undeniably the result of two forces—heredity and environment (with the latter including training). If turned out on the range, an identical twin to the placid bull would present an entirely different appearance. By the same token, optimum environment could never make a champion out of a bull with scrub ancestry, but it might well be added that "fat and hair will cover up a multitude of sins."

These are extreme examples, and they may be applied to any class of farm animals; but they do emphasize the fact that any particular animal is the product of heredity and environment. Stated differently, heredity may be thought of as the foundation, and environment as the structure. Heredity has already made its contribution at the time of fertilization, but environment works ceaselessly away until death.

Admittedly, after looking over an animal, a breeder cannot with certainty know whether it is genetically a high or a low producer; and there can be no denying the fact that environment—including feeding, management, and disease —plays a tremendous part in determining the extent to which hereditary differences that are present will be expressed in animals.

Experimental work has long shown conclusively enough that the vigor and size of animals at birth are dependent upon the environment of the embryo from the minute the ova or egg is fertilized by the sperm, and now we have evidence to indicate that newborn animals are affected by the environment of the egg and sperm long before fertilization has been accomplished. In other words, perhaps due to storage of factors, the kind and quality of the ration fed to young, growing females may later affect the quality of their progeny. Generally speaking, then, environment may inhibit the full expression of potentialities from a time preceding fertilization until physiological maturity has been attained.

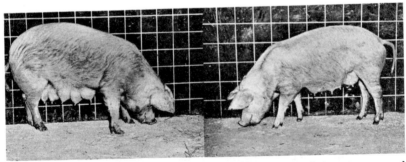

Fig. 2-11. Feed made the difference! The two sows are of the same age and breeding, but the sow shown in the picture at left received all she could eat from birth, whereas the gaunt sow shown in the picture at right was limited to 70 per cent of the ration consumed by the better fed animal. This 10-year experiment, conducted at Washington State University, was designed to study the effect of plane of nutrition on meat animal improvement. (Courtesy, Washington State University)

It is generally agreed, therefore, that maximum development of characters of economic importance—growth, body form, milk or wool production, speed, etc.—cannot be achieved unless there are optimum conditions of nutrition and management. However, the next question is whether a breeding program can make maximum progress under conditions of suboptimal nutrition (such as is often found under some farm and range conditions). One school of thought is that selection for such factors as body form and growth rate in animals can be most effective only under nutritive conditions promoting the near maximum development of those characters of which the animal is capable. The other school of thought is that genetic differences affecting usefulness under suboptimal conditions will be expressed under such suboptimal conditions, and that differences observed under forced conditions may not be correlated with real utility under less favorable conditions. Those favoring the latter thinking argue, therefore, that the production and selection of breeding animals for the range should be under typical range conditions and that the animals should not be highly fitted in a box stall.

In general, the results of a long-time experiment conducted at Washington State University support the contention that selection of breeding animals should be carried on under the same environmental conditions as those under which commercial animals are produced.[9]

Within the pure breeds of livestock—managed under average or better than average conditions—it has been found that, in general, only 30 to 45 per cent of the observed variation in a characteristic is actually brought about by hereditary variations. To be sure, if we contrast animals that differ very greatly in heredity—for example, a champion heifer and a scrub—90 per cent or more of the apparent differences in type may be due to heredity. The point is, however, that extreme cases such as the one just mentioned are not involved in the advancement within improved breeds of livestock. Here the comparisons are between animals of average or better than average quality, and the observed differences are often very minor.

The problem of the progressive breeder is that of selecting the very best animals available genetically—these to be parents of the next generation of offspring in his herd. The fact that only 30 to 45 per cent of the observed variation is due to differences in inheritance, and that environmental differences can produce misleading variations, makes mistakes in the selection of breeding animals inevitable. However, if the purebred breeder has clearly in mind a well-defined ideal and adheres rigidly to it in selecting his breeding stock, very definite progress can be made, especially if mild inbreeding is judiciously used as a tool through which to fix the hereditary material.

It is also quite likely that better adapted strains or breeds of animals need to be developed for different sections of the world and even for the diverse conditions existing in this large country. For example, the sparse vegetation under low-rainfall conditions in many sections of the Southwest offers considerable contrast to the lush pastures of the Corn Belt. Accordingly, it is quite likely that different types of animals should be produced in each area. In recognition of this fact, the King Ranch in Texas developed the Santa Gertrudis breed of cattle, and Brahman breeding has been and is being used in the development of other breeds adapted to the southern part of the United States. Finally, it may be said that it is highly questionable that a breed or strain of animals is well adapted to a certain area if, over a period of years, it is necessary constantly to go to outside areas for a high proportion of the breeding stock.

---

[9] Washington Agricultural Experiment Station Bul. 34, 1961.

SYSTEMS OF BREEDING

The many diverse types and breeds among each class of farm animals in existence today originated from only a few wild types within each species. These early domesticated animals possessed the pool of genes, which, through controlled matings and selection, proved flexible in the hands of man. In cattle, for example, through various systems of breeding, there evolved animals especially adapted to draft purposes, beef production, milk production, and dual-purpose needs. Animals with special adaptations and types were also developed in horses, sheep, and hogs. Each of the common systems of breeding will now be discussed briefly.

Perhaps at the outset it should be stated that there is no one best system of breeding or secret of success for any and all conditions. Each breeding program is an individual case, requiring careful study. The choice of the system of breeding should be determined primarily by size and quality of herd, finances and skill of the operator, and the ultimate goal ahead.

Purebreeding

A purebred animal may be defined as a member of a breed, the animals of which possess a common ancestry and distinctive characteristics; and he is either registered or eligible for registry in the herd book of that breed. The breed association consists of a group of breeders banded together for the purpose of: (1) recording the lineage of their animals, (2) protecting the purity of the breed, and (3) promoting the interest of the breed.

It must be emphasized that pure breeding and homozygosity may bear very different connotations. The term "purebred" refers to animals whose entire lineage, regardless of the number of generations removed, traces back to the foundation animals accepted by the breed or to any animals which have been subsequently approved for infusion. On the other hand, homozygosity refers to the likeness of the genes.

Yet there is some interrelationship between purebreds and homozygosity. Because most breeds had a relatively small number of foundation animals, the unavoidable inbreeding and linebreeding during the formative stage resulted in a certain amount of homozygosity. Moreover, through the normal sequence of events, it is estimated that purebreds become more homozygous by from 0.25 to 0.5 per cent per animal generation. It should be emphasized that the word "purebred" does not necessarily guarantee superior type or high productivity. That is to say, the word "purebred" is not, within itself, magic, nor is it sacred. Many a person has found to his sorrow that there are such things as purebred scrubs. Yet, on the average, purebred animals are superior to nonpurebreds.

For the man with experience and adequate capital, the breeding of purebreds may offer unlimited opportunities. It has been well said that honor, fame, and fortune are all within the realm of possible realization of the purebred breeder; but it should also be added that only a few achieve this high calling.

Purebred breeding is a highly specialized type of production. Generally speaking, only the experienced breeder should undertake the production of purebreds with the intention of furnishing foundation or replacement stock to other purebred breeders or purebred sires to the producer of grades. Although we have had many constructive animal breeders and great progress has been made, it must be remembered that only a few achieve sufficient success to classify as master breeders.

Inbreeding

Most scientists divide inbreeding into various categories, according to the closeness of the relationship of the animals mated and the purpose of the matings. There is considerable disagreement, however, as to both the terms used and the meanings that it is intended they should convey. For purposes of this book and the discussion which follows, the following definitions will be used:

Inbreeding is the mating of animals more closely related than the average of the population from which they came.

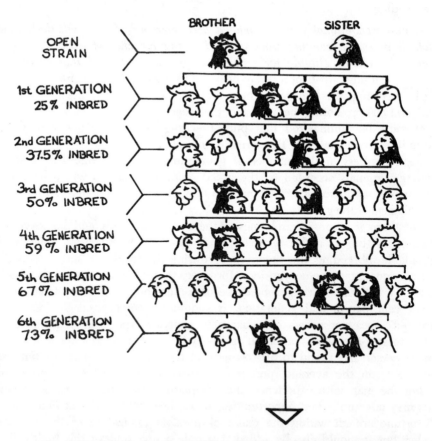

Fig. 2-12. Inbreds are the "building blocks" of the modern inbredcrossed chicken. The technique for making an inbred is illustrated in this figure. Of course, selections are made during each generation. (Courtesy, DeKalb Agricultural Assn., Inc., DeKalb, Ill.)

Closebreeding is the mating of closely related animals: sire to daughter, son to dam, and brother to sister.

Linebreeding is the mating of animals more distantly related than in closebreeding and in which the matings are usually directed toward keeping the offspring closely related to some highly admired ancestor; such as half-brother to half-sister, female to grandsire, and cousins.

CLOSEBREEDING

In closebreeding there are a minimum number of different ancestors. In the repeated mating of a brother with his full sister, for example, there are only 2 grandparents instead of 4, only 2 great-grandparents instead of 8, and only 2 different ancestors in each generation farther back—instead of the theoretically possible 16, 32, 64, 128, etc. The most intensive form of inbreeding is self-fertilization. It occurs in some plants, such as wheat and garden peas, and in some lower animals; but domestic animals are not self-fertilized. Closebreeding is rarely practiced by present-day stockmen, though it was common in the foundation animals of most of the breeds. For example, it is interesting to note that Comet (155), an illustrious sire and noted as the first Shorthorn to sell for $5,000, came from the mating of Favorite and Young Phoenix, a heifer that had been produced from the union of Favorite with his own dam. Such was the program of the Collings brothers and many another early-day beef cattle breeder, including those in all breeds.

The reasons for practicing closebreeding are:

1. It increases the degree of homozygosity within animals, making the resulting offspring pure or homozygous in a larger proportion of their gene pairs than in the case of linebred or outcross animals. In so doing, the less desirable recessive genes are brought to light so that they can be more readily culled. Thus, closebreeding, together with rigid culling, affords the surest and quickest method of fixing and perpetuating a desirable character or group of characters.

2. If carried on for a period of time, it tends to create lines or strains of animals that are uniform in type and other characteristics.

3. It keeps the relationship to a desirable ancestor highest.

4. Because of the greater homozygosity, it makes for greater prepotency. That is, selected closebred animals are more homozygous for desirable genes (genes which are often dominant) and they, therefore, transmit these genes with greater uniformity.

5. Through the production of inbred lines or families by closebreeding and the subsequent crossing of certain of these lines, it affords a modern approach to livestock improvement. Moreover, the best of the closebred animals are likely to give superior results in outcrosses.

6. Where a breeder is in the unique position of having his herd so far advanced that to go on the outside for seed stock would merely be a step backward, it offers the only sound alternative for maintaining existing quality or making further improvement.

The precautions in closebreeding may be summarized as follows:

1. As closebreeding greatly enhances the chances that recessives will appear during the early generations in obtaining homozygosity, it is almost certain to increase the proportion of worthless breeding stock produced—that with such so-called degenerate characteristics as reduction in size, fertility, and general vigor. Lethals and other genetic abnormalities often appear with increased frequency in closebred animals.

2. Because of the rigid culling necessary in order to avoid the "fixing" of undesirable characters, especially in the first generations of a closebreeding program, it is almost imperative that this system of breeding be confined to a relatively large herd or flock and to instances when the owner has sufficient finances to stand the rigid culling that must accompany such a program.

3. It requires skill in making planned matings and rigid selection, thus being most successful when applied by "master breeders."

4. It is not adapted for use by the man with average or below average stock because the very fact that his animals are average means that a goodly share of undesirable genes are present. Closebreeding would merely make the animals more homozygous for undesirable genes and, therefore, worse.

Judging from outward manifestations alone, it might appear that closebreeding is predominantly harmful in its effects—often leading to the production of defective animals lacking in the vitality necessary for successful and profitable production. But this is by no means the whole story. Although closebreeding often leads to the production of animals of low value, the resulting superior animals can confidently be expected to be homozygous for a greater than average number of good genes and thus more valuable for breeding purposes. Figuratively speaking, therefore, closebreeding may be referred to as "trial by fire," and the breeder who practices it can expect to obtain many animals that fail to measure up and have to be culled. On the other hand, if closebreeding is properly handled, he can also expect to secure animals of exceptional value.

Although closebreeding has been practiced less during the past century than in the formative period of the different pure breeds of livestock, it has real merit when its principles and limitations are fully understood. Perhaps closebreeding had best be confined to use by the skilled master breeder who is in a sufficiently sound financial position to endure rigid and intelligent culling and delayed returns and whose herd is both large and above average in quality.

LINEBREEDING

From a biological standpoint, closebreeding and linebreeding are the same thing, differing merely in intensity. In general, closebreeding has been frowned upon by stockmen, but linebreeding (the less intensive form) has been looked upon with favor in many quarters. In a line breeding program, the degree of relationship is not closer than half-brother and half-sister or matings more distantly related; cousin matings, grandparent to grand offspring, etc.

Linebreeding is usually practiced in order to conserve and perpetuate the good traits of a certain outstanding sire or dam. Because such descendents are of similar lineage, they have the same general type of germ plasm and therefore exhibit a high degree of uniformity in type and performance. During the past three decades, for example, a great many Hereford herds have been linebred to Prince Domino, that immortal Gudgell and Simpson bred bull who, in the hands of Otto Fulscher and the Wyoming Hereford Ranch, contributed so much to the improvement of the Hereford breed.

Fig. 2-13. Prince Domino 499611, calved September 13, 1914 and died April 4, 1930. Many great Herefords have been produced from linebreeding to this immortal sire. Prince Domino's final resting place at Wyoming Hereford Ranch, Cheyenne, Wyoming, is marked with the following epitaph: "He lived and died and won a lasting name." This is a rare tribute, indeed, to any beast—or man. (Courtesy, *The American Hereford Journal*)

In a more limited way, a linebreeding program has the same advantages and disadvantages of a closebreeding program. Stated differently, linebreeding offers fewer possibilities both for good and harm than closebreeding. It is a more conservative and safer type of program, offering less probability to either "hit the jackpot" or "sink the ship." It is a "middle-of-the-road" program that the vast majority of average and small breeders can safely follow to their advantage. Through it, reasonable progress can be made without taking any great risk. A degree of homozygosity of certain desirable genes can be secured without running too great a risk of intensifying undesirable ones.

Usually a linebreeding program is best accomplished through breeding to an outstanding sire rather than to an outstanding dam because of the greater number of offspring of the former. If a breeder found himself in possession of a great bull—proved great by the performance records of a large number of his get—a linebreeding program might be initiated in the following way: Select two of the best sons of the noted bull and mate them to their half-sisters, balancing all possible defects in the subsequent matings. The next generation matings might well consist of breeding the daughters of one of the bulls to the son of the other, etc. If, in such a program, it seems wise to secure some outside blood (genes) to correct a common defect or defects in the herd, this may be done through selecting one or more outstanding proved cows from the outside—animals whose get are strong where the herd may be deficient—and then mating this female or females to one of the linebred bulls with the hope of producing a son that may be used in the herd.

The owner of a small purebred herd or flock with limited numbers can often follow a linebreeding program by buying all of his sires from a large breeder who follows such a program—thus, in effect, following the linebreeding program of the larger breeder.

Naturally, a linebreeding program may be achieved in other ways. Regardless of the actual matings used, the main objective in such a system of breeding is that of rendering the animals homozygous—in desired type and performance—to some great and highly regarded ancestor, while at the same time weeding out homozygous undesirable characteristics. The success of the program, therefore, is dependent upon having desirable genes with which to start and an intelligent intensification of these good genes.

It should be emphasized that there are some types of herds that should almost never closebreed or linebreed. These include grade or commercial herds and purebred herds of only average quality.

The owner of a grade or commercial herd runs the risk of undesirable results, and, even if successful as a commercial breeder, he cannot sell his stock at increased prices for breeding purposes.

With purebred herds of only average quality, more rapid progress can usually be made by introducing superior outcross sires. Moreover, if the animals are of only average quality they must have a preponderance of "bad" genes that would only be intensified through a closebreeding or linebreeding program.

Outcrossing

Outcrossing is the mating of animals that are members of the same breed but which show no relationship close up in the pedigree (for at least the first four or six generations).

Most of our purebred animals of all classes of livestock are the result of outcrossing. It is a relatively safe system of breeding, for it is unlikely that two such unrelated animals will carry the same undesirable genes and pass them on to their offspring.

Perhaps it might well be added that the majority of purebred breeders with average or below average herds had best follow an outcrossing program, because, in such herds, the problem is that of retaining a heterozygous type of germ plasm with the hope that genes for undesirable characters will be counteracted by genes for desirable characters. With such average or below average herds, an inbreeding program would merely make the animals homozygous for the less desirable characters, the presence of which already makes for their mediocrity.

In general, continued outcrossing offers neither the hope for improvement nor the hazard of retrogression of linebreeding or closebreeding programs.

Judicious and occasional outcrossing may well be an integral part of line-breeding or closebreeding programs. As closely inbred animals become increasingly homozygous with germ plasm for good characters, they may likewise become homozygous for certain undesirable characters even though their general overall type and performance remains well above the breed average. Such defects may best be remedied by introducing an outcross through an animal or animals known to be especially strong in the character or characters needing strengthening. This having been accomplished, the wise breeder will return to the original closebreeding or linebreeding program, realizing full well the limitations of an outcrossing program.

Grading Up

Grading up is that system of breeding in which purebred sires of a given pure breed are mated to native or grade females. Its purpose is to develop uniformity and quality and to increase performance in the offspring.

Many breeders will continue to produce purebred stock. However, the vast majority of animals in the United States—probably more than 97 per cent—are not eligible for registry. In general, however, because of the obvious merit of using well-bred sires, farm animals are sired by purebreds. In comparison with the breeding of purebreds, such a system requires less outlay of cash, and less experience on the part of the producer. However, even with this type of production, grading up of the herd through the use of purebred sires is generally practiced. Thus, one of the principal functions of the purebred breeder is that of

Fig. 2-14. High-grade Shorthorn calves, the result of using registered Short-horn bulls on grade Shorthorn cows since 1911. Grand Champion load of feeder calves at the National Western Stock Show, Denver; bred by Josef Winkler, Castle Rock, Colorado. (Courtesy, Josef Winkler)

serving as a source of seed stock—particularly of sires—for the commercial producer. In brief, it is hoped that concentrated doses of "good" genes may be secured through the use of purebred sires. As the common stock is improved, this means that still further improvement and homozygosity for good genes is necessary in the purebreds, if they are to bring about further advancement in any grading up program.

Naturally, the greatest single step toward improved quality and performance occurs in the first cross. The first generation of such a program results in offspring carrying 50 per cent of the hereditary material of the purebred parent (or 50 per cent of the blood of the purebred parent, as many stockmen speak of it). The next generation gives offspring carrying 75 per cent of the blood of the purebred breed, and in subsequent generations the proportion of inheritance remaining from the original scrub females is halved with each cross. Later crosses usually increase quality and performance still more, though in less marked degree. After the third or fourth cross, the offspring compare very favorably with purebred stock in conformation, and only exceptionally good sires can bring about further improvement. This is especially so if the males used in grading up successive generations are derived from the same strain within a breed.

As evidence that cattle of high merit may be produced through grading up, it is interesting to note that many present-day champion steers are sired by purebred bulls but are out of high-grade cows. High-grade animals that are the offspring of several generations of outstanding purebred sires can be and often are superior to average or inferior purebreds.

Years of experience in grading up beef cattle through using registered Shorthorn bulls on good native red cows at Sni-A-Bar Farms, Grain Valley, Missouri, yielded the following results and conclusions:

1. The greatest single step toward improved quality, compared with common stock, occurred in the first cross. Subsequent crosses increased quality and market value still more, though in less marked degree.

2. After the third and fourth cross, the offspring compared very favorably with purebred stock in conformation and quality, and only exceptionally good sires could bring about further improvement.

3. The demonstration showed clearly that breeding is a dominant factor in the production of high-quality beeves and that good feeding and management will not return best results unless the element of good breeding is also present.

As evidence that horses of high merit may be produced through grading up, it is interesting to note that the champion draft gelding at the Chicago International in 1921 and again in 1923, Major MacFarlane, was a grade horse only two generations removed from a Cayuse or Indian Pony mare. This fact should also inspire purebred breeders to still further improvement, if the use of purebred sires is to continue to bring about improvement in grading up the commercial herds.

After some experience, the commercial producer who has successfully handled grade animals may add a few purebreds to the herd and gradually build into the latter, provided that his experience and his market for seed stock justifies this type of production.

Crossbreeding

Crossbreeding is the mating of animals of different breeds. In a broad sense, crossbreeding includes the mating of purebred sires of one breed with high-grade females of another breed. The vast majority of market swine and sheep are cross-breds; estimates are that two-thirds to three-fourths of all market hogs are crossbreds and a high percentage of western lambs are crossbreds.

No other system of breeding has been the object of more present-day controversy than crossbreeding. Perhaps, in the final analysis, however, all would agree that *any merits that crossbreeding may possess are and will continue to be based on improved "seed stock."* Certainly, from a genetic standpoint, it should be noted that crossbred animals generally possess greater heterozygosity than outcross animals—with the added virtue of hybrid vigor. It may also be added that, as in outcrossing, the recessive and undesirable genes remain hidden in the crossbred animal.

On purely theoretical grounds, it would appear that crossbreeding should result in some increase in vigor because the desirable genes from both breeds would be combined and the undesirable genes from each would tend to be overshadowed as recessives. That is to say, there has been an inevitable, though small, amount of inbreeding in all purebreds during the period of the last 100 to 150 years. This has been partly intentional and partly due to geographical limitations upon the free exchange of breeding stock from one part of the country to another. As a result of this slight degree of inbreeding, there has been a slow but rather constant increase in homozygosis within each of the pure breeds of livestock. Most of the factors fixed in the homozygous state are desirable; but inevitably some undesirable genes have probably been fixed, resulting in lowered vigor, slower growth rate, less ability to live, etc.

Theoretically, then, crossbreeding should be an aid in relegating these undesirable genes to a recessive position and in allowing more dominant genes to express themselves. Practical observation and limited experiments would indicate that this does occur in crossbreeding.

Today, there is renewed interest in crossbreeding, and increased research is under way on the subject. Crossbreeding is being used by stockmen to (1) increase productivity over straightbreds, because of the resulting hybrid vigor or heterosis, just as is being done by commercial corn and poultry producers; (2) produce commercial animals with a desired combination of traits not available in any one breed; and (3) produce foundation stock for developing new breeds.

The motivating forces back of increased crossbreeding in animals are: (1) more artificial insemination, thereby simplifying the rotation of sires of different breeds, and (2) the necessity for stockmen to become more efficient in order to meet their competition, both from within their respective industries and from without.

It is important that crossbreeding be well planned—that there be a systematic approach. Some possible systems are: (1) breeding straightbred females of one breed to males of another breed; (2) breeding crossbred females to males of a third breed; (3) crisscrossing by using males of two breeds (females sired by

males of one breed are bred to males of the other, generation after generation);
and (4) rotation crossing by using males of three breeds in sequence.

The proved value of crossbreeding in the creation of new breeds especially
adapted to certain conditions is generally recognized. For example, the Santa
Gertrudis breed of cattle, a breed derived from five-eighths Shorthorn and three-
eighths Brahman breeding, was developed to meet a need in the hot, dry, and
insect-infested area of the Southwest. Experienced cattlemen of the area will
vouch for the fact that this is a practical example of a planned system of crossbreeding which has high utility value under the environmental conditions common
to the country. Also, the Columbia breed of sheep, representing a Lincoln-
Rambouillet cross, is especially well adapted to the better ranges of the West.
Still other examples of crossbreeding in the creation of breeds may be cited.

In summary, it can be said that crossbreeding has a place, particularly from
the standpoint of increased vigor, growth rate, and efficiency of production; but
pure breeding will continue to control the destiny of further improvement in
any class of livestock and furnish the desired homozygosity and uniformity which
many stockmen insist is a part of the art of breeding better livestock.

SELECTION IN LIVESTOCK BREEDING

In simple terms, selection in livestock breeding is an attempt to secure or
retain the best of those animals in the current generation as parents of the next
generation. Obviously, the skill with which selections are made is all-important
in determining the future of the herd or flock. It becomes perfectly clear, therefore, that the destiny of livestock improvement is dependent upon selecting for
breeding purposes those animals which are genetically superior. The use of
genetically inferior animals for breeding purposes has ruined many a herd or flock.

The profitability of any individual animal or of a herd or flock of animals is
determined by the following two factors:

1. *Type* or *individuality* based upon the ability to produce high-quality
products for a discriminating market.

2. *Performance* or *efficiency of production,* which is the ability to utilize
feed efficiently in producing meat, milk, wool, or power. This also includes the
ability to reproduce regularly and to produce large litters in the case of litter-
bearing animals.

Bases of Selection

Whether establishing a new herd or flock or improving an old one, there are
four bases of selection; namely (1) selection based on type and individuality,
(2) selection based on pedigree, (3) selection based on show-ring winnings, and
(4) selection based on production testing. At the outset, it should be said that
each method of selection has its own particular place. Certainly the progressive
stockman will make judicious use of all of them, but with increasing emphasis
upon production testing.

SELECTION BASED ON TYPE AND INDIVIDUALITY

This implies selecting those animals that most closely approach an ideal or standard of perfection, and culling out those that fall short of these standards. The vast majority of animals, including those in both purebred and commercial herds and flocks, are selected on this basis.

SELECTION BASED ON PEDIGREE

In pedigree selection, which is used in most purebred herds, the individuality and performance of the ancestors are relied upon for an estimate of the probable transmitting ability. Pedigree selection is of special importance when production data is not available or when the animals are either so thin or so young that their individual merit cannot be ascertained with any degree of certainty. Also, when selection is being made between animals of comparable individual merit, the pedigree may well be the determining factor. In making use of pedigree selections, however, it must be remembered that ancestors close up in the pedigree are much more important than those many generations removed.

SELECTION BASED ON SHOW-RING WINNINGS

The show-ring has long been a major force in shaping the type of all classes of livestock. The first American show was held at Pittsfield, Massachusetts, in 1810, but livestock exhibitions had been initiated in Europe many years earlier.

As now conducted, our livestock shows have both advantages and disadvantages from the standpoint of breed improvement.

Among the advantages are the following:

1. The show-ring is the best medium yet discovered for molding breed type. For this reason, it behooves the breed registry associations and the purebred breeders alike to accept their rightful responsibility in seeing that the animals which win top honors are those that most nearly meet the efficiency of production demands on the part of the producer and the meat quality demands of the consumer.

2. It serves as one of the very best advertising or promotional mediums for both the breed and the breeder.

3. It brings breeders together for exchange of ideas and experiences.

4. It provides an incentive to breed better animals, for only by comparing animals in the show-ring can the breeder ascertain whether or not he is keeping up with his competitors.

Some of the disadvantages of the show-ring are as follows:

1. Heavy fitting, in order to win, often results in temporary or permanent sterility.

2. The desire to win often causes exhibitors to resort to "surgical means" and "filling" in order to correct defects. Admittedly, such man-made corrections

are not hereditary, and their effects are often not too durable—as is belatedly discovered by some innocent purchaser.

3. Valuable animals are frequently kept out of productive work or from reproduction in order to enhance their likelihood of winning in the show-ring.

Thus, in making selections from among show animals, one should do so with a full understanding of both the virtues and the limitations therein.

Selection based on show-ring winnings implies the selection of animals that have placed well in one or more livestock shows. Perhaps the principal value of selection based on show-ring winnings lies in the fact that shows focus the attention of the amateur to those types and strains of animals which at the moment are meeting with the approval of the better breeders and judges.

SELECTION BASED ON PRODUCTION TESTING

Selection of breeding stock on the basis of production records is a requisite in modern animal improvement. It should be emphasized that this involves the taking of accurate records rather than casual observation. Moreover, in order to be most effective, selection must be based on characteristics of economic importance (rather than breed fancy points), and an objective measure or "yard-stick" must be placed upon each of the characteristics that is to be measured. Finally, those breeding animals that fail to meet the high standards set forth must be removed from the herd promptly and unflinchingly.

As most characters of economic importance—for example, body type and efficiency of feed utilization—are due to many genes, a method of measuring and selecting for these characters must be devised.

Production testing embraces both (1) **performance testing** and (2) **progeny testing**. The distinction between and the relationship of these methods are set forth in the following definitions:

1. **Performance testing** *is the practice of evaluating and selecting animals on the basis of their individual merit or performance.* Thus, the measurement of the performance of an individual animal—his own birth weight, weaning weight, daily rate of gain, efficiency of feed utilization, and body type, as determined under standard conditions—is known as performance testing.

2. **Progeny testing** *is the practice of selecting animals on the basis of the merit of their progeny.* Thus, when an animal is evaluated on the basis of its get—the offspring's birth weight, weaning weight, daily rate of gain, efficiency of feed utilization, and body type and/or carcass evaluation, as determined under standard conditions—the system is known as progeny testing.

Production testing *is a more inclusive term, including progeny testing and/or performance testing.*

Progeny testing is more infallible than performance testing. Thus, if a sire has been proved through the uniformly outstanding quality of his get, one need not be greatly concerned over what he looks like, how he performs, or what is back of him. Then his record is in front of him, and this is the important thing. If the dam has also been proved, so much the better. Otherwise, it is desirable to ascertain that the female is sired by a good proved sire and out of a good female family. On the other hand, if there is progress (with the progeny slightly better on the average than the parents), then performance testing of a male and female—meaning their own performance records—may be more valuable than their breeding record as determined through progeny testing. This is true because:

1. Their own records are available at an earlier age.

2. It is difficult to apply progeny testing to females because of the relatively few offspring.

3. Progeny testing often does little more than confirm what is already known from performance testing.

4. Progeny testing records are available only after most of the effective selection has already been done.

5. It is usually impractical to progeny test enough bulls and cows so that selection can be effectively practiced among them.

6. When animals are highly selected before progeny testing, the tests will probably not reveal significant differences between them unless large numbers of offspring are obtained.

7. There is the hazard that the male being tested will only be bred to a few select females and that only the top offspring will be tested.

8. A regular practice of progeny testing will increase the length of generation, which reduces the rate of progress. Naturally, this is more important with cattle and horses than with hogs or sheep. For example, beef bulls are usually three to four years of age and dairy bulls six to seven years of age before a progeny test can be secured.

For these reasons, when a herd or flock is showing steady improvement, it may be best to select the most promising breeding animals as determined by performance testing rather than be delayed by progeny testing.

In production testing programs, it must be realized that training and feeding play a major role in producing outstanding animals, making it difficult to separate out environmental from hereditary influences. For greatest effectiveness and progress, therefore, the conditions under which the tests are made should be standardized as much as possible from year to year.

Despite all the difficulties enumerated, and the admitted fact that much more research work is needed in the testing of meat animals, there is ample evidence to indicate that selection on the basis of either performance testing or progeny testing is imperative if breed improvement is to take place at the maximum rate. To select intelligently on the basis of a testing program, the breeder must have adequate records and use them.

PRODUCTION TESTING NOT NEW

Production testing is not new. It was advocated by the Roman, Varro, two thousand years ago, and it was effectively used by Robert Bakewell in the eighteenth century in his practice of bull and ram letting.

The breeders of race horses have always followed a program of mating animals of proved performance on the track. It is interesting to note that the first breed register, which appeared in 1791, recorded the pedigrees of all the Thoroughbred horses winning important races. In a similar way, the Standardbred horse, which is an American creation, takes its name from the fact that, in its early history, animals were required to trot a mile in 2 minutes and 30 seconds or pace a mile in 2 minutes and 25 seconds before they could be considered as eligible for registry. The chief aim, therefore, of the early-day breeders of race horses was to record the pedigrees of outstanding performers rather than all members of the breed.

Milk production has long been used as a criterion for selecting dairy cattle, and with the invention of the Babcock test in 1890, butterfat content also became a measuring device. In the latter part of the nineteenth century, the Holstein-Friesian Breed Association introduced official weighing of milk and testing for butterfat per cent as a part of its program. In 1966-67, the Dairy Herd Improvement Registry (DHIR) became the official milk recording program of all the breeds. Dairy herd improvement associations are in existence throughout the dairy sections of the United States. These associations lend assistance to dairymen in keeping production records of each cow. Production testing in dairy cattle is now the most widely known record of performance used in the United States.

The invention of the trap nest shortly before 1900 made it possible to keep individual egg-production records on hens. Then, in the 1940's Random Sample Performance Tests evolved. In these centralized tests, stocks from several growers are hatched at the test station, the chicks raised, and the resultant pullets maintained to a fixed age (500 days or older) to determine egg production. More recently, a new kind of program, known as the Multiple Unit Poultry Test, was developed. In the latter, more than one type of test is carried out at more than one farm or location. These performance tests have exerted a powerful influence in developing high genetic merit of poultry.

PRODUCTION TESTING IN MEAT ANIMALS IS DIFFICULT

Unfortunately, the problem of using production records in meat animals is more difficult than in the classes of animals just mentioned; for no single yardstick or criterion accurately evaluates the worth of an animal. For example, breeders of dairy cattle have measured the milk and butterfat production of the animals; breeders of race horses have used speed as the criterion; and poultry breeders have used egg production. With sheep, beef cattle, and swine, it is more difficult to place a "yardstick" upon the characteristics that should be measured. On the other hand, extensive studies have been made of the factors that should be evaluated in breeding meat animals, and today we have a fairly clear idea of the things which should be considered. Perhaps the relative importance of each character varies under different conditions. In a discriminating market, quality of product may be the most important factor influencing profitability, whereas under market conditions in which a premium is not paid for quality, economy of production is the most important. Perhaps all would agree that the most profitable type of meat animal over a period of years is the one that most efficiently produces (at the lowest cost) the quantity and quality of carcass which brings the most money over the block.

THE DANISH SYSTEM OF PRODUCTION TESTING SWINE

Without doubt, the outstanding example of production testing with fat stock is the swine breeding work of Denmark. This work was started in 1907, and

Fig. 2-15. Interior view of the world's first swine production testing station established in 1907 at Elsesminde, Denmark. In Denmark four pigs of each litter are tested under standard conditions, with evaluation based on (1) rate and economy of gain and (2) carcass quality of 200 pounds weight. (Courtesy, Danish Embassy)

since then, it has operated continuously, except for three years during World War I when shortage of feed forced the suspension of all testing. In the Danish system, the registration of swine is supervised by a national committee in charge of swine breeding. Only animals bred at organized swine-breeding centers are eligible for registration, because these are the farms where the breeders have complied with certain regulations, including sending each year to the testing stations half as many litters as they have sows in their herd. At the testing stations, these test litters of four pigs each are fed under standard conditions, and the rate and economy of gain are recorded. When each pig reaches a weight of 200 pounds, it is slaughtered at a nearby bacon factory, and its dressing percentage and the type, conformation, and quality of its carcass are measured and scored. Twice annually, each breeding center is inspected by a committee that scores it for: (1) management and general appearance of the farm, (2) conformation of breeding animals, (3) fertility of the breeding animals, (4) efficiency in the use of feed by the test pigs from this center, and (5) slaughter quality of the test pigs. The advances made in the carcass qualities (body length, belly and backfat thickness), plus efficiency of feed utilization, have been phenomenal. Swine selection in Denmark is strictly based on utility considerations.

GENERAL CONSIDERATIONS RELATIVE TO PRODUCTION TESTING

The "yardsticks" or criteria used in testing will vary somewhat with the class of farm animals. For example, in sheep both wool and lamb production are important; and, with both sheep and swine, multiple births are a major factor. A detailed discussion of the production records applicable to each species will be given in the breeding section devoted to each class of farm animals.

A prerequisite for any testing data, regardless of species, is that each animal be positively identified—by means of ear notches, ear tags, or tattoos. With purebred breeders, who must use a system of animal identification anyway, this is not an additional detail. But the taking of weights and grades does require additional time and labor—an expenditure which is highly worth-while, however.

Body-type scores had best be taken at a standard weight or a standard age (at weaning time and perhaps annually thereafter), probably being evaluated in terms of either a numerical score or a letter. It is important that all animals be evaluated and their scores made a part of the permanent record. Consistently good production is to be desired; the hazard being that it is all too easy for a breeder to remember the good individuals produced by a given animal and to forget those which are mediocre or culls.

Record forms should be relatively simple. Furthermore, they should be in a form that will permit easy summarization—for example, the record of one female should be on one sheet if possible.

Information on the productivity of close relatives (the sire and the dam and the brothers and sisters) can supplement that on the animal itself and thus be a distinct aid in selection. The records of more distant relatives are of little significance, because, individually, due to the sampling nature of inheritance, they contribute only a few genes to an animal many generations removed.

Under practical conditions, testing with meat animals is usually confined to the sire; for a male produces during his lifetime many more offspring than a female. Because of the relatively small numbers of offspring, testing with females (except with litter-bearing sows) is somewhat more difficult, and as a rule a female cannot be thoroughly progeny tested until she has spent half or more of her lifetime in a herd. Certainly, the intelligent breeder should study his females and cull those which consistently fail to produce good offspring. If possible, the females should also be tested, especially those that may become the dams of future sires.

A good plan in progeny testing young sires consists of retaining and mating one or more—the numbers depending upon the size of the herd—on a limited number of females during their first season of breeding. The progeny are then tested and evaluated, and only those males that have proved to be best on the basis of their progeny are retained for further breeding purposes. Thus, if young bulls 18 months of age are each mated to 8 to 12 females, calves should be born 9 months later, and the progeny can be tested between the ages of 7 and 12 months. With good fortune, it is possible to have progeny data on a beef bull when he is approximately 39 months of age. With dairy bulls, whose daughters must be in lactation in order to make the test, it is not possible to make an evaluation until the animal is six to seven years of age.

SUMMARY OF PRODUCTION TESTING

In summary, it should be pointed out that progressive livestock breeders are beginning to look for sires backed by records. This interest will increase, and the far-seeing purebred breeder will start now to get his herd on a tested basis. Even though production testing is one of the keenest tools available to the breeder, for best results one should continue to use all four major methods of selection—individuality, pedigree, show-ring winnings, and either performance or progeny testing—but with increasing emphasis upon one of the latter methods. In other words, *testing should be used to supplement individual, pedigree, and show-ring selection rather than to displace them,* as is sometimes advocated. Individuality tells us what an animal seems to be; his pedigree tells us what he ought to be; but his performance and progeny tell us what he really is.

Selection for Several Characters

Sometimes stockmen have been burdened by attempting to select for too many characters. For example, horsemen may select for speed, beauty, temperament, size, color, etc. It must be remembered, however, that selection for two or more characteristics automatically cuts down the effectiveness of selection for any one of them. Thus, the breeder who selects with equal intensity for type and speed is likely to be left in the position of the dog that chased two rabbits and caught neither. A realization of this fact, together with the fact that in many cases such things as type and beauty are correlated only slightly, if at all, with productivity is undoubtedly behind the current emphasis on production testing with all classes of animals.

Determining Relative Emphasis to Place on Each Character

A replacement animal seldom excels in all of the economically important characters. The stockman must decide, therefore, how much importance shall be given to each character. Thus, the beef cattle producer will have to decide how much emphasis shall be placed on birth weight, how much on weaning weight, how much on daily rate of gain, how much on efficiency of feed utilization, and how much on body type and carcass evaluation.

Perhaps the relative emphasis to place on each character should vary according to the circumstances. Under certain conditions, some characters may even be ignored. Among the factors determining the emphasis to place on each character are the following:

1. **The economic importance of the character to the producer.**—By economic importance is meant their dollars and cents value. Thus, those characters which have the greatest effect on profits should receive the most attention.

2. **The heritability of the character.**—It stands to reason that the more highly heritable characters should receive higher priority than those which are less heritable, for more progress can be made thereby.

3. **The genetic correlation between traits.**—One trait may be so strongly correlated with another that selection for one automatically selects for the other. For example, rate of gain and economy of gain in meat animals are correlated to the extent that selection for rate of gain tends to select for the most economical gains as well; thus, economy of gain may be largely disregarded if rate of gain is given strong consideration. Conversely, one trait may be negatively correlated with another so that selection for one automatically selects against the other.

4. **The amount of variation in each character.**—Obviously, if all animals were exactly alike in a given character, there could be no selection for that character. Likewise, if the amount of variation in a given character is small, the selected animals cannot be very much above the average of the entire herd, and progress will be slow.

5. **The level of performance already attained.**—If a herd or flock has reached a satisfactory level of performance for a certain character, there is not much need for further selection for that character. Thus, if sheep are almost free of wrinkles, there is not much need to select against them; in fact, if sheep are entirely free of wrinkles, it would be impossible to select against them since there would be no wrinkled individuals to cull.

Systems of Selection

Finally, the stockman needs to follow a system of selection which will result in maximum total progress over a period of several years or animal generations. The three common systems are:

1. **Tandem selection.**—This refers to that system in which there is selection for only one trait at a time until the desired improvement in that particular trait is reached, following which selection is made for another trait, etc. This system makes it possible to make rapid improvement in the trait for which selection is being practiced, but it has two major disadvantages: (a) usually, it is not possible to select for one trait only and (b) generally, income is dependent on several traits.

Tandem selection is recommended only in those rare herds and flocks where one character only is primarily in need of improvement; for example, where a certain flock of fine-wool sheep needs improving primarily in staple length.

2. **Establishing minimum standards for each character, and selecting simultaneously but independently for each character.**—This system, in which several of the most important characters are selected for simultaneously but independently, is without doubt the most common system of selection. It involves establishing minimum standards for each character and culling animals which fall below these standards. For example, it might be decided to cull all calves weighing less than 55 pounds at birth, or weighing less than 375 pounds at weaning, or gaining less than 1¼ pounds daily, or requiring more than 900 pounds of feed per 100 pounds gain, or grading *three* or less. Of course, the minimum standards may have to vary from year to year if environmental factors change markedly (for example, if calves average light at weaning time due to a severe drought and poor pasture).

The chief weakness of this system of selection is that an individual may be culled because of being faulty in one character only, even though he is well nigh ideal otherwise.

3. **Selection index.**—Selection indexes combine all important traits into one overall value or index. Theoretically, a selection index provides a more desirable way in which to select for several traits than either (a) the tandem method or (b) the method of establishing minimum standards for each character and selecting simultaneously but independently for each character.

Selection indexes are designed to accomplish the following:

a. To give emphasis to the different traits in keeping with their relative importance; for example, to give emphasis to the mutton and wool qualities of sheep in keeping with the economic importance of each (thus, generally speaking, about two-thirds of the income from sheep is derived from the sale of lambs; one-third from the sale of wool).

b. To balance the strong points against the weak points of each animal.

c. To obtain an overall total score for each animal, following which all animals can be ranked from best to poorest.

d. To assure a constant and objective degree of emphasis on each trait being considered, without any shifting of ideals from year to year.

e. To provide a convenient way in which to correct for environmental effects, such as type of birth (single or twin), age of dam, etc.

Despite their acknowledged virtues, selection indexes are not perfect. Among their weaknesses are the following:

a. Practical indexes are not available for all classes of animals.

b. Their use may result in covering up or masking certain bad faults or defects.

c. They do not allow for year to year differences, generally speaking.

d. Their accuracy is dependent upon (1) the correct evaluation of the net worth of the economic traits considered, (2) the correctness of the estimate of heritability of the traits, and (3) the genetic correlation between the traits. These estimates are often difficult to make.

In practice, the selection index is best used as a partial guide or tool in the selection program. For example, it may be used to select twice as many animals as are needed for herd or flock replacements, and this number may then be reduced through rigid culling on the basis of a thorough visual inspection for those traits that are not in the index, which may include such things as quality, freedom from defects, and market type.

ARTIFICIAL INSEMINATION[10]

By definition, *artificial insemination is the deposition of spermatozoa in the female genitalia by artificial rather than by natural means.*

Legend has it that artificial insemination had its origin in 1322, at which time an Arab chieftain used artificial methods to impregnate a prized mare with semen stealthily collected by night from the sheath of a stallion belonging to an enemy tribe. There is no substantial evidence, however, to indicate that the Arabs practiced artificial insemination to any appreciable degree.

The first scientific research in artificial insemination of domestic animals was conducted with dogs by the Italian physiologist, Lazarro Spallanzani, in 1780. A century later, American veterinarians employed artificial means to get mares in foal that persistently had failed to settle to natural service. They noticed that because of obstructions the semen was often found in the vagina and not in the uterus following natural service. By collecting the semen into a syringe from the floor of the vagina and injecting it into the uterus, they were able to impregnate mares with these anatomical difficulties.

The Russian physiologist, Ivanoff, began a study of artificial insemination of farm animals, particularly horses, in 1899; and in 1922, he was called upon by the Russian government to apply his findings in an effort to re-establish the livestock industry following its depletion during World War I. Crude as his methods were, his work with horses must be considered the foundation upon which the success of the more recent work is based.

The shifting of the large-scale use of artificial insemination to cattle and sheep, two decades after it was first introduced for horses, was not caused by the fading importance of the horse and the increased demand for cattle and sheep. Rather, it was found that progress was quicker and more easily achieved with these animals, because the physiological mechanism of reproduction in cattle and sheep is more favorable than in horses. It was also discovered that the sperm of bulls and rams survive better in storage than stallion sperm, and that the estrus period of cows and ewes is shorter than in the mare with the result that it is easier to inseminate at the correct time for conception. In more recent years, considerable progress has been made in the treatment of stallion and jack semen; currently, frozen stallion semen is in limited use—a development which offers much opportunity for the future.

Following World War II, British scientists were called upon to make wide use of artificial insemination in re-establishing the livestock industry of England.

[10]This section was authoritatively reviewed by Dr. Harry Herman, Executive Secretary, National Association of Animal Breeders, Columbia, Mo.; and Dr. H. L. Self, Department of Animal Science, Iowa State University, Ames, Iowa.

They looked upon it as: (1) a way in which to increase more rapidly the efficiency and utility value of their animals through making wider use of outstanding sires, (2) a means of controlling certain diseases, and (3) the best way in which to increase breeding efficiency.

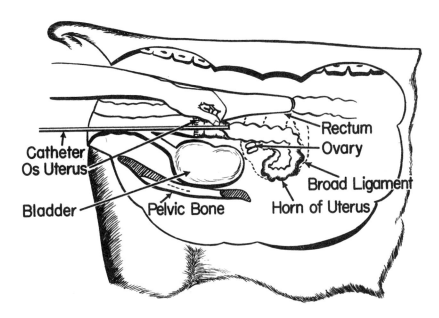

Fig. 2-16. Deep uterine insemination of the cow. The cervix is grasped *per rectum* and the inseminating tube is carefully worked into and through the cervical canal. (Courtesy, Dr. H. A. Herman, Executive Secretary, National Association of Animal Breeders)

Today, artificial insemination is more extensively practiced with dairy cattle than with any other class of farm animals. In 1938, only about 7,000 cows were bred by this means in organized groups in the U.S.; whereas, in 1965, 6,301,178 head, or 44 per cent of the dairy cows and heifers were bred by artificial insemination. Additionally, in that same year, 615,147 head of beef cattle were bred by artificial insemination. Also, it is noteworthy that the average number of cows bred per bull increased from 228 in 1939—when the first artificial breeding association was organized in this country—to 3,053 in 1965 (that's approximately 100 times more than by natural service); and that certain outstanding sires are now being used to breed 10,000 to 15,000 cows annually, and this is not the upper limit.

Advantages of Artificial Insemination

Some of the advantages of artificial insemination are:

1. **It increases the use of outstanding sires.**—Through artificial insemination, many breeders can avail themselves of the use of an outstanding sire, whereas

the services of such an animal were formerly limited to one owner or, at the most, to a partnership.

2. **It alleviates the danger and bother of keeping a sire.**—Some hazard and bother are usually involved in keeping a sire, especially a bull or a stallion. Cooperative dairy cattle breeding programs are fast eliminating the necessity of owning a bull.

3. **It makes it possible to overcome certain physical handicaps to mating.**—Artificial insemination is of value (a) in mating animals of greatly different sizes—for example, in using heavy mature bulls on yearling heifers—and (b) in using stifled or otherwise crippled sires that are unable to perform natural service. It may also increase the use of monogamous species, such as the fox. Artificial insemination is also useful in hybridization.

4. **It lessens sire costs.**—In smaller herds (for example, in dairy herds with fewer than 50 cows), artificial insemination is usually less expensive than the ownership of a worth-while sire together with the accompanying building, feed, and labor costs.

5. **It reduces the likelihood of costly delays through using sterile sires.**—Because the breeding efficiency of sires used artifically is constantly checked, it reduces the likelihood of breeding females to a sterile sire for an extended period of time.

6. **It helps control disease.**—Artificial insemination reduces the spread of venereal diseases, such as vibriosis, trichomoniasis, and vaginitis in cattle. Its value in this respect is appreciated by beef and dairy herd owners alike.

7. **It makes it feasible to prove more sires.**—Because of the small size of the herds in which they are used in natural service, many sires are never proved. Still others are destroyed before their true breeding worth is known. Through artificial insemination, it is possible to determine the genetic worth of a sire at an earlier age and with more certainty than in natural service.

8. **It creates large families of animals.**—The use of artificial insemination makes possible the development of large numbers of animals within a superior family, thus providing uniformity and giving a better basis for a constructive breeding program.

9. **It increases pride of ownership.**—The ownership of progeny of outstanding sires inevitably makes for pride of ownership, with accompanying improved feeding and management.

10. **It increases profits.**—The offspring of outstanding sires are usually higher and more efficient producers and thus more profitable. Artificial insemination provides a means of using such sires more widely.

Limitations of Artificial Insemination

Like many other wonderful techniques, artificial insemination is not without its limitations. A full understanding of such limitations, however, will merely accentuate and extend its usefulness. Some of the limitations of artificial insemination are:

1. **It must conform to physiological principles.**—One would naturally expect that the practice of artificial insemination must conform to certain physiological principles. Unfortunately, much false information concerning the usefulness of artificial insemination has been encountered—for example, the belief that females will conceive if artificially inseminated at any time during the estrual cycle. Others have even accepted exaggerated claims that the quality of semen may be improved through such handling, only to be disappointed.

2. **It requires skilled technicians.**—In order to be successful, artificial insemination must be carried out by skilled technicians who have had considerable training and experience.

3. **It necessitates considerable capital to initiate and operate a cooperative breeding program.**—Considerable money is necessary to initiate a cooperative artificial insemination program, and still more is needed to expand and develop it properly. It is noteworthy, however, that 38 per cent of all cows bred artificially in 1965 were serviced with semen provided by privately-owned establishments; thus, private enterprise is playing an increasingly important role in this rapidly growing industry.

4. **It may accentuate the damage of a poor sire.**—It must be realized that when a male sires the wrong type of offspring his damage is merely accentuated because of the increased number of progeny possible. For this reason, untried or untested males are seldom used extensively in a stud; for example, 60 per cent of the dairy sires are proved, and these sires account for about 80 per cent of the matings made. This precautionary measure virtually eliminates the possibility of using a genetically inferior sire.

5. **It may restrict the sire market.**—The fact that the market demand for poor or average sires will decrease if artificial insemination is widely adopted should probably be considered an attribute rather than a limitation. Also, it is noteworthy that a sizeable number of the nation's beef cattle are still bred to "scrub" or nondescript bulls.

6. **It may increase the spread of disease.**—As previously indicated, the careful and intelligent use of artificial insemination will lessen the spread of disease. On the other hand, carelessness or ignorance may result in the rapid spread of disease. However, artificial insemination organizations follow rigid sire health standards and, to date, no outbreaks of disease attributable to artificial insemination have been reported.

7. **It may be subject to certain abuses.**—If semen is transported from farm to farm, the character of the technician must be above reproach. Trained workers can detect differences in the spermatozoa of the bull, ram, boar, stallion, or cock; but even the most skilled scientist is unable to differentiate between the semen of a Thoroughbred and a Morgan, to say nothing of the difference between two stallions of the same breed. However, it appears that such abuse is more

suspicioned than real. In a blood type study[11] with cattle, Rendel found 4.2 per cent family records in error out of 615 animals by natural service, compared to 4.0 per cent family records in error out of 199 sired by artificial insemination.

Of course, with skilled workers performing the techniques required in artificial insemination, there usually is more check on the operations and perhaps less likelihood of dishonesty than when only the owner is involved, such as is usually the situation with natural service.

Some Practical Considerations of Artificial Insemination

Artificial insemination finds useful application in large breeding establishments, especially with dairy and beef cattle; but, as yet, it has only limited practical application with other classes of farm animals. Someday it may. The knowledge of the reproductive processes gained from artificial insemination, however, can contribute materially to the increased efficiency of animal production.

In the wild state, when a female was served several times during her heat period, an annual conception rate of 90 to 100 per cent was common rather than the exception. Aside from frequency of service, the outdoor exercise, vigor, good nutrition, and regular breeding habits and lack of contamination were conducive to conception. On the other hand, when handled under unnatural conditions in confinement, when the female is generally bred as soon as she starts to show signs of heat, it is not surprising that the conception rate rarely ranges from 50 to 80 per cent and is frequently much less. Perhaps, among its virtues, artificial insemination does offer some promise of assuring a higher conception rate.

Based on present knowlege, gained through research and practical observation, it may be concluded that stockmen can make artificial insemination more successful through the following:

1. Give the female a reasonable rest following parturition and before rebreeding; in cows this should be about 60 days, in sows 35 to 49 days.

2. Keep record of heat periods and note irregularities.

3. Watch carefully for heat signs, especially at the approximate time.

4. Where an association is involved, notify the insemination technician promptly when an animal comes in heat.

5. Avoid breeding diseased females or females showing cloudy mucus. The latter condition indicates an infection somewhere in the reproductive tract.

6. Have the veterinarian examine females that have been bred three times without conception or that show other reproductive abnormalities.

BREED REGISTRY ASSOCIATIONS

The typical history of the formation of the various breeds of livestock may be summarized as follows:

---

[11] *Acta Agric. Scand.* VIIII, p. 140.

1. A recognition of the existence of what was considered to be a more desirable and useful type.

2. The best animals of that type were gathered into one or a few herds which ceased to introduce outside blood.

3. Intense inbreeding to fix characters followed.

4. With greater numbers of animals, more herds were established.

5. When the breed became so numerous and the number of animal generations in the pedigrees increased until no man could remember all of the foundation animals far back in the pedigree, the necessity for a herd book arose. In addition to supplying knowledge of foundation animals, the herd books were designed to prevent, insofar as possible, unscrupulous traders from exporting grades or common stock as purebreds.

6. The breed associations or societies that publish the stud book were also organized for the purposes of improving the breed and promoting the general interests of the breeders.

Naturally, not all breed histories were identical. Circumstances often varied the pattern that molded the breed, but the end results and objectives were similar. The first herd book of any breed or class of animals, known as "An Introduction to the General Stud Book," published in 1791, was for Thoroughbred horses. In it were included the pedigrees of horses winning the important races. Thus, it was really a record of performance. The Shorthorn herd book, first undertaken as the private venture of Mr. and Mrs. George Coates, followed in 1822. Other societies and herd books for the various breeds were originated in due time.

It is interesting to note that some of the early breeders objected to furnishing pedigrees of their sale animals, fearing that they would thus give away valuable trade secrets.

A list of the breed registry associations is given in Section VI, Appendix, of this book.

NEW ANIMAL FRONTIERS THROUGH BREEDING

Many livestock breeders are aware of the phenomenal success that has been attained by inbreeding corn and then producing crossbreds, popularly known as hybrid corn. Hybrid corn research, covering a period of 30 years, cost an estimated 15 million dollars. Yet, it has paid handsome dividends. In 1933, only 0.2 per cent of the maize acreage of the great Corn Belt was planted to hybrid seed, whereas today it is conservatively estimated that 98 per cent of the corn grown in the corn-producing sections of the United States is of hybrid origin. In general, such corn has been found to yield 8 to 10 bushels more per acre than the best open-pollinated varieties; or about ⅔ billion bushels more annually, valued at approximately one billion dollars. This amount of corn would be sufficient to produce 3,750,000,000 pounds of beef, or 5,625,000,000 pounds of lamb, or 10,012,500,000 pounds of pork—enough to supply each man, woman and child in the nation with from one-fourth to one-half their annual per capita meat requirement. It has been further estimated that the two billion dollars spent in the development of the atom bomb was more than retrieved through the increased yields of hybrid corn alone during the years 1942 to 1945, the period of the atom bomb development.

Purely from a biological standpoint, there appears to be no reason why similar breeding methods to those used in hybrid corn should not bring about equally effective improvement in the quality of commercial livestock. That is, highly inbred strains of hogs, cattle, or sheep could be formed and then the inbred strains crossed for commercial production. Poultry breeders are doing so.

From a practical production standpoint, however, there are several factors that make this breeding system more difficult to follow with animals than with corn. These are as follows:

1. Corn can be self-pollinated and therefore self-fertilized, whereas the closest inbreeding that can be accomplished with livestock is brother-sister matings. From a genetic standpoint, this brings about homozygosis less than one-half as fast as self-fertilization.

2. Corn breeding requires very much less outlay of cash than animal breeding. With corn it is easily possible to start a thousand inbred lines in any one year and maintain them as long as they show desirable characteristics. However, the maintenance of a thousand inbred lines of any class of livestock is quite a different problem.

3. The production of abnormal animals, which is almost inevitable in inbreeding—even if it occurs only to a limited extent—represents a considerable economic loss to the stockman; whereas no such costly economic losses are encountered by the plant breeder.

Even these difficulties, however, do not appear to be insurmountable provided that there is cooperative effort. Thus, the problem is being attacked through the regional swine-, sheep-, and cattle-breeding laboratories—each of which represents a huge cooperative venture between the U.S. Department of Agriculture and the several cooperating state agricultural experiment stations. In these laboratories, inbred lines of the respective classes of livestock are being formed with the eventual purpose of: (1) determining whether crosses between them will produce more desirable commercial animals than now available and (2) using them further to improve purebred livestock. This system is what may be described as a modern approach to livestock improvement. At the present time, it is very much in the experimental stage, and it is impossible to predict whether or not the results will be as phenomenal as the production of hybrid corn. Certainly, it is both slower and more costly, and more difficulties must be surmounted. Nevertheless, the stakes are great.

Production testing techniques are being refined rapidly, with wider and more practical applications inevitable.

Research gave us several new breeds of livestock, and it is likely that the introduction and formation of new and better-adapted breeds of livestock will continue.

We need to know how to rectify appalling and costly sterility and reproductive failures. Fourteen per cent of the nation's cows never calve, 6 to 10 per cent of all ewes are barren, 15 to 20 per cent of all sows fail to pig, and 40 to 60 per cent of all mares that are bred fail to foal.

These and other approaches and problems in animal breeding deserve careful exploration.

QUESTIONS FOR STUDY AND DISCUSSION

1. What unique circumstances surrounded the founding of genetics by Mendel?
2. How can you determine whether a polled bull is homozygous or heterozygous?
3. In order to make intelligent selections and breed progress, is it necessary to fit, stall-feed, or place animals in show conditions; or may they be selected in their "work clothes" off the farm or ranch?
4. When abnormal animals are born, (a) what conditions tend to indicate a hereditary defect; (b) what conditions indicate a nutritional deficiency?
5. The "sire is half the herd or flock." Is this an under- or over-statement?
6. What system of breeding do you consider to be best adapted to your herd or flock, or to a herd or flock with which you are very familiar? Justify your choice.
7. How may a progressive stockman make use of each basis of selection?
8. List the factors which should be considered in determining the relative emphasis to place on each character in a selection program. What system of selection—(a) tandem, (b) establishing minimum culling levels, or (c) selection index—would you recommend and why?
9. Must a new breed of livestock be approved by someone, or can anyone start a new breed?

SELECTED REFERENCES

Title of Publication	Author(s)	Publisher
Adaptation of Domestic Animals	E. S. E. Hafez	Lea & Febiger, Philadelphia, Pa., 1968.
Animal Breeding	A. L. Hagedoorn	Crosby Lockwood & Son, Ltd., London, England, 1950.
Animal Breeding	L. M. Winters	John Wiley & Sons, Inc., New York, N. Y., 1948.
Animal Breeding Plans	J. L. Lush	Collegiate Press, Inc., Ames, Iowa, 1963.
Artifical Insemination in Livestock Breeding	A. H. Frank	U.S. Department of Agriculture, Circ. No. 567, Washington, D. C., 1952.
Breeding and Improvement of Farm Animals	V. A. Rice F. N. Andrews E. J. Warwick J. E. Legates	McGraw-Hill Book Co., Inc., New York, N. Y., 1967.
Breeding Better Livestock	V. A. Rice F. N. Andrews E. J. Warwick	McGraw-Hill Book Co., Inc., New York, N. Y., 1953.
Elements of Genetics, The	C. D. Darlington K. Mather	The Macmillan Co., New York, N. Y., 1950.
Farm Animals	John Hammond	Edward Arnold & Co., London, England, 1952.

Title of Publication	Author(s)	Publisher
Gene . . . the Universal Calf	L. N. Hazel L. F. Johnson	Fred Hahne Printing Co., Webster City, Iowa, 1956.
Genetics and Animal Breeding	E. J. Warwick	Agri. Expt. Sta. Popular Bull. 189, Washington State University, Pullman, Wash., 1948.
Genetics of Livestock Improvement	J. F. Lasley	Prentice-Hall, Inc., Englewood Cliffs, N. J., 1963.
Highlight of Breeding Systems	V. A. Rice	Holstein-Friesian Assn. of Amer., Brattleboro, Vermont.
Improvement of Livestock	Ralph Bogart	The Macmillan Co., New York, N. Y., 1959.
Inheritance in Cattle and Sheep	C. B. Roubicek	Wyo. Agri. Expt. Sta. Circ. 45, Univ. of Wyoming, Laramie, Wyo.
Physiology of Reproduction and Artificial Insemination of Cattle	G. W. Salisbury N. L. VanDewark	W. H. Freeman & Co., San Francisco, Calif., 1961.
Reproduction in Farm Animals	E. S. E. Hafez	Lea & Febiger, Philadelphia, Pa., 1968.
Reproductive Physiology	A. V. Nalbandov	W. H. Freeman & Co., San Francisco, Calif., 1958.

Chapter III

FEEDING LIVESTOCK

Contents Page

The Functions of Feeds.. 85
  Maintenance 85
  Growth 85
  Finishing (or Show-Ring Fitting).. 86
  Reproduction and Lactation... 86
  Work (or Running).. 87
  Wool 87
Essentials of an Adequate Diet; A Balanced Ration................................. 88
  Protein Needs 88
    Quality of Proteins.. 89
    Rumen Synthesis.. 90
    Practical Protein Sources.. 91
  Energy Needs 91
    Carbohydrates 92
    Fats 93
    Methods of Measuring Energy... 97
      The Total Digestible Nutrients (TDN) System............................. 97
      The Calorie System.. 98
  Mineral Needs...100
    Function of and Essential Minerals...101
    Complex Mineral Mixtures..115
    Value and Economy of Commercial Mineral Mixtures....................115
    Methods of Feeding Mineral Supplements..115
  Vitamin Needs 116
    The Known Vitamins..118
  Water Needs...129
Feed Additives 130
  Antibiotics 131
    Nutritional Role of Antibiotics...131
  Hormones and Other Accessory Ration Ingredients...........................132
Good Livestock Require Good Soils...132
Feeding as an Art...134
  Starting Animals on Feed..134
  Amount to Feed...135
  Frequency, Regularity, and Order of Feeding.....................................136
  Feeds Should Not Be Changed Abruptly...136
  Selection of Feeds..136
  Attention to Details Pays...136
Hand-feeding Versus Self-feeding..137
Creep Feeding Young Animals..138
Preparation of Feeds...139
Home-mixed Versus Commercial Feeds..142
  How to Select Commercial Feeds...142
Nutritional Diseases and Ailments...143
Nutrition Research of the Future..143
Questions for Study and Discussion...161
Selected References 162

Animals inherit certain genetic possibilities, but how well these potentialities develop depends upon the environment to which they are subjected; and the most important influence in the environment is the feed. In turn, all feeds come directly or indirectly from plants which have their roots in the soil. Thus, we have the cycle as a whole—from the soil, through the plant, thence to the animal and back to the soil again.

Lush pastures and well-cured, dry forages produced on fertile soils, to-gether with a multitude of grains and by-product feeds—many of which are inedible by man—constitute the basis of successful livestock production. In this category are hay, pasture, certain grains, mill feeds, and other by-products which are converted into meat, eggs, milk, and wool. Moreover, 49.4 per cent of the land area of the United States is pastured all or part of the year. Much of this forage is produced on lands unsuited for the growth of bread grains or gardens.

Also, feeding is important from an economic standpoint; it is the major item of expense in producing livestock. For example, feed accounts for approx-imately 80 per cent of the total cost of producing pork, for 80 per cent of the cost of finishing cattle exclusive of the initial purchase price of the animals, for 50 per cent of the cost of milk production, and for 50 to 70 per cent of the total production cost of poultry.

RELATIVE IMPORTANCE OF PRINCIPAL LIVESTOCK FEEDS

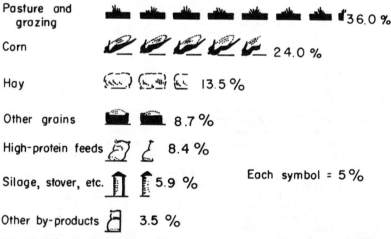

Pasture and grazing	36.0 %
Corn	24.0 %
Hay	13.5 %
Other grains	8.7 %
High-protein feeds	8.4 %
Silage, stover, etc.	5.9 %
Other by-products	3.5 %

Each symbol = 5%

Fig. 3-1. These principal livestock feeds are converted into meat, eggs, milk, and wool. About two-thirds of the feed consumed by animals is not suited for human consumption. Data based on average of the feeding years 1963 and 1964; provided by Earl F. Hodges, Agricultural Economist, Farm Production Division, Economic Research Service, USDA.

It is important, therefore, that feeding practices on the farm be as effi-cient and economical as possible. To this end, every livestock producer should endeavor to provide a ration that is both satisfactory and inexpensive—a ration which makes for the maximum production of a quality product per unit of feed consumed.

THE FUNCTIONS OF FEEDS

The feed consumed by animals is used for a number of different purposes, the exact usage varying somewhat with the class, age, and productivity of the animal. With all animals, a certain part of the feed is used for the maintenance of bodily functions aside from any useful production. This is known as the maintenance requirement. In addition, the various classes of animals use feed to take care of the functions for which they are kept. Thus, young, growing animals need nutrients suitable for building muscle tissue and bone; finishing animals need a surplus of energy feeds for the formation of fat; breeding females require feed for the development of their fetuses, and, following parturition, for the production of milk; whereas work (or running) animals use feed to supply energy for productive work. Still other classes of animals require feed for the production of eggs and wool. Each of these needs will be discussed separately.

Maintenance

An animal differs from an engine in that the latter has no fuel requirement when idle; whereas an animal requires fuel every second of the day, whether it is idle or not.

The maintenance requirement may be defined as a ration which is adequate to prevent any loss or gain of tissue in the body when there is no production. Although these requirements are relatively simple, they are essential for life itself. A mature animal must have heat to maintain body temperature, sufficient energy to cover the internal work of the body and the minimum movement of the animal, and a small amount of proteins, vitamins, and minerals for the repair of body tissues.

No matter how quietly an animal may be lying in the stall, it still requires a certain amount of fuel, and the least amount on which it can exist is called its basal maintenance requirement. The animal (man, cattle, and sheep, but not horses) requires about 9 per cent more fuel when standing than when lying and still more for any movement it may make. This explains why it is desirable for economic reasons that finishing animals should eat and then lie down as much as possible. Even under the best of conditions, about one-half of all the feed consumed by animals is used in meeting the maintenance requirements.

Growth

Growth may be defined as the increase in size of the muscles, bones, internal organs, and other parts of the body. Naturally, the growth requirements become increasingly acute when animals are forced for early usage, such as the training and racing of a two- or three-year-old horse.

Growth has been referred to as the foundation of animal production. Young cattle, sheep, and swine will not make the most economical finishing gains unless they have been raised to be thrifty and vigorous. Likewise, breeding females may have their productive ability seriously impaired if they have been raised improperly. Nor can one expect the most satisfactory yields of milk from dairy cows, unless they have been well developed as heifers. Work horses and mules cannot perform the maximum amount of work, and running horses do not possess the desired speed and endurance, if their growth has been stunted or if their skeletons have been injured by inadequate rations during the growth period.

Finishing (or Show-Ring Fitting)

This is the laying on of fat, especially in the tissues of the abdominal cavity and in the connective tissues just under the skin and between the muscles.

The composition of a ration for fitting may be the same as for maintenance, but it must be supplied in larger quantities.

In practical fitting rations, higher condition in mature animals is usually obtained through increasing the allowance of feeds high in carbohydrates and fats—a more liberal allowance of grains. Any surplus of protein may also serve for the production of fat, but usually such feeds are more expensive and are not used for economy reasons. In fitting mature animals, very little more proteins, minerals, and vitamins are required than for maintenance. In fitting young, growing animals, however, it is essential that—in addition to supplying more carbohydrates and fats—ample proteins, minerals, and vitamins be provided.

In general, the more feed a growing or finishing animal consumes, the more economical will be its gains. For example, it may be assumed that a calf requires 6 pounds of feed daily to maintain itself, when making no gain. With an additional 3 pounds of feed, or a daily ration of 9 pounds, it gains 1 pound daily in weight. If the ration is increased by another 3 pounds, bringing the daily allowance to 12 pounds, it gains 2 pounds daily in weight. Thus, each 3 pounds of feed over and above the maintenance requirement (6 pounds per day for maintenance) produced a gain of 1 pound in live weight. On the basis of total feed consumed, however, the first pound of gain required a total of 9 pounds of feed (the first 6 pounds for maintenance and an additional 3 pounds for gain), whereas the next pound of gain only required an additional 3 pounds of feed. These facts, as illustrated in this oversimplified way, are the basis for the statement that for economical finishing the feeder should get every possible ounce of feed "under their hides." The chief difference between good and poor feeders is in the amount of feed above the maintenance requirement that they are able to consume. This also shows why it is necessary to have animals with ample feed capacity.

Reproduction and Lactation

Regular and normal reproduction is the basis for profit on any farm or ranch. Despite this undeniable fact, it has been estimated that from 20 to 50 per cent of all matings are infertile, that 25 per cent of all cows culled from dairy herds are removed because of reproductive inefficiency, that the overall average United States calf crop of beef cattle is only 86 per cent, that 6 to 10 per cent of all ewes are sterile, that only 40 to 60 per cent of all mares bred actually produce foals, and that 15 to 20 per cent of all sows bred fail to produce litters. Certainly, there are many causes of reproductive failure, but most scientists are agreed that inadequate nutrition is a major one.

With all species, most of the growth of the fetus occurs during the last third of pregnancy, thus making the reproductive requirements most critical during this period. The ration of the pregnant female should supply sufficient amounts of protein, minerals, and vitamins.

With females of all species, the nutritive requirements for moderate to heavy milk production are much more rigorous than the pregnancy requirements. There is special need for a rather liberal protein, mineral, and vitamin allowance.

In the case of young, growing, pregnant females, additional protein, minerals, and vitamins, above the ordinary requirements, must be provided; otherwise, the fetus will not develop properly or milk will be produced at the expense of the tissues of the dam.

It is also known that the ration exerts a powerful effect on sperm production and semen quality. Too fat a condition can even lead to temporary or permanent sterility. Moreover, there is abundant evidence that greater fertility of herd sires exists under conditions where a well-balanced ration and plenty of exercise are provided.

Work (or Running)

In many respects, work requirements are similar to the needs for finishing, both functions requiring high-energy feeds. The function of work (or running) is, for the most part, limited to horses, though in certain parts of the world oxen furnish the chief source of power.

For mature work horses, not in reproduction, work is performed primarily at the expense of the carbohydrates and fats of the ration—energy that can be supplied in the form of additional grain. Theoretically, the protein is not drawn upon so long as the other nutrients are present in adequate amounts. From a practical standpoint, however, it is usually desirable to feed more proteins than the maintenance requirement, merely to insure that the animal can make efficient use of the remainder of the nutrients in the ration. In other words, when a ration too low in protein is fed, more feed is required because the animal is unable to utilize the ration efficiently. For work animals, the mineral and vitamin requirements are practically the same as for comparable idle animals—except for the greater need for salt because of increased perspiration.

Wool

Wool is a high-protein product. Thus, a shortage of protein in the ration will lessen wool production, even though the total amount of the ration is adequate. It is also known that both the quality and quantity of fiber may be materially lowered if the animals are subjected to unfavorable thrift or health. If such periods are of relatively short duration, tender spots (weak spots) appear in the growth of the fiber.

ESSENTIALS OF AN ADEQUATE DIET;
A BALANCED RATION

To supply all the needs—maintenance, growth, finishing, reproduction and lactation, work (or running), and wool—the different classes of animals must receive sufficient feed to furnish the necessary quantity of proteins, energy (carbohydrates and fats), minerals, vitamins, and water. Perhaps under certain conditions feed additives may be desirable, although it is not likely that they are essential. A ration that meets all these needs is said to be balanced. More specifically, by definition, *a balanced ration is one which provides an animal the proper proportions and amounts of all the required nutrients for a period of 24 hours.*

Protein Needs

For more than a century, proteins and their structural units, the amino acids, have been studied and recognized as important dietary constituents. Pro-

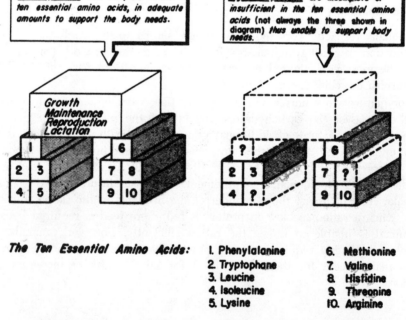

The Ten Essential Amino Acids:

1. Phenylalanine
2. Tryptophane
3. Leucine
4. Isoleucine
5. Lysine
6. Methionine
7. Valine
8. Histidine
9. Threonine
10. Arginine

Fig. 3-2. The amino acids are sometimes referred to as the building stones of proteins. Rations that furnish an insufficient amount of the essential building stones (amino acids) are said to have proteins of poor quality. In general, proteins of animal origin are of good quality, whereas proteins of plant origin are of poor quality. (Drawing by R. F. Johnson)

teins are complex organic compounds made up chiefly of amino acids, which are present in characteristic proportions for each specific protein. This nutrient always contains carbon, hydrogen, oxygen, and nitrogen, and in addition it usually contains sulphur and frequently phosphorus. Proteins are essential in all plant and animal life as components of the active protoplasm of each living cell.

In plants, the protein is largely concentrated in the actively growing portions, especially the leaves and seeds. Plants also have the ability to synthesize their own proteins from such relatively simple soil and air compounds as carbon dioxide, water, nitrates, and sulfates. Thus, plants, together with some bacteria which are able to synthesize these products, are the original sources of all proteins.

In animals, proteins are much more widely distributed than in plants. Thus, the proteins of the animal body are primary constituents of many structural and protective tissues—such as bones, ligaments, hair, hoofs, skin, and the soft tissues which include the organs and muscles. The total protein content of animal bodies ranges from about 10 per cent in very fat mature animals to 20 per cent in thin, young animals. By way of further contrast, it is also interesting to note that, except for the bacterial action in the rumen, animals lack the ability of the plant to synthesize proteins from simple materials. They must depend upon plants or other animals as a source of dietary protein. In brief, except for the high quality proteins built by the bacterial action in the paunch of ruminants, the animal must have amino acids or more complete protein compounds in the ration.

Animals of all ages and kinds require adequate amounts of protein of suitable quality; this being required for maintenance, growth, finishing, reproduction, work, and wool production. Of course, the protein requirements for growth and reproduction are the greatest and most critical.

QUALITY OF PROTEINS

In addition to supplying an adequate quantity of proteins, it is essential that the character of proteins be thoroughly understood. Proteins are very complex compounds with each molecule made up of hundreds of thousands of amino acids combined with each other. The amino acids, of which some 23 are known, are sometimes referred to as the building stones of proteins. Certain of these amino acids can be made by the animal's body to satisfy its needs. Others cannot be formed fast enough to supply the body's needs and, therefore, are known as essential (or indispensable) amino acids. These must be supplied in the feed. Thus, rations that furnish an insufficient amount of any of the essential amino acids are said to have proteins of poor quality, whereas those which provide the proper proportions of the various necessary amino acids are said to supply proteins of good quality. In general, proteins of plant origin (linseed meal, cottonseed meal, soybean meal, and peanut meal) are of poor quality. Proteins of animal origin (meat, fish, eggs, milk, and their by-products) are of good quality.

The necessity of each amino acid in the diet of the experimental rat has been thoroughly tested, but less is known about the requirements of large animals or even the human. According to our present knowledge, based largely on work with the rat, the following division of amino acids as indispensable and dispensable seems proper:

Indispensable	Dispensable
Arginine	Alanine
Histidine	Aspartic acid
Isoleucine	Citrulline
Leucine	Cystine
Lysine	Glutamic acid
Methionine	Glycine
Phenylalanine	Hydroxyglutamic acid
Threonine	Hydroxyproline
Tryptophane	Proline
Valine	Serine
	Tyrosine

Fortunately, the amino-acid content of proteins from various sources varies. Thus, the deficiencies of one protein may be improved by combining it with another, and the mixture of the two proteins often will have a higher feeding value than either one alone. It is for this reason that a considerable variety of feeds in the ration is usually recommended.

The feed proteins are broken down into amino acids by digestion. They are then absorbed and distributed by the blood stream to the body cells, which rebuild these amino acids into body proteins.

RUMEN SYNTHESIS

In the case of ruminants (cattle and sheep), there is a tremendous bacterial action in the paunch. These bacteria build body proteins of high quality from sources of inorganic nitrogen that nonruminants (humans, rats, chickens, swine, poultry, and dogs) cannot use. Farther on in the digestive tract, the ruminant digests the bacteria and secures good proteins therefrom. Although the horse is not a ruminant, apparently the same bacterial process occurs to a more limited extent in the caecum (or cecum), that greatly enlarged blind pouch of the large intestine of the horse.

In ruminant nutrition, therefore, even such nonprotein sources of combined nitrogen as ammonia and urea have a protein replacement value. In general, meeting the protein requirements of ruminants is not a critical problem insofar as quality is concerned. An exception is the very young ruminant (or horse) in which the rumen (or caecum) and its synthetic ability are not yet well developed. For such an animal, high quality proteins in the diet are requisite to normal development.

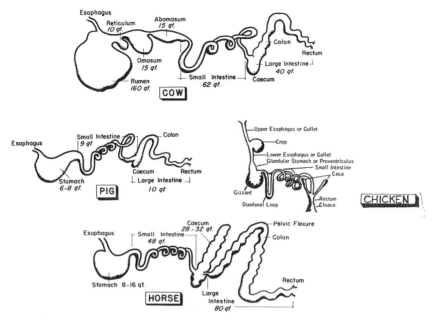

Fig. 3-3. Schematic diagram of digestive tracts of the cow, pig, horse, and chicken. The rumen of the cow is the seat of tremendous bacterial action through which high quality proteins are synthesized. Because of this arrangement, high quality proteins are unimportant in the ration of ruminants, except in the case of young stock. (Drawing by R. F. Johnson)

PRACTICAL PROTEIN SOURCES

In practical feeding operations, hogs and chickens are usually provided with some protein feeds of animal origin in order to supplement the proteins found in grains and forages. In feeding mature cattle, sheep, and horses, a safe plan to follow is to provide a liberal supply of high-quality legume hay or lush young pasture along with the concentrates. Also, as previously indicated, the quality of the proteins in the ration is likely to be higher if a variety of feeds is combined.

In general, feeds of high protein content are more expensive than those high in carbohydrates or fats. Accordingly, there is a temptation to feed too little of the proteins. On the other hand, when protein feeds are the cheapest— as is often true of cull peas in certain sections of the West—excess quantities of them may be fed as energy feeds without harm, provided that the ration is balanced out in all other respects. Any amino acids that are left over, after the protein requirements have been met, are deaminated or broken down in the body. In this process, a part of each amino acid is turned into energy, and the remainder is excreted via the kidneys.

Energy Needs

It is common knowledge that a ration must contain proteins, fats, and carbohydrates. Although each of these has specific functions in maintaining a normal body, they can all be used to provide energy for maintenance, for work, or for finishing. From the standpoint of supplying the normal energy needs of both humans and animals, however, the carbohydrates are by far the most important, more of them being consumed than any other compound, whereas the fats are next in importance for energy purposes. Carbohydrates are usually more abundant and cheaper, and they are very easily digested, absorbed, and transformed into body fat. Also, carbohydrate feeds may be more easily stored in warm weather and for longer periods of time. Feeds high in fat content are likely to become rancid, and rancid feed is unpalatable, if not actually injurious in some instances.

CARBOHYDRATES

The carbohydrates are organic compounds composed of carbon, hydrogen, and oxygen. This group includes the sugars, starch, cellulose, gums, and related substances. They are formed in the plant by photosynthesis as follows: $6CO_2 + 6H_2O$ + energy from sun $= C_6H_{12}O_6$ (glucose) $+ 6O_2$. On the average, the carbohydrates comprise about three-fourths of all the dry matter in plants, the chief source of animal feed. They form the woody framework of plants as well as the chief reserve food stored in seeds, roots, and tubers. When consumed by animals, carbohydrates are used as a source of heat and energy, and any excess of them is stored in the body as fat.

No appreciable amount of carbohydrate is found in the animal body at any one time, the blood supply being held rather constant at about 0.05 to 0.1 per cent for most animals but, with the pig, ranging from 0.05 to 0.25 per cent. However, this small quantity of glucose in the blood, which is constantly replenished by changing the glycogen of the liver back to glucose, serves as the chief source of fuel with which to maintain the body temperature and to furnish the energy needed for all body processes. The storage of glycogen (so-called animal starch) in the liver amounts to 3 to 7 per cent of the weight of that organ.

CARBOHYDRATE FEEDS CONSIST OF NITROGEN-FREE EXTRACT AND FIBER

From a feeding standpoint, the carbohydrates consist of nitrogen-free extract (N.F.E.) and fiber. The nitrogen-free extract includes the more soluble, and, therefore, the more digestible, carbohydrates—such as the starches, sugars, hemicelluloses, and the more soluble part of the celluloses and pentosans. Also, N.F.E. contains some lignin. The fiber is that woody portion of plants (or feeds) which is not dissolved out by weak acids and alkalies. Fiber, therefore, is less easily digested. It includes cellulose, hemicellulose, and lignin.

Use of Fibrous Roughages Possible
Because of Bacterial Action

The ability of animals to utilize roughages—to digest the fiber therein—depends chiefly on bacterial action. It is a true symbiotic type of relationship, carried out chiefly by anaerobic bacteria. This action is confined largely to the first three compartments of the stomach of ruminants, to the cecum and colon of the horse, and to a lesser extent in the large intestine of all animals. This bacterial digestion breaks down the cellulose and pentosans of feeds into usable organic acids (chiefly acetic, propionic, and butyric acid). These so-called volatile fatty acids are absorbed directly through the ruminal wall, and may furnish one-third or more of the maintenance energy requirements of the animal. This process also results in (1) the production of gases (principally carbon dioxide and methane) which are eliminated as wastes, and (2) the production of heat, which is of no value unless it is needed in maintaining body temperature.

Bacterial digestion is of great practical importance in the nutrition of mature cattle, sheep, and horses and is the fundamental reason why they can be maintained chiefly on roughages. It has been estimated that 78 and 89 per cent of the total feed supply of beef cattle and sheep, respectively, consists of forages.

Fiber of Young Grasses and Early Cut Hay More Digestible

The fiber of growing pasture grass, fresh or dried, is more digestible than the fiber of most hay. Likewise, the fiber of early cut hay is more digestible than that of hay cut in the late-bloom or seed stages. The difference is due to both chemical and physical structure, especially to the presence of certain encrusting substances (notably lignin) which are deposited in the cell wall with age.

Optimum Fiber Content of Ration Variable

Young stock of all classes, finishing steers and lambs, high-producing dairy cows, swine, poultry, and work (or running) horses must have rations in which a large part of the carbohydrate content of the ration is low in fiber and is in the form of nitrogen-free extract. On the other hand, a considerable amount of fiber or bulk in the ration is believed desirable for mature breeding animals of all classes of livestock, especially when too high condition is not desired. Likewise, with young animals being developed for breeding purposes, the increased fiber will tend to develop more growth and not so much fat.

To promote normal physiological activity of the gastrointestinal tract, one must feed a certain amount of coarse roughage to all classes of farm animals, except possibly to swine.

FATS

Lipids (fat and fat-like substances), like carbohydrates, contain the three elements: carbon, hydrogen, and oxygen. Fats are soluble in such organic solvents as ether, chloroform, and benzene. For this reason, grease spots on clothing are usually removed with one of these solvents. As livestock feeds, fats function much like carbohydrates in that they serve as a source of heat and energy and for the formation of fat. Because of the larger proportion of carbon and hydrogen, however, fats liberate more heat than carbohydrates when digested, furnishing approximately 2.25 times as much heat or energy per pound on oxidation as do the carbohydrates. A smaller quantity of fat is required, therefore, to serve the same function.

FATS VARY IN MELTING POINT AND DEGREE OF UNSATURATION

The physical and chemical properties of fats are quite variable. From a chemical standpoint, a molecule of fat consists of a combination of three molecules of certain fatty acids with one molecule of glycerol. Fats differ in their melting points and other properties depending on the particular fatty acids which they contain. Thus, because of the high content of unsaturated acids (such as oleic and linoleic) and acids of low molecular weight, corn fat is a liquid at ordinary temperatures; whereas, because of the high content of stearic and palmitic acids, beef fat is solid at ordinary temperatures.

Some fatty acids are unsaturated, which means that they have the ability to take up oxygen or certain other chemical elements. Chemically, these unsaturated acids contain one or more pairs of double-bond carbon atoms. These characteristics are important. The value of linseed oil and varnish is due ' their high content of unsaturated fatty acids, by virtue of which oxygen absorbed when they are exposed to air, resulting in a tough, resistant coating. Likewise, because of their high content of unsaturated fats, soybeans or peanuts, when fed liberally, will produce soft pork.

An unsaturated fat readily unites with iodine, two atoms of this element being added for each double bond. Thus, in experimental work, the iodine number (the number of grams of iodine absorbed by a hundred grams of fat) is an excellent criterion of the degree of unsaturation. In the past, the iodine test was commonly applied in studying the soft pork problem. At the present time, the chief measure used in such determinations is the refractive index, as determined by the refractometer.

RANCIDITY OF FATS

Because of their unsaturation, fats often become rancid through oxidation or hydrolysis, resulting in disagreeable flavors and odors which lessen their desirability as feeds. The development of rancidity may be retarded through proper storage or by adding antioxidants. The hydrogenation of fats (adding hydrogen to the double bonds) also lessens rancidity. The latter process has long been effectively used in improving the keeping qualities of vegetable shortenings, and is now used in lard.

FEED FATS AFFECT BODY FATS

The nature of the body fat in animals is markedly influenced by the character of the fat in feeds. This phenomenon is of considerable practical importance, as the degree of hardness of the fat is a major factor in determining carcass quality and value. This is particularly true of hogs in which, because of the nature of the feeds consumed in certain areas, the soft-pork problem exists. Likewise, the kind of fat consumed by cows has a similar influence on the nature of the milk fat.

Fig. 3-4. Feed fats affect body fats. The soft lard sample (left) came from hogs fed on a high soybean ration. Both samples of lard had been exposed to room temperature, 70° F., for two hours prior to photographing. (Courtesy, University of Illinois)

ME FATS IN RATION DESIRABLE

Common belief to the contrary, animals can tolerate a rather high fat content in the ration. As evidence of this, it is to be noted that sucklings normally handle a relatively large amount of fat, for milk contains 25 to 40 per cent of this nutrient on a dry-matter basis. Also, except for the soft-pork problem, no apparent difficulty is encountered in feeding hogs on a rather high fat diet, such as results when large quantities of peanuts or soybeans are fed.

A small amount of fats in the ration is desirable, as these fats are the carriers of the fat-soluble vitamins. There is evidence that some species (humans, swine, rats, and dogs) require certain of the fatty acids. Although the fatty-acid requirements of farm animals have not been settled, it is thought that ordinary farm rations contain ample quantities of these nutrients.

ANIMAL VS. VEGETABLE FATS

The comparative food value of animal and vegetable fats has long been a stormy issue, particularly in regard to the relative merits of butter versus oleomargarine or of lard versus vegetable shortenings. In general, except for the vitamins which they carry, there is no conclusive experimental work to indicate that, as a source of fatty acids, animal fats are superior to vegetable fats. There is reason to believe that margarine, when fortified with vitamins A and D, is—from a nutritional standpoint—just as effective as butter in promoting growth, good health, reproduction, and lactation. There is, however, evidence that some species (humans, swine, rats, and dogs) require certain of the fatty acids, but it is quite likely that these differences are unimportant when a normal mixed diet is used. Of course, many people still prefer butter, and many

Lard Is Effective in the Treatment of Many Cases of Eczema

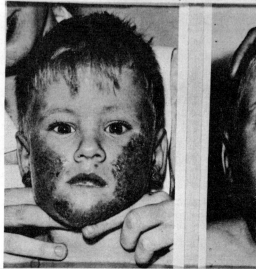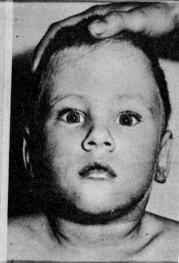

Two and one-half year old child

Eruption present since 2 months of age

One month after fresh lard was added to the diet

(Studies by Dr. A. E. Hansen, U. of Texas, Medical Branch, Galveston; supported by National Live Stock and Meat Board)

Fig. 3-5. Humans require certain of the fatty acids. Thus, as shown in the illustration, often lard—which contains a relatively large amount of the essential unsaturated fatty acids—is effective in the treatment of eczema. (Studies by Dr. A. E. Hansen, University of Texas, Medical Branch, Galveston; supported by National Live Stock and Meat Board)

desire to patronize it as a more genuinely and naturally home-produced product than margarine.

FEEDING FATS

The feeding of fats was prompted in an effort to find a profitable outlet for surplus packing house fats. For the most part, fats were formerly used for soap making, but they are not used extensively in detergents. Thus, with the rise in the use of detergents in recent years, fats became a "drug on the market."

From 2 to 6 per cent fat can be added successfully to most rations of farm animals and poultry, provided the fat is first stabilized to prevent rancidity.[1] Also,

---

[1] In order to prevent rancidity and to increase the utilization and stability of vitamin A and carotene, the use of the antioxidants butylated hydroxyanisole (BHA), butylated hydroxytoluene (BHT), etoxyquin, or some formulation containing them is recommended.

in compounding such rations, consideration must be given to the fact that fats do not provide proteins, vitamins, or minerals.

Animal and vegetable fats seem to be equally effective additions to feed; hence, selection should be determined solely by comparative price. Ordinarily, animal fats are much cheaper than such vegetable fats as soybean, cottonseed, or safflower oil.

With favorable prices—that is, if price relationships are such that fats can be used to furnish energy more cheaply than carbohydrates—they are popular in mixed feeds, because, in addition to feed efficiency and possible other animal benefits, there are several advantages to adding fats to rations from the standpoint of feed processing. Among the latter are: (1) control of dustiness, (2) decreased wear on mixing machinery, (3) improved appearance and feel of the ration, and (4) greater ease in pelleting.

METHODS OF MEASURING ENERGY

Two methods of measuring energy are commonly employed in the United States: (1) the older total digestible nutrient (TDN) system and (2) the newer calorie system. Most scientists favor a transition from the TDN system to the calorie system.

THE TOTAL DIGESTIBLE NUTRIENTS (TDN) SYSTEM

Total digestible nutrients (TDN) is the sum of the digestible protein, fiber, nitrogen-free extract, and fat x 2.25.

Back of TDN values are the following steps:

1. **Digestibility.**—The digestibility of a particular feed for a specific class of stock is determined by a digestion trial. It is made by determining the percentage of each nutrient in the feed through chemical analysis; giving the feed to the test animal for a preliminary period, so that all residues of former feeds will pass out of the digestive tract; giving weighed amounts of the feed during the test period; collecting, weighing, and analyzing the feces; determining the difference between the amount of the nutrient fed and the amount found in the feces; and computing the percentage of each nutrient digested. The latter figure is known as the *digestion coefficient* for that nutrient in the feed.

2. **Computation of digestible nutrients.**—Digestible nutrients are computed by multiplying the percentage of each nutrient in the feed (protein, fiber, nitrogen-free extract [N.F.E.], and fat) by its digestion coefficient. The result is expressed as digestible protein, digestible fiber, digestible N.F.E., and digestible fat. Thus, for corn the digestible nutrients could be estimated as shown in the table on the following page.

In this example, corn grain has 6.2 per cent digestible protein. Every feed has a digestible protein value which was determined in this manner.

Total % of nutrient in feed	X	Digestion coefficient / 100	=	% Digestible nutrient	
				Digestible Nutrient	
				(%)	(lbs.)
9.3% protein	X	67 / 100	=	6.2 (protein)	6.2
1.9% fiber	X	39 / 100	=	0.7 (fiber)	0.7
70.1% nitrogen-free extract (NFE)	X	85 / 100	=	59.6 (NFE)	59.6
3.9% ether extract (fat)	X	85 / 100	=	3.3 (fat)	3.3

3. **Computation of total digestible nutrients.**—To approximate the greater caloric value of fat, the percentage of digestible fat is multiplied by 2.25. Hence, for the sample of corn, the TDN may be calculated as follows:

Digestible protein	6.2	X	1	= 6.2
Digestible crude fiber	0.7	X	1	= 0.7
Digestible NFE	59.6	X	1	= 59.6
Digestible either extract (fat)	3.3	X	2.25	= 7.4

73.9% TDN, or
73.9 lbs.TDN/100 lbs. corn

4. **Animal requirements or feeding standards.**—In the TDN system, the feed requirements (energy) of farm animals are given as pounds of total digestible nutrients; and, in addition, the pounds of dry matter are given also to insure that the stated amount of TDN is fed.

THE CALORIE SYSTEM

Energy is used in many forms—as light, electricity, atomic force, work, or heat—and it is measured by several units such as candle power, kilowatts, foot pounds, joules, and calories. In animals, energy is expended as work and/or heat or stored as products. It would appear, therefore, that it should be measured in units suitable for these purposes. Thus, a heat unit is an excellent way in which to measure the potential energy of feeds, the energy of animal products, and the heat that results from body processes. The heat unit used by animal nutritionists is the calorie.

A calorie (cal/-always written with a small c) is the amount of heat required to raise the temperature of one gram of water one degree Centigrade. To measure this heat, an instrument known as the bomb calorimeter is used, in which the feed (or other substance) tested is placed and burned with the aid of oxygen (see Fig. 3-6).

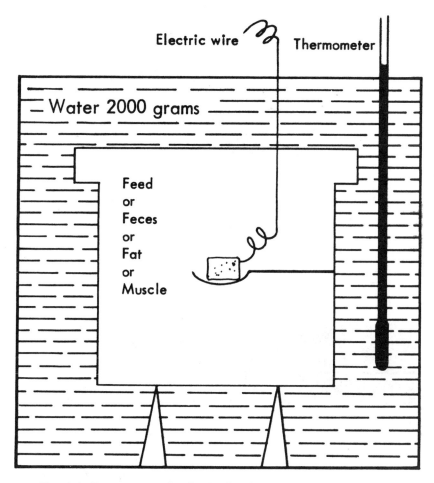

Fig. 3-6. Diagrammatic sketch of a bomb calorimeter used for the determination of the gross energy value (caloric content) of various materials. (Courtesy, Dr. Lorin E. Harris, Utah State University)

It is noteworthy that the determination of the heat of combustion with a bomb calorimeter is not as difficult or as time-consuming as the chemical analyses used in arriving at TDN values. Briefly stated, the procedure is as follows: An electric wire is attached to the material being tested, so that it can be ignited by remote control; 2,000 grams of water are poured around the bomb; 25 to 30 atmospheres of oxygen are added to the bomb; the material is ignited; the heat given off from the burned material warms the water; and a thermometer registers the change in temperature of the water. For example, if one gram of material is burned and the temperature of the water is raised one degree Centigrade, 2,000 cal are given off. Hence, the material contains 2,000 cal per g, or 907,200 cal per pound.

The energy utilization by a lactating cow is illustrated in Fig. 3-7. As shown, the feces and heat production make up the largest losses of energy.

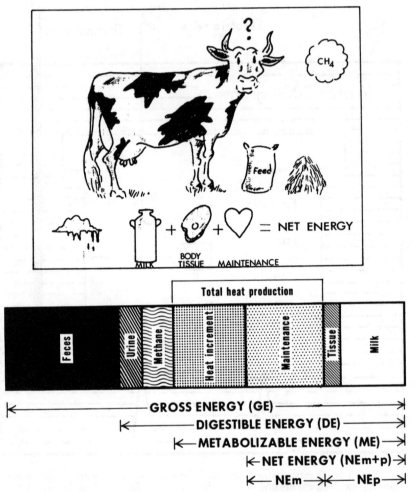

Fig. 3-7. Energy utilization by a lactating cow. (Adapted by the author from drawings provided by Dr. W. P. Flatt, Research Dairy Husbandman, Dairy Research Branch, USDA; and Dr. Lorin E. Harris, Utah State University)

Mineral Needs[2]

It has long been known that minerals play an important role in animal nutrition. Aside from furnishing structural material for the growth of bone, teeth, and tissue, the minerals regulate many of the vital life processes.

Also, it is recognized that mineral allowances given with the ration or in a mineral mix should vary according to the mineral content of the soil on which feeds are grown.

---

[2]In the preparation of this section on mineral needs, the author had the benefit of the authoritative help and review of Dr. Oscar O. Thomas, Professor, Montana State Univ., Bozeman; Dr. F. R. Klay, Head, Nutrition Research Division, Moorman Mfg. Co., Quincy, Ill.; Dr. Marvin G. Moose, Feed Ingredients Dept., International Minerals & Chemical Corp., Skokie, Ill.; and Mr. John W. Megown, Vigortone Products, Inc., Cedar Rapids, Iowa.

Although acute mineral-deficiency diseases and actual death losses are relatively rare, inadequate supplies of any one of the 15 essential mineral elements may result in lack of thrift, poor gains, inefficient feed utilization, lowered reproduction, and decreased production of work, milk, or wool. Thus, like a thief in the night, subacute mineral deficiencies in farm animals each year steal away millions of dollars in profits from the farmers and ranchers of America, and, for the most part, go unnoticed. Only when the mineral deficiency reaches such proportions that it results in excess emaciation, reproductive failure, or death is it likely to be detected.

FUNCTION OF AND ESSENTIAL MINERALS

Animal bodies contain but small amounts of minerals, the common range being from 2 to 5 per cent, but these constituents are very important. Mineral matter makes up a large part of the skeleton and teeth of the animal, and minerals are essential constituents of the soft tissues, the blood, the fluids of the body, and certain of the secretions.

Approximately 70 per cent of the mineral content of the animal body consists of calcium and phosphorus. About 99 per cent of the calcium and over 80 per cent of the phosphorus are found in the bones and teeth. Since the greatest development of the skeleton takes place in the young, growing animal, it is evident that adequate minerals must be provided at an early age if the bone is to be sound.

The 15 mineral elements which, up to the present time, have been shown to be essential are: calcium, phosphorus, sodium, chlorine, iodine, iron, copper, manganese, magnesium, sulfur, zinc, potassium, cobalt, selenium, and molybdenum. This list of essential mineral elements is based upon experiments with one or more species, for all elements have not been tested with all species. It is highly probable, however, that all 15 are required by each specie of farm animal. This does not mean that all 15 of these minerals must always be included in the mineral supplement. As a matter of fact, through careful selection of feeds, most of these elements can be supplied in natural rations. Sometimes, however, special mineral supplements are needed and should be added. Such supplements should supply only the specific minerals that are deficient—and in the quantities necessary. Excesses and mineral imbalances are to be avoided.

The evidence available today would indicate that the following four elements may be of practical concern in animal feeding in most sections of the United States: the constituents of common salt—sodium and chlorine, calcium, and phosphorus. In addition, iodine, cobalt, and copper deficiencies exist in certain areas; and, under certain conditions, deficiencies of magnesium and iron (and copper) may be encountered with suckling calves and pigs, respectively. Also, growing pigs may need supplementary zinc when fed rations that are high in calcium. The other mineral elements appear to be secured in ample quantities through the natural feeds produced in the various sections of the United States and for this reason will not receive individual consideration in the discussion that follows.

There is renewed interest in trace elements, and general recognition of the importance of many of them in livestock rations.

Sodium Chloride or Salt

Salt, which serves as both a condiment and a nutrient, is needed by all classes of animals, but more especially by herbivora (grass-eating animals). It may be provided in the form of granulated-, rock-, or block-salt. In general, the form selected is determined by price and availability. It is to be pointed out, however, that very hard block and rock salt are difficult for stock to eat, often resulting in sore tongues and inadequate consumption. Also, if there is much competition for the salt block, the more timid animals may not get their requirements.

Both sodium and chlorine are essential for animal life. They are necessary in maintaining the osmotic pressure of body cells (thereby assisting in the transfer of nutrients to the cells and the removal of waste materials). Also, sodium is important as one of the main body buffers and in making bile, which aids in the digestion of fats and carbohydrates. Chlorine is required for the formation of the hydrochloric acid in the gastric juice so vital to protein digestion. The blood contains 0.25 per cent chlorine, 0.22 per cent sodium, and 0.02 to 0.22 per cent potassium; thus, the chlorine content is higher than that of any other mineral in the blood. The salt requirement is greatly increased under

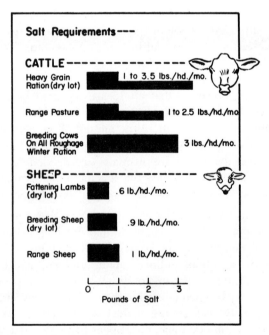

Fig. 3-8. The average salt requirements of cattle and sheep. (**Drawing by** Steve Allured)

conditions which cause heavy sweating, thereby resulting in large losses of this mineral from the body. Unless replaced, fatigue will result. For this reason, when engaged in hard work and perspiring profusely, both horses and humans should receive liberal allowances of salt.

Precautions in Feeding Salt

Salt can be fed free-choice to cattle, sheep, swine, and horses provided that they have not previously been salt-starved. That is, if the animals have not been fed salt for a considerable length of time, they may overeat, resulting in digestive disturbances and even death. Salt-starved animals should first be hand-fed salt, and the daily allowance should be increased gradually until they start leaving a little in the mineral box. When this point is reached, self-feeding may be followed. The Indians and the pioneers of this country handed down many legendary stories about the huge numbers of buffalo and deer that killed themselves simply by gorging at a newly found "saltlick" after having been salt-starved for long periods of time.

CALCIUM AND PHOSPHORUS

Farm animals are more likely to suffer from a lack of phosphorus and of calcium than from any of the other minerals except common salt. These two minerals comprise about three-fourths of the ash of the skeleton and from one-third to one-half of the minerals of milk.

Calcium is essential for the development and maintenance of normal bones and teeth; for the formation of egg shell in poultry; for blood coagulation and lactation; for the functioning of the heart, nerves and muscles; and for regulating the permeability of tissue cells.

Phosphorus is essential for sound bones and teeth, for the assimilation of carbohydrates and fats, for enzyme activity; and it acts as a buffer in blood tissue, occupies a key position in biologic oxidation and energy reactions, and serves as a vital ingredient of the chief protein in the nuclei of all body cells.

Fig. 3-9. Bone chewing by cattle is a common sign of phosphorus deficiency. (From Texas Station Bulletin 344, through the courtesy of The National Fertilizer Association)

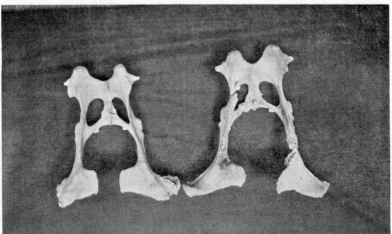

Fig. 3-10. Lactating cows need calcium. Both hips of the cow shown above have been broken (knocked down) as a result of feeding a low-calcium ration. At lower left, the pelvis of a cow which suffered three breaks while the cow received a low-calcium ration. At lower right, the pelvis of the cow pictured above, showing the breaks involving both hip bones. (From Florida Agr. Exp. Sta. Tech. Bul. 262; through the courtesy of Dr. R. B. Becker)

Liberal allowances of calcium and phosphorus are especially important for young, growing animals, for those that are pregnant, and for those that are producing milk.

The following general characteristics of feeds in regard to calcium and phosphorus are worth noting:

1. The cereal grains and their by-products and straws, dried mature grasses, and protein supplements of plant origin are low in calcium.

2. The protein supplements of animal origin and legume forage and rape are rich in calcium.

3. The cereal grains and their by-products are fairly high or even rich in phosphorus, but a large portion of the phosphorus is not readily available.

4. Most all protein-rich supplements are high in phosphorus. But, here again, plant sources of phosphorus contain much of this element in a bound form.

5. Beet by-products and dried, mature, non leguminous forages (such as grass hays and fodders) are likely to be low in phosphorus.

6. The calcium and phosphorus content of plants can be increased through fertilizing the soil upon which they are grown.

The Calcium-Phosphorus Ratio and Vitamin D

In considering the calcium and phosphorus requirements of animals, it is important to realize that the proper utilization of these minerals by the body is dependent upon three factors: (1) an adequate supply of calcium and phosphorus in an available form, (2) a suitable ratio between them (somewhere between 1 to 2 parts of calcium to 1 to 2 parts of phosphorus), and (3) sufficient

Fig. 3-11. Calf with severe rickets. Note the emaciation, humping of back, swelling of joints, knuckling of pasterns, and bowing of legs. Rickets may be caused by a lack of either calcium, phosphorus, or vitamin D, or by an incorrect ratio of the two minerals. (From Michigan State University Bulletin 150, through the courtesy of The National Fertilizer Association)

vitamin D to make possible the assimilation and utilization of the calcium and phosphorus.

Generally speaking, nutritionists have advocated a calcium-phosphorus ratio somewhere between 1 to 2 parts of calcium to 1 to 2 parts of phosphorus. However, there is much evidence that a calcium-phosphorus ratio of 1:1 to 1:2 for nonruminants (hogs and horses) and 1:1 to 7:1 for ruminants are equally satisfactorily, but ratios below 1:1 are disastrous.

If plenty of vitamin D is present (as provided either by sunlight or through the ration), the ratio of calcium to phosphorus becomes less important. Also, less vitamin D is needed when there is a desirable calcium-phosphorus ratio.

Calcium and Phosphorus Deficiencies

Young and high-producing animals are most likely to be affected by de-

Fig. 3-12. Lamb fed a ration deficient in phosphorus. Note the knock-kneed conformation. (Courtesy, University of Idaho)

ficiencies of calcium and/or phosphorus because of their greater needs for these minerals, but older animals do suffer from deficiencies. A decided deficiency of calcium or phosphorus or a lack of vitamin D will cause rickets in growing animals and osteomalacia in mature animals. A summary of each of these nutritional diseases is given in Table 3-5.

Recommended Calcium and Phosphorus Supplements

Table 3-1 gives several sources of calcium and phosphorus and the approximate percentages of the two elements in various mineral supplements.

TABLE 3—1

COMPOSITION OF CALCIUM AND PHOSPHORUS SUPPLEMENTS[1]

Mineral Supplement	Calcium			Phosphorus		
	(per cent)	(gm/lb)	(gm/kg)	(per cent)	(gm/lb)	(gm/kg)
Oyster shells, ground................	38.05	172	379	—	—	—
Limestone, ground....................	33.84	154	339	—	—	—
Bone black, spent.....................	22.00	100	220.5	13.10	60	132
Bone meal, raw feeding.............	22.70	103	227	10.10	46	101
Bone meal, steamed..................	30.00	136	229.8	13.90	63	138.9
Dicalcium phosphate................	26.50	120	264.6	20.50	93	205
Tricalcium phosphate...............	32.00	145	319.7	18.00	82	180.8
Defluorinated phosphate...........	33.00	150	330.7	18.00	82	180.8
Monosodium phosphate............	—	—	—	22.40	102	224.9
Diammonium phosphate........... (N=2%)	—	—	—	23.00	104	229

[1]From *Nutrient Requirements of Domestic Animals*, Number 3, Pub. 1349, 3rd Ed., 1966, NRC, National Academy of Sciences.

The relative importance of phosphorus supplements in 1966 was as follows:

Dicalcium phosphate...250,000 tons
Defluorinated phosphate...250,000 tons
Low fluorine rock phosphates...125,000 tons
Salt phosphate with colloidal clay... 75,000 tons
Bone meal.. 50,000 tons
Other chemical phosphates.....................................15,000 to 25,000 tons

Where calcium alone is needed, ground limestone or oyster-shell flour are commonly used, either free choice or added to the ration in keeping with nutrient requirements.[3]

Precautions Relative to Calcium and Phosphorus Supplements

Earlier experiments cast considerable doubt on the availability of phosphorus

---

[3]For requirements, see Sec. II of *The Stockman's Handbook*, a book by the same author and publisher as *Animal Science*.

TABLE 3—2

MAXIMUM FLUORINE CONTENT FOR (1) MINERAL SUBSTANCES
AND (2) CONCENTRATE FEEDS[1]

Class of Animal	Maximum Fluorine Content of Any Mineral or Mineral Mixture Shall Not Exceed	Fluorine Content of Rock Phosphate (or other ingredients) Shall Be Such That the Maximum Fluorine Content of the Total Concentrate (Grain) Shall Not Exceed
	(%)	(%)
Cattle......................	0.30	0.009
Sheep.......................	0.35	0.01
Swine.......................	0.45	0.014
Poultry.....................	0.60	0.035

[1]*Feed Control,* Official publication, Association of American Feed Control Officials, 1968, p. 25.

when the phosphorus was largely in the form of phytin. Although wheat bran is very high in phosphorus, containing 1.32 per cent, there was some question as to its availability due to the high phytin content of this product. More recent studies, however, indicate that cattle, and perhaps mature swine, can partially utilize phytin phosphorus. Cattle can utilize about 60 per cent of the total phosphorus from most plant sources, whereas swine can utilize only about 50 per cent. It must be emphasized, however, that phosphorus availability depends to a large extent on phosphorus sources, dietary supplies of calcium, and adequate vitamin D. Recent work indicates that high-calcium levels enhance the formation of the insoluble phytin salt from phytic acid, whereas high vitamin-D levels aid materially in the utilization of phosphorus in the form of phytin. On the other hand, in the case of man, livestock, and poultry, the evidence seems clear that phytin phosphorus is a less satisfactory source of phosphorus.

Likewise, for humans, the availability of the calcium of certain leafy materials is impaired by the presence of oxalic acid—the acid precipitating the calcium and preventing its absorption. Thus, it was a great consolation to many people to discover that, due to the high oxalic-acid content of spinach, this food possesses very questionable value in human nutrition from the standpoint of calcium. On the other hand, the deleterious effects of oxalic acid are reduced in the ruminant because of its apparent ability to metabolize oxalic acid in the body.

During World War II, the shortage of phosphorus feed supplements led to the development of defluorinated phosphates for feeding purposes. Raw, unprocessed rock phosphate usually contains from 3.25 to 4.0 per cent fluorine, whereas feeding steamed bone meal normally contains only 0.05 to 0.10 per cent. Fortunately, through heating at high temperatures under conditions suitable for elimination of fluorine, the excess fluorine of raw rock phosphate can be removed. Such a product is known as defluorinated rock phosphate.

Under the definition of the Association of American Feed Control Officials,

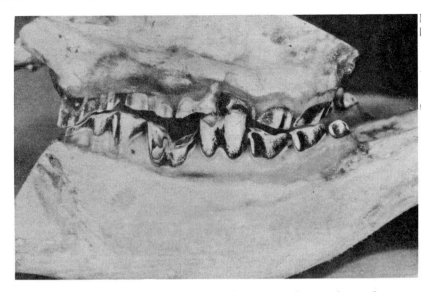

Fig. 3-13. Excess fluorine results in softening, mottling, and irregular wear of the teeth in both animals and man. (From Michigan Bulletin 129, through the courtesy of The National Fertilizer Association)

to qualify as a defluorinated phosphate, rock phosphate cannot contain more than 1 part of fluorine to 100 parts of phosphorus.

Excess fluorine results in abnormal development of the bones; softening, mottling, and irregular wear of the teeth; roughened hair coat; delayed maturity; and less efficient utilization of feed.

IRON AND COPPER

Although the body contains only approximately 0.004 per cent of iron,[4] this element is vital to life itself, because the oxygen needed by the tissues for the life processes is transported in the blood by the hemoglobin, an iron-containing compound. Also, minute amounts of iron are present in other cells and tissues, and iron is important to certain enzyme systems. Traces of copper are necessary, along with iron, for hemoglobin formation. A variable body store of both iron and copper is located in the liver and spleen, with some iron being found in the kidneys.

Iron and Copper Deficiencies

If animals are fed diets that are too low in iron, or in iron and copper, nutritional anemia will result. The incidence of nutritional anemia is widespread —particularly in young pigs. Among cattle and sheep, anemia is closely associated with internal parasite infection. Also, it is prevalent in Florida in this country and in certain areas of New Zealand, Tasmania, southern Scotland, and

---

[4] The body of a mature human contains a total of about 1/10 ounce of this mineral.

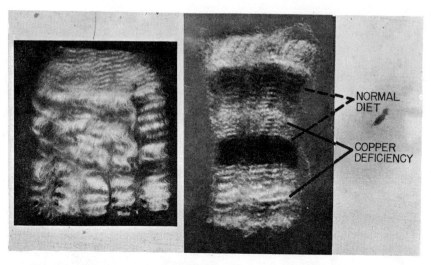

Fig. 3-14. Two samples of Australian wool, both of which show what may happen when sheep are on a copper-deficient diet.

Left: The outer (bottom) two-thirds of this sample was produced by a sheep on a copper-deficient ration, resulting in hair-like or "steely wool." Then copper was added to the sheep's diet, and normal, well-crimped wool was produced.

Right: Wool sample from a normally black sheep. The white bands appeared at intervals when copper was deficient in the ration, because copper is essential for melanin or pigment production.

Where such deficiencies occur under natural conditions, it is recognized that copper deficiencies result in the production of wool of lowered elasticity, tensile strength, and affinity for dyes. (Courtesy, Dr. Gene Erwin, former Fulbright Fellow, who studied in Australia; now, E. S. Erwin & Associates, Tolleson, Ariz.)

in Kenya Colony of British East Africa. A summary of anemia is given in Table 3-5.

Recommended Iron and Copper Supplements

There is seldom any lack of iron or copper in the normal rations of farm animals, except perhaps during the suckling period. Young mammals are born with a store of these minerals in their bodies. As a result, as long as they have access to iron-rich soil, they will subsist until they normally begin to eat feeds which supply these constituents. This is most fortunate, as milk is very low in iron and copper. When young animals are continued on a milk diet for a long period of time, particularly under confined conditions and with little or no supplemental feeds, nutritional anemia will likely develop.

In such iron- and copper-deficient areas as found in Florida, anemia in cattle, sheep, goats, and hogs (an ailment commonly called "salt sick") may be prevented by providing the animals with salt containing a mixture of copper sulfate. Likewise, ferrous sulfate and injectable iron are widely used in the prevention and treatment of anemia in young pigs.

Rich natural sources of iron include the leafy portions of plants, meats, legume seeds, cereal grains, and cane molasses. As most of the iron in cereal grains is located in the outer coatings and germ, milling increases the supply to animals

Fig. 3-15. Suckling pig with nutritional anemia, caused by a lack of iron, characterized by swollen condition about the head and shoulders and paleness of the mucus membranes. (Courtesy, College of Veterinary Medicine, University of Illinois)

but decreases it so far as humans are concerned.

In high molybdenum areas, it is recommended that the copper levels for horses and cattle be about five times higher than the normal level.

Precautions in Feeding Iron and Copper

In obtaining sources of iron, it is well to remember that simple inorganic iron salts, such as ferric chloride, are readily utilized, whereas the iron in the complex organic compounds in the hemoglobin of the blood is much less readily available, if at all. Also, though certain small amounts of iron are very essential, too much of this element in the diet may be actually deleterious—interfering with phosphorus absorption by forming an insoluble phosphate—and rickets may thus result on a diet otherwise adequate.

In any mineral mixtures containing copper, thorough mixing must be obtained in order to prevent copper toxicity or poisoning. Only limited quantities of copper can be put into the mineral mixture for the same reason. (For example, five parts per million appear adequate for sheep.)

IODINE

It is estimated that the mature animal body contains less than 0.00004 per cent of iodine, but, if this minute amount is not maintained by the diet, disaster results. More than half of the total iodine content of the body is located in the thyroid gland of the neck. Iodine, which is secreted by the thyroid gland in the form of thyroxin (an iodine-containing hormone), controls the rate of metabolism of the body.

Iodine Deficiencies

If the soil—and the water and food crops coming therefrom—is low in iodine, the body is likely to show deficiency symptoms in the form of simple goiter, unless an adequate source of iodine is provided artificially. A goiter is simply an enlargement of the thyroid gland, which is nature's way of trying to make enough thyroxin when there is insufficient iodine in the feed. However, iodine-deficiency symptoms are not always evidenced by the appearance of goiter, though this is the most common characteristic of such deficiency in humans, calves, lambs, and kids. In pigs, the outstanding symptom of the deficiency is hairlessness, whereas in foals the only symptom may be extreme weakness at birth, resulting in an inability to stand and suck. Cows and ewes give birth to goiterous (big-neck) calves and lambs, respectively. Where soils

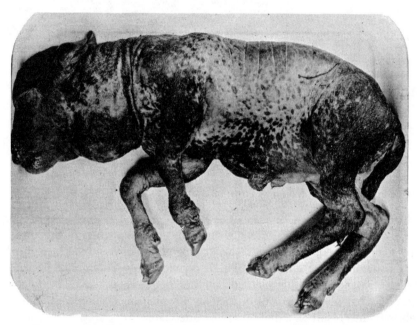

Fig. 3-16. Woolless, goitered (big-necked) lamb stillborn due to iodine deficiency. (Courtesy, Dr. E. A. Tunnicliff, Montana State University, Bozeman, Mont.)

are deficient in iodine, animals may be born weak and not be able to stand and suck. There is also some evidence to indicate that navel-ill in foals may be lessened by feeding iodine to brood mares. In general, it may be said that goiter is an advanced symptom of iodine deficiency but that the chief loss is from interference with reproductive processes and the birth of weak, deformed offspring that fail to survive.

Iodine deficiencies are world-wide. In the United States, the northwestern states, the Pacific Coast, and the Great Lakes region are classed as goiter areas. A summary of goiter is given in Table 3-5.

Recommended Iodine Supplements

The simplest method of supplying iodine in deficient areas is through use of salt containing (1) 0.01 per cent potassium iodide (0.0076 per cent iodine), or (2) calcium iodate. Most of the salt companies now manufacture stabilized iodized salt.

With the exception of fish meal (made from saltwater fish), dried kelp (a sea plant), and cod-liver oil, none of the common feedstuffs is a rich source of iodine.

Precautions in Feeding Iodized Salt

Although iodized salt is an effective preventive measure, no satisfactory treatment has been developed for animals which have developed pronounced deficiency symptoms. In fact, studies with goiter in humans have clearly established that, although iodine is an effective preventative, it may be harmful rather than beneficial as a treatment after the goiter has developed.

Iodized salt should always be kept in a dry place and it should be kept as fresh as possible. It should also be provided in such form and quantities as to insure an adequate intake of iodine.

In no instance should iodine be fed in excess. Such excesses have proved toxic to lambs, and very probably the same hazard applies to other classes of livestock. For this reason, thorough mixing of iodized salt is important, whether it be a commercial or a home-prepared product.

COBALT

Cobalt has been demonstrated to be essential in the nutrition of cattle

Fig. 3-17. A typical cobalt-deficient sheep. Note the emaciation that results from a failing appetite, the dominant symptom of the deficiency. (Courtesy, Dr. S. E. Smith, Cornell University)

and sheep. It is part of vitamin B_{12} and, along with copper and iron, is needed for the formation of hemoglobin in the prevention of anemia. Also, rumen microorganisms use cobalt for the synthesis of vitamin B_{12} and the growth of rumen bacteria. Cobalt-deficient areas have been reported in Australia and western Canada, and in the states of Florida, Michigan, Wisconsin, New Hampshire, North Carolina, and New York. Other areas are suspected.

Animals suffering from a cobalt deficiency grow listless, lose appetite and weight, become weak and anemic, and finally die. Frequently a depraved appetite is noted. The disease known as "salt sick" in Florida is probably due to a cobalt deficiency, usually associated with a copper deficiency.

In different sections of the world, a cobalt deficiency is known as Denmark disease, coast disease, enzootic marasmus, bush sickness, salt sickness, nakuritis, and pining disease.

Only minute quantities of cobalt are required. Although more experimental work is sorely needed, it is assumed that an intake of 0.1 mg daily for a 120-pound sheep is adequate. A cobaltized mineral mixture may be prepared by adding cobalt at the rate of 0.2 oz. per 100 lbs. of salt as cobalt chloride, cobalt sulfate, cobalt oxide, or cobalt carbonate.

Also, several good cobalt-containing commercial minerals are on the market. In no instance should cobalt be added to the ration if it is not needed, and then excesses are to be avoided because of possible toxicity.

OTHER TRACE MINERALS

There is renewed interest in the trace elements, and a general recognition

Fig. 3-18. Perosis or slipped tendon resulting from a deficiency of manganese. A deficiency of either choline or biotin may also result in perosis. (Courtesy. Department of Poultry Science, Cornell University)

of the importance of many of them in livestock rations. Thus, in addition to those trace elements already discussed (iron, copper, iodine, and cobalt), and bearing in mind specie differences, scientists agree that consideration should be given to zinc, manganese, magnesium, selenium, and molybdenum.

COMPLEX MINERAL MIXTURES

Most animal husbandmen favor the use of simple mineral mixtures. Providing either an excessive amount of minerals or a complex mineral mixture when it is not necessary is expensive and wasteful, and any imbalances may actually be injurious to animals. In general, the wise policy consists in knowing the mineral content of the available feeds and providing, in proper amounts, only those essential minerals which are deficient.

VALUE AND ECONOMY OF COMMERCIAL
MINERAL MIXTURES

Commercial mineral mixtures are just what the name implies—minerals mixed by manufacturers who specialize in the commercial mineral business, either handling minerals alone or a combination feed and mineral business. Most commercial minerals are very good.

The commercial mineral manufacturer has the distinct advantages over farm- or ranch-mixing of (1) purchase of minerals in quantity lots, thereby obtaining price advantages, (2) economical and controlled mixing, (3) the hiring of scientifically trained personnel for use in determining the formulations, and (4) quality control. Additionally, most farmers and ranchers do not have the equipment with which to mix minerals properly. Besides, mineral mixes have become more complicated with recognition of the increasing importance of trace elements and interrelationships. For these reasons, commercial minerals are finding a place of increasing importance in all livestock feeding.

Good mixtures supply only the specific minerals that are deficient, and in the quantities necessary. Excesses and mineral imbalances are avoided. Thus, the value of any mineral mixture can easily be determined by how well it meets the needs.

METHODS OF FEEDING MINERAL SUPPLEMENTS

Needed minerals may be incorporated in rations. In addition, it is recommended that all animals be allowed free access to a two-compartment mineral box, with (1) salt (iodized salt in iodine-deficient areas) in one side, and (2) a suitable mineral mixture in the other. Free-choice feeding is in the nature of cheap insurance, with the animals consuming the minerals if they are needed. If the minerals are incorporated in the ration (or in the protein supplement), such additions should be in keeping with known requirements;[5] otherwise animals may either consume too much or not enough, with the result that

---

[5] For requirements, see Sec. II of *The Stockman's Handbook.*

Fig. 3-19. The free-choice method of feeding minerals. (Drawing by R. F. Johnson)

mineral imbalances may be forced upon them. Where the free-choice method is followed, it is necessary to guard against "mineral-starved" animals. Such animals should be gradually accustomed to the minerals in order to prevent gorging and digestive disturbances.

Vitamin Needs[6,7]

Until early in the twentieth century, if a ration contained proteins, fats, carbohydrates, and minerals—together with a certain amount of fiber—it was considered to be a complete diet. True enough, the disease known as beriberi made its appearance in the rice-eating districts of the Orient when milling machinery was introduced from the West, having been known to the Chinese as early as 2600 B.C.; and scurvy was long known to occur among sailors fed on salt meat and biscuits. However, for centuries these diseases were thought to be due to toxic substances in the digestive tract caused by pathogenic organisms rather than food deficiencies, and more time elapsed before the discovery of vitamins. Of course, there was no medical profession until 1835, the earlier treatments having been based on superstition rather than science.

Largely through the trial-and-error method, it was discovered that specific foods were helpful in the treatment of certain of these maladies. In 1747,

[6]For requirements, see Sec. II of *The Stockman's Handbook.*
[7]In the preparation of this section the author had the authoritative review and help of Dr. W. E. Dinusson, Professor and Nutritionist, North Dakota State University, Fargo.

Lind, a British naval surgeon, showed that the juice of citrus fruits was a cure for scurvy. Lunin, as early as 1881, had come to the conclusion that certain foods, such as milk, contain, beside the principal ingredients, small quantities of unknown substances essential to life. Eijkman, working in Java in 1897, had satisfied himself that the disease beriberi was due to the continued consumption of a diet of polished rice. We are told also that, at a very early date, the Chinese used a concoction rich in vitamin A as a remedy for night blindness. Also, cod-liver oil was used in treating or preventing rickets long before anything was known about the cause of the disease.

The significance of these observations relative to diet, however, was not fully appreciated until scientists found it desirable in many types of investigations to use the biological approach, with purified diets to supplement chemical analyses in measuring the value of feeds. These rations were made up of relatively pure nutrients—proteins, carbohydrates, fats, and minerals—from which the unidentified substances were largely excluded. With these purified rations, all investigators shared a common experience; the animals limited to such diets not only failed to thrive, but they even failed to survive if the investigations were continued for any length of time. At first, many investigators explained such failures on the basis of unpalatability and monotony of the rations. Finally, it was realized that these purified rations were lacking in certain substances, minute in amount and the identity of which was unknown to science. These substances were essential for the maintenance of health and life itself and the efficient utilization of the main ingredients of the food. With these findings, a new era of science was ushered in. The modern approach to nutrition was born.

Funk, a Polish scientist working in London, first referred to these nutrients as "vitamines" in 1912. Presumably, the name vitamines alluded to the fact that they were essential to life, and they were assumed to be chemically of the nature of amines (the chemical assumption was later proved incorrect, with the result that the "e" was dropped—thus, the word "vitamin").

The actual existence of vitamins, therefore, has been known only since 1912, and only within the last few years has it been possible to see or touch any of them in a pure form. Previously, they were merely mysterious invisible "little things" known only by their effects. In fact, most of the present fundamental knowledge relative to the vitamin content of both human foods and animal feeds was obtained through measuring their potency in promoting growth or in curing certain disease conditions in animals—a most difficult and tedious method. For the most part, small laboratory animals were used, especially the rat, guinea pig, pigeon, and chick.

The lack of vitamins in a ration may, under certain conditions and in a more limited way, be more serious than a short supply of feed and may result in serious economic losses. On the other hand, such vitamin deficiencies are less widespread throughout the world than hunger itself, for actual starvation has always stalked across much of the world, being referred to as famine only when the numbers killed approach the millions.

Under practical conditions, the rations of farm animals usually contain adequate quantities of each of the several vitamins. However, deficiencies may occur during periods (1) of extended drought or in other conditions of restriction in diet, (2) when production is being forced, (3) when large quantities of highly refined feeds are being fed, or (4) when low-quality forages are utilized. Also, deficiencies may occur as a result of lack of availability of vitamins or because of the presence of antimetabolites. Both are important concepts. For example, analyses show corn to be adequate in niacin. Yet, due either to an antimetabolite or unavailability, there may be niacin deficiencies when corn is fed—deficiencies that can be remedied by niacin supplementation.

The absence of one or more vitamins in the ration may lead to a failure in growth or reproduction, or to characteristic disorders known as deficiency diseases. In severe cases, death itself may follow. Although the occasional deficiency symptoms are the most striking result of vitamin deficiencies, it must be emphasized that, in practice, mild deficiencies probably cause higher total economic losses than do severe deficiencies. It is relatively uncommon for a ration, or diet, to contain so little of a vitamin that obvious symptoms of a deficiency occur. When one such case does appear, it is reasonable to suppose that there must be several cases that are too mild to produce characteristic symptoms but which are sufficiently severe to lower the state of health and the efficiency of production. It is also to be emphasized that different species of animals vary in their needs for the vitamins. Also, not all animals suffer from the same deficiency diseases. Thus, man, the monkey, and the guinea pig react severely to the absence of the antiscorbutic vitamin in the ration, whereas fowl and ruminants are unaffected.

It has long been known that the vitamin content of feeds varies considerably according to soil, climatic conditions, and curing and storing, More recently, scientists have found that it is possible to increase the content of certain vitamins in milk, eggs, and meat by liberal feeding of those vitamins.

THE KNOWN VITAMINS

Table 3-3 contains a list of the known vitamins, the existence of which is undisputed, each one having been proved an essential dietary constituent for one or more species. It is also quite likely that several others will be added to the list. A number of the known vitamins have been isolated chemically and even synthesized. Also, many of them can be distinguished by chemical and physical properties as well as by biological and bacteriological assay. Each of the vitamins is as much a distinct chemical compound as is cane sugar, for example. Although they are present in foods in exceedingly minute amounts, the vitamins are extraordinarily potent.

In Table 3-3, only a brief presentation is made relative to (1) animals most affected, (2) the function of the vitamins, (3) some deficiency symptoms, and (4) good animal sources of each of the vitamins. In reviewing this, it must be remembered that single, uncomplicated vitamin deficiencies are the exception rather than the rule. Multiple deficiencies are altogether too common, making diagnosis difficult even to the trained observer. In addition to the summary in Table 3-3, some general comments of interest are contained in the section which

TABLE 3—3

ANIMAL VITAMIN CHART

Name of Vitamin	Animals Most Affected	Functions	Some Deficiency Symptoms	Good Sources for Animals	Comments
Vitamin A	Affects all farm animals, including poultry.	Promotes growth and stimulates appetite, helps to keep the mucus membranes of respiratory and other tracts in a healthy condition so that they will resist bacterial infection. Necessary in the regeneration of visual purple, helps to maintain a normal and healthy nervous system, and assists in reproduction and lactation.	Stunted growth or loss in weight and loss of appetite, xerophthalmia (an eye disease), night blindness, nervous incoordination as shown by a staggering gait, and sterility in males and females or young which are born weak or dead.	Green, leafy hays, not over 1 year old Grass silages Lush, green pastures Yellow corn Green and yellow peas Fish oils Carrots Whole milk Dehydrated alfalfa meal Synthetic vitamin A	Vitamin A is found only in animals; plants contain the precursor, carotene. Animals are able to store considerable vitamin A, but because of their greater requirements and less storage, young animals suffer from a deficiency much sooner than those that are mature. Both carotene and vitamin A are readily destroyed by oxidation, thus resulting in considerable losses in processing and storing (as in making hay or storing of hay).
Vitamin D	Affects all farm animals, including poultry.	Aids in the assimilation and utilization of calcium and phosphorus and is necessary in normal bone development of animals, including the bone of the fetus.	Rickets in young and osteomalacia in mature animals, and congenital malformations in the newborn, which may be due to a lack of vitamin D.	Sun-cured hays Cod and certain other fish-liver oils Direct sunlight Irradiated yeast Irradiated ergosterol Vitamin D₃, the animal form, should be used for poultry.	When animals are exposed sufficiently to direct sunlight, the ultraviolet light in the sunlight penetrates the skin and produces vitamin D from traces of certain cholesterols in the tissues. Tissue storage is very limited. The vitamin D requirement is less when a proper balance of calcium and phosphorus exists.
Vitamin E	Calves, sheep, poultry, rats, and perhaps certain other animals.	Necessary for normal reproduction in rats and poultry; necessary for proper health of all animals and the development of the muscular and vascular systems.	Stiff lamb disease in sheep, and white muscle disease in calves. "Crazy chick disease" and poor hatchability.	Wheat-germ oil Cereal grains and other seeds Green pastures Good-quality hay	This factor is widely distributed in all natural feeds, even in corncobs. Thus, the addition of wheat-germ oil to ordinary farm rations is of doubtful value.
Vitamin K	Deficiency symptoms have been reported in various birds and in mice, rats, rabbits, and man. Thought to be needed by all species but probably synthesized in the rumen or intestines.	Aids in the clotting of blood and the prevention of hemorrhage.	Blood failing to clot; sweet clover disease.	Green pastures Well-cured hays Fish meal Menadione In general, this factor is widely distributed in normal farm rations. Also, all classes of farm animals synthesize it.	Vitamin K has definite value in human therapy where clotting of the blood needs to be induced. It has also been helpful in the treatment of hemorrhagic sweet clover disease in animals.
Vitamin C or Ascorbic Acid	Dietary need is limited to man, the guinea pig and the monkey. Probably required by other species but synthesized in the body.	Formation of the intercellular substances of the teeth, bones, and soft tissues, increases resistance to infection, promotes firm gums.	Scurvy: swollen, bleeding, and ulcerated gums, loosening of teeth, and weak bones.	Citrus fruits Green pastures Well-cured hays	Ordinary farm rations and body synthesis appear to provide adequate vitamin C.

(Continued)

TABLE 3—3 (Continued)

Name of Vitamin	Animals Most Affected	Functions	Some Deficiency Symptoms	Good Sources for Animals	Comments
THE KNOWN B VITAMINS B_1 or Thiamine	All animals must have a dietary source, unless there is rumen synthesis, as in cattle and sheep	Promotes appetite and growth, required for normal carbohydrate metabolism, aids reproduction.	Beriberi in man and ployneuritis in birds. In most species, there appears to be loss of appetite and retarded growth, enlarged heart and slowing of the heart beat, lower body temperature, and lowered reproduction or failures in both sexes with prolonged deficiencies.	Green pastures Well-cured, green, leafy hays Cereal grains Peas Brewer's yeast	Although farm animals require thiamine, it is not of practical importance since all natural rations containing even a small percentage of cereal grains will most likely be adequate in B_1
Riboflavin	Thought to be required by all animals but deficiency symptoms not observed in ruminants, perhaps due to rumen synthesis. Deficiency symptoms noted in poultry, swine, and horses.	Promotes growth and functions in the body as a constituent of several enzyme systems and as such is important in carbohydrate and amino-acid metabolism.	Retarded growth in most species, with a wide variety of other symptoms somewhat variable with the species. Periodic ophthalmia (moon blindness) in horses; reproductive failure in the sow, and slow growth, anemia, diarrhea, unthrifty appearance, eye opacities, and an abnormal gait in the young pig.	Green pastures Well-cured, green, leafy hays Grass silage Milk and milk products Meat scraps and fish meal Synthetic riboflavin	Grains are poor source of riboflavin. Many common rations are borderline or deficient in riboflavin, especially swine and poultry rations.
Niacin or Nicotine Acid	It is a dietary essential of pigs, chickens, monkeys, and man. Apparently synthesized in the digestive tract of ruminants (sheep and cattle) and the horse.	Functions as a hydrogen carrier in the oxidation of food, essential to growth and health.	Pellagra in man and black tongue in dogs. Swine exhibit loss of appetite, vomiting, slow growth, diarrhea, and a dry and harsh hair and skin.	Cereals and their by-products, except corn, are good sources. Animal by-products Green alfalfa is a fair source.	This factor is widely distributed among common feeds, thus making deficiencies in natural rations rather unlikely. May be of benefit in swine rations high in corn.
Vitamin B_6 or Pyridoxine	B_6 is a dietary essential for the rat, pig, chick, and dog. It is synthesized in the rumen of cattle and sheep and perhaps in the caecum of the horse; thus no deficiency symptoms in these species have been reported.	Basic in amino-acid and fat metabolism.	Rats develop a symmetrical dermatitis (acrodynia) and fail to grow; pigs exhibit poor appetite, slow growth, unsteady gait, convulsions, anemia, and fatty livers.	Cereal grains and their by-products Rice bran and polished rice Green pastures Well-cured alfalfa hay Yeast	Normally, the ration is not lacking in vitamin B_6

(Continued)

TABLE 3—3 (Continued)

Name of Vitamin	Animals Most Affected	Functions	Some Deficiency Symptoms	Good Sources for Animals	Comments
THE KNOWN B VITAMINS (Continued) Pantothenic Acid	Rats, dogs, pigs, chickens, and turkeys. Synthesized in rumen of cow and sheep; perhaps the horse also synthesizes it.	Not clearly established, but probably important in carbohydrate metabolism.	There seems to be a specie difference in symptoms. Swine exhibit an uncoordinated, goose-stepping gait, enteritis, slow growth, abnormal appetite, and some loss of hair. In rats and dogs, there is graying and loss of hair.	Fish solubles	Grain is very deficient in pantothenic acid. Of all B vitamins, it is most likely to be deficient under dry-lot conditions.
Biotin	It is required in the diets of rats, poultry, dogs, rabbits, monkeys, pigs, and probably other species.	Known to be necessary for the maintenance of health in some species. Biotin is involved in carbohydrate metabolism.	Pigs exhibit spasticity of the hind legs, cracks in the feet, and a dermatitis. There is also lowered efficiency of feed utilization.	Animal feeds have been little studied relative to biotin content. Yeast, milk, egg yolk, liver, and kidney are especially rich.	Ordinary farm rations probably contain ample biotin, or farm animals synthesize all they need.
Folic Acid	Not too much is known about species, but deficiency symptoms have been produced in chicks, monkeys, rats, swine, and humans.	Of importance in hemoglobin formation; necessary for normal reproduction in swine.	Lowered reproduction in swine.	Some animal proteins; well-cured, green leafy alfalfa; green pastures.	Folic acid is widely distributed in both plants and animals. It was given this name because of the abundance of the factor in plant leaves.
Inositol	Little is known as to animals affected.	Not clearly established.	It stimulates biotin synthesis in the pig.		
Para-amino Benzoic Acid.	Little known but of no benefit to the pig when added to purified ration.	Not clearly established.	Loss of hair color in the rat.		
Choline	Swine, rats, and poultry. Choline deficiency has not been observed in man.	Functions in amino-acid and fat metabolism, necessary for normal reproduction in swine.	Fatty livers in most species, perosis in poultry. Gestating-lactating sows on choline deficient rations farrow an abnormal number of weak pigs; pigs exhibit muscular incoordination, heavy mortality, and fatty livers.	Choline content of normal feed is sufficient.	With a high protein diet, enough choline is synthesized from certain precursors and amino acids. Deficiency symptoms are more readily obtained as the protein content is lowered.
Vitamin B_{12}	Swine, rats, and poultry.	Stimulates appetite, increases the rate of growth and the efficiency of feed utilization, and necessary for normal reproduction in pigs, chickens, and turkeys.	Retarded growth. Reproductive failure in swine, rats, and poultry.	Protein supplements of animal origin	B_{12} is apt to be lacking in swine rations. A specific treatment for human anemias.

follows, and a summary of each of the vitamin deficiency diseases is contained in Table 3-5. It is noteworthy that the water-soluble B vitamins, which are present in every living tissue, are chiefly concerned with the transfer of energy. By contrast, the fat-soluble vitamins are required for the regulation of metabolism of structural units, and each of them appears to have a specific and independent role. This explains why so many of the deficiency symptoms of the B-complex vitamins are so similar, and why those of the fat-soluble vitamins are usually specific—and dissimilar to each other.

The vitamin requirements of poultry, which differ considerably from those of the four-footed animals, are given in Table 40-3 of this book.

For further information on this voluminous subject, the reader is referred to texts on biological chemistry and to books, articles, and current journal articles dealing exclusively with this subject.

VITAMIN A

Vitamin A is required by all farm animals and man. It is strictly a product of animal metabolism, no vitamin A being found in plants. The counterpart in plants is known as carotene, which is the precursor of vitamin A. Because the animal body can transform carotene into vitamin A, this compound is often spoken of as *provitamin A*.

Carotene is the yellow-colored, fat-soluble substance that gives the characteristic color to carrots and to butterfat (vitamin A is nearly a colorless substance). Carotene derives its name from the carrot, from which it was first isolated over one hundred years ago. Although its empirical formula was established in 1906, it was not until 1919 that Steenbock discovered its vitamin A activity. Though the yellow color is masked by the green chlorophyll, the green parts of plants are rich in carotene and thus have a high vitamin A value. Also, the degree of greenness in a roughage is a good index of its carotene content provided it has not been stored too long. Early cut, leafy green hays are very high in carotene.

Aside from yellow corn, practically all of the cereal grains used in livestock feeding have little carotene or vitamin A value. Even yellow corn has only about 1/10 as much carotene as well-cured hay. Dried peas of the green and yellow varieties, carrots, yellow sweet potatoes, yellow pumpkins, and squash are also valuable sources of carotene.

On most farms and ranches, adequate vitamin A can be supplied for all classes of animals by allowing access to green pastures in the grazing season and through providing green, leafy hay (ground legumes for swine) not over one year old, or good quality grass or legume silage for winter feeding. The circumstances most conducive to vitamin A deficiencies are (1) extended periods of drought, resulting in the pastures becoming dry and bleached; (2) a long winter feeding period on bleached hays or straws, especially overripe cereal hays and straws; (3) using feeds which have lost their vitamin A potency through extended storage (for example, it has been found that alfalfa-leaf meal may lose 9/10 of its vitamin A value in a year's storage); or (4) the dry-lot feeding of

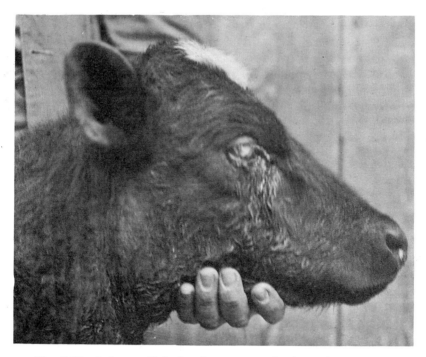

Fig. 3-20. A 3-year-old heifer showing typical advanced eye lesions accompanying a vitamin A deficiency. (From California Agricultural Experiment Station Bulletin 560)

Fig. 3-21. An advanced stage of vitamin A deficiency. Note the exudate from the eye and the general ruffled appearance. (Courtesy, Department of Poultry Science, Cornell University)

swine predominantly on cereals, especially if yellow corn is not included in the ration. There is reason to believe that mild deficiencies of vitamin A, especially in the winter and early spring, are fairly common.

When deficiency symptoms appear, it is recommended that there be added to the ration either (1) dehydrated alfalfa or grass, (2) a stabilized vitamin A product, or (3) cod-liver or a vitamin A feeding oil.

VITAMIN D

Like vitamin A, vitamin D is required by all farm animals and man. Most of the commonly used feeds contain little or no vitamin D, yet there is no widespread need for special supplements containing this factor. Fortunately, the skin of animals and many feeds contain the provitamins in certain forms of cholesterol and ergosterol, respectively, which, through the action of ultraviolet light (light of such short wave length that it is invisible) from the sun, is converted into vitamin D. These certain forms of cholesterol and ergosterol themselves have no antirachitic effect.

Of all the known vitamins, vitamin D has the most limited distribution in common feeds. Very little of this factor is contained in the cereal grains and their by-products, in roots and tubers, in feeds of animal origin, or in growing pasture grasses. The only important natural sources of vitamin D are sun-cured hay and other roughages. The chief vitamin D-rich concentrates include sun-cured hay, codliver and other fish oils, irradiated cholesterol and ergosterol, and irradiated yeast. Vitamin D_3, the animal form, is more active for poultry and should be used instead of vitamin D_2, the plant form of the vitamin.

As might be suspected from the preceding discussion, artificially behydrated hay contains little vitamin D.

The effectiveness of sunlight is determined by the lengths and intensity of the ultraviolet rays which reach the body. It is more potent in the tropics than elsewhere, more potent at noon than earlier or later in the day, more potent in

Fig. 3-22. A pig with rickets caused by a vitamin D deficiency. (Courtesy, Ohio Agricultural Experiment Station)

the summer than in the winter, and more potent at high altitudes. The ultraviolet rays are largely screened out by clothing, window glass, clouds, smoke, or dust.

Vitamin E

Although it has been established that vitamin E is necessary for normal reproduction in the rat and chick and other small animals, there is no conclusive evidence to indicate that it is necessary for reproduction in the larger farm animals. Moreover, there appears to be an abundance of this factor in all natural feeds; even corncobs are a good source. Thus, the addition of vitamin E-rich concentrates, such as wheat-germ oil, to ordinary farm rations is of doubtful value.

A deficiency of vitamin E may produce deficiency diseases in lambs and calves, known as stiff lamb disease and white muscle disease, respectively (see Table 3-5). Also, a deficiency of vitamin E will produce "crazy chick disease" in poultry.

Fig. 3-23. Lamb afflicted with stiff lamb disease, which in this case was associated with a lack of vitamin E in the ration. (Courtesy, Dr. John Willman, Cornell University)

Vitamin K

Present information would indicate that there is no need of giving consideration to the vitamin K content of the ration of farm animals, except in the case of poultry. Green pastures and green, leafy hays are rich sources of this vitamin, and various other products contain substantial amounts. Also, there is rumen and intestinal synthesis in farm animals.

Vitamin C

Apparently this vitamin is not of importance in feeding farm animals. Although this factor is probably required for various species—other than man, monkeys, and guinea pigs—it is synthesized in ample quantities in the body. Moreover, all green forages (pastures, hays, and silages) are high in vitamin C.

The Known B Vitamins

The original vitamin, known as vitamin B, has now been found to be composed of a large number of vitamins or vitamin-like factors. This condition has made the terminology most confusing. Some of these factors have been isolated and recognized; whereas others are not so well known.

In 1948, vitamin B_{12} was isolated by Merck and Company as the anti-anemia factor in liver; subsequent experimental studies have revealed that this is the elusive factor long known to be of importance in swine nutrition and to exist in animal proteins (the "animal protein factor") and cow manure (the "cow manure factor"). Table 3-3 contains a brief summary of our present knowledge of vitamin B_{12}.

The known B vitamins either appear in adequate quantities in normal farm rations or are sufficiently synthesized by micro-organisms in the digestive tract (the rumen of sheep and cattle, or the cecum and colon of the horse) to satisfy properly the requirements of sheep, cattle, and horses. Therefore, the requirements of these classes of animals for the B vitamins will not be pursued further in this discussion.

Unlike these classes of livestock, however, pigs and poultry have one stomach

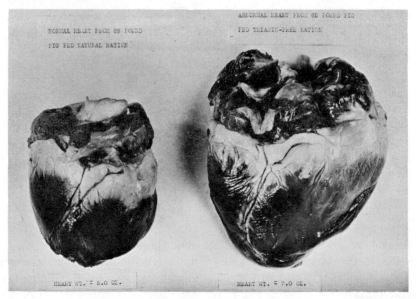

Fig. 3-24. Enlargement of the heart of a pig caused by a B_1 or thiamine deficiency. (Courtesy, Washington State University)

Fig. 3-25. All pigs from sows that received a riboflavin deficient ration during gestation were either born dead or died within 48 hours. (Courtesy, Washington State University)

Fig. 3-26. Retarded growth in a pig as a result of a niacin deficiency. The ages of the two pigs were approximately the same, and the rations were identical except that the one vitamin, niacin, was left out of the feed of the stunted pig on the right. (Courtesy, *Journal of Nutrition;* and Dr. M. M. Wintrobe, University of Utah)

(and no large cecum like the horse). As a result, they do not synthesize enough of certain B vitamins. Consequently, these factors must be provided through the ration if deficiencies are to be averted.

It is also to be emphasized that subacute deficiencies can exist although the actual deficiency does not appear. In fact, borderline deficiencies are both the most costly and the most difficult to cope with, going unnoticed and unrectified. Such borderline deficiencies result in poor and expensive gains.

Also, under farm conditions one will usually not find a vitamin deficiency

Fig. 3-27. Vitamin B₆ deficiency. This pig is having an epileptic-like fit. (Experimental work, University of Calif.; photo courtesy, Dr. T. J. Cunha, University of Florida.)

Fig. 3-28. Pig showing pantothenic acid deficiency symptoms. Note high, goose-stepping gait. (Courtesy, University of California)

which involves only a single vitamin. In other words, deficiencies usually represent a combination of factors, and usually the deficiency symptoms will not be clear-cut.

Inspection of Table 3-3 would indicate that, even with swine, the farmer can meet the B vitamin requirements of the pig by (1) making the maximum use of pastures throughout the grazing season, and (2) feeding generous quantities (5 to 10 per cent for growing-finishing pigs and 15 to 35 per cent or more for brood sows) of high quality ground alfalfa or other suitable forage during the winter or under dry-lot conditions. During the critical periods—young, growing pigs under 75 pounds weight; gestation; and lactation—especially under dry-lot conditions, the essential B vitamins may be provided by adding to the ration yeast (2 to 4 per cent), distillers solubles, or animal or marine protein supplements. The B vitamin requirements of poultry are given in Table 40-3.

Fig. 3-29. Pigs from a sow that received a choline-deficient ration during the gestation period. Note the weak, spraddle-legged condition of the pigs. (Courtesy, Washington State University)

Water Needs

Water is one of the most vital of all nutrients. In fact, animals can survive for a longer period without feed than they can without water. Yet comparatively little discussion will be given to this nutrient simply because, under ordinary conditions, it can be readily provided in abundance and at little cost.

Water is one of the largest single constituents of the animal body, varying in amount from 40 per cent in fat hogs to 80 per cent in newborn pigs, 50 per cent in a 1,000 pound steer to 70 per cent in a newborn calf, and 50 per cent in a fat lamb to 80 per cent in a newborn lamb. In general, the percentage of water in the bodies of animals varies with their species, condition, and age. The younger the animal, the more water it contains. Also, the fatter the animal, the lower the water content. Thus, as an animal matures, it requires proportionately less water on a weight basis, because it consumes less feed per unit of weight and the water content of the body is being replaced by fat. This accounts for the fact that gains in older animals are more costly than those in younger animals.

Water performs the following important functions in animals:

1. It is necessary to the life and shape of every cell and is a constituent of every body fluid.

2. It acts as a carrier for various substances, serving as a medium in which nourishment is carried to the cells and waste products are removed therefrom.

3. It assists with temperature regulation in the body, cooling the animal by evaporation from the skin as perspiration.

4. It is necessary for many important chemical reactions of digestion and metabolism.

5. As a constituent of the synovial fluid, it lubricates the joints; in the cerebrospinal fluid, it acts as a water cushion for the nervous system; in the perilymph in the ear, it transports sound; and in the eye it is concerned with sight and provides a lubricant for the eye.

Surplus water is excreted from the body, principally in the urine, and to a slight extent in the perspiration, feces, and water vapor from the lungs.

The specific water requirements of each class of animals will receive further consideration in the sections devoted to the respective species. In general, however, under practical conditions, the needs for water can best be taken care of by allowing the animals free access to plenty of clean, fresh water at all times.

FEED ADDITIVES

Without doubt, most animal scientists and stockmen would agree that antibiotics and hormones stand out as the two nutritional discoveries of recent years that have had the greatest impact on the livestock industry. In 1949, it was discovered that antibiotics were something new to be added to livestock feeds. Then, late in 1954, stilbestrol was approved by the Food and Drug Administration for use in cattle finishing rations. In each case, a new era in livestock feeding was ushered in—comparable to the vitamin era which was born in 1912; and more feed additives followed. Today, it is estimated that 75 per cent of the nation's growing-finishing pigs and dry-lot finished cattle receive feed additives, and a lesser, but growing number, of finishing lambs are being so fed.

Some glowing reports to the contrary, there is no evidence to indicate that the use of these additives can or will alleviate the need for vigilant sanitation, improved nutrition, and superior management. Instead, with the unfolding and applying of scientific information relative to these promotants, the producer will be able to achieve still greater efficiency of production. Also, practical producers will weigh the benefits of each one against its cost.

Antibiotics

The newer knowledge of antibiotics—products of molds, bacteria, and green plants—dates from the discovery of penicillin by Dr. Alexander Fleming, a British scientist, in 1928.[8] Quite by accident, a stray mold spore floated in on the breeze, and landed on a culture plate of bacteria with which Dr. Fleming was working. It inhibited the growth of the bacteria. Dr. Fleming correctly interpreted his observation; the possible value of the mold in the treatment of disease, thus ushering in the antibiotic era. However, penicillin did not come into prominence until 10 years later, and it was not until 1944 that streptomycin, the second most widely known of the antibiotics, was discovered by Waksman, a soil microbiologist, and his colleagues at the New Jersey station.

Penicillin, streptomycin, and other antibiotics were rushed into use against a long list of human ailments, ranging from common flu to radiation sickness. They were hailed as the "wonder drugs" of our time, but no one thought of them, even remotely, as something to be added to livestock feeds. Finally, in 1949, quite by accident, while conducting nutrition studies with poultry, Jukes of Lederle Laboratory and McGinnis of Washington State University, obtained startling growth responses from feeding a residue from aureomycin production. Later experiments revealed that the supplement used by McGinnis and Jukes— the residue from aureomycin production—supplied the antibiotic aureomycin. Such was the birth of feeding antibiotics to livestock.

Commercially produced antibiotics are thought of as substances produced by mold-like organisms grown in nutrient solutions in large steel tanks. Hundreds of antibiotics are known—including commercially produced penicillin, streptomycin, aureomycin, chloromycetin, terramycin, bacitracin, etc.—and each is effective against one or more kinds of bacteria. The vast majority of antibiotics are too toxic for medical use.

At the present time, crystalline (pure) antibiotics are too expensive for feeds, and, besides, they cannot be purchased from the corner drugstore without a prescription from a medical doctor (M.D.) or a veterinarian (D.V.M.). However, crude supplements, which are entirely satisfactory for livestock feeding purposes, can be purchased from reputable manufacturers or feed stores.

NUTRITIONAL ROLE OF ANTIBIOTICS

At the present time, our knowledge of the nutritional role, or mode of action, of antibiotics is incomplete. However, based on studies conducted at Notre Dame, it appears that antibiotics are effective because of eliminating harmful, toxic-producing micro-organisms found in the intestinal tract. In experiments, antibiotics were ineffective in producing growth when given to germ-free animals, but they gave the expected response when given to "contaminated" animals. Subsequent experiments in other laboratories have confirmed the Notre Dame findings.

---

[8] Actually, the presence of antibiotics was known much earlier than the discovery of penicillin, but no commercial use was made of them.

Hormones and Other Accessory Ration Ingredients

Most stockmen are familiar with, or have used, one or more of the hormones or other accessory ration ingredients in addition to antibiotics. Late in 1954, stilbestrol (diethylstilbestrol)—a synthetic female hormone, and not a nutrient—was released by the Food and Drug Administration for use in cattle finishing rations; and two years later, in 1956, the Food and Drug Administration approved the use of stilbestrol implants for steers. Soon, the race was on; other hormones and accessory ration ingredients were rushed in—and more will follow.

Today, many of these growth promotants are being tested, and being incorporated in practical rations, for purposes of stimulating live weight gains, improving feed utilization, and lessening diseases. Among such products are live rumen cultures, vermifuges, antibiotics, surface active agents, arsenical compounds, hormones, tranquilizers, and enzymes (singly and in combination). Perhaps many of them have real merit and will come to find practical application. At the present time, however, our knowledge of the role of many of these hormones and other additives is merely opened up; more research work is needed. For example, the mode of action of most of them is not known.

GOOD LIVESTOCK REQUIRE GOOD SOILS

The good stockman can be identified by the appearance of his animals. A good animal is proof of good breeding and superior nutrition, and proper nutrition is obtained by feeding hays, grains, and pastures which are grown on fertile soils.

In the wild state, animals did not possess the many bone unsoundnesses and nutritional deficiencies common to domesticated livestock. They roved over the prairies or through the forests, gleaning the feeds provided by nature—vegetation produced on highly mineralized, unleached soils—whereas on a modern farm the range is restricted, leached, and sometimes entirely devoid of vegetation. Domestic animals have little or no choice in the selection of their diet, being able to consume only what the caretaker provides or what can be grazed within the confines of fenced holdings. The condition is further aggravated by forcing early development and high production, such as is obtained in racing two- or three-year-olds, in producing high yields of milk and butterfat, the finishing of baby beeves, the farrowing of gilts at one year of age and the marketing of pigs at four to six months of age, and the simultaneous production of a heavy fleece and a fat market lamb.

Present research, together with practical observation, points to the fact that the mere evaluation of yields in terms of tons of forage or bushels of grain produced per acre is not enough. Neither do standard feed analyses tell the whole story. Rather, there appears to be a direct and most important relationship of the fertility of the soil to the composition of the plant in terms of calcium, phosphorus, proteins, vitamins, and other nutrients. Moreover, the animal cannot be expected to be well nourished when forced to subsist on plants which

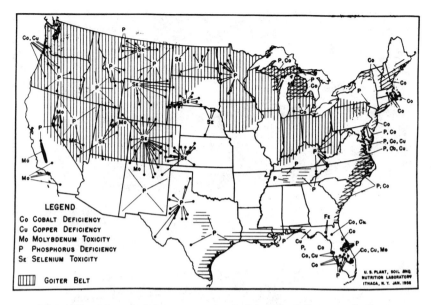

Fig. 3-30. Mineral deficiency areas of the United States and the excess selenium area of the northern and central Great Plains. (From USDA Yearbook, 1948)

themselves are suffering from such nutritive deficiencies. Since the need for these nutritive constituents for the development of strong bone and healthy bodies is fully understood, it may truly be said that good animals require good soils.

Unsuccessful attempts are constantly being made to overcome these nutritive deficiencies of plants by dosing the animal with patent mineral and vitamin mixtures. Unfortunately, at times, such "curealls" may even accentuate the difficulty, because of harmful imbalances in calcium or phosphorus and possibly other nutrients. Therefore, the wise policy consists of first improving the fertility of the soil, which in turn means well-nourished and highly nutritious forages and grains for the animal. Soil fertility can best be improved through adding crop residues, manure, and certain commercial fertilizers as required. Restoring depleted soils not only increases the mineral, protein, and perhaps vitamin content of plants; but the tonnage yield of the crop will be higher.

The rapidity of soil leaching is always greatest in areas of high rainfalls and high temperatures, which means the eastern and southern parts of the United States. It can also be stated that the failure of a soil to grow an adapted legume is an indication of lack of calcium. In such areas, the nutritive deficiencies of animals are more prevalent.

Under certain conditions and in certain areas where mineral deficiencies become very severe, deficiency areas become known. Thus, southwestern United States is known as a phosphorus-deficient area, northwestern United States as an iodine-deficient area, and southeastern United States as a cobalt-deficient area.

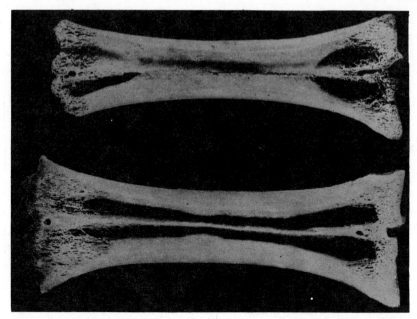

Fig. 3-31. Split bones from two calves of similar breeding and age. Small bone (above) obtained from calf pastured on belly deep grasses grown on highly weathered soils low in mineral content. Big bone (below) obtained from calf grown on moderately weathered, but highly mineralized, residual limestone soil. (Courtesy, Dr. W. A. Albrecht, University of Missouri)

FEEDING AS AN ART

The feed requirements of animals do not necessarily remain the same from day to day or from period to period. The age and size of the animal; the kind and degree of activity; climatic conditions; the kind, quality, and amount of feed; the system of management; and the health, condition, and temperament of the animal are all continually exerting a powerful influence in determining the nutritive needs. How well the feeder understands, anticipates, interprets, and meets these requirements usually determines the success or failure of the ration and the results obtained. Although certain principles are usually followed by all good feeders, no book knowledge or set of instructions can substitute for experience and born livestock intuition. Skill and good judgment are essential to the feedlot. Indeed, there is much truth in the old adage that "the eye of the master fattens his animals."

The discussion that follows will primarily be directed at the finishing operations of cattle, sheep, and hogs. The maintenance of the breeding herds and flocks will receive special attention in the respective sections devoted to each class of farm animals. Dairy and poultry feeding are covered in Chapters XX and XL, respectively.

Starting Animals on Feed

In cattle and lamb feeding operations, it is important that the animals be accustomed to feed gradually. In general, upon arriving at the feedlot, the animals may be given as much nonlegume roughages as they will consume. On the other hand, it is necessary that they be gradually accustomed to high-quality legumes which may be too laxative. The latter can be accomplished by slowly replacing the nonlegume roughage with greater quantities of legumes. Of course, as the grain ration is increased the consumption of roughages will be decreased.

Starting cattle and lambs on grain requires care and good judgment. With both classes of stock, it is usually advisable first to accustom them to a bulky type of ration, a starting ration with considerable oats or beet pulp being excellent for this purpose. A common "rule of thumb" in starting cattle on feed is to give them 2 pounds per head the first day; increase the ration by from ½ to 1 pound daily until they reach approximately the halfway mark of what is anticipated will be a full feed; and then increase the ration by 1 pound every third day until full feeding is obtained. Lambs are usually started on grain by feeding about ¼ pound per head daily, gradually increasing the allowance so that they are getting a feed of about 2 pounds per head daily when on full feed about four weeks later.

In general, little difficulty is ever encountered in starting hogs on feed. Although the same precautions that apply to cattle and sheep should be observed, swine are less sensitive to feed changes than other classes of farm animals.

The keenness of the appetites and the consistency of the droppings of the animals are an excellent index of their capacity to take more feed. In all instances, scouring, the bane of the feeder, should be avoided.

Amount to Feed

Many farm animals throughout the United States are underfed all or some part of the year. Temporary underfeeding is most likely to occur in the winter months or during periods of extended droughts. Fortunately, during such times of restricted feed intake, animals have nutritive reserves upon which they can draw. Although they may survive for a considerable period of time under these conditions, there is an inevitable loss in body weight and condition.

Overfeeding is also undesirable, being wasteful of feeds and creating a health hazard. Animals that suffer from mild digestive disturbances are commonly referred to as off feed. When overfeeding exists, there is usually considerable leftover feed and wastage, and there is a high incidence of bloat (colic in horses), founder, scours, and even death.

When on full feed, finishing cattle will consume 1¾ to 2½ pounds of concentrates and from ¾ to 2 pounds of hay per 100 pounds of live weight daily. Lambs on full feed will consume about 2 pounds of grain per head daily and about the same amount of roughage. The proportion of grain to roughage for cattle and sheep should be varied according to their comparative price and the age and quality of the animals. Finishing hogs will consume 4 to 5 pounds of feed, mostly concentrates, per 100 pounds of live weight. The pig, therefore, is capable of consuming more feed in proportion to body weight than can either the cow or sheep. This is a major factor in the greater efficiency with which pigs convert feeds into meats. Regardless of the ration or class of stock, however, finishing animals should receive a maximum ration over and above the maintenance requirement.

Frequency, Regularity, and Order of Feeding

In general, finishing animals are fed twice daily. With animals that are being fitted for show, where maximum consumption is important, it is not uncommon to find three or even four feedings daily. When self-fed, animals eat at more frequent intervals, though they consume smaller amounts each time.

Animals learn to anticipate their feed. Accordingly, they should be fed *with great regularity*, as determined by a time piece. During warm weather, they will eat better if the feeding hours are early and late, in the cool of the day.

Usually, the grain ration is fed first, with the roughage following. In this manner, the animals eat the bulky roughages more leisurely.

Feeds Should Not Be Changed Abruptly

Sudden changes in diet are to be avoided, especially when changing from a less-concentrated ration to a more-concentrated one. When this rule of feeding is ignored, digestive disturbances result, and animals go off feed. In either adding or omitting one or more ingredients, the change should be made gradually. Likewise, caution should be exercised in turning animals out to pasture or in transferring them to more lush grazing. If it is not convenient to accustom them to new pasture gradually, they should at least be well filled with hay (or with the former pasture) before being turned out.

Selection of Feeds

In general, the successful feeder balances out the ration through selecting those feeds which are most readily available at the lowest possible cost. In addition, consideration is given to supplying quality proteins, the proper minerals, and the necessary vitamins. Attention is also given to the laxative or constipating qualities of feeds and the palatability of the ration. Furthermore, the relation of the feeds to the quality of product produced should not be overlooked. In dairy cows it is known that certain feeds have a tendency to produce soft or "salvy" butter, and in finishing hogs, excessive quantities of soybeans or peanuts produce soft pork.

Attention to Details Pays

The successful feeder pays great attention to details. In addition to maintaining the health and comfort of the animals and filling their feed troughs, consideration is also given to their individual likes and temperaments.

It is important to avoid excessive exercise, which results in loss of energy by the animals through unnecessary muscular activity. Rough treatment, excitement, and noise usually result in nervousness and inefficient use of feed. Finishing animals and milking cows should not be required to exercise any more than is deemed necessary for the maintenance of health. Dehorning is usually necessary in order to reduce fighting and possible bruises or injury. Likewise, all males should be castrated, for they will be much quieter.

HAND-FEEDING VERSUS SELF-FEEDING

Self-feeding is the most common method of feeding employed in finishing hogs and feeding poultry. Though less prevalent, the practice is increasing in cattle- and lamb-finishing operations, but it is almost never used with horses.

Self-feeding may be accomplished satisfactorily in either of two ways: (1) providing a suitable self-feeder or hopper-type of container, or (2) keeping a large-type feed bunk (trough for swine) well-filled at all times. In order to self-feed cattle or sheep, they must be hand-fed until they are on full feed, after which they may have free access to the self-feeder.

The principal **advantages** derived from the use of self-feeders are:

1. Less labor and time are required in the feeding operations. By using self-feeders with large bins or hoppers, a large quantity of feed—enough for a week or two—may be mixed and placed before the animals at one time. Hand-feeding is a twice-a-day chore, whereas it is merely necessary to check the filled self-feeders at intervals to make certain that the feed has not clogged.

2. Slightly higher feed consumption and larger daily gains are secured. This is especially true when hand-feeding is done by an inexperienced feeder or when more or less irregularity occurs in time of feeding and quantity and character of rations—conditions which sometimes prevail under ordinary farm conditions.

3. Self-fed animals are usually ready for market earlier than hand-fed animals because of their slightly more rapid gains.

4. The animals are less likely to go off feed. This is because they learn that feed is available at all times, with the result that they are inclined to eat leisurely. On the other hand, greedy steers or lambs are likely to gorge when hand-fed, particularly at those times when weather conditions may cause them to come to the feed trough with very keen appetites.

5. Often self-feeders are especially well adapted to grain feeding on pastures due to the distance of the pastures from the feed storage and mixing facilities.

6. With most feeds, pigs can be relied upon to balance out their own rations when fed cafeteria style; thus, considerable time can be saved in the mixing of feeds.

The principal **disadvantages** of using self-feeders are the following:

1. Unless chopped roughage is thoroughly mixed with the grain ration, self-feeding is not adaptable where it is desired to utilize the maximum quantity of roughage. This is simply due to the fact that, under self-fed conditions, the animals elect to eat a large proportion of grain. Thus, where roughages are abundant and low in price, hand-feeding may be more practical.

2. The gains of self-fed cattle and sheep may cost slightly more, particularly where grains are relatively higher than roughages. However, the slightly

higher feed cost is usually offset by the slightly higher selling price of the finished animals.

3. If hopper-type feeders are used, rather than bunks, there is usually a slightly higher equipment cost in self-feeding.

4. Somewhat more time and expense is usually required in preparing feeds (shelling, grinding, and mixing) for the self-feeder.

5. Practical cattle feeders usually consider that self-feeding is not adapted to an extended feeding period, whereas they feel that it is quite a satisfactory method to use for a short-feed of 90 to 120 days.

6. Unlike pigs, cattle and sheep cannot be trusted to balance their own rations when different feeds are made available on a free-choice basis.

In general, because of the greater quantities of concentrates consumed in self-feeding, it is advisable that the ration used be slightly more bulky than when hand-feeding is used. The extra bulk may be obtained either by (1) adding a small amount of chopped or ground hay to the grain ration, or (2) using in the ration a considerable proportion of such bulky, fibrous feeds as oats, beet pulp, or bran. With favorable feed prices, it may be well to have as much as one-third of the ration of cattle and sheep made up of oats, beet pulp, or bran. With brood sows, a generous supply of ground alfalfa should be mixed in the ration, thus providing a bulky, less-fattening ration and furnishing a desirable source for vitamins, minerals, and proteins.

CREEP FEEDING YOUNG ANIMALS

It has always been said that young gains are cheap gains. This is due to (1) the higher water and lower fat content of the young animal in comparison with older animals, and (2) the higher feed consumption per unit of weight of young animals. Also, there has been an increasing demand for lighter cuts of

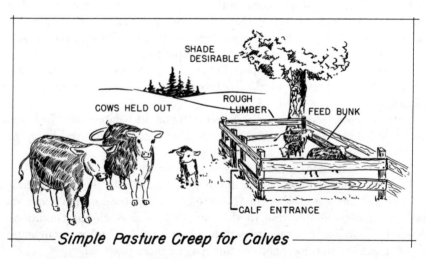

Simple Pasture Creep for Calves

Fig. 3-32. A creep of this general type can be provided for any class of animals. Note the small creep entrance for the calves and the nearby shade. (Drawing by R. F. Johnson)

meat, with meat animals of all species being marketed at younger ages and lighter weights. These factors have encouraged more and more creep-feeding of calves, pigs, and lambs. *The practice of self-feeding of concentrates to young animals in a separate enclosure away from their dams is known as creep-feeding.*

PREPARATION OF FEEDS

Perhaps no problem is so perplexing to the amateur feeder as the proper preparation of feeds. Usually, the confusion is further accentuated by the propaganda of manufacturers and distributors of various feed preparation equipment, not to mention the pet theories of experienced feeders. Table 3-4 is a summary of pertinent information relative to the preparation of feeds for cattle, sheep, swine, and horses.

Some additional pointers relative to the preparation of feeds follow:

1. **Grinding or Rolling Grains.—**
   a. Avoid grinding any feed too finely; fine, floury particles are unpalatable and it costs more to prepare them. Finely ground feeds are more palatable when pelleted for all classes of animals or when used in a slop for pigs.
   b. When whole grains are fed to finishing cattle, follow cattle with pigs.

2. **Steam Rolling.—**Based on University of Arizona studies, it is recommended that milo and barley (and perhaps other cereal grains) for finishing cattle be processed under 20 pounds of steam pressure for 20 minutes, at approximately 205° F.; then, at 18 to 20 per cent moisture content, rolled thinly.

3. **Soaking, Cooking, or Slopping.—**
   a. Cooking may slightly increase the digestibility of the starches, but it is apt to decrease the digestibility of the proteins.
   b. Soaking does not improve feeding value.

4. **Shredding and Cutting, or Grinding Roughages.—**
   a. The preparation of roughages does not increase the value of the initial product.
   b. Except for hogs, roughages should be coarsely chopped (not less than 2 inches in length)—if they are prepared.
   c. Chopping forages for cattle, sheep, and horses is more common in the West than elsewhere; primarily because in this area forages are relatively more abundant and cheaper than the grains, with the result that a higher proportion of them is fed. Also, it follows that there is apt to be greater waste of forage under liberal feeding, unless precautions are taken to alleviate it.
   d. In preparing forages, avoid processing those (1) with high moisture, which may heat and produce spontaneous combustion, and (2) in which there are foreign objects (wire, etc.) which the animals may not be able to select out, and which may ignite a fire when being processed.

TABLE 3—4

PREPARATION OF FEEDS

Class of Animal	Grinding or Rolling Grains	Soaking, Cooking, or Slopping	Shredding and Cutting or Grinding Roughages	Pelleting
Cattle	Grind cereal grains coarsely for cattle other than those fitted for show. Professional herdsmen prefer steamrolled grains for show cattle; as ration is lighter and fewer digestive disturbances are encountered. It may not be profitable to grind grain for calves under 9 to 12 mo. of age, for young calves masticate grains well.	Professional herdsmen often cook (or steam) feeds, thereby increasing palatability and feed consumption. Also, some commercial cattle feeders cook grains.	Cut or shred such coarse forages as corn fodder or stover; they are easier to handle and there is less waste. In the West, hay is frequently chopped because (1) it is easier to handle, (2) it can be stored in a smaller area at less cost, and (3) it is fed with less waste.	Many western stockmen prefer pellets or cubes for cattle, especially for range feeding.
Sheep	Unless grains are extremely hard (such as millet) or the teeth are poor, sheep prefer to do their own grinding, and there is no saving from processing. Professional shepherds prefer steamrolled grains for show sheep; as ration is lighter and fewer digestive disturbances are encountered.		(Same as cattle)	Many western stockmen prefer pellets or cubes for sheep, especially for range feeding. Also many lamb feeders are pelleting the grain alone, or the mixed forage and grain rations.
Swine	Grind hog feeds rather than roll, as latter are too bulky.	Potatoes and beans should always be cooked when fed to swine. Professional herdsmen prefer to feed some slop to swine being fitted for show, feeling that they obtain greater feed consumption and gains thereby.	Grind or finely chop alfalfa or other forages that are added to swine rations.	The pelleting of swine feeds is increasing rapidly. Pelleting will increase the value of the ration used by 10% or more. Smaller pigs should have smaller pellets.
Horses	For horses with good teeth, the value of oats is increased only 5% by grinding or rolling. Feed corn on cob or shelled. Rolling is preferred to grinding for horses; the ration is lighter and fewer digestive disturbances are encountered.		Finely ground hay is apt to be dusty which is especially undesirable for horses.	All-pelleted rations for horses are increasing. They are especially popular with horse owners who keep them in the suburbs.

5. **Pelleting.**—This type of feed preparation may be, and is, applied to (a) concentrates alone, (b) forage alone, and (c) concentrates and roughage combined in a complete ration.

  a. *Pelleting concentrates*—the practice of pelleting concentrates is increasing because:
   (1) Pelleted feeds are less bulky and easier to store and to handle, thus lessening storage and labor costs.
   (2) Pelleting prevents animals from selectively wasting ingredients likely to be high in certain dietary essentials; each bite is a balanced feed.
   (3) Pelleting alleviates wastage of relatively unpalatable feeds, such as barley.
   (4) Pelleting reduces losses from wind blowing—an especially important factor on the range.
  b. The increased value of pelleting should be appraised against the increased cost of pelleting.
  c. *Pelleted forages; all-pelleted rations*—pelleted forage refers to forage pelleted alone, whereas all-pelleted rations are those in which the grain and forage are first mixed and then pelleted together.

The biggest deterrents to pelleting forages at the present time are: (a) the cost factor, and (b) the difficulty of processing chopped forage which is coarse enough to allow for optimum cellulose digestion in the rumen, and which will not increase the incidence of bloat. As a rule of thumb, one would be on the safe side if the forage were not chopped more finely than silage. Also, it is recommended that the ratio of roughage to concentrate be higher in all-pelleted rations than where long hay is fed.

Among the virtues ascribed to an all-pelleted ration are: (a) it prevents selective eating—if properly formulated, each mouthful is a balanced diet; (b) it alleviates waste; (c) it eliminates dust; (d) it lessens labor and equipment—just fill self-feeders; and (e) it lessens storage.

The benefits to be derived from practical pelleted forages may be even greater. It will (a) simplify hay making; (b) lessen transportation costs and storage space—pelleted roughages require only one-fifth to one-third as much space as when forage is in loose or chopped form; (c) reduce labor; (d) make automatic hay feeding feasible; (e) decrease nutrient losses; and (f) eliminate dust.

With pelleting, the spread between high and low quality roughages is narrowed; that is, the poorer the quality of roughage, the greater the advantage from pelleting. This is so primarily because such preparation assures complete consumption of the roughage.

6. **Wafering (Cubing) Hay.**—This refers to the practice of compressing long and/or coarsely cut hay in wafers or cubes which are larger and coarser than pellets. This method of hay making is increasing. It alleviates fine grinding, and it facilitates automation in both hay making and feeding.

HOME-MIXED VERSUS COMMERCIAL FEEDS

The value of farm-grown grains—plus the cost of ingredients which need to be purchased in order to balance the ration, and the cost of grinding and mixing—as compared to the cost of commercial ready-mixed feeds laid down on the farm, should determine whether it is best to mix feeds at home or depend on ready-mixed feeds. Although there is nothing about the mixing of feeds which is beyond the capacity of the intelligent farmer or rancher, under many conditions a commercially mixed feed supplied by a reputable dealer may be the most economical and the least irksome. The commercial dealer has the distinct advantages of (1) purchase of feeds in quantity lots, making possible price advantages; (2) economical and controlled mixing; and (3) the hiring of scientifically trained personnel for use in determining the rations. Because of these advantages, commercial feeds are finding a place of increasing importance in American agriculture.

Also, it is to the everlasting credit of reputable feed dealers that they have been good teachers; often getting stockmen started in the feeding of balanced rations, a habit which is likely to remain with them whether or not they continue to buy commercial feeds.

How to Select Commercial Feeds

There is a difference in commercial feeds! That is, there is a difference from the standpoint of what a stockman can purchase with his feed dollars. The smart operator will know how to determine what constitutes the best in commercial feeds for his specific needs. He will not rely solely on how the feed looks and smells or on the feed salesman. The most important factors to consider or look for in buying a commercial feed are:

1. **The reputation of the manufacturer.**—This should be determined by (a) checking on who is back of it, (b) conferring with other stockmen who have used the particular products, and (c) checking on whether or not the commercial feed under consideration has consistently met its guarantees. The latter can be determined by reading the bulletins or reports published by the respective state departments in charge of enforcing feed laws.

2. **The specific needs.**—Feed needs vary according to (a) the class, age, and productivity of the animals, and (b) whether animals are fed primarily for maintenance, growth, finishing (or show-ring fitting), reproduction, lactation, or work (running). The wise operator will buy different formula feeds for different needs.

3. **The feed tag.**—Most states require that mixed feeds carry a tag that guarantees the ingredients and the chemical make-up of the feed. Feeds with more protein and fat are better, and feeds with less fiber are better.

In general, if the fiber content is less than 8 per cent, the feed may be considered as top quality; if the fiber is more than 8 but less than 12 per cent, the feed may be considered as medium quality; while feeds containing more than 12 per cent fiber should be considered carefully. Occasionally, a high fiber feed is good; the Iowa Economy Supplement is such an example. In this particular feed, corncobs are used primarily as an agent to absorb the molasses and to act as a carrier for the urea, minerals, and stilbestrol. This formula is fed at the rate of about 1 pound per head daily and provides a convenient amount for even distribution in the daily feed. Likewise, many feeds are high in fiber simply because they contain generous quantities of alfalfa; yet they may be perfectly good feeds for the purpose intended. On the other hand, if oat hulls and similar types of high fiber ingredients are responsible for the high fiber content of the feed, the quality should be questioned. The latter type of fiber is poorly digested and does not provide the nutrients required to stimulate the digestion of the fiber in roughages.

4. **Flexible formulas.**—Feeds with flexible formulas are usually the best buy. This is because the price of feed ingredients in different source feeds varies considerably from time to time. Thus, a good feed manufacturer will shift his formulas as prices change in order to give the stockman the most for his money. This is as it should be, for (a) there is no one best ration, and (b) if substitutions are made wisely, the price of the feed can be kept down and the feeder will continue to get equally good results.

NUTRITIONAL DISEASES AND AILMENTS

More animals (and people) throughout the world suffer from hunger—from just plain lack of sufficient feed—than from the lack of a specific nutrient (or nutrients); therefore, it is recognized that nutritional deficiencies may be brought about either by (1) too little feed, or (2) rations that are too low in one or more nutrients.

Also, forced production (such as very high milk yields and marketing of animals at early ages) and the feeding of forages and grains which are often produced on leached and depleted soils have created many problems in nutrition. This condition has been further aggravated through the increased confinement of stock, many animals being stall-fed all or a large part of the year. Under these unnatural conditions, nutritional diseases and ailments have become increasingly common.

Although the cause, prevention, and treatment of most of these nutritional diseases and ailments are known, they continue to reduce profits in the livestock industry simply because the available knowledge is not put into practice. Moreover, those widespread nutritional deficiencies which are not of sufficient proportions to produce clear-cut deficiency symptoms cause even greater economic losses because they go unnoticed and unrectified. Table 3-5, contains a summary of the important nutritional diseases and ailments affecting animals.

NUTRITION RESEARCH OF THE FUTURE

Research in the field of animal nutrition has brought amazing results. In fact, it has been well said that we are gradually learning to feed our children

TABLE 3—5 –NUTRITIONAL DISEAS

Disease	Species Affected	Cause	Symptoms (and age or group most affected)	Distribution and Losses Caused By
Acetonemia in Cattle (see Ketosis)				
Alkali Disease (See Selenium poisoning)				
Anemia, nutritional	All warm blooded animals and man.	Commonly an iron deficiency, but it may be caused by a deficiency of copper, cobalt, and/or certain vitamins, (riboflavin, pyridoxine, pantothenic acid and/or folic acid).	Loss of appetite, progressive emaciation, and death. Pigs show labored breathing and a swollen condition about the head and shoulders, commonly called "thumps." Most prevalent in suckling young, especially young pigs.	Worldwide. Losses consist of sl and inefficient ga and deaths.
Aphosphorosis	Cattle, and sheep to lesser extent.	Low phosphorus in feed.	Depraved appetite; chewing bones, wood, hair, rag, etc. Stiff joints and fragile bones. Breeding problems and a high incidence of milk fever in dairy cattle.	Worldwide; in S United States
Azoturia (Hemoglobinuria, Monday morning disease, Blackwater)	Horses	Associated with faulty carbohydrate metabolism, and with work following a period of idleness in the stall on full rations.	Profuse sweating, abdominal distress, wine-colored urine, stiff gait, reluctance to move, and lameness. Finally, animal assumes a sitting position, and eventually falls prostrate on the side.	Worldwide, but t disease is seld seen in horses at p ture and rarely horses at consta work.
Baby pig shakes (See Hypoglycemia)				
Bloat	Cattle, Sheep	Unknown. Most common on lush legume pastures.	Greatly distended paunch noticeable on the left side in front of the hip bone.	Widespread, althou some areas appear have more bloat th others. Often results in deat Causes average annu losses in beef a dairy cattle (includ milk) of $104,940,0

Footnotes on last page of table.

D AILMENTS OF ANIMALS[1]

Treatment	Control and Eradication	Prevention	Remarks
ide dietary sources of the trient or nutrients the deiency of which is known to use the condition.	When nutritional anemia is encountered, it can usually be brought under control by supplying dietary sources of the nutrient or nutrients the deficiency of which is known to cause the condition.	Supply dietary sources of iron, copper, cobalt, and certain vitamins. Keep suckling animals confined to a minimum and provide feeds at an early age. Anemia in pigs can be prevented by any of the following: 1. Injecting into the ham muscle an iron-dextran compound (containing 150 mg of iron), at one to three days of age. Repeat at 2 to 3 weeks if necessary. 2. Placing clean, hog-manure-free sod in each farrowing pen several times each week. 3. Giving iron pills or liquids to pigs at weekly intervals. 4. Using iron fortified baby pig feeds in the creep area.	Anemia is a condition in which the blood is either deficient in quality or quantity (a deficient quality refers to a deficiency in hemoglobin and /or red cells). Levels of iron in most feeds believed to be ample, since most of them contain 40 to 400 mg per pound.
	Controlled by feeding phosphorus, either free choice or added to the ration.	Feed phosphorus. Keep the Ca:P ratio proper.	Generally caused by lack of P in the pasture. P fertilizing may help.
olute rest and quiet. While waiting the veterinarian, ply heated cloths or blants, or hot water bottles the swollen and hardened uscles.	Azoturia is non-contagious. When trouble is encountered, decrease the ration and increase the exercise on idle days.	Restrict the ration and provide daily exercise when the animal is idle. Give a wet bran mash the evening before an idle day or turn the idle horses to pasture.	
e permitting, severe cases bloat should be treated a veterinarian. Puncturg of the paunch should be last resort. l cases may be home-treat by (1) keeping the animal its feet and moving, and drenching (preferably by omach tube). For a cow, ve one pint of vegetable l such as peanut oil, corn l, or soybean oil. For a ature sheep, give about ¼ a pint.	When there is high incidence of bloat, it may be desirable to change the feed. For control of legume bloat, use Poloxalene according to manufacturer's directions.	The incidence is lessened by (1) avoiding straight legume pastures, (2) feeding dry forage along with pasture, (3) avoiding a rapid fill from an empty start, (4) keeping animals continuously on pasture after they are once turned out, (5) keeping salt and water conveniently accessible at all times, and (6) avoiding frosted pastures. Use poloxalene according to manufacturer's directions.	Legume pastures, alfalfa hay, and barley appear to be associated with a higher incidence of bloat more than many other feeds. Legume pastures are particularly hazardous when moist, after a light rain or dew.

(Continued)

TABLE 3-

Disease	Species Affected	Cause	Symptoms (and age or group most affected)	Distribution and Losses Caused By
Colic	Horses	Improper feeding working, or watering.	Excruciating pain; and, depending on the type of colic, other symptoms are: distended abdomen, increased intestinal rumbling, violent rolling and kicking, profuse sweating, constipation, and refusal of feed and water.	Worldwide.
Crooked calf disease (See Manganese deficiency)				
Fluorine poisoning (Fluorosis)	All farm animals, poultry and man.	Ingesting excessive quantities of fluorine through either the feed or water.	Abnormal teeth (especially mottled enamel) and bones, stiffness of joints, loss of appetite, emaciation, reduction in milk flow, diarrhea, and salt hunger.	The water in parts Arkansas, Californi South Carolina, ar Texas has been r ported to contain e cess fluorine. Occ sionally throughou the U.S. high fluorin phosphates are use in mineral mixture
Founder	Horses, Cattle, Sheep, Goats	Overeating, overdrinking, or from inflammation of the uterus following parturition. Also intestinal inflammation.	Extreme pain, fever (103° to 106° F.), and reluctance to move. If neglected, chronic laminitis will develop, resulting in a dropping of the hoof soles and a turning up of the toe walls.	Worldwide. Actual death losse from founder are no very great.
Goiter (See Iodine Deficiency)				
Grass Tetany (Grass staggers)	Cattle Sheep, particularly on wheat pasture.	Exact cause unknown, but it does appear to be nutritional.	Generally occurs during first 2 weeks of pasture season. Nervousness, twitching of muscles (usually of head and neck), head held high, accelerated respiration, high temperature, gnashing of the teeth, and abundant salivation. Slight stimulus may precipitate a crash to the ground. Death usually occurs within a few hours.	Reported in Nebraska Kentucky, Missouri, Iowa, Washington, and perhaps in other states. Also, found in New Zealand, England and Holland. Highly fatal. Causes estimated aver age annual losses ir beef and dairy cattle (including milk) o $662,000.
Heaves	Horses, Mules	Exact cause unknown, but it is known that the condition is often associated with the feeding of damaged, dusty, or moldy hay. Also, it often follows severe respiratory infections such as strangles. Probably an allergy.	Difficulty in forcing air out of the lungs, resulting in a jerking of flanks (double flank action), and coughing. The nostrils are often slightly dilated and there is a nasal discharge.	Worldwide. Losses are negligible

Footnotes at end of table.

ontinued)

Treatment	Control and Eradication	Prevention	Remarks
l a veterinarian. To avoid danger of inflicting self-injury, (1) place the animal in a large well-bedded table, or (2) take it for a slow walk. Depending on the diagnosis, the veterinarian may use one or more of the following: sedatives, laxatives such as mineral oil, drugs (to increase peristalsis), or surgery.	Follow a good management program, including parasite control.	Proper feeding, working and watering.	Bloodworms can cause a thromboembolic colic.
y damage may be permanent, but animals which have not developed severe symptoms may be helped to some extent, if the sources of excess fluorine are eliminated.	Discontinue the use of feeds, water, or mineral supplements containing excessive fluorine.	Avoid the use of feeds, water, or mineral supplements containing excessive fluorine. 100 ppm (0.01%) fluorine of the total dry ration is the borderline in toxicity for cattle, sheep, and pigs. At levels of 25-100 ppm some mottling of the teeth may occur over periods of 3-5 years. In breeding animals, whose usefulness exceeds 3-5 years, the permissible level is 30 ppm of the total dry ration. Not more than 65-100 ppm fluorine should be present in dry matter of rations when rock phosphate is fed.	Fluorine is a cumulative poison.
nding arrival of the veterinarian, the attendant should stand the animal's feet in a cold water bath.	Alleviate the causes, namely (1) overeating, (2) overdrinking, and/or (3) inflammation of the uterus following parturition.	Avoid overeating and overdrinking (especially when hot). Veterinary attention should be given if mares retain the afterbirth longer than 12 hours.	Swine do not founder, because they can unload their stomachs by vomiting. Unless foundered animals are quite valuable, it is usually desirable to dispose of them following a case of severe founder.
travenous injection of a solution of calcium and/or magnesium salt by a qualified veterinarian.	Access to a mineral supplement such as the following: Bone meal 65% Tra. min. mix 30% Mg carbonate or Mg oxide or > 5% Mg sulfate	Grass tetany can be prevented by not turning animals to pasture, but this is not practical. Feeding hay at night during the first two weeks of the pasture season is helpful. Feed magnesium-containing mineral free-choice.	Affected animals show low blood Mg.; often low serum Ca. Treated cattle may be aggressive on arising; so watch out!
ntihistamine granules added to feed will control coughing due to lung congestion. Affected animals less bothered if turned to pasture, worked lightly, and fed water-sprinkled hay or all-pelleted ration.	(See Prevention)	Avoid the use of damaged feeds. Feed an all-pelleted ration.	

(Continued)

TABLE 3—

Disease	Species Affected	Cause	Symptoms (and age or group most affected)	Distribution and Losses Caused By
Hypoglycemia (or Baby pig shakes)	Swine	Low-blood sugar level accompanies the trouble, but cause of the low blood sugar in unknown. The hog cholera virus can also cause this disease.	Shivering, weakness, failure to nurse, with no evidence of scouring. If disturbed, the pigs emit a weak, crying squeal. Hair becomes erect and rough, and the heart action slow and feeble. Without treatment, death usually comes in 24 to 36 hours after the first symptoms appear. Confined to baby pigs only.	Throughout the U. S. mortality may be high.
Iodine Deficiency (Goiter)	All farm animals and man	A failure of the body to obtain sufficient iodine from which the thyroid gland can form thyroxin (an iodine-containing compound).	Goiter (big neck) is the most characteristic symptom in humans, calves, lambs, and kids. Also, there may be reproductive failures and weak offspring that fail to survive. Pigs may be born hairless, and foals may be weak.	Northwestern U.S. and the Great Lakes region.
Ketosis (Acetonemia in cattle, or Pregnancy Disease in Sheep)	Cattle, Sheep, Goats	A metabolic disorder thought to be a disturbance in the carbohydrate metabolism.	In cows, ketosis or acetonemia is usually observed within 1 to 6 weeks after calving. Affected animals show loss in appetite and condition, a marked decline in milk production, and the production of a peculiar, sweetish, chloroform-like odor of acetone that may be present in the milk and pervade the barn. In sheep, ketosis or pregnancy disease generally strikes during the last 2 weeks of pregnancy, and usually the affected ewes are carrying twins or triplets. Symptoms include grinding of the teeth, dullness, weakness, frequent urination, and trembling when exercised—with the final stage being complete collapse, followed by death in 90% of the cases (see Fig. 3-33).	Worldwide. Ketosis or acetonemia affects dairy cattle throughout the U.S. Ketosis or pregnancy disease of sheep affects farm flocks more than range bands, the losses in the former sometimes being as high as 25%. Causes estimated average annual loss in dairy cattle (including milk) of $1,899,000
Manganese deficiency (or Crooked calf disease)	All farm animals and poultry	Deficiency of manganese.	Young born with stiff, curved, or crooked necks and backs, and permanently bent forward legs caused by contracted tendons.	Reported in Washington, Montana, and Utah.
Milk Fever	Cattle, Sheep, Goats, Swine	Low blood calcium. In milk cows, the Ca:P ratio should not exceed 2:1.	Commonly occurs soon after calving and in high-producing cows. Rarely occurs at first calving. First symptoms are loss of appetite, constipation, and general depression. This is followed by nervousness and finally collapse and complete loss of consciousness. The head is usually turned back.	A common, widespread disease of dairy cows. Losses are not great although untreated animals are likely to die. Causes average annual losses in dairy cattle (including milk) of $10,619,000.
Molybdenum Toxicity (commonly called teartness)	Ruminants, especially calves and cows in milk	As little as 10 to 20 ppm in forages result in toxic symptoms.	Toxic levels interfere with copper metabolism, thus increasing the copper requirement and producing typical copper deficiency symptoms. The physical symptoms are anemia and extreme diarrhea, with consequent loss in weight and milk yield.	England; and in Florida; California; and Manitoba, Canada.

Footnotes at end of table.

ontinued)

Treatment	Control and Eradication	Prevention	Remarks
ovide heat lamps for pigs. earliest symptoms either 1) force feed at frequent intervals a mixture of 1 part orn syrup diluted with 2 barts of water or (2) give ntraperitoneal injections of % glucose solution every to 6 hours. Consult veterinarian.	Apparently not contagious.	Adequate rations and good-care and management of the gestating sows may lessen the incidence of the disease. Be sure there is adequate milk for baby pigs during first days of life.	One of the hazards of hypo-glycemia is that the milk flow of the sow will not be stimulated or may even cease, due to the inactivity of the affected pigs. In the latter case, the pigs may have to be either transferred to a foster mother or hand-fed.
nce the iodine-deficiency symptoms appear in farm animals, no treatment is very effective.	At the first signs of iodine-deficiency, iodized salt should be fed to all farm animals.	In iodine-deficient areas, feed iodized salt to all farm animals throughout the year. Stabilized iodized salt containing 0.01% potassium iodide is recommended.	The enlarged thyroid gland (goiter) is nature's way of attempting to make sufficient thyroxine under conditions where a deficiency exists.
eat affected cows and ewes by adding molasses to the ation. e of the following is commonly used by the veterinarian in the treatment of ketosis: (1) glucose injection, 2) chloral hydrate in warm water, (3) cortisone, (4) ACTH, or (5) sodium propionate.	When ketosis is encountered in cattle, sheep, or goats, add molasses to the ration to stimulate appetite.	No sure prevention, but the following will help: Ketosis (Acetomemia) in cattle:—Feed a well-balanced ration, and, for high producing cows, add ½ lb. molasses/head daily, and feed a sodium-propionate-containing feed (2½ lbs./100 lbs. feed); from one week before to six weeks after calving. Ketosis (Pregnancy Disease) in sheep:—Give the ewes a well-balanced ration (including ½ to ¾ lb. grain daily) and plenty of clean, fresh water during pregnancy; provide regular and moderate exercise during this period; and follow good management practices. Adding molasses (3 qts./100 ewes) to the daily ration of pregnant ewes may be helpful.	The clinical findings are similar in the case of affected cattle and sheep, but it usually strikes ewes just before lambing, whereas cows are usually affected within the first 1 to 6 weeks after calving.
	(See Prevention.)	Feed a mineral containing manganese; 30 ppm of total feed, or 27.24 gm/ ton feed.	The Utah station has also produced crooked calves by feeding lupine. Alkali can tie up the manganese in water, soils, or plants.
atment consists of (1) having the veterinarian give an atravenous injection of a alcium salt or (2) inflating he udder with filtered air.	(See Prevention.)	During last month of dry period, (1) increase the P and achieve a Ca:P ratio of 1:2 or 3, and (2) feed more concentrate; or Feed 20 million units of vitamin D in form of irradiated yeast 4 to 7 days before calving (never longer than 7 days).	The name "milk fever" is a misnomer, because the disease is not accompanied by fever, the temperature really being below normal.
e gram of copper sulphate er head daily will cure ymptoms of molybdenum oxicity.		One gram of copper sulfate per head daily will prevent molybdenum toxicity.	When feeds are high in sulfate, toxic symptoms will be produced on lower levels of molybdenum and, conversely, higher levels of molybdenum can be tolerated with low levels of sulfate.

(Continued)

TABLE 3–

Disease	Species Affected	Cause	Symptoms (and age or group most affected)	Distribution and Losses Caused By
Moonblindness (See Periodic Ophthalmia)				
Nitrate-Nitrite-Poisoning (oat hay poisoning, cornstalk poisoning)	Cattle, sheep, and horses; but especially cattle.	1. The forages (seeds do not appear to accumulate nitrate nitrogen) of most grain crops (oats, wheat, barley, rye, corn, and sorghum), Sudan grass, and numerous weeds; especially (1) under stress— drought, insufficient sunlight, following spraying by weed killers, or after frost or (2) following the application of high soil nitrate nitrogen (through nitrogen fertilizer, green manure crops, or barnyard manure) which may boost the nitrate nitrogen of plants to dangerous levels. Also, sometimes nitrate appears to be formed after forage is stacked. 2. Inorganic salts of nitrate or nitrite (including fertilizers) carelessly applied to fields or left where animals have access to them. Sometimes these chemicals are also mistakenly used in place of common salt. 3. Pond or shallow well water into which heavy rains have washed a high concentration of nitrate from (1) fertilizer from heavily fertilized fields or (2) feed lot drainage (ammonium nitrate).	Accelerated respiration and pulse rate; diarrhea; frequent urination; loss of appetite; general weakness, trembling, and a staggering gait; frothing from the mouth; lowered milk production; abortion; blue color of the mucous membrane, muzzle, and udder due to lack of oxygen; and death in 4½ to 9 hrs. after eating lethal doses of nitrate. A rapid and accurate diagnosis of nitrate poisoning may be made by drawing and examining a venous (jugular) blood sample. Normal blood is red and becomes brighter on standing. Brown-colored blood, due to the formation of methemoglobin, is characteristic of animals suffering from nitrate poisoning; chemically, the nitrate oxidizes the ferrous hemoglobin (oxyhemoglobin) to ferric hemoglobin (methemoglobin) which cannot transport oxygen, with the result that death due to nitrate poisoning may be compared to asphyxiation or strangulation. Death occurs when about ¾ of the oxyhemoglobin (the oxygen carrier in the blood) has been converted to methemoglobin.	Excessive nitrate co tent of feeds is a increasingly impo tant cause of poisor ing in farm animal due primarily to mor and more high nitro gen fertilization. Bu nitrate toxicity is no new, having been re ported as earl as 1850, and occurre in semi-arid regior of this and othe countries for year
Oat Hay Poisoning (See Nitrate-nitrite poisoning)				
Osteomalacia	All species	Lack of vitamin D. Inadequate intake of calcium and phosphorus, and/or Incorrect ratio of calcium to phosphorus.	Phosphorus deficiency symptoms are: depraved appetite (gnawing on bones, wood, or other objects, eating dirt), lack of appetite, stiffness of joints, failure to breed regularly, decreased milk production, and an emaciated appearance. Calcium deficiency symptoms are: fragile bones, reproductive failures, and lowered lactations. Mature animals most affected. Most of the acute cases occur during pregnancy and lactation.	Southwestern U. is classed as a pho phorus-deficient ar whereas calcium-d cient areas have be reported in parts Florida, Louisia Nebraska, Virgin: and West Virginia.

Footnotes at end of table.

ontinued)

Treatment	Control and Eradication	Prevention	Remarks
4% solution of methylene blue (in a 5% glucose or a .8% sodium sulfate solution) administered by a veterinarian intravenously at the rate of 100 cc./1000 lbs. live weight.	(See Prevention.)	Regard any amount of nitrate nitrogen over 0.5% of the total ration (moisture-free basis) as a potential source of trouble. When in doubt, have the feed analyzed (first make a rapid, qualitative field test, using a commercial test kit according to direction; then, if high-nitrate samples are spotted, follow with a quantitative laboratory chemical test). Nitrate poisoning may be lowered by (1) feeding high levels of carbohydrates or energy feeds (grain or molasses) and vitamin A, (2) feeding limited amounts of high nitrate forage, (3) alternating or mixing high and low-nitrate forages, and (4) ensiling forages high in nitrates, since fermentation reduces some of the nitrates to gas (but beware of nitric oxide and nitrogen dioxide gas, which is released as yellow-red fumes in the early stages of fermentation and may cause silo gas poisoning to both humans and animals). After 3-4 weeks the silage has usually lost most of its nitrate and is safe to feed.	Nitrate from nitrogen does not appear to cause the actual toxicity. During digestion, the nitrate is reduced to nitrite, a far more toxic form (10 to 15 times more toxic than nitrates). In cows and sheep, this conversion takes place in the rumen (paunch); in horses in the cecum. Lethal dose varies with (1) nutritional state, size and type of animal and (2) the consumption of feed other than nitrate-containing material. Nitrate over 5% of total ration is a potential source of trouble; 0.75% content nitrate forages must be fed with caution, and milk production will be lowered; and at 1.5% death will likely occur. Where nitrate troubles are suspected, consult the local veterinarian or county agent.
ase the calcium and phosrus content of feeds ough fertilizing the soils. t natural feeds that con-n sufficient quantities of cium and phosphorus. a special mineral supple-nt or supplements. disease is far advanced, atment will not be suc-sful.	(See Treatment.)	Feed balanced rations, and allow animals free access to a suitable phosphorus and calcium supplement.	Calcium deficiencies are much more rare than phosphorus deficiencies in cattle, sheep and horses. Calcium deficiencies are fairly common in swine because grains, which are their chief feed, are low in this mineral.

(Continued)

TABLE 3—

Disease	Species Affected	Cause	Symptoms (and age or group most affected)	Distribution and Losses Caused By
Parakeratosis (greasy skin disease)	Swine	High calcium levels in the diet—above 0.8%.	Pigs have mangy look, reduced appetite and growth rate, diarrhea, and vomiting. It affects pigs 1—5 months of age.	Mortality is not high; economic loss is mainly in reduced gains and lowered feed efficiency.
Periodic Ophthalmia (Moodblindness)	Horses, Mules, Asses	It appears that it may be caused by (1) leptospirosis, (2) a localized hypersensitivity or allergic reaction, or (3) lack of riboflavin.	Periods of cloudy vision, in one or both eyes, which may last for a few days to a week or two and then clear up; but it recurs at intervals, eventually culminating in blindness in one or both eyes.	In many parts of the world. In the U. S. it occurs most frequently in the states east of the Missouri River.
Pine Needle Abortion[2]	Cattle	Needles of Yellow Pine (*Pinus ponderosa*); commonly called Yellow Pine, British Columbia Pine, or Jack Pine. It is suspected that the high turpentine content of Yellow Pine needles actually causes the abortion, for there is evidence that turpentine can cause abortion in the human female.	Pregnant cows, free of brucellosis, abort.	British Columbia, Canada, and in the states of Washington, Idaho, and Oregon.
Pregnancy Disease in Sheep (See Ketosis)				
Rickets	All farm animals and man	Lack of either calcium, phosphorus, or vitamin D, or An incorrect ratio of the two minerals.	The knee and hock joints are enlarged, and the animal may exhibit great pain when moving about. Irregular bulges (beaded ribs) at juncture of ribs with breastbone and bowed legs. Swine are frequently paralyzed in the hind legs. Rickets is a disease of young animals— of calves, foals, pigs, lambs, kids, pups, and chicks.	World wide It is seldom fatal.
Salt poisoning (sodium chloride)	All farm animals, but swine and sheep most frequently affected.	Brine from cured meats; wet salt. Where large amounts of brine or salt have been mixed in hog slop. When excess salt is fed following salt starvation. When salt is improperly used to govern self-feeding of concentrate.	Sudden onset—1 to 2 hours after ingesting salt; extreme nervousness; muscle twitching and fine tremors; much weaving, wobbling, staggering, and circling; blindness; weakness; normal temperature, rapid but weak pulse, and very rapid and shallow breathing; diarrhea; death from a few hours up to 48 hours. Convulsions seldom occur, except in pigs.	Salt poisoning is relatively rare.
Salt (Sodium chloride) deficiency	All farm animals and man	Lack of salt (Sodium chloride).	Loss of appetite, retarded growth, loss of weight, a rough coat, lowered production of milk, and a ravenous appetite for salt.	Worldwide, especially among grass-eating animals and the pig
Salt Sick	Cattle, Sheep, Goats	Probably cobalt deficiency, associated with copper and perhaps iron deficiencies.	Loss of appetite, depraved appetite, scaliness of skin, listlessness, and lack of thrift.	Florida; on sandy soils

Footnotes at end of table.

(Continued)

Treatment	Control and Eradication	Prevention	Remarks
Add 0.4 lb. of zinc carbonate or 0.9 lb. of zinc sulfate heptahydrate/ton of feed.	It is not contagious.	Add 0.4 lb. of zinc carbonate or 0.9 lb. of zinc sulfate heptahydrate/ton of feed where the disease is encountered.	
Antibiotics administered promptly are helpful.	If symptoms of moonblindness are observed, immediately, (1) change to greener hay or grass or (2) add riboflavin to the ration at the rate of 40 mg per horse per day.	Feed riboflavin-high green grass or well-cured green leafy hays; or Add riboflavin to the ration at the rate of 40 mg per horse per day.	This disease has been known to exist for at least 2,000 years.
No treatment known.		Keep pregnant cows away from Yellow Pine trees.	Lodgepole Pine (Pinus contoria) —Commonly called Black Pine, Jack Pine, Western Jack Pine, White Pine, or Cypress —does not appear to cause abortion in cattle. Pregnant cows will consume quantities of pine needles even though fed an adequate ration.
If the disease has not advanced too far, treatment may be successful by supplying adequate amounts of vitamin D, calcium, and phosphorus, and/or adjusting the ratio of calcium to phosphorus.	(See Prevention.)	Provide (1) sufficient calcium, phosphorus, and vitamin D, and (2) a correct ratio of the two minerals.	Rickets is characterized by a failure of growing bone to ossify, or harden, properly. In adult animals this disease is called osteomalacia (bone softening).
Provide large quantities of fresh water to affected animals. Those that can and do drink seldom need additional treatment. Those unable to drink should be given water via stomach tube, by the veterinarian. The vet may also give (I.V. or intraperitoneally) calcium gluconate to severely affected animals.	(See Prevention.)	If animals have not had salt for a long time, they should first be hand-fed salt, gradually increasing daily allowance until they leave a little in the mineral box; then self-feed.	Indians and pioneers handed down many legendary stories about huge numbers of wild animals that killed themselves simply by gorging at a newly found salt lick after having been salt-starved for long periods of time.
Salt-starved animals should be gradually accustomed to salt; slowly increasing the hand-fed allowance until the animals may be safely allowed free access to it.	(See Treatment and Prevention.)	Provide plenty of salt at all times, preferably by free-choice feeding.	Common salt is one of the most essential minerals for grass-eating animals, and one of the easiest and cheapest to provide. Excess salt intake can result in toxicity.
		Mix 0.2 oz. of cobalt chloride or cobalt sulfate/100 lbs. of either (1) salt or (2) the mineral other than salt.	

(Continued)

TABLE 3—

Disease	Species Affected	Cause	Symptoms (and age or group most affected)	Distribution and Losses Caused By
Selenium Poisoning (Alkali Disease)	All farm animals and man	Consumption of plants grown on soils containing selenium.	Loss of hair from the mane and tail in horses, from the tail in cattle, and a general loss of hair in swine. In severe cases, the hoofs slough off (see Fig. 3—34), lameness occurs, feed consumption decreases, and death may occur by starvation.	In certain regions o western U. S., espe cially certain areas i South Dakota, Mon tana, Wyoming, N braska, Kansas, an perhaps areas i other states in th Great Plains an Rocky Mountains. Also in Canada.
Stiff Lamb Disease (white muscle disease, Muscular dystrophy)	Lambs [Also a similar condition (white muscle disease) appears in calves].	Selenium deficiency and lack of vitamin E; or perhaps for some as yet unknown reason the vitamin E of the ration is not available to the animal due to an inhibitor, or for other reasons.	A stiff, stilted way of moving, chiefly in hind legs, although front legs and shoulders may be involved. Back usually humped or "roached." Lambs that live are usually stunted. Young, rapidly growing lambs one to five weeks of age especially susceptible.	Throughout the U. S but incidence is high est in inter-mountai area, between th Rocky and Cascad Mountains. Affected lambs ofte die.
Sweet Clover Disease	Cattle; rarely affects sheep, horses.	Usually produced only by moldy or spoiled sweet clover hay or silage. Caused by presence of dicumarol which interferes with vitamin K in blood clotting.	Loss of clotting power of the blood. As a result, blood forms soft swellings beneath skin of different parts of body (see Fig. 3—35). Serious or fatal bleeding may occur at the time of dehorning, docking, castration, parturition, or following injury. All ages affected. A newborn animal may also have the condition at birth.	Wherever sweet clove is grown.
Urinary Calculi (gravel, stones, water belly)	Cattle, Sheep, Horses, Man	Unknown, but it does seem to be nutritional. Experiments have shown a higher incidence of urinary calculi when there is (1) a high potassium intake, (2) an incorrect Ca:P ratio, or (3) a high proportion of beet pulp or grain sorghum in the ration.	Frequent attempts to urinate, dribbling or stoppage of the urine, pain, and renal colic. Usually only males affected, the females being able to pass the concretions (see Fig. 3—36). Bladder may rupture, with death following. Otherwise, uremic poisoning may set in.	Worldwide. Affected animals se dom recover cor pletely. Causes estimated ave age annual loss beef cattle of $4,052,000.
Vitamin A Deficiency (night blindness and xerophthalmia)	All farm animals and man	Vitamin A deficiency.	Night blindness, the first symptom of vitamin A deficiency, is characterized by faulty vision, especially noticeable when the afflicted animal is forced to move about in twilight in strange surroundings. Xerophthalmia develops in the advanced stages of vitamin A deficiency, the eyes become severely affected, and blindness may follow. Severe diarrhea in young calves and intermittent diarrhea in advanced stages in adults. In finishing cattle, generalized edema or anasarca with lameness in hock and knee joints and swelling in the brisket area.	Worldwide. Especial prevalent in weste U.S. where one of t following conditio frequently prevai (1) extended droug and (2) winter feedi on bleached gra cured on the stalk on bleached hay.

Footnotes at end of table.

Continued)

Treatment	Control and Eradication	Prevention	Remarks
lthough arsenic has been shown to counteract the effects of selenium toxicity, there appears to be no practical method of treating other than removal of animals from affected areas.	(Control measures based on Prevention.)	Abandon areas where soils contain selenium, because crops produced on such soils constitute a menace to both animals and man.	Chronic cases of selenium poisoning occur when animals consume feeds containing 8.5 ppm of selenium over an extended period; acute cases occur on 500 to 1,000 ppm. The toxic level of selenium is in the range of 2.27 to 4.54 mg/lb. of feed.
njections of selenium and tocopherol give dramatic results.	If stiff-lamb disease occurs in the flock, give prompt attention to any possible improvements in the ration. In season, turn animals on good pasture.	Inject lambs with a solution of vitamin E and selenium (1) at docking time (3-4 days) and (2) 2-4 weeks of age. Since several concentrations are available, follow the directions on the label.	Most natural rations, even corn cobs, contain an abundance of vitamin E. At Cornell, a high incidence of stiff lamb disease occurred when a ration high in cull red kidney beans was fed. Stiff lamb disease is most common (1) in rapidly growing lambs and (2) on lush pastures. Linseed meal is probably effective in preventing stiff lamb disease because it contains selenium. Selenium is not approved by the Food and Drug Administration as a feed additive.
emove the offending material and administer Menadione (vitamin K₃).· he veterinarian usually gives the affected animal an injection of plasma or whole blood from a normal animal that was not fed on the same feed.	When a case of sweet clover disease is observed in the herd, either (1) discontinue feeding the damaged product or (2) alternate it with a better quality hay, especially alfalfa.	Properly cure any sweet clover hay or ensilage.	The disease has also been produced from feeding moldy lespedeza hay and from sweet clover pasture.
nce calculi develop, dietary treatment appears to be of little value. mooth muscle relaxants may allow passage of calculi if used before rupture of bladder. rgery may save the animal, but such treatment will result in bulls becoming nonbreeders. hen the condition strikes in feedlot cattle or lambs, increase the salt content of the diet if the animals are not ready to market.	If severe outbreaks of urinary calculi occur in finishing steers or lambs, it is usually well to dispose of them if they are carrying acceptable finish. For feed lot cattle, add ammonium chloride at rate of 1¼ to 1½ oz./head/day, or add 1.7 to 2.0 oz. of ammonium sulfate/head/day. For feedlot wether lambs, add to the ration 0.5% ammonium chloride (1 oz./head/day) or 0.9% ammonium sulfate.	Good feed and management, and delayed castration (castration of bull calves at 4-5 mo. of age) appear to lessen the incidence, but no sure preventative is known. Avoid high phosphorus and low calcium; keep the Ca:P ratio at about 2:1. Provide adequate vitamin A, salt, and water. 1 to 1½% salt in the ration will induce more water consumption and lower the incidence of urinary calculi.	Calculi are stone-like concretions in the urinary tract which almost always originate in the kidneys. These stones block the passage of urine. Avoid high P and low Ca. Keep the Ca:P ratio about 2:1. Provide adequate vitamin A, salt, and water.
reatment consists of correcting the dietary deficiencies.	(See Prevention and Treatment.)	Provide good sources of carotene (vitamin A) through green, leafy hays; silage; lush, green pastures; yellow corn or green and yellow peas; whole milk or fish oils; or add stabilized vitamin A to the ration.	Sheep will not develop xerophthalmia on a vitamin A deficiency. High levels of nitrates interfere with the conversion of carotene to vitamin A.

(Continued)

TABLE 3—5

Disease	Species Affected	Cause	Symptoms (and age or group most affected)	Distribution and Losses Caused By
White Muscle Disease (muscular dystrophy; also see stiff lamb disease.	Calves, Lambs (See stiff lamb disease)	A deficiency of selenium and vitamin E.	Symptoms range from mild "founder-like" stiffness to sudden death. Calves continue to nurse as long as they can reach the cow's teats. Many calves stand or lie with protruded tongue, fighting for breath against a severe pulmonary edema. It seems that more calves than lambs develop fatal heart damage. Affected calves show pathological lesions similar to those of "stiff lambs"; namely, whitish areas or streaks in the heart and other muscles. Affects calves from birth to 3 months of age.	Throughout the U.S. but incidence is highest in inter-mountain area, between the Rocky and Cascade Mountains.

¹In the preparation of Table 3-5, the author had the authoritative help of Dr. Robert F. Behlow, DVM, Professor and Extension Veterinarian, North Carolina State University, Raleigh, North Carolina.
Unless otherwise indicated, the estimated average annual loss (in dollars) figures given under the column headed "Distribution and Losses Caused By," of Table 3-5, were taken from *Losses in Agriculture*, Agriculture Handbook No. 291, 1965.

Fig. 3-33. Ewe with ketosis or pregnancy disease. The specific cause of this disease is unknown, but it is attributed to disturbances in metabolism resulting from pregnancy, poor feeding, and lack of exercise. (Courtesy, Dept. of Veterinary Pathology and Hygiene, College of Veterinary Medicine, University of Illinois)

ntinued)

Treatment	Control and Eradication	Prevention	Remarks
ine affected animals in a ll and give plenty of rest. :t selenium and vitamin	(See Prevention and Treatment.)	Feed 1¼ lbs. linseed meal per cow daily during last 2 months of gestation. It is thought that linseed meal contains sufficient selenium to serve as a preventative. See preventive measures successfully used in lambs as reported under "stiff lamb disease."	White muscle disease is often overlooked in calves.

²This summary is based on a Master's Thesis, dated October, 1953, by Mr. H. H. Nicholson, prepared under the supervision)r. A. J. Wood, University of British Columbia.

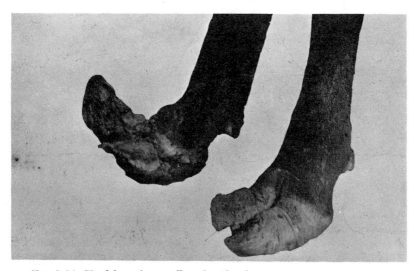

Fig. 3-34. Hind feet of cow afflicted with selenium poisoning. In severe cases, the hoofs slough off. (Courtesy, Alvin L. Moxon, South Dakota State University)

Fig. 3-35. Calf with sweet clover disease. Note the collection of blood at the point of the left shoulder. (Courtesy, Dept. of Veterinary Pathology and Hygiene, College of Veterinary Medicine, University of Illinois)

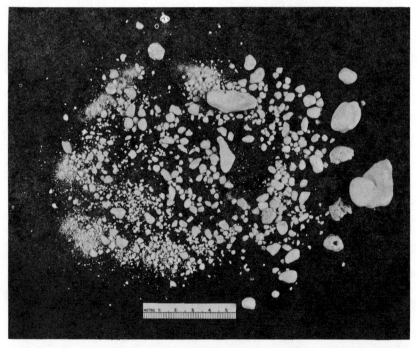

Fig. 3-36. Concretions or stones obtained from a $6,500 imported Shorthorn bull that died from urinary calculi. The cause of urinary calculi is unknown, but it does seem to be tied up with nutrition. (Courtesy, Washington State University)

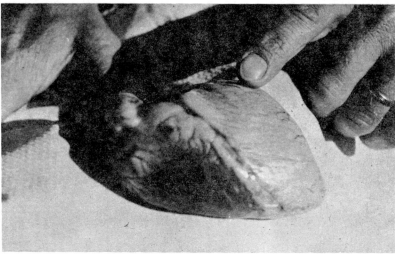

Fig. 3-37. White muscle disease in a calf.
Upper picture shows the generalized weakness of muscles, lameness, and difficulty in locomotion of an afflicted calf.
Lower picture shows abnormal white areas in the heart muscles of a six-week-old calf afflicted with white muscle disease. (Courtesy, O. H. Muth, Oregon Agricultural Experiment Station)

as well as our animals. Despite this remarkable progress, it is recognized that a combination of forced production, feeds produced on depleted soils, and the purification of feeds has created many problems.

Table 3-6 points up the continued need for greater efficiency of animal production, the urgency of which becomes altogether too apparent in light of population increases and impending world food shortages. Even the dairy cow, the most efficient of all animal producers, is only (1) 26 per cent efficient in con-

TABLE 3-6

FEED TO FOOD EFFICIENCY RATING BY SPECIES OF ANIMALS

(Based on energy as TDN or DE and crude protein in feed eaten by various kinds of animals converted into calories and protein content of ready-to-eat human food)

Species	Unit of Production (on foot)	Feed Required to Produce One Production Unit[1]				Dressing Yield		Ready-to-eat; Yield of Edible Product (meat and fish deboned and after cooking)				Efficiency Rating		Total Score (calories + protein)	Rank (calories & protein)
		Pounds	TDN	DE[2]	Protein	Per Cent	Net Left	As % of Raw Product (carcass)	Amount Remaining From One Unit of Production	Calorie[3]	Protein[3]	Calorie Efficiency[4]	Protein Efficiency[5]		
		(lb.)	(lb.)	(kcal)	(lb.)	(%)	(lb.)	(%)	(lb.)	(kcal)	(lb.)	(%)	(%)		
Dairy cow .... 1 lb. milk		.85[6]	.60	1,200	.11	100	1.0	100	1.0	309	.037	25.8	33.6	59.4	1
Fish............... 1 lb. fish		1.6[7]	.90	1,800	.57	65[8]	.65	57[9]	.37	285	.093	15.8	16.3	32.1	2
Layer............. 1 lb. eggs (8 eggs)		4.0[10]	2.96	5,920	.68	100	1.0	100[11]	1.0[11]	616	.106	10.4	15.6	26.0	3
Broiler............ 1 lb. chicken		3.0[6]	2.37	4,740	.66	72[12]	.72	54[13]	.39	274	.11	5.8	16.7	22.5	4
Turkey............ 1 lb. turkey		5.2[10]	3.95	7,900	1.19	79.7[12]	.797	57[14]	.45	446	.146	5.6	12.3	17.9	5
Hog (birth to 200 lb.)... 1 lb. pork		4.9[6]	3.67	7,340	.69	70[15]	.70	44[16]	.31	341	.088	4.6	12.7	17.3	6
Beef steer (yearling finishing period in feedlot).......... 1 lb. beef		10.0[7]	6.50	13,000	1.00	58[15]	.58	49[16]	.28	342	.085	2.6	8.5	11.1	7
Lamb (finishing period in feedlot).. 1 lb. lamb		9.0[8]	5.58	11,160	.96	47[15]	.47	40[16]	.19	225	.052	2.1	5.4	7.5	8

[1]Includes provision for body maintenance, for the reason that feed energy must be expended in body maintenance before there can be any production; for example, the dairy cow must be maintained before there can be any milk production.

[2]Digestible Energy (DE) in this column given in kcal, which is 1 Calorie (written with a capital C), or 1,000 calories (written with a small c). Kilocalories computed from TDN values in column to immediate left as follows:1 lb. TDN=2,000 kcal.

[3]From Lessons on Meat, 1965, National Livestock and Meat Board.

[4]Kilocalories in ready-to-eat food=kilocalories in feed consumed, converted to percentage.

[5]Protein in ready-to-eat food=protein in feed consumed, converted to percentage.

[6]Computations made by the author.

[7]Data from Feedstuffs, April 15, 1967, report by Dr.,Phillip J. Schaible, Michigan State University.

[8]Industrial Fishery Technology, ed. by Maurice E. Stansby, Reinhold Pub. Corp., 1963, Ch. 26, Table 26—1.

[9]Ibid. Reports that, "Dressed fish averages about 73% flesh, 21% bone, and 6% skin." In limited experiments conducted by A. Ensminger, it was found that there was a 22% cooking loss on filet of sole. Hence, these values—73% flesh from dressed fish, plus 22% cooking losses—give

57% yield of edible fish after cooking, as a per cent of the raw, dressed product.

[10]Handbook of Agriculture Charts 1965, Agric. Handbook No. 300, p. 58, USDA, Oct., 1965.

[11]Calories and protein computed basis per egg; hence, the values herein are 100% and 1.0 lb., respectively.

[12]Marketing Poultry Products, p. 147.

[13]Factors Affecting Poultry Meat Yields, Univ. of Minn. Sta. Bul. 476, Table 11 (fricassee), p. 29,1964.

[14]Ibid. Table 10, p. 28, 1964.

[15]The Stockman's Handbook, 4th Ed., Sec. XII.

[16]Allowance made for both cutting and cooking losses following dressing. Thus, values are on a cooked, ready-to-eat basis of lean and marbled meat, exclusive of bone, gristle, and fat. Values provided by National Livestock and Meat Board (personal communication of June 5, 1967, from Dr. Wm. C. Sherman, Director, Nutrition Research to the author; and based on data from The Nutritive Value of Cooked Meat, by Ruth M. Leverton and George V. Odell, Misc. Pub. MP-49, Appendix C, March 1958).

[17]Beef Cattle Science, 4th Ed. Ch. 14, Table 14-21.

[18]Sheep and Wool Science, 3rd Ed., p. 250.

verting the energy of feed to food, and (2) 34 per cent efficient in converting protein of feed to food. Granted, feed is only one factor responsible for the productivity rating given in Table 3-6; other environmental factors and heredity play a part. Nevertheless, feed is a costly and important item, and, historically, hungry people throughout the world have been forced to eliminate considerable animals and to consume grains directly to avoid famine.

In recent years, science and technology have teamed up and made for great strides in improving the productive efficiency of poultry. No doubt, further progress with all animals lies ahead. Also, as increasing quantities of cereal grains are needed for human consumption, ruminants will utilize higher proportions of roughages to concentrates.

QUESTIONS FOR STUDY AND DISCUSSION

1. Why is knowledge of livestock feeding so important?
2. Why are proteins so important in animal nutrition?
3. In 1949, Dr. J. K. Loosli of Cornell submitted evidence (*Science*, 110:144-145, 1949), that microbial action in the rumen can synthesize from urea all of the 10 amino acids which are essential for rat growth. Loosli fed a nearly protein-free, purified diet to lambs, with the following results:

AVERAGE DAILY AMINO ACID BALANCE OF SHEEP
(In grams)

Amino Acid	Intake	Excreted		
		Urine	Feces	Total
Arginine	0.19	0.48	0.06	0.54
Histidine	0.05	0.18	0.02	0.20
Isoleucine	0.00	0.52	0.06	0.58
Leucine	0.15	0.61	0.08	0.69
Lysine	0.24	0.71	0.12	0.83
Methionine	0.03	0.21	0.02	0.23
Phenylalanine	0.05	0.48	0.04	0.52
Threonine	0.07	0.67	0.06	0.73
Tryptophane	0.01	0.13	0.01	0.14
Valine	0.14	0.69	0.08	0.77

This showed that 3 to 10 times as much of each amino acid was excreted as was fed. Since the lambs were gaining in weight and were in positive nitrogen balance, the excreted acids could not have come from tissue breakdown but must have been synthesized in the rumen. On the basis of analysis of rumen samples, the concentration of the various amino acids in the rumen contents was estimated to be 9 to 20 times greater than in the feed.

Discuss the significance and the application of the experiment referred to above.

4. Discuss the utilization of fibrous roughages by animals.
5. What factors should be considered in feeding fats?
6. Compare the price of one or more commercial minerals with the price of a home-mixed product; and relate their respective analyses to the needs of the class of livestock for which they are intended.
7. For each class of farm animals, list the vitamins most apt to be deficient; then (a) list some of the deficiency symptoms and (b) give practical sources of each vitamin for use on your farm or ranch.

8. What two nutritional discoveries of the past decade have had the greatest impact on the livestock industry? Justify your answer.

9. When would you use antibiotics in the ration; when wouldn't you?

10. When would you use hormones in the ration; when wouldn't you?

11. What factors should be considered in the selection of feeds; and why?

12. Under what conditions should commercial feeds be used instead of home-mixed rations?

13. How would you go about selecting a commercial feed for a specific purpose?

SELECTED REFERENCES

Title of Publication	Author(s)	Publisher
Animal Nutrition	L. A. Maynard J. K. Loosli	McGraw-Hill Book Co., New York, N. Y., 1962.
Applied Animal Nutrition	E. W. Crampton L. E. Harris	W. H. Freeman and Co., San Francisco, Calif., 1968.
Antibiotics in Agriculture	Proceedings	American Cyanamid Co., Lederle Laboratories Div., Pearl River, N. Y.
Comparative Nutrition of Farm Animals	H. R. Guilbert J. K. Loosli	Reprint from Journal of Animal Science, Feb. 1951, Vol. 10, No. 1, pp. 22-41. Pub. by National Res. Council, Washington, D. C.
Composition of Cereal Grains and Forages	Pub. 585	National Academy of Sciences, National Res. Council, Washington, D. C.
Composition of Concentrate By-Product Feeding Stuffs	Pub. 449	National Academy of Sciences, National Res. Council, Washington, D. C.
Better Feeding of Livestock	Farmers' Bull. 2052	U. S. Department of Agriculture, Washington, D. C.
Feed Bag, Red Book, The	Annual	Editorial Serv. Co., 1712 West St. Paul Ave., Milwaukee, Wisc.
Feed Formulations Handbook	T. W. Perry	The Interstate Printers & Publishers, Inc., Danville, Ill., 1966.
Feeders' Guide and Formulae for Meal Mixtures	Quebec Provincial Feed Board	Department of Agriculture, Quebec, Canada.
Feeding Practices	Educational Serv.	National Cottonseed Products Assn., Inc., 618 Wilson Bldg., Dallas, Tex.
Feeds and Feeding, Abridged	F. B. Morrison	Morrison Pub. Co., Ithaca, N. Y. 1949.
Feeds and Feeding, 22nd Ed.	F. B. Morrison	Morrison Pub. Co., Ithaca, N. Y., 1956.
Feeds of the World	B. H. Schneider	Agr. Exp. Sta., West Virginia University, Morgantown, W. Va., 1947.
Feed Trade Manual		National Miller Pub., Inc., 6 E. McDonald Rd., Prospect Heights, Ill.
Frontiers in Nutrition		Dawe's Manufacturing Co., Chicago, Ill.
Handbook of Feedstuffs, The	Rudolph Seiden W. H. Pfander	Springer Publishing Co., New York, N. Y., 1957.
Health from the Ground Up	K. B. Mickey	International Harvester Co., Chicago, Ill., 1946.

Title of Publication	Author(s)	Publisher
Inadequate Diets and Nutritional Deficiencies in the United States		National Res. Council, National Academy of Sciences, Washington, D. C., 1943.
Mineral Nutrition of Plants and Animals	F. A. Gilbert	University of Oklahoma Press, Norman, Okla., 1948.
Minerals for Livestock	Pop. Bul. 183 T. J. Cunha	Wash. Agri. Exp. Sta., Washington State University, Pullman, Wash., 1946.
Minerals for Livestock	Circ. 297 Gus Bohstedt	Extension Service, University of Wisconsin, Madison, Wisc., 1957.
Minerals for Livestock Feeding	Circ. 688 H. H. Mitchell	Extension Service, University of Illinois, Urbana, Ill., 1951.
Nutritional Deficiencies in Livestock	R. T. Allman T. S. Hamilton	Food and Agric. Organization Studies No. 5, Rome, Italy.
Nutrition of Plants, Animals, Man	Centennial Symp. 1855-1955	College of Agriculture, Michigan State University, East Lansing, Mich.
Phosphate Fertilization of Alfalfa and Some Effects on the Animal Body	W. W. Heinemann M. E. Ensminger W. E. Ham J. E. Oldfield	Tech. Bul. 24, 1957, Wash. Agr. Exp. Sta., Washington State University, Pullman, Wash.
Practical Explanation of Some Terms in Animal Nutrition	M. J. Brinegar	E.C. 252, Revised, 1951, Ext. Serv., University of Nebraska, Lincoln, Neb.
Proceedings, Nutritional Council, American Feed Manufacturers Assn.		American Feed Manufacturers Assn., 53 West Jackson Blvd., Chicago, Ill.
Proceedings Annual Research Conf.		Charles Pfizer & Co., Terre Haute, Ind.
Proceedings of the Symposium of Mineral Nutrition		International Minerals and Chemicals, 20 No. Wacker Drive, Chicago, Ill.
Proteins and Amino Acids in Animal Nutrition	H. J. Almquist	U. S. Industrial Chemicals Co., 99 Park Avenue, New York, N. Y.
Salt in Animal Nutrition		Salt Institute, 33 No. LaSalle St., Chicago, Ill., 1957.
Scientific Feeding of Farm Animals		Armour and Co., Chicago, Ill.
Through the Leaves	E. J. Maynard	Great West. Sugar Co., Denver, Colo.
Vitamin Manual		Upjohn Co., Kalamazoo, Mich., 1957.
Vitamin Reviews		Merck & Co., Rahway, N. J.
Vitamins and Hormones, Vol. XV		Academic Press Inc., New York, N. Y., 1957.

Also, literature on the subject of feed additives may be secured from the several pharmaceutical companies selling these products.

CHAPTER IV

LIVESTOCK BUILDINGS AND EQUIPMENT[1]

Contents   Page
Location of Farm or Ranch Headquarters..............................166
Farmstead Arrangement...167
Requisites of Livestock Buildings..169
   Confinement; Environmental Control..............................174
Requisites of Livestock Equipment......................................175
   Automation 176
Space Requirements of Buildings and Equipment...................177
   Recommended Minimum Width for Service Passages............177
   Storage Space Requirements for Feed and Bedding.............178
Types of Barn Roofs..178
Types of Floors for Stalls or Stables..................................178
   Slotted Floors 179
Paved Lots and Feeding Floors..181
The Silo...182
   Types of Silos...182
     Tower Silo...183
     Pit Silo...184
     Trench Silo 184
     Self-feeder or Bunker Silo...184
     Aboveground Temporary Silos.....................................185
     Plastic Silos..186
Manure Handling 187
Scales 188
Fences for Livestock...189
Paint for Buildings and Equipment.....................................189
Questions for Study and Discussion.....................................189
Selected References 189

Properly constructed and arranged buildings and equipment are an asset to the farm or ranch. They increase animal production, make for feed efficiency, conserve crops and manure, provide comfort for man and beast, and add to the beauty of the farm landscape. In serving these purposes, it is not necessary that buildings and equipment be either elaborate or expensive.

It is generally recognized that the mechanization and modernization of livestock operations—especially of buildings and equipment—has lagged behind the mechanization and modernization in crop production and in certain other phases of agriculture. Thus, it is estimated (1) that more than 50 per cent of livestock work is still hand labor, and (2) that through mechanization and modernization at least one-half of the hours spent in animal production could be saved annually, despite the well-recognized fact that animals cannot ever be as completely mechanized as crops.

---

[1] The author acknowledges his indebtedness to the following authorities who reviewed Chapter IV: Prof. June Roberts, Chairman, Department of Agricultural Engineering, Washington State University, Pullman, Wash.; and Prof. C. H. Zuroske, Agricultural Economist, Department of Agricultural Economics, Washington State University, Pullman, Wash.

Because of variations in climatic conditions, sizes and types of enterprises, and systems of management, no attempt will be made herein to present detailed building and equipment plans and specifications. Rather, it is desired merely to convey suggestions regarding some of the desirable features of buildings and equipment in use in various parts of the country. For detailed plans and specifications for a particular locality, the farmer or rancher should (1) study successful buildings and equipment on neighboring farms and ranches, (2) consult the local county agricultural agent, vocational agriculture instructor, or lumber dealer, and/or (3) write to the state college of agriculture.

LOCATION OF FARM OR RANCH HEADQUARTERS

When planning an entirely new farm or ranch headquarters, the choice of location for the buildings is the first consideration. Likewise, when appraising the desirabilty of an existing headquarters, the same factors should be considered. These are:

Fig. 4-1. The attractive headquarters of High Valley Ranch, a famous 100,000 acre cattle outfit near Ellensburg, Washington. (Courtesy, L. T. Murray)

1. **Water supply.**—Water should be available and plentiful. With the availability of electricity and automatically operated pumps, many farmers and ranchers can locate the headquarters farther from the source of water supply when it is desirable to do so to obtain other advantages.

2. **Topography.**—The topography should be high and level with no abrupt slopes. A relatively level area requires less site preparation, thus lowering building costs.

3. **Drainage.**—The soil should be porous and the slope gentle, for this makes for dry corrals and lots. Animal health is much more easily maintained when the yards and buildings are well drained, and the work of the caretaker is more pleasant and easier under such conditions.

4. **Size and shape.**—The area for the headquarters should be of adequate size, usually from two to five acres, and nearly square in shape. With further mechanization, smaller farmsteads are now needed than in the era when horses were extensively used. In general, the tendency is to have too large a farmstead; this adds to maintenance and weed-control costs and keeps valuable land out of production.

5. **Soil type.**—A good fertile soil is desirable for the garden and yard.

6. **Accessibility to fields.**—In general, centrally located headquarters have the advantage of efficiency of field work. Headquarters so located also facilitate the movement of stock to and from all fields with the least inconvenience.

7. **Roads.**—It is preferable that the headquarters be located near an all-weather road that is well maintained, but one should avoid having the farmstead on both sides of a road.

8. **View.**—A scenic view, especially from the living side of the house, makes for a "heap of living."

9. **Sun exposure and wind protection.**—The farm or ranch headquarters should be located to obtain the maximum sun exposure in the North and the minimum sun exposure in the South, and protection from strong prevailing winds.

10. **Electricity.**—If possible, the headquarters should have access to a power line.

11. **Schools and churches.**—The farm or ranch family should have convenient access to a good school and the church of their preference.

12. **Telephone.**—Farming or ranching is a business, and it is difficult to conduct any kind of modern business without access to a telephone. The headquarters should be near a well-maintained telephone line.

13. **Mail route.**—The headquarters should be served by an established mail route, which will provide daily communication with the outside.

14. **Service facilities.**—The headquarters should be served by school buses, delivery services, and cream or milk routes.

15. **Erosion control.**—On those farms or ranches in which soil erosion is a problem, it is desirable that the headquarters and fields be located to permit contour farming.

16. **Vegetation.**—Natural shade, trees for windbreaks, and a well-sodded area are valuable attributes.

FARMSTEAD ARRANGEMENT

In planning a new farm or ranch headquarters or in altering an old one, buildings, fences, lots, trees, etc., should be added according to an established master plan; for, once constructed, buildings are difficult and expensive to move. In general, for conservation of space and time, the barn and other service buildings should be located around a central court and should be so arranged that most of them can be seen from the house. In arriving at the best arrangement—which means the location and arrangement of individual buildings within the site—the farmstead cannot and should not be modeled after one popular pattern. Consideration should be given to the following pertinent factors:

1. **The house location comes first.**—As the farm or ranch house is the headquarters or office of the farm business as well as a home, its location is of greatest importance in farmstead arrangement. The ranch house should be located: (a) on a high area which is well drained away from the house and will command a view of other buildings as well as one or more scenic views; (b) where it is easily accessible; (c) in the direction of the prevailing winds but sheltered from strong winds; (d) to obtain the maximum of sunlight in the North and a minimum of sunlight in the South; (e) with access to either the front or back door but with best access to the front door; (f) where there is adequate yard which can be well landscaped; and (g) approximately 150 feet from the road.

2. **Orientation.**—Fortunately, the farm or ranch headquarters need not be oriented with the compass. Although in general the farmstead plan will be developed to present the front to the road, most buildings can be turned, quarter-turned, or reversed, as may be necessary to take advantage of the prevailing winds, sunlight, view, etc. In general, livestock barns are placed with the long axis north and south, whereas, when possible, livestock sheds in northern areas are faced to secure direct sunlight and yet to face away from the direction of the prevailing winds. In the South, sheds are usually oriented for maximum shade and storm protection.

3. **Direction of wind.**—The house should be located on the windward side of the headquarters, with special consideration given to summer winds. Swine barns should be located at the greatest distance from the other farm buildings, especially from the house and dairy barn, and so that the prevailing winds will not blow from the swine barn to the house. Unless hills form a natural windbreak, it is desirable to arrange suitable tree plantings for this purpose. Usually, a tree windbreak is located 75 to 150 feet from the buildings to be protected, with three to seven rows of trees 20 to 75 feet wide.

4. **Efficiency.**—The buildings should be located so as to require a minimum of walking when doing the chores. This means that those buildings in which the most time is spent—such as the dairy barn, poultry house, and machine shop—should be closest to the house and that the buildings should be near enough to gether to permit efficiency of labor without making a fire hazard. Likewise, animal barns should be convenient to feedlots and pastures.

5. **Corrals and lots.**— The buildings and their adjacent corrals and lots should be arranged so that the buildings are accessible without walking through feedlots and corrals.

6. **Fire protection.**—Farm buildings should be far enough apart so that fire

will not spread easily from one building to another. In general, this means at least 100 feet apart in the case of large buildings. In acquiring added fire protection through spacing buildings further apart, one should avoid extreme distances that will mean inefficiency in operation; fire insurance is probably cheaper than labor.

7. **Appearance.**—Careful attention to the headquarters arrangement can add to the attractiveness of the entire unit. Manure piles and unsightly objects should not be visible from the main highway or house; shrubbery and trees should be planted to screen unsightly objects; fences and buildings should be repaired and painted regularly; and yards, driveways, and corrals should be kept free from rubbish, scattered farm machinery, etc.

8. **Gates and lanes.**—The adoption of larger machinery has necessitated wider gates and lanes than have been commonplace in the past. Often the wider lanes can serve as pasture as well as roadway.

REQUISITES OF LIVESTOCK BUILDINGS

Each farm or ranch is different, and the type and size of buildings will vary accordingly. Among the factors determining the type and size of buildings are: (1) kind and fertility of the soil, (2) available markets, (3) size of farm, (4) tenant or owner operation, (5) kind and amount of livestock and crops to be grown, (6) personal preference, (7) climatic conditions of the region, and (8) storage requirements. Thus, the specific requisites of animal buildings will vary according to the needs of the region, state, community, and individual farm or ranch. There are, however, certain general requirements of animal buildings that should always be considered; and it is with these that the ensuing discussion will deal. Once buildings are constructed, there is a definite limit to the changes that can be made in remodeling. Consequently, it is most important that very careful consideration be given to their initial design.

1. **Reasonable construction and maintenance cost.**—The word "reasonable" is used herein, because, as is true in the automobile business, low-cost buildings of durable construction are a thing of the past.

If buildings are to be practical and economical, there must be reasonable construction and maintenance costs. In the first place, they cannot be built if the necessary capital is not available. Secondly, livestock barns and shelters must be paid for out of the enterprises they house, if desirable economic relationships are to be maintained.

In addition to the practical aspects, however, certain intangible values accrue from having good buildings, such as the pride and satisfaction derived in caring for animals under such circumstances, reduced hazards, and, in the case of purebred herds and flocks, the advertising value that accompanies an attractive set of buildings.

2. **Flexible design.**—In order that buildings may be adapted to changes in a changing world, they should be as flexible in design as possible. This needed

flexibility can best be achieved by constructing a one-story building with the maximum of movable partitions and equipment.

At the present time, it is impossible to predict the kind and extent of changes that will come with further mechanization and by such developments as pelleted forages. It is obvious, however, that they will materially affect conventional storage and feeding practices, and that one will not be able to take full advantage of these and other developments unless maximum flexibility in building design exists.

3. **Reduce labor.**—Because of the high cost of labor, now and in the future, labor requirements must be held to a minimum. To this end, and to the extent that it is practical, all possible labor-saving considerations and devices should be a part of building construction.

4. **Utility value.**—Buildings should have utility value; that is, they should be designed so that they will best serve their intended purpose. Generally, it may be said that the chief purpose or function of livestock buildings is to make it possible for animals to convert plants into more nutritious products. They should be constructed with this and other utility purposes in mind. To accomplish this, it is important that the man who is to use the building—the farmer or rancher— have the most to say about the design, provided that the design is well planned.

5. **Provide protection from the elements.**—Livestock barns and shelters should provide protection from rain, snow, sun, and wind. Hogs, dairy cattle, and poultry have less resistance to weather changes than other classes of farm animals. It is important, therefore, that their quarters provide desirable temperature.

6. **Protect newborn animals.**—Young calves, lambs, pigs, and foals are "animal babies" and must be protected as such. Suitable buildings make it possible to save more newborn animals.

7. **Attractiveness.**—Any structure that has utility value and is erected in good proportions and in harmony with the natural surroundings will add to the value of the farm or ranch and the general enjoyment of rural living. Attractive buildings also add materially to the sale value of farm or ranch property.

8. **Durability.**—Livestock barns and shelters should be adequately durable to stand firm against wind and weather and to last for a sufficient span of time without excessive maintenance cost, but they need not be so expensively or permanently constructed that there is danger of their becoming obsolete before being worn out. Thus, it is noteworthy that, with the mechanization of farms and ranches, many a horse barn throughout the country is either idle or has been remodeled, after a fashion, for the storage of the tractor.

Income tax authorities recognize the need for replacing farm buildings with new and modern structures. Thus, a barn depreciated at the rate of 4 per cent annually is entirely written off the books in 25 years.

9. **Dryness.**—Buildings should be constructed to assist in providing a reasonably dry bed for animals. This means that the barn or shelter should be

located on high ground with drainage away from the building and that, except in dry areas, the structure should be provided with eave troughs and down spouts which empty into a tile line draining away from the building. Proper ventilation and direct sunlight also aid materially in providing dry bedding. In open sheds, it is important that there be sufficient depth to assure dryness.

10. **Well ventilated.**—Ventilation refers to the changing of air—the replacement of foul air with fresh air. Livestock barns and shelters should be well ventilated, but care must be taken to avoid direct drafts. Animals cannot do well in poorly ventilated stalls or sheds. If a choice must be made between warmth and ventilation, secure the latter. The primary purposes of ventilation are to remove excess moisture and foul odors. A desirable ventilation system accomplishes these objectives with a minimum temperature variation inside the building.

Ventilation may be secured by various systems. The simplest method usually consists of one or more of the following: (a) open shed, (b) open doors, (c) windows that open inwardly from the top, or (d) building or stall partitions left slatted or open at the top. A more complete method of ventilating tight buildings consists of a system of intake and outtake flues operated on the basis of either gravity or forced ventilation. Whatever the system, proper ventilation is one in which the foul air is drawn off and harmful humidity conditions are eliminated without excess heat loss or creation of drafts.

11. **Well lighted.**—Proper lighting is essential for visibility and the convenience of the caretaker. A well-lighted building may be obtained in the following ways: (a) through an open shed or door arrangement, (b) by providing adequate windows or plastic materials designed to let light through, (c) by artificial lights, or (d) through a combination of the previous three ways as is usually the case.

12. **Direct sunlight.**—Direct sunlight is a good germicide, and arrangements should be made to obtain its benefits. An open shed or door arrangement is the best means of securing direct sunlight.

13. **Sanitary.**—Sanitation is essential for disease prevention and parasite control. This means that livestock barns should be constructed so that they may be easily cleaned, thoroughly disinfected, and free from vermin. Sanitation is also promoted structurally by providing for direct sunlight and elimination of moisture. Smooth walls and hard-surfaced floors are the most satisfactory from this standpoint. It must be recognized, however, that hard-surfaced floors are hard on animals, especially cattle, sheep, and horses.

14. **Easily cleaned.**—A barn or shelter which is arranged so that it may be easily cleaned is more likely to be kept in a sanitary condition. Construction that will permit mechanical manure disposal, in addition to such things as smooth walls and floors, is an asset from the standpoint of ease in cleaning.

15. **Proper provision for manure disposal.**—The manure disposal system should be adapted to the particular conditions. Whatever the method, it should

dispose of the manure efficiently and as intended; and it should make for the maximum degree of sanitation with a minimum amount of odor and flies.

16. **Convenient.**—Livestock buildings should be constructed to furnish the greatest possible convenience, which means fewer steps and man-hours. This means that attention should be given to the most convenient arrangement for feeding, watering, and bedding the animals and for cleaning of barns. Among the most important points to be considered are the locations of the silo, water tanks, feed rooms or bins, hay chutes, driveways, feed alleys, stalls, doors, and windows, and the arrangement for removing manure with a minimum of labor. Greater convenience usually means that one man can and will care for more animals, and this means greater profits. It is significant to note that an hour saved each day is equivalent to eliminating a full month's work in a year.

17. **Adequate space for animals.**—Livestock barns and shelters should be of adequate size to accommodate the existing herds and flocks, expected young stock, and any contemplated early expansion in operations. In general, less space than indicated may jeopardize the health and well-being of animals; whereas more space may make the buildings and equipment more expensive than necessary.

18. **Adequate space for feed and bedding storage.**—In arriving at the space needs for feeds and bedding storage, consideration should be given to: (a) the crop productivity of the farm, (b) the size of animal population to be maintained, (c) the management practices, and (d) the length of the winter feeding period. The proper storage of hay or grain, in a barn that keeps out rain, means more tons of sound, properly cured roughage or grain for feed. See Section III of the Appendix of this book for storage space requirements for feed and bedding.

19. **Multiple use.**—For greater use, buildings should be designed to have multiple usages; that is, to serve more than one type of farm enterprise. Without doubt, this is one of the main reasons why an open shed is so popular; the use of a structure of this type is sufficiently flexible to accommodate cattle, sheep, hogs, or horses, or it may serve for machinery, feed, and bedding storage.

Flexibility of use is especially important on tenant-operated farms. In 1964, 17.1 per cent of U.S. farms were operated by tenants.

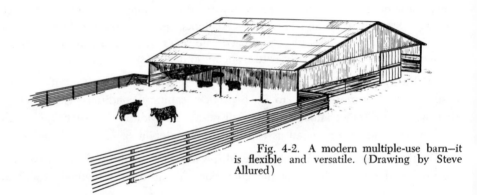

Fig. 4-2. A modern multiple-use barn—it is flexible and versatile. (Drawing by Steve Allured)

20. **Minimum fire risk.**—The principal causes of fire losses in farm buildings are smoking, spontaneous combustion (usually from heat generated by moist hay or forage), lightning, defective flues, sparks on roof, faulty wiring, ignition caused by accidents with equipment, trash fires, gasoline, and matches. The structural safeguards against fire include tile-lined flues, spark arrestors on chimneys, fire-resistant or fire-proof shingles, masonry construction, approved wiring that is inspected at intervals, approved installations of equipment, lightning protection in those areas where thunderstorms are frequent and intense, and "no smoking" signs which are observed. In addition to these precautions, exit doors should be provided so that animals may be removed from the building quickly in case of fire.

21. **Safety.**—In the construction of livestock buildings, it is important that safety features be given consideration. For example, doors and ceilings should have adequate height; doors should be of sufficient width; door sills should be low or omitted; and paved lots should not be dangerously smooth and slick.

22. **Rodent control.**—Livestock barns, and especially the feed storage parts thereof, should be constructed to provide the maximum protection against rats and mice. This is important both from the standpoint of feed conservation and disease prevention. New buildings may be rat proofed as follows:

    a. By installing a concrete curtain wall around the foundation. This prevents rats from burrowing under the buildings.

    b. By using hardware cloth around feed storage bins.

23. **Surrounded by suitable corrals or lots.**—Animal buildings should be provided with adjacent, well-drained, safe, durably fenced, and attractive corrals or lots. In small lots and in muddy areas, pavement is recommended. If the entire corral or lot is not surfaced, it will be helpful at least to pave a strip in front of feed racks and around watering tanks. It is recommended that small corrals or lots be fenced with steel, boards, or poles. For larger yards, heavy wire fencing—sometimes with the wire doubled—and heavy posts set 8 to 10 feet apart may be used. Barbed wire fences are hazardous when used to confine animals in small yards; many an animal has been injured and made useless through such an arrangement.

24. **Near water.**—Water may be piped a considerable distance, but it is important that most barns or shelters either have water in the building or in the lots adjacent thereto. When separate and long pipelines are needed to serve livestock in rotation fields, tank wagons for hauling water may be more economical than pipelines. Water is also important from the standpoint of providing fire protection. For the latter purpose, there should be adequate volume and pressure.

25. **Modify extreme temperatures.**—Good livestock buildings should make for a uniform temperature to provide greater comfort to both man and beast. In order to accomplish this requisite, buildings in northern areas are constructed for warmth in the winter; whereas in the South they are made cool for summer. Fortunately, nature has provided warm coats for most animals, and it is not

necessary that they have exceedingly warm buildings, although such shelter is needed for the newborn offspring. In no case should warmth of a building be obtained at the cost of poor ventilation.

26. **Keep proper humidity.**—Humidity refers to the amount of moisture in the air. The air inside animal buildings picks up moisture from respiration and excrement. When the humidity of a building is high, the evaporation from the surface of the body practically ceases. This causes a sensation of warmth in the summer and coldness in the winter. When there is a difference of several degrees between inside and outside temperatures, the moisture condenses on the cold surfaces. In freezing weather, this condensation forms frost. Condensation on the walls or other surfaces is evidence of unsatisfactory moisture conditions. Such condensation is objectionable because it is harmful for animals to go from a moist, warm barn into the cold outside air and because the excess moisture causes the structure to decay or deteriorate.

Experimental studies indicate that a 1,000-pound cow breathes into the air approximately 10 pounds of moisture per day. Thus, from a herd of 42 cows there would be given off 420 pounds or about 50 gallons of water per day. This amount of moisture must be removed daily in order to keep the barn free from dampness, thus necessitating proper ventilation.

Strawlofts in sheds or one-story barns and haymows in two-story barns reduce moisture condensation and frosting on the ceiling.

27. **Properly insulated.**—Proper insulation, which slows up the passage of heat, is desirable in the summer as well as in the winter. In the winter, it helps to hold the heat within the building, while in the summer it tends to prevent the heat from entering the structure.

28. **Adapted to present and future needs.**—In building a livestock barn or shelter, the farmer or rancher should give consideration to present needs and future plans, the present and potential production, and the various uses for which the barn is needed now and in the future. Thus, in constructing a barn, it is desirable that it be of a size that will meet the existing conditions and be so built as to permit the erection of additions without disturbing the convenient arrangement or without tearing down any part of the structure.

29. **Protect animal health.**—Animal barns and shelters should provide healthful indoor living conditions for the occupants. This is most important, for healthy animals are the profitable and efficient ones.

Confinement; Environmental Control

Confinement refers to limited quarters, with or without shelter. Where there is shelter, it may range all the way from an open shed to a completely enclosed building with air circulation and temperature, humidity, and light control—known as environmental control.

Environmental-controlled buildings are costly to construct, but they lend themselves to automation and make for the ultimate in animal comfort and health and efficiency of feed utilization. Today, environmental control is rather

Fig. 4-3. Environmental-controlled dairy barn in Wisconsin; well insulated and ventilated (note fan). Also, note (1) automatic feed auger at top of rack for conveying chopped hay and silage, (2) automatic waterer at end of feed rack, and (3) curb along rack to encourage cows to stay near feed bunk while eating. (Courtesy, Babson Bros. Co., Chicago, Ill.)

common in poultry and swine housing, and it is on the increase with other classes of livestock.

REQUISITES OF LIVESTOCK EQUIPMENT

Generally speaking, livestock equipment refers to structures other than barns or shelters used in the care and management of animals. Much of this equipment is portable.

The size and design of livestock equipment may differ; that is, not all hayracks or self-feeders, for example, are the same. Yet there are certain fundamentals of livestock equipment that are similar regardless of the kind of equipment, the design, or the size. These requisites are:

1. **Utility value.**—Equipment should be useful, practical, and efficient.

2. **Simple construction.**—As most livestock equipment is home-made, simple construction is essential.

3. **Durable.**—Livestock equipment receives rough use. Thus, it should be strongly and durably built.

4. **Dependable.**—Livestock equipment should be dependable, so that it will function without getting out of order.

5. **Low initial cost and upkeep.**—Like animal barns and shelters, livestock equipment must be paid for out of animal profits. It is important, therefore, that it have a low initial and upkeep cost.

6. **Movable.**—Equipment that is used away from buildings should be movable. Bunks, racks, and self-feeders should be built on skids so that they may be moved from one location to another.

7. **Accessible.**—Stationary or less-portable equipment, such as stocks and dipping vats, should be readily accessible.

8. **Save feed.**—Much grain and hay may be saved when fed in properly constructed equipment. When such equipment is used, animals clean up grain and hay and do not throw or root it out of the feeder.

9. **Reduce labor.**—Modern equipment, such as large self-feeders and large hayracks that require infrequent filling, reduces the labor required in feeding operations.

10. **Conserve manure.**—Feeding equipment may be either located in the barn or feed yard from whence the accumulated manure is hauled directly to the fields or is placed in the manure pit. Or, by carefully moving the feeding facilities about in the fields, the fertility may be scattered where it is most needed.

Automation

Automation is a coined word meaning the mechanical handling of materials. Stockmen automate to lessen labor and cut costs.

Fig. 4-4. Silage being fed by a self-unloading box. (Courtesy, Gehl Bros. Manufacturing Co., West Bend, Wisc.)

Fig. 4-5. Broilers with automatic feed and water. (J. C. Allen and Son photo)

Modern equipment has practically eliminated the pitch fork, bucket, and basket. Such chores as feeding, watering, bedding, and barn cleaning have been, or are being, mechanized. Stockmen are using more self-unloading trucks and trailers, self-feeders, feed bunk augers and belts, labor-saving grain and forage processing equipment (pellets, cubes, or wafers, etc.), automatic waterers, and manure disposal units. Automation of the livestock industry will increase.

SPACE REQUIREMENTS OF BUILDINGS AND EQUIPMENT

One of the first and frequently one of the most difficult problems confronting the farmer or rancher who wishes to construct a building or item of equipment is that of arriving at the proper size or dimensions. In general, less space than indicated in the sections which follow may jeopardize the health and well-being of animals, whereas more space may make the buildings and equipment more expensive than necessary.

Recommended Minimum Width for Service Passages

In general, the requirements for service passages are similar, regardless of the kind of animals. Accordingly, the suggestions contained in Table 4-1 are equally applicable to beef and dairy cattle, sheep, swine, and poultry, and horse facilities.

TABLE 4—1

RECOMMENDED MINIMUM WIDTHS FOR SERVICE PASSAGES

Kind of Passage	Use	Minimum Width
Feed alley............................	for feed cart	4'-0"
Driveway.............................	for wagon, spreader, or truck	9'-0"
Doors and gate......................	drive-through	9'-0"
Doors and gate......................	to small pens	4'-0"

Storage Space Requirements for Feed and Bedding

The space requirements for feed storage for the livestock enterprise vary so widely that it is difficult to provide a suggested method of calculating space requirements applicable to such diverse conditions. The amount of feed to be stored depends primarily upon: (1) length of pasture season, (2) method of feeding and management, (3) kind of feed, (4) climate, and (5) the proportion of feeds produced on the farm or ranch in comparison with those purchased. Normally, the storage capacity should be sufficient to handle all feed grain and silage grown on the farm and to hold purchased supplies. Forage and bedding may or may not be stored under cover. In those areas where weather conditions permit, hay and straw are frequently stacked in the fields or near the barns in loose, baled, or chopped form. Sometimes, poled framed sheds or a cheap cover of waterproof paper or wild grass is used for protection. Other forms of low-cost storage include temporary upright silos, trench silos, and temporary grain bins.

Section III in the Appendix of this book gives the storage space requirements for feed and bedding. This information may be helpful to the individual operator who desires to compute the barn space required for a specific livestock enterprise. This table also provides a convenient means of estimating the amount of feed or bedding in storage.

TYPES OF BARN ROOFS

Figure 4-6 illustrates various roof shapes. The shape, style, slope, and type of roof construction selected should be based upon the function to be served, the economy of construction, strength, and appearance.

On permanent buildings, the roofing should last 15 to 20 years without replacement. Among the more durable roofings are: cedar shingles; cement-asbestos shingles; 250-pound asphalt shingles; 28-gauge, 2-ounce coated steel sheets; and aluminum.

TYPES OF FLOORS FOR STALLS OR STABLES

Solid floors for animals may be and are constructed of numerous materials—including clay, clay with a concrete border, plank, concrete, concrete with board surfacing, cork brick, creosoted wooden blocks, cinders, or various com-

Barn Roofs

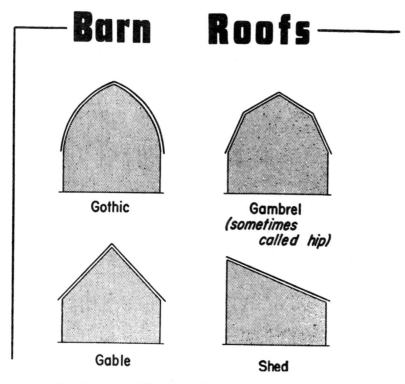

Gothic

Gambrel
(sometimes
called hip)

Gable

Shed

Fig. 4-6. Types of barn roofs. (Drawing by R. F. Johnson)

binations of these materials. Regardless of the type of flooring material, for a good dry bed there should be a combination of surface and subsurface drainage together with a cover provided by a suitable absorbent litter.

Most stockmen feel that a perfect flooring material has not yet been developed, as each of the existing types has certain disadvantages. Rough wooden floors furnish good traction for animals and are warm to lie upon; but they are absorbent and unsanitary. They also lack durability and often harbor rats and other rodents. Concrete floors are durable, impervious, easily drained, and sanitary; but they are rigid and without resilient qualities, are slippery when wet, and are cold to lie upon. Clay floors are noiseless, springy; and they afford a firm natural footing unless wet, but they are difficult to keep clean and level. After considering both the advantages and disadvantages of the many types of flooring materials, most practical stockmen are agreed that, under average conditions and where solid floor is desired, concrete is the most satisfactory flooring for central hog houses and poultry houses and that clay is the most satisfactory flooring for cattle, sheep, and horse barns or shelters.

Slotted Floors

Slotted floors are floors with slots through which the feces and urine pass to a storage area below or nearby. Such floors are not new; they have been used

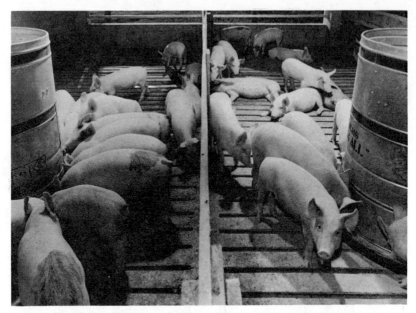

Fig. 4-7. Pigs in confinement on slotted floors. (J. C. Allen and Son photo)

Fig. 4-8. Layers on slotted floor. (J. C. Allen and Son photo)

in Europe for over 200 years. More and more slotted floors are being used for swine and poultry in this country, and there is increased interest in using them for sheep and cattle.

The main **advantages** of slotted floors are: (1) less space per animal is needed, (2) bedding is eliminated, (3) manure handling is reduced, (4) increased sanitation, and (5) saving in labor.

The chief **disadvantages** of slotted floors are: (1) higher initial cost than conventional solid floors, (2) less flexibility in the use of the building, (3) any spilled feed is lost through the slots, (4) animals raised on slotted floors resist being driven over a solid floor, and (5) environmental conditions become more critical.

PAVED LOTS AND FEEDING FLOORS

In those areas in which barnyard mud is a usual winter problem, a concrete lot floor for beef and dairy cattle, hogs, and sheep may constitute one of the most profitable improvements. A properly constructed paved feedlot results in: (1) a saving in time and labor; (2) less waste in feed and bedding, especially when hogs follow cattle; (3) greater conservation of manure; (4) greater sanitation and fewer diseases; and (5) more animal comfort, which means greater gains and production. Corn Belt cattle feeders generally figure that paving for a six-months' period of winter and spring feeding pays for itself at the rate of $5.00 per steer. This is the saving computed on the cattle and hogs running with them and does not include the greater recovery of manure.

Fig. 4-9. A paved corral lot used for finishing steers on the Frandsen Farm, Story City, Iowa. Note that the cattle are clean and free from mud and manure. (Courtesy, Dale Woolsoncroft, Iowa State University, and the Portland Cement Association)

The paved feedlot should be located where it will make for convenience in feeding and watering operations and will be sheltered from the prevailing winds and exposed to the sun. In most areas, these conditions are met by locating the paved lot adjacent to the building housing the animals and on the south or east side thereof.

Concrete feeding floors for hogs should be about 4 inches thick; for cattle, 5 inches. Subsurface drainage can be assured and proper footing obtained by placing the concrete slab on a well-tamped fill consisting of 3 to 6 inches of fine stone, gravel, or cinders. Adequate surface drainage may be provided by sloping the floor about ¼ inch per foot. In order to provide for expansion and contraction, the floor should be formed in sections about 10 feet square. An apron or cutoff wall should be added to prevent undermining of the floor. A low curb around the edge of the paving will also hold the manure; but some openings should be left to let rain water escape. The floor should be finished with a wood float or broom, leaving an even, yet gritty, nonslip surface. The size of the paved lot will depend upon the class and number of animals kept and on management practices. Some stockmen also prefer to have a part of the lot unpaved to permit the animals to loiter on bare ground during dry weather. The latter point is of special importance to purebred breeders; for it is recognized that a long stay on a hard-surfaced floor may make for crooked legs on young animals.

Hard-surfaced lots may be constructed with crushed limestone, gravel, paving brick, or concrete. Although concrete is the most costly, it is also the most permanent and satisfactory—all factors considered.

Properly constructed paved lots or floors are easy to clean, and the manure is not trampled into the mud. It may be scooped up with a shovel or manure loader. On large floors, cleaning is facilitated by first bunching the refuse with a tractor equipped with a blade.

THE SILO

The first silo built by white man in the United States is said to have been erected by F. Morris in Maryland in 1876. But Columbus found that the Indians used pits or trenches in which to store their grain, and centuries earlier in the Old World silos were used as a means of preserving both grain and green forage.

The value and use of silage in feeding the respective classes of livestock are fully covered in the chapters on feeding. The ensuing discussion will be devoted to a discussion of types and requisites of silos—especially from structural and utility standpoints.

Types of Silos

The general kinds of silos are: tower silos, pit silos, trench silos, self-feeder or bunker silos, aboveground temporary silos, and plastic silos. The kind of silo decided upon and the choice of construction material should be determined primarily by the cost and by the suitability to the particular needs of the farm or ranch.

Some pertinent information relative to each kind of silo is given in the discussion which follows, but it is not within the intent of this book to give

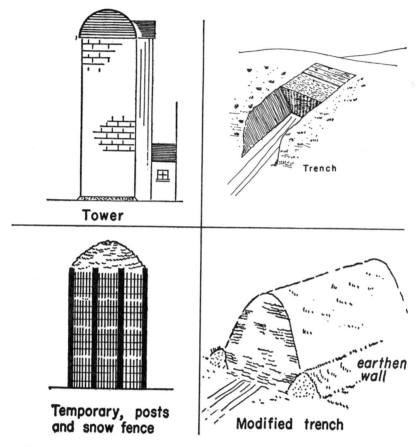

Fig. 4-10. Four kinds of silos: (1) tower silo (upper left), (2) trench silo (upper right), (3) enclosed stack silo (lower left), and (4) modified trench-stack silo (lower right). The latter two are aboveground temporary silos. (Drawing by R. F. Johnson)

detailed silo plans and specifications. The latter may be obtained from local authorities, from silo manufacturers, or by writing to the state agricultural college.

TOWER SILO

The tower silo, which is sometimes referred to as the "watch-tower of prosperity," is a cylinder built aboveground. Its round shape withstands pressure well and is adapted to good packing.

The tower silo is a permanent farm structure and, as such, should be constructed to withstand long usage. Among the materials used are concrete, brick, tile, stone, metal, and wood. Although tower silos are usually both durable and handy, they are the most expensive of all types.

PIT SILO

The pit silo is shaped like the tower silo, but inverted into the ground. It resembles a well or cistern. The walls of a pit silo may or may not be lined. Where the water table is low enough that the silo will not fill with water, such as in semi-arid areas, the pit silo is very satisfactory.

In comparison with tower silos, pit silos have the following advantages: (1) they are never damaged by storm or fire, (2) they require less reinforcing, (3) they minimize silage losses because of not having doors, and (4) they avoid frozen silage. But they have the following disadvantages: (1) they are dangerous, due to the frequent presence of suffocating carbon dioxide gas and (2) considerable work is involved in removing the silage, despite the development of a number of hoist devices.

Before entering a pit silo, it is recommended that a lighted cigarette lighter, candle, or lantern be lowered into the silo. If the flame goes out, assume that the pit is dangerous to enter and replenish it with fresh air before entering.

TRENCH SILO

The trench silo is a trench-like structure that can be built quickly and at low cost. It is the most popular in areas where the weather is not too severe and where there is good drainage. The walls of a trench silo may or may not be lined, but for the making of good silage they should always be smooth. A trench silo should be wider at the top than at the bottom, and the bottom should slope away from one end in order that excess juices will drain off.

The trench silo has the advantages of: (1) low initial cost, (2) low cost of filling machinery, for a blower is not necessary, (3) relative freedom from freezing, and (4) ease of construction. The chief disadvantage of the trench silo in comparison with the tower silo is the larger area to seal to prevent spoilage. Because of shallowness, the forage should be packed very thoroughly in a trench silo by driving a tractor or team of horses back and forth over it. When filling is completed, the top should be carefully sealed (1) by 3 to 12 inches of dirt, with or without a seeding of rye or winter wheat, (2) by wet straw, poor-quality hay, marsh grass, or sawdust, (3) by a mixture of dirt and straw, (4) by a waterproof paper lapped about 12 inches at the joints and covered with dirt or straw, or (5) by plastic, aluminum, or other materials.

SELF-FEEDER OR BUNKER SILO

As a labor-saving measure, some operators are now constructing silos aboveground (or slightly recessed)—usually with concrete floors, and side walls of wood, concrete, or other materials—and self-feeding silage to cattle by making use of a portable hurdle or fence.

In this method, the fence (or gate or hurdle or stanchion) through which the animals put their heads, is placed at the end (or side) of the silo and moved back as the silage is eaten. Feed wastes are reduced if the bottom section of the gate or hurdle is solid and the top slopes away from the silo (about 7½ inches out at the top, on gates 5 feet high), so that the animals are forced to eat down toward the bottom of the stack.

Most of those who have used bunker silos successfully, recommend the following:

1. That there be about 6 inches of space per cow.

2. That the silage not be piled higher than 6 feet.

3. That the silage be loosened in front of the rack.

4. That manure be removed from the feeding area at intervals of 7 to 14 days in order to facilitate drainage.

ABOVEGROUND TEMPORARY SILOS

Several kinds of aboveground temporary silos are used. Generally, this kind of storage is used to meet emergencies, to supplement permanent silos, or to ensile such by-product feeds as cannery refuse, pea vines, and beet tops or pulp. Aboveground temporary silos are low in cost, can be erected at short notice, require no special foundation, and can be set up on almost any site convenient for filling and feeding.

The amount of spoilage in aboveground temporary silos can be kept to a minimum by having straight sides, considerable height, proper packing, and protection with fiber-reinforced paper or other suitable material. The spoilage on the sides will vary from 4 to 20 inches, with greater spoilage in grass silage than in easier-keeping corn or sorghum silage.

Perhaps most aboveground temporary silos can be classed as belonging to one of the following three kinds:

1. **The enclosed stack.**—These are built entirely aboveground, without trenches or holes. They are upright, are generally circular, and are enclosed by snow or picket fences, poles, wooden staves, heavy woven wire, or other materials. Most of them are lined with tar paper or tough fiber-reinforced paper made especially for the purpose. Because of the relatively weak walls of these silos, their height should not be greater than twice their diameter unless poles are set at four to six points around their circumference and tied together at the top.

2. **The open stack.**—These are similar to enclosed stack silos, except that no supports or walls are used. As would be expected, greater spoilage is encountered in the open stack than in the enclosed stack, because of the greater evaporation and spoilage which accompanies the exposed sides.

3. **The modified trench-stack silo.**—This silo, which is intermediate between a trench and a stack silo, is adapted to areas where the ground-water level is high. It is constructed by excavating a shallow trench 12 to 18 inches deep, by piling the excavated earth on either side of the trench to support the silage and to keep out surface water, by packing silage thoroughly in and over the

trench to a height of 10 to 15 feet, and by covering the stack with any one of the materials recommended for covering a trench silo (see "Trench Silo"). The modified trench-stack silo is designed to give greater protection and less spoilage than can be accomplished by open stacks. Also, this type of silo is easier to feed out of than a trench silo.

PLASTIC SILOS

Plastics for trench and stack silo covers are now on the market. The material is fitted over the silage, and a seal is effected (in a trench silo, by burying the outside edges of the plastic in dirt to a depth of about 12 inches; in a stack silo, by tying at the top). Also, a patented, vacuum-sealed plastic is on the market.

Among the special advantages attributed to plastic silos are: (1) economy (a cost of less than $1.00 per ton of silage) where a permanent silo is not

Fig. 4-11. Automatic gutter cleaner at swine barn of Hunter Bros. Farm, Brook, Indiana. This type of equipment offers a way of eliminating much of the hand labor in stanchioned dairy barns and in swine barns. (Courtesy, James Mfg. Co.)

desired, (2) adaptation to small quantities of silage and for out-of-the-way places, and (3) reduction of spoilage to less than 5 per cent. But there is a disadvantage: present plastic materials are very susceptible to puncture by sharp objects (fingernails, plant stems, implements, etc.).

Gases begin collecting in a plastic silo immediately upon sealing, with the bag reaching its maximum extension in 36 hours.

MANURE HANDLING

Until recent years, the use of manure was considered the logical and economical way for a stockman to make and keep his soil productive; many farmers and ranchers "fed livestock so that the animals could produce manure, so that they could grow more grain to feed more livestock, to produce more manure." But times have changed! The use of commercial fertilizers has expanded manyfold; labor costs have risen to the point where it may be uneconomical to conserve and spread manure on the land; and more animals are being raised in confinement, thus producing more manure. As a result, the choice of a method of handling manure has become a major question mark on many livestock establishments. Should it be conserved and applied to the land, or should it be disposed of in the cheapest manner possible, without any attempt to make use of its fertility value?

Fig. 4-12. Farm scales take the "guess" out of many farm and ranch operations. Where it is not convenient or practical to weigh, often reasonably accurate estimates can be calculated from certain measures. (Courtesy, Swift & Company)

Where field spreading is not possible or practical, complete disposal through the use of lagoons and septic tanks, or a combination of the two, is receiving increased attention.

Where manure is put back on the land, automation is being applied to obtain (1) saving of labor, (2) expediency, and (3) a minimum loss of nutrients.

SCALES

Scales are a valuable piece of equipment for the modern stock farm or ranch; for they make it possible to determine weights of animals on production testing studies, to secure the accurate rate of gains of animals being finished, to sell animals on the farm or ranch on a weight basis, and to buy and sell feed on a weight basis. For greatest usefulness, scales should be so arranged that a pen may be set up quickly when weighing mature animals or may be removed when weighing feed.

A convenient place for the farm scales is in the farm court, next to the

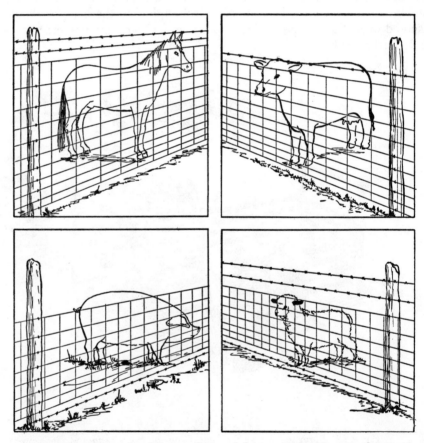

Fig. 4-13. Fences for different classes of farm animals. (Drawing by Steve Allured)

corrals or feedlot. In this location, the scale is convenient for weighing livestock or loads of feed and supplies.

FENCES FOR LIVESTOCK

Good fences (1) maintain farm boundaries, (2) make livestock operations possible, (3) reduce losses of both animals and crops, (4) increase land values, (5) promote better relationships between neighbors, (6) lessen accidents from animals getting on roads, and (7) add to the attractiveness and distinctiveness of the premises.

Wire is the leading fence material, although such materials as steel, poles, boards, stone, and hedge have a place and are used under certain circumstances.

PAINT FOR BUILDINGS AND EQUIPMENT

The chief purposes of painting farm buildings and equipment are: (1) to preserve them from the effects of the weather and (2) to add to their attractiveness. In addition, interior painting, such as is done in most homes, makes walls and ceilings more sanitary and dark rooms lighter.

QUESTIONS FOR STUDY AND DISCUSSION

1. One of the first and frequently one of the most difficult problems confronting the stockman who wishes to construct a building or item of equipment is that of arriving at the proper size or dimensions. In planning to construct new buildings and equipment for beef cattle, for example, what factors and measurements for buildings and equipment must be considered?

2. List and discuss the factors determining the type and size of farm buildings.

3. List and discuss the steps in determining the size barn to build on any given farm or ranch.

4. List and discuss the steps in determining the size silo to build on any given farm or ranch.

5. List and discuss the needed and desirable features of a modern multiple-use barn such as shown in Figure 4-2.

6. In the selection of woven wire fence, what is meant by the following number: 1155? What other factors should be considered in the selection of woven wire? What specifications may be used in ordering barbed wire?

SELECTED REFERENCES

Title of Publication	Author(s)	Publisher
Automatic Livestock Waterers	Leaflet 395	U.S. Department of Agriculture, Washington, D. C.
Doane Ideas on Farm Buildings		Doane Agricultural Service, Inc., 5144 Delmar Blvd., St. Louis, Mo.
Farm Book, The		Doane Agricultural Digest, 5144 Delmar Blvd., St. Louis, Mo.
Farm Buildings	D. G. Carter W. A. Foster	John Wiley & Sons, New York, N. Y., 1947.
Farm Buildings	J. C. Wooley	McGraw-Hill Book Co., New York, N. Y., 1946.

Title of Publication	Author(s)	Publisher
Farm Building Design	L. W. Neubauer H. B. Walker	Prentice-Hall, Inc., Englewood Cliffs, N. J., 1961.
Farm Service Buildings	H. E. Gray	McGraw-Hill Book Co., New York, N. Y., 1955.
Farm Structures	H. J. Barre L. L. Sammet	John Wiley & Sons, Inc., New York, N. Y., 1950.
Plans of Farm Buildings for Southern States	Misc. Publication No. 360	U.S. Department of Agriculture, Washington, D. C.
Plans of Farm Buildings for Western States	Misc. Publication No. 319	U.S. Department of Agriculture, Washington, D. C.
Stockman's Handbook, The	M. E. Ensminger	Interstate Printers & Publishers, Inc.. Danville, Illinois., 1969.

Chapter V

ANIMAL HEALTH, DISEASE PREVENTION, AND PARASITE CONTROL[1]

Contents | Page
Signs of Good Health...........192
Animal Disease...........194
Causes of Disease...........195
   Bacteria...........195
   Viruses...........196
   Parasites...........196
   Poisonous Plants...........198
Animal Health...........201
   Immunity...........202
   Vaccination...........202
   Biologics...........203
      Vaccines...........204
      Bacterins...........205
      Serums...........205
      Toxoids (or Antitoxins)...........205
   Other Artificial Protective Mechanisms Against Disease...........205
   Diagnostic Agents...........206
   Drugs...........206
General Animal Sanitation and Disease Prevention...........206
   Ventilation...........207
   Housing...........207
   Adequate Manure Disposal...........208
   Pasture Rotation...........209
   Carcass Disposal...........209
   Disinfectants and Their Use...........210
Regulations Relative to Disease Control...........214
   Animal Disease Eradication Division, Agricultural Research Service...........214
   State Veterinarians, Sanitary Commissions, and Boards...........214
   Quarantine...........214
   Stockyards Inspection...........215
   Meat Inspection...........215
   Biologic Standardizing...........215
   Indemnity Payments in Disease Eradication...........216
Glossary of Animal Health Terms...........216
Questions for Study and Discussion...........218
Selected References...........219

In the natural state, animals roved over the broad prairies or through virgin forests, gleaned the feeds provided by nature, and bedded down on new sites each night. Finally, as civilization advanced and herds and flocks increased in size, animals were placed in restricted areas. Simultaneously, they were bred and fed for greater production of meat, milk, eggs, fiber, or for power and speed. Under unnatural conditions of close confinement, greater numbers, forced

[1]In the preparation of this chapter, the co-authorship of Dr. Robert F. Behlow, D.V.M., Professor and Extension Veterinarian, North Carolina State University, Raleigh, is gratefully acknowledged.

production, and eating and sleeping in close contact with their own body discharges, the control of diseases and parasites became of paramount importance.

Each year, many American farmers and ranchers, from one end of the country to the other, are robbed of their profits in livestock production—robbed by diseases and parasites. Death losses take a tremendous toll, but even greater economic losses result from the decreased growth, gains, or production among the living—from the increased production costs of meat, milk, eggs, wool, and power. It has been conservatively estimated that the annual United States losses from the more important diseases, parasites, and pests of livestock and poultry aggregate nearly $2.8 billion, with a breakdown as follows:[2]

Infectious and non-infectious diseases	$1,569,358
Internal parasites	340,206
Insects	877,850
Total	$2,787,414

It is hoped that the information presented in this chapter will be of special value in assisting stockmen in the prevention of diseases and parasites. Although final diagnosis of disease and prescribed treatment should be left in the hands of a veterinarian, a well-enlightened producer will: (1) be in a better position to institute a program designed to assure herd health, (2) more readily recognize any serious outbreak of disease and promptly call a veterinarian, (3) prevent unnecessary suffering of sick animals, (4) be better qualified to assist the veterinarian in administering treatment, and (5) be more competent in carrying out a program designed to bring the disease under control with a minimum spread of the infection.

SIGNS OF GOOD HEALTH

In order that stockmen may know when animal disease strikes, they must first know the signs of good health; any departure from which constitutes a warning of trouble. Some of the signs of good health are:

1. **Contentment.**—Healthy animals appear contented; the cow will stretch on rising, the sheep will stand or lie quietly, the pig will curl his tail, and the horse will look completely unworried when resting.

2. **Alertness.**—Healthy animals are alert and bright-eyed and will prick their ears up on the slightest provocation.

3. **Eating with relish, and cudding by ruminants.**—In healthy animals, the appetite is good and the feed is attacked with relish (as indicated by eagerness to get to the trough, wagging the tail, etc.). In cattle and sheep, cudding is a sure sign of good health, and is one of the first things to disappear in sickness.

---

[2] *Losses in Agriculture,* Agriculture Handbook No. 291, 1965, Pub. by Agricultural Research Service, USDA, Tables 26-32.

4. **Sleek coat and pliable and elastic skin.**—A sleek, oily coat and a pliable and elastic skin characterize healthy animals. When the hair coat loses its luster and the skin becomes dry, scurfy, and hide-bound, there is usually trouble.

5. **Bright eyes and pink eye membranes.**—In healthy animals, the eyes are bright and the membranes—which can be seen when the lower lid is pulled down—are pink in color and moist.

6. **Normal feces and urine.**—The consistency of the feces varies with the diet; for example, when animals are first turned on lush grass they will be loose. Also, the consistency and dryness of the feces vary between species, but they should be firm and not dry. And there should not be large quantities of undigested feed. The urine should be clear. Both the feces and urine should be passed without effort, and should be free from blood, mucus, or pus.

7. **Normal temperature, pulse rate, and breathing rate.**—Table 5-1 gives the normal temperature, pulse rate, and breathing rate of farm animals. In general, any marked and persistent deviations from these normals may be looked upon as a sign of animal ill-health.

TABLE 5—1

NORMAL TEMPERATURE, PULSE RATE, AND BREATHING
RATE OF FARM ANIMALS

Animal	Normal Rectal Temperature		Normal Pulse Rate	Normal Breathing Rate
	Average	Range		
	(degrees F.)	(degrees F.)	(rate/min.)	(rate/min.)
Cattle	101.5	100.4-102.8	60-70	10-30
Sheep	102.3	100.9-103.8	70-80	12-20
Goats	103.8	101.7-105.3	70-80	12-20
Swine	102.6	102.0-103.6	60-80	8-13
Horses	100.5	99.0-100.8	32-44	8-16
Poultry	106.0	105.0-107.0	200-400	15-36

Every stockman should provide himself with an animal thermometer, which is heavier and more rugged than the ordinary human thermometer. The temperature is measured by inserting the thermometer full length in the rectum, where it should be left a minimum of three minutes. Prior to inserting the thermometer, a long string should be tied to the end.

In general, infectious diseases are ushered in with a rise in body temperature, but it must be remembered that body temperature is affected by stable or outside temperature, exercise, excitement, age, feed, etc. It is lower in cold weather, in older animals, and at night.

The pulse rate indicates the rapidity of the heart action. The pulse of different farm animals is taken at the following body areas: Cattle, either on the outside of the jaw just above its lower border, on the soft place immediately above the inner dewclaw, or just above the hock joint; sheep and swine, on the inside of the thigh where the femoral artery comes in close proximity to the skin; and horse, either at the margin of the jaw where an artery winds around from the inner side, at the inside of the elbow, or under the tail. It should be remembered that the younger, the smaller, and the more nervous the animal, the higher the pulse rate. Also, the pulse rate increases with exercise, excitement, digestion, and high outside temperature.

The breathing rate can be determined by placing the hand on the flank, by observing the rise and fall of the flanks, or, in the winter, by watching the breath condensate in coming from the nostrils. Rapid breathing due to recent exercise, excitement, hot weather, or stuffy buildings should not be confused with disease. Respiration is accelerated in pain and in febrile conditions.

ANIMAL DISEASE

In general, *disease is defined as any departure from the state of health*. Beyond a doubt, the most serious menace threatening the livestock industry is animal ill-health. There are many degrees of ill-health, but by far the largest loss is a result of the diseases that are due to a common factor transmitted from animal to animal. These disorders are classed as infectious, contagious, and parasitic diseases and are considered theoretically controllable. Today, with the modern rapid transportation facilities and the dense livestock population centers, the opportunity for animals to become infected are greatly increased compared with a generation ago.

Few people realize the extent of losses caused by diseases and parasites. One is inclined to consider only those costs due to death or depreciation, but actual animal disease losses are far more extensive. For example, considerable cost is involved in keeping out diseases that do not exist in the United States. To the latter end, during the period 1946 to 1954, the United States spent $127 million in trying to eradicate foot-and-mouth disease in Mexico. Also, quarantine of a diseased area may cause depreciation of land values, or may even restrict whole agricultural programs.

The fact that many animal diseases are transmissible to man is well known, and, as a result, the ever-present human danger adds to the economic loss. Approximately 90 different types of infectious and parasitic diseases can be spread from animals to human beings.[3] Of most concern in this respect are such animal diseases as brucellosis (undulant fever), anthrax, Q fever, rabies, trichinosis, tuberculosis, and tularemia. Rigid meat and milk inspection is necessary for the protection of human health.

Although it is difficult to estimate the actual death loss due to parasites, it is even more difficult to make a proper appraisal of the losses due to unthriftiness and stunting that invariably result from parasitic invasions.

Despite all of these disturbing factors, it is satisfying to know that the United States is regarded as the safest country in the world for a flourishing livestock industry. In order to insure further progress, however, thousands of

---

[3] Table 67 of the fourth edition of *Diseases Transmitted from Animals to Man*, by Dr. Thomas G. Hull, published by Charles C Thomas, Springfield, Illinois, lists 92 diseases which animals transmit to man.

workers—including scientists with the U.S. Department of Agriculture, colleges, pharmaceutical houses, practicing veterinarians, and others—are constantly striving to make this country even healthier for both man and beast.

Causes of Disease

Any agent that may bring about an abnormal condition of any or all tissues of the body is a disease-producing entity. Among the chief causes may be listed infectious agents, such as bacteria, viruses, and parasites; and noninfectious agents, including chemicals, poisons of various types, faulty nutrition, and injuries. In addition to the actual causative agents, any of the following conditions may predispose disease: overwork, exposure to cold, and long shipments—especially in cold weather. The present discussion will be limited to bacteria, viruses, parasites, and poisonous plants—the other causative agents being covered elsewhere; for example, nutritional diseases and ailments are included in the chapter devoted to feeding livestock (Chapter III).

The activity of disease in the animal body results in a change in the tissues invaded. It is usually marked by inflammation, which is manifested by increased blood supply to the part affected and by heat, redness, swelling, and pain in the affected part.

Diseases are often named after the part affected with the suffix "itis" (meaning inflammation) attached—for example, conjunctivitis (inflammation of the conjunctiva of the eye) or enteritis (inflammation of the intestines, or entrails).

The infection of a tissue and the production of a disease by a living agent is not always easily accomplished. The agent must first gain entrance to the animal by one of the body openings (respiratory, digestive, or genital tract) or through the skin. It then usually multiplies and attacks the tissues. To accomplish this, it must be sufficiently powerful (virulent) to overcome the defenses of the animal body. The defenses of the animal body vary and may be weak or entirely lacking, especially under conditions of a low nutritional plane and poor management practices.

BACTERIA

Bacteria are one of the smallest and simplest known forms of plant life. They possess just one cell, vary in size and shape, multiply by transverse fission, and possess no chlorophyll. Bacteria are exceedingly numerous in nature, and the majority of them are beneficial; for example, those that create the fermentation processes used in the manufacture of vinegar and the ripening of cheese. The few that cause disease are referred to as pathogens.

Bacteria are classified by various distinguishing features. In shapes, they are either rods (bacilli), spheres (cocci), or spirals (spirilla). Some bacteria will grow only on special types of media in varying amounts of oxygen. Some are motile, whereas others lack the power of locomotion. Then there are those bacteria that under certain conditions form spores that are highly resistant to destruction and may live for years. Some also possess the ability to elaborate toxic products within themselves or in the media in which they grow, as does, for example, the fatal and relatively common toxin which causes botulism poisoning.

VIRUSES

Viruses may be defined as disease-producing agents that (1) are so small that they cannot be seen through an ordinary microscope (they can be seen by using an electron miscroscope), (2) are capable of passing through the pores of special filters which retain ordinary bacteria, and (3) propagate only in living tissue. They are generally classified according to the tissues they invade, although this is a very arbitrary method, as some viruses invade many tissues.

Viruses cause over 30 diseases of animals, including foot-and-mouth disease, hog cholera, rabies, and equine sleeping sickness—all of which are highly contagious. Virus diseases are often complicated by the presence of secondary bacterial invaders. In some cases, a virus is unable to produce a disease in the absence of so-called secondary bacteria; for example, as in swine influenza.

PARASITES

Broadly speaking, parasites are organisms living in, on, or at the expense of another living organism. They include fungi, protozoa (or unicellular animals), arthropods (or insects, ticks, and related forms), and helminths (or worms). Bacteria come under this definition, but are being eliminated here since they already have been discussed.

Any animal that serves as a residence for a parasite is referred to as a host. In order to complete their life span (cycle), some parasites require only one host while others need more.

While in residence, parasites usually seriously affect the host, but there are notable exceptions. Among the ways in which parasites may do harm are: (1) absorbing food, (2) sucking blood or lymph, (3) feeding on the tissue of the host, (4) obstructing passages, (5) causing nodules or growths, (6) causing irritation, and (7) transmitting diseases. These may result in death of the affected animal; or they may cause large financial loss through stunted growth, lowered production, general unthriftiness, and emaciation.

Although thousands of parasites affect human beings and animals, only a few will be discussed.

Protozoa

Protozoa are the simplest form of animal life; they consist of only a single cell. There are many classifications of protozoa depending upon their method of reproduction and locomotion and general shape and structure. Since most of them are free-living (occurring in the soil, water, etc.), only a few concern human and animal health. Malaria and amoebic dysentery are examples of devastating human parasitic diseases caused by micro-organisms known as protozoa; among the protozoan diseases of animals are coccidiosis and trichomoniasis.

Helminths (or Worm Parasites)

Helminths (or worm parasites) are many-celled animals varying greatly in size, shape, structure, and physiology. With few exceptions, the eggs or larvae must leave the host animal in which they originate to undergo further development on the ground, elsewhere in the open, or in intermediate hosts. For purposes of description they are classified here as (1) flukes (or trematodes), (2) tapeworms (or cestodes), (3) roundworms (or nematodes), and (4) thorny-headed worms (or acanthocephala).

Flukes

Flukes (or trematodes) are soft, flat, leaf-shaped parasitic worms. With few exceptions, they are hermaphroditic (the generative organs combine those of both sexes), and they usually have two or more hosts, one of which always includes a mollusk (snail). The only flukes of known livestock importance in this country are the liver flukes that commonly parasitize cattle, wild ruminants, sheep and goats, and, less frequently, swine. Liver flukes rarely, if ever, infect horses.

Tapeworms

Without exception tapeworms are parasitic. They range in size from a fraction of an inch to over 10 yards in length. They occur as adult worms in the intestines and as larvae or bladder worms in various locations outside the alimentary canal—including the muscles, abdominal cavity, liver, lungs, brain, eye, and other organs and tissues. Although there appears to be little resemblance between an adult tapeworm and a bladder worm, the latter is really only the larval stage of the former.

Because bladder worms live in the tissue of animals, they cause more damage than the adult worm that resides mainly in the digestive tract. For example, the disease of sheep known as gid is caused by the presence in the brain of a bladder worm an inch or so in diameter. The pork tapeworm sometimes affects the brain and eye of man.

The adult worms injure the lining of the digestive tract and probably rob food from the host animal.

Roundworms

Roundworms, or nematodes, are unsegmented worms, usually cylindrical and elongate in shape and with tapered ends. They may be free-living or parasitic, and they vary greatly in size. Some are barely visible to the naked eye; others are a foot in length and as thick as an ordinary lead pencil.

The forms of infection by nematodes vary a great deal. The worms enter a variety of locations outside of the intestinal tract and wander, apparently aimlessly, in various organs and cavities, sometimes dying there.

Roundworms are among the most important parasites of man and animals. They suck blood, carry disease, excrete toxins, disturb digestion and respiration, and generally cause emaciation. Hookworms, trichinella, strongyles, nodular worms, and stomach worms of cattle, sheep, and goats are a few examples.

Thorny-headed Worms

Thorny-headed worms (or acanthocephala) derive their name from the peculiar anatomical structure characteristic of these worms—a retractible snout armed with hooks. The sexes are separate. Only one species, the thorny-headed worm of swine, is of importance to the livestock industry.

ARTHROPODS (INSECTS, TICKS, ETC.)

Some parasites are transmitted directly from one host animal to another, without the intervention of intermediate hosts; whereas the propagation and spread of others necessitates the presence of an intermediate host or hosts. Those hosts that transmit parasites are known as vectors or carriers. Knowledge of the intermediate hosts and vectors is extremely important in control programs. Thus, without mosquitoes, there would be no malaria; and without ticks, there would be no tick or Texas fever. Other intermediate hosts and vectors include flies, beetles, snails, and slugs. In fact, almost any animal, and even human beings, may serve as an intermediate host for parasites.

POISONOUS PLANTS

Poisonous plants have been known to man since time immemorial. Biblical literature alludes to the poisonous properties of certain plants, and history records that poison-hemlock (made from the plant from which it takes its name) was administered by the Greeks to Socrates and other state prisoners.

No section of the United States is entirely free of poisonous plants, for there are hundreds of them. Also, surprising as it may seem, plants do not readily fall into poisonous and nonpoisonous groups. Some are poisonous only at certain seasons of the year and under other specific conditions. Others are even excellent and nutritious forages providing they do not constitute the sole diet.

The heaviest livestock losses from poisonous plants occur on the western ranges because (1) there has been less cultivation and destruction of poisonous plants in range areas, and (2) the frequent overgrazing on some of the western ranges has resulted in the elemination of some of the more nutritious and desirable plants, and these have been replaced by increased numbers of the less desirable and poisonous species. It is estimated that poisonous plants account for 3 to 5 per cent of all range animal losses each year; and in some areas more. It is further estimated that poisonous plants cause average annual losses of beef cattle, sheep, and horses of $23,281,000.[4]

The list of poisonous plants is so extensive that no attempt is made herein to discuss them. Instead, those who are interested in pursuing further the subject are referred to specific books and bulletins relative to poisonous plants.

---

[4] *Losses in Agriculture,* Agricultural Handbook No. 291, 1965, Tables 26-30.

Both the stockman and the veterinarian should have a working knowledge of the principal poisonous species in the area in which they operate.

Conditions That Indicate Plant Poisoning

Since plants contain many different poisons, there are no general symptoms by which to recognize plant poisoning in animals. It may be suspected, however, if the following conditions prevail:

1. If there is sudden onset of obscure illness without visible cause.

2. If a number of animals in a herd show acute disorders of the central nervous system or of the digestive tract without fever, but with prostration or rapid loss of weight.

3. If there is rapid heart action, stomach and intestinal irritation, general distress, and repeated attempts to void feces.

4. If these symptoms are followed by extreme weakness, coma, and collapse, and accompanied by difficult breathing.

It should be recognized, however, that plant poisoning may differ considerably in intensity, depending on (1) the kind and amount of plant eaten, (2) the stage of plant growth, (3) the kind and amount of other feed eaten simultaneously, and (4) the tolerance of the individual animal to the poison.

Fig. 5-1. Cow with snakeroot poisoning. Marked weakness results in the "trembles" characteristic of this condition. (Courtesy, College of Veterinary Medicine, University of Illinois)

In addition to these facts, diagnosis is made more complicated because it is difficult to differentiate certain types of plant poisoning from sickness due to chemicals or to certain infectious diseases. Thus, diagnosis had best be left to the skill of a trained veterinarian.

Preventing Losses from Poisonous Plants

With poisonous plants, the emphasis should be on prevention of losses rather than on treatment, no matter how successful the latter. The following are effective preventive measures:

1. **Follow good pasture or range management** in order to improve the quality of the pasture or range. Plant poisoning is nature's sign of a "sick" pasture or range, usually resulting from misuse. When a sufficient supply of desirable forage is available, poisonous plants are not often eaten, for they are less palatable. On the other hand, when overgrazing reduces the available supply of the more palatable and safe vegetation, animals may, through sheer hunger, consume the toxic plants.

2. **Know the poisonous plants common to the area.** This can usually be accomplished through (a) studying drawings, photographs, and/or descriptions, (b) checking with local authorities, or (c) sending two or three fresh whole plants (if possible, include the roots, stems, leaves, and flowers) to the state agricultural college—first wrapping the plants in several thicknesses of moist paper.

By knowing the poisonous plants common to the area, it will be possible—

a. To avoid areas heavily infested with poisonous plants which, due to animal concentration and overgrazing, usually include waterholes, salt grounds, bed grounds, and trails.
b. To control and eradicate the poisonous plants effectively, by mechanical or chemical means (as recommended by local authorities) or by fencing off.
c. To recognize more surely and readily the particular kind of plant poisoning when it strikes, for time is important.
d. To know what first aid, if any, to apply, especially when death is imminent or where a veterinarian is not readily available.
e. To graze with a class of livestock not harmed by the particular poisonous plant or plants, where this is possible. Many plants seriously poisonous to one kind of livestock are not poisonous to another, at least under practical conditions.
f. To shift the grazing season to a time when the plant is not dangerous, where this is possible. That is, some plants are poisonous at certain seasons of the year, but comparatively harmless at other seasons.
g. To avoid cutting poison-infested meadows for hay when it is known that the dried cured plant is poisonous. Some plants are poisonous in either green or dry form, whereas others are harmless when dry. When poisonous plants (or seeds) become mixed with hay (or grain), it is difficult for animals to separate the safe from the toxic material.

3. **Know the symptoms that generally indicate plant poisoning,** thus making for early action.

4. **Avoid turning to pasture in very early spring.** Nature has ordained most poisonous plants as early growers—earlier than the desirable forage. For this

reason, as well as from the standpoint of desirable pasture management, animals should not be turned to pasture in the early spring before the usual forage has become plentiful.

5. **Provide supplemental feed during droughts or after early frost.** Otherwise, hungry animals may eat poisonous plants in an effort to survive.

6. **Avoid turning very hungry animals where there are poisonous plants,** especially those that have been in corrals for shearing, branding, etc., that have been recently shipped or trailed long distances, or that have been wintered on dry forage. First feed the animals to satisfy their hunger or allow a fill on an area known to be free from poisonous plants.

7. **Avoid driving animals too fast when trailing.** On long drives, either allow them to graze along the way or stop frequently and provide supplemental feed.

8. **Remove promptly all animals from infested areas when plant poisoning strikes.**

9. **Treat promptly,** preferably by a veterinarian.

TREATMENT

Unfortunately, plant-poisoned animals are not generally discovered in sufficient time to prevent loss. Thus, prevention is decidedly superior to treatment.

When trouble is encountered, the owner or caretaker should *promptly* call a veterinarian. In the meantime, the animal should be (1) placed where adequate care and treatment can be given, (2) protected from excessive heat and cold, and (3) allowed to eat only feeds known to be safe.

The veterinarian may determine the kind of poisonous plant involved (1) by observing the symptoms, and/or (2) by finding out exactly what poisonous plant was eaten through looking over the pasture and/or hay and identifying leaves or other plant parts found in the animal's digestive tract at the time of autopsy.

It is to be emphasized, however, that many poisoned animals that would have recovered had they been left undisturbed have been killed by attempts to administer home remedies by well meaning but untrained persons.

ANIMAL HEALTH

Keeping livestock healthy and sound not only entails the reduction of death losses of animals generally but also includes reduction of losses from unthriftiness. In addition to being economically important in profitable and successful livestock production, animal health is important in the maintenance and protection of human health.

Although modern science has conceived many artificial protective mechanisms against disease, there is no substitute for livestock sanitation and disease prevention. The artificial achievements, valuable as they are, are merely an adjunct to a high state of natural health that is built around a program of improved breeding, feeding, and management.

Immunity

When an animal is immune to a certain disease, it simply means that it is not susceptible to that disease.

The animal body is remarkably equipped to fight disease. Chief among this equipment are large white blood cells, called phagocytes, which are able to overcome many invading organisms.

The body also has the ability, when properly stimulated by a given organism or toxin, to produce antibodies and/or antitoxins. When an animal has enough antibodies for overcoming particular (disease-producing) organisms, it is said to be immune to that disease.

When immunity to a disease is inherited, it is referred to as a natural immunity. For example, when sheep are exposed to hog cholera they never contract the disease because they have a type of natural immunity referred to as species immunity. Algerian sheep are said to be highly resistant to anthrax, and this constitutes a type of natural immunity called racial immunity.

Acquired immunity or resistance is either active or passive. When the animal is stimulated in such manner as to cause it to produce antibodies, it is said to have acquired active immunity. On the other hand, if an animal is injected with the antibodies (or immune bodies) produced by an actively immunized animal, it is referred to as an acquired passive immunity. Such immunity is usually conferred by the injection of blood serum from immunized animals, the serum carrying with it the substances by which the protection is conferred. Passive immunization confers immunity upon its injection, but the immunity disappears within three to six weeks.

In active immunity, resistance is not developed until after one or two weeks; but it is far more lasting, for the animal apparently keeps on manufacturing antibodies. It can be said, therefore, that active immunity has a great advantage. There are exceptions, however—for example, when a disease must be checked immediately as in a virulent outbreak of swine erysipelas, when immune serum from actively immunized horses is injected.

It is noteworthy that young suckling mammals secure a passive immunity from the colostrum that they obtain from the mother for the first few days following birth.

Vaccination

Vaccination may be defined as the injection of some agent (such as a bacterin or vaccine) into an animal for the purpose of preventing disease.

In regions where a disease appears season after season, it is advised that healthy susceptible animals be vaccinated before being exposed and before there is a disease outbreak. This practice is recommended not only because it takes time to produce an active immunity but also because some animals may be about to be infected with the disease. The delay of vaccination until there is a disease outbreak may increase the seriousness of the infection. In addition, a new outbreak will "reseed" the premises with the infective agent.

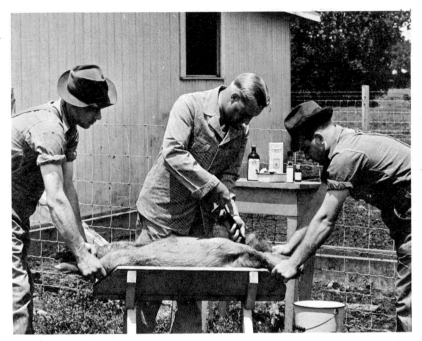

Fig. 5-2. Vaccinating a pig. In vaccination, the object is to produce in the animal a reaction that in some cases is a mild form of the disease. (Courtesy, Pitman-Moore Company)

In vaccination, the object, as has been previously pointed out, is to produce in the animal a reaction that in some cases is a mild form of the disease.

It is a mistake, however, to depend on vaccination alone for disease prevention. One should always insure its success by the removal of all interfering adverse conditions. It must also be said that varying degrees of immunity or resistance result when animals are actively immunized. Individual animals vary widely in their response to similar vaccinations. Heredity also plays a part in the determination of the level of resistance. In addition, nutritional and management practices play an important part in degrees of resistance displayed by animals.

Biologics

Biologics may be defined as medicinal preparations made from microorganisms (bacteria, protozoa, or viruses) and their products. They include various vaccines, bacterins, serums, and similar preparations. These agents are one of the most valuable contributions to animal health, and they are constantly being improved. They are used essentially for rendering animals immune to various infections.

It is noteworthy, however, that not all attempts to confer immunity by biologics are successful. In some cases, it seems impossible to create an immunity against infection. The common cold is a case in point. In other cases, the animal may die from the disease or its complications, in spite of an in-

Fig. 5-3. Inoculation of eggs for the production of vaccine. Some vaccines are made by growing virus on chick embryos. For this process, the two main constituents are fertile chicken eggs and a stock culture of virus. (Courtesy, Dr. Salsbury's Laboratories, Charles City, Iowa)

oculation; because of a biologic of poor quality, infection before the treatment is begun, or improper administration of the biologic.

VACCINES

Usually vaccines are defined as suspensions of live micro-organisms (bacteria or virus) or micro-organisms that have had their pathogenic properties removed but their antigenic properties retained. As pointed out previously, vaccines are purposely administered to produce a mild attack of disease, thus stimulating the resistance of that animal to that specific disease, often resulting in permanent immunity. Vaccines are employed mainly in the prevention rather than in the curing of disease. Examples are strain 19 vaccine of *Brucella abortus*, anthrax vaccine, and hog cholera vaccine. Great care must be used in their preparation, storage, and administration. Since the improper use of vaccines may result in disease outbreaks, it is strongly recommended that a veterinarian be consulted about their use.

BACTERINS

Bacterins are standardized suspensions of bacteria (and their products) that have been killed by heat or chemical means and are unable to produce disease. When introduced into the body, they stimulate the production of protective antibodies which act against subsequent attacks of organisms of the kind contained in the bacterin. They produce an active immunity.

Theoretically, bacterins should be useful in the prevention of every infectious disease in which the causative agent is known. Unfortunately, they do not always give the desired results, especially in diseases of a chronic nature.

Often a product may be a mixed bacterin; that is, it may contain more than one organism. This usually includes secondary invaders when the true causative agent is unknown.

Among the common bacterins in use are those for blackleg in cattle, enterotoxemia in sheep, and malignant edema in all animals.

SERUMS

Serums, also known as immune blood serum or immune serum, are obtained from the blood of animals (often horses) that have developed a solid immunity from having received one or more doses of infectious organisms. They do not contain any organisms, either dead or alive. Serums are used for the protective nature of the antibodies that they contain, which stop the action of an infectious agent or neutralize a product of that agent. They give a passive immunity. Among the serums that have proved successful are those for hog cholera, erysipelas, tetanus, and anthrax.

TOXOIDS (OR ANATOXINS)

A toxoid is a "tamed" toxin. Some bacteria, such as the germs that cause diphtheria and tetanus, produce powerful poisons or toxins. These are the substances that actually cause the damage; the bacteria themselves may produce only very mild symptoms. The same toxin is formed when the bacteria are grown in the laboratory, but it is then treated chemically. It loses the poisonous or toxic properties but still retains the power to stimulate the body cells; they form the appropriate antibody (antitoxin). Among toxoids are diphtheria toxoid and tetanus toxoid.

OTHER ARTIFICIAL PROTECTIVE MECHANISMS
AGAINST DISEASE

In addition to the vaccines, bacterins, serums, and toxoids, the following products are employed for the protection of animals against disease: sensitized vaccines, sensitized bacterins, germfree extracts, natural and artificial aggressins, and bacterial filtrates. Although these products are prepared differently, they all serve to provide protective substances against corresponding infections.

DIAGNOSTIC AGENTS

Other biological products are used solely for the diagnosis of diseases. Tuberculin is an example of such an agent, and it is considered accurate enough to cause the slaughter of an apparently normal animal that reacts positively. Another agent now employed for diagnosis is an antigen which is made up of *Brucella* organisms and is employed in the detection of brucellosis disease reactors. Use is made here of the fact that when an animal is infected with *Brucella* organisms it produces an antibody called agglutinin. When serum from a positive animal is brought in contact with the specific antigen, a characteristic agglutination or clumping occurs.[5]

Drugs

Drugs, or medicinal agents, are substances of mineral, vegetable, or animal origin used in the relief of pain or for the cure of disease. Much superstition cloaks the reasons for the recommended use of many drugs that have been employed for centuries. An example of this is liver wort, which was heralded as a sure cure for liver disorders only because it was shaped like a liver. Unfortunately, there is no known cure-all for a large number of diseases or for the relief of a great number of different parasitisms.

Lacking the knowledge of limitations of drugs and the nature of disease, many farmers and ranchers have been sold worthless products. There is a flourishing business in various "cure-alls" that are sold under such names as "tonic," "reconditioner," "worm expeller," "liver medicine," "mineral mixture," "mineral and vitamin mix," "regulator," and numerous others. It is poor practice to disregard the advice of reputable veterinarians and experimental workers and to rely on claims made by unscrupulous manufacturers of preparations of questionable or fraudulent nature. Most of these patent drugs are sold for fantastic prices, considering their actual cost, and most of their ingredients are never indicated. To avoid being swindled, purchases should be limited to preparations of reliable firms and then confined to those recommended by the local veterinarian. Fortunately, the Food and Drug Administration has been very vigilant and has been instrumental in the disappearance of many misbranded drugs and remedies from interstate channels.

General Animal Sanitation and Disease Prevention

In order to reduce the possibility of disease, one must adopt certain management practices relative to the environment of the animal. It has been said

---

[5] The milk ring test is now being used extensively as a screening test in brucellosis control programs. It is convenient and practical, in that the milk samples can be collected directly from producers' milk samples. Out of 100 ring-test-reacting herds, one can expect that the follow-up blood test will reveal, on the average, 25 negative, 50 suspect, and 25 reactor herds.

that domestication and increased animal numbers imply sort of a contract. Man, in fulfilling his obligation for services rendered, must protect his animals from the elements, parasites, and diseases, and furnish them sanitary quarters and suitable rations. Abuse leads to the reduction of profit—a case in which money and decency are on the same side of the ledger.

Animals require sanitary quarters. In the wild state, they had access to plenty of fresh air, clean feed, and plenty of room. They are naturally of clean habits and if given the choice will not voluntarily consume contaminated feed nor lie in filth.

VENTILATION

The need for ventilation is not as great for the animal as it is for human beings, for most of the animal's life is spent out of doors where plenty of fresh air is available. Ventilation is significant only when animals are housed in crowded quarters.

Ventilation is the act of causing the movement of air through buildings with the objective of supplanting foul air with fresh air containing needed oxygen. Contrary to common opinion, when a feeling of discomfort is noticed, it is the result of oxygen starvation rather than carbon dioxide poisoning.

The amount of moisture in the air is important. When improper ventilation prevents proper evaporation, the moisture content of the air increases. If humidity rises too high, interfering with heat elimination, heat stroke may ensue. Moist air generally is a more favorable medium for the existence of micro-organisms, thus lending itself well to the transmission of contagious diseases. When one animal is infected with a contagious disease and is closely housed with others, an epidemic will usually follow. The air may also pick up various noxious gases, such as ammonia from decomposing urine, which may cause irritation to the sensitive membranes of the mouth, eyes, nose, and respiratory tract.

Ventilation is measured in cubic feet per minute (cfm). The required ventilation differs according to species of animal, size of animal, and outside temperature. (See Table 7-13 of *The Stockman's Handbook*, 4th ed., a book by the same author and publisher as *Animal Science*.)

HOUSING

Although housing and close confinement predispose animals to more disease, it is often very necessary. Housing must frequently be provided to facilitate handling, to combat the elements, or to furnish protection during illness or when young are arriving. Proper drainage and dryness, adequate space, and good lighting are some of the requirements for good housing. In addition, animal quarters must be of such construction as to facilitate proper cleaning, disinfection, and maintenance of sanitary conditions. This includes suitable floors, adequate waste disposal, and proper absorbent bedding. Further discussion of the requisites of livestock buildings is found in Chapter IV.

Fig. 5-4. Visitors can bring diseases, so precautions must be taken to insure that a healthy flock or herd stays that way. Plastic boots help insure against disease and parasite introduction. (Courtesy, DeKalb Agricultural Association, Inc., DeKalb, Illinois)

ADEQUATE MANURE DISPOSAL

Situations that compel animals to live in close contact with their own body excreta are most injurious to physical well-being. Urine, feces, exhalations, and nose and mouth discharges may often contain disease-producing agents, and furnish an ideal medium for the growth of micro-organisms. Stockmen are fully aware of the miraculous recovery many animals undergo when taken from small, unsanitary enclosures to good, clean pastures.

The importance of removing excrement frequently from the immediate surroundings (enclosures, barns, and loafing sheds) cannot be stressed too much. The method of disposal of solid and liquid manure is also very important. As this manure may contain a variety of parasites and eggs, proper disposal offers an excellent opportunity for breaking the life cycles of these parasites. On the other hand, if left in an accessible place for animals, manure can be a rich, never-ending source of disease and parasitism.

In order to insure the killing of many harmful parasites, one may store manure (for two weeks to a month) so that the heat generated will cause their death. It should be stored in a covered concrete pit and located far enough away from the buildings to prevent contamination. These enclosures should be inaccessible to all animals. Spraying manure pits with DDT makes it possible to inhibit fly development. If the manure is believed to be free of specific infectious micro-organisms (for example, tuberculosis, brucellosis, and blackleg), it may be spread daily on arable land containing no animals. Here the purifying elements—such as rain, sunshine, soil, and vegetable processes— will tend to render the manure sanitary. Food and water should always be protected from contamination by manure.

PASTURE ROTATION

Pasture rotation provides a very practical method of control of many diseases and parasites. Permanent pastures used by one species of animal may be regarded as highly dangerous for profitable endeavors. A method by which land areas for pasturage are systematically changed periodically to crop production is recommended.

As many parasites (including bacteria) are often specific for a certain host (for example, bots of horses affect no other animal), frequently pastures may be rotated between different species.

CARCASS DISPOSAL

In the disposal of carcasses, it is a safe rule to assume that all are a source of some infection and subsequently to adopt the proper sanitary precautions.

The most sanitary method of destroying a carcass is to burn it, preferably at the site of death in order to prevent the contamination of surrounding ground. A trench of sufficient size should be prepared, a fire built, and the animal placed on top so that it will be consumed in its entirety. An incinerator may be used for poultry.

The most common method of large animal carcass disposal is by burial. So that this method will be effective, the carcass should be buried deep and covered with quicklime. The top of the carcass should be at least 4 feet below the surface of the ground and in soil from which there is no danger of contamination by drainage. Burial should not be near a flowing stream, for this will only serve to spread the disease downstream.

Near large centers of population, rendering plants will take carcasses, and they afford the easiest method of disposal.

When an animal dies, it is recommended that a veterinarian be called immediately to perform a post-mortem examination. This is done in an attempt to determine the cause of death or study the abnormal conditions present. It is never safe for one who is uninformed about specific disease lesions to open an animal carcass. Such practice may not only serve to spread a very highly contagious disease but may also expose the operator to a dangerous infection.

It is also unsafe to feed the carcass to other animals. Such procedure may cause the animal consuming it to become sick, or it may serve only to spread the disease.

DISINFECTANTS AND THEIR USE

A disinfectant is defined as any biological, physical, or chemical agent capable of exerting changes in environment unfavorable for the continued survival of micro-organisms.

Under ordinary conditions, proper cleaning of barns removes most of the micro-organisms, along with the filth, thus eliminating the necessity of disinfection. In case of disease outbreak, however, the premises must be disinfected.

Effective disinfection depends on the following five conditions:

1. Thorough cleaning before application.

2. The phenol coefficient of the disinfectant, which indicates the killing strength of a disinfectant as compared to phenol (carbolic acid). It is determined by a standard laboratory test in which the typhoid fever germ often is used as the test organism.

3. The dilution at which the disinfectant is used.

4. The temperature; most disinfectants are much more effective if applied hot.

5. Thoroughness of application, and time of exposure.

Disinfection must in all cases be preceded by a very thorough cleaning, for organic matter serves to protect disease germs and otherwise interferes with the activity of the disinfecting agent. This includes the burning of all inflammable refuse and the spreading out of the remainder on arable land (cultivated land not occupied by animals). Included also is the moistening of all litter and its subsequent removal. All walls, ceilings, and woodwork must be brushed down and also washed down with water and scrubbed. Old sacks should be disinfected or destroyed. Contaminated feed should be destroyed. Having accomplished this cleaning, one is ready to choose the disinfectant.

Unfortunately, there is no one best germ killer, nor is there anything like a general disinfectant that is effective against all types of micro-organisms under all conditions. This stems partially from the fact that not all disease-producing bacteria are susceptible to the same chemical agents. A few bacteria—such as those which cause blackleg, tetanus, and anthrax—possess the ability of forming seed-like spores that can remain dormant for years and resist destruction. Others, like those organisms causing tuberculosis, are resistant to oxidizing disinfectants such as the chlorine compounds. The organisms that cause brucellosis, strangles, and some other diseases are, fortunately, very readily killed by almost any disinfectant that reaches them.

Sunlight possesses disinfecting properties, but it is variable and superficial in its action. Heat and some of the chemical disinfectants are more

TABLE 5–2

HANDY DISINFECTANT GUIDE

Kind of Disinfectant	Usefulness	Strength	Limitations and Comments
Alcohol	Effective against the less resistant disease germs provided there is adequate exposure.	70 per cent alcohol—the content usually found in rubbing alcohol.	Limited application. Not recommended for general use. Often used as a local antiseptic in obtaining blood samples or making hypodermic injections. Not reliable for sterilization of instruments.
Bichloride of Mercury (mercuric chloride; corrosive sublimate)	Destroys less resistant bacteria under favorable conditions. Tends to prevent growth rather than actually destroying bacteria. Organic mercurials, sometimes used as local antiseptics, are less poisonous and more reliable.	Tablets used in a dilution of 1 to 1,000.	Unreliable as a germ killer in the presence of organic matter. **Also cattle are especially susceptible to mercury poisoning.** For farm disinfection, bichloride of mercury is inferior to iodine, lye, saponified cresols, and the cationic bactericides.
Boric Acid[1]	As a wash for eyes, and other sensitive parts of the body.	1 oz. in 1 pt. water (about 6% solution).	It is a weak antiseptic. It may cause harm to the nervous system if absorbed into the body in large amounts. For this and other reasons, antibiotic solutions and saline solutions are fast replacing it.
Cationic Bactericides (many commercial products available, including QAC, i.e., quarternary ammonium compounds)	Primarily detergents but some are actively bactericidal. Often used in sanitizing dairy or other equipment and utensils. **Use only as recommended by competent sanitarian.**	Concentration varies with different products and under different conditions. Follow authoritative recommendations.	They have only a slight toxicity and are non-irritant and odorless. They are neutralized by soap, anionic detergents, and even by mineral content of some waters. Superior to chlorine compounds in the presence of organic matter. They are not effective against TB organisms and spores.
Cresols (many commercial products available)	A generally reliable class of disinfectant. Effective against brucellosis, shipping fever, swine erysipelas, and tuberculosis.	4 oz. per gal.; or according to the directions found on the container.	Cannot be used where odor may be absorbed, and therefore, not suited for use around milk and meat.

Footnote on last page of table.

(Continued)

TABLE 5–2 (Continued)

Kind of Disinfectant	Usefulness	Strength	Limitations and Comments
Heat (by steam, hot water, burning, or boiling)	In the burning of rubbish or articles of little value, and in disposing of infected body discharges. The steam "Jenny," is effective for disinfection if properly employed—particularly if used in conjunction with a phenolic germicide.	10 min. exposure to boiling water is usually sufficient.	Exposure to boiling water will destroy all ordinary disease germs but sometimes fails to kill the spores of such diseases as anthrax and tetanus. Moist heat is preferred to dry heat, and steam under pressure is the most effective. Heat may be impractical or too expensive.
Hypochlorites (chlorine compounds)	For deodorizing manure, sewers, drains, and for disinfecting milk cans and bottles and around dairy barns.	200 parts available chlorine per million of water. **Unstable: replace solution frequently as recommended.**	Excellent for disinfection, but with following limitations: not effective against the TB organism and spores. Its effectiveness is greatly reduced in presence of organic matter, such as milk, even in small quantities. **Hypochlorites deteriorate rapidly when exposed to air.**
Iodine[1]	Extensively used as skin disinfectant, for minor cuts and bruises.	Generally used as tincture of iodine 2% or 7%.	Never cover with a bandage. Clean skin before applying iodine.
Iodophor (iodine complexed with a detergent which releases free iodine at a controlled rate)	For disinfecting milk cans and bottles around dairy barns and for area disinfection where large quantities of organic soil are not present.	75 parts available iodine per million is minimum under ideal circumstances. 150 ppm is recommended for most practical uses. Unstable—replace solution frequently.	An excellent disinfectant but with the following practical limitations: Germicidal agent rapidly consumed requiring frequent replacement. Functions best in a highly acid range. Solution strength must be increased to get necessary available iodine when mixture is made with alkaline water. Iodine slowly volatilizes from solution. Considerable control should be exercised.
Lime (quicklime, burnt lime, calcium oxide)	As a deodorant when sprinkled on manure and animal discharges; or as a disinfectant when sprinkled on the floor or used as a newly-made "milk of lime" or as a whitewash.	Use as a dust; as "milk of lime"; or as a whitewash, but **use fresh.**	Not effective against organisms of TB and the spore formers. Wear goggles when adding water to quicklime.

Footnote on last page of table.

(Continued)

TABLE 5–2 (Continued)

Kind of Disinfectant	Usefulness	Strength	Limitations and Comments
Lye (sodium hydroxide, caustic soda)	On concrete floors; in milk houses because there is no odor; against microorganisms of brucellosis and the viruses of foot-and-mouth disease, hog cholera, and vesicular exanthema. In strong solution (5%), effective against anthrax and blackleg.	1 can (13 oz.) to 12 to 15 gal. water. To prepare a 5% solution, add 5 (13 oz.) cans to 10 gals. water.	Damages fabrics, aluminum, and painted surfaces. Be careful, for it will burn the hands and face. Not effective against organisms of TB, Johne's disease, or strangles, or most spores. When used in hog houses, lye should be mixed with hot water, as the heat of the water will destroy the worm eggs. Diluted vinegar can be used to neutralize lye.
Phenolic Germicides, Synthetic (those containing odorless non-toxic phenols such as orthophenyl phenol or orthobenzyl parachlorophenol)	A very reliable class of disinfectants effective against all disease-producing fungi and bacteria including the TB organism.	Varies with different formulations; follow directions on manufacturer's label.	Excellent for disinfection. They are not inactivated by soap, anionic detergents, hard water, or organic matter. They are effective against all bacteria and fungi including the TB organism but not the spores of anthrax and tetanus.
Sal Soda	It may be used in place of lye against foot-and-mouth disease and vesicular exanthema.	10½% solution (13½ oz. to 1 gal. water).	
Soap	Its power to kill germs is very limited. Greatest usefulness is in cleansing and dissolving coatings from various surfaces, including the skin, prior to application of a good disinfectant.	As commercially prepared.	Although indispensable for sanitizing surfaces, soaps should not be considered as disinfectants. They are not regularly effective, staphylococci and the organisms which cause diarrheal diseases are resistant.
Soda Ash (or sodium carbonate)	It may be used in place of lye against foot-and-mouth disease and vesicular exanthema.	5% solution (1 lb. to 3 gal. water). Most effective in hot solution.	Commonly used as a cleaning agent, but has disinfectant properties, especially when used as a hot solution.

¹Sometimes loosely classed as a disinfectant but actually an antiseptic and practically useful only on living tissue.

effective. Table 5-2 gives a summary of the usefulness, strength, and limitations of some of the common disinfectants.

REGULATIONS RELATIVE TO DISEASE CONTROL

Certain animal diseases are so devastating that no individual farmer or rancher could long protect his herds and flocks against their invasion. Moreover, where human health is involved, the problem is much too important to be entrusted to individual action. In the United States, therefore, certain regulatory activities in animal-disease control are under the supervision of various federal and state organizations. The duties and responsibilities of some of the more important of these agencies will be discussed briefly.

Animal Disease Eradication Division, Agricultural Research Service

The year 1884 marked the beginning of an organized cooperative effort, under legal authority, for the control and eradication of animal disease. In that year, Congress passed an act creating the Federal Bureau of Animal Industry (now the Animal Disease Eradication Division, Agricultural Research Service). It was first established to prevent exportation of diseased cattle and to eradicate contagious pleuropneumonia and other contagious diseases. In three years, it had succeeded in completely eliminating contagious pleuropneumonia, a dread disease.

In the famous Bulletin No. 1, the Bureau of Animal Industry revealed that Texas fever ticks were the biological bearer of the protozoa causing Texas fever. The description of this type of disease relationship laid the foundation for the subsequent work on such diseases as yellow fever and malaria of humans.

Since then, great progress has been made. To list a few examples, bovine tuberculosis has all but been eradicated, and the cattle tick fever has been reduced to negligible proportions by a very extensive eradication program. Present programs have brought under control much of the devastation formerly wrought by hog cholera. Advances are being made on the control of brucellosis and mastitis. In addition, there are many methods by which the Animal Disease Eradication Division, Agricultural Research Service, makes less spectacular, though equally important, contributions to human and animal welfare in the United States.

State Veterinarians, Sanitary Commissions, and Boards

In addition to the work of the Agricultural Research Service, most states have state veterinarians, or comparable officials, who also direct their effort to livestock sanitary and regulatory problems.

Quarantine

By quarantine is meant the segregation and confinement of one or more animals in the smallest possible area to prevent any direct or indirect contact with animals not so restrained.

Many highly infectious diseases are prevented from gaining a foothold in this country by strict enforcement of local quarantine at points of entry. By such means rinderpest, surra, and other diseases have never gained a foothold in the United States. When an infectious disease outbreak occurs, drastic quarantine must be imposed to restrict movement out of an area or within areas. The type of quarantine varies from one involving a mere physical examination and movement under proper certification to the complete prohibition against the movement of animals, produce, vehicles, and even human beings.

Stockyards Inspection

With the advent of large public markets, public stockyards inspection was initiated. This is an addition to the regular inspection performed on animals by meat inspectors prior to slaughter. Among the principal diseases for which inspections are made are: anthrax, scabies of cattle and sheep, tick or splenetic fever, hog cholera, and erysipelas of swine.

Not only are the incoming shipments of livestock inspected, but a reinspection is made of outgoing shipments. Tests for tuberculosis and brucellosis are accomplished, and dipping for scabies is performed before shipments are allowed to return to farms and ranches.

Meat Inspection

Federal meat inspection is required by law for all meat and meat products prepared for interstate commerce.[6] Its purpose is to protect the consumer against infected meats and fraudulent and unsanitary preparation of meat products. The inspection first consists of an examination of the live animal so that any unfit beast may be removed and disposed of properly. Secondly, the carcasses and internal organs are inspected for any abnormalities of animals carrying infectious diseases. Centers of infection sources may be located, thus assisting the livestock owners in the vicinity. The records of meat inspection also serve as a useful purpose to the research scientist. Additional discussion of meat inspection is contained in Chapter VI.

Biologic Standardizing

Regulations now in effect are designed not only to standardize but to improve the quality of biological products and drugs of licensed establishments. Considering the millions of inoculations that are made each year, it is not difficult to imagine the havoc that could be wrought by infected products. It is required that the products be of standard quality and properly labeled.

---

[6] The Wholesome Meat Act of December 15, 1967, (1) requires that the state standards of meat inspection be at least equivalent to those of federally inspected plants, and (2) assures consumers that all meat in the U.S. is either inspected by the federal government or an adequate state program.

Indemnity Payments in Disease Eradication

Where certain animal diseases are involved, stockmen can obtain financial assistance in eradication programs through federal and state sources.

Information relative to indemnities paid to owners by the federal government for animals disposed of as a result of outbreaks of certain diseases is given in the following two publications, of Sub-chapter B, Title 9, of the Code of Federal Regulations, which can be obtained from the U.S. Department of Agriculture:

1. Part 51—Cattle Destroyed Because of Brucellosis (Bang's Disease), Tuberculosis or Paratuberculosis (Johne's Disease).

2. Part 53—Foot-and-Mouth Disease, Pleuropneumonia, Rinderpest, and Other Contagious or Infectious Animal Diseases which constitute an emergency and threaten the livestock industry of the country.

Regulations pertaining to each state can be secured by writing to the respective state departments of agriculture.

GLOSSARY OF ANIMAL HEALTH TERMS

Animal health, like other subjects in the field of animal science, has a language somewhat of its own. Here is a list of some of the most frequently used words and their definitions:

Allergy.—A severe reaction, or sensitivity, which occurs in some individuals following the introduction of certain antigens into their bodies.

Anthelmintic (vermifuge).—A product which removes worm parasites.

Antibiotic.—A chemical substance, produced by molds or bacteria, which has the ability to inhibit the growth of, or to destroy, other micro-organisms.

Antibody.—A substance that opposes the action of another substance.

Antigen.—A foreign substance which, when introduced into the body, stimulates formation of protective antibodies.

Antiseptic.—A compound that inhibits the growth of micro-organisms, and which is usually applied to the skin.

Autopsy.—Inspection, and partial dissection, of a dead body to determine the cause of death.

Bacteria.—One-celled micro-organisms, smallest of the non-green plants, which are chiefly parasitic.

Bactericide.—A product which kills bacteria.

Bacteriostat.—A product which retards bacterial growth.

Broad-spectrum antibiotic.—An antibiotic which attacks both gram-positive and gram-negative bacteria, and which may also show activity against other disease agents.

Culture.—The propagation of micro-organisms, or of living tissue cells, in special media conducive to their growth.

Debilitating.—Weakening.

Disinfectant.—A product which, at certain concentrations, will kill on contact a wide range of disease organisms.

Emaciated.—A severe loss of weight.

Enzootic.—A disease confined to a certain locality.

Excreta.—Excreted material; waste matter.

Exudate.—A fluid oozing from tissue.

Filterable virus.—An organism so small that it is capable of passing through filters which will retain the ordinary bacteria.

Fungi.—Certain vegetable organisms such as molds, mushrooms, and toadstools.

Gram-negative bacteria.—Those bacterial species which are decolorized by acetone or alcohol.

Gram-positive bacteria.—Those bacterial species which retain a crystal-violet color even when exposed to alcohol or acetone.

Hypersensitivity.—A state in which the body reacts to a foreign agent more strongly than normal.

Ingestion.—The taking in of food and drink.

Intradermal.—Into, or between, the layers of the skin.

Intramuscular.—Within the substance of a muscle.

Intraperitoneal.—Within the peritoneal cavity.

Intrauterine.—Within the uterus.

Intravenous.—Within the vein or veins.

In vitro.—Occurring in a test tube.

In vivo.—Occurring in the living body.

Medium-spectrum antibiotic.—An antibiotic which attacks a limited number of gram-positive and gram-negative bacteria.

Metabolic.—Pertaining to the nature of metabolism.

Metabolism.—Refers to all the changes which take place in the nutrients after they are absorbed from the digestive tract including (1) the building-up processes in which the absorbed nutrients are used in the formation or repair of body tissues and (2) the breaking-down processes in which nutrients are oxidized for the production of heat and work.

Micro-organism.—Any organism of microscopic size, applied especially to bacteria and protozoa.

Morbidity.—Sick rate.

Mortality.—Death rate.

Narrow-spectrum antibiotic.—An antibiotic whose activity is restricted to either gram-negative or gram-positive bacteria. For example, penicillin is active primarily against gram-positive organisms, whereas streptomycin attacks only gram-negative organisms.

Necrosis.—Death or dying of local tissue.

Oral.—Given by mouth.

Pathogenic.—Disease-producing.

Pathological.—Diseased, or due to disease.

Post-mortem.—Examination after death.

Prophylaxis.—Preventive treatment against disease.

Protozoa.—One-celled animals which reproduce by splitting in half; found largely in water, and include many parasitic forms.

Rigor mortis.—Stiffening of the body after death.

Secondary invaders.—Infective agents which attack after a primary organism has established an infection.

Serum, blood.—The clear portion of blood separated from its more solid elements.

Subcutaneous.—Under the skin.

Sulfa drug (sulfonamide).—A synthetic organic drug which has the ability to inhibit the growth of, or to destroy, micro-organisms.

Supportive treatment.—Treatment of individual symptoms of a disease where diagnosis is obscure or where a specific treatment has not been established.

Therapy.—Treating disease.

Toxemia.—A condition produced by the presence of poisons (toxins) in the blood.

Virus.—The smallest living micro-organisms, not visible under an ordinary microscope, which lives parasitically upon plants and animals, and sometimes causes disease.

QUESTIONS FOR STUDY AND DISCUSSION

1. Why are such publications as (a) the 1942 Yearbook of Agriculture entitled *Keeping Livestock Healthy*, and (b) The 1956 Yearbook of Agriculture entitled *Animal Diseases* of value to livestock producers?

2. Select (a) a specific farm or ranch (either your own or one with which you are familiar) and (b) a specific class of farm animals (beef cattle, dairy cattle, sheep, swine, poultry, or horses), and outline (in 1, 2, 3, order) a program of animal health, disease prevention, and parasite control.

3. Obtain the following publications from The Animal Disease Eradication Division, Agricultural Research Service, USDA, Washington, D.C.: Subchapter B. Title 9, of the Code of Federal Regulations, parts 51 and 53. Also, write to your state department of agriculture for information about indemnity payments. Then determine the indemnity payments that you could expect were you to encounter an outbreak in cattle or (a) brucellosis or (b) foot-and-mouth disease.

4. Assume that a specific contagious disease (you name it) has broken out in your herd or flock. What steps would you take to meet the situation (list in 1, 2, 3, order; be specific)?

5. Assume that a specific parasite (you name it) has become troublesome in your herd or flock. What steps would you take to meet the situation (list in 1, 2, 3, order; be specific)?

6. Assume that you have encountered death losses from a certain poisonous plant (you name it). What steps would you take to meet the situation (list in 1, 2, 3, order; be specific)?

7. Justify "meat inspection" as a federal and/or state expense, as opposed to letting such inspection be handled by the individual processor.

SELECTED REFERENCES

Title of Publication	Author(s)	Publisher
Animal Diseases	Yearbook of Agriculture, 1956	U.S. Department of Agriculture, Washington, D. C., 1956.
Animal Sanitation and Disease Control	R. R. Dykstra	Interstate Printers and Publishers, Danville, Ill., 1961.
Brucellosis	A Symposium— 1949	American Association for the Advancement of Science, 1515 Massachusetts Ave., N.W., Washington, D. C.
Diseases of Cattle		U.S. Department of Agriculture, Washington, D. C., 1942.
Diseases of Cattle	W. J. Gibbons	American Veterinary Publications, Inc., Wheaton, Ill., 1963.
Diseases of Feedlot Cattle	Rue Jensen D. R. Mackey	Lea & Febiger, Philadelphia, Pa., 1965.
Diseases of Swine	H. W. Dunne	Iowa State College Press, Ames, Iowa, 1958.
Diseases of the Horse		U.S. Department of Agriculture, Washington, D. C., 1942.
Equine Medicine and Surgery	J. F. Bone, et al.	American Veterinary Publications, Inc., Wheaton, Ill., 1963.
Farmer's Veterinary Handbook	J. J. Haberman	Prentice-Hall, New York, N. Y. 1953.
Home Veterinarian's Handbook	E. T. Baker	Macmillan Company, New York, N. Y., 1949.
Infectious Diseases of Domestic Animals, The	W. A. Hagan D. W. Bruner	Comstock Publishing Associates, Ithaca, N. Y., 1957.
Insecticide Recommendations	Agricultural Handbook No. 120	U.S. Department of Agriculture, Washington, D. C.
Keeping Livestock Healthy	Yearbook of Agriculture, 1942	U.S. Department of Agriculture, Washington, D. C., 1942.
Livestock Health Encyclopedia	Rudolph Seiden	Springer Publishing Co., New York, N. Y., 1951.
Merck Veterinary Manual, The		Merck & Co., Rahway, N. J., 1967.
Principles of Veterinary Science	F. B. Hadley	W. B. Saunders Co., Philadelphia, Pa., 1949.
Sheep Diseases	I. E. Newsom	Williams & Wilkins Co., Baltimore, Md., 1952.
Sheep Management and Diseases	H. G. Belschner	Angus & Robertson, Sydney, Australia, 1965.
Stockman's Handbook, The	M. E. Ensminger	Interstate Printers and Publishers, Danville, Ill., 1969

Veterinary Handbook for Cattlemen	J. W. Bailey	Springer Publishing Co., New York, N. Y., 1958.
Veterinary Medicine	D. C. Blood J. A. Henderson	The Williams and Wilkins Company, Baltimore, Md., 1960.
Veterinary Notebook	W. R. McGee	The Blood Horse, Lexington, Ky. 1958.

In addition to the above selected references, valuable publications on different subjects pertaining to animal diseases, parasites, disinfectants, and poisonous plants can be obtained from the following sources:

1. Division of Publications
   Office of Information
   U.S. Department of Agriculture
   Washington, D.C.

2. Your state agricultural college

3. Several biological, pharmaceutical, and chemical companies

/

CHAPTER VI

MARKETING LIVESTOCK

Contents Page

Importance of Livestock Marketing.....222
The Development of American Markets.....223
The Development of Livestock Transportation.....225
The Development and Extension of Meat Packing.....227
  Modern Meat Packing.....228
    Efficiency and Low Cost of Operation.....229
  Geography of Meat Production and Consumption.....230
  The Large National Meat Packers.....231
  Decentralization of Meat Packing.....232
Methods of Marketing Livestock.....232
  Terminal Public Markets.....233
    Essential Factors Operating in a Terminal Public Market.....235
    Terminal Marketing Procedure.....235
    Charges at Terminal Public Markets.....237
  Livestock Auction Markets.....238
    Charges at Auctions.....240
  Country Selling.....240
  Selling on Basis of Carcass Grade and Weight.....241
  Selling Purebred Animals.....243
  Choice of Market Outlets.....243
Preparing and Shipping Livestock.....244
  How to Prevent Bruises, Crippling, and Death Losses.....247
  Number of Animals in a Railroad Car and in a Truck.....250
  Shrinkage in Marketing Animals.....250
Dockage.....251
Livestock Market News Services.....252
  Market Information Supplied by Commission Companies.....253
Federal and State Livestock Marketing Agencies.....253
  Federal Meat Inspection.....253
  State Meat Inspection.....256
  Packers and Stockyards Act of 1921.....256
  The 28-Hour Law Regulating Transportation of Livestock.....256
  Health-Control Officials.....257
  Brand Inspection.....257
Development of Market Classes and Grades of Livestock.....257
  Use Made of Market Classes and Grades.....258
  Definition of Market Classes and Grades.....259
  Factors Determining Market Grades.....259
Supply and Demand Determine Prices of Market Livestock.....260
  Factors Which Influence Market Supplies and Prices.....260
    Longtime (or Secular) Trends.....260
    Cyclical Trends.....261
    Seasonal Changes.....261
    Short-time Changes.....262
    Jewish Holidays.....263
The Future of Livestock Marketing.....263
Promotional and Research Organizations of Importance to the Livestock
  and Meat Industry.....264
Questions for Study and Discussion.....265
Selected References.....265

Livestock marketing embraces those operations beginning with loading animals out on the farm, ranch, or feedlot and extending until they are sold to go into processing channels. In this chapter, the term is conceived to include processing as it reflects on livestock marketing. However, treatment is limited to the marketing of four-footed animals—cattle, sheep, and hogs. Because of their distinct and different market channels and procedures, separate chapters are accorded to marketing milk and dairy products (Chapter XXII) and marketing poultry and eggs (Chapter XLV).

In the past, the livestock producer could be successful if he knew how to breed, feed, and manage his stock. Today, this is not enough; preconsidered, if not prearranged, markets are essential. In brief, livestock marketing is going through a revolution.

IMPORTANCE OF LIVESTOCK MARKETING

Livestock marketing is the end of the line. From the producer's standpoint, it is that part which gives point and purpose, and profit or loss, to all that has gone before. Market receipts constitute the only source of reimbursement to the producer for his work; market day is the producer's pay day—hence it is the most important single day or operation to him. The importance of marketing is further attested to by the following facts:

1. In 1966, 152,476,000 head of meat animals were marketed in the United States; 129,355,000 head of meat animals were slaughtered; and 32.6 billion pounds of red meat were produced.[1]

2. In 1966, U.S. farmers and ranchers received $24.8 billion, or 57.5 per cent of their cash income, from livestock and livestock products.[1]

3. Livestock markets establish values for all animals, including those down on the farm or ranch. On January 1, 1968, there were 617,037,000 cattle, sheep, hogs, chickens, and turkeys in the U.S., with an aggregate value of $18,961,094.

4. There are approximately 2,300 auctions and 60 terminal markets operating in the United States. In addition, there are innumerable concentration yards and other private market places.

5. About three-fifths of the livestock in the United States is produced west of the Mississippi River, whereas more than two-thirds of the meat is consumed east of this area. This points up the enormity of the task of marketing the nation's livestock; keeping in mind that marketing is the process through which livestock is moved from where it is produced to where it is consumed.

6. About 10 million full-time workers are engaged in marketing and distributing (assembling, transporting, processing, wholesaling, and retailing) of farm products, of whom about half are in the food industry;[2] it is not known, however, what proportion of this total is engaged specifically in livestock and meat marketing. But these figures do not tell the whole story; another 6 million are employed in the production and distribution of farm production supplies—

---

[1] *Agricultural Statistics, 1967*, USDA.
[2] *Agricultural Economics Research*, USDA, Agricultural Marketing Service, April, 1955, Vol. 7, No. 2, p. 42.

things the farmer buys to operate.[3] Add to these figures the 7½ million farm workers, and we have more than 23½ million people—over a third of all those gainfully employed in the United States—making their living from agriculture (they are in agribusiness); they are either producing, marketing, or processing farm commodities, or they are supplying production goods used on the farm.[4]

Fig. 6-1. Two Egyptian cattlemen taking an ox to market. (An old photograph from Bas Relief found in Sakara in the tomb of King Ephto Stoptep.) At first, meat animals were bartered for articles made by craftsmen. (Courtesy, The Bettmann Archive)

THE DEVELOPMENT OF AMERICAN MARKETS

Until the latter part of the seventeenth and early part of the eighteenth centuries, American livestock markets were small and largely local in character. At that time, the West was comprised of Ohio, Kentucky, and Indiana. There were no railroads, no refrigerator cars, and no large central markets. For the most part, meat animals were slaughtered on the farm, and the carcasses were exchanged for the goods and services supplied by the artisans and tradesmen.

As the eastern seaboard towns and cities became larger, direct barter between farmers and consumers was gradually replaced by the services of the local meat merchant. For a time, however, slaughtering continued to be done on the farm. The town meat merchant merely served as a middleman, buying the dressed carcasses from farmers and selling the meat to consumers and sometimes curing a portion of it for later use. But because farmers often slaughtered on a convenience basis rather than according to the demand, less reliance was placed upon farm slaughter as the requirements for meat increased. This gave rise to the town butcher who purchased animals on the hoof, slaughtered them,

---

[3] From an address by Marvin L. McLain, Assistant Secretary of Agriculture, Washington, D.C., April 14, 1959.
[4] *Ibid.*

and distributed the meat. In the beginning, his slaughter plant and selling place were located together, and most of the house-to-house selling was done by means of a little covered one-horse butcher's cart.

With this transformation, it was an easy and logical step for the slaughter-houses to be operated under separate ownership and for one such plant to take care of the slaughter needs of more than one meat market. Thus, these local slaughterhouses gradually increased in size and importance. They were the forerunners of the modern packing plants.

As the volume of slaughtering increased, the operators no longer had the necessary time in which to go greater distances into the country for the purpose of buying slaughter animals. They found it more convenient to depend upon drovers who purchased animals in the country, assembled them, and trailed them to the local slaughterhouses. These early livestock drovers operated as employees of the slaughterer, employees of the butcher, or on their own account. They were called drovers because the major portion of their time was spent in driving slaughter animals from farm to market. A few hundred miles travel meant nothing to these men whose lives were filled with adventure and hardship. Often they forded or swam their herds across dangerous streams, braved storms and thieves, and overcame difficulties which would have driven men less resolute out of business. They were truly the pioneers of livestock trans-portation.

As production areas shifted farther westward, increasing numbers of cattle, hogs, and sheep were driven overland from the newly settled areas to the ex-panding eastern cities. But there were no market reports, and communication was largely by word of mouth. Thus, it was mere happenstance if supply and demand coincided in any reasonable degree. Most generally, there was either

Fig. 6-2. Stone gate entrance to the Union Stock Yards, Chicago, at 39th and Halsted Streets. The Chicago Stock Yards was founded in 1865. (Courtesy, Chicago Historical Society)

Fig. 6-3. View of the Chicago Stock Yards today. (Courtesy, The Union Stock Yard and Transit Company, Chicago)

a vast oversupply or too few animals available. The situation between different markets also usually varied at any given time, even though they might not be separated by many miles. In addition to these complications, drovers often found it difficult to get in touch with prospective buyers. This led to the establishment of private markets in close proximity to the larger cities.

In the private markets, livestock were assembled and buyers and sellers met. In some instances, special market days were designated for the convenience of both the buyers and sellers. The more enterprising market operators provided feed and water for the animals, and served as go-betweens for the buyers and sellers.

Gradually the centers of livestock production shifted to the West, and the leading markets shifted with it. At one time, it was believed that Albany was to be the final gateway for western shipments. Next, Buffalo, Pittsburgh, and Cincinnati were, in turn, regarded as the future great livestock markets of the country. But eventually it became evident that Chicago—by virtue of its proximity to both producers and consumers—was destined to become the greatest central market in the world. Now, it's Omaha.

THE DEVELOPMENT OF LIVESTOCK TRANSPORTATION

In no phase of livestock marketing have the developments been more phenomenal than in transportation. With the humble beginning of marketing on foot or by a combination of trailing and boat transportation, transportation progressed to the luxury of the railroad, to the development of the refrigerator car designed for carrying and preserving fresh meats, and finally to the construction of modern highways and the speed and flexibility of the motor truck.

Fig. 6-4. Texas cattle fording a stream in "trailing" north. A few hundred miles travel meant nothing to the "drovers"—those men who drove slaughter animals overland to eastern markets. Their lives were filled with adventure and hardship. (After a woodcut; courtesy, The Bettmann Archive)

Fig. 6-5. Unloading cattle at railroad unloading dock, Union Stock Yards, Chicago. Cattle were first shipped by rail in 1852. The day of the drover ended with the advent of the railroads. (Courtesy, The Union Stock Yard and Transit Company, Chicago)

There are wide variations in the proportion of livestock arriving by motor truck at different markets. In general, a higher proportion of hogs and calves than cattle and sheep arrive by motor truck. Rail shipments predominate when long movements are involved, whereas truck shipments are favored for short hauls. The latter point probably explains why a lower percentage of sheep and

Fig. 6-6. Unloading hogs at truck unloading dock, Union Stock Yards, Chicago. (Courtesy, Producers Live Stock Marketing Association)

cattle are transported by truck, for longer shipments are involved for these animals, especially with western-range consignments.

Table 6-1 shows the percentage of total livestock receipts at several leading terminal public markets received by rail versus truck.

TABLE 6—1

PERCENTAGE OF MARKET LIVESTOCK, BY CLASSES, RECEIVED
AT PUBLIC STOCKYARDS BY RAIL VERSUS TRUCK, 1957[1]

Truck or Rail	Cattle	Calves	Hogs	Sheep and Lambs
	(%)	(%)	(%)	(%)
Rail......................	13.9	15.8	10.6	37.5
Truck....................	86.1	84.2	89.4	62.5

[1]*Livestock Receipts and Disposition at Public Markets*, 1957, USDA, Agricultural Marketing Service, p. 7.

THE DEVELOPMENT AND EXTENSION OF MEAT PACKING

The development of the livestock business has truly gone hand in hand with the transformation and extension of the nation itself, and progress in each phase of livestock marketing and processing has unwittingly stimulated the whole. Thus, the growth of cities brought about the demand for meats. Progressively this was followed by farm slaughtering for barter, the establishment of the town butcher, the operation of the local slaughterhouse, the trailing of animals and the drover, the advent of rail transportation, the development of refrigeration, further opening up of the western range, improved highways, and shipment by motor truck. These changes were not alone, for the local slaughterhouse was gradually increasing in size and eventually we had the birth of the modern meat packing industry.

Fig 6-7. Old-time farm slaughter scene. When nearly all the people lived on the land—prior to the growth of cities and the rise of the town butcher—each family did its own slaughtering. (Courtesy, Swift and Company)

Modern Meat Packing

Today the name packing is a misnomer, for the barreled or pickled pork from whence the name originated is now packed only for a few lumber camps and a limited export demand. But modern meat slaughtering and processing developed slowly, and the original name was so well established that there has never been any attempt to rename the industry.

It may be said that there have been four distinct eras in the evolution of the modern meat packing industry: (1) the era of cured pickled pork and dry salted beef which correctly resulted in the early-day meat processors being designated as packers, (2) the era of rail transportation and the development of artificial refrigeration and the refrigerator car, (3) the era of complete utilization of by-products, and (4) the era of truck transportation of livestock and meat products, and of decentralization.

The first era extended from the time when operators in the eastern cities first devoted the major share of their time to meat curing to approximately the time of the Civil War, a span of nearly 200 years. The second era occupied a relatively

Fig. 6-8. The first Swift and Company packing plant. Small, local slaughter-houses of this type were the forerunners of modern packing houses. (Courtesy, Swift and Company)

short period of time, spanning only about two decades during and immediately following the Civil War. The era of the utilization of by-products was somewhat less rapid and devoid of much of the glamour of the first two periods. Truck transportation had its beginning in 1911.

At first, the packing plants were local in nature and small in size. But as transportation facilities improved and the services were broadened, the plants increased in both numbers and volume of business. Today, there are about four thousand meat packing companies—large and small, national, sectional, and local—in all parts of the country. In volume of business, the industry as a whole ranks as one of the big three, along with the automobile and steel businesses. It is also interesting to note that the meat packing concerns regularly provide about one-fourth of the nation's manufactured food products. The American meat processing industry, humbly originating with the home slaughtering and curing by the colonists, has thus risen to the status of big business. This position has not been achieved by mere chance, but because of the services that these plants render to both the producer and the consumer.

EFFICIENCY AND LOW COST OF OPERATION

In addition to rendering these many valuable services, the modern meat packing industry has become great because of the efficiency and relatively low cost at which it has operated over a period of years. During the five-year period extending from 1959 to 1964, the net profit on each dollar of sales of meat and other products amounted to a mere 0.85 cent—earnings of 0.8 cent per dollar of sales. By contrast, it is noteworthy that the average earnings of 19 manufacturing companies in 1964 was 9.6 cents per dollar of sales, or more than 9 times greater.

Fig. 6-9. A Swift and Company branch house, Norfolk, Va. The nation-wide meat packing organizations maintain branch houses in the larger towns and cities. Here they receive their supplies in refrigerated cars and trucks directly from the meat packing plants, and they distribute their products to the customers in the area served. (Courtesy, Swift and Company)

As further evidence of efficiency and low cost of operation in the meat packing industry, it is interesting to note that from 1960 to 1964 the net profit of packing companies per 100 pounds live weight totaled 26 cents.[5] Thus, based on averages, for each 1,000-pound steer purchased, the packer netted $2.10 in profit; for each 200-pound hog, 52 cents; and for each 100-pound lamb, only 26 cents. Of course, the volume of sales (the number of hams sold in a given year), the efficiency in operations, and the utilization of by-products make it possible for the industry to operate on these comparatively small margins.

Obviously, the net profits in the meat packing industry have never been large enough to have any appreciable effect upon either meat or livestock prices. The gross margin is too small. Consequently, there is no justification for the housewife blaming the meat packer for high meat prices. Neither is there any basis for the producer blaming the packer for low market livestock prices. This situation is largely true because of the keen competition within the industry and the thousands of meat slaughtering and processing plants located throughout the country.

It should also be realized that, however much the consumer may complain about the high price of meat, the price would be higher if it were not for the careful attention that has been given to the manufacture and sale of by-products. Many times the packer actually pays out for a live animal more than is received from the sale of the dressed carcass. Under these conditions, the 30 to 55 percent non-meat portion of the live weight of a slaughter animal must be handled most efficiently in order to come out with any profit at all from the operations.

Geography of Meat Production and Consumption

About three-fifths of the livestock in the United States is produced west of the Mississippi River, whereas more than two-thirds of the meat is consumed east

[5] *Financial Facts About the Meat Packing Industry,* 1964, American Meat Institute, Chicago, Ill.

of this area. Specifically, the geography of meat production and consumption as applied to each class of meat animals is as follows:

1. About 70 per cent of the cattle are raised west of the Mississippi, whereas about 70 per cent of the beef is consumed east of the Mississippi.

2. About 53 per cent of the hogs are raised west of the Mississippi, whereas about 70 per cent of the pork is consumed east of the Mississippi.

3. About 80 per cent of the lambs are raised west of the Mississippi, whereas about 78 per cent of the lamb is consumed east of the Mississippi.

Fig. 6-10. This shows the geography of meat production and consumption. Note that the majority of production is in the West, whereas the majority of the consumption is in the East—thus making for a transportation problem. (Drawing by R. F. Johnson)

Under these conditions, either livestock or meats, or both, must be moved great distances from the surplus-producing regions of the West to the deficit-producing areas of the East. From a practical standpoint, it has been found to be more economical to slaughter animals in plants located in close proximity to the surplus-producing sections, to save the by-products, and then to transport the meat in refrigerator cars to the consuming sections than to ship the live animals. Also, it is not economical to ship live animals farther than necessary on account of deaths, injuries, bruises, shrinkage, and freight costs. With this procedure the average pound of meat is moved about one thousand miles from where it is produced to where it is consumed.

The Large National Meat Packers

Certain names loom large in the packing industry. In 1863, Philip D. Armour, in partnership with a Mr. Plankinton, established a meat packing enterprise at Milwaukee; and four years later Armour and Company set up business in Chicago. Gustavus F. Swift first opened a retail meat market of his own at Eastham, Massachusetts, in 1859; gradually he moved westward and opened up the Swift and Company, Chicago plant in 1877. The names of Armour and Swift, therefore, have long been landmarks in the meat packing industry. Later, the Cudahy Packing Company and Wilson and Company rounded out the "Big Four."

Swift, Armour and Wilson still hold a commanding lead in volume of business, but Cudahy is now in seventh place. The 10 leading packers in dollar sales value, based on the year 1964, are:[6]

Swift & Company	$2,610,056,365
Armour & Company	1,887,026,000
Geo. A. Hormel & Company	1,272,495,015
Wilson & Co., Inc.	766,392,826
John Morrell & Co.	655,678,682
Hygrade Food Products Corp.	454,333,499
Cudahy Packing Company	329,604,252
Oscar Mayer & Co., Inc.	295,965,795
Rath Packing Company	277,295,517
Tobin Packing Co., Inc.	177,552,794

Decentralization of Meat Packing

Following World War I, a trend toward geographical decentralization of the industry became apparent. This represented attempts to seek the optimum plant location between supplies of livestock and the market for meat. These new plants are commonly referred to as interior plants.

This gradual shift in location of slaughter has decreased the relative importance of some of the leading terminal markets. The major packers, located on the old established central markets, have countered this move through decentralization of their own operations, chiefly through direct buying and purchases of some of the interior plants.

Without doubt, the most important single factor contributing to the decentralization of meat packing was the development and use of motor trucks, together with the extension of hard-surfaced roads. Other factors that have favored the development of interior plants are: improved market information, increased feed and livestock production in certain areas, saving in transportation rates by marketing closer to home, and more favorable labor costs in certain areas.

METHODS OF MARKETING LIVESTOCK

The producer of livestock is confronted with the perplexing problem of determining where and how to market his animals. Usually there is a choice of outlets, and the one selected often varies with different species of livestock and among sections of the country. The methods of marketing also differ between slaughter and feeder animals, and all of these differ from the marketing of purebreds.

---

[6]*Moody's Industrial Manual, 1965,* Moody's Investor's Service, New York, N. Y.

Prior to the advent of terminal public markets in 1865, country selling accounted for virtually all sales of livestock. But sales of livestock in the country declined with the growth of terminal markets, until the latter method reached its peak at the time of World War I. Country selling was reactivated by the large nation-wide packers beginning about 1920, in order to meet the increased buying competition of the small interior packers. The decline in the proportion of all livestock moving through terminal public markets was largely accounted for by the growth in country selling until the late 1930's and by the growth in auctions since.

In 1966, meat packers (1,337 of them) purchased their animals through the following channels:[7]

	Cattle (%)	Calves (%)	Sheep (%)	Hogs (%)
Direct, country dealers, etc..............	49.2	33.7	64.6	62.7
Terminal markets	31.0	15.7	21.9	22.1
Auctions..	19.8	50.6	13.5	15.2

Of course, it is generally recognized that these figures are continuing to shift, with terminal market sales decreasing and with auction and country sales increasing.

Recently, a number of states have enacted "livestock market development acts," designed to (1) assure financial responsibility, (2) favor competitive selling, in contrast to non-market channels in the purchase and sale of livestock, and (3) make for improved market facilities and practice.

Terminal Public Markets

Terminal public markets (also referred to as terminal markets, central markets, public stockyards, and public markets) *are livestock trading centers, where livestock are assembled at a single geographic location in large numbers to be sold on a private treaty basis, and which possess facilities for receiving, caring for, handling, and selling livestock.* Sixty U.S. markets are so classified. Various numbers of commission firms, depending on the size of the market, sell livestock at these markets; and all buyers and sellers of livestock are privileged to use these facilities.

The first of the present terminal public markets was established at Chicago in 1865; and most of the larger terminal markets operating today were established in the latter half of the nineteenth century.

Up through World War I, the majority of slaughter livestock in the United States was sold through terminal public markets by farmers and local buyers shipping to them. Since then, the importance of these markets has declined in relation to other outlets, as shown in Fig. 6-11 and Table 6-2. But these figures do not tell the whole story. When the total slaughter of all commercial establishments

---

[7] *Packers and Stockyards Résumé,* Packers and Stockyards Administration, U. S. Department of Agriculture, Vol. V, No. 12, Nov. 24, 1967.

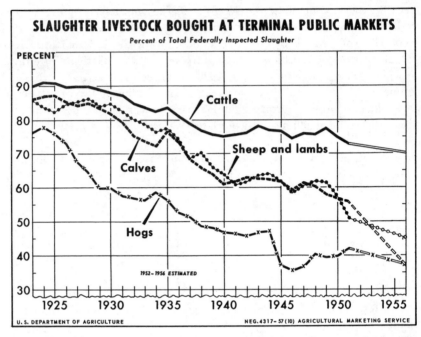

Fig. 6-11. Terminal public markets have declined in relation to other market channels.

TABLE 6—2

PER CENT OF CATTLE AND HOGS BOUGHT BY PACKERS
ON TERMINAL MARKETS[1]

Class of Animal	1950	1964
Cattle...	75	36.5
Hogs..	40	24

[1]*Food from Farmer to Consumer,* Report of the National Commission on Food Marketing, June 1966, p. 22.

is considered, the percentage bought at terminal markets is somewhat less; this is so because nonfederally inspected slaughterers tend to buy larger proportions of their livestock at markets other than terminal markets.

Despite the declining importance of terminal public markets in relation to other market channels, it is noteworthy that (1) they are still a major livestock market outlet, and (2) since 1920, their receipts of cattle and calves have remained fairly steady, although their receipts of hogs, sheep, and lambs have declined (see Fig. 6-12). In 1966, terminal public markets handled almost 16.5 million head of cattle, 2.1 million head of calves, 23.7 million head of hogs, and 6.4 million sheep and lambs.[8]

_____

[8]*Agricultural Statistics, 1967,* USDA, pp. 375, 386 and 403.

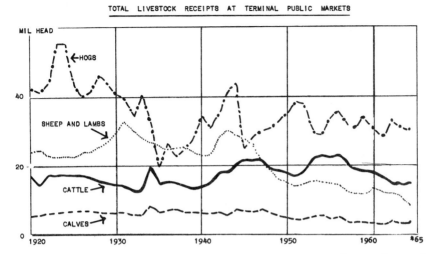

Fig. 6-12. Terminal public markets are still an important and integral part of the livestock marketing system.

Most of the large public markets are located in or adjacent to the Corn Belt. However, several large markets for calves are in Texas and Oklahoma, while several of the large lamb markets are in Texas, Colorado, and Utah.

ESSENTIAL FACTORS OPERATING IN A TERMINAL PUBLIC MARKET

A modern terminal market is a very complex organization, and the larger it is the more complex it becomes. Among the more essential factors operating in each large terminal market are: (1) stockyards company, (2) commission companies or firms, (3) buyers, (4) livestock exchange, (5) traders livestock exchange, (6) banks, (7) market news services, and (8) federal and state agencies.

TERMINAL MARKETING PROCEDURE

Briefly, the steps through which slaughter animals usually pass from the farm or ranch to and through the terminal market and on to their final destination are as follows:

1. Animals are transported to the terminal market by truck or rail, with the former method most commonly used for short hauls and the latter for long distances. When rail shipments are used, federal supervisors check for the compliance with the 28 hour law, requiring that animals in transit for more than 28 hours be fed, watered, and rested for 5 hours before resuming transportation.

2. Representatives of the stockyard company receive, unload, count, yard the animals in pens assigned to the commission company to which the shipment is consigned, and feed and water the animals as directed by the commission company.

3. The salesman for the commission company makes the best sale possible to a packer buyer, order buyer, yard trader, or local butcher.

4. The stockyards company then weighs, counts, records, and delivers or reships the animals to their final destination.

5. Following the sale of the animals, the commission company promptly remits to the consignor the net proceeds, deducting transportation charges, yardage, feed, commission, insurance, etc. The proper commission is retained by the commission company; and it assumes full responsibility for payment of the other bills for which deductions are made from the proceeds.

6. At the larger market one or more conveniently located banks facilitate

Fig. 6-13. Terminal public market functional chart. (Prepared by the American Stockyards Association)

prompt payment by the buyer and the earliest possible remittance to the consignor by the commission company.

7. The livestock exchange and traders' livestock exchange, which exist on most of the larger markets, insure fair dealings and integrity on the part of their members and require that they post bond as a guarantee of financial responsibility.

8. Federal meat inspectors, functioning under the Meat Inspection Act of 1906, make ante-mortem and post-mortem inspections of all slaughter animals. They also enforce sanitary regulations covering both the yards and packing plants. In intrastate yards and plants, similar service is rendered by the respective state departments of agriculture.

9. Federal officials, operating under the provisions of the Packers and Stockyards Act, ascertain that fair and competitive practices are observed by the packers and commission companies and that reasonable charges are made for marketing services rendered.

10. Health-control officials, both state and federal, enforce such practices as will prevent the spread of contagious diseases. They especially supervise shipments of stocker, feeder, and breeding animals back to the farm or ranch or the reshipment of fat animals to another market.

11. In marketing western cattle, brand inspectors maintain a constant vigilance for stolen or stray animals.

12. The various market news services—including Federal Market News Service (operating through the media of newspapers, radio broadcasts, and their own federal publications), the *Drovers Journal,* and market information supplied by commission men—keep both buyers and sellers well informed regarding supplies and prices.

CHARGES AT TERMINAL PUBLIC MARKETS

Stockmen need to be acquainted with livestock marketing costs, although it is recognized that rates vary slightly (1) according to services and facilities utilized and the size of consignment, and (2) between markets. Table 6-3 shows the average terminal marketing charges per head paid by producers.

TABLE 6—3

AVERAGE TERMINAL PUBLIC MARKET CHARGES PER HEAD
PAID BY PRODUCERS IN 1966[1]

Species	Yardage	Feed	Sales Commission	Services[2]	Total
	←——————— (dollars per head) ———————→				
Cattle	1.40	.25	1.50	.20	3.35
Calves	.65	.10	.65	.03	1.43
Sheep and lambs	.28	.10	.32	.02	.72
Hogs	.42	.10	.50	.03	1.05

[1]Figures provided by the *Drovers Journal,* in a personal communication to the author from Allan W. McGhee, Editor.
[2]Includes bedding.

Commission fees are the major charges paid by producers or other shippers at terminal markets, usually accounting for about one-half of the total charges. Yardage charges account for approximately one-third of the total marketing charges, whereas feed and service charges are relatively minor.

Livestock Auction Markets

Livestock auctions (also referred to as sales barns, livestock auction agencies, community sales, and community auctions) *are trading centers where animals are sold by public bidding to the buyer who offers the highest price per hundredweight or per head.*

This method of selling livestock in this country is very old, apparently being copied from Great Britain where auction sales date back many centuries.

Apparently the auction method of selling was used in many of the colonies as a means of disposing of property, imported goods, secondhand household furnishings, farm utensils, and animals.

According to available records, the first public livestock auction sale was held in Ohio in 1836 by the Ohio Company, whose business was importing English cattle. This event also marked the first sale of purebred cattle ever held in America.

Although there are some records of occasional livestock auction sales during the nineteenth century, there is no indication of any auction market that continued operation throughout the period of the greatest development of terminal public stockyards markets. It is within the current century that present auction

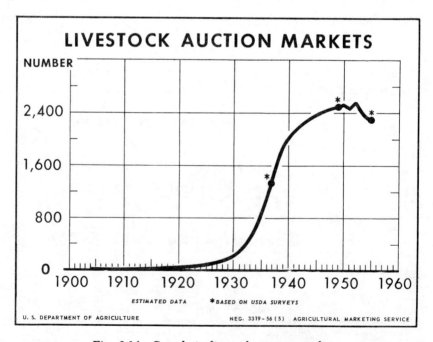

Fig. 6-14. Growth in livestock auction markets.

development had its beginning. In fact, livestock auction markets have had their greatest growth since 1930, both in numbers established and the extensiveness of the area over which they operate.

Figure 6-14 shows the growth in numbers of livestock auctions. About 200 auctions were operating by 1930; by 1937, this number had increased to 1,345. The peak in numbers was reached in 1952, when over 2,500 different livestock auctions were holding sales; but, by 1959, the total number had declined to about 2,300.

Several factors contributed to the phenomenal growth in auction markets during the 1930s, chief of which were the following:

1. The decentralization of markets. Associated with this was the improvement and extension of hard-surfaced roads accompanied by the increased use of trucks as a means of transporting livestock to and from the market place. Use of trucks increased flexibility in handling of various sized lots of livestock and in the direction of movement; and, with the advent of better roads, trucks could be used for transporting livestock moderate distances both quickly and economically. Also, growing numbers of small packers, located at distant points from terminal markets, were able to procure livestock more efficiently at auction markets.

2. The development of more uniform class and grade designations for livestock.

3. Improvements made by the federal government in providing more extensive collection and dissemination of market news.

4. The greater convenience afforded in disposing of small lots of livestock and in purchasing stockers, feeders, and breeding animals.

5. The recognized educational value of these nearby markets, which enabled producers to keep currently informed of local market conditions and livestock prices.

6. The Depression of 1930-33. When livestock prices are low—such as was true during the depression years—transportation and other marketing expenses comprise a greater part of the total gross value received from the sale of livestock. Since at this time the commission charges at most auctions were based on a percentage of the gross sale value of the animal, marketing expenses at auctions tended to be low when prices were low. Also, with the proximity of auctions to producing areas, out-of-pocket transportation expenses were less for livestock sent to local auction than for shipments to more distant market outlets.

7. The abnormal feed distribution. This was caused by the droughts of 1934 and 1936 in the western Corn Belt and Range states, which created conditions favoring increased sales at auctions. Some immature and unfinished stock in these areas were sold at nearby auctions to farmers having a plentiful supply of feed on hand. Also, stocker and feeder cattle were shipped out of the drought sections to auctions located in areas where feed supplies were more abundant.

8. The desire to sell near home. By contrast to large public terminal markets which receive some livestock from considerable distances, auction markets draw their supplies largely from communities in which they are located.

Prior to the advent of community livestock auctions, the small livestock operator had two main market outlets for his animals: (1) shipping them to the nearest terminal public market or (2) selling them to buyers who came to his farm or ranch. Sometimes, the first method was too expensive because of the transportation distance involved and the greater expense in shipping small lots. The second method pretty much put the producer at the mercy of the buyer, because he had no good alternative to taking the price he was offered, and often he did not know the value of his animals. By contrast, the big operator is not particularly concerned about these things. Because of his large scale, usually he can take advantage of any of several terminal markets, and he knows enough about values that he can deal satisfactorily with buyers who come to his farm or ranch. Thus, community livestock auctions are really of greatest importance to the small operator.

In 1955, Iowa was the leading state in numbers of auctions, with 185 in operation; Texas was second with 151. The nation's largest livestock auction market, in total animals sold and gross dollar volume, is the Norfolk Live Stock Sales Co., Norfolk, Nebraska; whereas the world's largest cattle auction market is the Amarillo Livestock Auction, Amarillo, Texas.

CHARGES AT AUCTIONS

Rates charged for marketing livestock vary at different auctions. Services for which charges are levied may include selling, yardage, weighing, insurance, brand inspection, and health inspection. Many auctions do not provide all of these services. A commission or selling fee, however, is charged at all markets and is the primary source of income to auction operators. At some auctions, the commission covers yardage and weighing in addition to the selling service. Some operators levy a separate charge for each service provided, while others charge a single rate to cover all services.

Auction operators levy their charge, on a per head basis, on a percentage of gross value, or by a combination of these two methods.

Straight per head charges vary considerably. However, it is estimated that they will average about as follows on a per head basis: cattle, $2.90; calves, $2.50; sheep, $0.70; and hogs, $0.70. For auctions reporting straight percentage charges, the most usual rates are from 3 to 5 per cent.

Country Selling

Country selling refers to producers' sales of livestock direct to packers, local dealers, or farmers without the support of commission men, selling agents, buying agents, or brokers.

Prior to the advent of terminal public markets in 1865, country selling accounted for virtually all sales of livestock. Sales of livestock in the country declined with the growth of terminal markets until the latter method reached its peak of selling at the time of World War I. But country buying was accelerated by the large nation-wide packers following World War I in order to meet the increased buying competition of the small interior packers. The decline in the proportion of all livestock moving through terminal public markets was largely accounted for by the growth in country selling until the late 1930's and by the growth in auctions since.

Like auction selling, direct selling has a certain appeal, inasmuch as it permits producers to observe and exercise some control over selling while it takes place; whereas consignment to distant terminal public markets at times represents an irreversible commitment to sell. Large and more specialized livestock farmers feel competent to sell their livestock direct.

Improved highways and trucking facilitated the growth of country selling. Farmers were no longer tied to outlets located at important railroad terminals or river crossings. Livestock could move in any direction. Improved communications, such as the radio and telephone, and an expanded market information service, also aided in the development of country selling of livestock, especially in sales direct to packers.

Direct selling to meat packers is an important outlet for slaughter animals in many areas. Some packers buy direct from producers at the plant; others send their buyers into the country, from farm to farm or feedlot to feedlot, where they make bids on the livestock that they inspect.

Local dealers operate in all parts of the country. These include country buying operations by local buyers, by contract buyers for later delivery, by buyers purchasing on order for others, and by a variety of speculative buyers. Speculative buyers are known by a variety of names in different parts of the country; they are sometimes called livestock buyers, traders, scalpers, truck buyers, stock buyers, pin-hookers, and scavengers. Some of the country buyers purchase livestock at fixed establishments similar to packer-owned country buying points.

Selling on Basis of Carcass Grade and Weight

It is generally agreed that there is need for a system of marketing which favors payment for a high cut-out value of primal cuts and a quality product. Selling on the basis of carcass grade and weight fulfills these needs.

This is the most common method of marketing hogs in Denmark, Sweden, and Canada. The bargaining is in terms of the price to be paid per hundred pounds dressed weight for carcasses that meet certain grade specifications. It is the most accurate and unassailable evaluation of the value of a carcass. From the standpoint of the packer, this procedure is more time-consuming than the conventional basis of buying, and there is less flexibility in the operations.

In general, farmers who produce superior animals benefit from selling on the basis of carcass grade and weight, whereas the producers of lower quality animals usually feel that this method unjustly discriminates against them. In countries where rail grading has been used extensively, there has been an unmistakable improvement in the breeding and feeding of swine. Denmark, Sweden, and Canada have effectively followed this type of program in producing high quality bacon, chiefly for export to the London market.

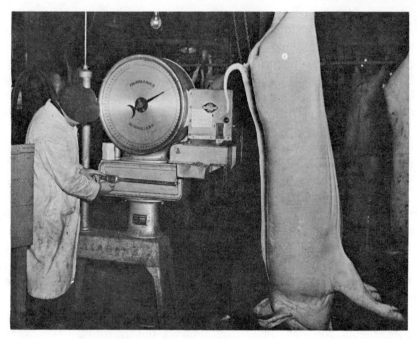

Fig. 6-15. Weighing Canadian hog carcasses. Selling on the basis of carcass grade and yield is the most common method of marketing hogs in Denmark, Sweden, and Canada. (Courtesy, Dept. of Agri., Ottawa, Canada)

The **factors favorable** to selling on the basis of carcass grade and weight may be summarized as follows:

1. It encourages the breeding and feeding of quality animals.

2. It provides the most unassailable evaluation of the product.

3. It eliminates wasteful filling on the market.

4. It makes it possible to trace losses from condemnations, bruises, and soft pork to the producer responsible for them.

5. It is the most effective approach to animal improvement.

The **factors unfavorable** to selling on the basis of carcass grade and weight are:

1. The procedure is more time-consuming than the conventional basis of buying.

2. There is less flexibility in the operations.

3. The physical difficulty of handling the vast United States volume of animals on this basis is great.

An estimated 8 to 10 per cent of cattle were marketed on grade and yield in 1964—over 25 per cent in Iowa and as high as 20 per cent in some western states.[9] About 3 per cent of hogs were sold on grade and yield in 1964, with some large firms buying over 15 per cent on that basis.[10]

---

[9] *Food from Farmer to Consumer,* Report of the National Commission on Food Marketing, June 1966, p. 23.
[10] *Ibid.*

Effective April 6, 1968, the U.S. Department of Agriculture issued the following uniform regulations where meat packers buy livestock on the basis of carcass grade, carcass weight, or a combination of the two:

1. Make known to the seller, before the sale, the significant details of the purchase contract.

2. Maintain the identity of each seller's livestock and carcass.

3. Maintain sufficient records to substantiate settlement for each purchase transaction.

4. Make payment on the basis of actual carcass weight before carcasses are shrouded.

5. Use hooks, rollers, gambrels and similar equipment of uniform weight in weighing carcasses from the same species of livestock in each packing plant; and include only the weight of this equipment in the actual weight of the container.

6. Make payment on the basis of final USDA carcass grades or furnish the seller with detailed written specifications for any other grades used in determining final payment.

7. Grade carcasses by the close of the second business day following the day of slaughter.

Selling Purebred Animals

Selling purebred animals is a highly specialized and scientific business. Purebred animals are usually sold at private treaty directly to other purebred breeders or commercial producers or through auctions which may either be sponsored by one or a few breeders (joint sales or consignment sales).

In general, the vast majority of males of all species saved for breeding purposes go into commercial herds and flocks. Only the elite sires are retained with the hope of effecting further breed improvement in purebred herds. On the other hand, the sale of purebred females is fairly well restricted to meeting the requirements for replacement purposes in existing purebred herds or for establishing new purebred herds.

Most consignment sales are sponsored by a breed association, either local, state-wide, or national in character. Such auctions, therefore, are usually limited to one breed. Purebred auction sales are conducted by highly specialized auctioneers. In addition to being good salesmen, such auctioneers must have a keen knowledge of values and be familiar with blood lines of the breeding stock.

Choice of Market Outlets

Marketing is dynamic; thus changes are inevitable in types of market outlets, market structures, and market services. Some outlets have gained in importance; others have declined.

The choice of a market outlet represents the seller's evaluation of the most favorable market among the number of alternatives available to him. No simple

Fig. 6-16. A purebred bull sale at Toronto, Ontario, Canada. Note the ring and the bull in it, the auction stand, and the large crowd. Purebred auction sales are conducted by highly specialized auctioneers. (Photo by James E. Rose, Toronto, Canada)

and brief statement of criteria can be given as a guide to the choice of the most favorable market channel. Rather, an evaluation is required of the contributions made by alternative markets in terms of available services offered, selling costs, the competitive nature of the pricing process, and ultimately the producer's net return. Thus, an accurate appraisal is not simple.

From time to time, producers can be expected to shift from one type of market outlet to another. Because price changes at different market outlets do not take place simultaneously, nor in the same amount, nor even in the same direction, one market may be the most advantageous outlet for a particular class and grade of livestock at one time, but another may be more advantageous at some other time. The situation may differ for different classes and kinds of livestock and may vary from one area to another.

Regardless of the channel through which the producer markets his livestock, in one way or another he pays, or bears, either in the price received from the livestock or otherwise, the entire cost of marketing. Because of this, he should never choose a market because of convenience or habit, or because of personal acquaintance with the market and its operator. Rather, the choice should be determined strictly by the net returns from the sale of his livestock; effective selling and net returns are more important than selling costs.

PREPARING AND SHIPPING LIVESTOCK

Improper handling of livestock immediately prior to and during shipment may result in excess shrinkage; high death, bruise, and crippling losses; disappointing sales; and dissatisfied buyers. Unfortunately, many stockmen who do a superb job of producing animals dissipate all the good things that have gone before by doing a poor job of preparing and shipping to market. Generally speaking, such omissions are due to lack of know-how, rather than any deliberate attempt to take advantage of anyone. Even if the sale is consummated prior to delivery, negligence at shipping time will make for a dissatisfied customer. Buyers soon learn what to expect from various producers and place their bids accordingly.

In addition to the important specific considerations covered in the sections which follow, these general considerations should be accorded in preparing livestock for shipment and in transporting them to market:

1. **Select the best suited method of transportation.**—The stockman should decide between truck and rail transportation on the basis of which method best suits his particular situation.

2. **Feed properly prior to loading out.**—Never ship animals on an excess fill. Instead, withhold grain feeding 12 hours before loading (omit one feed), and do not allow cattle and sheep access to water within 2 to 3 hours of shipment. Cattle and sheep may be allowed free access to dry, well-cured grass hay up to loading time, but more laxative-type hays, such as alfalfa or clover, should not be fed within 12 hours of shipment even if the animals were accustomed to them previously. Likewise, animals on green or succulent feed should be conditioned to dry feeds prior to shipment.

Animals that are too full of concentrated or succulent feeds or full of water at the time of loading will scour and urinate excessively. As a result, the floors become dirty and slippery and the animals befoul themselves. Such animals undergo a heavy shrink and present an unattractive appearance when unloaded. Abrupt ration changes of any kind prior to shipment should be avoided. Occasionally, a misinformed cattleman withholds water, but gives a liberal feeding of salt prior to shipment to obtain maximum water consumption and fill on the market. This "sharp" practice cannot be condemned too strongly; it is cruel to animals and experienced buyers are never deceived.

3. **Keep animals quiet.**—Prior to and during shipment, animals should be handled carefully. Hot, excited animals are subject to more shrinkage, disease, and injury; and with cattle, there is more dark cutting[11] if they are slaughtered following shipment.

If the cattle or sheep are trailed on-foot to the shipping point, they should be moved slowly and allowed to rest and to drink moderately prior to loading. Although loading may be exasperating at times, take it easy; never lose your temper. Avoid hurrying, loud hollering, and striking. Never beat an animal

---

[11]Brady, D. E. and H. B. Hedrick, *Journal of Animal Science*, Nov. 1956, Vol. 15, No. 4, p. 1290; and
Hedrick, H. B., D. E. Brady, and C. W. Turner, *Proceedings of the Ninth Research Conference*, sponsored by the Council on Research, American Meat Institute, at the University of Chicago, March 22-23, 1957.

with such objects as pipes, sticks, canes, or forks; instead, use either (a) a flat, wide canvas slapper with a handle or (b) an electric prod (the latter judiciously).

4. Consider health certificates, permits, and brand inspection in interstate shipments.—When animals are to be shipped into another state, the shipper should check into and comply with the state regulations relative to health certificates, permits, and brand inspection. Usually, the local veterinarian or railroad agent will have this information. Should there be any question about the health regulations, however, the state livestock sanitary board (usually located at the state capital) of the state of destination should be consulted. Knowledge of any compliance with such regulations well in advance of shipment will avoid frustrations and costly delays.

5. Comply with the 28-hour law in rail shipments.[12]—Actually, the shipper has no alternative to taking advantage of feed and rest stops during long hauls by rail; by federal law, passed in 1873, livestock cannot be transported by rail for a longer period than 28 consecutive hours without unloading for the purpose of giving feed, water, and rest for a period of at least 5 consecutive hours before resuming transportation. The period may be extended to 36 hours upon written request from the owner of the animals; and most experienced shippers routinely so request. With less than carload lots (LCL shipments), the owner may provide feed and water in the car with instructions that the animals be fed and watered enroute.

The shipper may instruct the railway company on the kind and amount of feed to be given in transit, with these instructions written on the waybill or on the livestock contract which each shipper signs. If no such instructions are given by the owner of the livestock, the amount of feed prescribed by the U.S. Department of Agriculture is given at the livestock feeding yards. The feeding is done by the railway company crew, and charge is made to the shipper for the amount of feed consumed.

Where two or more cars of stock are shipped, the railroad will provide a free ticket for a caretaker, including return to the point of origin. When shipping by rail and where possible, it is recommended that the shipper take advantage of this arrangement. When this is done, the caretaker can make certain that the animals are properly fed and given access to clean water at the stops enroute; also, under certain circumstances, it may be wise to allow animals to make as much as a 12-hour rest stop and to feed twice before reloading.

6. Feed or graze in transit if advantageous.—In some cases, where stockmen graze or finish cattle or sheep at points distant from their base of operations, privileges are granted so that animals may be grazed or fed in transit from 1 day to 12 months. For example, through this arrangement, a Montana rancher might bill his livestock to the Chicago stockyards, but with the privilege of stopping in Minnesota (or some other intermediate point) to

---

[12] No such law applies to truck transportation of animals.

finish them out over a period up to one year, before finally putting them on the Chicago market. Under these circumstances, the shipper would pay one rate with the stopover charge instead of paying a rate from his shipping point in Montana to the point in Minnesota, and another from the intermediate point in Minnesota to Chicago. These regulations apply only to certain specified conditions, which can be determined by making inquiry of the local railroad agent.

7. **Use partitions when necessary.**—When mixed loads (consisting of cattle, sheep, and/or hogs) are placed in the same truck or car, partition each class off separately. Also, partition younger animals from older animals, and separate cripples, stags, and males; tie bulls.

8. **Avoid shipping during extremes in weather.**—Whenever possible, avoid shipping when the weather is either very hot or very cold. During such times, shrinkage and death losses are higher than normal. During warm weather, avoid transporting animals during the heat of the day; travel at night, or in the evening or early morning.

Additional points pertinent to proper preparing and shipping livestock are covered in the sections which follow.

How to Prevent Bruises, Crippling, and Death Losses

Losses from bruising, crippling, and death that occur during the marketing process represent a part of the cost of marketing livestock; and, indirectly, the producer foots most of the bill.

Most bruises are caused by horned cattle; by projections in feed lots, motor trucks, cars, and stockyards; by failure to partition off different kinds and classes of livestock in cars or trucks properly; by overloading or underloading; and by rough and careless handling. A careful analysis of the cause of bruises indicates that most of this loss could be prevented. Unfortunately, unless cuts or bumps are present, most bruises cannot be detected until after the animals have been slaughtered. This being true, and because market animals are purchased on the basis of live weight in the United States, slaughter buyers take the probable loss into consideration at the time of purchase. This procedure is entirely justified because bruises render the particular spot unfit for human food.

It is estimated that the annual losses accruing from bruises, crippling, and death have a monetary value of $25,000,000. In a nationwide survey, involving 775,000 hogs and 163,000 cattle, Livestock Conservation, Inc., found that 8.5 per cent of all market hogs and 6.4 per cent of all market cattle show unmistakable and costly carcass bruises.

The same factors that are responsible for bruising are also responsible for much of the loss from death and crippling. The following observations have been made relative to crippling and death losses:

1. Crippling in hogs is more common than in other species; the incidence of crippling in calves, cattle, and sheep ranks after hogs in the order named.

2. Death losses in calves are higher than is encountered in any other kind

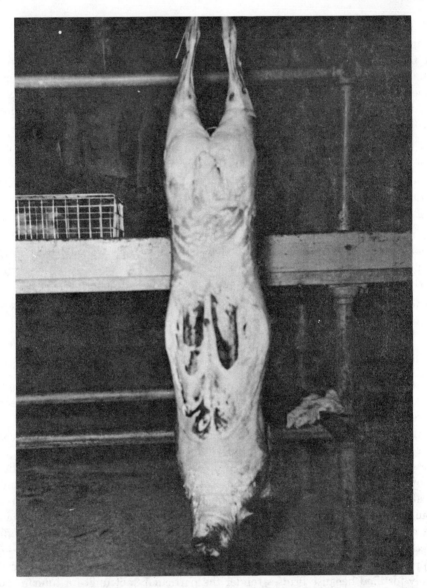

Fig. 6-17. A bruised lamb carcass showing trimming losses. Total losses from bruises trimmed out in U.S. slaughter plants cost millions of dollars, and, indirectly, the producer foots most of the bill. (Courtesy, Armour and Company, Spokane)

or class of livestock. From the standpoint of species, sheep have the highest death loss in marketing, followed by hogs and cattle.

3. In-transit losses from crippling and death are higher among thin, emaciated, or overfinished animals than among animals in a strong, vigorous condition.

4. Extreme heat or cold, or sudden temperature changes, lead to increased crippling and death losses.

5. The nutrition of the animals during the growing-finishing period is a major factor.

Although the connotation of the word "crippled" varies somewhat from market to market, usually an animal that arrives in such condition that it cannot walk into pens unassisted is recorded as a cripple. Badly crippled animals are generally bought subject to inspection. Dead animals are sent to the rendering tanks.

The following precautions are suggested as a means of reducing market losses from bruises, crippling, and death:

1. Dehorn cattle, preferably when young.

2. Remove projecting nails, splinters, and broken boards in feed racks and fences.

3. Keep feedlots free from old machinery, trash, and any obstacles that may bruise.

4. Do not feed grain heavily just prior to loading.

5. Use good loading chutes; not too steep.

6. Bed with sand free from stones, to prevent slipping.

7. Cover sand with straw in cold weather (especially for calves, sheep, goats, and hogs), but use no straw for hogs in hot weather.

8. Wet the sand bedding in summer before loading hogs and while enroute. Drench when necessary.

9. Partition all packing sows from lightweight butchers.

10. Provide covers for trucks to protect from sun in summer and cold in winter.

11. Always partition mixed loads into separate classes, and partition calves from cattle.

12. Have upper deck of truck high enough to prevent back bruises on calves below.

13. Remove protruding nails, bolts, or any sharp objects in truck or car.

14. Load slowly to prevent crowding against sharp corners and to avoid excitement. Do not overload.

15. Use canvas slappers instead of clubs or canes.

16. Tie all bulls in truck or car, and partition boars, stags, and cripples.

17. Place "bull board" in position and secure before car door is closed on loaded cattle.

18. Drive carefully. Slow down on sharp turns and avoid sudden stops.

19. Inspect load enroute to prevent trampling of animals that may be down.

20. Back truck slowly and squarely against unloading dock.

21. Unload slowly. Do not drop animals from upper to lower deck; use cleated inclines.

22. Never lift sheep by the wool.

All of these precautions are simple to apply; yet all are violated every day of the year.

Number of Animals in a Railroad Car and in a Truck

Overcrowding of market animals causes heavy losses. Sometimes a railroad car or a truck is overloaded in an attempt to effect a saving in hauling charges. More frequently, however, it is simply the result of not knowing space requirements.

Normally, railroad cars are either 36 or 40 feet in length, but truck beds are variable in size. The size of the car or truck, and the class and size of animals, determine the number of head that should be loaded therein. For comfort in shipping, the car or truck should be loaded heavily enough so that the animals stand close together, but both overloading and underloading should be avoided. Tables 6-4 and 6-5 give some indication as to the number of market animals that may be loaded in a railroad car or truck.

TABLE 6—4

ANIMALS PER RAILROAD CAR[1]

Car Size	Kind and Weight of Animals		
	Cattle, 1,000 Pounds (454 kg)	Lambs, 100 Pounds (45.4 kg)	Hogs, 225 Pounds (102 kg)
36 foot car (11 m)..........	26	110	73
40 foot car (12 m)..........	28	125	81

[1]Recommendations of Western Weighing and Inspection Bureau, Chicago, Illinois. In loading double deck cars, the upper deck should contain 10% fewer than the lower deck.

TABLE 6—5

NUMBER OF ANIMALS FOR SAFE LOADING IN A TRUCK[1]

Length of Truck Floor	Kind and Weight of Animals		
	Cattle	Lambs	Hogs & Calves
(ft.)	(1,000 lbs.) (454 kg)	(100 lbs.) (45.4 kg)	(222 lbs.) (100.8 kg)
8 (2.4 m)....................	4	20	16
12 (3.7 m)....................	7	31	24
15 (4.6 m)....................	9	40	30
20 (6.1 m)....................	12	54	40
24 (7.3 m)....................	15	65	48

[1]Recommendations of Livestock Conservation, Inc., Chicago, Illinois.

Shrinkage in Marketing Animals

The shrinkage (or drift) refers to the weight loss encountered from the time animals leave the farm or feedlot until they are weighed over the scales at the market. Thus, if a steer weighed 1,000 pounds at the feedlot and had a market weight of 970 pounds, the shrinkage would be 30 pounds or 3.0 per cent. Shrink is usually expressed in terms of percentage. Most of this weight loss is *excretory shrink,* or in the form of feces and urine, and the moisture in the expired air. On the other hand, there is some *tissue shrinkage*, which results from metabolic or breaking-down changes.

Shrinkage is of importance because the carcass meat is the most valuable portion of the animal. For this reason, dressed yield is one of the most important factors taken into consideration by packers in buying livestock for slaughter.

The most important factors affecting shrinkage are:

1. **Fill.**—The fill refers to the amount of feed and water consumed by animals upon their arrival at the market and prior to selling. Normally, the fill of hogs consists of a feed or some grain (small grains are ground) common to the area, and water, whereas the fill of cattle and sheep consists of hay and water, although grain-fed animals may be given some concentrate. Naturally, the larger fill animals take, the smaller the shrinkage.

Because animals transported via motor truck may not have remained off feed too long, there is an increasing tendency not to feed and water them prior to selling on the market. This saving in feed and expense seems to be economically sound.

2. **Time and distance in transit.**—The longer the animals are in transit and the greater the distance, the higher the total shrinkage. Also, the shrink takes place at a rapid rate during the first part of the haul, and then decreases as time in transit progresses.

3. **Truck vs. rail transportation.**—Based on practical experience and observation, most stockmen are of the opinion (1) that truck shipments result in less shrinkage than rail shipments for short distances, and (2) that rail shipments result in less shrinkage than truck shipments for long distances.

4. **Season.**—Extremes in temperature, either very hot or very cold weather, result in higher shrinkage.

5. **Age and weight.**—Young animals of all species shrink proportionally more than older animals, because of their lower carcass yield caused by less body fat and greater amount of fill in proportion to live weight. Likewise, feeder cattle shrink about 25 per cent more than finished cattle.

6. **Overloading.**—Overloading always results in abnormally high shrinkage.

7. **Rough ride, abnormal feeding, and mixed loads.**—Each of these factors will increase shrinkage.

On the average, the following shrinkage is obtained on market animals:

Cattle . . . . from 3 to 6 per cent
Sheep . . . . from 6 to 10 per cent
Hogs . . . . from 1 to 2 per cent

DOCKAGE

Dockage refers to deductions made in the live weight of market animals because of excessive dressing losses, or because part of the product is of low quality. Some common dockages on livestock markets are:

1. **Piggy sows.**—Usually docked 40 pounds, but may range from 0 to 50 pounds, depending on the market.

2. **Stags (hogs).**—Usually docked 70 pounds, but may range from 40 to 80 pounds, depending on the market.

3. **Cattle with lumpy jaw.**—Usually bought subject to the amount of wastage.

LIVESTOCK MARKET NEWS SERVICES

Accurate market news is essential to the efficient marketing of livestock, both from the standpoint of the buyer and the seller. In the days of trailing, the meager market reports available were largely conveyed by word of mouth. Moreover, the time required to move livestock from the farm or ranch to market was so great that detailed market information would have been of little benefit even if it had been available. With the speed in transportation afforded by railroads and trucks, late information on market conditions became important.

The Federal Market News Service was initiated by the U.S. Department of Agriculture, beginning in 1916. This service was established for the purpose of providing unbiased and uniformly interpretable market information. Livestock markets are covered by the Federal Market News Service. This network of branch offices is connected by a system of leased telegraph wires so that the central office in Washington, D.C., as well as each of the branches, receive several reports daily from every other office. Practically all of the branch offices collect and report livestock information, but only a few cover meat and wool. Nevertheless, livestock, meat, and wool statistics are included in the service. The market information is assembled and widely disseminated through the media of (1) newspapers, (2) the radio, and (3) a considerable number of daily, weekly, monthly, and annual reports distributed directly by the Federal Market News Service. The Federal Market News Service relies upon local and privately owned newspapers and radios, merely supplying them with the market reports. Because at least a part of the readers or listeners are interested in this type of information, the local papers and radio stations are usually glad to serve as media for disseminating these reports.

The chief contributions of the Federal Market News Service may be summarized as follows: (1) A common terminology has come to be established from market to market, thus a slaughter steer which will grade Good at Chicago would be designated the same grade at every other market in the country, and (2) more adequate facilities for the dissemination of market information have been provided.

But as terminal markets came to represent a decreasing fraction of livestock trading, market reports emanating therefrom were not the only, if indeed the best, price barometer. U.S. Department of Agriculture market news reporters are endeavoring to improve livestock sales coverage by reporting more prices from non-terminal sales. But the latter is not without its problems; such transactions are widely scattered, gathering this information is costly and difficult, and market reporters lack authority to examine actual invoices or to verify the accuracy of reports given them. Better information is needed to help keep sellers abreast of changing market conditions and current and prospective prices at available alternative outlets.

Market Information Supplied by Commission Companies

Cards or circulars are issued by some commission companies as a convenient means of keeping their patrons informed on market conditions and also as a means of soliciting shipments.

FEDERAL AND STATE LIVESTOCK MARKETING AGENCIES

With the growth of the far-flung livestock marketing system and meat slaughtering, processing, and distribution, it soon became apparent that federal and state supervision was necessary to prevent unfair and discriminatory trade practices, to protect the public health, to insure humane methods of handling animals, and to establish fair and equitable rates and charges for all agencies operating on a given public market. The various services rendered, legislative acts, and state and federal organizations carrying out these functions will be discussed briefly.

Federal Meat Inspection

The federal government requires supervision of establishments which slaughter, pack, render, and prepare meats and meat products for interstate shipment and foreign export; it is the responsibility of the respective states to have and enforce legislation governing the slaughtering, packaging, and handling of meats shipped intrastate, but state standards cannot be lower than federal levels. The meat inspection laws do not apply to farm slaughter for home consumption, although most states require inspection if the meat is sold or transported away from the farm.

The meat inspection service of the U.S. Department of Agriculture was inaugurated and is maintained by the Meat Inspection Act of June 30, 1906.

This 61-year old act was updated and strengthened by the Wholesome Meat Act of December 15, 1967. The latter statute (1) requires that state standards be at least to the levels applied to meat sent across state lines, and (2) assures consumers that all meat in the United States is either inspected by the federal government or by an adequate state program.

The purposes of meat inspection are: (1) to safeguard the public by eliminating diseased or otherwise unwholesome meat from the food supply, (2) to enforce the sanitary preparation of meat and meat products, (3) to guard against the use of harmful ingredients, and (4) to prevent the use of false or misleading names or statements on labels. Personnel for carrying out the provisions of the act are of two types: professional or veterinary inspectors who are graduates of accredited veterinary colleges, and nonprofessional or lay inspectors who are required to pass a Civil Service examination. In brief, the inspections consist of the following two types:

1. **Ante-mortem (before death)** inspection is made in the pens or as the animals move from the scales after weighing. The inspection is performed to detect evidence of disease or any abnormal condition that would indicate a disease. Suspects are provided with a metal ear tag bearing the notation "U.S. Suspect No.......," and are given special post-mortem scrutiny. If in the ante-mortem examination there is definite and conclusive evidence that the animal is not fit for human consumption, it is "condemned," and no further post-mortem examination is necessary.

Fig. 6-18. Ante-mortem (before death) inspection of cattle being made by a federal veterinarian. Animals that are clearly diseased, emaciated, or otherwise unfit for human food are destroyed. Their carcasses may be used only in making inedible grease, fertilizers, or other nonfood products. Animals that appear slightly abnormal on foot are tagged "U.S. Suspect," and are given special post-mortem scrutiny. (Courtesy, USDA)

2. **Post-mortem (after death)** inspection is made at the time of slaughter and includes a careful examination of the carcass and the viscera (internal organs). All good carcasses are stamped "U.S. Inspected and Passed," whereas the inedible carcasses are stamped "U.S. Inspected and Condemned." The latter are sent to the rendering tanks, the products of which are not used for human food.

In addition to the ante-mortem and post-mortem inspections referred to, the government meat inspectors have the power to close a plant that is not sanitary in every respect. The floors and tables in the plant must be washed every day, tools must be thoroughly sterilized, and workmen must have clean garments and adequate lavatory facilities for keeping their person clean.

Fig. 6-19. Post-mortem (after death) inspection of the viscera (internal organs). The carcass is also carefully examined. (Courtesy, USDA)

Proportion of Total U.S. Meat Slaughter Produced in:

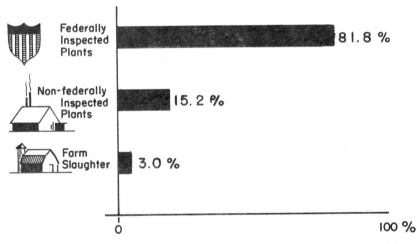

Fig. 6-20. Proportion of total United States meat slaughter produced in (1) federally inspected plants, (2) nonfederally inspected plants, and (3) farm slaughter, 1964. (From *Agricultural Statistics, 1965,* USDA, p. 356)

Meat inspection regulations condemn the carcasses of animals suffering from anthrax, peritonitis, enteritis, uremia, septicemia, pleurisy, parturient paresis, tetanus, extreme emaciation, pseudotuberculosis, generalized tuberculosis, and shipping fever.

Other ailments and conditions that are given careful scrutiny but which may or may not render a carcass unfit for food, depending upon the stage of the disorder, are: lumpy jaw, tuberculosis, tumors, and advanced pregnancy.

Only 15 to 20 per cent of all commercial meat packers are under federal inspection, but these establishments average much larger in size than the non-federally inspected ones, thus making it possible for them to account for the major portion of total United States slaughter. Figure 6-20 shows the proportion of the total United States meat slaughter that was produced in (1) federally inspected plants, (2) nonfederally inspected plants, and (3) farm slaughter in 1964. Inasmuch as the Wholesome Meat Act of 1967 requires that state standards meet the minimal federal standards, it is anticipated that, from that date forward, most meat packing plants will be federally inspected, thereby giving them the added flexibility of shipping interstate if they so desire.

State Meat Inspection

Different states have varying legislation governing the slaughtering, packaging, and handling of meats shipped intrastate. Local slaughterhouses also are often supervised by community or city ordinances. Usually, state permits are issued to plants operating in a state, and inspection is administered by the state department of agriculture. The Wholesome Meat Act of 1967 requires that the standards be just as tight, and that the inspection be just as rigid, for state meat inspection as for federal inspection.

Packers and Stockyards Act of 1921

On August 15, 1921, Congress passed the Packers and Stockyards Act which gives the Secretary of Agriculture supervision of packers and all others engaged in business at public stockyards. This law was enacted in order to prevent packers from engaging in unfair, discriminatory, or deceptive practices tending to restrain trade or create a monopoly or from indulging in practices having the effect of manipulating or controlling prices. The law also decrees that all rates charged by stockyards companies and market agencies shall be just, reasonable, and nondiscriminatory. Until 1938, the Packers and Stockyards Act was administered by the Bureau of Animal Industry, but on October of that year responsibility was shifted to the Agricultural Marketing Service of the U.S. Department of Agriculture. Fines are levied as penalties for violations, but the accused has the recourse of courts, which must uphold any ruling of the Secretary of Agriculture before the action is considered final.

The 28-Hour Law Regulating Transportation of Livestock

In 1873, Congress passed a law making it prohibitive for any carrier to transport livestock by rail for a longer period than 28 consecutive hours without unloading for the purpose of giving feed, water, and rest for a period of at least 5 consecutive hours before resuming the transportation. The period may be extended to 36 hours upon written request from the owner of the animals or his agent. With less than carload lots (LCL shipments), the owner may provide feed and water in the car with instructions that the animals be fed and watered enroute.

The purpose of the 28-hour law was to prevent cruelty incident to the shipment of livestock. Prior to enactment of this legislation, it was not uncommon for carriers to confine animals to cars without feed and water for periods of 50 to 60 hours or even longer.

At the present time, no such law applies to the truck transportation of animals.

Health-Control Officials

At every large central market, two groups of health-control officials are represented: the U.S. Department of Agriculture and regulatory officials of the state department of agriculture. These health-control officials are vested with the responsibility of preventing the spread of animal diseases. The federal government has jurisdiction over interstate shipments, and the laws governing such movement apply uniformly to all parts of the country. The several states have separate and different laws governing the in-shipment of livestock from other states and the control of livestock diseases within the state.

Although the act has been considerably modified and extended, the first federal legislation designed to control the spread of animal diseases was passed in 1884. State regulations have concerned themselves primarily with the eradication of tuberculosis, hog cholera, and Bang's disease. Because of lack of uniformity in state laws, there has been considerable controversy in the regulations governing the control of the latter disease, particularly when calfhood vaccination is involved.

Brand Inspection

Brand inspection of western cattle is undertaken primarily to prevent the stealing (rustling) of animals on the range and their subsequent shipment and sale to innocent parties at the big markets. This service is also very useful in recovering stray animals that have become mixed in with other cattle and cattle that, through oversight, have been shipped to market by parties other than the real owners. Brand inspection is supported by and is under the supervision of the different stock growers' associations of the range states. In Montana, however, the state government manages the work. Brand inspection is taken care of by men expert in the reading and deciphering of brands. They examine each individual in every shipment of branded cattle.

DEVELOPMENT OF MARKET CLASSES AND GRADES OF LIVESTOCK

With the turn of the century, the importance of having some uniform system of marketing livestock according to their relative merits or values was clearly recognized. Sensing this need, investigators of the Illinois Agricultural Experiment Station made a careful study of markets and published their findings and recommendations relative to market classes and grades in three different bulletins which appeared successively between 1902 and 1908.[13]

The need for uniform nation-wide standards also soon became evident. Thus, in 1916, the U.S. Department of Agriculture was authorized to report market conditions and transactions at the various livestock markets in the United States. Using the earlier publications of the University of Illinois as a basis—and with the help of market specialists, representatives of producer organizations, and land-grant colleges—the U.S. Department of Agriculture undertook to define tentative standards for uniform market classes and grades of cattle, sheep, and hogs. Through the years, these standards have been further refined, and more and more people have come to interpret them in a like manner regardless of the market or section of the country.

In addition to being rather specific and uniform—for example, so that a Choice lightweight, yearling, slaughter steer would be so designated on the several markets throughout the United States—it was recognized that the terminology must be easily understood and reasonably permanent in order to be workable. Moreover, the terminology must serve the market needs of producers, selling agencies, and buyers.

Use Made of Market Classes and Grades

Standard market classes and grades of animals have demonstrated their practicality in a number of ways. They have been especially valuable in rendering the following services:

1. In providing a means of selling animals according to their values.

2. As the standard vocabulary in market reporting, thus making possible more accurate and useful market reports.

3. As a guide to producers in shaping their breeding and feeding operations to meet market demands.

4. As a standard to insure fair dealing when animals are purchased on order.

5. As a means of keeping various markets fairly well in line with each other.

6. As a means of insuring that direct buying prices are on an equitable basis to those prevailing at the terminal markets.

7. In providing a producer with a method of selecting the market in which he may secure the best returns. The producer may review market reports based on standard classes and grades, and, with the flexibility of modern truck transportation, take advantage of the best market.

8. In providing a basis for compiling important statistical data used in analytical studies of supplies, demands, prices, and movements of livestock.

---

[13] H. W. Mumford, *Market Classes and Grades of Cattle*, Illinois Agri. Expt. Sta. Bull. No. 78, 1902; William Dietrich, *Market Classes and Grades of Swine*, Illinois Agri. Expt. Sta. Bull. No. 97, 1904; and W. C. Coffey, *Market Classes and Grades of Sheep*, Illinois Agri. Expt. Sta. Bull. No. 129, 1908.

Definition of Market Classes and Grades

Grading livestock is the act of sorting, dividing, or designating animals of similar classes and grades. When grading is properly and expertly done, each individual of a specific class and grade group is quite similar to other individuals in that group, regardless of whether the animals are in the same pen or in separate markets hundreds of miles removed from each other.

Broadly speaking, *the market class is the use to which animals are put,* whereas *the market grade is a measure of how well the animal fulfills the requirements for the class.* More accurately, however, the market class is determined by all of those factors affecting the use and value of the animal, except the final grade. Thus, in cattle, the market class is determined by whether the animals are cattle or calves; by the general use to which the animals are put (slaughter cattle, stocker and feeder cattle, milkers and springers, vealers, slaughter calves, and stocker and feeder calves); by the sex (steers, heifers, cows, bulls, or stags); by the age (yearling or two-year-old or over steers), and by weight.

The grade is the final subdivision in the classification process. It indicates the relative degree of excellence of an animal or group of animals.

Factors Determining Market Grades

In cattle, sheep, and hogs, the "quality grade" is determined by the following three factors, singly and in combination:

1. **Conformation.**—Conformation is the form, shape, outline, or contour of the animal. Superior conformation makes for a high dressing percentage, the maximum cutout value of the primal cuts, and the most desirable relationship between the lean, fat, and bone of the carcass. Breeding is chiefly responsible for variations in conformation, although the sex and the quality and distribution of fat also affect the build of an animal.

Though requiring experience to appraise, the conformation of a stocker or feeder animal indicates the shape the animal will have when it is finished.

2. **Finish.**—Finish refers to the degree of fatness of an animal, including the quality and distribution of the fat. For the most part, finish is determined by the amount and kind of feed consumed, although breeding, age, and sex are also factors. Finish is important in slaughter animals because it affects the palatability and nutritive qualities of the product, the dressing percentage, and the attractiveness of meats.

In stocker and feeder animals, the degree of fatness is usually referred to as condition rather than finish.

3. **Quality.**—Quality is a more intangible sort of thing, but nonetheless important. In a slaughter animal, quality is denoted by breeding, refinement, degree of finish, and to some extent by age and sex. The quality of a feeder animal is indicated primarily by its breeding and refinement.

Additionally, there are the following "yield grades" of slaughter cattle and slaughter sheep: Yield Grade 1, Yield Grade 2, Yield Grade 3, Yield Grade 4, and Yield Grade 5. Thus, slaughter cattle and sheep may be graded for (1) quality alone, (2) yield grade alone, or (3) both quality and yield grades.

SUPPLY AND DEMAND DETERMINE PRICES OF
MARKET LIVESTOCK

The price that prevails for slaughter animals on foot is primarily determined by supply and demand.

Because meat animals normally provide about one-third of the entire cash income of United States farmers and ranchers, the importance of market prices is self-evident. But livestock raised for market are valuable only to the extent to which the meat and by-products obtainable from them are valuable.

The price of meat and animal by-products is largely determined by supply and demand, with the demand being affected primarily by buying power and competition from other products.

Contrary to the opinion held by some, packers do not control livestock and meat prices. Rather, like most commodities, they are dominated chiefly by supply-and-demand forces. That is, fluctuations in livestock prices are due either to changes in the demand for meat or to changes in the supply of slaughter animals. The amount of meat that people will buy is affected by a wide variety of circumstances, such as industrial conditions and buying power, the competition of other foods in season, holidays, and weather. On the other hand, the number of animals available for slaughter and the meat supply is largely determined by whether the animals return a profit or incur a loss to the producer, and by the extent of each.

Factors Which Influence Market Supplies and Prices

Studies reveal that livestock prices change in keeping with a somewhat regular pattern according to the period of time. These types of price changes are: (1) long-time trends, (2) cyclical trends, (3) seasonal changes, (4) short-time changes, and (5) Jewish holidays.

LONGTIME (OR SECULAR) TRENDS

Longtime price trends are those which operate so slowly that they may not be detected for a number of years, perhaps for a period of 50 years or more. They are caused by such factors as changes in the standard of living or earning power of the masses of people in a country, by major population increases or decreases, or by longtime changes in production costs. The longtime price trends of cattle, sheep, and hogs have been very similar. In general, prices tended downward from the close of the Civil War to about 1896, after which price trends started upward. With the replacement of draft horses and mules by mechanical power, there has been a steady decrease in the demand for work animals accompanied by a longtime decrease in horse and mule prices. Aside from the recent wartime experience, the increase in numbers of meat animals has not kept pace with the increase of human population.

CYCLICAL TRENDS

The price cycle as it applies to livestock may be defined as that period of time during which the price for a certain kind of livestock advances from a low point to a high point and then declines to a low point again. In reality, it is a change in animal numbers that represents the stockman's response to prices. Although there is considerable variation in the length of the cycle within any given class of stock, currently, the price cycle of the different classes of animals is about as follows: hogs, 3 to 5 years; sheep, 9 to 10 years; and cattle, 10 to 12 years.

The specie cycles are a direct reflection of the rapidity with which the numbers of each class of farm animals can be shifted under practical conditions to meet consumer meat demands. Litter-bearing and early-producing swine can be increased in numbers much more rapidly than either sheep or cattle. When market hog prices are favorable, established swine enterprises are expanded,

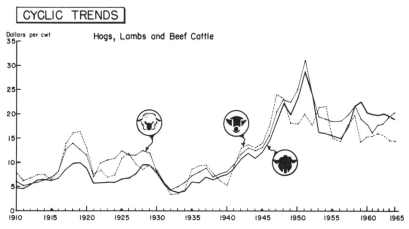

Fig. 6-21. Average price received by U.S. farmers for each class of live-stock, 1910 through 1965. In general, this shows that, currently, the price cycle of each class of animals is approximately as follows: hogs, 3 to 5 years; sheep, 9 to 10 years; and cattle, 10 to 12 years. (Based on data obtained from USDA; drawing by Steve Allured)

and new herds are founded, so that about every 3 to 5 years, on the average, the market is glutted and prices fall, only to rise again because too few hogs are being produced to take care of the demand for meats.

It is noteworthy that cattle cycles were formerly 15 years or longer, but that they have shortened to 10 to 12 years, due to the earlier maturity of modern cattle and the marketing of cattle at younger ages.

Normal cycles are disturbed by droughts, wars, general periods of depression or inflation, and federal controls.

SEASONAL CHANGES

Progressive stockmen are well aware of seasons of high and low market

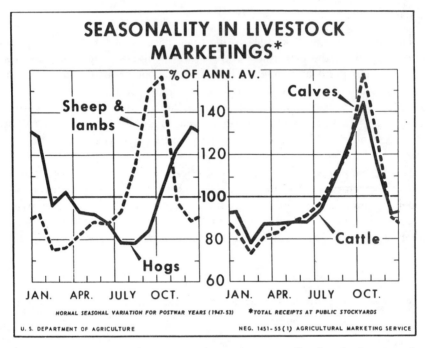

Fig. 6-22. Livestock prices tend to vary seasonally, largely because of seasonal marketing. This figure shows the seasons of largest and lightest receipts at terminal markets.

prices and plan their buying and selling operations accordingly. As would be expected, (1) seasons of high market prices are generally associated with light marketings, and seasons of low market prices with heavy marketings, and (2) the seasons of high and low market prices vary with different classes of livestock. It must be realized, however, that the normal seasons of high and low market prices may be changed by such factors as (1) federal farm programs and controls, (2) business conditions and general price levels, (3) feed supplies and weather conditions, (4) wars, etc. Also, it is not always wise to plan production to hit the highest market, for sometimes that would push up production costs more than enough to offset the gains from higher prices. Nevertheless, a careful study of normal seasonal prices will usually reveal the best time to buy and to sell livestock in order to reap the greatest profits (see Table 6-6).

SHORT-TIME CHANGES

Day-to-day variations in livestock prices usually are caused by uneven distribution of receipts on a given market because of such factors as weather, interference with transportation, strikes, uncertain or threatened federal policies, and stock market fluctuations. Although such changes are not large, the shrewd producer and market specialist is quick to take advantage of fluctuations that are in his financial interest.

TABLE 6—6

WHEN TO BUY AND WHEN TO SELL FARM ANIMALS[1]

Kind and Class of Animal	Lowest Prices (When to Buy)	Highest Prices (When to Sell)
Slaughter steers:		
Prime	June, and Oct. to Feb.	April and Sept.
Choice	June, and Oct. to Feb.	April and Sept.
Good	June, and Oct. to Feb.	April and Sept.
Other	Dec. to March	Aug. to Oct.
Slaughter heifers (top grades)	Sept. thru Nov.	Jan. and April
Cows	Nov. to Feb.	March to July
Feeder steers	Dec.	March to May
Slaughter lambs	Oct. thru Dec.	May and June
Fed lambs	Dec. to Feb.	Feb. thru April
Feeder lambs	May thru Nov.	Dec. to Apr.
Slaughter barrows and gilts	Nov. to May	June thru Aug.
Sows (packing)	Dec.	June to Oct.
Feeder pigs	July	Feb. thru April

[1]Based on averages.

JEWISH HOLIDAYS

The Jewish abstinence from eating meat during certain holidays exerts a minor influence on livestock prices. The important thing is that no kosher slaughtering is done on certain of these holidays. Likewise, producers should know that no animals are kosher slaughtered on Saturdays (the Jewish Sabbath). Normally, therefore, it is not good business to have too many kosher-type cattle, calves, or lambs on the eastern markets just prior to or during these holidays.

THE FUTURE OF LIVESTOCK MARKETING

The following transformation appears to be inevitable in future livestock marketing:

More animals will be marketed, for we shall need more meat to feed our expanding population; fewer farms and larger livestock production units, more ably managed and more deft in the market place; continued decentralization of meat packing and decline in terminal markets; continued growth of supermarkets and commercial feed companies, both of which will become more active in livestock marketing; continued growth of direct marketing, with increased contract arrangements and specification buying as added ingredients; a modest increase in numbers of animals marketed through livestock auctions, with increased government supervision and elimination of small, inefficient auction markets; some shifting of the geography of production and consumption—with expanded cattle feeding and swine production in the West and the South; the continued age-old fight on freight rates, on carcasses versus live animals; an attempt to feed our way out of surplus grains, with consequent over-production and low prices; increased government in business, including more supervision and anti-trust action; unionization of more areas in the agribusiness chain; more futures trading; and increased meat promotion, which, unfortunately, is likely to be poorly correlated, and not as effective as it could be, for many years to come.

A real challenge and a real opportunity lies ahead, provided stockmen are not stymied by traditions and old allegiances—if they have the "tomorrow mind" instead of the "yesterday mind." The improvement of livestock marketing is in the hands of the producer, the seller, the processor, and the retailer. To meet this challenge, there must be understanding, patience, and an open mind, and all segments of the industry must work together. The future belongs to those who make wise and timely changes in a changing world.

PROMOTIONAL AND RESEARCH ORGANIZATIONS OF IMPORTANCE TO THE LIVESTOCK AND MEAT INDUSTRY

There are a number of nation-wide promotional and research organizations whose business it is to work for the betterment of the livestock industry, especially in the areas of livestock marketing and/or meats. Among these are the following:

American Meat Institute
   Dr. Herrell DeGraff, President, 59 E. Van Buren Street, Chicago, Illinois 60605.

American Stock Yards Association
   Charles B. Jennings, President, 1712 "Eye" Street, N.W., Washington, D.C. 20006.

Certified Livestock Markets Association
   C. T. "Tad" Sanders, General Manager, 4900 Oak Street, Room 201, Kansas City, Missouri 64112.

Livestock Conservation, Inc.
   Paul Zillman, Executive Director, Room 405, Livestock Exchange Building, Union Stock Yards, Chicago, Illinois 60609.

National Independent Meat Packers Association
   John A. Killick, Executive Secretary, 1820 Massachusetts Avenue, N.W., Washington, D.C. 20036.

National Live Stock and Meat Board
   David H. Stroud, President, 36 S. Wabash Avenue, Chicago, Illinois 60603

National Live Stock Exchange
   James Magner, President, Bourbon Stock Yards, Louisville, Kentucky.

National Live Stock Producers Association
   Mylan Ross, Executive Vice President, 155 N. Wacker Drive, Chicago, Illinois 60606.

United States Live Stock Sanitary Association
   Dr. R. D. Hendershott, Secretary-Treasurer, 33 Oak Lane, Trenton, New Jersey 08618.

Western States Meat Packers Association
L. Blaine Liljenquist, President-General Manager, 917-15th Street, N.W., Washington, D.C. 20005.

QUESTIONS FOR STUDY AND DISCUSSION

1. Present facts that attest to the importance of livestock marketing.
2. Enumerate the transition stages through which early-day marketing passed, finally culminating in the development of terminal markets.
3. In succession, market animals were transported by (a) drovers and water, (b) rail, and (c) truck. What factors caused each of these types of transportation, except trucking, to decline in importance?
4. Obviously, the term packer no longer connotes the total functions of meat processors. Should it be changed? If so, what name would you propose?
5. Are packer profits too big? Justify your answer.
6. Enumerate and discuss some of the factors that keep packer profits in line.
7. List the primary factors which caused a decentralization of meat packing. Are these factors likely to cause further decentralization? How have the major packers countered this move?
8. What method or methods of marketing (what market channels) do you consider most advantageous for the stock of your home farm or ranch, and why?
9. What market avenues appear destined to increase in importance in the future; what market channels are apt to decline? Why is this likely to be so?
10. *Animal Science* lists the several factors operating on a large central (or terminal) market. Are any of these factors obsolete; should any of their functions be changed?
11. Is there adequate assurance of honesty, of sanitation, and of humane treatment of animals on markets?
12. What steps would you take in preparing and shipping cattle, sheep, and swine (a) by truck and (b) by rail?
13. Define on-foot market (a) classes and (b) grades, and tell of their value.
14. Is the dockage of piggy sows and stags justified?
15. Do packers control livestock and meat prices?
16. How may a stockman take advantage of cyclical trends and seasonal changes?
17. List and discuss the forces that are currently reshaping livestock marketing.
18. List and discuss the deficiencies and grievances in livestock marketing.
19. List the livestock marketing areas in which you feel more research is needed and give the economic importance of each.
20. What help, direct or indirect, does the producer obtain from the meat promotional organizations?
21. Discuss the future of livestock marketing.

SELECTED REFERENCES

Title of Publication	Author(s)	Publisher
American Live Stock Market, The, How It Functions	A. C. Davenport	Drovers Journal Print, Chicago, Ill., 1922.
Beef Marketing Margins and Costs	Misc. Pub., No. 710	U.S. Department of Agriculture, Washington, D. C.
Charting the Seasonal Market for Meat Animals	H. F. Breimyer Charlotte Kause	Agriculture Handbook No. 83, U.S. Department of Agriculture, Washington, D. C., 1955.

Title of Publication	Author(s)	Publisher
Competition in the Meat Packing Business	Bert Horan	Swift and Company, Chicago, Ill.
Economic Effects of U. S. Grades for Beef	Marketing Research Report No. 298	U.S. Department of Agriculture, Washington, D. C.
Essentials of Marketing Livestock	R. C. Ashby	(For The National Live Stock Exchange) Morningside College, Sioux City, Iowa.
Hired Truck Transportation in Marketing Livestock	Marketing Research Report No. 297	U.S. Department of Agriculture, Washington, D. C.
Improving Livestock Marketing Efficiency	I. M. Stevens R. L. Fox	General Report 39, Farmer Cooperative Service, U.S. Department of Agriculture, Washington, D. C.
Lamb Marketing Costs and Margins	Marketing Research Report No. 159	U.S. Department of Agriculture, Washington, D. C.
Livestock Auction Markets in the Southeast	G. E. Turner C. F. Brasington	Marketing Research Report No. 141, U.S. Department of Agriculture, Washington, D. C., 1956.
Livestock Auction Markets in the United States	Gerald Engelman Betty Sue Pence	Marketing Research Report No. 223, U.S. Department of Agriculture, Washington, D. C.
Livestock Marketing	A. A. Dowell Knute Bjorka	McGraw-Hill Book Company, New York, N. Y., 1941.
Livestock Marketing in the United States	H. H. Smith	Bulletin 442-A, Agricultural Extension Service, Colorado State University, Fort Collins, Colo.
Livestock Shrinkage		Western Livestock Marketing Research Committee, Denver, Colo.
Livestock Terminal Markets in the United States	Marketing Research Report No. 299	U.S. Department of Agriculture, Washington, D. C.
Losses of Livestock in Transit in Midwestern and Western States	J. E. Rickenbacker	Marketing Research Report 247, Farmer Cooperative Service, U.S. Department of Agriculture, Washington, D. C.
Margins and Costs— Special Studies	Marketing Research Report No. 167	U.S. Department of Agriculture, Washington, D. C.
Marketing Livestock in the Corn Belt Region	Knute Bjorka Corn Belt Lvstk. Mktg. Res. Com.	Agri. Exp. Sta. Bull. 365, South Dakota State College, Brookings, S. D., 1942.
Marketing Meat-Type Hogs	Marketing Research Report No. 227	U.S. Department of Agriculture, Washington, D. C.
Marketing of Livestock and Meat, The	S. H. Fowler	Interstate Printers and Publishers, Danville, Ill., 1961.
Market Outlets for Livestock Producers	Marketing Research Report No. 216	Agricultural Marketing Service, U.S. Department of Agriculture, Washington, D. C.

Title of Publication	Author(s)	Publisher
Organization and Competition in the Livestock and Meat Industry, Tech. Study, No. 1	National Commission on Food Marketing	Supt. of Documents, U.S. Govt. Printing Office, Washington, D.C., June, 1966.
Pork Marketing Margins and Costs	Miscellaneous Publication No. 711	U.S. Department of Agriculture, Washington, D. C.
Problems and Practices of American Cattlemen	M. E. Ensminger M. W. Galgan W. L. Slocum	Wash. Agri. Expt. Sta. Bull. 562, Washington State University, Pullman, Wash., 1955.
Stockman's Handbook, The	M. E. Ensminger	Interstate Printers and Publishers, Danville, Ill., 1969.
Trade in Western Livestock at Auctions: 1, Development Relative Importance Operations	Harold Abel D. A. Broadbent	Utah Agricultural Experiment Stations Bulletin 352, University of Utah, Logan, Utah, 1952.
Trade in Western Livestock at Auctions; 2, Analysis of Livestock Marketings	C. R. Harston E. C. Voorhies	Wash. Agri. Expt. Sta. Bull. 537, A Western Regional Research Publication, Washington State University, Pullman, Wash., 1952.
Trends in Prices of Purebred Cattle	A. A. Dowell Arnold Brekke	Agri. Expt. Sta. Bull. 398, University of Minnesota, St. Paul, Minn., 1948.
What Governs Livestock Prices?	F. A. Kutish	Swift and Company, Agricultural Research Department, Chicago, Ill.

Chapter VII

MEAT AND ANIMAL BY-PRODUCTS[1]

Contents

	Page
Meat Through the Ages	270
Meat Over the Block the Ultimate Objective	272
Qualities in Meats Desired by the Consumer	274
Need for Meat Grading	276
Early Grade Terms Were Confusing	278
Federal Grading	278
The Federal Grades of Meats	280
Advantages and Disadvantages of Federal Meat Grading	282
American Meat Institute System of Grading	284
Packer Brand Names	285
Kosher Meats	286
The Nutritive Qualities of Meats	287
What Determines the Price of Meat?	291
The Available Supply of Meat	291
The Demand for Meat	292
Where the Consumer's Food Dollar Goes	294
World and U.S. Meat Production	297
Per Capita Meat Consumption in Various Countries	298
Per Capita Meat Consumption in the United States	299
Trends in Per Capita Consumption of Meat and Other Foods	300
Meat Imports and Exports	301
Meat Preservation	305
Methods of Meat Cookery	307
Dry-heat Cooking	308
Moist-heat Cooking	308
Packing House By-products from Slaughter	308
Important By-products from Animal Slaughter	310
Meat Promotion	315
Questions for Study and Discussion	315
Selected References	316

Meat may be defined as the edible flesh of mammals used for food. In a broad sense, the term meat may also include the flesh of fish, shellfish, poultry, and game. In this chapter, the discussion of meat is limited to red meat—to beef, lamb, and pork. Poultry meat is treated in the poultry section.

Meat by-products include all products, both edible and inedible, other than the carcass meat. The edible glands and organs are usually classed as by-products, but lard is usually grouped along with pork.

Although this chapter is devoted primarily to the final animal product—meat—it must be remembered that the top grades of this important food constituent represent the culmination of years of progressive breeding, the best in nutrition, vigilant sanitation and disease prevention, superior care and manage-

[1] Acknowledgment, with sincere thanks is given to staff members of the following organizations who reviewed this chapter: National Live Stock and Meat Board, and the American Meat Institute, Chicago, Ill.

ment, and modern marketing, slaughtering, processing, and distribution. In brief, the efficient availability of the highest quality meat is dependent upon the well-coordinated operation of the whole field of animal science. Much effort and years of progress have gone into the production of luscious steaks or chops.

MEAT THROUGH THE AGES

For thousands of years, meat has been a pillar of the human diet. Primitive man chose it instinctively, if not through necessity. At first, it was a matter of securing meats from wild animals; later, animals were domesticated and eventually used for power and recreation as well as for food and clothing. The story of meat through the ages is a romantic one.

The development and extension of civilization itself has gone hand in hand with the existence of animals. The fragmentary evidence—mostly in the form of bones and tools collected from buried camp sites, caves, and graves and the carving on the walls of caves or on utensils, tools, and weapons—constitutes the first historical record of what is known about early man and his surroundings. From such archeological evidence, it is clear that during the Paleolithic Period (the Old Stone Age)—long before there were any domestic animals, except perhaps the dog—man hunted down certain animals and used their meat for food and their skins for clothing. Neolithic man (New Stone Age man) found it more convenient to domesticate animals, thus providing a more stable food supply. He appears to have had nearly all of our domestic animals in Europe,

Fig. 7-1. Expeditionary Force sent to Persia and India in 1670. Formerly live animals had to be carried along to be slaughtered as the army proceeded into uninhabited regions. Today, frozen, dehydrated, and canned meat simplifies the problem. It is also interesting to note that the search for spices for use in meat preservation prompted much of the early-day sailing. (Courtesy, the Bettmann Archive)

except the cat and poultry and those animals which were found only in America or in the tropics. During the Bronze and Iron Ages, especially the latter period, man began to use animals as a source of power, as well as for food and clothing. Thus, with each succeeding step in his advancing civilization, man became more and more dependent upon animals and animal products.

Down through the ages, meat continued to exert a powerful influence on history. Columbus set forth on his famous voyage of 1492, seeking a shorter route to the East Indies, primarily because it would then be easier to secure needed supplies of spices for Europe. In those early days, refrigeration was unknown, and spices were in great demand to preserve meat and make it more palatable. Likewise, Marco Polo's overland journey to the Far East had much the same incentive behind it.

The stories surrounding the names of some of the meat cuts is also fascinating. For example, according to an old English legend which dates back many

Fig. 7-2. King Charles II was so impressed with a platter of beef that was served at one of his feasts, that—according to an old English legend—he ceremoniously arose, touched his sword to the steaming platter and said, "A noble joint it shall have a title. Loin, I dub thee Knight—henceforth thou shall be Sir Loin."

years, King Charles II was responsible for naming the sirloin of beef (see Fig. 7-2).

Meat from the native wild animals had, presumably, always formed a major part of the food of the early American Indians. In fact, it is thought that the Red Man taught the first white settlers how to cure and smoke meats. But the colonists were not willing to become nomadic hunters of wild animals. At a very early time, they imported domestic animals from the mother country. Hogs had preceded the Jamestown settlement, having been brought to Tampa Bay (now Florida) by De Soto in 1539. Cattle and sheep were first brought over from England by the colonists in 1609 and 1610, respectively. At first, cattle were primarily used for work purposes, and sheep were valued chiefly for their wool. As grains became more plentiful, however, it was possible to share the crops, other than pasture, with the animals. When this time arrived, meat became an article of trade and a source of income. In fact, the colonists used both grain and pork as sources of money. In early New England, to be destitute of pork was even considered disreputable.

MEAT OVER THE BLOCK THE ULTIMATE OBJECTIVE

Except for the wool produced by sheep, meat over the block is the ultimate objective in producing cattle, sheep, and swine To be sure, this has not always been true. Time was, even in colonial America, when the greatest utility value of cattle was as work oxen. The production of meat and milk was purely incidental, and hides were the most valuable product of slaughter. Yet, as feeds and animals increased in abundance, the colonists showed their fondness for beef, as well as for pork and lamb.

Of course, the type of animals best adapted to the production of meat over the block has changed in a changing world. Thus, in the early history of this country, the very survival of animals was often dependent upon their speed, hardiness, and ability to fight. Moreover, long legs and plenty of bone were important attributes when it came time for animals to trail hundreds of miles as drovers took them to market. The Texas Longhorn, Arkansas Razorback, and multi-colored sheep of the Navajo Indians were adapted to these conditions.

With the advent of rail transportation and improved care and feeding methods, the ability of animals to travel and fight diminished in importance. It was then possible, through selection and breeding, to produce meat animals better suited to the needs of more critical consumers. With the development of large cities, artisans and craftsmen and their successors in industry required fewer calories than those who were engaged in the more arduous tasks of logging, building railroads, etc. Simultaneously, the American family decreased in size. The demand shifted, therefore, to smaller and less fatty cuts of meats; and, with greater prosperity, high quality steaks and roasts were in demand. To meet the needs of the consumer, the producer gradually shifted to the breeding and marketing of younger animals with maximum cut-out value of the primal cuts. The need was for a blocky conformation, with short legs and a short neck. Instead of marketing large, ponderous, fat, three-to-five-year-old steers, baby beef came into prominence; the 600- to 1,000-pound packing hogs were transformed into 200-pound meat-type barrows; and instead of marketing mature sheep as unrelished mutton, the marketing of lamb increased in importance.

Thus, throughout the years, consumer demand has always exerted a powerful influence upon the type of animals produced. To be sure, it is necessary that such production factors as prolificacy, economy of feed utilization, rapidity of

Fig. 7-3. A modern meat market. There are about 278,616 U.S. grocery stores, most of which handle meat, plus 23,844 meat markets; or a total of about 300,000 retail meat outlets.

Fig. 7-4. Cattle fashions have changed! "Firly," a prize ox of Britain in 1835; shown at 4 years and 8 months of age and weighing 3,000 pounds. The near animal is Royal Jupiter, a Shorthorn steer that was Grand Champion over all breeds at the Chicago International; shown by Oklahoma State University. (Courtesy, *The Shorthorn World*)

gains, size, longevity, etc., receive due consideration along with consumer demands. But once these production factors have received due weight, the producers of all meat animals—whether they be purebred or commercial producers—must remember that meat over the block is the ultimate objective.

QUALITIES IN MEATS DESIRED BY THE CONSUMER

Until 25 years ago, big lardy hogs were preferred; families were large and engaged in strenuous outdoor occupations, there was a lively export for lard, and lard was in demand for use as shortening and for the manufacture of soaps and munitions. But times have changed! Vegetable oils have largely replaced lard as a shortening, and we have lost much of our export market. From a position of minor importance in 1946, synthetic detergents had 77 per cent, by weight, of our combined soap-detergent sales in 1963. As a result of these changes, there has been a rather constant widening of the gap between the prices of the primal lean cuts of pork (hams, loins, picnics, and butts) and of fat for lard. Whereas fat was worth nearly as much as lean cuts in the early part of the century, in 1964,[2] the lean cuts, pound for pound, were worth three times as much as fat.

But excess lard production is not the only problem facing the swine producer. Currently, consumers are showing a definite preference for leaner cuts of meat and there is a declining demand for pork in relation to beef. Expendi-

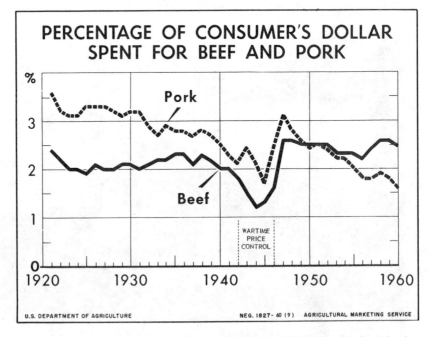

Fig. 7-5. About 1950, U.S. consumer preference shifted from pork to beef.

---

[2] *Agricultural Statistics, 1965*, USDA, Table 223, p. 153.

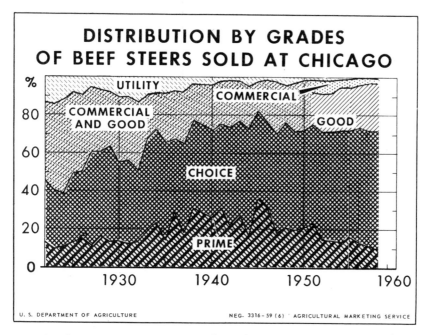

Fig. 7-6. In response to consumer demand, more Choice and less Prime beef is being produced.

tures for pork dropped from around 3¼ per cent of consumer income in the early 1930's to about 1.6 per cent in 1960; at the same time, consumer expenditures for beef increased from 2⅓ per cent of income in those earlier years to 2½ per cent now.[3]

Nor have such changes been limited to pork; consumers desire more red meat and less fat in both beef and lamb.

Because consumer preference is such an important item in the production of meats, it is well that the farmer and rancher, the packer, and the meat retailer be familiar with these desired qualities, which are summarized as follows:

1. **Palatability.**—First and foremost, people eat meat because they like it. Palatability is influenced by the tenderness, juiciness, and flavor of the fat and lean.

2. **Attractiveness, eye appeal.**—The general attractiveness is an important factor in selling meats to the housewife. The color of the lean, the degree of fatness, and the marbling are leading factors in determining buyer appeal. Most consumers prefer a white fat and a light or medium red color in the lean.

3. **Moderate amount of fat and bone.**—Middle- and low-income groups discriminate against too much fat, especially when it must be trimmed heavily.

4. **Small cuts.**—Most purchasers prefer to buy cuts of meat that are of a

---

[3] Engelman, Gerald and Raymond O. Gaarder, *Marketing Meat-Type Hogs,* Marketing Research Report No. 227, Agricultural Marketing Service, USDA, April 1958.

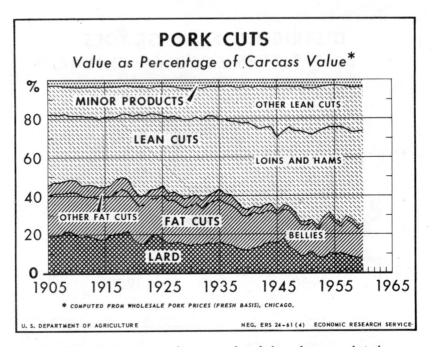

Fig. 7-7. In recent years, lean cuts of pork have become relatively more valuable than fat cuts and lard.

proper size to meet the needs of their respective families. Because the American family has decreased in size, this has meant smaller cuts. This, in turn, has had a profound influence on the type of animals and on market age and weight.

5. **Ease of preparation.**—More and more women are working; the rest are spending more time at the club. The net results is that they wish to rush home and, without much work, prepare a meal at maximum speed. Prepackaged and/ or frozen meats—especially steaks, chops, hamburger, and variety meats—are the answer. But the housewife must expect to pay for these added services and conveniences.

6. **Repeatability.**—The housewife wants to be able to secure a standardized product; meat of the same tenderness and other eating quality as her last purchase. Perhaps this can be achieved through the use of chemical tenderizers and other processing methods. If successful, such developments will help promote increased sales of meats at favorable prices. To this end, more research is needed.

If these qualities are not met by meats, other products will. Recognition of this fact is important, for competition is keen for space on the shelves of a modern retail food outlet.

NEED FOR MEAT GRADING

Slaughtering and selling meats have progressed from a purely local enterprise to a highly complex system. The early-day butcher bought animals on the hoof, did his own slaughtering, and sold the meat to his neighbors and friends. There were no standard wholesale cuts. In fact, the carcass was usually halved and then meat was cut from end to end, with the particular location of the cut obtained by any purchaser being determined largely by the progress in cutting the carcass at the time the purchase chanced to be made. Neither was there any grading. Based on the quality of animals purchased, some butchers simply acquired a reputation for supplying better meats than others.

With the westward expansion, the development of large meat packing plants nearer the source of production, and the advent of meat shipment in refrigerated cars, the slaughterers and consumers tended to become more widely separated. Because an individual retailer usually could not handle an entire carlot of meat, the wholesaler took over the assignment of buying large quantities of meats from packers and selling in small lots to individual retailers. But it was

Fig. 7-8. Early-day (about 1840) butcher shop, from a painting by W. S. Mount (1807-1869). There were neither standard wholesale cuts nor grades. (Courtesy, The Bettmann Archive)

no longer practical for the eastern meat buyer personally to inspect and purchase meat supplies from packers located many miles to the west. To a lesser extent, many retailers found it a nuisance to go to the wholesaler's warehouse to inspect the meats before buying. It was further realized that price is not always an indication of quality in meats and that most meats look alike to the inexperienced buyer and consumer. Thus, there was a need for some practical and standard means of describing quality in meats. Out of this need has arisen four systems of meat grading: (1) federal grading, (2) American Meat Institute grading, (3) packer brands, and (4) O.P.A. grades, which are now obsolete.[4]

Packer brands are usually used in combination with either federal grades or institute grades. The O.P.A. grades were strictly a World War II measure and are no longer used. Regardless of the system used, it is generally acknowledged that carcass grading is a more accurate evaluation of the value of slaughter animals than can be arrived at on foot, even by experienced packer buyers (for example, dark cutters cannot be detected prior to slaughter).

EARLY GRADE TERMS WERE CONFUSING

Prior to establishing federal grading, each packing plant and meat market had a certain vocabulary peculiar to itself and most likely not known to other markets. Nor was there any particular correlation between designations on foot and in carcass form. In a broad way, the early terms emphasized the geographical origin of animals. It was common to refer to "native" or "western" beef and lamb. Presumably, the native carcasses were from grain-fed animals; whereas the western carcasses were from grass-fat animals. Yet, it was soon realized that these designations were inaccurate because many western cattle and lambs are now grain fed, either in the Corn Belt or in the irrigated valleys of the West. Many so-called native cattle and lambs received no grain whatsoever prior to marketing. At most markets, the broad classifications, native and western, were further subdivided to show narrower ranges of quality, such as choice, good, and medium natives or westerns, respectively. Yet, these designations had very different connotations on different markets. Both buyers and sellers of meats were in a constant state of confusion, especially in going to a different market; and misunderstandings could not be avoided without a personal inspection.

FEDERAL GRADING[5]

A scientific study of meat grading was first undertaken by the University of Illinois, beginning in 1902. The results of these studies were used as a basis by the U.S. Department of Agriculture workers in setting up tentative standards for classes and grades of beef carcasses. They were first used in market news reporting work in 1916. As would be expected in such pioneering and in a changing industry, several revisions of the early meat standards have been made through the years, thus keeping them in line with consumer demands and production practices.

Federal grading of beef was first started as a special service to United States Steamship Lines in 1923; and on February 10, 1925, the 68th U.S. Congress

---

[4] Under O.P.A., compulsory federal grading existed from 1942 to 1946. The grades Prime and Choice were combined into a new grade designated as AA, the Good grade was designated A, the Commercial grade B, the Utility grade C, and the Cutter grade D.

[5] This section was authoritatively reviewed by Mr. J. C. Pierce, Director, Livestock Division, Consumer and Marketing Service, USDA.

passed an act setting up a federal meat grading service. But commercial meat grading was not inaugurated until 1927, at which time Prime and Choice grades of steer and heifer beef were stamped at Boston, New York City, Philadelphia, Washington, Chicago, Omaha, and Kansas City. A year later, the Good grade was added, and finally the service was broadened to include beef of all classes and grades.

At first, federal grading of meats was limited to beef, but it now includes mutton, lamb, calf, veal, and pork carcasses.

Government grading, unlike meat inspection, was not compulsory prior to July 13, 1942. During the period of World War II, O.P.A. grading was required as a part of price controls, but following the war the service was again placed on a permissive basis. Official graders are subject to the call of anyone who wishes their services, (packer, wholesaler, or retailer) with a charge of $8.20 per hour being made (with a minimum charge of $4.10).[6] The time includes both travel and the actual time required to do the grading. Government meat graders are appointed from a list of eligibles submitted by the Civil Service Commission. To qualify, a candidate must have had at least six years of suitable practical experience in wholesale meat marketing or grading. Be-

Proportion of U.S. Commercial Meat Slaughter Federally Graded, 1965

(Dark area represents % federally graded of total slaughter)

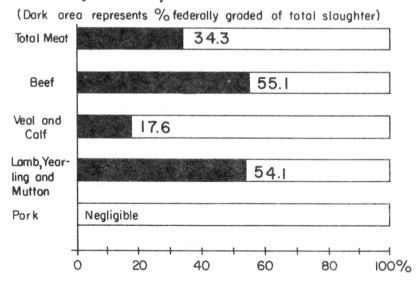

Fig. 7-9. Proportion of U.S. meat slaughter (including federally inspected, nonfederally inspected, and farm slaughter) federally graded in 1965. (Data provided by Mr. J. C. Pierce, Director, Livestock Division, Agricultural Marketing Service, USDA; drawing by Steve Allured)

---

[6]The grading service is nearly self-supporting, depending largely upon fees for the payment of expenses.

ginners are also trained for a period of time under experienced graders. Figure 7-9 shows the proportion of the total United States meat slaughter (including federally inspected, nonfederally inspected, and farm slaughter) which was federally graded in 1965. It is noteworthy that only 34.3 per cent of all meats (beef, veal, lamb, mutton and pork combined) were federally graded during the year. No farm-produced meat is federally graded, but a limited amount of federal grading is used by some plants that do not have federal inspection for sanitation.

The Federal Grades of Meats

The grade of meat may be defined as a measure of its degree of excellence based on conformation, finish, and quality; factors which determine selling and eating qualities. It is intended that the specifications for each grade shall be sufficiently definite to make for uniform grades throughout the country and from season to season, and that on-hook grades shall be correlated with on-foot grades.

Both producers and consumers should know the federal grades of meats and have a reasonably clear understanding of the specifications of each grade. From the standpoint of producers—including both purebred and commercial operators—this is important, for, after all, meat over the block is the ultimate objective. From the standpoint of consumers, especially the housewife who buys most of the meat, this is important, because (1) in these days of self-service, pre-packaged meats there is less opportunity to secure the counsel and advice of the meat cutter when making purchases, and (2) the average consumer is not the best judge of the quality of the various kinds of meats on display in the meat counter.

The following are definitions of the grade factors as they apply to meats, both carcasses and wholesale cuts, coming from all species[7]:

1. **Conformation.**—Conformation refers to the general build, form, shape, contour or outline of the carcass, side, or cut. Superior conformation implies a plump or blocky carcass that is thick in relation to its length; with short neck and shanks; full loins; deep, plump rounds; well-fleshed ribs; and smooth shoulders. This is in contrast to the ranginess and angularity associated with inferior conformation. Superior conformation assures retail cuts that will be shapely and have full muscles and a large percentage of edible meat to bone and that will make for the maximum cut-out value of primal cuts.

2. **Finish.**—Finish refers to the amount, quality, and distribution of fat. Superior finish implies a smooth, even covering of fat over most of the exterior surface of the carcass, a much thinner covering over the interior surface of the ribs, and a liberal intermixture of fat with lean, called marbling. In grading, it is recognized that the degree of finish and marbling is related to some extent to the age of the animal from which it is produced. Thus, less

---

[7] Some specific ways in which pork carcasses differ from beef, veal, mutton and lamb carcasses will be discussed later in this section.

finish and marbling is required for top-grade meats obtained from younger animals, but it is necessary that the character of the fat and the conformation and quality meet the degree of perfection required for the grade.

3. **Quality.**—Quality refers to the eating quality of the meat and is indicated by certain characteristics of the fat and lean tissue, maturity, and the marbling. Superior quality implies well-marbled lean that is firm and fine in texture, a minimum of connective tissue, and a desirable color of lean typical of the species. The finish is also firm (not soft or oily) and the meat is produced from young animals as indicated by the bones. Quality is considered the most important of the three grade factors because it furnishes for consumers the most dependable criterion of the merit of meat.

Federally graded meats are so stamped (with an edible vegetable dye) that the grade will appear on the retail cuts as well as on the carcass and wholesale cuts. These are summarized in Table 7-1.

TABLE 7—1

FEDERAL GRADES OF MEATS, BY CLASSES[1]

Beef	Veal	Mutton and Lamb	Pork
1. Prime[2]	1. Prime	1. Prime[3]	1. U.S. No. 1
2. Choice	2. Choice	2. Choice	2. U.S. No. 2
3. Good	3. Good	3. Good	3. U.S. No. 3
4. Standard	4. Standard	4. Utility	4. U.S. No. 4
5. Commercial	5. Utility	5. Cull	5. Medium
6. Utility	6. Cull		
7. Cutter			
8. Canner			

[1] In rolling meat, the letters U.S. precede each federal grade name. This is important, as only government-graded meat can be so marked. For convenience, however, the letters U.S. are not used in this table or in the discussion which follows.
[2] In addition to the quality grades given herein, there are the following yield grades of beef and lamb (and mutton) carcasses: Yield Grade 1, Yield Grade 2, Yield Grade 3, Yield Grade 4, and Yield Grade 5. Thus, beef and lamb carcasses may be graded for (1) quality alone, (2) yield grade alone, or (3) both quality and yield grade.
[3] Cow beef is not eligible for the Prime grade.
[4] Limited to lamb and yearling carcasses.

Because of the different grade designation and the smaller number of grades in comparison with beef, the following elucidation is given relative to the grades of pork: Pork is more uniform in quality than any other class of meat and, therefore, there is need for fewer grades. Also, the grades of barrow and gilt carcasses are based on two general considerations: (1) the quality-indicating characteristics of the lean and (2) the expected combined yields of the four lean cuts (ham, loin, picnic shoulder, and Boston butt). Although the quality of the lean is best evaluated by a direct observation of its characteristics in a cut surface, such observations are impractical in grading carcasses. Thus, in carcasses, the quality of the lean is evaluated indirectly, on the basis of such quality-indicating characteristics as: (1) firmness of fat and lean; (2) amount of feathering between the ribs; (3) color of lean; and (4) belly thickness, determined primarily by the thickness of the belly pocket. Research has shown that the actual average thickness of the backfat in relation to carcass length is a rather reliable guide to the yield of the four lean cuts. Therefore, in determining the grade of pork carcasses, the actual average thickness of backfat and the carcass length are considered.

Some additional and pertinent facts relative to federal grades of meats are:

1. **There is no sex differentiation between steer, heifer, and cow beef.** —Federal grades make no distinction between steer, heifer, and cow beef. It is not intended that this should be construed to imply that there is no carcass difference between these sex classes. As a matter of fact, it is generally recognized that there is a pronounced difference between the sex classes of cattle, with a lesser difference between the sex classes of sheep and hogs. This step in simplification was taken so that it might be easier for the buyer or consumer to purchase meat on the basis of quality, without the added confusion of a more complicated system.

2. **Bull and stag beef is identified.**—Bull and stag beef is identified by class as bull beef and stag beef, respectively. Within each of these classes, there are the following six grades: (a) Choice, (b) Good, (c) Commercial, (d) Utility, (e) Cutter, and (f) Canner. However, no designated grade of bull beef or of stag beef is comparable in quality to a similarly designated grade of beef obtained from steers, heifers, or cows. Neither is the quality in a designated grade of bull beef comparable to a similarly designated grade of stag beef.

3. **Lower grades seldom sold as retail cuts.**—It is seldom that the lower grades—Cutter and Canner beef, and Cull veal, mutton, and lamb—are sold as retail cuts. The consumer, therefore, only needs to become familiar with the upper grades of each kind of meat.

As would be expected, in order to make the top grade in the respective classes, the carcass or cut must possess a very high degree of conformation and quality, and adequate finish. The lower grades of meats are deficient in one or more of these grade-determining factors. Because each grade is determined on the basis of a composite evaluation of all three factors (conformation, finish, and quality), a carcass or cut may possess some characteristics that are common to another grade. It must also be recognized that all of the wholesale cuts produced from a carcass are not necessarily of the same grade as the carcass from which they are secured. Figure 7-10 gives the percentage distribution by grades of the total beef graded during 1965.

Advantages and Disadvantages of Federal Meat Grading

Any system of evaluating products is certain to possess advantages and disadvantages, and meat grading is no exception.

Some of the advantages of competent federal grading are:

1. Because the federal grade is applied by an independent agency, rather than an employee of the packing house, the average consumer is less likely

Percentage Distribution by Grade of Total Beef Federally Graded, in 1965

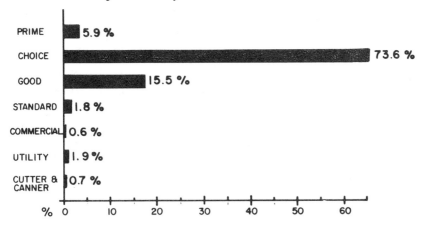

Fig. 7-10. Percentage distribution of beef by grades, in 1965. However, slightly less than half the beef is not federally graded (Fig. 7-9). (Data provided by Mr. John C. Pierce, Director, Livestock Division, Consumer and Marketing Service, USDA)

to question it. Moreover, it reduces possible misunderstanding between buyers and sellers of meats.

2. The average consumer is not a good judge of the quality of the various kinds of meat that are on display. However, if the meat were correctly graded and labeled, the consumer would be in a position to select the grade that meets his particular requirements.

3. Because there are fewer federal grades, the consumer is likely to become familiar with their significance more readily than with the more numerous Meat Institute numbers and the still more numerous packer brands.

4. Federal grading facilitates large-scale purchasing by federal, state, county, and city institutions and by hotels, restaurants, dining cars, and other large users of meats, chiefly because they can place large orders through one or several channels and obtain uniform products. Such large orders are usually on a contract basis, with grade specifications set forth.

5. The federal grades of meats correspond rather closely to the on-foot grades. They, therefore, provide a very important correlation for the benefit of producers. The payment of a premium for a quality product is a definite stimulation to improved breeding and feeding.

6. There is hardly any limit to the packer brands as established by different companies; whereas the federal grades are fairly comparable regardless of the area or ownership of the plant.

7. It is but natural that there should be less area or seasonal variation in appraisal of meat value or grades when a large overall agency is functioning than when men are trained by many organizations, with only limited effort toward standardization between them.

8. Federal grading avoids any suspicion or temptation of upgrading, an alleged practice when demand for top grades exceeds the supply.

9. It makes meat market reports more intelligible.

10. The purchaser need not inspect carcasses or wholesale cuts to secure uniform products of merit to meet his requirements.

Some of the disadvantages of federal grading are:

1. It ignores sex classes that are important. It would hardly be expected that a cow carcass grading U.S. Good could be comparable to a steer carcass of the same grade.

2. It does not provide sufficiently narrow classifications for a critical trade.

3. Many feel that packer brand names are more alluring to buyers than the rather unglamorous federal grades. Naturally, this feeling has been accentuated through advertising.

4. A meat packer's reputation is an individual proposition more than a collective one. It is argued, therefore, that he is more likely to uphold the reputation of his particular brand.

5. The national packers prefer advertising their brand names, claiming that to advertise federal grades places them in the position of helping the small packer, who does little or no advertising but who would greatly benefit therefrom.

AMERICAN MEAT INSTITUTE SYSTEM OF GRADING

Claiming that government grades are too wide (too few in number to meet trade requirements), the meat packing industry has devised its own system of beef classes and grades. This system, which was put into effect by the Institute of American Meat Packers (now the American Meat Institute) in January, 1931, provides for ten grades and gives to each grade a number, using "0" for the top grade and "9" for the bottom grade. A few packers also use additional grades or subgrades of their own. Like federal grading, the Institute system of grading is based on conformation, finish, and quality. It differs from the federal system chiefly in that consideration is given to sex classes and it provides ten grades instead of eight as used in federal grading.

Under the Institute system, the packer may designate the sex classes (steer, heifer, cow, bull, and stag) simply by prefixing the Institute name by a certain number, but different packers use different numbers to represent each of the sex classes. In a certain plant the prefixes used may be as follows: "1" for steer, "2" for heifer, "3" for cow, "4" for bull, and "5" for stag. With this system, "10" would indicate prime steer beef; the prefix "1" would designate steer beef and the "0" the top grade.

In addition to the sex classes and grades, there are also carcass weight divisions ranging from 400 to 1,200 pounds, in either 50- or 100-pound differentials. It is obvious therefore, that when sex classes, grades, and weight divisions are all taken into consideration, the subdivisions number into the hundreds.

In the Institute system, the grading is done by the employees of the packing company. The numbers are not stamped on the carcass but are merely marked on tags which are hooked to the carcass in the packing plant and removed before the carcass is delivered to the retailer. Thus, the Institute grades are never seen by the consumer, but they are a great aid to packer salesmen and retail meat dealers in transacting their business.

Table 7-2 shows the comparison between the two grading systems. It will be noted that in some cases a federal grade covers more than one Institute grade. Although no cow beef qualifies for U.S. Department of Agriculture grade of Prime, the Institute does assign its second top grade to this sex class, and the packer usually prefixes it with his own sex class designation. The largest percentage of all beef sold to retail dealers is on the basis of Institute grades.

TABLE 7—2

COMPARISON BETWEEN USDA GRADES, AND AMERICAN MEAT
INSTITUTE (AMI) GRADES OF CARCASS BEEF
(steer, heifer, and cow beef)

USDA Grades (steer, heifer, and cow beef)	AMI Grades (steer and heifer beef)	AMI Grades (cow beef)
Prime[1]	0	No USDA Prime Cow Beef
	1	
	2	
Choice	3	1
Good	4	2
Standard	5	3
Commercial	6	4
Utility	7	5
Cutter	8	6
		7
Canner	9	8
		9

[1]Cow beef is not eligible for Prime grade.

PACKER BRAND NAMES

In addition to the Institute grades, practically all packers identify their higher grades of meats with alluring private brands so that the consumer as well as the retailer can recognize the quality of a particular cut. Thus, the top brand names synonymous with the names of four national meat packers and applied to their highest quality beef, pork, and lamb are: Armour's *Star*, Swift's *Premium*, Wilson's *Certified*, and Cudahy's *Puritan*.

A meat packer's reputation depends upon consistent standards of quality for all meats that carry his brand names. The brand names are also effectively used in advertising campaigns.

KOSHER MEATS

Meat for the Jewish trade—known as kosher meat—is slaughtered and processed according to ancient Biblical laws, called *Kashruth*, dating back to the days of Moses, more than three thousand years ago. The Hebrew religion holds that God issued these instructions directly to Moses, who, in turn, transmitted them to the Jewish people while they were wandering in the wilderness near Mount Sinai.

The Hebrew word kosher means fit or proper, and this is the guiding principle in the handling of meats for the Jewish trade. Also, only those classes of animals considered clean—those that both chew the cud and have cloven hooves—are used. Thus, cattle, sheep, goats and poultry—but not hogs—are koshered.[8]

Contrary to common belief, both forequarters and hindquarters of kosher slaughtered meat may be used by orthodox Jews. But because all veins must be removed before the meat is delivered to the consumer, the Jewish trade usually confines itself to the forequarters, from which the veins can be removed with a minimum of tearing of the flesh. In order to devein a hind-quarter, it is necessary to cut it up into such small pieces that it is very unattractive and unsaleable for anything but ground meat or stews. Because the forequarters do not contain such choice cuts as the hinds, the kosher trade attempts to secure the best possible fores; thus this trade is for high-grade slaughter animals. Also, there is a secondary reason why the kosher trade demands well finished beef; namely, the ban against the use of lard in cooking, and the need for beef fat therefor.

Kosher meat must be sold by the packer or the retailer within 72 hours after slaughter, or it must be washed (a treatment known as *begiss,* meaning to wash) and reinstated by a representative of the synagogue every subsequent 72 hours. At the expiration of 216 hours after the time of slaughter (after begissing three times), however, it is declared *trafeh,* meaning forbidden food, and is automatically rejected for kosher trade. It is then sold in the regular meat channels. Because of these regulations, kosher meat is moved out very soon after slaughter. Also it is easier to devein the meat while it is still warm than after it has been chilled.

Kosher sausage and prepared meats are made from meats which are deveined, soaked in water one-half hour, sprinkled with salt, allowed to stand for an hour, and washed thoroughly. This makes them kosher indefinitely.

The Jewish law also provides that before kosher meat is cooked, it must be soaked in water for one-half hour. After soaking, the meat is placed on a perforated board in order to drain off the excess moisture. It is then sprinkled

---

[8] Deuteronomy 14:4-5 and Leviticus 11:1-8.

liberally with salt. One hour later, it is thoroughly washed. Such meat is then considered to remain kosher as long as it is fresh and wholesome.

As would be expected, the volume of kosher meat is greatest in those eastern seaboard cities where the Jewish population is most concentrated. New York City alone uses about one-fourth of all the beef koshered in the United States.

While only about half of the total of more than six million U.S. Jewish population is orthodox, most members of the faith are heavy users of kosher meats.

THE NUTRITIVE QUALITIES OF MEATS

Perhaps most people eat meats simply because they like them. They derive a rich enjoyment and satisfaction therefrom. For flavor, variety, and appetite appeal, meat is unsurpassed.

But meat is far more than just a very tempting and delicious food. From a nutritional standpoint, it contains certain essentials of an adequate diet. This is important, for how we live and how long we live are determined in large part by our diet.

It is estimated that the average American gets the following percentages of his food nutrients from meat.[9]

63% of his protein
47% of his iron
28% of his phosphorus
42% of his vitamin B_1 (thiamine)
24% of his vitamin B_2 (riboflavin)
79% of his niacin
    (Plus generous amounts of other B vitamins—including the important B_{12})

The nutritive qualities of meats may be summarized as follows:

1. **Proteins.**—The word protein is derived from the Greek word *proteous,* meaning *in first place.* **Protein is recognized as a most important body builder.** Fortunately, meat contains the proper quality and quantity of protein for the building and repair of body tissues. On a fresh basis, meat contains 15 to 20 per cent protein. Also, it contains all of the amino acids, or building stones, which are necessary for the making of new tissue; and the proportion of amino acids in meat almost exactly parallels that in human protein.

2. **Calories.**—Meat is a rich source of energy, the energy value being dependent largely upon the amount of fat it contains. A pound of moderately fat beef provides about 1,350 calories, or nearly half the daily energy requirement of the average adult.

---

[9] From a study conducted by the USDA. The percentages of daily dietary allowance are based on recommendations of the National Research Council for an average 154-lb. sedentary man.

Fig. 7-11. Meat on the table. (Courtesy, USDA)

Fig. 7-12. Shows that meat is a good source of phosphorus. Minerals are necessary in order to build and maintain the body skeleton and tissues and regulate body functions. Although meat is a rich source of several minerals, it is especially good as a source of phosphorus and iron. (Demonstration conducted by the National Live Stock and Meat Board in the laboratory of Rush Medical College)

3. **Minerals.**—Minerals are necessary in order to build and maintain the body skeleton and tissues and to regulate body functions. Meat is a rich source of several minerals, but it is especially good as a source of phosphorus and iron. Phosphorus combines with calcium in building the bones and teeth. Phosphorus also enters into the structure of every body cell, helps to maintain the alkalinity of the blood, is involved in the output of nervous energy, and has other important duties.

Iron is necessary for the building of blood, and its presence protects against nutritional anemia. With these important functions, however, it is interesting to know that the iron in the body of an average adult is equivalent to only about the weight of a penny, yet it enters into the structure of every active body cell. Iron is a constituent of the hemoglobin or red pigment of the 25 trillion or more body corpuscles. Thus, it helps to carry the life-giving oxygen to every part of the body. In 1934, Doctors Minot, Murphy, and Whipple were jointly awarded the Nobel Prize in Medicine for the discovery that liver was effective in the treatment of anemia, a disease which once was regarded as fatal. The average adult would be assured an adequate supply of iron if two servings of meat were taken daily along with one serving of liver each week.

4. **Vitamins.**—Today we are vitamin conscious. Even so, the word vitamin is not very old. In fact, it was not until the year 1912 that Dr. Casimar Funk, a Polish physician, originated the word. He coined it from the word vita, meaning life. Although the name vitamins is relatively new and we are still making discoveries relative to these substances, thousands of years ago people knew that certain foods possessed certain unidentified nutritive properties. For example, as early as 1500 B.C. the Egyptians and Chinese hit upon the discovery that eating livers would improve one's vision in dim light. We now know that livers furnish vitamin A, a very important factor for night vision. In fact, medical authorities

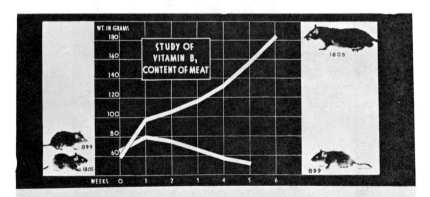

Rat No. 899 received adequate diet except for Vitamin B₁

Rat No. 1805 received same diet + 2% dried pork ham
which is rich in Vitamin B₁

Fig. 7-13. Meat is a good source of vitamin B₁ (or thiamine). (Studies by the University of Wisconsin; supported by National Live Stock and Meat Board)

recognize that night blindness, glare blindness, and poor vision in dim light are all common signs pointing to the fact that the person so affected is not getting enough vitamin A in his diet.

Meat is one of the richest sources of the important B group of vitamins, especially thiamine, riboflavin, niacin, and vitamin B_{12} (see Table 7-3)—the vitamins now being used to reinforce certain foods and which are indispensable in our daily diet. Thiamine stimulates appetite, prevents beriberi, aids in the utilization of carbohydrates, and promotes the health of the body cells. Ribo-

TABLE 7—3

VITAMIN CONTENT OF FRESH MEATS[1]

Meat Product	Thiamine	Riboflavin	Niacin	Vitamin B12
	(mg /100 g)	(mg /100 g)	(mg /100 g)	(mcg /100 g)
Beef liver...........................	0.23	3.39	13.5	51.0
Beef round.........................	0.17	0.16	5.7	1.8
Pork ham..........................	1.13	0.21	3.5	1.3
Lamb leg...........................	0.20	0.30	6.3	1.7
Salami sausage..................	0.21	0.20	4.0	1.4

[1]*Nutritional Observatory*, Heinz Nutritional Research Division, Mellon Institute of Industrial Research, Vol. 14, No. 2, April 1953.

Fig. 7-14. Meat is a good source of niacin which prevents and cures pellagra in man and "black tongue" in dogs. (Studies by the University of Wisconsin; supported by National Live Stock and Meat Board)

flavin is necessary for cell oxidation and protects against nervous disorders and also liver disturbances. Niacin prevents and cures pellagra, a diet deficiency disease which formerly afflicted hundreds of thousands of persons in this country, especially in the South. Vitamin B_{12} stimulates the appetite, increases the rate of growth and the efficiency of feed utilization, and is necessary for normal reproduction. Indeed, one of the reasons for the rapid decline in B-vitamin deficiencies in America may well be the increased amount of meat and other B-vitamin-containing foods in the daily diet.

5. **Digestibility.**—Finally, in considering the nutritive qualities of meats, it should be noted that this food is highly digestible. About 97 per cent of meat proteins and 95 per cent of meat fats are digested.

We come to realize, therefore, the important part that meat is playing in the nutrition of the nation. It should play an even greater part, for we are told that 35 to 40 per cent of our population is now failing to receive an adequate diet to maintain health and vigor.

WHAT DETERMINES THE PRICE OF MEAT?

During those periods when meat is high in price, especially the choicest cuts, there is a tendency on the part of the consumer to blame either or all of the following: (1) the farmer or rancher, (2) the packer, (3) the meat retailer, or (4) the government. Such criticisms, which often have a way of becoming quite vicious, are not justified. Actually, meat prices are determined by the laws of supply and demand; that is, the price of meat is largely dependent upon what the consumers as a group are able and willing to pay for the available supply.

The Available Supply of Meat

Because the vast majority of meats are marketed on a fresh basis rather than cured and because meat is a perishable product, the supply of this food is very much dependent upon the number and weight of cattle, sheep, and hogs available for slaughter at a given time. In turn, the number of market animals is largely governed by the relative profitability of livestock enterprises in comparison with other agricultural pursuits. That is to say, farmers and ranchers—like any other good businessmen—generally do those things that are most profitable to them. Thus, a short supply of market animals at any given time usually reflects the unfavorable and unprofitable production factors that existed some months earlier and which caused curtailment of breeding and feeding operations.

Historically, when short meat supplies exist, meat prices rise, and the market price on slaughter animals usually advances, making livestock production profitable. But, unfortunately, livestock breeding and feeding operations cannot be turned on and off like a spigot. For example, a heifer cannot be bred until she is about 1½ years of age; the pregnancy period requires another 9 months; for various reasons only an average of 86 out of 100 cows bred in the United

States conceive and give birth to young; and finally, the young are usually grown and fed until at least a year and a half of age before marketing. Thus, under the most favorable conditions, this production process, which is controlled by the laws of nature, requires about four years in which to produce a new generation of market cattle.

History also shows that if livestock prices remain high and feed abundant, the producer will step up his breeding and feeding operations as fast as he can within the limitations imposed by nature, only to discover when market time arrives that too many other producers have done likewise. Overproduction, disappointingly low prices, and curtailment in breeding and feeding operations are the result.

Nevertheless, the operations of livestock farmers and ranchers do respond to market prices, producing so-called cycles. Thus, the intervals of high production, or cycles, in cattle occur about every 10 to 12 years. In sheep, they occur about every 9 to 10 years, and in hogs—which are litter bearing, breed at an earlier age, have a shorter gestation period, and go to market at an earlier age—they occur every 3 to 5 years.

The Demand for Meat

The demand for meat is primarily determined by buying power and competition from other products. Stated in simple terms, demand is determined by the spending money available and the competitive bidding of millions of housewives who are the chief home purchasers of meats. On a nation-wide basis, a high buying power and great demand for meats exist when most people are employed and wages are high.

It is also generally recognized that in boom periods—periods of high personal income—meat purchases are affected in three ways: (1) more total meat is desired; (2) there is a greater demand for the choicest cuts; and (3) because of the increased money available and shorter working hours, there is a desire for more leisure time, which in turn increases the demand for those meat cuts or products that require a minimum of time in preparation (such as steaks, chops, and hamburger). In other words, during periods of high buying power, people not only want more meats, but they compete for the choicer and easier prepared cuts of meats—porterhouse and T-bone steaks, lamb and pork chops, hams, and hamburger (chiefly because of the ease of preparation of the latter).

Because of the operation of the old law of supply and demand, when the choicer and easier prepared cuts of meat are in increased demand, they advance proportionately more in price than the cheaper cuts. This results in a great spread in prices, with some meat cuts very much higher than others. While porterhouse steaks, or pork or lamb chops, may be selling for four or five times the cost per pound of the live animal, less desirable cuts may be priced at less than the cost per pound of the animal on foot. This is so because a market must be secured for all the cuts.

But the novice may wonder why these choice cuts are so scarce, even though people are able and willing to pay a premium for them. The answer is

STORY OF THE STEER

Cattle are not all beef		Beef is not all steak
1000 lbs STEER	**590 lbs BEEF**	**465 lbs RETAIL CUTS**

			Lbs	Price	Total
		Porterhouse, T-Bone & Club steak	35	$1.19	$41.65
		Sirloin steak	40	1.09	43.60
		Round steak	65	.89	57.85
		Rib roast	45	.79	35.55
		Boneless rump roast	25	.99	24.75
		Chuck roast	100	.59	59.00
		Hamburger	45	.55	24.75
		Stew meat & misc. cuts	110	.65	71.50
		Bones, Fat, Waste & Shrink	125		1.50

at 29½¢ per lb.	at 45¢ per lb.	
Packer pays $295	**Retailer pays $265**	**Consumer pays $360**

Value of by-products, such as hides, fats, hair, animal feeds, fertilizer, etc., in part offsets packers' dressing, handling and selling expenses, so that the beef from a steer generally sells at wholesale for less than the live animal cost.	Retailer mark-up must cover such costs as rent, labor, depreciation on equipment and fixtures, etc., as well as trimming loss and natural shrinkage in weight of beef carcass when converted into retail cuts.

Based on average market prices prevailing in Chicago for April, 1958

DEPARTMENT OF MARKETING
AMERICAN MEAT INSTITUTE

Chart No. 685-R1
April, 1958

Fig. 7-15. Cattle are not all beef, and beef is not all steak! It is important therefore, that those who produce and slaughter animals and those who purchase wholesale and/or retail cuts know the approximate (1) percentage yield of chilled carcass in relation to the weight of the animal on foot and (2) yield of different retail cuts. This figure illustrates these points. As noted, an average 1,000 pound steer will yield about a 590 pound carcass or 465 pounds of retail cuts, only 35 pounds of which will be porterhouse, T-bone, and club steaks. (Courtesy, American Meat Institute)

simple; nature does not make many choice cuts or top grades, regardless of price. Moreover, a hog is born with merely two hams, a lamb with two hind legs; and only two loins (a right and a left one) can be obtained from each carcass upon slaughter. In addition, not all weight on foot can be cut into meat. For example, the average steer weighing 1,000 pounds on foot and grading Good will only yield 465 pounds of retail cuts (the balance consists of hide, internal organs, etc.). Secondly, this 465 pounds will cut out only about 35 pounds of porterhouse, T-bone, and club steaks. The balance of the cuts are equally wholesome and nutritious; and, although there are other steaks, many of the cuts are better adapted for use as roasts, stews, and soup bones. To make bad matters worse, not all cattle are of a quality suitable for the production of steaks. For example, the meat from most worn-out dairy animals and thin cattle of beef breeding is not sold over the block. Also, if the moneyed buyer insists on buying only the top grade of meat, namely U.S. Prime or its equivalent, it must be remembered that only a small proportion of slaughter cattle produce carcasses of this top grade. To be sure, the lower grades are equally wholesome, but they are simply graded down because the carcass is somewhat deficient in conformation, finish, and/or quality.

Thus, when the national income is exceedingly high, there is a demand for the choicest but limited cuts of meat from the very top but limited grades. This is certain to make for high prices, for the supply of such cuts is limited, but the demand is great. Under these conditions, if prices did not move up to balance the supply with demand, there would be a marked shortage of the desired cuts at the retail counter.

It must also be remembered that meats must compete with other food products for the consumer's dollar. In 1965, 18.2 per cent of the disposable income was spent for food.[10] In addition to preference, therefore, relative prices are an important factor in determining food selection.

Meat must also compete with certain nonfood items, for there are people who would literally go hungry in order to be able to spend their money for other purposes. On the average, U.S. consumers spend 4.3 per cent of their total income for meat.

WHERE THE CONSUMER'S FOOD DOLLAR GOES

Food is the nation's largest industry. A total of $85 billion, nearly one-fifth of the total consumption expenditures, was spent for food in 1965. This vast sum included the bill for about 300,000 retail food stores; a large majority of the nation's 3,300,000 farms; thousands of wholesalers, brokers, eating establishments, and other food firms; and the transportation, equipment, and container industries. Food processors and distributors alone employed 3,000,000 persons.

In recognition of the importance of food to the nation's economy and the welfare of its people, The National Commission on Food Marketing was established by Public Law 88-354, signed by President Johnson on July 3, 1964. The voluminous report of the Commission was issued in June, 1966. Tables 7-4,

TABLE 7—4

WHERE THE CONSUMER'S FOOD DOLLAR GOES[1]
(as shown by "market basket" comprised
of 62 farm-produced foods)

	1964	1965
Retail value of market basket	$1,014	$1,042
Farm value	374	409
Farm-retail spread	640	633
Farm share of consumer's dollar.............	.37	.39

[1]*Food from Farm to Consumer*, Report of the National Commission on Food Marketing, June 1966, p. 11.

---

[10]It is noteworthy that food expenditures as a per cent of income have decreased as follows:

1937-39	23.1
1947-49	24.7
1957-59	20.6
1965	18.2

These figures are from: *Food from Farmer to Consumer*, Report of the National Commission on Food Marketing, June 1966, p. 9.

TABLE 7—5

DISTRIBUTION OF CONSUMER'S DOLLAR ACCORDING TO MARKETING FUNCTION, SELECTED FOOD PRODUCTS, 1964[1]

	Beef Choice Grade (lb.)	Pork (lb.)	Lamb Choice Grade (lb.)	Veal (lb.)	Broiler (lb.)	Turkey (lb.)	Oranges Florida (90 lb. box)	Apples Washington Delicious (42 lb. box)	Canned Corn (cream style) (303 can)	White Bread (1 lb.)	Breakfast Cereal (1 lb.)
	(¢)	(¢)	(¢)	(¢)	(¢)	(¢)	($)	($)	(¢)	(¢)	(¢)
Retail price	70.8	52.3	70.0	78.1	36.3	40.6	11.37	9.79	19.0	20.7	41.6
Retailing	17.0	12.3	17.5	20.9	7.9	4.0	4.27	3.70	3.3	3.7	6.4
Wholesaling, transportation, other distribution	2.3	1.6	2.4	2.6	4.5	3.0	2.25	2.15	3.0	6.1	3.4
Processing	5.3	10.1	7.4	10.4	3.6	7.0	2.11	2.19	10.3	6.7	25.0
Assembly	3.8	1.7	3.2	3.6	.6	.6	......	......	......	.2	2.5
Farm value	42.4	26.6	39.5	40.6	19.7	26.0	2.74	1.75	2.4	4.0	4.3
Farmer's share of retail price, %	60	51	56	52	54	64	24	18	13	19	10

[1] *Food from Farmer to Consumer*, Report of the National Commission on Food Marketing, June 1966, Table 4, pp. 14-15.

TABLE 7—6

RETAIL AND FARM VALUES OF THE FOOD MARKET BASKET,
WITH RELATED DATA[1]

Year	Market Basket Values			Share of Retail	
	Retail	Farm	Farm-Retail Spread	Farm	Farm-Retail Spread
	($)	($)	($)	(%)	(%)
1939..........	425	160	265	38	62
1947-49......	890	441	449	50	50
1950..........	870	409	461	47	53
1955..........	917	373	544	41	59
1962..........	1,006	384	622	38	62
1965..........	1,042	409	633	39	61

[1]*Food from Farmer to Consumer*, Report of the National Food Commission on Food Marketing, June 1966, Table 9, p. 18.

7-5, and 7-6 of this book, based on data from the Commission report, are particularly pertinent to the livestock industry.

Table 7-4 reveals that of each food dollar, the farmer's share is only 39 cents, the rest—61 cents—goes for processing and marketing. This means that almost two-thirds of today's food dollar goes for preparing, processing, packaging, and selling—and not for the food itself.

Table 7-5 gives a further breakdown, by selected food items, of where the consumer's food dollar goes. Among the products shown, the farmer's share of the consumer's dollar ranges from 10 per cent for breakfast cereal to 60 per cent for beef. The farmer's share of the retail price of beef is relatively high because processing is simple and inexpensive, transportation costs are low due to the concentrated nature of the product, and retailer's handling costs are moderate because stores frequently sell beef at special, low prices—as an attraction. On the other hand, the farmer's share of breakfast cereal is low due to the high processing and container costs, and its bulky, costly transportation.

Table 7-6 shows (1) that the farmer's share of the consumer's food dollar rose to a historic high during the sharp inflation immediately following World War II, and (2) that it has fluctuated considerably over the past three decades. Among the reasons advanced as to why farm prices of foods failed to go up in keeping with rising marketing costs, thereby giving the farmer a greater share of the consumer's food dollar, are: (1) rapid technological advances on the farm, making it possible for the farmer to stay in business despite smaller margins; (2) overproduction; and (3) the relative ease with which cost pressures within the marketing system can be passed backward rather than forward.

Over the years, processing and marketing costs have increased and the farmer's share has decreased, primarily because consumers have demanded, and gotten, more and more processing and packaging—more built-in services. For example, few consumers are interested in buying a live hog—or even a whole carcass. Instead, they want a pound of pork chops—all trimmed, packaged, and ready for cooking. Likewise, few housewives are interested in buying flour and baking bread. But consumers need to be reminded that, fine as these services are, they cost money—hence, they should be expected to pay for them. Without realizing it, American consumers have three million maids working for them in food processing and distributing alone. These mysterious maids do not do any work in the kitchen; they're the three million people who work on the food from the time it leaves the farms and ranches until it reaches the nation's kitchens. They're the people who make it possible for the housewife to choose between quick frozen, dry frozen, quick cooking, ready to heat, ready to eat, and many other conveniences. Hand in hand with this transition, and accentuating the demand for convenience foods, more women work outside the home. The proportion of the nation's labor force made up of women rose from 28 per cent in 1947 to 35 per cent in 1965. All this is fine, but we need to remind some folks that the three million maids engaged in processing and distributing foods must be paid, for they want to eat too.

WORLD AND U.S. MEAT PRODUCTION

The 1966 meat production for the principal livestock countries of the world, reached 120,722 million pounds. In general, the meat-surplus-producing countries are the newer countries and those that are more sparsely settled.

The United States production of meat (total and by kinds) and lard from 1961 to 1966, is shown in Table 7-7.

TABLE 7—7
UNITED STATES PRODUCTION OF MEAT AND LARD
FROM 1961 to 1966[1]

Year	All Meats (Excluding Lard)		Beef		Veal		Lamb and Mutton		Pork (Excluding Lard)		Lard	
	(lbs.)	(kg)	(lbs.)	(kg)	(lbs.)	(kg)	(lbs.)	(kg)	(lbs.)	(kg)	(lbs.)	(kg)
1961	28,585	12,978	15,298	6,945	1,044	474	832	378	11,411	5,181	2,517	1,143
1962	28,956	13,146	15,296	6,944	1,015	461	809	367	11,841	5,376	2,480	1,126
1963	30,559	13,874	16,423	7,456	927	421	770	350	12,439	5,647	2,476	1,124
1964	32,673	14,834	18,424	8,364	1,011	459	715	325	12,523	5,685	2,476	1,124
1965	31,527	14,313	18,693	8,487	1,018	462	651	296	11,165	5,069	2,050	931
1966	32,582	14,810	19,694	8,952	910	414	650	296	11,328	5,149	1,929	877

(Million)

[1]Agricultural Statistics, 1965, USDA, pp. 356 and 358, and 1967, p. 418.

Table 7-8 shows the number of animals of each of the respective classes slaughtered in the United States in the year 1966 and the proportions of these animals slaughtered in federally inspected plants, nonfederally inspected plants, and farm slaughter.

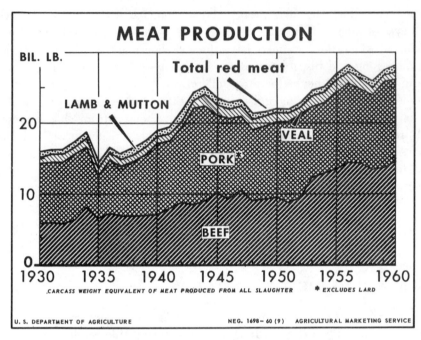

Fig. 7-16. United States red meat production.

TABLE 7—8

UNITED STATES MEAT SLAUGHTER (FEDERALLY AND NON-
FEDERALLY INSPECTED AND FARM SLAUGHTER)
BY CLASSES OF ANIMALS, 1966[1]

Federal, Nonfederal or Farm Slaughter	Cattle	Calves	Sheep and Lambs	Hogs
	(1,000 hd.)	(1,000 hd.)	(1,000 hd.)	(1,000 hd.)
Federally inspected............	27,319	4,432	11,553	63,729
Other wholesale	6,408	2,215	1,184	10,282
Farm...............................	442	214	264	1,313
Total................	34,169	6,861	13,001	75,324

[1]*Livestock and Meat Statistics*, Supp. for 1966 to Statistical Bul. No. 333, USDA, p. 63.

PER CAPITA MEAT CONSUMPTION IN VARIOUS COUNTRIES

In general, consumption of meat is higher in new or frontier-type countries that are sparsely populated than in the older and more densely populated regions of the world. In many of the latter areas, insufficient grain is produced to support the human population when consumed directly. This eliminates any possibility of keeping animals, except as scavengers. Certainly when it is a choice between the luxury of meat and animal by-products or starvation, people will elect to accept a lower standard of living and go on a grain diet. In addition to the available meat supply, food habits and religious restrictions affect the amount of meat consumed.

TABLE 7—9

PER CAPITA MEAT CONSUMPTION IN SPECIFIED COUNTRIES, 1966[1]

Country	Per Capita Meat Consumption		Country	Per Capita Meat Consumption	
	(lb.)	(kg)		(lb.)	(kg)
New Zealand	229	104	France	152	69
Uruguay	224	102	Canada	148	67
Argentina	207	94	United Kingdom	138	63
Australia	198	90	Paraguay	133	60
United States	171	78	West Germany	123	56

[1]Foreign Agriculture Circular, FLM 11-67, Foreign Agricalatural Service, USDA, Nov., 1967.

Table 7-9 gives a summary of per capita meat consumption in several countries of interest.

Although the United States is an important meat-eating country, four other countries consume more meat per capita; namely, New Zealand, Uruguay, Argentina, and Australia. All of these countries possess vast expanses of grasslands, and are sparsely populated.

PER CAPITA MEAT CONSUMPTION IN THE UNITED STATES

Although comprising less than 6 per cent of the world's population, the people of the United States eat over one-fourth of the total world production of meat. The amount of meat consumed in this country varies from year to year (see Fig. 7-17). In 1966, the average per capita meat consumption, exclusive of lard, was 170 pounds; with 8.6 pounds of lard in addition. That was about 44 pounds per person more than was consumed in the pre-war period, 1935-39. In 1966, when the per capita civilian consumption of meats, exclusive of lard, totaled 170 pounds, the distribution of types of meat was as shown in Table 7-10.

During the war years, the American servicemen received about 300 pounds of meat per capita, or more than twice the amount eaten by civilians at home during this same period. The Office of the Surgeon General of the Army issued figures showing that meat supplied 43.4 per cent of the protein in the soldier's daily diet, 36.5 per cent of the iron, 35.4 per cent of the riboflavin, 33.4 per cent of the thiamine, and 31.0 per cent of the phosphorus. In addition, meat ranked as the number-one morale food for the armed forces.

For the most part, meat consumption in this country is on a domestic basis, with only negligible amounts being either imported or exported. Although cured meats furnish somewhat of a reserve supply—with more meats going into cure during times of meat surpluses—our meat consumption generally is up when livestock production is high. Also, when good crops are produced and feed prices are favorable, market animals are fed to heavier weights. On the other hand, when feed-livestock ratios are unfavorable, breeding operations are curtailed, and animals are marketed at lighter weights. But during the latter periods, numbers are liquidated, thus tending to keep the meat supply fairly stable.

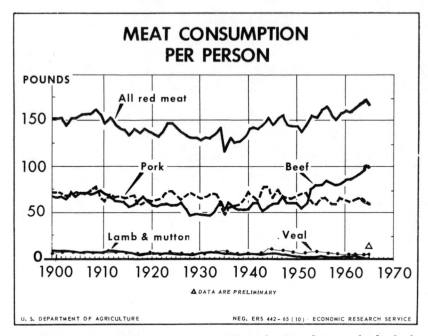

Fig. 7-17. Per capita meat consumption in the United States, by kind of meat. As noted, the amount of meat consumed in this country varies from year to year. In recent years, the average American has consumed more beef than any other kind of meat. (Courtesy, Agricultural Marketing Service, USDA)

TABLE 7—10

UNITED STATES PER CAPITA CONSUMPTION OF MEAT
(BY KINDS) AND LARD FOR 1966[1]

Type of Meat	1966 Annual per Capita Consumption	
	(lbs.)	(kg)
Beef	103.8	47.2
Veal	4.5	2.0
Lamb and Mutton	4.0	1.8
Pork (excluding lard)	58.0	26.4
Total meat	170.3	77.4
Lard	8.6	4.0

[1]Agricultural Statistics, 1967, USDA, pp. 424 and 425.

TRENDS IN PER CAPITA CONSUMPTION
OF MEAT AND OTHER FOODS

Figure 7-18 shows the trends in per capita consumption of meat and other foods, by groups. As will be noted, the consumption of grain products and potatoes has gone steadily downward, whereas the per capita consumption of fruits and vegetables and dairy products has increased. Until recently, the long-time trend in meat consumption was downward.

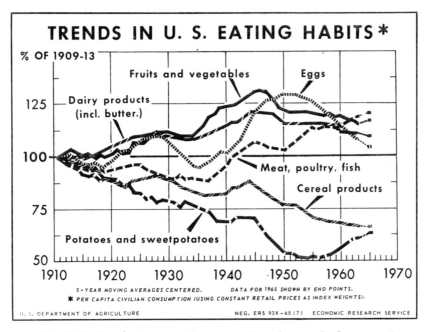

Fig. 7-18. Trends in per capita consumption of major food groups, 5-year moving averages, with 1909 to 1913=100. Until 1937, the long-time trend in meat consumption was downward.

The selection of foods is based on taste preference and relative prices, with different foods competing with each other for a place in the consumer's diet. In prosperous times and with increased buying power, the preferred foods increase in demand and price. Because grain products and potatoes are not luxury foods, their per capita consumption is little affected by buying power.

MEAT IMPORTS AND EXPORTS

Stockmen are prone to ask why the United States, which produces over one-fourth of the world's meat, buys meat from abroad. Conversely, consumers sometimes wonder why we export meat. Occasionally, there is justification for such fears. Table 7-11 gives a comparison of U.S. meat imports and production.

Table 7-12 reveals that the United States imports more meat than it exports, but, as shown in Table 7-11, total meat imports actually constitute a very small percentage of the available U.S. supply.

The quantity of meat and animals imported from abroad depends to a substantial degree on (1) the level of U.S. meat production, (2) consumer buying power, (3) livestock prices, and (4) quotas and tariffs. When animal prices are high, more meat is imported (see Fig. 7-19). Actually, there may be some virtue in judiciously increasing imports of meat and animals during times of scarcity and high prices, as an alternative to pricing meat out of the market. The position of butter versus oleomargarine is proof enough of this assertion, for butter was priced out of the market.

TABLE 7—11

U.S. IMPORTS[1] OF MEATS AND LIVESTOCK COMPARED
WITH U.S. MEAT PRODUCTION[2]
(Average 1961-65, Annual 1966)

Commodity	Average 1961-65			1966		
	Imports	Production	Imports Compared with Production	Imports	Production	Imports Compared with Production
	(million) (lbs.) (kg)	(million) (lbs.) (kg)	(%)	(million) (lbs.) (kg)	(million) (lbs.) (kg)	(%)
Beef and veal..........	856 389	17,835 8,107	4.8	893.3 406.0	20,604 9,365	4.3
Pork......................	212 96	11,854 5,388	1.8	298.3 135.6	11,328 5,149	2.6
Lamb and mutton...	61 28	755 343	8.1	75.4 34.3	650 295	11.6
Total...............	1,129 513	30,444 13,838	3.7	1,267.0 575.9	32,582 14,809	3.9

[1]Livestock and Meat Products Division, Foreign Agricultural Service, USDA, March 1967.
[2]*Agricultural Statistics 1967*, USDA pp. 424, 425.

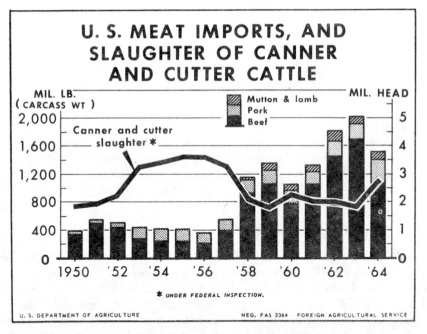

Fig. 7-19. Meat imports increase when slaughter of Cutter and Canner cattle is down. (Courtesy, USDA)

The quantity of meat and animals exported from this country is dependent upon: (1) the volume of meat and the number of animals produced in the United States, (2) the volume of meat and the number of animals produced abroad, and (3) the relative vigor of international trade, especially as affected by buying power and trade restrictions.

Our meat imports come from many countries, but chiefly: **beef**—from Australia, New Zealand, South America (Argentina, Uruguay, Paraguay, and

TABLE 7—12

U.S. MEAT IMPORTS AND EXPORTS[1]

Imports (Million)

Year	Beef and Veal (lb)	(kg)	Pork (lb)	(kg)	Lamb, Mutton, and Goat (lb)	(kg)	Other Meats; Canned, Prepared, or Preserved (lb)	(kg)	All Meats (lb)	(kg)
1961	689.1	312.9	173.7	78.9	55.8	25.4	2.0	.9	920.7	418.0
1962	967.4	439.2	203.8	92.5	78.1	35.5	3.1	1.4	1252.4	568.6
1963	1122.4	509.6	212.6	96.5	81.8	37.1	5.0	2.3	1421.7	645.5
1964	800.4	363.4	215.2	97.7	44.7	20.3	1.8	.8	1062.1	482.2
1965	941.8	427.5	333.0	151.2	72.5	32.9	2.2	1.0	1349.5	612.7

Exports

Year	Beef and Veal (lb)	(kg)	Pork (lb)	(kg)	Lamb, Mutton, and Goat (lb)	(kg)	Other Meats; Canned, Prepared, or Preserved (lb)	(kg)	All Meats (lb)	(kg)
1961	29.9	13.6	68.3	31.0	1.6	.7	129.6	58.9	229.5	104.2
1962	27.1	12.3	63.7	28.9	2.2	1.0	129.9	59.0	222.9	101.2
1963	27.3	12.4	138.1	62.7	1.0	.5	169.7	74.3	330.2	149.9
1964	57.3	26.0	133.0	60.4	1.3	.6	239.1	108.6	430.6	195.5
1965	53.9	24.5	55.3	25.1	2.0	.9	220.8	100.2	332.0	150.7

[1]Livestock and Meat Products Division, Foreign Agricultural Service, USDA.

Brazil), Canada, Mexico, and Ireland; **lamb**–from New Zealand, Australia, and Argentina; and **pork**–from Canada, Denmark, and Ireland.

Because of restrictions designed to prevent the introduction of foot-and-mouth disease, neither fresh nor salted refrigerated beef can be imported to the United States from South America; beef importations from these countries must be canned or fully cured (*i. e.* corned beef). Some animals of all classes are imported for breeding purposes,[11] but the vast majority of on-foot importations consist of feeder cattle shipments from Canada and Mexico (see Table 7-13). Currently, on-foot importations are starting from New Zealand and Australia.

The most important U.S. livestock products that move into export channels are lard, tallow, hides and skins, and variety meats; and the major markets for

TABLE 7—13

U.S. LIVE ANIMAL IMPORTS
(1961-1965)

Year	Cattle	Sheep and Lambs	Hogs
	(no.)	(no.)	(no.)
1961[1]	1,042,721	979	3,252
1962	1,250,029	20,845	3,277
1963	852,278	3,091	4,323
1964	546,606	12,680	5,094
1965[2]	1,128,278	19,073	14,453

[1]Data for 1961 through 1964 from *Livestock and Meat Statistics*, USDA, Supp. for 1964 to Statistical Bull. No. 333, p. 149.

[2]Data for 1965 from *USDA Report*, LMS-149, Tables 11 and 12, pp. 27-28, May 1966. (Courtesy, John C. Pierce, Director, Livestock Division, Consumer and Marketing Service, USDA)

Fig. 7-20. Indians drying and smoking venison. (Photo from a water color original by Ernest Smith. Owned by the Rochester Museum of Arts and Sciences)

---

[11] Certified (registered) purebred animals are permitted free entry into the United States.

each of these products are: **lard**—the United Kingdom is our largest customer, but we also ship lard to West Germany, Yugoslavia, Canada, Belgium, Denmark, France, the Netherlands, Poland, and Latin America; **tallow**—mostly to Europe, but we also ship tallow to South America; **hides and skins**—primarily to Japan, Western Europe, and Canada; **variety meats**—mostly to Europe.

MEAT PRESERVATION

From time immemorial, one of man's major food problems has been that of preserving meats over a period of time and in a condition suitable as a food. Fundamentally, meat preservation is a matter of controlling putrefactive bacterial action. Various methods of preserving meats have been practiced through

Fig. 7-21. Smoking meats in early colonial days. This method of preserving meats is very old. Smoking is still a common practice in the homecuring of pork, and modern meat packers smoke many of their products. (Courtesy, Swift and Co.)

the ages, the most common of which are: (1) drying, (2) smoking, (3) salting, (4) freezing, (5) canning, and (6) sausages.

In this country, meat curing is largely confined to pork, primarily because of the keeping qualities and palatability of cured-pork products. Considerable beef is dried or corned and some lamb and veal are cured, but none of these is of such great importance as cured pork.

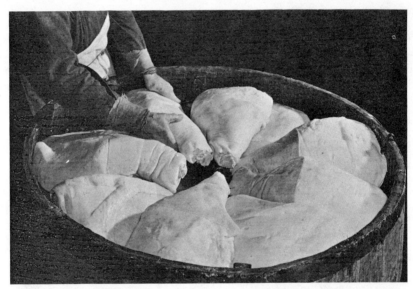

Fig. 7-22. Hams in barreled sweet-pickle cure.

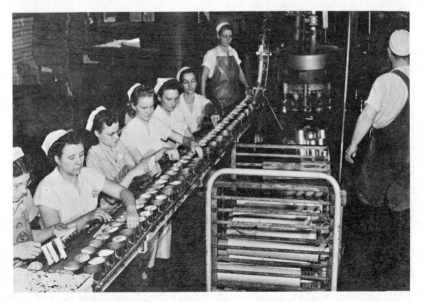

Fig. 7-23. Canning meat. This popular method of meat preservation was first initiated by Arthur Libby in 1874. (Courtesy, Mr. H. A. Rothra, Ed., *Meat Magazine*)

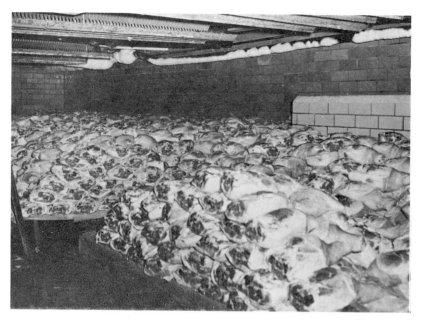

Fig. 7-24. Hams in dry cure (or dry-sugar cure). Most dry-cured pork is smoked following the formula treatment. (Courtesy, Mr. H. A. Rothra, Ed., *Meat Magazine*)

Fig. 7-25. Dry-salting bacon for curing. (Courtesy, Mr. H. A. Rothra, Ed., *Meat Magazine*)

METHODS OF MEAT COOKERY

The method used in meat cookery depends on the nature of the cut to which it is applied. In general, the types of meat cookery may be summarized as follows:

Fig. 7-26. Some of the many different varieties of sausage. Some are fresh; others are dry, smoked, or cooked. Sausage represents both a method of meat preparation, and—except for fresh sausage—a means of meat preservation. The making of sausage antedates recorded history. (Courtesy, National Live Stock and Meat Board)

Dry-heat Cooking

Dry-heat cooking is used in preparing the more tender cuts, those that contain little connective tissue. This method of cooking consists of surrounding the meat by dry air in the oven or under the broiler. The common methods of cooking by dry heat are: (a) roasting, (b) broiling, and (c) panbroiling.

Moist-heat Cooking

Moist-heat cooking is generally used in preparing the less-tender cuts, those containing more connective tissues that require moist heat to soften it and make it tender. In this type of cooking, the meat is surrounded by hot liquid or by steam. The common methods of moist-heat cooking are: (a) braising and (b) cooking in water (called stewing when small pieces of meat are so cooked).

PACKING HOUSE BY-PRODUCTS FROM SLAUGHTER

The meat or flesh of animals is the primary object of slaughtering. The numerous other products are obtained incidentally. Thus, all products other than the carcass meat are designated as by-products, even though many of them are wholesome and highly nutritious articles of the human diet. Yet it must be realized that, upon slaughter, cattle, sheep, and hogs produced in the United States yield an average of 47, 53, and 30 per cent, respectively, of products other than carcass meat. When a meat packer buys a steer, lamb, or hog, he buys far more than the cuts of meat that will eventually be obtained from the carcass; that is, only about 50 per cent of a meat animal is meat.

In the early days of the meat packing industry, the only salvaged by-

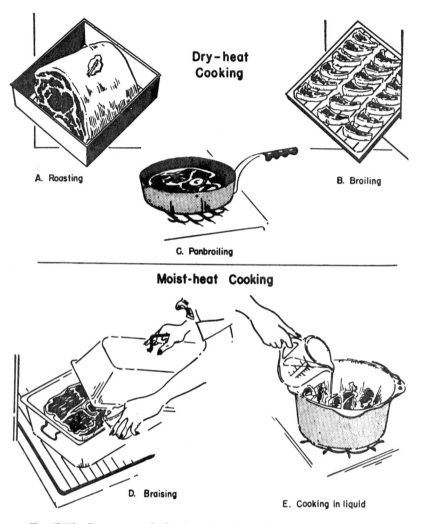

Dry - heat Cooking

A. Roasting

B. Broiling

C. Panbroiling

Moist-heat Cooking

D. Braising

E. Cooking in liquid

Fig. 7-27. Common methods of meat cookery: *Dry-heat cooking:* A, roasting; B, broiling; and C, panbroiling; *moist-heat cooking:* D, braising; and E, Cooking in liquid. (Drawing by R. F. Johnson)

products, were hides, wool, tallow, and tongue. The remainder of the offal was usually carted away and dumped into the river or burned or buried. In some instances, packers even paid for having the offal taken away. In due time, factories for the manufacture of glue, fertilizer, soap, buttons, and numerous other by-products sprang up in the vicinity of the packing plants. Some factories were company-owned, and others were independent industries. Soon much of the former waste material was being converted into materials of value.

Naturally, the relative value of carcass meat and by-products varies, both according to the class of livestock and from year to year. It is estimated that packers retrieved the following percentages of the live cost of different classes of slaughter animals from the value of the by-product in 1966: 1,000-pound steer,

7.77 per cent; 100-pound lamb, 8.75 per cent; and 235-pound hog, 9.56 per cent. Sheep pelts and cattle hides alone account for 4.50 per cent and 2.88 per cent, respectively, of the total income from these classes of animals.[12] The decreasing value of by-products is especially noticeable in cattle, for which by-products contributed over 15 per cent of the value in 1930.[13] This is primarily due to the decreasing value of hides and tallow in recent years; and, in turn, this has been reflected in cattle prices.

In contrast to the 4 early-day by-products—hide, wool, tallow, and tongue—modern cattle slaughter alone produces approximately 80 by-products which have a great variety of uses. Although many of the by-products from cattle, sheep, and hogs are utilized in a like manner, there are a few special products which are peculiar to the class of animals (e. g., wool and "catgut" from sheep).

The complete utilization of by-products is one of the chief reasons why large packers are able to compete so successfully with local butchers. Were it not for this conversion of waste material into salable form, the price of meat would be much higher than under existing conditions. In fact, under normal conditions, the wholesale value of the carcass approaches the cost of the animal on foot.

Important By-products from Animal Slaughter

The following is a list of some of the commercially important by-products of meat packing and the products that are made from them:

GELATIN
Confectionery
Marshmallow
Ice cream
Gelatin desserts
Pharmaceutical products (capsules for medicine, coating for pills, etc.)
Photographic materials and processes
Culture media for bacteria

LIVESTOCK AND POULTRY FEEDS
Various types, especially protein concentrates

WOOL
Wool cloth
Sheepskin
Mouton coats
Lanolin
Cosmetics and medical ointments
Surgical dressings
Shoe polishers
Upholstery
Yarn

HIDES
Leather
    shoes and soles

wearing apparel
suitcases
belting
furniture
harness
athletic equipment
rawhide
drumheads
luggage
saddlery
gloves
wallets
show awards and badges
jewelry
chamois
razor strops
"sheepskins" for diplomas
Hide trimmings
    glue
    fertilizer

BLOOD
Livestock feeds
Adhesives
Leather preparations
Textile sizing
Plaster retardant
Pharmaceuticals

---

[12] Data provided to the author in a communication of December 16, 1966, from Charles E. Hughes, Manager-Agricultural Relations, Armour and Company, Chicago.
[13] *Agricultural Markets in Change*, USDA Report No. 95, July 1966.

HAIR

Brushes (artist, paint and tooth)
Upholstering material (for furniture,
   automobiles, and passenger planes)
Insulating material
Felt padding
Plastering material
Air filters
Rug pads

FATS

Lard
Soap
Oleomargarine
Animal feeds
Candles
Glycerine
   nitroglycerine
   food preservatives
   ointments
   solvents
   vehicle for medicants
   antifreeze
   paints
   cellophane
Industrial oils
   lubricating oils
   cutting oils
   automotive additive
   ceramics
Neats-foot oil and other oils for leather
Oleo stearine
   used in candies, chewing gum, lard
   compounds, frozen desserts, shortenings
Base for ointments and salves
Fatty acids
   insecticides, weed killer, lubricants,
   candles, detergents, wetting agents,
   chemicals, plastics, synthetic rubber, tar, wool finisher, metal polish,
   asphalt binder
Fertilizer

FERTILIZER

Various types used for lawns, gardens
and in farms for increasing crop
yields

BONES, HORNS, AND HOOVES

Inedible bone meal
Plant foods and fertilizer
   gelatin
   glue
   bone china
Stock feeds
Ornaments and novelties, such as
   combs, buttons, knife and umbrella
   handles, crochet needles, teething
   rings, napkin rings, chess men, dice
Ground for use in case hardening
   steel products
Pulverized and burned, used in refin-
   ing sugar and other industrial processes

"CATGUT"

(Made from intestines of meat ani-
   mals)
Tennis racket strings
Musical strings
Surgical sutures
Sausage casings
Gold beater skins for manufacture of
   gold leaf

GLUE

Various types developed for use in
   paper manufacture, book binders,
   cabinet making and other specialized industrial processes

MEDICINAL PRODUCTS

Made from glands, blood fractions,
   etc.

It is not intended that this book should describe all of the one hundred or more by-products obtained from animal slaughter. Rather, only a few of the more important ones will be discussed briefly.

1. **Hides.**—Hides are particularly important as a by-product of cattle slaughter. Thus, most of the discussion in this section will be especially applicable to cattle hides.

Cattle hides have been used by man since the dawn of time; and leather, particularly cowhide, has held an important place in commerce throughout recorded history. It was an important part of the clothing and armour of ancient and medieval times, and today it has hundreds of industrial uses.

There are two great classes of cattle hides, based on their place of origin; packer hides and country hides. Packer hides are the more valuable of the two because they are more uniform in shape, cure, and handling; much freer from cuts and gashes; and uniformly graded and available in larger lots.

Fig. 7-28. It is not within the scope of this book to picture and describe all the products which are manufactured from by-products obtained from slaughter. Instead, Fig. 7-28 is presented in order to show some of the more important items for which by-products are used; items which contribute to the convenience, enjoyment, and health of people in all walks of life. (Courtesy, American Meat Institute)

1. Bone for bone china.
2. Horn and bone handles for carving sets.
3. Hides and skins for leather goods.
4. Rennet for cheese making.
5. Gelatin for marshmallows, photographic film, printers' rollers.
6. Stearin for making chewing gum and candies.
7. Glycerin for explosives used in mining and blasting.
8. Lanolin for cosmetics.
9. Chemicals for tires that run cooler.
10. Binders for asphalt paving.
11. Medicines such as various hormones and glandular extracts, insulin, pepsin, epinephrine, ACTH, cortisone, and surgical sutures.
12. Drumheads and violin strings.
13. Animal fats for soap and feed.
14. Wool for clothing.
15. Camel's hair (actually from cattle ears) for artists' brushes.
16. Cutting oils and other special industrial lubricants.
17. Bone charcoal for high-grade steel, such as ball bearings.
18. Special glues for marine plywoods, paper, matches, window shades.
19. Curled hair for upholstery. Leather for covering fine furniture.
20. High-protein livestock feeds.

The presence of needlessly large brands lowers the value of the hide. Cattle grubs (ox-warbles) also damage hides. It is estimated that one-third of all cattle hides produced in the United States are damaged by grubs. If there are five or more grub holes in the hide, it is classed as No. 2 and is discounted one cent per pound. Because of the larger throat cut, hides from kosher-killed cattle are less valuable.

2. **Sheep pelts.**—The sheep pelt is the most valuable by-product of sheep slaughtering. Sheep skins with short wool, ¾ inch or less in length, are usually tanned with the wool on and are used for coats, robes, rugs, felts, slippers, and other articles. Pelts with longer wool are sent to the pullery. Usually they are temporarily preserved by the addition of salt until the wool is

removed. The pulling process consists of applying a depilatory solution (made of sodium sulphide, slaked lime, and water) to the skin side of the pelt and then pulling the wool loose from the skin after the chemical action has loosened the hold of the fibers.

3. **The fats.**—Next to hides and pelts, the fats (not including lard) are the most valuable by-product derived from slaughtering.

Oleomargarine, which is one of the better known of the products in which rendered animal fat is incorporated, is usually a mixture of vegetable oils and select animal fat.[14] Oleo oil, one of the chief animal fats of this product, is obtained from beef and mutton or lamb. Oleomargarine was first perfected in 1869 by the Frenchman, Mege, who won a prize offered by Napoleon III for a palatable table fat which would be cheaper than butter, keep better, and be less subject to rancidity.

4. **Variety meats.**—The heart, liver, brains, kidneys, tongue, cheek meat, tail, feet, sweetbreads (thymus and pancreatic glands), and tripe (pickled rumen of cattle and sheep) are sold over the counter as variety meats or fancy meats.

5. **Hair.**—Artist and camel-hair brushes are made from the fine hair on the inside of the ears of cattle. Other hair from cattle and hogs is used as indicated in the listing of by-products.

6. **Intestines and bladders.**—Intestines and bladders are used as sausage, lard, cheese, snuff, and putty containers. Lamb casings are used in making surgical sutures, strings for various musical instruments, and strings for tennis rackets.

7. **Glands.**—Various glands of the body are used in the manufacture of numerous pharmaceutical preparations (see Fig. 7-29).

Proper preparation of glands requires quick chilling and skillful handling. Moreover, a very large number of glands must be collected in order to obtain any appreciable amount of most of these pharmaceutical products. For example, the glands from more than 100,000 lambs are necessary to produce one pound of adrenalin, a powerful heart stimulant; and it takes pancreas glands from 1,500 cattle or 7,500 hogs to produce one precious ounce of insulin. But, fortunately, only minute amounts of insulin are required—the insulin from two hogs per day, or from 750 hogs per year, will suffice for each diabetic.

8. **Collagen.**—The collagen of the connective tissues—sinews, lips, head, knuckles, feet, and bones—is made into glue and gelatin. The most important use for glue is in the wood-working industry. About 50 per cent of the United States production of gelatin comes from veal

9. **Contents of the stomach.**—Contents of the stomach are used in making fertilizer.

---

[14] Oleomargarine is of two kinds: (1) a mixture of 50 to 80 per cent animal fat and 20 to 50 per cent vegetable oil, churned with pasteurized skimmed milk or (2) 100 per cent vegetable oil, churned with pasteurized skimmed milk.

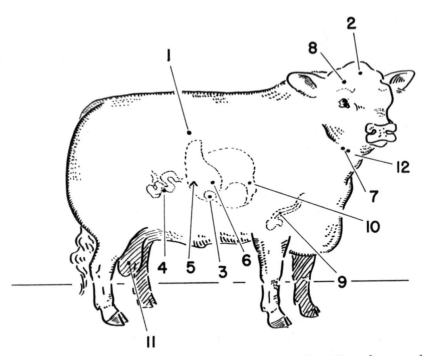

Fig. 7-29. Meat animals are the source of more than 100 medicines and medical products, which doctors and veterinarians administer daily to millions of people and animals to save lives, battle disease, relieve pain, and restore health. This figure shows the approximate location of a few of the glands and other tissues used in the manufacture of some of the pharmaceutical products of human and veterinary medicine. (Drawing by R. F. Johnson. Also, the author gratefully acknowledges the helpful suggestions of the following authorities who reviewed this figure and caption: P. A. Klavano, D.V.M. and Pharmacologist, and W. M. Dickson, Physiologist)

1. **Adrenal (suprarenals)**—Source of (1) epinephrine (used for asthma, hay fever, allergies and shock) and (2) adrenal cortex extract (used for Addison's Disease, and in post surgical and burn shock).

2. **Brain**—Source of kephalin or (cephalin), used on oozing surfaces to check bleeding.

3. **Gall Bladder**—Source of (1) bile salts, (2) dehydrocholic acid—used for gall bladder disturbances and abnormalities of fat digestion, and (3) cortisone (used for rheumatic fever, arthritis, various allergies, inflammatory eye diseases, etc.).

4. **Intestines**—Lamb intestines are used for surgical sutures.

5. **Liver**—Source of (1) liver extract (used for pernicious anemia) and (2) heparin (used to delay clotting of shed blood of ulcers and following surgery).

6. **Pancreas**—Source of (1) insulin (the only substance known to medical science which can control diabetes), (2) trypsin (the protein-digesting enzyme), (3) amalase (the starch-splitting enzyme), and (4) lipase (the fat-splitting enzyme). Each enzyme is used for digestion of these respective nutrients; and trypsin is also used to soften scar tissue or digest necrotic tissue in wounds and ulcers.

7. **Parathyroid**—Parathyroid extract is used for tetany, which follows removal of these glands.

8. **Pituitary**—Source of (1) posterior pituitary extract (used to increase blood pressure during shock, to promote uterine contraction during and after childbirth, and to control excessive urination of diabetes insipidus) and (2) ACTH (used for rheumatic fever, arthritis, acute inflammation of eyes and skin, acute alcoholism, severe asthma, and hay fever and other allergy conditions).

9. **Red Bone Marrow**—Bone marrow concentrates used in treatment of various blood disorders.

10. **Stomach**—Sourse of rennin, used to aid milk digestion.

11. **Testes**—Source of the enzyme hyaluronidase.

12. **Thyroid**—Thyroid extract is used for malfunctions of the thyroid gland (some goiters, cretinism, and myxedemal).

13. **Blood**—Source of thrombin, applied locally to wounds to stop bleeding.

14. **Bones and Hides**—Source of gelatin, used as a plasma extender.

15. **Lard**—With 1% benzoin added, it produces benzoinated lard, which is used as a medical ointment base.

Thus, in a modern packing plant, there is no waste; literally speaking, "every thing but the squeal" is saved. These by-products benefit the human race in many ways. Moreover, their utilization makes it possible to slaughter and process beef, lamb, and pork at a much lower cost. But this is not the end of accomplishment! Scientists are continually striving to find new and better uses for packing house by-products in an effort to increase their value.

MEAT PROMOTION

Effective meat promotion—which should be conceived in a broad sense and embrace research, educational, and sales approaches—necessitates full knowledge of the nutritive qualities of the product. To this end, we need to recognize that (1) meat contains 15 to 20 per cent high quality protein, on a fresh basis; (2) meat is a rich source of energy, the energy value being dependent largely upon the amount of fat it contains; (3) meat is a rich source of several minerals, but it is especially good as a source of phosphorus and iron; (4) meat is one of the richest sources of the important B group of vitamins, especially thiamine, riboflavin, niacin, and vitamin B_{12}; and (5) meat is highly digestible, about 97 percent of meat proteins and 95 percent of meat fats are digested. Thus, meat is one of the best foods with which to alleviate human malnutrition; a most important consideration when it is realized that (1) Selective Service records show that one out of eight draftees of World War II was turned down because of ailments directly or indirectly traceable to malnutrition and (2) it is estimated that 35 to 40 percent of the U.S. population is now failing to receive an adequate diet.

Also, it is noteworthy that the per capita consumption of meat in four countries exceeds that of the United States; by rank, based on 1966 meat consumption, these are (1) New Zealand, 229 lbs.; (2) Uruguay, 224 lbs.; (3) Argentina, 207 lbs.; (4) Australia, 198 lbs.; and (5) United States, 171 lbs.[15]

Thus, based on (1) its nutritive qualities and (2) the per capita consumption in those four countries exceeding us, it would appear that there is a place and a need for increased meat promotion; thereby increasing meat consumption and price.

There is considerable controversy as to how meat promotion funds should be raised, whether by voluntary deductions (check offs) or otherwise. There can be no doubt, however, that all segments of the meat industry would benefit by working together in a unified approach.

QUESTIONS FOR STUDY AND DISCUSSION

1. How did meat prompt early sailing?
2. Explain how consumer demand has influenced the type of animals produced.
3. What qualities in meats are desired by consumers; what effects will present consumer preferences exert on the livestock production and meat processing of the future?

---

[15] From Table 7-9 of this chapter.

4. Trace the development of federal meat grading, and explain the forces or motives which prompted each step.

5. Should we have only one system of grading; if so, which system should we select?

6. Why should meat be included in the diet?

7. What determines meat prices?

8. Why do we not consume more meat per capita in the U.S.?

9. What factors favor the increased use of freezing as a means of meat preservation?

10. Why are packing house by-products important?

SELECTED REFERENCES

Title of Publication	Author(s)	Publisher
Adventures in Diet	Vilhjalmur V. Stefansson	Reprinted from *Harper's* magazine by the Institute of American Meat Packers, 59 East Van Buren Street, Chicago, Ill.
By-Products in the Packing Industry	R. A. Clemen	The University of Chicago Press, Chicago, Ill., 1927.
Financial Facts about the Meat Packing Industry		American Meat Institute, 59 East Van Buren Street, Chicago, Ill.
Food from Farmer to Consumer	National Commission on Food Marketing	U.S. Government Printing Office, Washington, D. C., June 1966.
Inspection Stamp as a Guide to Wholesome Meat, The	Agricultural Information Bulletin 92	U.S. Department of Agriculture, Washington, D. C.
Meat Inspection, Regulations Governing the, of the United States	USDA	U.S. Government Printing Office, Washington, D. C.
Meat for the Family	J. J. Wanderstock J. I. Miller	Cornell Extension Bulletin 732, Cornell University, Ithaca, N. Y., 1947.
Meat for the Table	Sleeter Bull	McGraw-Hill Book Company, New York, N. Y., 1951.
Meat Reference Book		American Meat Institute, 59 East Van Buren Street, Chicago, Ill.
Meat We Eat, The	P. Thos. Ziegler	Interstate Printers and Publishers, Danville, Ill., 1966.
Official United States Standards for Grades of Carcass Beef		U.S. Department of Agriculture, Washington, D. C.
Stockman's Handbook, The	M. E. Ensminger	The Interstate Printers & Publishers, Danville, Ill., 1969.
Ten Lessons on Meat for Use in Schools	Department of Home Economics	National Live Stock and Meat Board, 407 South Dearborn Street, Chicago, Ill.

Titles of Publication	Author(s)	Publisher
Spread Between Prices of Livestock and Meat, The	J. C. Bottum	Swift and Company, Agriculture Research Department, Chicago, Ill.

Also, literature on meats may be secured by writing to meat packers and processors and trade organizations; in particular, the following two trade organizations:

American Meat Institute
59 East Van Buren Street
Chicago, Illinois 60605

National Live Stock and Meat Board
36 South Wabash Avenue
Chicago, Illinois 60603

CHAPTER VIII

BUSINESS ASPECTS OF ANIMAL PRODUCTION[1]

Contents

	Page
Capital Needs	320
Credit in the Livestock Business	320
Types of Credit	321
Helpful Hints for Building and Maintaining a Good Credit Rating	321
Borrow Money to Make Money	322
Manager	322
Traits of a Good Manager	322
Organization Chart and Job Description	323
An Incentive Basis for the Help	323
Indirect Incentives	325
Farm Records and Accounts	326
Budgets in the Livestock Business	327
Computers in the Livestock Business	327
Futures Trading	329
Tax Management and Reporting	330
Estate Planning	331
Inheritance and Partnerships	331
Liability	332
Questions for Study and Discussion	333
Selected References	333

Farming has changed from a way of life to a way of making a living. It's big and important business, and intricate, too; and it is destined to get bigger and more complicated.

From 1935 to 1967, within a span of 32 years, the number of farms decreased from 6.8 million to 3.1 million and the size of farms increased from 154.8 acres to 350 acres. Thus, within 32 years, over one-half of the farms disappeared from American agriculture and the average size of farms more than doubled. With this transition, herds, flocks, and feedlots became bigger. This trend will continue. By 1980, it is predicted that farms will increase from 350 to over 550 acres in size. In 1966, each farm worker supplied enough food and fiber

---

[1] In recognition of the great importance of this chapter, the author obtained the review and suggestions of many knowledgeable persons in its preparation. It was reviewed by the following: Mr. John A. Hopkins, Vice President, Bank of America, San Francisco, Calif.; Dr. Raymond J. Doll, Vice President and Senior Economist, Federal Reserve Bank of Kansas City, Kansas City, Mo.; Mr. C. P. Moore, Senior Vice President, The Great Falls National Bank, Great Falls, Mont.; Mr. M. F. Parker, Vice President, and Mr. Ralph Chaffee, Agricultural Loan Supervisor, United California Bank, Fresno, Calif.; Mr. Forest L. Goetsch, Senior Vice President, Doane Agricultural Service, Inc., St Louis, Mo.; Mr. Robert C. Liebenow, President, Corn Refiners Association, Inc., Washington, D. C., and formerly President of the Chicago Board of Trade; Mr. Everette B. Harris, President, Chicago Mercantile Exchange, Chicago, Ill.; Mr. Wendell A. Clithero, International Business Machine Corporation (IBM), Chicago, Ill.; Dr. T. C. Cartwright, Texas A. & M. University, College Station, Texas; Mr. John McGregor, McGregor Land and Livestock Company, Hooper, Wash.; Dr. Wilton W. Heinemann, Washington State University, Prosser, Wash.; Mr. Ronald Baker, C & B Livestock, Inc., Hermiston, Oregon.; and Dr. J. B. Wyckoff, Head, Department of Agricultural and Food Economics and Education, University of Massachusetts, Amherst, Mass.

for 33 persons, including himself; by 1975, it's expected that the latter figure will be increased to 43.

With this transition, however, the business and management aspects of animal production will be increasingly important. More capital will be required, competent management will be in demand, margins will become smaller, greater efficiency of production will be essential, and computers will be used more extensively. The net result is that those engaged in the business of agriculture must treat it as the big business that it is, and become more sophisticated and efficient in operation; otherwise, they won't be in business very long.

CAPITAL NEEDS

U.S. farm investment in land, improvements, machinery and equipment, animals, feed, and supplies totals $273 billion, which (1) ranks it as America's biggest single industry and (2) is equivalent to about two-thirds the value of all the stocks of all corporations represented on the New York Stock Exchange. Another noteworthy statistic is that it takes about $14 in farm assets to produce $1 of net farm income.

CREDIT IN THE LIVESTOCK BUSINESS

Total farm assets are estimated at $273 billion, while farm debt is about $40 billion. This means that, in the aggregate, farmers have nearly an 85 per cent equity in their business, and 15 per cent borrowed capital. Perhaps they have been too conservative, for it is estimated that one-fourth to one-third of American farmers could profit from the use of more credit in their operations.

Credit is an integral part of today's livestock business. Wise use of it can be profitable, but unwise use of it can be disastrous. Accordingly, stockmen should know more about it. They need to know something about the lending agencies available to them, the types of credit, and how to go about obtaining a loan.

The common lending sources of farm credit are: commercial banks, production credit associations, federal land banks, individuals and other private lenders, life insurance companies, merchants and dealers, and Farmers Home Administration.[2]

Data showing the amount of money borrowed by stockmen, by sources, is not available. However, it is known that farmers and ranchers borrow over $6 billion a year (which is about one-sixth of the credit which they use) from the farm credit system—which includes the federal land banks, the federal intermediate credit banks, production credit associations, and banks for cooperatives. Also, it was reported that, on January 1, 1964, commercial banks held 85 per cent of the reported non-real estate loans to farmers in California, production credit associations held 12 per cent, and all other sources had only 3 per cent.[3] Hay

---

[2] Information relative to each of these credit sources is given in *The Stockman's Handbook,* 4th Ed., Sec. XVII.

[3] *Cattle Feeding in California,* Bank of America, Economic Research Department, Feb. 1965, p. 52.

dealers, grain companies, feed companies, and various other suppliers are also important sources of credit to stockmen.

Types of Credit

Following are the three general types of agricultural credit to consider, based on length of life and type of collateral needed:

1. **Short-term or production credit.**—This is used for one production period or up to one year. It is used for purchase of feeders or birds, feed, and operating expenses; and it's repaid when the animals are sold.

2. **Intermediate credit.**—This type of credit may be for one to seven years. It is used for the purchase of breeding stock, machinery, equipment, and semi-permanent investments. Repayment is made from the profits over several production periods.

3. **Long-term credit.**—This type of credit is used for land and major farm building, and physical plant construction. Repayments are made over several years from profits.

Helpful Hints for Building and Maintaining a Good Credit Rating

Stockmen who wish to build up and maintain good credit are admonished to do the following:

1. **Keep credit in one place, or in few places.**—Generally, lenders frown upon "split financing." Borrowers should shop around for a creditor (a) who is able, willing, and interested in extending the kind and amount of credit needed, and (b) who will lend at a reasonable rate of interest; then stay with the borrower.

2. **Get the right kind of credit.**—Don't use short-term credit to finance long-term improvements or other capital investments.

3. **Be frank with the lender.**—Be completely open and above board. Mutual confidence and esteem should prevail between borrower and lender.

4. **Keep complete and accurate records.**—Complete and accurate records should be kept by enterprises. By knowing the cost of doing business, decision making can be on a sound basis.

5. **Keep annual inventory.**—Take an annual inventory for the purpose of showing progress made during the year.

6. **Repay loans when due.**—Borrowers should work out a repayment schedule on each loan, then meet payments when due. Sale proceeds should be promptly applied on loans.

7. **Plan ahead.**—Analyze the next year's operation and project ahead.

Borrow Money to Make Money

Stockmen should never borrow money unless they are reasonably certain that it will make or save money. With this in mind, borrowers should ask, "How much should I borrow?" rather than, "How much will you lend me?"

MANAGER

According to Webster, *a Manager is one who conducts business affairs with economy, and management is the act, or art, of managing, handling, controlling or directing.*

Three major ingredients are essential to success in the livestock business: (1) good animals, (2) good feeding, and (3) good management. A manager can make or break any livestock enterprise. Unfortunately, this fact is often overlooked in the present era, primarily because the accent is on scientific findings, automation, and new products.

Management gives point and purpose to everything else. The skill of the manager materially affects how well animals are bought and sold, the quality of the animals, the health of the animals, the results of the ration, the stress of the stock, efficiency of production, the performance of labor, the public relations of the establishment, and even the expression of the genetic potential. Indeed, a livestock manager must wear many hats—and he must wear each of them well.

The bigger and the more complicated the operation, the more competent the management required. This point merits emphasis because currently (1) bigness is a sign of the times, and (2) the most common method of attempting to "bail out" of an unprofitable business venture is to increase its size. Although it's easier to achieve efficiency of equipment, labor, purchases, and marketing in big operations, bigness alone will not make for greater efficiency, as some owners have discovered to their sorrow, and others will experience. Management is still the key to success. When in financial trouble, owners should have no illusions on this point.

In manufacturing and commerce, the importance and scarcity of top managers are generally recognized and reflected in the salaries paid to persons in such positions. Unfortunately, agriculture as a whole has lagged; and altogether too many owners still subscribe to the philosophy that the way to make money out of the livestock business is to hire a manager cheap, with the result that they usually get what they pay for—a "cheap" manager.

Traits of a Good Manager

There are established bases for evaluating many articles of trade, including animals, hay, and grain. They are graded according to well defined standards. Additionally, we chemically analyze feeds and conduct feeding trials with them. But no such standard or system of evaluation has evolved for livestock managers, despite their acknowledged importance.

The author has prepared the "Livestock Manager Check List," given in Table 8-1, which (1) students may use for guidance as they prepare themselves

TABLE 8—1

LIVESTOCK MANAGER CHECK LIST

☐ CHARACTER—
    Absolute sincerity, honesty, integrity, and loyalty; ethical.

☐ INDUSTRY—
    Work, work, work; enthusiasm, initiative, and aggressiveness.

☐ ABILITY—
    Livestock know-how and experience; business acumen—including ability
    systematically to arrive at the financial aspects and convert this informa-
    tion into sound and timely management decisions; knowledge of how to
    automate and cut costs; common sense; organization; imagination;
    growth potential.

☐ PLANS—
    Sets goals, prepares organization chart and job description, plans work,
    and works plans.

☐ ANALYZES—
    Identifies the problem, determines pros and cons, then comes to a
    decision.

☐ COURAGE—
    To accept responsibility, to innovate, and to keep on keeping on.

☐ PROMPTNESS AND DEPENDABILITY—
    A self-starter; has "T.N.T.," which means that he does it today, not
    tomorrow.

☐ LEADERSHIP—
    Stimulates subordinates and delegates responsibility.

☐ PERSONALITY—
    Cheerful, not a complainer.

for managerial positions, (2) employers may find useful when selecting or evaluating a manager, and (3) managers may apply to themselves for self-improvement purposes. No attempt has been made to assign a percentage score to each
trait, because this will vary among livestock establishments. Rather, it is hoped
that this check list will serve as a useful guide (1) to the traits of a good manager
and (2) to what the boss wants.

Organization Chart and Job Description

It is important that every worker know to whom he is responsible and for
what he is responsible; and the bigger and the more complex the operation, the
more important this becomes. This should be written down in an organization
chart and a job description. Samples of an organization chart and a job description are given on the next page.

An Incentive Basis for the Help

Big farms and ranches must rely on hired labor, all or in part. Good help—
the kind that everyone wants—is hard to come by; it's scarce, in strong demand,
and difficult to keep. And the farm manpower situation is going to become more
difficult in the years ahead. There is need, therefore, for some system that will
(1) give a big assist in getting and holding top-flight help and (2) cut costs and

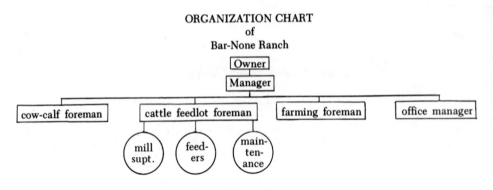

ORGANIZATION CHART
of
Bar-None Ranch

JOB DESCRIPTIONS
of
Bar-None Ranch

Owner	Manager	Cattle Feedlot Foreman	Cattle Feeder No. 1
Responsible for:	Responsible for:	Responsible for:	Responsible for:
1. Making policy decisions 2. Borrowing capital 3. (list others)	1. Supervising all staff 2. Preparing proposed long-time plan 3. Budgets 4. (list others)	1. Directing feedlot staff 2. Buying and selling cattle 3. Processing incoming cattle 4. Animal health 5. Feedlot rations 6. (list others)	1. Morning and evening feedings 2. Clean water troughs 3. (list others)

boost profits. An incentive basis that makes hired help partners in profit is the answer.

Many manufacturers have long had an incentive basis. Executives are frequently accorded stock option privileges, through which they prosper as the business prospers. Common laborers may receive bonuses based on piece-work or quotas (number of units, pounds produced). Also, most factory workers get overtime pay and have group insurance and a retirement plan. A few industries have a true profit-sharing arrangement based on net profit as such, a specified percentage of which is divided among employees. No two systems are alike. Yet, each is designed to pay more for labor, provided labor improves production and efficiency. In this way, both owners and laborers benefit from better performance.

Family-owned and family-operated farms have a built-in incentive basis; there is pride of ownership, and all members of the family are fully cognizant that they prosper as the business prospers.

Many different incentive plans can be, and are, used. There is no best one for all operations. The various plans in Table 8-2 are intended as guides only.

The incentive basis chosen should be tailored to fit the specific operation; with consideration given to kind and size of operation, extent of owner's supervision, present and projected productivity levels, mechanization, and other factors.

For most livestock operations, the author favors a "production sharing and prevailing price" type of incentive.

INDIRECT INCENTIVES

Normally, we think of incentives as monetary in nature—as direct pay-

TABLE 8—2

INCENTIVE PLANS FOR LIVESTOCK ESTABLISHMENTS

Types of Incentives	Pertinent Provisions of Some Known Incentive Systems in Use	Advantages	Disadvantages	Comments
1. Bonuses	A flat, arbitrary bonus; at Christmas time, year-end, or quarterly or other intervals. A tenure bonus such as (1) 5 to 10% of the base wage or 2 to 4 weeks additional salary paid at Christmas time or year-end, (2) 2 to 4 weeks vacation with pay, depending on length and quality of service, or (3) $3.00 to $20/week set aside and to be paid if employee stays on the job a specified time.	It's simple and direct.	Not very effective in increasing production and profits.	
2. Equity-building plan	Employee is allowed to own a certain number of animals. In breeding operations, these are usually fed without charge.	It imparts pride of ownership to the employee.	The hazard that the owner may feel that employee accords his animals preferential treatment; suspicioned if not proved.	
3. Production Sharing	$1 to $3/calf weaned, 50¢/cwt. on gain of feeder cattle; 25¢ to $1/head on fed cattle marketed; 50¢ to $1/pig marketed above 7 pigs/litter; 50¢ to $1 per 100 lbs. of milk sold over an agreed amount /cow (say 5,000 to 7,000 pounds); so much per 100 dozen eggs or 100 lbs. of broilers; 25¢ to 50¢ /lamb weaned; 50¢/cwt. of gain on lambs fed; 10¢ to 50¢/head on fed lambs marketed.	It's an effective way to achieve higher production.	Net returns may suffer. For example, a higher rate of gain than is economical may be achieved by feeding stockers more concentrated and expensive feeds than are practical. This can be alleviated by (1) specifying the ration and (2) setting an upper limit on the gains to which the incentive will apply. If a high performance level already exists, further gains or improvements may be hard to come by.	Incentive payments for production above certain levels —for example, above 450 lbs. calf weaned/cow bred—are more effective than paying for all units produced.
4. Profit Sharing		Net income sharing works better for managers, supervisors, and foremen than for common laborers because fewer hazards are involved to opening up the books to them.	Per cent of gross does not impart cost of production consciousness. Both (1) per cent of gross income and (2) per cent of net income expose the books and accounts to workers, who may not understand accounting principles. This can lead to suspicion and distrust.	There must be prior agreement on what constitutes gross or net receipts, as the case may be, and how it is figured.
a. Per cent of gross income	1% to 2% of the gross.			
b. Per cent of net income	10% to 20% of the net after deducting all costs.	It's an effective way to get hired help to cut costs. It's a good plan for a hustler.	Controversy may arise (1) over accounting procedures—for example, from the standpoint of the owner a fast tax write-off may be desirable on new equipment but this reduces the net shared with the worker and (2) because some owners are prone to overbuild and overequip, thereby decreasing net.	

(Continued)

TABLE 8—2 (Continued)

Types of Incentives	Pertinent Provisions of Some Known Incentive Systems in Use	Advantages	Disadvantages	Comments
5. Production sharing and prevailing price.	*Cow-calf, ewe-lamb, or sow operation*—Basis (1) per cent offspring weaned and (2) weaning weight (which means pounds offspring weaned/female bred). *Finishing cattle, or finishing hogs*—Basis (1) pounds feed/lb. gain and (2) daily rate of gain. *Horse breeding establishment*—Basis (1) per cent foal crop weaned and (2) price of yearlings. In each of the above, establish break-even point(s), then split profit(s) beyond this point(s) basis (1) 80% (owner) and 20% (help), or (2) use escalator arrangement, giving help greater percentage as profits rise.	It embraces the best features of both production sharing and profit sharing, without the major disadvantages of each. It (1) encourages high productivity and likely profits, (2) is tied in with prevailing prices, (3) does not necessitate opening the books, and (4) is flexible—it can be split between owner and employee on any basis desired, and the production part can be adapted to a sliding scale or escalator arrangement—for example, the incentive basis can be higher for the quarter pound of feedlot gain made in excess of 2-¾ pounds than for a quarter pound gain in excess of 2¼ pounds.	It is a bit more complicated than some other plans, and it requires more complete records.	When properly done, and all factors considered, this is the most satisfactory incentive basis for a livestock enterprise.

ments or bonuses for extra production or efficiency. However, there are other ways of encouraging employees to do a better job. The latter are known as indirect incentives. Among them are: (1) good wages; (2) good labor relations; (3) adequate house plus such privileges as the use of the farm truck or car, payment of electric bill, use of a swimming pool, hunting and fishing, use of a horse, and furnishing meat, milk, and eggs; (4) good buildings and equipment; (5) vacation time with pay, time off, and sick leave; (6) group health insurance; (7) security; (8) the opportunity for self-improvement that can accrue from working for a top man; (9) the right to invest in the business; (10) an all-expense-paid trip to a short course, show, or convention; and (11) year-end bonus for staying all year. These indirect incentives will be accorded to the help of more and more establishments, especially the big ones.

FARM RECORDS AND ACCOUNTS

Modern farming necessitates adequate records and accounts, the chief functions of which are:

1. To provide information from which the farm business may be analyzed, with its strong and its weak points ascertained. From the facts thus determined, the operator may adjust current operations and develop a more effective plan of organization.

2. To provide a net worth statement, showing financial progress during the year.

3. To furnish an accurate, but simple, net income statement for use in filing tax returns.

4. To keep production records on livestock and crops.

5. To aid in making a credit statement when a loan is needed.

6. To keep a complete historical record of financial transactions for future reference.

A farmer can make his own record book by simply ruling off the pages of a bound notebook to fit his specific needs, but the saving is negligible. Instead, it is recommended that he obtain a copy of a farm record book prepared for and adapted to his area. Such a book may usually be obtained at a nominal cost from the agricultural economics department of each state college of agriculture. Also, certain commercial companies distribute very acceptable farm record and account books at no cost.

BUDGETS IN THE LIVESTOCK BUSINESS

A budget is a projection of records and accounts and a plan for organizing and operating ahead for a specified period of time. A short-time budget is usually for one year, whereas a long-time budget is for a period of years. The principal value of a farm budget is that it provides a working plan through which the operation can be coordinated. Changes in prices, droughts, and other factors make adjustments necessary. But these adjustments are more simply and wisely made if there is a written budget to use as a reference.

It's unimportant whether a printed form (of which there are many good ones) is used or one made up on an ordinary ruled 8½" x 11" sheet placed sidewise. The important things are (1) that a budget is kept, (2) that it be on a monthly basis, and (3) that the operator be "comfortable" with whatever forms or system evolved.

No budget is perfect. But it should be as good an estimate as can be made—despite the fact that it will be affected by such things as droughts, diseases, markets, and many other unpredictables.

COMPUTERS IN THE LIVESTOCK BUSINESS

Accurate and up-to-the-minute records and controls have taken on increasing importance in all agriculture, including the livestock business, as the investment required to engage in farming and ranching has risen and profit margins have narrowed. Today's successful farmers and ranchers must have, and use, as complete records as any other business. Also, records must be kept current; it no longer suffices merely to know the bank balance at the end of the year.

Big and complex agricultural enterprises have outgrown hand record keeping. It's too time-consuming, with the result that it doesn't allow management enough time for planning and decision making. Additionally, it does not permit an all-at-once consideration of the complex interrelationships which affect the economic success of the business. This has prompted a new computer technique known as linear programming.

Linear programming is similar to budgeting, in that it compares several plans simultaneously and chooses from among them the one likely to yield the highest returns. It is a way in which to analyze a great mass of data and consider many alternatives. It is not a managerial genie; nor will it replace decision-making managers. However, it is a modern and effective tool in the present age, when just a few dollars per head or per acre can spell the difference between profit and loss.

There is hardly any limit to what computers can do if fed the proper information. Among the difficult questions that they can answer for a specific farm or ranch are:

1. **How is the entire operation doing so far?** It is possible to obtain a quarterly or monthly progress report; often making it possible to spot trouble before it's too late.

2. **What farm enterprises are making money; which ones are freeloading or losing?** By keeping records by enterprises—cow-calf, cattle feedlot, dairy, hogs, broilers, layers, wheat, corn, etc.—it is possible to determine strengths and weaknesses; then either to rectify the situation or shift labor and capital to a more profitable operation. Through "enterprise analysis," some operators have discovered that one part of the farm business may earn $5 or more per hour for labor and management, whereas another may earn only $1 per hour, and still another may lose money.

3. **Is each enterprise yielding maximum returns?** By having profit, or performance, indicators in each enterprise, it is possible to compare these (a) with the historical average of the same farm or ranch or (b) with the same indicators of other farms or ranches.

4. **How does this ranch stack up with its competition?** Without revealing names, the computing center (local, state, area, or national) can determine how a given ranch compares with others—either the average, or the top (say, 5 per cent).

5. **How to plan ahead?** By using projected prices and costs, computers can show what moves to make for the future—they can be a powerful planning tool. They can be used in determining when to plant, when to schedule farm machine use, etc.

6. **How can income taxes be cut to the legal minimum?** By keeping accurate record of expenses and figuring depreciations accurately, computers make for a saving in income taxes on most farms and ranches.

For providing answers to these questions and many more, computer accounting costs an average of about 1 per cent of the gross farm income. By comparison, it is noteworthy that city businesses pay double this amount.

There are three requisites for linear programming a farm or ranch:

1. Access to a computer.

2. Computer know-how, so as to set the program up properly and be able to analyze and interpret the results.

3. Good records.

The pioneering computer services available to farmers and ranchers were operated by universities, trade associations, and government—most of them were on an experimental basis. Subsequently, others have entered the field, including commercial data processing firms, banks, machinery companies, feed and fertilizer companies, and farm suppliers. They are using it as a "service sell," as a replacement for the days of "hard sell."

Information on "How to Balance a Ration by the Computer Method" is contained in Section II of the fourth edition of *The Stockman's Handbook*, a book by the same author and publisher as *Animal Science*.

FUTURES TRADING

Futures trading is not new. It is a well accepted, century-old procedure used in many commodities for protecting profits, stabilizing prices, and smoothing out the flow of merchandise. For example, it has long been an integral part of the grain industry; grain elevators, flour millers, feed manufacturers, and others, have used it to protect themselves against losses due to price fluctuations. Also, a number of livestock products—hides, tallow, frozen pork bellies, hams, eggs, and turkey toms—were traded on the futures market before the advent of live cattle and hog futures. Many of these operators prefer to forego the

Fig. 8-1. A view of the trading floor on the Chicago Mercantile Exchange. (Courtesy, Everette B. Harris, Pres., Chicago Mercantile Exchange)

possibility of making a high speculative profit in favor of earning a normal margin or service charge through efficient operation of their business. They look to futures markets to provide (1) an insurance medium in the marketing field and (2) the facilities and machinery for underwriting price risks.

Futures trading is a place where buyers and sellers meet on an organized market and transact business on paper, without the physical presence of the commodity. The exchange neither buys nor sells; rather, it provides the facilities, establishes rules, serves as a clearing house, holds the margin money deposited by both buyers and sellers, and guarantees delivery on all contracts. Buyers and sellers either trade on their own account or are represented by brokerage firms. Except for dealing in futures, and in paper contracts instead of live animals, futures trading on an exchange is very similar to terminal livestock markets.

The unique characteristic of futures markets is that trading is in terms of contracts to deliver or to take delivery, rather than on the immediate transfer of the physical commodity. In practice, however, very few contracts are held until the delivery date. The vast majority of them are cancelled by offsetting transactions made before the delivery date.

Many cattlemen have long contracted their cattle for future delivery without the medium of an exchange. They contract to sell and deliver to a buyer a certain number and kind of cattle at an agreed upon price and place. Hence, the risk of loss from a decrease in price after the contract is shifted to the buyer; and, by the same token, the seller foregoes the possibility of a price rise. In reality, such contracting is a form of futures trading. Unlike futures trading on an exchange, however, actual delivery of the cattle is a must. Also, such privately arranged contracts are not always available, the terms may not be acceptable, and the only recourse to default on the contract is a lawsuit.

The Chicago Mercantile Exchange initiated trading in live beef cattle on November 30, 1964. Shortly thereafter, they added dressed beef carcasses, as did the Chicago Board of Trade. Then, early in 1966, the Chicago Board of Trade announced plans for trading in live cattle, which they initiated on October 4, 1966. The Chicago Mercantile Exchange first offered hog futures on February 28, 1966. The Kansas City Board of Trade offered feeder cattle futures beginning on June 20, 1966.

TAX MANAGEMENT AND REPORTING

Good tax management and reporting consists in complying with the law, but in paying no more tax than is required. It is the duty of revenue agents to see that taxpayers do not pay less than they should, but it is the business of taxpayers to make sure that they do not pay more than is required. From both standpoints, it is important that farmers and ranchers should familiarize themselves with as many of the tax regulations as possible.

The cardinal principles of good tax management are: (1) maintenance of adequate records so as to assure payment of taxes in amounts no less or no more than required by law, and (2) conduct of business affairs to the end that the tax required by law is no greater than neccessary.

Also, farmers and ranchers need to recognize that good tax management and good farm management do not necessarily go hand in hand. In fact, they may be in conflict. When the latter condition prevails, the advantages of one must be balanced against the disadvantages of the other to the end that there shall be the greatest net return.

Under the cash system, farm income includes all cash or value of merchandise or other property received during the taxable year. It includes all available receipts from the sale of all items produced on the farm and profits from the sales of items which have been purchased, exclusive, generally speaking, of one-half of the profits received from the sale of property used by the farmer in his trade or business, such as breeding stock and farm machinery. It does not include the value of products sold or services performed for which payment was not actually available during the taxable year.

The accrual basis necessitates that complete annual inventories be kept. On the accrual basis, tax is paid on all income earned during the taxable year regardless of whether payment is actually received, and on increases of inventory values of livestock, crops, feed, produce, etc., at the end of the year as compared with the beginning of the year. All expenses incurred during the year's business are deducted from gross income regardless of whether payment is actually made, and deductions are made for any decrease in inventory values of livestock, etc., during the year.

ESTATE PLANNING

Human nature being what it is, most farmers shy away from suggestions that someone help plan the disposition of their property and other assets. Also, they have a long-standing distrust of lawyers, legal terms, and trusts, and, to them, the subject of taxes seldom makes for pleasant conversation.

If no plans are made, estate taxes and settlement costs often run considerably higher than if proper estate planning is done and a will is made to carry out these plans. Today, farming is big business; many farmers have more than $100,000 invested in land, animals, and equipment. Thus, it is not a satisfying thought to one who has worked hard to build and maintain a good farm during his lifetime to feel that his heirs will have to sell the farm or ranch to raise enough cash to pay federal estate and inheritance taxes. By using a good estate planning service, a farmer can generally save thousands of dollars for his family in estate and inheritance taxes and in estate settlement costs. For assistance, farmers should go to an estate planning specialist—an individual or company specializing in this work, or the trust department of a commercial bank.

Inheritance and Partnerships

Nothing pleases parents more than seeing their children succeed, and, generally speaking, having them take over the home farm or ranch makes for the ultimate in parental pride and satisfaction. Moreover, such an arrangement can make for a fine financial start in life for the young man who desires to carry on, provided, while the parents are still living, advantage is taken of the very considerable savings in federal inheritance taxes, as provided by law.

Regulations permit parents to make (1) one specific gift of $60,000 tax free and (2) an annual tax free gift, repeated for a number of years, of $6,000; and these gifts may be in the form of interest in the livestock operation. Thus, in the first year, it is possible to transfer a maximum interest of $66,000 in the dairy farm to an heir without entailing the payment of any federal inheritance tax. It is necessary, however, to file a gift tax return.

Frequently, even where it is the full intent and desire of the parents and the children that the latter continue with the farming or ranching operation, the gift tax provision is not considered. Then, upon death of the parent, the heir(s) may be required to raise such a large amount of cash to pay the inheritance taxes that a part or all of the operation may have to be liquidated.

A second logical step in this transfer is a partnership contract between the parents and their heir(s) recorded with the Clerk of Court in the county in which the farm is located. Appropriate counsel should be consulted in the preparation and recording of this agreement. Where the partnership contract is between the father and the heir, a provision should be included permitting the heir to purchase the father's share of the partnership for a fixed amount. The amount stipulated will then go into the father's estate. This will provide for proper and uninterrupted operation of the farm, because, upon the father's death, the partnership is legally terminated.

LIABILITY

Most farmers are in such financial position that they are vulnerable to damage suits. Moreover, the number of damage suits arising each year is increasing at an almost alarming rate, and astronomical damages are being claimed. Studies reveal that about 95 per cent of the court cases involving injury result in damages being awarded.

Several types of liability insurance offer a safeguard against liability suits brought as a result of injury suffered by another person or damage to their property.

Comprehensive personal liability insurance protects a farm operator who is sued for alleged damages suffered from an accident involving his property or family. The kinds of situations from which a claim might arise is quite broad including suits for injuries caused by animals, equipment, or personal acts.

Both workmen's compensation insurance and employers liability insurance protect farmers against claims or court awards resulting from injury to hired help. Workmen's compensation usually costs slightly more than straight employer's liability insurance, but it carries more benefits to the worker. An injured employee must prove negligence by his employer before the company will pay a claim under employer's liability insurance, whereas workmen's compensation benefits are established by state law and settlements are made by the insurance company without regard to who was negligent in causing the injury. Conditions governing participation in workmen's compensation insurance vary among the states.

QUESTIONS FOR STUDY AND DISCUSSION

1. Why have the business aspects of livestock production become so important in recent years?
2. Assume that you are going to enter the livestock business, and that you have decided on the particular kind (with you making the decision between beef, cow-calf, dairy, broilers, etc.). What types of credit may be needed, and how would you go about obtaining it?
3. How may a student acquire the traits of a good manager?
4. Take your own farm or ranch, or one with which you are familiar, and develop a workable incentive basis for the help.
5. Develop a yearly budget for your own farm or ranch, or for one with which you are familiar.
6. How may computers be used, on a practical basis, for a livestock enterprise?
7. Under what circumstances would you use computers?
8. Under what circumstances would you use futures trading?
9. Discuss the importance of each of the following: (a) tax management, (b) estate planning, (c) a father-son partnership, and (d) workmen's compensation insurance and employer's liability insurance.

SELECTED REFERENCES

Title of publication	Author(s)	Publisher
Cowboy Arithmetic	H. L. Oppenheimer	The Interstate Printers & Publishers, Inc., Danville, Ill., 1964.
Cowboy Economics	H. L. Oppenheimer	The Interstate Printers & Publishers, Inc., Danville, Ill., 1966.
Farmer's Handbook, The	John M. White	University of Okla. Press, Norman, Okla., 1948.
Farm Management	Robert R. Hudelson	The Macmillan Company, New York, N. Y., 1939.
Farm Management Economics	Earl O. Heady Harold R. Jensen	Prentice-Hall, Inc., Englewood, N. J., 1955.
Stockman's Handbook, The	M. E. Ensminger	The Interstate Printers & Publishers, Inc., Danville, Ill., 1969.

CHAPTER IX

THE BEEF CATTLE INDUSTRY

Contents   Page

Origin and Domestication of Cattle..336
   Bos taurus 336
   Bos indicus 337
Position of the Oxen in the Zoological Scheme.............................338
Use of Cattle in Ancient Times...338
Bakewell's Improvement of English Cattle....................................339
The Introduction of Cattle to America..340
Draft Oxen More Prized by Colonist than Beef.............................342
The Far-western Expansion of the Cattle Industry........................343
Growth of the U.S. Cattle Industry..344
World Distribution of Cattle...345
   Beef Production in South America..346
   Beef Production in Canada...349
   Beef Production in Mexico...350
   Beef Production in Australia...350
Beef Production in the United States..351
   Areas of Beef Production..352
      The Western Range...352
      The Corn Belt..353
      The Appalachian and Great Lakes Region.......................353
      The Cotton Belt...354
   Leading States in Beef Production...355
Factors Favorable to Beef Production...355
Factors Unfavorable to Beef Production...356
The Future of the American Beef Cattle Industry..........................357
Questions for Study and Discussion...359
Selected References 360

Cattle are the most important of all the animals domesticated by man, and, next to the dog, the most ancient. There are about 1,084 million cattle in the world.[1]

The word "cattle" seems to have the same origin as chattle, which means possession. This is a very natural meaning, for, when Rome was in her glory, a man's wealth was often computed in terms of his cattle possessions, a practice which still persists among primitive people in Africa and Asia. That the ownership of cattle implied wealth is further shown by the fact that the earliest known coins bear an ox head; and the Roman word "pecunia" for money (preserved in our adjective pecuniary) was derived from the Latin word *pecus*, meaning cattle. It is also noteworthy that the oldest known treatise on agriculture, written by the Greek poet Hesiod, referred to cattle. Apparently having had some disturbing experiences with young oxen, Hesiod advised: "For draught and yoking together nine-year-old oxen are best because, being past the mis-

---

[1]*Agricultural Statistics, 1965,* USDA.

chievous and frolicsome age, they are not likely to break the pole and leave the plowing in the middle."

ORIGIN AND DOMESTICATION OF CATTLE

It seems probable that cattle were first domesticated in Europe and Asia during the New Stone Age. In the opinion of most authorities, today's cattle bear the blood of either or both of two ancient ancestors—namely, *Bos taurus* and *Bos indicus*. Other species or subspecies were frequently listed in early writings, but these are seldom referred to today. Perhaps most, if not all, of these supposedly ancestral species were also descendants of *Bos taurus* or *Bos indicus* or crosses between the two.

Bos taurus

Bos taurus includes those domestic cattle common to the more temperate zones, and it, in turn, appears to be derived from a mixture of the descendants

Fig. 9-1. Artist's conception of an Aurochs (*Bos primigenius*) based on historical information. This was the mighty wild ox that was hunted by our ancestors. Most cattle are believed to have descended mainly from the Aurochs.

of the Aurochs (*Bos primigenius*) and Celtic Shorthorn (*Bos longifrons*).

Most cattle, including the majority of the breeds found in the United States, are believed to have descended mainly from the massive Aurochs (also referred to as Uri, Ur, or Urus). This was the mighty wild ox that was hunted by our forefathers. It roamed the forests of central Europe down to historic times, finally becoming extinct about the year 1627. About the year 65 B.C., Caesar mentioned this ox in his writings, but it was domesticated long before (perhaps early in the Neolithic Age) and probably south of the Alps or in the Balkans or in Asia Minor. Caesar referred to these animals as "approaching the elephant in size but presenting the figure of a bull." Although this is somewhat of an exaggeration as to the size of Aurochs, it was a tremendous beast, standing 6 or 7 feet high at the withers, as is proved by complete skeletons found in bogs.

In addition to the Aurochs, another progenitor of some of our modern breeds and earliest known domestic race of cattle was the Celtic Shorthorn or Celtic Ox. These animals, which have never been found except in a state of domestication, were the only oxen in the British Isles until 500 A.D., when the Anglo-Saxons came bringing with them animals derived from the Aurochs of Europe. The Celtic Shorthorn was of smaller size than the Aurochs and possessed a dished face. It may have had a still different wild ancestor, or may have been an independent domestication from the Aurochs.

Bos indicus

Bos indicus includes those humped cattle common to the tropical countries that belong to the Zebu (or Brahman) group. They are wholly domestic creatures, no wild ancestors having been found since historic times. It has been variously estimated that cattle of this type were first domesticated anywhere from 2100 to 4000 B.C. The Zebu is characterized by a hump of fleshy tissue over the withers (which sometimes weighs as much as 40 to 50 pounds), a very large dewlap, large drooping ears, and a voice that is more of a grunt than a low. These peculiar appearing animals seem to have more resistance to certain

Fig. 9-2. Zebu (*Bos indicus*). These wholly domestic animals were the ancestors of the humped cattle common to the tropical countries.

diseases and parasites and to heat than the descendants of *Bos taurus*. For this reason, they have been crossed with some of the cattle of Brazil and in the southern states of this country, especially in the region bordering the Gulf of Mexico.

POSITION OF THE OXEN IN THE ZOOLOGICAL SCHEME

Domesticated cattle belong to the family *Bovidae*, which includes ruminants with hollow horns. Members of this family possess one or more enlargements for food storage along the esophagus, and they chew their cuds. In addition to what we commonly call oxen or cattle, the family *Bovidae* (and the sub-family *Bovinae*) includes the true buffalo, the bison, musk-ox, banteng, gaur, gayal, yak, and zebu.

The following outline shows the basic position of the domesticated cow in the zoological scheme:

Kingdom *Animalia:* Animals collectively; the animal kingdom.

Phylum *Chordata:* One of approximately 21 phyla of the animal kingdom, in which there is either a backbone (in the vertebrates) or the rudiment of a backbone, the chorda.

Class *Mammalia:* Mammals or warm-blooded, hairy animals that produce their young alive and suckle them for a variable period on a secretion from the mammary glands.

Order *Artiodactyla:* Even-toed, hoofed mammals.

Family *Bovidae:* Ruminants having polycotyledonary placenta, hollow, nondeciduous, up-branched horns; and nearly universal presence of a gall bladder.

Genus *Bos:* Ruminant quadrupeds, including wild and domestic cattle, distinguished by a stout body and hollow, curved horns standing out laterally from the skull.

Species *Bos taurus* and *Bos indicus: Bos taurus* includes the ancestors of the European cattle and of the majority of the cattle found in the United States; *Bos indicus* is represented by the humped cattle (Zebu) of India and Africa and the Brahman breed of America.

USE OF CATTLE IN ANCIENT TIMES

Like other animals, cattle were first hunted and used as a source of food and other materials. As civilization advanced and man turned to tillage of the soil, it is probable that the domestication of cattle was first motivated because of their projected value for draft purposes. Large, well-muscled, powerful beasts were in demand; and any tendency to fatten excessively or to produce more milk than was needed for a calf was considered detrimental rather than desirable. Not all cattle were used for work purposes, however, in the era following their domestication. Instead of planting seeds, some races of people chose a pastoral existence—moving about with their herds as they required new pastures. These nomadic people lived mainly on the products of their herds and flocks.

As populations became more dense, feed became more abundant, and cattle became more plentiful, man became more interested in larger production of meat and milk. The pastoral people adopted a more settled life and began selecting out those animals that possessed the desired qualities—including rapid growth, fat storage, and milk production. Following this transformation, Biblical and other literature referred to milk cows, the stall-fed ox, and the fatted calf.

BAKEWELL'S IMPROVEMENT OF ENGLISH CATTLE

Robert Bakewell of Dishley (1726 to 1795)—an English farmer of remarkable sagacity and hard, common sense—was the first great improver of cattle in England. His objective was to breed cattle that would yield the greatest quantity of good beef rather than to obtain great size. Bakewell had the imagination to picture the future needs of a growing population in terms of meat and set about creating a low-set, blocky, quick-maturing type of beef cattle. He paid little or no attention to fancy points. Rather, he was intensely practical, and no meat animal met with his favor unless it had the ability to put meat on the back.

Bakewell's efforts with cattle were directed toward the perfection of the English Longhorn, a class of cattle common to the Tees River area. He also contributed greatly to the improvement of the Leicester breed of sheep, and the Shire horse. Success crowned his patient skill and unwearied efforts. But success in breeding was no mere happenstance in Bakewell's program. Careful analysis of his methods reveals that three factors were paramount: (1) a definite goal as evidenced by the joints that he preserved in pickle and the skeletons of the more noted animals that adorned his halls, (2) a breeding system characterized by "breeding the best to the best" regardless of relationship rather than crossing breeds as was the common practice of the time, and (3) a system of proving sires by leasing them at fancy prices to his neighbors rather than selling them. Because of Bakewell's methods and success, he has often been referred to as the founder of animal breeding.

Bakewell's experiments were the top news of the day, and his successes, the subject of much comment, both oral and written. The American poet, Emerson, for example, said of the British farmer, "He created sheep, cows, and horses to order . . . the cow is sacrificed to her bag, the ox to his sirloin."

By the beginning of the Napoleonic Wars, Bakewell's methods were widely practiced in England, and sheep and cattle were raised more for their flesh than formerly. A new era in livestock improvement was born. As an indication of this change, it is interesting to observe the increase in weights of animals

Fig. 9-3. Robert Bakewell of Dishley (1726 to 1795), noted agriculturalist and the first great improver of cattle in England. Bakewell also contributed greatly to the improvement of the Leicester breed of sheep, and the Shire horse.

at the famous Smithfield market. In 1710, beeves had averaged 370 pounds, calves 50 pounds, sheep 28 pounds, and lambs 18 pounds; whereas in 1795 they had reached 800, 148, 80, and 50 pounds, respectively. Although the effect of improved agriculture is not to be minimized, the main influence in this transformation can be attributed to Robert Bakewell, whose imagination, initiative, and courage put a firm foundation under improved methods of livestock breeding.

THE INTRODUCTION OF CATTLE TO AMERICA

Cattle were not native to the Western Hemisphere. They were first brought to the West Indies by Columbus on his second voyage in 1493. According to historians, these animals were intended as work oxen for the West Indies colonists. Cortez took cattle from Spain to Mexico in 1519. Then, beginning about 1600, other Spanish cattle were brought over for work and milk purposes in connection with the chain of Christian missions which the Spaniards established among the Indians in the New World. These missions extended from the east coast of Mexico up the Rio Grande, thence across the mountains to the Pacific Coast. Here, in a land of abundant feed and water, these Longhorns multiplied at a prodigious rate. By 1833, the Spanish priests estimated that their missions owned a total of 424,000 head of cattle,[2] many of which were running

---

[2] Yearbook of Agriculture, 1921, U.S. Department of Agriculture, p. 233.

in a semi-wild state. The hardy Texas Longhorn, animals of Spanish extraction, were of little commercial value except for their hides. Today, only a few of these animals remain, more as a novelty and for show purposes than for use as meat producers.

The colonists first brought cattle from England in 1609. Other English importations followed, with Governor Edward Winslow bringing a notable importation to the Plymouth Colony in 1623. The latter shipment included three heifers and a bull. Three years later, at a public court, these animals and their progeny—and perhaps some subsequent importations—were apportioned among the Plymouth settlers on the basis of one cow to six persons. It is further reported that three ships carried cattle to the Massachusetts Bay Colony in 1625. Other colonists came to the shores of New England bringing with them their oxen from the mother country. As would be expected, the settlers brought along the kind of cattle to which they had been accustomed in the mother country.

Fig. 9-4. Texas Longhorn steer. Today, only a few of these hardy animals remain, primarily as a novelty for rodeo and show purposes. (Courtesy, *The Cattleman*, Fort Worth, Tex.)

This made for considerable differences in color, size, and shape of horns, but all of these colonial imported cattle possessed ruggedness and the ability to perform work under the yoke.

For a number of years, there were very few cattle in the United States. Moreover, those animals that the colonists did possess went without winter feed and shelter, and the young suffered the depredations of the wolves. It was difficult enough for the settlers to build houses for themselves, and they could barely raise enough corn in their fields to sustain human life.

Conditions presently changed for the better. The cattle of earlier importations multiplied, new shipments were received, and feed supplies became more abundant. Cambridge, Massachusetts, enjoyed the double distinction of being the seat of Harvard College, the first institution of higher learning in what later came to be the United States, and the most prosperous cattle center in early New England. In order to provide ample grass and browse for the increased cattle population, it was necessary that the animals range some distance from the commons (the town pasture). Thus, the tale that the streets of Boston were laid out along former cowpaths is not legend but fact. Usually in their travels, the cattle were under the supervision of a paid "cowkeeper" whose chief duty consisted in safely escorting the cattle to and from pasture.

In the village economy, the bull was an animal of considerable importance. Usually the town fathers selected those animals that they considered most desirable to retain as sires, and those citizens who were so fortunate as to own animals of this caliber were paid an approved service fee on a per-head basis.

DRAFT OXEN MORE PRIZED BY COLONIST THAN BEEF

From the very beginning, the colonists valued cattle for their work, milk, butter and hides; but little importance was attached to their value for meat. In fact, beef was considered as much a by-product as hides are today. After all, wild game was plentiful, and the colonists had learned to preserve venison, fish, and other meats by salting, smoking, and drying. So necessary were cattle for draft purposes that, in some of the early-day town meetings, ordinances were passed making it a criminal offense to slaughter a work oxen before he had passed the useful work age of seven or more years. The work requirement led to the breeding of large rugged cattle, with long legs, lean though muscular bodies, and heavy heads and necks. Patient oxen of this type were well adapted for clearing away the forest and turning the sod on the rugged New England hill-

Fig. 9-5. Oxen pulling a Prairie Schooner (a type of covered wagon). Draft oxen were more prized by the colonist than beef. (Courtesy, The Bettmann Archive—from an engraving)

sides, for hauling the harvested produce over the rough roads to the seaport markets, and for subsisting largely on forages.

THE FAR-WESTERN EXPANSION OF THE CATTLE INDUSTRY

From the very beginning, cattle raising on a large scale was primarily a frontier activity. As the population of eastern United States became more dense, the stock raising industry moved farther inland. The great westward push came in the nineteenth century. By 1800, the center of the cow country was west of the Alleghenies, in Ohio and Kentucky; in 1860, it was in Illinois and Mis-

Fig. 9-6. Early Abilene, Kansas, shipping point. This end of the Texas cattle trail in eastern Kansas on the Kansas Pacific Railroad was established in 1867, for the purpose of providing safe transportation to the east, unmolested by the Ozark outlaws. (Courtesy, Abilene Chamber of Commerce)

souri; and by the 1880's, it was in the Great Plains. The ranches and cowboys of the far West were the counterpart of the New England commons and cow-drivers of the seventeenth and eighteenth centuries.

The western range was recognized as one of the greatest cattle countries that the world had ever known. Plenty of water and unlimited grazing area were free to all comers, and the market appeared to be unlimited. Fantastic stories of the fabulous wealth to be made from cattle ranching caused a rush comparable to that of the gold diggers of 1849. All went well until the severe winter of 1886. It was the type of winter that is the bane of the cattleman's existence. Then, but all too late, it was realized that too many cattle had been kept and too little attention had been given to storing up winter feed supplies. The inevitable happened. With the melting of the snow in the spring of 1887, thousands of cattle skeletons lay weathering on the western range, a grim reminder of overstocking and inadequate feed supplies. Many ranchers went broke, and the cattle industry of the West suffered a crippling blow that plagued it for the next two decades. Out of this disaster, however, the rancher learned the never-to-be-forgotten lessons of (1) avoiding overexpansion and too-close grazing, and (2) the necessity of an adequate winter feed supply.

GROWTH OF THE U.S. CATTLE INDUSTRY

Figure 9-7 shows the growth of the U.S. cattle industry. The group designated as milk cows includes all cows and heifers two years old and over kept for milk; whereas the curve showing total cattle and calves embraces milk cows and all other cattle combined. As can be observed, milk cows have shown a decrease in recent years. Although beef cattle numbers have increased, the increases have not kept pace with increases in human population. It is interesting to note, however, that per capita beef consumption has gone up, made feasible primarily because of the increased productive rate of the cattle—the marketing of cattle as baby beeves or at slightly older ages instead of as two-year-old steers. Also, currently, cattle are receiving better care. There is a marked improvement in feeding; more newborn animals are saved; more attention is given to sanitation, disease prevention, and parasite control; animals are more adequately housed; waste resulting from death, crippling, and bruises in transit has decreased; and other improved management factors are receiving attention.

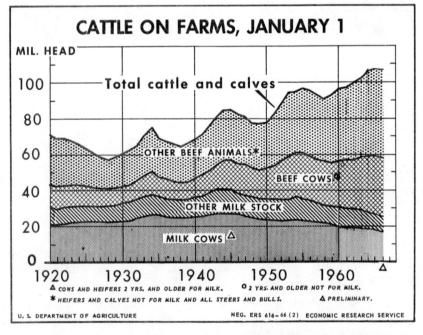

Fig. 9-7. Cattle on U.S. farms, January 1, 1920 to 1966. Although beef cattle numbers have increased somewhat, the increases have not kept pace with increases in human population. (Courtesy, Agricultural Marketing Service, USDA)

WORLD DISTRIBUTION OF CATTLE

It is important that producers be well informed concerning world-wide beef production in order to know which countries are potential competitors. Like the price of all commodities in a free commerce, the price of beef is determined chiefly by supply and demand—that is, by the demand existing in those countries

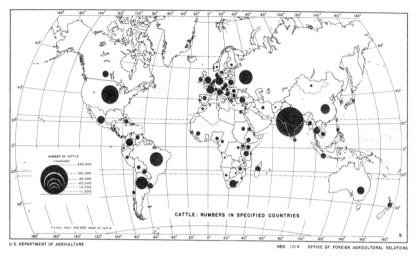

Fig. 9-8. World distribution of cattle. (Courtesy, USDA, Office of Foreign Agricultural Relations)

Fig. 9-9. Scene in India, showing cattle in a village. Usually Indian cattle are herded by the young or the old. (Photo by Dr. A. D. Weber, The Ford Foundation)

that do not produce enough to meet their domestic needs and by the supply which can be spared by those nations producing a surplus.

The production of beef cattle is world-wide. Table 9-1 gives the size and density of cattle population of the 10 leading cattle-producing countries of the world, by rank. In 1965, world cattle numbers were estimated at 1,084.2 million head.

The United States is excelled in aggregate cattle numbers only by India. But India is of very negligible importance so far as world trade is concerned. This is due to a large number of Indian cattle either being sacred or used for draft or milk purposes and the fact that water buffalos are included along with cattle numbers.

At the present time, certain of the South American nations and Mexico, Canada, Australia, and New Zealand are the chief countries which produce more than their domestic needs and thus have surpluses or potential surpluses of beef for export.

Beef Production in South America

Of the South American countries, Argentina is recognized as the outstanding beef producer. In fact, taken as a whole, Argentine cattle probably possess better breeding and show more all-round beef excellence than do the cattle of any other country in the world. The excellence of the Argentine cattle can be attributed to two factors: their superior breeding and the lush pastures of the country. Beginning in 1850 and continuing to the present time, large numbers of purebred animals have been imported from England and Scotland. No price has been considered too high for bulls of the right type; and, again and again, British and American breeders have been outbid by Argentine estancieros in the auction rings of Europe. These bulls and their progeny have been crossed on the native stock of Spanish extraction. Shorthorns are the most numerous cattle of the country, with Herefords ranking second, and Angus third.

The finest cattle pastures of the Argentine are found along the La Plata River, in the region known as the Pampas. Much of this fertile area is seeded to alfalfa upon which cattle are pastured the year round. Instead of finishing cattle largely on grains, as we do, the cattlemen in the Argentine finish their stock on alfalfa pastures. The corn of the Pampas region, which represents an acreage one-half as great as that devoted to alfalfa, is largely exported. Usually two- and three-year-old steers are finished by turning them into a lush alfalfa pasture for a period of four to eight months prior to marketing. The surplus beef of Argentina is marketed as frozen or chilled beef to the European countries, especially to Great Britain. None of the frozen or chilled beef from the Argentine is admitted into the United States because of the hazard of foot-and-mouth disease; it must be canned or fully cured (i.e., corned beef).

Other South American countries of importance in beef production are Brazil, Colombia, Uruguay, and Paraguay.

Generally speaking, Brazil, which is slightly larger than the United States, produces hardy cattle of rather low quality, predominantly of Zebu breeding.

TABLE 9–1

SIZE AND DENSITY OF CATTLE POPULATION OF
TEN LEADING CATTLE-PRODUCING
COUNTRIES OF THE WORLD, BY RANK

Country	Cattle[1]		Human Population[2]		Size of Country		Cattle Per Capita[4]	Cattle Per	
	Number	When Estimated	Number	When Estimated	(sq. mi.)	(sq. km.)		(sq. mi.)	(sq. km.)
India..........	207,119,000[3]	1956-60	471,627,000	1964	1,261,597	3,267,536	.44	164.2	63.3
United States.	107,152,000	1965	194,600,000	1965	3,548,974	9,191,843	.55	30.2	11.6
U.S.S.R........	87,100,000	1965	229,100,000	1965	8,655,890	22,418,755	.38	10.1	3.8
Brazil..........	81,515,000[3]	1965	78,809,000	1964	3,286,270	8,511,439	1.03	24.8	9.5
China (mainland)	63,000,000[3]	1965	750,000,000	1964	2,279,134	5,902,957	.08	27.6	10.6
Argentina......	43,000,000	1965	22,045,000	1964	1,072,700	2,778,293	1.95	40.1	15.4
Pakistan.......	29,762,000[3]	1965	100,762,000	1964	365,529	946,724	.30	81.4	31.4
Mexico........	28,400,000	1965	39,643,000	1964	758,259	1,963,891	.72	37.5	14.4
France.........	20,155,000	1965	48,492,000	1965	212,659	550,787	.42	94.8	36.5
Australia.......	19,500,000	1965	11,185,167	1964	2,971,081	7,695,100	1.74	6.6	2.5
World Total..	1,084,200,000	1965	3,220,000,000	1964	52,403,746	135,725,702	.32	20.7	7.9

[1]*Agricultural Statistics, 1965*, USDA.
[2]*World Almanac*, 1966, New York World-Telegram.
[3]Includes Buffaloes.

[4]Cattle per capita computed from most recent cattle and human census figures reported; in some cases, this necessitated using data for different years.

Fig. 9-10. Well-bred cattle on lush pastures in Argentina. (Courtesy, Counselor Office Cultural Relations, Republic of Argentina, Washington, D. C.)

Colombia, which is as large as the four states of Texas, Oklahoma, Arkansas, and Louisiana combined, ranks eighth in world cattle numbers. Although beef production is one of the nation's principle industries, it is handicapped by lack of improved breeding, poor transportation facilities, and limited refrigeration.

Uruguay, which is but little larger than the state of Missouri, is noted (1) as an ideal cattle country (because of its rich pastures, abundant water supply, and temperate climate), (2) for Hereford and Shorthorn cattle of good breeding, although they are not equal in quality to the cattle in Argentina, (3) as one of the most highly specialized beef cattle countries in the world, and (4) as a beef exporting country, despite its small size (80 per cent of the nation's exports consisting of animal products).

Paraguay, which is about two and one-half times larger than Uruguay, produces cattle of similar breeding and quality to those in Brazil.

As in the Argentine, year-round grazing constitutes the basis of the beef cattle industry of the other South American countries. Virtually no grain is used in finishing animals, except for those being fitted for show. No attempt is made to finish steers until they are fully mature.

In general, the foremost obstacles or unfavorable factors affecting South American beef production are the following:

1. The ever-present foot-and-mouth disease, which, though seldom fatal, results in enormous economic losses through arrested growth and emaciation and which limits the foreign sale of both beef and cattle on foot.

2. Droughts are rather frequent in many of the cattle sections, and they are likely to be of rather long duration.

3. Parasites and certain diseases other than foot-and-mouth disease are rather prevalent in the warmer sections.

4. Prices are very much dependent upon the export trade, thus making for an uncertain market.

5. Local markets are often unsatisfactory; modern packing plants are not too plentiful; and refrigeration facilities are limited. Many of the cattle slaughtered in the more isolated areas of South America, especially in Brazil and Paraguay, are still made into jerked or salted beef.

6. Transportation facilities are few and far between.

7. Except for the cattle of Argentina and Uruguay, much improvement in breeding is needed; but the introduction of improved blood is difficult because of the heavy infestation of diseases and parasites to which the native and Zebu cattle are more resistant.

Because of the glowing reports about the cattle industry of Argentina, many young men from the United States have, from time to time, been interested in establishing a cattle enterprise in South America. Without exception, experienced United States cattlemen who have visited in South America in person and who know whereof they speak point out the almost impossible odds of success in such a venture. In the first place, the land is in the hands of a comparatively few families who hold a monopoly on the cattle industry; and secondly, the political unrest in these countries is usually not conducive to such private foreign investments in land or cattle.

Beef Production in Canada

Canada is still a frontier type of country with almost unlimited opportunities for expansion of the beef cattle industry. In general, Canadian cattle are noted for their size, scale, and ruggedness. This is due to the fact that in the great expanses of frontier agriculture cattle production is on a cost-per-head rather than on a cost-per-pound basis; that is, it costs little more to produce a sizeable beast than to produce a small one. The main obstacles to increased beef production in Canada are: (1) the long severe winters in much of the cattle country centered primarily in the eastern and western provinces where up to seven months feeding is required; (2) the high duty and frequently closed borders for exports to the United States, the most natural potential market; and (3) the need for a permanent outlet for stocker and feeder cattle, as Canada has no finishing area comparable to the Corn Belt.

The cattlemen of Canada appear to be optimistic about the future of the industry. It is predicted that more and more cattle will be finished on the small grains which are produced in great abundance. Also, the opening up of the St. Lawrence-Great Lakes waterway to shipping provides economical transportation (1) to eastern Canada and (2) for the export trade. Many authorities predict that sizeable meat packing plants will be established at Port Arthur.

Fig. 9-11. Cattle roundup in Canada. On their way to summer pasture, long lines of cattle wind their way over the hills of the prairies. (Courtesy, Canadian National Film Board)

Beef Production in Mexico

Since January 1, 1955, Mexico has been free of foot-and-mouth disease and the border has been open, subject to the usual quotas and duties.

In addition to the foot-and-mouth disease hazard, other factors unfavorable to beef production in Mexico are: (1) the ravages of parasites, particularly the Texas tick; (2) lack of improved breeding, which is made difficult because of the susceptibility of newly imported cattle to diseases and parasites; and (3) frequent droughts, which, next to foot-and-mouth disease, constitute the greatest of all obstacles.

Despite all the difficulties now existing in Mexico, the fact remains that cattle are afforded a long grazing season and that labor is cheap and abundant. Cattle can be produced very cheaply. Also, in recent years, the better cattlemen of Mexico have made marked progress in improving both the quality of their cattle and the efficiency of their production. It is reasonable to expect, therefore, that Mexico will annually provide several thousand head of steers for finishing on the ranges of the Southwest or for shipment to U.S. feedlots.

Beef Production in Australia

In Australia, most of the cattle are grazed the year round on unfenced ranges where they are herded by musterers, who are the counterpart of the American cowboy. Slaughter animals usually consist of four-year-old steers which are grass fattened. Many of the cattle operations in Australia are very large; the ranches varying in size from 100,000 to 1,000,000 acres each, and the cattle numbers from 10 to 50 thousand head per unit.

The beef cattle industry of Australia is subjected to unfavorable factors much like those of South America, except that the country is free from foot-and-mouth disease. In comparison with South America, however, the greater distance from Europe makes shipping expensive. Improved technology in proc-

Fig. 9-12. Cattle on the 9,000-acre Angus stud near Narrabri in north-western New South Wales.

essing and in transporting beef are overcoming the latter obstacle. This, along with government policies favorable toward the development of the cattle in-dustry of the nation, indicates a bright future for the expanding beef cattle industry of Australia.

BEEF PRODUCTION IN THE UNITED STATES

The present importance of beef cattle in the agriculture of the nation rests chiefly upon their ability to convert coarse forage, grass, and grain crops into a palatable and nutritious food for human consumption.

In 1968, there were 108,813,000 cattle and calves on the farms and ranches of the U.S., of which 86,582,000 were kept primarily for beef.

The production of beef cattle differs from that of most other classes of live-stock in that the operation is frequently a two-phase proposition: (1) the pro-duction of feeders and (2) the finishing of cattle. In general, each of these phases is distinctive to an area. The production of feeders, or the cow-and-calf proposition, is characteristic of the western range, whereas the finishing of cattle is characteristic of the Corn Belt and the irrigated areas of the West and Southwest.

Areas of Beef Production

In addition to phases of production found in the two major cattle-producing areas—the western range and the Corn Belt—there are some rather characteristic production practices common to the other two less extensive areas: the Cotton Belt and the Appalachian and Great Lakes region. Certainly, within each area, variations from the most common practice are noted. For example, a goodly number of cattle are finished out in feedlots located in or near irrigated districts in the western range area, and many Corn Belt farmers have long successfully adhered to a cow-and-calf type of enterprise.

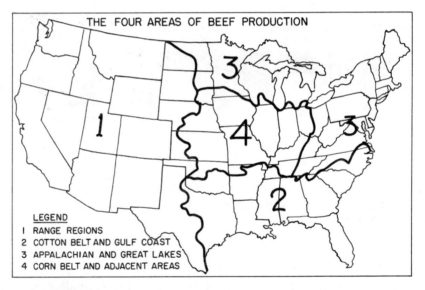

THE FOUR AREAS OF BEEF PRODUCTION

LEGEND
1 RANGE REGIONS
2 COTTON BELT AND GULF COAST
3 APPALACHIAN AND GREAT LAKES
4 CORN BELT AND ADJACENT AREAS

Fig. 9-13. The four important U.S. areas of beef production. In each area the methods followed are determined largely by the climate, feed supply, and economic conditions.

THE WESTERN RANGE

This area lies west of an irregular north and south line cutting through the Dakotas, Nebraska, Kansas, Oklahoma, and Texas. It is characterized by great diversity of topography, soil, rainfall, and temperature. Accordingly, the amount of vegetation and the resulting carrying capacity are variable factors. Except in some small areas under irrigation, the units of operation are large in size, and much of the range remains unfenced. In general, the western ranges supply an abundance of cheap grass but only a very limited amount of grain. Under these conditions, the cow-and-calf system is the dominant type of enterprise.

THE CORN BELT

The Corn Belt is noted for its fertile soil, medium-sized farms, high-priced land, and its livestock-feeding operations. Most of the land is well suited to crop production, especially to corn. It is not surprising, therefore, that it is the cattle finishing center of the United States. Beef cattle, dairy cattle, and hogs compete for the available feeds.

Many of the farmers maintain small commercial breeding herds, the off-spring of which are finished out on home-grown feeds and sold at an early age. Luxuriant pastures furnish practically all the feed for the breeding herds from May to November, and cornstalks and other roughages are utilized as winter feeds.

In addition to keeping small breeding units, many Corn Belt farmers make a regular practice of buying in feeder cattle from the western ranges. These cattle are usually purchased in the fall of the year and are obtained through public stockyards, at auctions, through dealers, or direct from the range. Some of these are roughed through the first winter by utilizing stubble or stalk fields and then finished on pastures the next season. Other cattle are carried on a program of winter feeding.

The Corn Belt occupies a unique location, with the range country to the West and the industrial meat-deficit area to the East. Thus, the natural movement of cattle is from west to east; and, in typical two-phase production, the feeder cattle are produced on the western ranges and are finished and slaughtered in the Corn Belt. The carcasses are then shipped east for consumption. About 70 per cent of the cattle and calves of the United States are produced west of the Mississippi River, whereas 70 per cent of the beef and veal consumption is east of this location.

The Corn Belt is also noted for its excellent purebred herds. Because of their proximity to the western ranges and the demands of the ranch owners for bulls, there has always been a good market for superior breeding stock.

THE APPALACHIAN AND GREAT LAKES REGION

The Appalachian and Great Lakes region is a densely populated area with great cities; it is noted for its manufacturing and commerce. The topography varies all the way from small, fertile valleys to mountainous territory. The valley areas are devoted to intensive methods of cultivation, whereas much of the up-land area produces pasture and hay crops for the dairy enterprise. Much of this land is rough and stony, making it unsuited to cultivation. The agriculture is of a most intensive type, with small farm units and very limited diversification. Many of the more distant areas that cannot be used to advantage for the production of a perishable product like market milk are used for dual-purpose or beef pro-duction.

The production of beef cattle was formerly an important and highly devel-oped industry through the Northeast. However, the opening up of the western ranges; the rapid increase in population of the East with the resulting industri-alization; the division of the eastern farming lands into smaller units; and the adoption of more intensive systems of farming caused a decline of beef production in the eastern states. With these changes in economic conditions, beef production has to a large extent been supplanted by dairying. With the existence of these favorable conditions for milk production, beef cattle cannot compete with dairy cattle, particularly on small farms. On the other hand, where dairying is not feasible because of overproduction and consistent low prices for market milk, where the distance to market is too great, or where labor difficulties exist, beef cattle may come into increasing importance. But this industry, in the East, can never regain its former magnitude or hold the place it does in the West or Middle West.

In general, the less accessible areas of the Appalachian and Great Lakes region are devoted to dual-purpose production rather than to either straight dairy or beef enterprises. More dual-purpose herds are found in this area than in any other section of the country. Western Pennsylvania, Ohio, and upper New York enjoy a national reputation for Milking Shorthorns; whereas in the New England states, both the Milking Shorthorn and Devon breeds are very popular.

Included in this region are also the famous residual limestone lands of Kentucky (the best of which are used for horses) and the excellent pastures of Virginia, West Virginia, and North Carolina. Feeders of commercial cattle are located in Lancaster and Chester counties in Pennsylvania, where cattle are finished primarily on corn.

THE COTTON BELT

The Cotton Belt—which includes all or portions of each of the 12 southern states, stretching from eastern Texas to Virginia—has always been noted for its great acreage of cotton. However, with several years of low prices for this commodity prior to World War II and with ruinous soil erosion and farm abandonment caused by careless cultivation of rolling lands, there has been in recent years a decided interest in more diversification throughout the South. Mild winters and the fact that grazing throughout the year can usually be depended upon have encouraged many a southern farmer to turn to beef production.

Another factor which in the past has seriously retarded beef production throughout a part of the South has been the presence of the cattle fever tick together with a heavy infestation of numerous internal and external parasites. With the eradication of the tick and the pushing of the quarantine line toward the Gulf, this difficulty has been almost completely removed. Furthermore, it has been found that Brahman cattle are more resistant to cattle tick fever than other breeds, and the infusion of blood from this breed has been of great importance.

In addition to a reduction in the cotton acreage and the control of cattle tick fever, scientific findings also have assisted the livestock program of the South through providing suitable supplements for mineral deficiencies and methods of improving pastures and controlling parasites. The cattle of the area have also been improved through shipping in large numbers of purebred and high-grade cattle from the Corn Belt and the West. All of these improved conditions, together with year-round grazing of the area and a surplus of feed grains for cattle finishing operations, would indicate that the South can and will expand its beef production on a sound basis.

Leading States in Beef Production

A ranking of the 10 leading states in beef cattle production, together with total numbers for the United States, is given in Table 9-2. As may be noted, Texas is far in the lead, with Iowa and Nebraska in second and third positions, respectively. The large cattle numbers in the state of Texas may be attributed to the fact that it represents a truly great range-cattle country, to increased cattle finishing, and to the immense size of the state. The cattle population of Iowa,

TABLE 9—2

TEN LEADING STATES IN BEEF CATTLE NUMBERS, BY RANK, 1968[1]

State	No. Beef Cattle
Texas	10,383,000
Iowa	6,178,000
Nebraska	6,139,000
Kansas	5,218,000
Missouri	4,087,000
Oklahoma	4,077,000
South Dakota	3,997,000
California	3,590,000
Montana	2,907,000
Colorado	2,847,000
United States Total (50 states)	86,582,000

[1]*Livestock and Poultry Inventory*, January 1, Statistical Reporting Service, USDA, February 13, 1968.

Nebraska and the other central states consists of native breeding herds and the sizeable cattle-finishing operation that go hand in hand with the great acreage of corn.

FACTORS FAVORABLE TO BEEF PRODUCTION

Some of the special advantages of cattle as compared to other kinds of livestock on the farm or ranch are:

1. Beef cattle efficiently utilize large quantities of coarse, low-grade roughages produced on the farm or ranch, including straws and stover, coarse or low-grade hays, and coarser pastures or ranker growth.

2. Beef cattle are well adapted to the use of the millions of acres of land unsuited for the production of bread grains or for any other type of farming. Such areas include the arid and semi-arid grazing lands of the West and Southwest (which beef cattle share with sheep) as well as the brush, forest, and cutover lands and swamp areas found in various sections of the United States.

3. Cattle can use the total home-grown production of grains and roughages, with or without the purchase of other feeds, more efficiently than any other class of livestock.

4. Beef cattle require less labor for their care than do other farm animals. Under average commercial range conditions, one man is required for about 250 to 300 cows.

5. Beef cattle greatly help to distribute the labor requirements throughout the year; they require but little attention except during the winter months.

6. Cattle afford a splendid means of maintaining soil fertility. In addition to returning to the soil approximately 80 per cent of the fertilizing constituents in their feeds, cattle offer a profitable way in which to utilize soil-building legumes that are usually a part of improved crop rotations.

7. Beef cattle require a comparatively small investment in buildings and equipment.

8. Cattle entail little death risk, as they are susceptible to comparatively few diseases and parasites. For example, it is usually assumed that the death losses of steers in the finishing lot will not exceed 1 per cent.

9. Beef cattle production provides an elastic outlet for grain. When plentiful, more grain can go into beef. When scarce, less grain and more grass and roughage will still produce beef.

It is recognized that certain of the favorable factors listed above apply to both beef and dairy cattle.

FACTORS UNFAVORABLE TO BEEF PRODUCTION

Some factors which, under certain conditions, may be unfavorable to beef cattle production are:

1. A beef cattle herd cannot be built up quickly. Ordinarily, a heifer should not calve until at least 24 months of age, and usually only one young is produced at a time. Thus, cattle are neither as prolific nor as early breeders as either sheep or hogs.

2. Should the federal controls on beef (tariffs, quotas, and embargoes) ever be completely lifted, the cattlemen of the United States would suffer ruinously low prices.

3. The presence of foot-and-mouth disease in certain other countries always constitutes a hazard.

4. During boom periods, high-quality purebred bulls are usually excessively high in price and difficult to obtain.

5. The operation of a cattle ranch requires a sizeable investment in cattle. Likewise, it is costly to establish a purebred herd.

6. The grazing regulations on the various federal- and state-controlled lands are often difficult to comply with.

7. Cattle finishing is often a risky venture; many a cattle feeder has literally "lost his shirt" in the enterprise.

8. Under conditions in which it is desired that the maximum economy be obtained in converting concentrated feeds into meat, both the pig and the sheep are superior to beef cattle.

9. The spread in price in market cattle is usually greater than is obtained

in any other class of livestock. Shelly old cows that have outlived their life of usefulness in the breeding herd will bring comparatively less than an old brood sow. In other words, a great spread usually exists between the price of Prime steers and Canner cows.

10. Unless cold-storage facilities are available, beef cannot be cured and stored on the farm as easily as pork.

THE FUTURE OF THE AMERICAN BEEF CATTLE INDUSTRY

The far-seeing cattleman is constantly projecting his thoughts into the future. This is but natural. Some of the factors of importance to the beef cattle industry of the future are:

1. **Foreign competition.**—Most of the South American countries—especially Argentina, Brazil, Uruguay, and Paraguay—and Canada, Mexico, Australia, and New Zealand are well adapted to beef cattle production. Many of these countries produce great surpluses; for example, in Argentina there are 1.95 head of cattle per capita and in Australia there are 1.74 cattle per capita. In the present scientific age, it is quite likely that rather rapid advances will be made in the control of parasites and diseases affecting cattle in the South American countries. Moreover, because of cheaper labor and feed supplies, ranchers in all the surplus beef producing countries can produce beef at a lower cost than the American cattleman. Transportation distances and costs are not prohibitive in obtaining beef from any of these countries, and even this will improve. It would appear, therefore, that only protective walls—tariffs, quotas, and embargo legislation enacted by the U.S. government—can stand in the way of increased beef competition from foreign sources.

The same factors enumerated as affecting beef imports operate relative to possible beef exports from the United States. Because of our higher production costs—even if other factors were favorable for expansion—it is not likely that we could compete on a longtime basis with these foreign countries in exporting beef to the deficit areas of the world.

Thus, exports of beef offer little possibility, but possible imports are likely to harass the cattle producers of this nation for some years to come.

The current quotas and tariffs on beef are given in Table 9-3.

2. **Increased human population.**—The population of the U.S. continues to expand.

It is reasonable to surmise that—as has happened in the older and more densely populated areas of the world—gradually less meat per capita will become available, dairy and poultry production will increase, and more and more grains will be consumed directly as human foods. This does not mean that the people of the U.S. are on the verge of going on an Asiatic grain diet, but history often has an uncanny way of repeating itself—even though such changes come about ever so slowly. Certainly, these conditions would indicate the desirability of eliminating the less efficient animals.

TABLE 9—3

U.S. CATTLE IMPORT TARIFF DUTIES[1]

Import Item	Quotas[2]	Tariff
	(No. of head per year)	(per pound)
Beef and veal (fresh, frozen, or chilled)[3]	———	3¢
Cattle weighing:		
under 200 lbs.[4]	200,000	1½¢
between 200 and 700 lbs.	———	2½¢
Dairy cattle weighing over 700 lbs.	———	1³/₁₀¢
Other cattle[5]	400,000	1½¢
Cattle for breeding	none	duty free

[1]Table 9-3 provided by Mr. C. V. McMillan, Executive Vice President, American National Cattleman's Association.
[2]Includes Canada, Mexico, and all other countries.
[3]Legislation of August 1964 established a basic limit of 725.4 million pounds plus an added factor based on U.S. production.
[4]For not over 200,000 head entered in the 12-month period beginning April 1 in any year. (2½¢ per pound for any in excess of limitation.)
[5]For not over 400,000 head entered in the 12-month period beginning April 1 in any year of which not over 120,000 shall be entered in any quarter beginning April 1, July 1, October 1, or January 1 and 2½¢ per pound for such "other" cattle entered in excess of any of the foregoing limitations.

3. **Land use and cattle expansion.**—The two major beef-producing areas of the U.S. are the Corn Belt and the western range. With the drastic reduction in the range sheep industry, beginning in 1941, a considerable acreage of grazing land has been released for cattle production or for other purposes. Certain range areas of the West are not now stocked to capacity. It must be remembered, however, that maximum stocking cannot be based on the good pasture years which usually are determined by moisture conditions. The unfortunate experiences resulting from overstocking and inadequate forage supplies during the drought years is not pleasantly recalled by many cattlemen.

Each year, more areas are being brought under irrigation in the far West. Without doubt, these will provide for some expansion of the beef industry, particularly from the standpoint of supplying a greater abundance of cheap feed, some of which will be utilized in cattle-finishing operations and some for wintering the breeding herd. It is quite likely also that much of the more marginal land of the West, which was plowed and placed in grain production because of the remunerative grain prices received with the outbreak of World War II, will be turned back to pastures.

It is predicted that the greatest future expansion in cow-calf operations will be in the Great Plains and Corn Belt. Also, with year-round pastures and an abundance of feeds suitable for cattle finishing, the southern states are in a very strong position. Moreover, recent scientific developments offer new possibilities of controlling the parasites so common to the warmer climates. In the final analysis, however, the future development of the beef industry of the South is dependent upon (1) the comparative profits to be derived from cotton, peanut, and tobacco farming in relation to livestock farming; (2) the steps which may be taken toward controlling the ravages of soil erosion, either through private initiative or government subsidy programs; and (3) the comparative profits to be realized from other types of animal agriculture, particularly swine and poultry production.

The industrial East is and will continue to support a predominantly intensive type of agriculture, with dairy and poultry dominating the livestock situation. There is room for increased beef cattle numbers, however, in some of the more isolated areas of the Northeast and East. Dual-purpose production also has a place in such areas.

4. **Breeding and quality of cattle.**—In 1930, the last year that this particular census item was taken, only 3 per cent of the total cattle population of the United States consisted of registered purebreds. Certainly, there is no halo around purebreds, and animals are not outstanding merely by virtue of being pure-breds. But this is one criterion of the status of cattle improvement. Perhaps the most convincing evidence of the great need for further improvement in beef cattle numbers may be gained through casually inspecting the daily livestock receipts on any public terminal market.

Despite the acknowledged needs for continued improvements, it must be admitted to the everlasting credit of the American cattlemen that we have travelled a long way from the days of the Texas Longhorn to the prime bullock of today. Improved breeding together with improved feeding and management practices—including the marketing of cattle at earlier ages—have made it possible to increase per capita beef consumption throughout the years, even though the human population of this country has expanded much more rapidly than the cattle population since 1890. But this is not the end of beef cattle improvement! With our present knowledge of genetics, nutrition, pathology, and production and management, new achievements in beef cattle improvement are on the horizon.

In the years ahead, there will be increased crossbreeding, production testing, and marketing to specification by grade and weight.

5. **Business aspects.**—The business aspects of cattle production will become more important in the years ahead. Cow-calf operations will continue to get bigger, and many of the farm-type feedlots of the Corn Belt will be replaced by "beef factories" like those of the West. Size of enterprise, both cow-calf and feed-lot, will be limited primarily by scarcity of competent management.

More capital will be required, credit will be more important and better tailored for cattle needs, production costs and labor problems will mount, computers will replace cowboy arithmetic, beef futures will be widely used, and consultants will assist owners and managers.

QUESTIONS FOR STUDY AND DISCUSSION

1. How do you account for the fact that most of the cattle in the U.S. are descendants of *Bos taurus* rather than *Bos indicus?*

2. Throughout the ages, and in many sections of the world, cattle have been used for work purposes more than horses and mules. Why has this been so?

3. Compare Robert Bakewell's breeding methods with those used in modern production testing programs. What three factors contributed most to his success as an animal breeder?

4. What accounts for the fact that per capita beef consumption has not changed materially through the years, although beef cattle numbers have not kept pace with the increases in human population?

5. What factors will continue to keep out or discourage more foreign imports of beef or veal, or of cattle on-foot?

6. What factors relative to beef production characterize the major potential beef competitors of the U.S.; namely, the South American nations, Mexico, Canada, Australia, and New Zealand?

7. Why is not the cattle per capita necessarily indicative of the type of agriculture predominating in an area?

8. Assuming that a young man had no "roots" in a particular location, in what area—(a) the western range, (b) the Corn Belt, (c) the Appalachian and Great Lakes region, or (d) the Cotton Belt—would you recommend that he establish a beef cattle enterprise? Justify your answer.

9. On the whole, do you feel that the future of U.S. beef cattle production warrants optimism or pessimism? Justify your answer.

SELECTED REFERENCES

Title of Publication	Author(s)	Publisher
American Cattle Trials 1540-1900	G. M. Brayer H. O. Brayer	Western Range Cattle Industry Study and American Pioneer Trails Assn., Bayside, N. Y., 1952.
Beef Cattle	Roscoe R. Snapp A. L. Neumann	John Wiley & Sons, Inc., New York, N. Y., 1960.
Beef Production and Distribution	Herrell DeGraff	Univ. of Okla. Press, Norman, Okla., 1960.
Cattle and Men	C. W. Towne E. N. Wentworth	University of Oklahoma Press, Norman, Okla., 1955.
Encyclopaedia Britannica		Encyclopaedia Britannica, Inc., Chicago, Ill.
History of Livestock Raising in the United States 1607-1860	J. W. Thompson	Agricultural History Series No. 5 U.S. Department of Agriculture, November, 1942, Washington, D.C.
Meat on the Nation's Table		American National Live Stock Assn., Denver, Colo., 1948-1949.
Our Friendly Animals and Whence They Came	K. P. Schmidt	M. A. Donohue & Co., Chicago, Ill., 1938.
Principles of Classification and a Classification of Mammals, The	G. G. Simpson	Bulletin of the American Museum of Natural History, Vol. 85, New York, N. Y., 1945.
Stock Raising in the Northwest, 1884	H. O. Brayer G. Weis	The Branding Iron Press, Evanston, Ill., 1951.
Yearbook of Agriculture, 1921	pp. 232 thru 264	U.S. Department of Agriculture, Washington, D.C.

Chapter X

TYPES AND BREEDS OF BEEF AND DUAL-PURPOSE CATTLE[1]

Contents   **Page**

Types of Cattle..361
Breeds of Beef and Dual-Purpose Cattle...363
Popularity of Breeds..363
Characteristics of Breeds..363
Questions for Study and Discussion..374
Selected References 374

Early in the progress of cattle improvement, especially during the development of fenced holdings in England, man began to select out certain animals for specific purposes and to plan matings with such uses in mind. Fortunately, because of the diversity of genes carried by the parent stock, it was possible, through selection, to mold certain types, each of which proved superior to the common cattle or even to other types for specific purposes. Thus, there evolved beef-type, dairy-type, dual-purpose-type, and draft-type cattle, and the several breeds of each.

TYPES OF CATTLE

Type may be defined as an ideal or standard of perfection combining all the characteristics that contribute to the animal's usefulness for a specific purpose. It should be noted that this definition of types does not embrace breed fancy points. These have certain value as breed trademarks and for promotional purposes, but in no sense can it be said that they contribute to an animal's utility value. There are four distinct types of cattle: beef-type, dairy-type, dual-purpose-type, and draft-type.

Beef-type animals are characterized by great width and depth of body. Their primary purpose is to convert feed efficiently into the maximum of high quality meat for human consumption.

Dairy-type animals are characterized by a lean, angular form and a well-

---

[1] Sometimes folks construe the write-up of a breed of livestock in a book or in a U.S. Department of Agriculture bulletin as an official recognition of the breed. Nothing could be further from the truth, for no person or office has authority to approve a breed. The only legal basis for recognizing a breed is contained in the Tariff Act of 1930, which provides for the duty-free admission of purebred breeding stock provided they are registered in the country of origin. But the latter stipulation applies to imported animals only.

In this book, no *official* recognition of any breed is intended or applied. Rather, the author has tried earnestly, and without favoritism, to present the factual story of the breeds in narrative and picture. In particular, such information relative to the new and/or less widely distributed breeds is needed, and often difficult to come by.

Fig. 10-1. Beef-type cow (above), characterized by great width and depth of body. Dairy-type cow (below), characterized by a lean, angular form and a well-developed mammary system.

Fig. 10-2. Dual-purpose-type cow (above), intermediate between the beef-type and dairy-type in conformation. Draft-type ox (below), characterized by great size and ruggedness with considerable length of leg.

developed mammary system. Their type is especially adapted to convert feed, efficiently, into the maximum of high quality milk.

Dual-purpose-type animals are intermediate between the beef type and dairy type in conformation and also in the production of both meat and milk.

Although many breeders have the dual-purpose type clearly in mind and although many fine specimens of the respective breeds have been produced, there is less uniformity in dual-purpose cattle. This is as one would expect when two important qualifications, beef and milk, are being combined.

Draft-type animals, when true to form, are characterized by great size and ruggedness with considerable length of leg. Although oxen are seldom seen in the United States, except in the New England states, it must be remembered that these patient, steady, plodding beasts are still the chief source of power in many parts of the world.

Several distinct breeds of cattle of each of the types have been developed in different parts of the world. Although each of these breeds possesses one or more characteristics peculiar to the group (breed characteristics), in general the type of cow that will produce a large flow of milk is the same the world over, despite acknowledged differences in size, color, shape of head and horns, or in any other distinctive breed characteristic. Likewise, there is a general similarity between all the beef-type breeds. Moreover, because of the great diversity of genes within any given breed, there is more difference within beef breeds than between them from the standpoint of beef type.

BREEDS OF BEEF AND DUAL-PURPOSE CATTLE

A breed may be defined as a group of animals having a common origin and possessing certain well-fixed and distinctive characteristics not common to other members of the same species; these characteristics are uniformly transmitted. A breed may come about as a result of planned matings; or, as has been more frequently the case, it may be purely a happenstance. Once a breed has evolved, a breed association is usually organized.

The breeds of beef and dual-purpose cattle in the United States, classed according to type or purpose for which they are primarily produced, are:

Beef Breeds

Angus	Devon	Polled Shorthorn
Beefmaster	Dexter	Red Angus
Belted Galloway	Galloway	Red Brangus
Brahman[2]	Hereford	Santa Gertrudis
Brangus	Indu Brazil	Scotch Highland
Charbray	Polled Hereford	Shorthorn
Charolais		

Dual-Purpose Breeds

Milking Shorthorn	Red Poll

POPULARITY OF BREEDS

Table 10-1 shows the 1965 and total registrations to date of the common breeds of beef and dual-purpose cattle. In these changing times, the recent annual figures are probably more meaningful than the all-time registrations, although it is recognized that one year's data fail to show trends.

CHARACTERISTICS OF BREEDS

The ultimate objective in beef production is the sale of beef over the block. But this is not enough. In this day and age, it is also imperative that feeds be converted *efficiently* into the maximum of high quality meat. How well the different breeds measure up to these requisites will determine their popularity in the future.

The characteristics of the different breeds of beef and dual-purpose cattle are summarized in Table 10-2.

---

[2] Actually, this embraces at least three breeds of *Bos indicus* cattle that have contributed or are contributing to beef production in the U.S.; namely American Brahman, Indu-Brazil, and Africander.

TABLE 10—1

1965 AND TOTAL REGISTRATIONS OF BEEF AND DUAL-PURPOSE CATTLE IN UNITED STATES BREED ASSOCIATIONS

Breed	1965 Registrations	Total Registrations
Hereford[1]....................	462,784	13,975,293
Angus........................	384,752	5,012,215
Polled Hereford...........	160,317	2,150,000
Shorthorn................... Polled Shorthorn[2]........	40,848	3,268,063
Charolais....................	31,114	151,129
Brahman.....................	15,616	369,770
Santa Gertrudis[3].........	12,331	172,312
Milking Shorthorn[4]......	5,656	322,295
Brangus.....................	4,264	30,316
Galloway....................	3,000	77,100
Charbray....................	2,741	35,772
Red Poll....................	1,712	232,862
Beefmaster[5]................	1,500	5,151
Scotch Highland.........	665	7,764
Devon........................	496	42,439
Red Brangus...............	326	1,207
Dexter.......................	45	1,287
Belted Galloway.........	35	345

[1]Including a considerable number of Polled Herefords most of which are registered in both the American Hereford Assn. and the American Polled Hereford Assn.
[2]Combined registration for Shorthorn and Polled Shorthorn.
[3]Not registrations but animals classified and, therefore, accepted by the Santa Gertrudis Breeders International.
[4]Registrations since 1948 when the American Milking Shorthorn Society separated from the American Shorthorn Breeders' Assn.
[5]First certificates issued in Feb. 1963.

Fig. 10-3. Black Jack, Grand Champion steer of the 1968 International Livestock Exposition; bred by Ankony Angus; and owned-exhibited by Gred, Al, and Peter Arendt of Highmore, South Dakota. Black Jack was 20 months of age, weighed 1,170 pounds, and sold for $10 per pound.

Fig. 10-4. Lasater Beefmaster two-year-old bull, Don Quixote. (Courtesy, Tom Lasater, The Lasater Ranch, Matheson, Colo.)

TABLE 10—2

BREEDS OF BEEF AND DUAL-PURPOSE CATTLE
AND THEIR CHARACTERISTICS

Breed	Place of Origin	Color	Distinctive Head Characteristics	Other Distinguishing Characteristics	Disqualifications; Comments
Beef Breeds:					
Angus	Scotland; in the northeastern counties of Aberdeen, Angus, Kincardine, and Forfar.	Black	Polled	Comparatively smooth coat of hair. Somewhat cyclindrical body.	Horns, scurs, or buttons. Red color. A noticeable amount of white above the underline, or in front of the navel, or on one or more legs. Calves from females less than 18 mo. of age when calf was dropped, or from bulls less than 6 mo. of age at the time of service.
Beefmasters (approx. ½ Brahman, and ¼ each Shorthorn and Hereford)	United States; on the Lasater Ranch, Falfurrias, Texas.	Red is the dominant color, but color is variable and is disregarded in selection.	The majority are horned, although a few are naturally polled.	Good milk producers under range conditions; heavy weaning and mature weights.	In order that each Beefmaster may be permanently identified with the breeder thereof, the breeds must use a prefix name such as "Jones Beefmaster," "Smith Beefmaster," etc., to designate his cattle. Thus, in a unique way, the responsibility for the continued improvement of the breed is placed squarely upon the individual breeder.
Belted Galloway	Scotland; in the southwestern district of Galloway.	Black with a brownish tinge, or dun; with a white belt completely encircling the body between the shoulders and the hooks.	Polled	Heavy coat of hair.	Red color, incomplete belt, other white marks, or scurs.

(Continued)

TABLE 10—2—(Continued)

Breed	Place of Origin	Color	Distinctive Head Characteristics	Other Distinguishing Characteristics	Disqualifications; Comments
Brahman	India (but a distinct American breed has been created through the amalgamation of several Indian types, probably with a small infusion of European breeding).	Gray or red preferred; either solid color, or a gradual blending of the two. However, there are brown, black, white, and spotted Brahmans.	Drooping ears. A long face.	Prominent hump over the shoulders. An abundance of loose, pendulous skin under the throat and along the dewlap. A voice that resembles a grunt rather than a low.	Brindle, gruella (a smutty or blackish red), or albino color. Cryptorchid bull. Freemartin heifer. Inherited lameness. Dwarf or midget characteristics.
Brangus (3/8 Brahman 5/8 Angus)	United States; on Clear Creek Ranch, Welch, Okla., owned by Frank Buttram, beginning in 1942.	Black	Polled	Slight crest over the neck. Smooth, sleek coat.	Horns. Off-color. White on underline or legs.
Charbray (3/4 Charolais, 1/4 Brahman to 7/8 Charolais, 1/8 Brahman, solid color, golden to white are registered)	United States; in the Rio Grande Valley of Texas.	Light tan at birth, but usually change to a cream white in a few weeks.	Horned	A slight hint of the Brahman dewlap remains.	To qualify for registration, Charbray cattle must have at least 1/4 Brahman. Charolais-Brahman of lesser percentages are recorded but not considered registered.
Charolais (usually spelled Charollais in France)	France; in the province of Charolles in Central France.	White or cream	Horned	Pink skin and mucus membranes.	The association disqualifies any animal that (1) has a black nose, (2) is spotted, or (3) has excessive dark skin pigmentation.
Devon	England; in the county of Devon.	Red; rich dark red is preferred.	Creamy white horns with black tips.	Yellow skin.	White other than in the switch or on small areas on the udder and belly.

(Continued)

TABLE 10–2–(Continued)

Breed	Place of Origin	Color	Distinctive Head Characteristics	Other Distinguishing Characteristics	Disqualifications; Comments
Dexter	Ireland, in the southern and southwestern parts. They were named after their founder, a Mr. Dexter.	Black or red.	Head is rather long.	Small size and short legs. Mature bulls should not exceed 900 lbs. and mature cows 800 lbs. Some mature animals are less than 40 inches high.	Animals having white other than on the belly, switch, udder, or scrotum are disqualified for registry.
Galloway	Scotland; in the southwestern province of Galloway.	Black; sometimes with a brownish or reddish tint; or dun.	Polled	Long curly hair.	White markings on feet or legs or above the underline.
Hereford	England; in the county of Hereford.	Red with white markings; white face and white on the underline, flank, crest, switch, breast, and below the knees and hocks. White back of the crops, high on the flanks, or too high on the legs is objectionable. Likewise, dark or smutty noses and red necks are frowned upon.			Calves from females less than 24 mo. of age when calf was dropped, or from bulls less than 12 mo. of age when service producing the calf occurred, cannot be registered.

(Continued)

TABLE 10—2—(Continued)

Breed	Place of Origin	Color	Distinctive Head Characteristics	Other Distinguishing Characteristics	Disqualifications; Comments
Indu Brazil (Zebu)	Brazil	Light grey to silver grey; dun to red.	Prominent—forehead and long drooping ears. Symmetrical horns drawing upward and to the rear.	Prominent hump over the shoulders. An abundance of loose, pendulous skin under the throat and along the dewlap. A voice that resembles a grunt rather than a low.	Brindle color combinations. White markings on the nose or switch. Absence of loose, thick, mellow skin. Weak and improperly formed hump.
Polled Hereford	United States; in Iowa.	Red with white markings, white face and white on underline, flank, crest, switch, breast, and below the knees and hocks. White back of the crops, high on the flanks, or too high on the legs is objectionable. Likewise, dark or smutty noses are frowned upon.	Polled		No calf is eligible for registration unless its sire was at least 12 mo. of age at the time of conception, and its dam at least 24 mo. of age at the time of calving. Horned animals.
Polled Shorthorn	United States; in the north central states, chiefly Ohio and Indiana.	Red, white or any combination of red and white. A "smutty nose" or dark nose is objectionable.	Polled		Horned animals.

TABLE 10—2—(Continued)

Breed	Place of Origin	Color	Distinctive Head Characteristics	Other Distinguishing Characteristics	Disqualifications; Comments
Red Angus	British Isles[1]	Red	Polled	Similar to black Angus, except for recessive red color.	Any color other than red.
Red Brangus	United States; from Brahman Angus cross, made in 1946. Registry chartered in 1956.	Red	Broad head with slightly curved forehead and straight profile; with medium sized, moderately drooping ears.	Males have crest immediately forward of the shoulders. Smooth, sleek coat.	White spotting other than on the underline, brindling or roan on the body, or black skin or mucus membrane. Long hair, or tight hide. Undersized; too rangy or too compact. Mature females with underdeveloped teats or udders. Mature males with an excessive or pendulous sheath, or the absence of a sheath.
Santa Gertrudis (5/8 Shorthorn and 3/8 Brahman)	United States; on the King Ranch in Texas.	Red or cherry red.		Hair should be short, straight, and slick. Hide should be loose, with surface area increased by neck folds and sheath or navel flap.	White or other spotting; fawn, cream, or brindle color; black skin; long wavy hair; absence of neck folds.
Scotch Highland (or Highland)	Scotland	Silver, golden, light red, brindle, black, or dun.	Long, widespread horns and heavy foretop.	Long, shaggy hair, short head and short legs.	Mottled or spotted with white (white permissible on tip of tail or on udder), or polled.
Shorthorn	England; in the northeastern counties of Durham, Northumberland, York, and Lincoln.	Red, white or any combination of red and white. A "smutty nose", or dark nose is objectionable.	Rather short, refined, incurving horns.		No calf is eligible for registration unless its sire and dam were each at least 18 mo. of age at the birth date of the calf.

Footnote on last page of table.

(Continued)

TABLE 10—2—(Continued)

Breed	Place of Origin	Color	Distinctive Head Characteristics	Other Distinguishing Characteristics	Disqualifications; Comments
Dual-Purpose Breeds:					
Milking Shorthorn	England	Red, white, or any combination of red and white.	Fine horns that are rather short.		No calf is eligible for registration unless its sire and dam were each at least 18 mo. of age at the birth date of the calf.
Red Poll	England; in the eastern middle coastal counties of Norfolk and Suffolk.	Red, varying from light to dark red. Any white except in the switch is discriminated against. Also a smoky nose or dark spots on the nose are objectionable.	Polled		White above underline, above switch of tail, or on legs. Bulls with white on underline forward of the navel region; or with only one testicle. Solid black or blue nose. Scurs or any horny growth. Total blindness.

[1]In England and Scotland, both reds and blacks are registered in same association, without distinction. In the U.S., however, red colored animals have been barred from registry in the American Angus Association since 1917. Red Angus Association of America was organized in 1954.

Fig. 10-5. Belted Galloway, Aldemere Farm, Rockport, Maine. (Courtesy, The American Belted Galloway Cattle Breeders' Assn.)

Fig. 10-6. HCK Miss Diann, Brahman female, bred by Koontz Ranch, Inez, Texas; sold to J. F. W. Herbst, Oor Pietersburg, N. Transvaal, South Africa. This female was Grand Champion in 11 major U.S. livestock shows. (Courtesy, American Brahman Breeders' Assn.)

Fig. 10-7. Junior yearling Brangus show heifer. (Courtesy, International Brangus Breeders' Assn.)

Fig. 10-8. A Charbray bull. (Courtesy, Mrs. Quinta Arrigo, Sec., The American Charbray Breeders' Assn.)

Fig. 10-9. Charolais bull. (Courtesy, American-International Charolais Assn.)

Fig. 10-10. The polled Devon female, Morse Marietta. Grand champion at Maryland State Fair and Eastern National Show. Weighed 1,000 pounds at 454 days of age. (Courtesy, American Devon Cattle Club, Inc.)

Fig. 10-11. J. F. Black Warrior, Dexter bull, owned by Peerless Herd, John Logsdon, Decorah, Iowa. (Courtesy, American Dexter Cattle Assn.)

Fig. 10-12. Emperor of Upper Barr, undefeated Champion Galloway bull of Scotland and England. This bull was bred and shown by Donald McQueen of Roughhills, Balgeattie, Scotland. He was imported to the U.S. and is owned by George S. Daniels, Forest Range Ranch, Laytonville, California. Galloway cattle are characterized by their long, curly, black hair; hardiness; and polled character. (Courtesy, American Galloway Breeders' Assn.)

Fig. 10-13. Hereford female, F. Colo. Ruperta. Owned by Fred Farrell Farms, Elgin, Oklahoma. The Hereford color is distinctive—a red body with a white face. (Courtesy, American Hereford Assn.)

Fig. 10-14. CEK Mixer Return, Champion Polled Hereford bull at many shows. He was bred by Joe O'Bryan, Hiatville, Kansas; and exhibited by Knowlton Hereford Farm, Bellefontaine, Ohio. One-third interest was sold to Huber Polled Hereford Ranch, Schneider, Indiana, for $40,000. Polled Herefords have a red body and a white face, and as the name indicates, they are polled. (Courtesy, American Polled Hereford Assn.)

Fig. 10-15. Lynnwood Nonpareil B 9th, Grand Champion Polled Shorthorn female at the International Livestock Exposition, Chicago; bred and shown by Lynnwood Farm, Carmel, Indiana. (Courtesy, American Shorthorn Assn.)

Fig. 10-16. The Red Angus bull, Beckton Larkabelang, bred by Mrs. W. E. Forbes, Beckton Stock Farm, Sheridan, Wyoming. (Courtesy, Mrs. Forbes)

Fig. 10-18. Lola, Santa Gertrudis female; bred and owned by King Ranch, Kingsville, Texas; shown weighing 1,590 pounds at 34 months of age. (Courtesy, Santa Gertrudis Breeders International)

Fig. 10-17. Red Brangus cow and her calf on the range. (Courtesy, Mike Levi, Paleface Ranch, Spicewood, Texas)

Fig. 10-19. Scotch Highland cow, on winter range, owned by Baxter Berry, XX Ranch, Belvidere, South Dakota. (Courtesy, American Scotch Highland Breeders' Assn.)

Fig. 10-20. Grand Champion Steer—a Shorthorn—over all breeds at the Grand National Livestock Exposition (Cow Palace), San Francisco, shown by Washington State University, Pullman, Washington. The 1,060-pound steer was bought by the Fairmont Hotel, San Francisco, at $5.25 per pound or a total of $5,565.00. Shorthorns are the largest of the beef breeds. (Courtesy, Washington State University)

Fig. 10-21. Fairy Lou, a National Milking Shorthorn Champion, owned by Bierhup Bros., Wellston, Ohio. As a four-year-old, she produced 11,212 lbs. of milk and 400.85 lbs. butterfat. The Milking Shorthorn is a strain of Shorthorns bred especially for milk production. (Courtesy, American Milking Shorthorn Society)

Fig. 10-22. Red Poll cow, Pinpur Ann Advancer A. R.; bred and owned by Purdue University, Lafayette, Indiana. (Photo by Abernathy; courtesy, Red Poll Cattle Club of America)

QUESTIONS FOR STUDY AND DISCUSSION

1. List the distinguishing characteristics and disqualifications of each breed of beef and dual-purpose cattle; then discuss the importance of these listings.
2. What makes a breed popular? Why are certain breeds more numerous than others?
3. Obtain breed registry association literature and a sample copy of a magazine of your favorite beef or dual-purpose breed of cattle. (See Appendix Tables VI and VII for addresses.) Evaluate the soundness and value of the material that you receive.
4. Justify any preference that you may have for one particular breed of beef or dual-purpose cattle.
5. Must a new breed of cattle be approved by someone, or can anyone start a new breed?

SELECTED REFERENCES

Title of Publication	Author(s)	Publisher
Beef-Cattle Breeds for Beef and for Beef and Milk	Farmer's Bull. 1779	U.S. Department of Agriculture, Washington, D.C., 1954.
Breeds of Livestock, The	C. W. Gay	The Macmillan Co., New York, N. Y., 1918.
Breeds of Livestock in America	H. W. Vaughan	R. G. Adams and Co., Columbus, Ohio, 1937.
Hereford in America, The	D. R. Ornduff	The author, Kansas City, Mo., 1957.
Hereford Heritage	B. R. Taylor	The author, University of Arizona, Tucson, Ariz., 1953.
History of Linebred Anxiety 4th Herefords, A	J. M. Hazelton	Assoc. Breeders of Anxiety 4th Herefords, Graphic Arts Bldg., Kansas City, Mo., 1939.
Modern Breeds of Livestock	H. M. Briggs	The Macmillan Co., New York, N. Y., 1958.
Santa Gertrudis Breeders International Recorded Herds	R. J. Kleberg, Jr.	Santa Gertrudis International, Kingsville, Tex., 1953.
Santa Gertrudis Breed, The	A. O. Rhoad	Inter-American Institute of Agriculture Sciences, Turrialba, Costa Rica, 1949.
Shorthorn Cattle	A. H. Sanders	Sanders Publishing Co., Chicago, Ill., 1918.
Stockman's Handbook, The	M. E. Ensminger	Interstate Printers & Publishers, Danville, Ill., 1969.
Study of Breeds in America, The	Thomas Shaw	Orange Judd Co., New York, N. Y., 1900.
Story of the Herefords, The	A. H. Sanders	Breeders Gazette, Chicago, Ill., 1914.
Types and Breeds of African Cattle	N. R. Joshi, E. A. McLaughlin, R. W. Phillips	Food and Agriculture Organization of the United Nations, Rome, Italy, 1957.
Types and Breeds of Farm Animals	C. S. Plumb	Ginn and Company, Boston, Mass., 1920.
World Dictionary of Breeds, Types and Varieties of Livestock, A	I. L. Mason	Commonwealth Agricultural Bureaux, Slough, Bucks, England, 1951.
Zebu Cattle of India and Pakistan	N. R. Joshi, R. W. Phillips	Food and Agriculture Organization of the United Nations, Rome, Italy, 1953.

Also, breed literature pertaining to each breed may be secured by writing to the respective breed registry associations. (See Sec. VI, Appendix, for the name and address of each Association.)

Chapter XI

ESTABLISHING THE HERD; SELECTING AND JUDGING BEEF CATTLE

Contents

Page

Factors to Consider in Establishing the Herd...376
   Purebreds or Grades..376
   Selection of the Breed..377
   Size of the Herd..377
   Uniformity 377
   Health 378
   Condition 378
   Age and Longevity...378
   Reproductive Ability 379
   Milking Ability...380
   Size 380
   Adaptation 382
   Price 382
Selection and Its Bases..382
   Selection Based on Type or Individuality...383
   Selection Based on Pedigree..383
   Selection Based on Show-Ring Winnings...384
   Selection Based on Production Testing..384
Herd Improvement Through Selection...384
Judging Beef Cattle...385
   Parts of a Cow..386
   Ideal Beef Type and Conformation...386
   Method of Examining...388
Questions for Study and Discussion...390
Selected References 390

Whether establishing or maintaining a herd, cattlemen must constantly appraise or evaluate animals; they must buy, sell, retain, and cull. Where the beef cattle herd is being neither increased nor decreased in size, on the average, about 20 per cent of the heifers are retained as replacements and about the same percentage of old cows are culled. In addition, bulls must be selected and culled, and steers and other surplus animals must be marketed. Thus, in normal operations, cattlemen are constantly called upon to cull out animals, to select replacements, and to market surpluses. Each of these decisions calls for an evaluation or appraisal, commonly called judging.

The great livestock shows throughout the land have exerted a powerful influence in molding animal types. At the same time, producers are ever aware of market demands as influenced by consumer preferences. It must be realized, however, that only a comparatively few animals on the farms and ranches are subjected annually to the scrutiny of experienced show-ring judges or market specialists. Rather, the vast majority of purebred animals and practically all commercial herds and flocks are evaluated by practical stockmen—men who select their own foundation or replacement stock and conduct their own culling operations. In general, these men are intensely practical; no animal meets with their favor unless it carries value in marketable products. Such stockmen have little interest in the so-called breed fancy points. These practical operators may not be able to express fluently their reasons for selecting certain animals while culling others, but usually they become quite deft in their evaluations. Whether young animals are being raised for market or for breeding stock, successful livestock operators are generally good judges of livestock.

FACTORS TO CONSIDER IN ESTABLISHING THE HERD

Except for the comparatively few persons who keep animals merely as a hobby, farmers and ranchers raise stock because, over a period of years, it has proved to be a profitable enterprise provided that the production and marketing phases are conducted in an enlightened and intelligent manner. Therefore, after it has been ascertained that the farm, feeds, and available labor are adapted to animal production, and that suitable potential markets exist, the next assignment is that of establishing a herd that is efficient from the standpoint of production and that meets market demands.

Purebreds or Grades

Many breeders will continue to produce purebred stock, but the vast majority of cattle producers will, for a long time to come, produce grade stock for market rather than purebreds. Such a system requires less outlay of cash, and less experience on the part of the producer. However, even with this type of production, grading up of the herd through the use of purebred sires is always advocated. In response to a survey made by Washington State University, 94 per cent of the cattlemen reported using purebred bulls only.[1]

After some experience, the commercial breeder who has handled grade cattle may add a few purebred cows to the herd and gradually build into purebreds, provided that his experience and his market for seed stock justifies the development of this type of production.

For the man with experience and adequate capital, the breeding of purebreds may offer unlimited opportunities. It has been well said that honor, fame, and fortune are all within the realm of possible realization in the purebred business, but it should also be added that only a few achieve this high calling.

During recent years, many successful industrialists have, as a hobby, established purebred herds of various classes of livestock. Ordinarily these men possess great ability, but they are inexperienced in the handling of animals. Such men are likely to derive more enjoyment from the venture and make a greater contribution to the livestock industry at less cost to themselves if they can be persuaded to (1) hire a competent manager in whom they have confidence and give him considerable freedom in the operation of the livestock

---

[1] Ensminger, M. E., M. W. Galgan, and W. L. Slocum, Wash. Agri. Expt. Sta. Bull. 562.

enterprise, and (2) start with the best animals obtainable and adhere to a sound breeding program.

Selection of the Breed

No one breed of cattle can be said to excel all others in all points of beef production for all conditions. The selection of a particular breed is most often a matter of personal preference, and usually the breed that the individual cattleman likes is the one with which he will have the greatest success. Where no definite preference exists, however, it is well to choose the breed that is most popular in the community—if any one breed predominates. If this procedure is followed, it is often possible to arrange for an exchange of animals, especially bulls. Moreover, if a given community is noted for producing good cattle of a particular breed, there are many advantages from the standpoint of advertisement and sales—this applies both to purebreds and grades. Above all, it should be remembered that *usually there are more differences among individuals within the same breed than between the different breeds.*

In selecting a purebred bull for a grade herd, the breed chosen should usually be one that the character of the cows most nearly approaches.

Size of the Herd

No minimum or maximum figures can be given as to the best size for the herd. Rather, each case is one for individual consideration. It is to be pointed out, however, that labor costs differ very little whether the herd numbers 10 or 80. The cost of purchasing and maintaining a herd bull also comes rather high when too few females are kept. The extent and carrying capacity of the pasture, the amount of hay and other roughage produced, and the facilities for wintering stock are factors that should be considered in determining the size of herd for a particular farm unit. The system of disposing of the young stock will also be an influencing factor. For example, if the calves are disposed of at weaning time or finished as baby beef, practically no cattle other than the breeding herd are maintained. On the other hand, if the calves are carried over as stockers and feeders or are finished at an older age, more feed, pasture, and shelter are required.

Then, too, whether the beef herd is to be a major or minor enterprise will have to be decided upon. Here again, each case is one for individual consideration. In most instances, replacements should be made from heifers raised on the farm.

Uniformity

In order to produce uniform calves, it is necessary that the cow herd be of similar type and breeding. This applies to both the purebred and grade herd. When this rule is followed, the herd bull can be selected with more intelligence. Secondly, uniform offspring sell at a premium at any age, whether they are sold as purebreds for foundation stock, as stocker and feeder calves, or as slaughter steers.

Health

All animals selected should be in a thrifty, vigorous condition and free from diseases and parasites. They should give every evidence of a life of usefulness ahead of them. The cows should appear capable of producing good calves, and the bull should be able to withstand a normal breeding season. Tests should be made to make certain of freedom from both tuberculosis and contagious abortion. In fact, all purchases should be made subject to the animals being free from these contagious diseases. With costly purebred animals, a health certificate should be furnished by a licensed veterinarian. Newly acquired animals should be isolated for several days before being turned with the rest of the herd.

Condition

Although an extremely thin and emaciated condition, which may mar reproduction, is to be avoided, it must be remembered that an overfat condition may be equally harmful from the standpoint of reproduction.

It takes a unique ability to project the effect of feeding a few hundred pounds of grain or hay to a thin animal, and fortunate indeed is the stockman who possesses this quality. This applies alike to both the purebred and the commercial producer. In fact, it is probably of greater importance with the commercial cattleman, for replacement females and stocker and feeder steers are usually in very average condition.

Age and Longevity

In establishing the herd, it is usually advisable to purchase a large proportion of mature cows (cows four to eight years of age) that have a record of producing uniformly high-quality calves. Perhaps it can be said that not over one-half of the newly founded herd should consist of untried heifers. Aside from the fact that some of the heifers may prove to be non-breeders, they require more assistance during calving time than is necessary with older cows. Perhaps the best buy of all, when they are available, consists of buying cows with promising calves at their side and which are rebred to a good bull; a three-in-one proposition.

Once the herd has been established, the replacements should be made from the top heifers raised on the farm. Old cows, irregular breeders, and poor milkers sell to best advantage before they become thin and "shelly."

A sound practice in buying a bull is to seek one of serviceable age that is known to have sired desirable calves—a proved sire. However, with limited capital, it may be necessary to consider the purchase of a younger bull. Usually a wider selection is afforded with the latter procedure and, also, such an individual has a longer life of usefulness ahead. Naturally, the time and number of services demanded of the bull will have considerable bearing on the age of the animal selected.

Since most beef females do not reproduce until they are approximately three years of age, their regular and prolonged reproduction thereafter has an important bearing upon the overhead cost of developing breeding stock in relation to the number of calves produced. The longer the good, proved, producing cows can be kept without sacrifice of the calf crop or too much decrease in salvage value, the less the percentage replacement required. Moreover, the proportion of younger animals that can be marketed is correspondingly increased. Washington State University found that old cows are culled or removed from the breeding herd at an average age of 9.6 years and bulls at 6.3 years.[2] It is recognized that the severity of culling will vary somewhat from year to year, primarily on the basis of whether cattle numbers are expanding or declining; and that purebred cattle are usually retained longer than commercial cattle. Selection and improvement in longevity are possible in all breeds and should receive more attention.

Reproductive Ability

For the U.S. as a whole, out of each 100 cows bred only 86 per cent drop calves annually. The other 14 per cent are nonproducers, either temporarily or permanently.[3] Many of the southern states have very low calf crop percentages, some state averages running as low as 50 per cent. With a 50 per cent calf crop, it simply means that two cows are being maintained an entire year for the production of one calf. As reproductive ability is fundamental to economical beef production, it can be readily understood that reproductive failure constitutes a major annual loss in the cattle business. In fact, cattlemen acknowledge that the calf crop percentage is the biggest single factor affecting profit in beef cattle production.[4] Improper feeding and disease are the two most common causes of low percentage calf crops in cattle.

Overfeeding accompanied by extremely high condition, or underfeeding accompanied by an emaciated and run-down condition, usually result in temporary sterility that may persist until the condition is corrected. Lack of exercise, inflammation and infection of the reproductive tract resulting from retained afterbirth or other difficulties encountered at calving, and infections of various other kinds may also result in temporary sterility. The most common

---

[2] Ensminger, M. E., M. W. Galgan, and W. L. Slocum, Wash. Agric. Expt. Sta. Bull. 562.

[3] The U.S. Department of Agriculture reports (in a personal communication of October 28, 1966, from Charles E. Bell, Jr., Director, Division of Agricultural Science, Technology and Management, to the author) that for the seven-year period, 1959 to 1965, the U.S. percentage calf crop (computed basis calves dropped in comparison with cows bred) for all cattle (beef and dairy) has been steady at 86 per cent.

[4] Methods of computing calf crop percentages vary, but the three most common methods are: (1) number of calves born in comparison with the number of cows bred, (2) number of calves marketed or branded in relation to the cows bred, or (3) the number of calves that reach weaning age as compared with the number of cows bred. Perhaps the first method is the proper and most scientific one, but, for convenience reasons, some ranchers use the other two.

causes of permanent sterility in cattle are: old age; diseased reproductive organs, such as cystic ovaries; diseased fallopian tubes; and heredity. The reproductive ability of an individual or an entire herd may also be greatly affected, either temporarily or permanently, by the presence of brucellosis.

Sterility may be present in either sex. Occasionally bulls are sterile even though sexually active. Differences in the fertility of bulls are especially revealed by the records kept and the semen studies made.

In addition to these factors which affect reproduction, the percentage calf crop may be affected by the proportion of bulls to cows and their distribution on the range, by the season of breeding, and by diseases.

Milking Ability

Most commercial cattle producers have long recognized the importance of good milking cows in producing heavy, thrifty calves. Unfortunately, insufficient attention is given to this factor by altogether too many purebred breeders. Instead, they have come to rely upon nurse cows for supplemental milk.

Beef cows that do not produce sufficient milk to raise their own calves satisfactorily should be culled from the herd. One can soon improve the milking ability of the herd by giving proper attention to this factor when selecting the herd bull. The best method is to select a bull whose sire and dam have both produced good milking daughters. If there is no opportunity to observe or secure information on the daughters of the parent animals, then the milking ability of the mother and of the sire's mother is the next best criterion. Even though good milking ability is desired, an excessive flow of milk in commercial cattle is equally undesirable, for it results in difficulty in milking them out and many spoiled udders.

Size

The question of size of beef cattle has been a point of considerable controversy among beef cattle producers. Fashions in beef cattle type have gradually changed during the past 50 or 60 years, moving from the big, rugged, beefy— but oftentimes rough "farmer or rancher type" that our grandfathers produced— to the smaller, earlier-maturing, blockier, smoother types in vogue from about 1935 to 1945, of which the comprest or compact represented the extreme. (These extremes were known as comprests in Herefords and compacts in Shorthorns.)

The reasons for this shift in cattle type were many and varied, but perhaps the smaller types evolved principally because of the demand on the part of the consumer for smaller cuts of meat. The show ring was, likewise, an important factor, and show-ring fashions for both the finished product and breeding animals tended to follow consumer preferences.

Unfortunately, the tremendously important utility factor or economy of production was largely overlooked in this shift, and little information was available in regard to whether the smaller types could be produced as economically as larger cattle. Many producers felt that bigger cattle could be produced more economically, especially under conditions where operating costs are on a per-head rather than on a per-pound basis and where profit in a cattle enterprise depends primarily upon the ability of the animals to utilize efficiently large amounts of roughage. The opinion was also prevalent that show-ring fashions toward the low-set, blocky, earlier-maturing, pony-type cattle went further than consumer demand justified. As a result, in recent years the pendulum has swung toward larger cattle; currently medium or medium to large type cattle are favored by most breeders.

Fortunately, some experimental work, designed to answer these and other questions, has been conducted. In a study[5]—involving large-, intermediate-, and small-type Hereford cattle—Stonaker of the Colorado station reported that wide variations in mature size are not antagonistic with present market demands, efficiency of feed use, or carcass cutout values and grades. However, the larger cattle produced a higher percentage calf crop and required some less fixed cost expenditure per pound of beef produced.

In the Colorado experiments, all groups of steers were fed to about the same degree of finish. This is important because fat is high in energy; and the fatter an animal becomes the less efficiently it utilizes its feed. Thus, it stands to reason that smaller-type animals, when fed to the same weight as large-type animals, will be fatter and, therefore, will require more feed per 100 pounds gain.

In a study[6] conducted cooperatively by the Kansas, Oklahoma, and Ohio Agricultural Experiment Stations involving steers sired by small-, medium-, and large-size bulls, medium-size steers were favored; it was found that medium-size cattle tend to combine the gaining ability of large cattle and the finishing ability of small cattle without sacrifice of efficiency of gain.

The New Mexico station compared the gains of and carcasses produced from compact, medium, and rangy steers. They found that the rangy steers weighed more when put on feed, gained more, and yielded a higher dressing percentage than the compact steers; and that the medium type was intermediate in each case. There was no indication of any differences in economy of gain, however.[7]

Perhaps, in the final analysis, the most practical size of cattle will vary according to: (1) the type and plane of nutrition available and (2) whether or not the market is a critical one. Thus, if large acreages of range are to be utilized and it is desired to market the cattle as heavy steers (about 1,200-pound weights)—as either grass-fat steers or with a minimum of grain feeding—perhaps the large-type animals would be preferable. It must also be remembered that the labor costs under range conditions are no greater for handling large animals with greater pounds than they are for the small animals.

On the other hand, under conditions where the available area is smaller, where a greater quantity of grain and less roughage is produced, and the

[5] Stonaker, H. H., Colorado State University Bull. 501-S, 1958.
[6] Weber, A. D., A. E. Darlow, and Paul Gerlaugh, Am. Her. Jour., 41 (22): 20, 1951.
[7] Knox, J. H. and Marvin Koger, Jour. of An. Sc., Vol. 5, No. 4, p. 331, 1946.

market is a discriminating one in which the consumers desire high quality but smaller cuts of meat, the situation may favor the production of smaller-type cattle.

Certainly animals can be too big. Huge size is usually accompanied by coarseness, poor fleshing qualities, loose rather than compact conformation, and slow maturity and finishing. Perhaps, under most conditions and in the final analysis, medium-type cattle are best from the standpoint of widest adaptability, general vigor, reproductive efficiency, milk production, longevity, and marketability. Yet it is reasonable to conjecture that there are environmental and market conditions under which one or the other extremes in beef type (the large type or the small type) may be more profitable.

Adaptation

As has already been indicated—except in those localities where a certain breed predominates, thus making possible the exchange of breeding stock and joint benefits in selling surplus stock—one will usually do best to select that breed for which the producer may have a decided preference. On the other hand, there are certain areas and conditions wherein the adaptation of the breed or class of animals should be given consideration. For example, in the South, Brahman cattle and certain strains of Brahman crossbreeds seem to thrive despite the extreme heat, heavy insect infestation, and less abundant vegetation common to the area. Because of this, Brahman blood is now being added to many herds of the South and Southwest, and new strains of beef cattle are in the making.

The livestock producer must always breed for a strong constitution—the power to live and thrive under the adverse conditions to which most animals are subjected sometime during their lifetime. Under natural conditions, selection occurs for this characteristic by the elimination of the unfit. In domestic herds and flocks, however, the constitution of foundation or replacement animals should receive primary consideration.

Price

With a grade herd, it is seldom necessary to pay much in excess of market prices for the cows. However, additional money paid for a superior bull, as compared to a mediocre sire, is always a good investment. In fact, a poor bull is high at any price. With the purebred breeder, the matter of price for foundation stock is one of considerable importance. Though higher prices can be justified in the purebred business, sound judgment should always prevail.

SELECTION AND ITS BASES

Four bases of selection are at the disposal of the cattle producer: (1) selection based on type or individuality, (2) selection based on pedigree, (3) selection based on show-ring winnings, and (4) selection based on production testing. Since each method of selection has its own particular place, the progressive cattleman will make judicious use of all of them.

Selection Based on Type or Individuality

The ultimate objective in beef production is that of selling meat over the block. Thus, fads or fancies in beef cattle selection that stray too far from this objective will, sooner or later, bring discredit and a penalty.

Strictly from the standpoint of the packer and the consumer, a meat animal should produce the maximum of the high-priced cuts, and there should be a very minimum of the less valuable bones and internal organs. On the other hand, in order to obtain efficiency of production under practical farm or ranch conditions, the producer must have animals with fairly good bone and a good middle. When such points of conflict exist, there must be a compromise. The most profitable beef animals, therefore, will be those that strike a happy balance between type, as related to the maximum production of a high-quality product, and the efficiency of production of this product.

Although environmental factors have a tremendous influence on animals, the fact remains that the performance and type of the animal itself (its phenotype or how it looks) are the best single indicators of the germ plasm that it carries (its genotype or what it actually is). Performance and type, therefore, are the most useful single factors in making selections. Naturally, this applies only to those characteristics that the animal itself can express. From a practical standpoint, this means that only those animals which are themselves average or preferably better than average should be used for breeding purposes, irrespective of the merit of near relatives.

The selection of animals on the basis of type or appearance alone is commonly called mass selection. This is the usual procedure followed in commercial herds, and, in a large part, it is responsible for the transformation of the Texas Longhorn to the present-day prime bullock.

In making selections based on type or individuality, it must be remembered that the characteristics found in the breeding herd are very likely to be reflected in the offspring; for here, as in any breeding program, a fundamental principle is that "like tends to produce like." Then, too, one must not overlook the fact that the herd bull is far more than half of the herd. A cow's inheritance will only influence one calf a year, whereas the herd bull may influence 20 to 50 times as many individuals in a given season.

Selection Based on Pedigree

In pedigree selection, the individuality and performance of the ancestors are relied upon for an estimate of the probable transmitting ability. This method is used in most purebred herds.

In making use of pedigree selections, one must not be misled nor must he overestimate the value of family names or favorite animals many generations removed from the foundation animal. Pedigree fads as such should be avoided, especially if there has not also been rigid culling and selection based on utility value. In all instances, poor individuals should not be saved, regardless of the excellence of relatives.

Selection Based on Show-Ring Winnings

Purebred cattle breeders have long used show-ring winnings as a basis of selection. Generally speaking, this has been wise, especially from the standpoint of providing guidance for the beginner. On the other hand, there are acknowledged weaknesses to this system; as evidenced by (1) the undersized, but generally popular, champion cattle of the 1930's and early 1940's, and (2) the overemphasis on breed fancy points, which admittedly have no utility value in commercial production.

Selection Based on Production Testing

As pointed out in Chapter II, production testing is the most infallible basis of selection. Further details relative to the traits of importance in beef cattle and the method of measuring each are presented in Chapter XIII.

Progressive cattle breeders are beginning to select bulls backed by either a performance test or progeny test. This interest will increase. The progressive purebred breeder, therefore, will start now to get his herd on a tested basis. It should be emphasized, however, that even though production testing is one of the keenest tools available to the breeder, for best results it is advocated that one continue to use all four methods of selection: individuality, pedigree, show ring, and production testing. But increasing emphasis should be placed upon the latter method. In other words, production testing should be used to supplement individual, pedigree, and show ring selection rather than to replace them as is sometimes advocated.

HERD IMPROVEMENT THROUGH SELECTION

Once the herd has been established, the primary objective should be to improve it so as to obtain the maximum production of quality offspring. In order to accomplish this, there must be constant culling and careful selection of replacements. The breeders who have been most constructive in such a breeding program have usually used great breeding bulls and then have obtained their replacements by selecting some of the outstanding, early-maturing heifers from the more prolific families.

Improvements through selection are really twofold: (1) the immediate gain in increased calf production from the better animals that are retained, and (2) the genetic gain in the next generation. The first is important in all herds, whereas the second is of special importance in purebred herds and in all herds where replacement females are raised. Most of the immediate gain is attained in selecting the cows, which are more numerous than the bulls; whereas the majority of the genetic gain comes from the careful selection of bulls. The genetic gain is small, but it is permanent and can be considered a capital investment.

Many good cattle breeders consider it a sound practice to plan on approximately a 20 per cent replacement each year. Under such a system of management, 20 (one-fifth) of the heifer calves are retained each year for each 100 cows.

JUDGING BEEF CATTLE

The discussion that follows represents a further elucidation of the first point discussed under selection—individuality. In addition to individual merit, judging implies the comparative appraisal or placing of several animals.

Judging beef cattle, like all livestock judging, is an art, the rudiments of which must be obtained through patient study and long practice. The master breeders throughout the years have been competent livestock judges. Shrewd traders have also been masters of the art, even to the point of deception.

The essential qualifications that a good judge of beef cattle must possess may be summarized as follows:

1. **Knowledge of the parts of an animal.**—This consists of mastering the language that describes and locates the different parts on an animal.

2. **A clearly defined ideal or standard of perfection.**—The successful livestock judge must know what he is looking for.

3. **Keen observation and sound judgment.**—The good judge possesses the ability to observe both good conformation and defects, and to weigh and evaluate the relative importance of the various good and bad features.

4. **Honesty and courage.**—The good judge of any class of livestock must possess honesty and courage, whether it be in making a show-ring placing or conducting a breeding and marketing program. For example, it often requires considerable courage to place a class of animals without regard to: (a) placings in previous shows, (b) ownership, and (c) public applause. It may take even greater courage and honesty with oneself to discard from the herd a costly animal whose progeny has failed to measure up.

5. **Logical procedure in evaluating.**—There is always great danger of the beginner making too close an inspection; he oftentimes gets "so close to the trees that he fails to see the forest." Good judging procedure consists of the following three separate steps: (a) observing at a distance and securing a panoramic view where several animals are involved, (b) using close inspection (and handling cattle), and (c) moving the animal in order to observe action. Also, it is important that a logical method be used in viewing an animal from all directions, as for example (a) side view, (b) rear view, and (c) front view; thus avoiding overlooking anything and making it easier to retain the observations that are made.

6. **Tact.**—In discussing either (a) a show-ring class or (b) animals on a stockman's farm or ranch, it is important that the judge be tactful. The owner is likely to resent any remarks that indicate that his animal is inferior.

Parts of a Cow

The first step in preparation for judging beef cattle consists of mastering the language that describes and locates the different parts of the animal. This information is set forth in Figure 11-1. Also, it is necessary to know which of these parts constitute items of major importance; that is, what comparative evaluation should be given to different parts of the animal? Having acquired this knowledge, long hours must be spent in patient study and practice in comparing animals. Even this will not make expert and proficient judges in all instances, for there may be a grain of truth in the statement that "the best judges are born and not made." Nevertheless, training in judging and selecting animals is effective when directed by a competent instructor or experienced stockman.

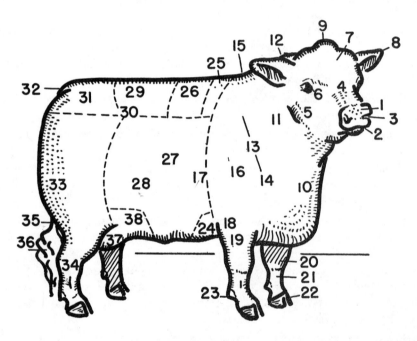

Fig. 11-1. Parts of a steer. The first step in preparation for judging beef cattle consists in mastering the language that describes and locates the different parts of the animal. (Drawing by R. F. Johnson)

1. Muzzle	11. Neck	20. Knee	30. Hip or hook
2. Mouth	12. Crest	21. Shank	31. Rump
3. Nostril	13. Shoulder vein	22. Foot	32. Tailhead
4. Face	14. Point of shoulder	23. Dew claw	33. Thigh
5. Jaw	15. Top of shoulder	24. Fore flank	34. Hock
6. Eye	16. Shoulders	25. Crops	35. Tail
7. Forehead	17. Foreribs or heart	26. Back	36. Switch
8. Ear	girth	27. Ribs	37. Cod
9. Poll	18. Elbow	28. Belly	38. Rear flank
10. Dewlap	19. Arm	29. Loin	

Ideal Beef Type and Conformation

The next requisite in judging is to have clearly in mind a standard or ideal. Presumably, this ideal should be based on a combination of: (1) the

efficient performance of the animal from the standpoint of the producer, and
(2) the desirable carcass characteristics of market animals as determined by
the consumer.

With beef animals, type is measured by the relative proportions between
rounds, loins, ribs, shoulders, chucks, legs, and other cuts as well as by the
estimated quality and the dressing percentage of the animal. The ideal beef
animal should be moderately low set and compact. The body should have great
width and depth throughout, with good lines, and with all parts smoothly blended

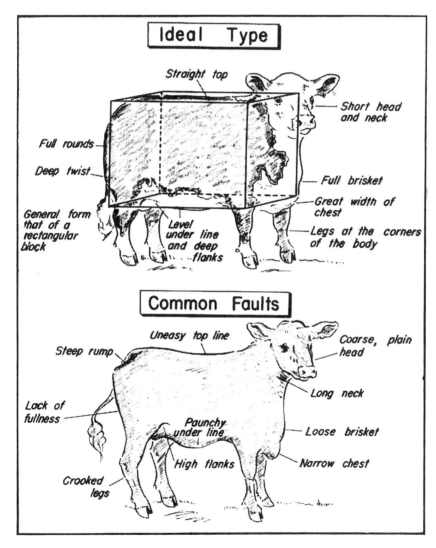

Fig. 11-2. Ideal beef type versus common faults. After mastering the
language that describes and locates the different parts of an animal, the next
requisite in judging is to have clearly in mind a standard or ideal. In brief, the
successful beef cattle judge must know what he is looking for, and be able to
recognize and appraise the common faults. (Drawing by R. F. Johnson)

together. The animal should be thickly and evenly fleshed, with superior development in the regions of the high-priced cuts. The legs should be straight, true, and squarely set; the bone should be ample and show plenty of quality. With this splendid beef type, there should be style, balance, and symmetry and an abundance of quality. Beef cows should show femininity and breediness. The bull should show great masculinity. He should be burly, bold, and rugged and have an energetic yet manageable disposition. The great breeders of the past were men who visualized an ideal better than the current standards and who were not stampeded by passing fads. They possessed both a goal and a program.

It must be recognized, however, that the perfect specimen has never been produced. Each animal possesses one or several faults. In appraising an individual animal, therefore, its good points and its faults must be recognized, weighed, and evaluated in terms of an imaginary ideal. In comparative judging—that is, in judging a class of animals—the good points and the faults of each animal must be compared with the good points and the faults of every other animal in the class. In no other manner can they be ranked.

In addition to recognizing the strong and weak points in an animal, it is necessary that the successful judge recognize the degree to which the given points are good or bad. A sound evaluation of this kind requires patient study and long experience. Figure 11-2 shows the ideal beef type versus some of the common faults.

Method of Examining

As in examining any class of livestock, in judging beef cattle the examination should be systematic and thorough. First, the animal (or animals) should be viewed from a distance, obtaining views from the side, rear, and front. Finally, the animal should be handled.

It makes little difference as to the order of the views in inspecting cattle, but it is important that the same procedure be followed each time. Though good judges differ, perhaps as logical a method of examining as any is illustrated in Figure 11-3.

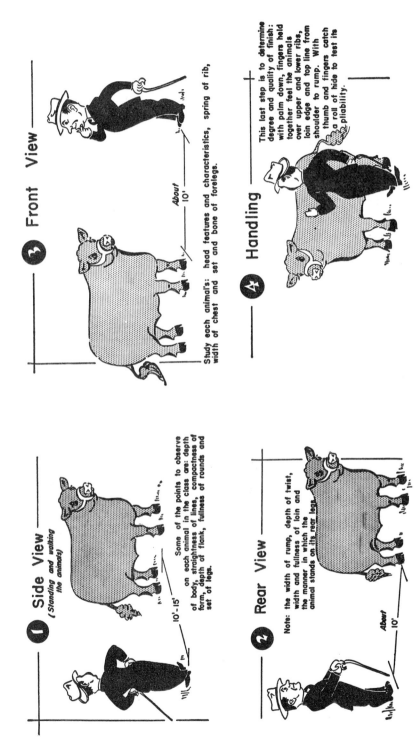

① Side View
(Standing and walking the animals)

10'-15'

Some of the points to observe on each animal in the class are: depth of body, straightness of lines, compactness of form, depth of flank, fullness of rounds and set of legs.

② Rear View

Note: the width of rump, depth of twist, width and fullness of loin and the manner in which the animal stands on its rear legs.

About 10'

③ Front View

About 10'

Study each animal's: head features and characteristics, spring of rib, width of chest and set and bone of forelegs.

④ Handling

This last step is to determine degree and quality of finish: with palm down, fingers held together feel the animals over upper and lower ribs, loin edge and top line from shoulder to rump. With thumb and fingers catch a roll of hide to test its pliability.

Fig. 11-3. Steps in examining: (1) side view, (2) rear view, (3) front view, and (4) handling. It is important that the judge follow a logical procedure in looking over animals. (Drawing by R. F. Johnson)

QUESTIONS FOR STUDY AND DISCUSSION

1. Select a certain farm or ranch (either your home farm or ranch, or one with which you are familiar). Assume that there are no beef cattle on this establishment at the present time. Then outline, step by step, (a) how you would go about establishing a herd, and (b) the factors that you would consider. Justify your decisions.

2. Cite examples as proof of the fact that show-ring standards have not always been practical.

3. What are the disadvantages to the score-card system of judging?

4. What bases of selection would you use, and why?

SELECTED REFERENCES

Title of Publication	Author(s)	Publisher
Breeding Better Livestock	V. A. Rice F. N. Andrews E. J. Warwick	McGraw-Hill Book Co., New York, N. Y., 1953.
Determining the Age of Farm Animals by Their Teeth	Farmer's Bul. 1721	U.S. Department of Agriculture, Washington, D.C.
Elements of Livestock Judging, The	W. W. Smith	J. B. Lippincott Co., Philadelphia, Pa., 1930.
Judging Livestock	E. T. Robbins	Cir. 579, Ext. Ser., University of Illinois, Urbana, Ill.
Livestock and Meat Manual, A	Ext. Misc. Pub. 40	Extension Service, Washington State University, Pullman, Wash.
Livestock Judging Handbook	J. E. Nordby W. M. Beeson David L. Fourt	Interstate Printers and Publishers, Danville, Ill., 1962.
Selecting, Fitting and Showing Beef Cattle	J. E. Nordby H. E. Lattig	Interstate Printers and Publishers, Danville, Ill., 1962.
Stockman's Handbook, The	M. E. Ensminger	Interstate Printers and Publishers, Danville, Ill., 1969.

Chapter XII

SYSTEMS OF BEEF PRODUCTION

Contents   Page

Breeding Purebreds 392
Cow-and-calf System..392
Growing of Stockers..393
Baby Beef Production..393
Finishing Cattle 394
Dual-Purpose Production..395
The Farm Herd Method..395
The Range Cattle Method..396
Questions for Study and Discussion..397
Selected References 397

The general systems of beef production that are most extensively practiced include: (1) breeding purebreds; (2) cow-and-calf system; (3) growing of stockers; (4) baby beef production; (5) finishing cattle; and (6) dual-purpose production. In these systems, two area methods of management are involved: the farm herd method and the range cattle method.

Fig. 12-1. Purebred Hereford herd on pasture, near San Marcos, California. The breeding of purebreds is a highly specialized type of production. (Courtesy, American Hereford Association)

Fig. 12-2. Cow-and-calf system of beef cattle production. In this system, the calves are run with their dams until weaned and the cows are not milked. It is the most common system of beef production on the western range. (Courtesy, Soil Conservation Service)

BREEDING PUREBREDS

This is a specialized type of production. Generally speaking, only the experienced breeder should undertake the production of purebreds with the intention of furnishing foundation or replacement stock to other purebred breeders, or purebred bulls to the commercial producer. Unless prices are unusually favorable, the beginner had best start with grade cows and a purebred bull. Although there have been many constructive beef cattle breeders and great progress has been made, it must be remembered that only those master breeders like Bakewell, Cruickshank, and Gentry are among the immortals. Few breeders achieve the success which was theirs.

It is estimated that only 3 per cent of the cattle of the United States are purebreds at the present time and that more than 88 per cent of the farms on which beef cattle are kept do not possess a single purebred cow. Although limited in numbers, purebred herds are scattered throughout the United States and include both farm and ranch operations.

COW-AND-CALF SYSTEM

This system is sometimes referred to as the production of stockers and feeders. In this type of operation, the calves run with their dams until weaned, and the cows are not milked. This particular type of production is followed more extensively than any other throughout the United States. It is especially adapted to regions where pasture is plentiful and land is cheap. As might be expected, it represents the more or less standard system of beef production in the western range country. The breeding herd needs but little grain or other expensive feeds, except when the ground is covered with snow.

GROWING OF STOCKERS

Stockers are thin animals, generally of beef breeding and yearlings or under, upon which it is intended that gains shall be produced on pasture or other cheap roughages. They may consist of steers or heifers that are intended for

Fig. 12-3. Santa Gertrudis stocker cattle calved in Texas, shipped to Pennsylvania, and turned to lush pastures; subsequently, finished in dry lot. (Courtesy, Pennsylvania Millers and Feed Dealers Association, Ephrata, Pa.)

finishing purposes at a later period, or heifers which will be used for breeding purposes. Usually such cattle are not held longer than a year, and, for the most part, they are fed chiefly on pasture and cheap roughage. This type of operation is conducted in both the farm and range states.

BABY BEEF PRODUCTION

Baby beef is the term applied to finished animals from 12 to 18 months of age, and which grade from Good to Prime. Although animals classed as baby beef vary somewhat in weight, it is noteworthy that during the 10-year period 1949 through 1958 the champion steers at the Chicago International averaged 1,063 pounds. In its truest form, the production of baby beeves involves the breeding, rearing, and finishing of the calves on the same farm. The first requirement for baby beef production is superior breeding. Secondly, the calves intended for such use should never be allowed to lose their baby fat. Ordinarily the calves are creep fed—grain is placed before them as soon as they are old enough to eat, usually when they are from four to six weeks old. Cows producing calves intended for baby beef are generally fed a little more liberally than those producing calves for other purposes.

Well-finished baby beeves command top prices, and demand is wide and insistent. An increasing number of beef men are therefore turning their efforts to this type of production. Boys' and girls' 4-H Club work has done much to focus attention on baby beef production.

FINISHING CATTLE

The cattle-finishing industry, in so far as grain feeding is concerned, is largely confined to the Corn Belt and the irrigated valleys of the West. Although some of the feeders in the central states maintain breeding herds from which

Fig. 12-4. Hereford steers being finished by Frank Friedricksen, Andover, Iowa. The grain finishing of cattle is confined almost entirely to the Corn Belt and the irrigated valleys of the West. (Courtesy, The Corn Belt Farm Dailies)

they produce their own feeder calves, the majority of feeders continue to rely on the western ranges for their young stock.

For the inexperienced feeder or the "in-and-outer," this type of production is surrounded by many hazards. When feeders have the opinion that profits are due largely to clever buying and selling, the enterprise is often a gamble. However, for the man who follows cattle feeding year after year as a method of marketing home-grown grain and who practices skillful feeding and management, this system will give good returns over a period of years. The subject of finishing cattle is more fully discussed in Chapter XIV.

DUAL-PURPOSE PRODUCTION

For the most part, dual-purpose production has been confined to the small farmer who lives upon the land and who makes his living therefrom. Cows of dual-purpose breeding are often referred to as the farmer's cow. In this type of production, an attempt is made to obtain simultaneously as much beef and milk as possible. That is to say, in its truest form, this type of management can be classified as neither beef nor dairy production.

One of the chief virtues of dual-purpose production is the flexibility which it affords. When labor is available and dairy products are high in price, the

Fig. 12-5. Red Poll steers on feed. Dual-purpose cattle provide considerable flexibility. (Courtesy, Red Poll Cattle Club of America)

herd may be managed for market milk production. On the other hand, when labor is scarce and dairy products are low in price, calves may be left running with their dams, and emphasis may be placed on beef production.

THE FARM HERD METHOD

In general, beef cattle production in the so-called farm states is merely part of a diversified type of farming. Grain and pasture crops are produced; and, on the same farm, beef cattle may compete with dairy cattle, hogs, and sheep for the available feeds. This applies to practically all the farms located to the east of the 17 western range states. In general, farm beef cattle herds are

Fig. 12-6. A farm herd of beef cattle. In general, farm herds are much smaller than range herds. (Courtesy, American Shorthorn Association)

much smaller than range herds of the West, and many of them lack the uniformity which now prevails in range cattle.

THE RANGE CATTLE METHOD

More than half of all the beef cattle in the United States are produced on the western range. Because a considerable portion of the range area is not suited to the production of grains, and sheep offer the only other major use of the grasses, it seems evident that range beef cattle production will continue to hold a place of prominence in American agriculture.

Fig. 12-7. Hereford cattle on a range in New Mexico. (Courtesy, New Mexico State University)

QUESTIONS FOR STUDY AND DISCUSSION

1. Select a certain farm or ranch (your home farm or ranch, or one with which you are familiar). Assume that there are no beef or dual-purpose cattle on this establishment at the present time. Which of the six systems of beef production would you elect to follow? Justify your decision.

2. If you were purchasing a cattle establishment, would you select a farm-type or a ranch-type operation? Justify your decision.

SELECTED REFERENCES

Title of Publication	Author(s)	Publisher
Beef Cattle	R. R. Snapp A. L. Neumann	John Wiley & Sons, New York, N. Y., 1960.
Beef Production	R. V. Diggins C. E. Bundy	Prentice-Hall, Inc., Englewood Cliffs, N. J., 1956.
Beef Cattle Production in the South	D. W. Williams	Interstate Printers and Publishers, Danville, Ill., 1941.
Livestock Book, The	C. S. Hobbs, *et al.*	Vulcan Service Co., 403 Tuscaloosa Ave., S.W., Birmingham, Ala.

CHAPTER XIII

BREEDING BEEF CATTLE

Contents

Page

Normal Breeding Habits of Cows.....399
  Age of Puberty.....399
  Age to Breed Heifers.....400
  Heat Periods.....401
    Signs of Estrus.....402
  Gestation Period.....402
Fertility in Beef Cattle.....402
Methods of Mating.....403
  Hand Mating.....403
  Pasture Mating.....403
Pregnancy Test.....403
Care and Management of the Bull.....403
Age and Service of the Bull.....405
Care of the Pregnant Cow.....406
Care of the Cow at Calving Time.....407
  Signs of Approaching Parturition.....407
  Preparation for Calving.....407
  Normal Presentation.....408
  Rendering Assistance.....409
  The Newborn Calf.....409
  The Afterbirth.....410
Normal Breeding Season and Time of Calving.....410
  Advantages of Spring Calves.....411
  Advantages of Fall Calves.....412
Abnormal Development of Sex in Cattle.....412
Lethals and Other Hereditary Abnormalities.....413
Dwarfism in Cattle.....413
Bull Grading.....415
Production Testing Beef Cattle.....416
Questions for Study and Discussion.....420
Selected References.....421

Although it is true that exactly the same laws of nature govern heredity in all animals, special breeding problems are peculiar to each class of stock, and cattle are no exception.

NORMAL BREEDING HABITS OF COWS

In general, cattle that are bred when out on pasture or range are mated under environmental conditions approaching those which existed in nature prior to domestication. Less breeding trouble is generally encountered among such animals than among beef or dairy animals that are kept in confined conditions and under forced production.

Age of Puberty

The normal age of puberty of cattle is 8 to 12 months. It is recognized, however, that the age at which puberty is attained varies according to: (1) breeds, with the smaller breeds having an earlier onset of puberty than the larger, slower maturing ones, and (2) nutritional and environmental factors, with puberty occurring when animals have reached about one-third of their adult size.

Age to Breed Heifers

The age at which to breed heifers will vary with their growth and development. However, when heifers are reasonably well grown and weigh 600 to 650 pounds, a safe rule is to breed at the first breeding season after they are 13 to 14 months old. Some breed registry associations will not register a calf born to a heifer under a certain stipulated age; thus, purebred breeders need to be informed relative to such rules.

There appears to be an increasing tendency among ranch operators to breed heifers at an earlier age. In a study made by Washington State University,[1] it was found that 48.6 per cent of the reporting cattlemen bred 80 per cent or more of their replacement heifers to calve as two-year-olds; another 27.3 per cent of the cattlemen bred up to 20 per cent of their replacement heifers as two-year-olds.

Some ranchers sort the young bred heifers out from the rest of the herd in order to provide the choicest range for them. Others use an Angus bull on young first-calf heifers, claiming that there is less trouble at calving time because of the smaller body size and smaller heads of such calves.[2] Certainly, if the dam and the calf are not adversely affected, breeding at an early age would be advantageous from the standpoint of cutting production costs.

Based on limited experiments plus observation, the following are some of the advantages and disadvantages of allowing heifers to calve for the first time as two-year-olds:

Advantages—

1. On a lifetime basis, it will result in the production of about one more calf and an added calf weight of approximately 350 pounds.

2. Cow cost per hundred pounds of weaned calf will be lower.

Disadvantages—

1. The conception rate of young heifers bred when just reaching puberty is lower than in older ones. This results in spreading the calving season over a longer period, with accompanying greater inconvenience and expense.

2. The percentage calf crop of heifers calving as twos will be about 10 per cent lower than of older cows.

---

[1] Ensminger, M. E., M. W. Galgan, and W. L. Slocum, Wash. Agri. Expt. Sta. Bull. 562, p. 59.

[2] In a study in which Hereford heifers were divided and mated to Angus and Hereford bulls, the Oklahoma station did not find a breed difference. (Thesis by Delbert Glenn Moore, Oklahoma State University, May, 1956)

3. More calving troubles and a higher death loss of both mothers and calves will be encountered.

4. Early calving heifers will likely be somewhat undersized until they reach 4 to 5 years of age.

5. The calves will wean at 25 to 50 pounds lighter weights.

6. It may not be desirable for the purebred breeder from the standpoints of (a) compliance with breed registry rules relative to minimum age at calving time (check them out; different breed registries have different rules), (b) selling of open heifers, (c) having well grown, young cows for visitors to see, and (d) distribution of birth dates so as to fill more show classifications; but, of course, these points do not affect commercial cattlemen.

From the preceding, it may be concluded that more cattlemen can, and should, breed yearling heifers to calve as two-year olds. But, in doing so, the following rules should be observed:

1. Breed only well-developed heifers, weighing 600 to 650 pounds (depending on breed) at 13 to 14 months of age. Size at breeding is more important than age. Also, some breeds come in heat and mature a little earlier than others.

2. Use young, small-headed, refined-type bulls; preferably, bulls known to sire calves that are smaller than average at birth—Angus bulls are widely used for this purpose because (a) the calves tend to be somewhat smaller at birth and (b) when crossed on other breeds, hybrid vigor is also obtained (of course, similar hybrid vigor applies to other crosses too).

3. Feed a well-balanced ration, and for continuous gain of about one pound during the pregnancy period; but don't get them too fat.

4. Give special care at calving time.

5. Provide superior nutrition—well balanced and rather liberal—during the lactation period. This requires a good ration—one containing adequate energy and proteins, and fortified with the necessary vitamins and minerals. In season, usually this can be accomplished by keeping these heifers on *good pastures*, with or without supplemental feeding, both during pregnancy and lactation. When good grass is not available—in the winter, early and late, or during droughts—proper feeding must be relied upon.

6. If practical, wean early; at around four to six months of age, rather than the normal seven months.

7. Try it out on half your replacement heifers to start with; make sure that you are ready before going all out.

For the average breeder, it is best not to have the heifers calve until they are about 30 months of age. This practice can be followed if calves are being dropped in both spring and fall. When the management practice calls for either spring or fall calving and no departure therefrom, it is necessary to have the heifers calve when either two or three years of age rather than somewhere between these limits.

Heat Periods

The period of duration of heat—that is, the time during which the cow will take the bull—is very short, usually not over 16 to 20 hours, although it may vary from about 6 to 30 hours. Cows tend to have a pattern of external behavior; for example, they come in heat during the morning hours, go out of heat in the evening or early part of the night, and then ovulate approximately 14 hours after the end of heat.

Females of all species bred near the end of the heat period are much more likely to conceive than if bred at any other time. The heat period recurs approximately at 19- to 20-day intervals, but it may vary from 16 to 24 days. In most cases, cows do not show signs of estrus until some six to eight weeks after parturition, or in some instances even longer. Occasionally, an abnormal condition develops in cows that makes them remain in heat constantly. Such animals are known as nymphomaniacs. This condition is due to the development of cysts and the failure of the follicle to rupture. Treatment, which may or may not be successful, consists of rupturing the cysts via rectum or hormone injection.

SIGNS OF ESTRUS

Experienced cattlemen can usually detect in-heat cows because they generally exhibit one or more of the following characteristic symptoms: (1) nervousness, (2) attempts to mount other members of the herd and standing to be mounted by another cow (the latter appears to be the best single characteristic of the heat period), (3) a noticeable swelling of the labia of the vulva, (4) an inflamed appearance about the lips of the vulva, (5) frequent urination, and (6) a mucus discharge. Dry cows and heifers usually show a noticeable swelling or enlargement of the udder during estrus, whereas in lactating cows a rather sharp decrease in milk production is often noted.

Gestation Period

The average gestation period of cows is 283 days, or roughly about 9½ months. Though there may be considerable breed and individual variation in the length of the gestation period, it is estimated that two-thirds of all cows will calve between 278 and 288 days after breeding.

FERTILITY IN BEEF CATTLE

Fertility refers to the ability of the male or female to produce viable germ cells capable of uniting with the germ cells of the opposite sex and of producing vigorous, living offspring. Fertility is lacking in very young animals, manifests itself first at puberty, increases for a time, then levels out, and finally recedes with the onset of senility. In cattle, as with other classes of farm animals, fertility is determined by heredity and environment.

Of course, the final test for fertility is whether young are produced, but unfortunately this test is both slow and expensive. Through evaluation of the quality of semen, it is possible to make a fairly satisfactory appraisal of the male's fertility, but no comparable measure of the female's relative fertility has yet been devised.

METHODS OF MATING

Two methods of mating beef cattle are as follows: (1) hand mating and (2) pasture mating. Each of these will be discussed.

Hand Mating

In hand mating, the bull is kept separate from the cows at all times, except when an individual cow is to be bred and is turned in with him for this purpose. As a rule, in hand mating only a single service is allowed, the cow being removed immediately after service. In the breeding of purebred cattle, when breeding records are so important, this method is frequently followed. Hand mating allows for a more accurate check on whether the bull is settling the cows. It also permits a larger number of cows to be served by a bull, an especially important consideration with a proved sire.

Pasture Mating

In this system the bull is turned in with the herd, either throughout the entire year or during the breeding season. Even with pasture breeding, when it is desired to have the calves all come within a few weeks of each other thereby assuring more uniformity in size and offspring, the herd bull should be separated from the cows except during the breeding season. Uniformity in size is very important from the standpoint of marketing the calves advantageously. Furthermore, by having the calves come as nearly as possible at one time, closer observation may be given the herd at the time of parturition.

Pasture breeding is most often followed with a commercial herd. As a rule, this system requires less labor, and there is less danger of missing cows when they are in heat. However, the convenience of pasture mating should not result in neglect to check whether the cows are being settled during the breeding season.

PREGNANCY TEST

Absence of heat is not always a sign of pregnancy, but a positive diagnosis can be made. By about the second month in heifers and the third month in cows, the uterus becomes enlarged, especially in the pregnant horn, and drops into the abdominal cavity. An experienced technician can ascertain this sign of pregnancy by *feeling with the hand through the rectum wall* (see Fig. 13-1). This is the most common test of pregnancy.[3] It is popular because it affords early diagnosis, and there is little hazard when performed by an experienced operator.

CARE AND MANAGEMENT OF THE BULL

Outdoor exercise throughout the year is one of the first essentials in keep-

---

[3] For other pregnancy tests, see *Beef Cattle Science;* by the same author and publisher as *Animal Science.*

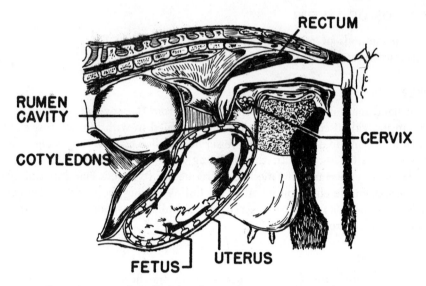

Fig. 13-1. Rectal method for determining pregnancy in the cow.

ing the bull virile and in a thrifty, natural condition. The finest and easiest method of providing such exercise is to arrange for a well-fenced, grassy paddock (about two acres is a good size for one bull). Many valuable sires have been ruined through close confinement in a small stall—or more likely yet— through being kept knee deep in mud within a small filthy enclosure. In addition

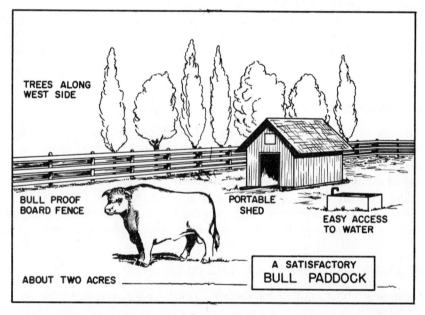

Fig. 13-2. This arrangement for the herd bull has proved most satisfactory at Washington State University. Note the size of the pasture paddock, the individual portable shelter, and the water tank, shade, and bull-proof board fence. (Drawing by R. F. Johnson)

to the valuable exercise obtained in the grassy paddock, the animal gets succulent pasture, an ideal feed for the herd bull.

A satisfactory and inexpensive shelter should be provided for the bull. The most convenient arrangement is to have this within or adjacent to the paddock, so that the bull may run in and out at will. Sufficient storage space for feed and conveniences for caring for the bull should be provided in this building. Normally, purebred bulls are kept in separate stalls and enclosures, though some successful purebred breeders regularly run several valuable bulls in one enclosure. Bulls used in commercial herds are usually run together, both on the range and when separated out from the cows. Because of their scuffling and fighting, there is more injury hazard when bulls are handled in a group.

Under range conditions, it is rather difficult to give the bulls much attention during the breeding season. Usually the proper number of bulls is simply turned with the cow herd. During the balance of the year, however, the bulls are usually kept separate. Thus, if the producer desires calves that are dropped from February 1 to June 1, the bulls are turned with the cows about May 1 and are removed September 1.

The feeding of the herd bull is fully covered in Chapter XIV. In brief, it may be said that the feeding program should be such as to keep the bull in a thrifty, vigorous condition at all times.

AGE AND SERVICE OF THE BULL

The number and quality of calves that a bull sires in a given season is more important than the total number of services. The number of services allowed will vary with the age, development, temperament, health, breeding condition, distribution of services, and system of mating (pasture or hand mating). With pasture mating, size of area, carrying capacity of the range, and the size of the herd are important factors. Therefore, no definite best number of services can be recommended for any and all conditions, and yet the practices followed by good cattlemen do not differ greatly. For best results, a bull should be at least 15 months old and well grown for his age before being put into service. Even then, it is best to follow a system of hand mating until the bull is two years of age.

Table 13-1 gives pertinent information relative to the use of the bull, including consideration that should be given to age and method of mating. In a survey,[4] Washington State University found that, on the average, one bull was used for every 21.5 cows and heifers bred.

Should the bull prove to be an uncertain breeder, he should be given rest from service, forced to take plenty of exercise, and then placed in proper condition—neither fat nor thin. Sometimes a bull that is being "let-down" in condition following showing will be temporarily sterile during the reducing process.

---

[4] Ensminger, M. E., M. W. Galgan, and W. L. Slocum, Wash. Agri. Expt. Sta. Bull. 562, p. 50.

TABLE 13—1

HANDY BULL MATING GUIDE

| | No. of Matings/Yr. | | |
Age	Hand Mating	Pasture Mating	Comments
Yearling...............	10-12	8-10	Most ranchers use 1 bull to 20 to 25 cows.
Two-year-old.........	25-30	20-25	A bull should remain a vigorous and reliable breeder up to 10 years or older; up to 6 to 7 years under range conditions.
Three-year-old or over...................	40-50	25-40	

Even though this lack of fertility may last for a year, usually such animals "bounce back."

CARE OF THE PREGNANT COW

The nutritive requirements of the pregnant cow are less rigorous than those during lactation. In general, pregnant cows should be provided as nearly year-round pasture as possible. During times of inclement weather or when deep snows or droughts make supplemental feeding necessary, dry roughages and silage are the common feeds. If produced on fertile soils, such forage will usually provide all the needed nutrients for reproduction. Further discussion of the nutritive needs of pregnant cows is obtained in Chapter XIV.

No shelter is necessary except during periods of inclement weather. Normally, the cows will prefer to run out-of-doors. This desire is to be encouraged

Fig. 13-3. Breeding cows on pasture at Brookview Farms, Pine Grove, Ky. Pregnant cows should be provided as nearly year-round pasture as is possible. (Courtesy, American Hereford Association)

—in order to provide exercise, fresh air, and sunshine. Where and when shelter is necessary, it should be neither elaborate nor expensive. An open shed facing away from the direction of prevailing winds is quite as satisfactory for the protection of dry cows as a warm bank barn with individual box stalls—and it is far less expensive. The chief requirements are that the shelter be tight overhead, that it be sufficiently deep to afford protection from inclement weather and remain dry (depths of 34 to 36 feet are preferred), that it is well drained, and that it is of sufficient size to allow the animals to move about and lie down in comfort.

CARE OF THE COW AT CALVING TIME

As has been previously indicated, the period of gestation of a cow is about 283 days, but it may vary a few days in either direction. The careful and observant caretaker, therefore, will be ever alert and will make definite preparations in ample time. It is especially important that first-calf heifers be watched at calving time, for frequently they will need some assistance. Older cows that habitually have trouble in parturition may well be culled from the herd.

Signs of Approaching Parturition

Perhaps the first sign of approaching parturition is a distended udder, which may be observed some weeks before calving time. Near the end of the gestation period, the content of the udder changes from a watery secretion to a thick, milky colostrum. As parturition approaches, there generally will be a marked shrinkage or falling away of the muscular parts in the region of the tail head and pin bones, together with a noticeable enlargement and swelling of the vulva.

The immediate indications that the cow is about to calve are extreme nervousness and uneasiness, separation from the rest of the herd, and muscular exertion and distress.

Preparation for Calving

At the time the signs of approaching parturition seem to indicate that the calf may be expected within a short time, arrangements for the place of calving should be completed.

During the seasons of the year when the weather is warm, the most natural and ideal place for calving is a clean, open pasture away from other livestock. Hogs should not be allowed in the same place with the cow, for they are likely to injure or kill the young calf. They have even been known to injure the cow.

Under pasture conditions, there is decidedly less danger of either infection or mechanical injury to the cow and calf. In commercial range operations, it is common practice to ride the range more frequently at calving time. A better procedure consists of having a smaller pasture adjoining headquarters into which

Fig. 13-4. A clean pasture makes for a good start in life.

heavy springing cows are placed a few days before calving. With the added convenience of such an arrangement, the animals can be given more careful attention.

During inclement weather, the cow should be placed in a roomy (10 or 12 feet square), well-lighted, well-ventilated, comfortable box stall or maternity pen which should first be carefully cleaned, disinfected, and bedded for the occasion.

Normal Presentation

Labor pains in a mild form usually start some hours before actual parturition. After a time, the water bag appears on the outside, usually increasing in size until it ruptures from the weight of its own contents. This is closely followed by the appearance of the amniotic bladder (the second water bag), with the fetus. With the rupture of the second water bag, the straining becomes more violent, and presentation soon follows. Most commonly in presentation, the front feet come first followed by the nose which is resting on them, then the shoulders, the middle, the hips, and then the hind legs and feet.

With posterior presentation (hind feet first), there is likely to be difficulty

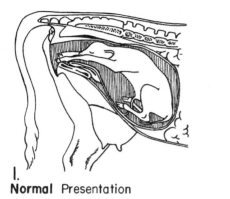
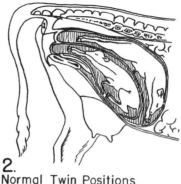

I.
Normal Presentation

2.
Normal Twin Positions

Fig. 13-5. 1. Normal single presentation; the back of the fetus is directly toward that of the mother, the forelegs are extended toward the vulva, and the head rests between the forelegs. If it is necessary to render assistance, apply ropes above the ankle joints and pull alternately downward on each leg as the cow strains.

2. Normal twin positions. If delivery does not proceed normally, this is a case for a veterinarian.

in calving. Moreover, there is considerably more danger of having the calf suffocate through rupture of the umbilical cord and strangulation.

Rendering Assistance

A good rule for the attendant is to be near but not in sight. If presentation is normal and within an hour or two after the onset of signs of calving, no assistance will be necessary. On the other hand, if the cow has labored for some time with little progress or is laboring rather infrequently, it is usually time to give assistance. Such aid will usually consist of fastening small ropes around the pasterns and pulling the young outward and downward as the cow strains. This should be done by an experienced caretaker or a competent veterinarian. It is always well to be reminded that rough, careless, or unsanitary methods at such a time may do more harm than good.

The Newborn Calf

If parturition has been normal, the cow can usually take care of the newborn calf, and it is best not to interfere. However, in unusual cases, it may be necessary to wipe the mucus from the nostrils to permit breathing; or, more rarely yet, artificial respiration methods must be applied to some calves. This may be done by blowing into the mouth, working the ribs, rubbing the body rather vigorously, and permitting the calf to fall gently. The cow should be permitted to lick the calf dry.

With calves born in sanitary quarters or out on clean pastures, there is little likelihood of navel infection. To lessen the danger of such infection, the navel cord of the newborn calf should be treated at once with a 10-per-cent solution of tincture of iodine.

A vigorous calf will attempt to rise in about 15 minutes and usually will be nursing in half an hour to an hour. The weaker the calf, the longer the time before it will be able to be up and nursing. Sometimes it may even become necessary to assist the calf by holding it up to the cow's udder.

The colostrum (the milk yielded by the mother for a short period following the birth of the young) is most important for the well-being of the newborn calf. Experiments have shown that it is almost impossible to raise a calf that has not received any colostrum. Aside from the difference in chemical composition, compared with later milk, the colostrum seems to have the following functions:

1. It contains antibodies which temporarily protect the calf against certain infections, especially those of the digestive tract.

2. It serves as a natural purgative, removing fecal matter which has accumulated in the digestive tract.

3. It contains a very high content of vitamin A, from 10 to 100 times that of ordinary milk. This provides the young calf, which is born with little body storage of this vitamin, with as much vitamin A on the first day as it would secure in some weeks from normal milk.

Usually it is best to keep the cow and calf in a small pasture for a few days. After this, they may be turned back with the main herd. Nothing is better for the cow at calving time than plenty of grass, and both the cow and calf will be helped by an abundance of fresh air and sunshine. The cow may deliberately hide the calf for the first few days, and the job may be so thoroughly done as to require considerable cleverness on the part of the caretaker to find it.

The Afterbirth

Under normal conditions, the fetal membranes (placenta or afterbirth) are expelled from three to six hours after parturition. Should they remain as long as 24 hours after calving, competent assistance should be given by an experienced caretaker or a licensed veterinarian. The operation of removing a retained afterbirth requires skill and experience; and, if improperly done, the cow may be made a nonbreeder. Furthermore, before doing this, the fingernails should be trimmed closely; the hands and arms should be thoroughly washed with soap and warm water, disinfected, and then lubricated with petroleum jelly or linseed oil. In no case should a weight be tied to the placenta in an attempt to force removal.

As soon as the afterbirth is ejected, it should be removed and burned or buried in lime, thus preventing the development of bacteria and foul odors. This step is less necessary on the open range, where animals traverse over a wide area.

NORMAL BREEDING SEASON AND TIME OF CALVING

The season at which the cows are bred depends primarily on the facilities at hand, taking into consideration the feed supply, pasture, equipment, labor, and weather conditions; whether the cattle are being produced for ordinary commercial or for purebred purposes; and whether they are strictly beef or dual-purpose cattle.

The purebred breeder who exhibits cattle should plan the breeding program so that maximum advantage will be taken of the various age groups. In most livestock shows throughout the country, the present classifications are based upon the dates of January 1, May 1, and September 1.

When it is intended to market milk from dual-purpose herds, the cows should be producing their largest flow of milk at a time when the product is likely to bring the highest price. Usually this means fall calves, in order that milk may be sold throughout the fall and winter months.

In the commercial herd of beef cattle, two systems of breeding are commonly practiced in regard to the season of the year. In one system, the bulls are allowed to run with the cows throughout the year so that calving is on a year-round basis. This system results in greater use of the bull, and there is less delay in the first breeding of the heifers as soon as they are sufficiently mature. On the other hand, often the calves arrive at undesired and poorly adapted times; the breeding system is without order and regularity; and the calves usually lack uniformity. This system is frequently followed in the central and southern states.

The other system of breeding followed with the commercial herd, and the most widely used system on the western range, is that of having all of the breeding done within a restricted season (of about three months) so that the calves arrive within a short spread of time—usually in the spring. Sometimes in the central and southern states this system is used. Having the calves born about the same time, whether it be fall or spring, results in greater uniformity. Thus, it is easier to care for (brand, dehorn, castrate, vaccinate, etc.) and market such animals. Each farm has its individual problems, and the decision must be made accordingly.

Advantages of Spring Calves

The production of spring calves has the following advantages:

1. In producing spring calves, the cows are bred during the most natural breeding season—at a time when they are on pasture, gaining in flesh, and more likely to conceive. The calving percentage is usually higher, therefore, with a system of spring calving.

2. The calves will be in shape to sell directly from the cows in the fall, at which time there is a good demand for feeder calves.

3. If the calves are to be sold as yearlings, one wintering is saved; or if they are to be sold at weaning time, no wintering is required.

4. Because of greater utilization of cheap roughage, dry cows may be wintered more cheaply.

5. Less labor and attention is required in caring for the calves the first winter.

6. Spring calves require less grain and utilize the maximum amount of pasture and roughage.

Advantages of Fall Calves

The production of fall calves has the following advantages:

1. The cows are in better condition at calving time.
2. The cows give more milk for a longer period.
3. The calves make better use of the grass during their first summer.
4. The calves escape flies, screwworms, and heat while they are small (this is especially important in the South).
5. Upon being weaned the following spring, the calves can be placed directly on pasture instead of in a dry lot; or, if it is desired to sell, they usually find a ready market ahead of the influx of fall feeder calves from the range area.
6. When it is intended to sell market milk from dual-purpose cows, fall calves are usually best. The greater flow of milk is obtained during the period of highest prices.

ABNORMAL DEVELOPMENT OF SEX IN CATTLE

A peculiar form of sterility usually occurs in heifers born twin to a bull. Such sterile heifers are called freemartins. This condition prevails in about 9 out of 10 twin births when a calf of each sex is involved. The fetal circulations fuse, and the male hormones get into the circulation of the unborn female where they interfere with the normal development of sex and modify the female embryo in the direction of the male. In about 10 per cent of heifers born twin to a bull, fusion of the circulation does not occur, and the animal is normal and fertile. As, on the average, only 1 out of each 10 heifers born twin to a bull is normal, it is usually considered best to sell such animals for slaughter; unless very valuable purebred cattle are involved, or it has been ascertained that such heifers are not freemar-

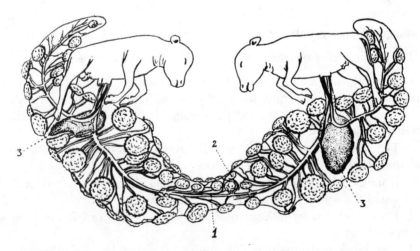

Fig. 13-6. Diagram showing fused fetal circulation of twin calves of opposite sex. Note (1) the fetal circulation of the male fused with that of the female, (2) fetal cotyledon free yolk sac, and (3) normal bull on the left and freemartin heifer on the right. (From *Physiology of Reproduction* by Marshall; courtesy, the publisher, Longmans, Green and Co., Ltd., London, England)

tins. An experienced person can, at the time of birth, determine if the circulatory systems were fused. Also, there are two blood tests for detecting freemartins: (1) a red blood cell test and (2) a white corpuscle test through which it is found that there is a deviation of some of the chromosomes in freemartin heifers.

In addition to freemartins, occasionally other abnormal sexual developments occur in animals; namely, hermaphrodites and intersexes. Hermaphrodites are animals that possess characteristics of both sexes, whereas intersexes do not possess definite characteristics of either sex. These conditions occur sporadically when something happens to the embryo to disturb normal development.

LETHALS AND OTHER HEREDITARY ABNORMALITIES[5]

Lethal characters in beef cattle or in any class of animals are caused by the presence of hereditary factors in the germ-plasm that produce an effect so serious as to cause the death of the individual either at birth or later in life. Breeding animals possessing hereditary lethals should be culled from the herd.

DWARFISM IN CATTLE

Beginning about 1940, a disturbing condition known as dwarfism appeared among beef cattle, probably in all breeds. Though very small (usually weighing about half as much as normal calves), these calves are exceedingly stocky and well built. The eyes protrude, giving a characteristic "pop-eyed" appearance. Some dwarfs are weak and unsteady in gait at birth. Others appear to be strong enough, but soon develop a large stomach, heavy shoulders, crooked hind legs, and sometimes labored breathing. Survival is somewhat lower than with normal calves, though most purebred breeders make no attempt to raise them.

Fig. 13-7. Normal (left) and dwarf (right) Hereford calves. The normal calf is 2½ months of age while the dwarf is 3½ months of age. Note the smaller size of the dwarf and its stocky, well-built conformation. (Courtesy, Washington State University)

---

[5]For a complete summary of Lethals and Other Abnormalities in Cattle, see *Beef Cattle Science*; a book by the same author and publisher as *Animal Science*.

There is complete agreement among scientists (1) that the dwarf condition is of genetic origin, and (2) that it is inherited as a simple autosomal recessive (the word autosomal meaning that the factor is not carried on the sex chromosome). One or the other of the conditions (or perhaps both conditions) shown in Figures 13-8 and 13-9 prevail in any herd of cattle in which dwarf-carrying animals are being used.

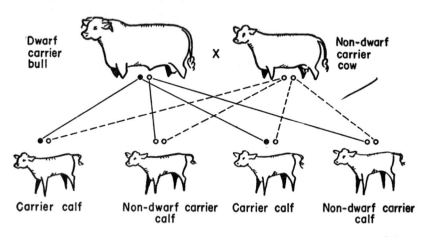

Fig. 13-8. Diagrammatic illustration of the inheritance of dwarfism, showing what to expect when a carrier (heterozygous) bull(s) is mated to a noncarrier (homozygous normal) cow(s); or the sexes may be reversed. As shown, carrier X noncarrier matings will, *on the average,* produce calves of which (1) 50% are carriers, although not dwarfs and (2) 50% are noncarriers and nondwarfs. Unfortunately, the two groups look alike and cannot be detected by sight. (Drawing by R. F. Johnson)

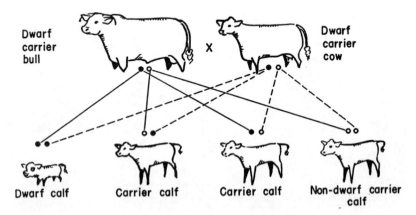

Fig. 13-9. Diagrammatic illustration of the inheritance of dwarfism, showing what to expect when a carrier (heterozygous) bull(s) is mated to a carrier (heterozygous) cow(s); or the sexes may be reversed. As shown, carrier X carrier matings will, *on the average,* produce calves of which (1) 25% are dwarfs, (2) 50% are carriers, although not dwarfs, and (3) 25% are noncarriers and nondwarfs. Unfortunately, only the dwarfs can be detected by sight; the two nondwarf groups look alike and cannot be distinguished by sight. (Drawing by R. F. Johnson)

BULL GRADING

In recent years, bull-grading programs have had a tremendous effect on improving the commercial cattle on the western ranges of this country. Perhaps this movement received its greatest impetus in those areas where several owners run herds on unfenced public grazing lands. Formerly, those progressive ranchers who believed that only purebred beef bulls of high quality should be used could do nothing to prevent the presence of inferior bulls on these public ranges. The man who bought superior bulls got no more use from them than his neighbor who turned out scrubs because he could buy them cheaply. But this problem was solved when groups of cattlemen using common ranges decided to have their bulls classified and to use only bulls of certain standards. Perhaps this movement has had its greatest following in the state of Utah, where it is estimated that 90 per cent of all range bulls have been graded.

Initially, in most bull-grading programs, the grades were designated as follows:

1. **"One-plus"** grade bulls (scoring 98 to 100) are well-nigh perfect specimens that are rarely produced.

2. **"One"** grade bulls (scoring 95 to 97) are very outstanding animals that are capable of making a good showing in the best of competition.

3. **"One-minus"** grade bulls (scoring 92 to 94) are top animals in most every respect; the kind that are good enough to head purebred herds.

4. **"Two-plus"** grade bulls (scoring 89 to 91) are outstanding bulls that have some minor faults. Some of them are used in purebred herds simply because there aren't enough "One" grade bulls available. "Two-plus" bulls are top range bulls; the kind that have enough type and quality to improve any range herd.

5. **"Two"** grade bulls (scoring 86 to 88) are good, useful kind of range bulls.

6. **"Two-minus"** grade bulls (scoring 83 to 85) are the lower end of range bulls; as far down in type and conformation as one should go in any commercial herd. Because of their deficiencies, no self-respecting rancher wishes to display "Two-minus" grade bulls.

7. **"Three"** grade bulls lack sufficient type and quality to give improvement in a commercial herd. They are the kind that should be castrated. In theory, "Three" grade bulls are divided further into (a) "Three-plus" grade bulls (scoring 80 to 82), (b) "Three" grade bulls (scoring 77 to 79), and (c) "Three-minus" grade bulls (scoring 74 to 76), but in actual practice generally all bulls grading below "Two-minus" are eliminated from sales and from use on the range.

Several college agricultural extension workers and some of the breed registry associations now use the following terms and values, based on U.S. feeder cattle grades:

High Prime	17	Prime	16	Low Prime	15
High Choice	14	Choice	13	Low Choice	12
High Good	11	Good	10	Low Good	9
High Medium	8	Medium	7	Low Medium	6
Common	5	Inferior	4	Very Inferior	3
Crippled	2	Deformed	1	Sick	0

In the West, the bull-grading program is firmly entrenched. In the future, it is predicted that production testing will become an added and useful adjunct to bull grading.

PRODUCTION TESTING BEEF CATTLE[6]

In comparison with that of chickens or even swine, production testing of beef cattle is slow, and, like most investigational work with large animals, it is likely to be expensive. Even so, in realization that such testing is absolutely necessary if maximum improvement is to be made, the progressive purebred beef cattle breeder will wish to make a start. The following items appear to be of greatest importance in evaluating the profitability of beef cattle:

1. **Regular production on the part of the cows.** (calving interval—fertility —has a heritability of 10 per cent).—Although a 100 per cent calf crop is desired, under practical conditions this is seldom achieved. Certainly any barrenness that may be hereditary had best be dealt with by removing the animals from the herd.

2. **Birth weight** (which has an approximate heritability of 41 per cent[7]).— The larger, more vigorous calves at birth seem to retain these advantages to maturity.

3. **Weaning weight** (which has an approximate heritability of 29 per cent).— Heavy weaning weight is important because (a) it is indicative of the milking ability of the cow, (b) gains made before weaning are cheaper than those made after weaning, and (c) those that sell calves at weaning make more profit due to effecting a saving in labor and making for a more rapid turnover in capital.

4. **Weaning conformation score** (which has an approximate heritability of 27 per cent).—Body type scores are difficult to make and are materially affected by condition. Yet they are important, for, after all, animals of dairy breeding may rank very high when judged by each of the other criteria. It is recommended that body type scores be taken at a standard age or ages, perhaps at weaning and at the close of the test feeding period.

5. **Daily rate of gain from weaning to marketing** (which has an approximate heritability of 47 per cent).—Daily rate of gain from weaning to marketing is important because (a) it is highly correlated with efficiency of gain, and (b) it makes for a shorter time in reaching market weight and condition, thereby effecting a saving in labor and making for a more rapid turnover in capital.

6. **Efficiency of feed utilization** (which has an approximate heritability of 40 per cent).—Where convenient, accurate feed records should be kept. The most profitable animals are the ones which require the least pounds of feed to make 100 pounds of gain.

---

[6] For further information on this subject see the section in Chapter II devoted to "Selection Based on Production Testing."

[7] The rest is due to environment. The heritability figures given herein are averages based on large numbers; thus, some variations from these may be expected in individual herds.

GET OF SIRE RECORD

Calf Crop for Year of ....

Sex: ....

Owner and Address: ....

Sire's Name .... Reg. No. ....

Date of Birth ....

Herd No. of Calf	Date of Birth	Weaning Data							———— Data					Dam Data						Remarks
		Weaning Date	Weaning Age in Days	Weight in Lbs.	Daily Gain from Birth Weight	Adj. —Day Weaning Weight	Rating on Weights and Gain Grade	Grade Percentage	Date Weighed	Weight	Wt. Adj. to —Mo.	Grade	Grade Percentage	Herd No.	Age This Year	Mature Weight	Grade	Grade Percentage	

Fig. 13-10. Get of Sire Record form.

(Seal: AGRICULTURAL EXTENSION SERVICE — U.S. DEPARTMENT OF AGRICULTURE AND STATE COLLEGE OF WASHINGTON)

INDIVIDUAL COW RECORD

Tattoo

Name...Reg. No..................

Sire...

Dam...

Bred by...Birth Date.................

Purchased from...Birth Weight[1].................

Address...Weaning Wt.........Age.........Type[1].........

Purchase Date...Yearling Wt.........Age.........Type[1].........

Disposition.................Price.................Two Year Wt.........Age.........Type[1].........

Price.................Average Daily Gain Weaning to 1 yr.................

Reason for Disposal...Feed Efficiency.................lbs. feed/100 lbs. gain

....Date.................Temperament.................

Faults & Abnormalities...

PRODUCE RECORD

Birth Date	Sex	Tattoo	Sire	Birth Wt.	Vigor[2] at Birth	Wean'g Age Days	Wean'g Wt. Act.	Wean'g Wt. Adj.	Wean'g Cond.	Wean'g Type	Yearling Age	Yearling Wt.	Yearling Type	Production Testing Days on Feed	Production Testing Ave. Daily Gain	Production Testing Lbs. Feed/100 lbs. gain	Disposition; Price Remarks

[1]100-90 = excellent; 90-80 = very good; 80-70 = good plus; 70-60 = good; 60-50 = good minus; 50-40 = fair; 40-30 = poor.

[2]0 = dead at birth; 1 = definitely undersized at birth; 2 = unthrifty; definite indications of disorders; 3 = moderately thrifty, slight indications of disorders; 4 = thrifty, no signs of disorders, dry hair coat; 5 = thrifty, no signs of disorders, sleek hair coat; 6 = very large, healthy, and vigorous.

Horn Brand or Neck Chain No.................

Fig. 13-11a. Individual Cow Record (see next page for reverse side of record form).

VACCINATION INFORMATION

Date¹	Blkg.	M. Edema	Bangs	Misc.	TB-Bangs	Johnes	Lepto	Anaplas.	Vib.	Trich.	Misc.	Remarks

Indicate vaccinations by check in appropriate column opposite date given; indicate test results by P (positive), N (negative), or S (suspect) opposite date of test.

GENERAL INFORMATION

Record all facts pertinent to the history of this cow, viz.: veterinary treatment (except immunizations), udder condition, mothering instinct, calving peculiarities, etc.

Date	Remarks

Fig. 13-11b. Individual Cow Record. This is the reverse side of the record form shown on the previous page.

Opinions differ as to the most desirable testing period or age and method. Most scientists recommend (a) testing from weaning (6 to 7 months) to 12 months, (b) either full- or self-feeding, and (c) group feeding where individual feeding is not practical.

Certainly, from the ultimate experiment standpoint, individual feed records should be obtained. But because this procedure is not always feasible, the practical cattleman may keep group feed records; through feeding young animals of similar ages together, or, if necessary, disregard this criterion and concentrate on the other points. In any event, individual feed records on prospective herd sires are extremely important.

7. **On-foot grade at slaughter time** (which has an approximate heritability of 44 per cent).—Sale of meat over the block is the ultimate objective in beef production. The body type of an individual should be based on the demands and prices of a discriminating market as projected into the future.

8. **Carcass grade** (which has an approximate heritability of 32 per cent).— Where steer progenies are slaughtered, their carcass grades will constitute the best possible evaluation of type. High carcass grade is important because it determines eating and selling qualities.

9. **Area of rib eye** (which has an approximate heritability of 69 per cent).— The rib eye (the large muscle which lies in the angle of the rib and vertebrae) is indicative of the bred-in muscling of the entire carcass. Thus, a large area of rib eye is much sought.

Widely used and highly satisfactory record forms are shown in Figures 13-10, 13-11a, and 13-11b.

QUESTIONS FOR STUDY AND DISCUSSION

1. Why is cattle breeding less flexible in the hands of man than swine or sheep breeding?

2. In a study made by Washington State University (and reported in Washington Agricultural Experiment Station Bulletin 562), it was found that there was a 79.5 per cent calf crop and that only 62.6 per cent of the cows weaned off calves. This means that there was an appalling calf loss of 21 per cent between birth and weaning. Discuss the economics and the causes of this situation.

3. Define the following: (a) nymphomaniac, (b) freemartin, (c) hermaphrodite, and (d) intersex.

4. How would you purge a herd of dwarfs (or any other undesirable recessive)?

5. Give the expected genetic picture of dwarfism of 100 offspring from mating of (a) carrier bulls x noncarrier cows and (b) carrier bulls x carrier cows. What steps can be taken to get rid of dwarfism?

6. How would you go about production testing a herd of beef cattle? List and discuss each step.

7. Under what conditions is bull grading particularly valuable?

8. For your home farm or ranch (or one which you select), what do you consider to be the most desirable breeding season and time of calving? Justify your answer.

9. How do you account for (a) so much pasture mating among purebred beef cattle breeders and (b) so little use of artificial insemination in beef cattle breeding?

10. How do you explain the following:
    a. Why so much crossbreeding on first-calf heifers?
    b. Why so few buy production-tested bulls?

11. Why are more and more cattlemen breeding heifers to calve as two-year-olds?

12. The "sire is half the herd"! Is this an under- or over-statement?

13. Under what conditions is bull grading particularly valuable?
    Why is bull grading generally more popular with buyers than sellers?

SELECTED REFERENCES

In addition to the Selected References listed in Chapter II, the following are recommended for Chapter XIII:

Title of Publication	Author(s)	Publisher
Beef Cattle for Breeding Purposes	Farmers' Bul. 1916	U.S. Department of Agriculture, Washington, D.C.
Beef Cattle Production	K. A. Wagnon Reuben Albaugh G. H. Hart	The Macmillan Company, New York, N. Y., 1960.
Beef Production and Distribution	Herrell DeGraff	University of Oklahoma Press, Norman, Okla., 1960.
Breeding Difficulties in Cattle	Charles Staff	General Mills, Larro Research Farm, P. O. Box 263, Indianola, Iowa.
Breeding Difficulties in Dairy Cattle	S. A. Asdell	Agri. Expt. Sta. Bul. 924, Cornell Univ., Ithaca, N. Y., 1957.
Cattle Fertility and Sterility	S. A. Asdell	Little, Brown & Co., Boston, Mass., 1955.
Crossbred Beef Cattle for the Northern Great Plains	Circ. 810	U.S. Department of Agriculture, Washington, D.C.
Crossbred Types of Beef Cattle for the Gulf Coast Region	Circ. 844	U.S. Department of Agriculture, Washington, D.C.
Factors Affecting Reproductive Efficiency in Dairy Cattle	Durward Olds D. M. Seath	Kentucky Agri. Expt. Sta. Bul. 605, Univ. of Kentucky, Lexington, Ky., 1954.
Genetics of Livestock Improvement	John F. Lasley	Prentice-Hall, Inc., Englewood Cliffs, N. J., 1963.
Problems and Practices of American Cattlemen	M. E. Ensminger M. W. Galgan W. L. Slocum	Wash. Agri. Expt. Sta. Bul. 562, Washington State University, Pullman, Wash., 1955.
Reproduction and Infertility	Centennial Symposium	Agri. Expt. Sta., Michigan State University, East Lansing, Mich., 1955.
Reproduction in Dairy Cattle	C. H. Boynton	Ext. Bul. 115, University of New Hampshire, Durham, N. H.
Robert Bakewell: Pioneer Livestock Breeder	H. Cecil Pawson	Crosby Lockwood & Son, Ltd., 26 Old Brompton Road, London SW7, England, 1957.

Chapter XIV

FEEDING BEEF CATTLE

Contents   Page

Specific Nutritive Needs of Beef Cattle...424
  Protein Needs 424
  Energy Needs 425
  Mineral Needs...426
    Salt 426
    Calcium 427
    Phosphorus 427
    Trace Elements..428
  Vitamin Needs 429
  Water Needs...431
Feeds for Beef Cattle...431
  Pastures for Beef Cattle...432
  Hays and Other Dry Roughages for Beef Cattle....................433
  Silages and Roots for Beef Cattle...434
  Concentrates for Beef Cattle..436
    Self-feeding Salt-Feed Mixtures to Range Cattle...............437
  Feed Additives 438
Feeding the Herd Bulls..438
Feeding the Beef Breeding Cows..438
  Feeding the Dry and Pregnant Cows......................................438
  Feeding at Calving Time..439
  Feeding the Lactating Cows...440
Feeding Grain to Suckling Calves...441
  Creep Feeding Calves..441
Feeding Stockers...442
Feeding Finishing Cattle..442
  Dry-lot Finishing 443
  Pasture Finishing..446
    Reducing Bloat on Pastures...447
  The Feeder's Margin..447
    Factors Determining the Necessary Margin......................448
  Finishing Cattle of the Various Market Grades.....................450
  The Value of Breeding and Type in Finishing Cattle..........451
  Age as a Factor in Finishing Cattle..452
  Heifers Versus Steers...454
  Buildings and Equipment for Finishing Cattle....................456
  Excess Finishing...457
  Hogs Following Cattle..457
  Contract (or Custom) Feeding Cattle.....................................458
Feed Allowance and Some Suggested Rations for Beef Cattle.....459
  Fitting Rations for Cattle...459
  Rules of Feeding Show Cattle...462
Questions for Study and Discussion..463
Selected References 463

Pastures and other roughages, preferably with a maximum of the former, are the very foundation of successful beef cattle production, for 78.8 per cent of the total feed of beef cattle is derived from roughages. If produced on well-fertilized soils, green grass and well-cured, green, leafy hay can supply all of the nutrient requirements of beef cattle, except the need for common salt and whatever energy-rich feeds may be necessary for additional conditioning or dry-lot finishing.

Fig. 14-1. Hereford steers grazing on a western range, with hay stacked for winter feeding. (Courtesy, U.S. Forest Service)

High-percentage calf crops, heavy weaning weights, continuous and rapid growth of young stock, and optimum utilization of feedlot rations in the finishing process are important; and all are based largely upon adequate nutrition. Improvements in each of these categories are well within the realm of realization on a practical basis.

SPECIFIC NUTRITIVE NEEDS OF BEEF CATTLE[1]

As feeds represent by far the greatest cost item in beef production, it is important that there be a basic understanding of the nutritive requirements. For convenience, these will be discussed under the following groups: (1) protein needs, (2) energy needs, (3) mineral needs, (4) vitamin needs, and (5) water needs.

Protein Needs

The protein requirements of beef cattle have become more critical with the shift in beef production practices. Steers were formerly permitted to make their growth primarily on roughages—pastures in the summertime and hay and other forages in the winter. After making moderate and unforced growth for two to four years, usually the animals were either turned in the feedlot or placed on more lush pastures for a reasonable degree of finishing. With this system, the growth and finishing requirements of cattle came largely at two separate periods in the life of the animal.

---

[1]Although Webster defines the noun **ration** as "the amount of food supplied to an animal for a definite period, usually for a day," to most stockmen the word implies the feeds fed to an animal or animals, without limitation to the time in which they are consumed. In this and other chapters of *Animal Science,* the author accedes to the common usage of the word rather than to dictionary correctness.

Under the old system of moderate growth rate, reasonably good pastures and good quality hay fully met the protein requirements as well as the mineral and vitamin needs. As the feeding period was not so long with these older cattle, in comparison with the period required in the finishing of calves or yearlings, there also was less tendency for vitamin deficiencies to show up in the feedlot; and the protein requirements were less important during the finishing period.

In recent years, there has been considerable change in beef production practices. The preference of the consumer for smaller cuts of beef—meats that are more tender and have less fat—made for a shift in management and marketing. Today, increasing numbers of cattle are finished at early ages. Such animals are in forced production. Their bodies are simultaneously laying on fat and growing rapidly in protein tissues and skeleton. Their nutritive requirements are more critical, therefore, than those of older cattle, especially from the standpoint of proteins, minerals, and vitamins.

The protein allowance of beef cattle, regardless of age or system of production, should be ample to replace the daily breakdown of the tissues of the body as well as to provide for the growth of hair, horns, hoofs, and tissue. In general, the protein needs are greatest for the growth of the young calf and for the gestating-lactating cow.

Cottonseed meal or cake, linseed meal or cake, and soybean meal or cake are generally the most economical protein supplements for beef cattle. Because of rumen synthesis of essential amino acids by micro-organisms, the quality of proteins is of less importance in the feeding of beef cattle than in feeding some other classes of stock. Also, these micro-organisms—which are a low form of plant life and are able to use inorganic compounds such as ammonia, just as plants utilize chemical fertilizers—build body proteins of high quality in their cells from sources of inorganic nitrogen that nonruminants cannot use. Since the life span of these bacteria is short, further on in the digestive tract, the ruminant digests the bacteria and obtains good protein therefrom. Except for the young calf, therefore, proteins from plant sources are quite satisfactory, and such nonprotein sources of nitrogen as urea and ammonia can be used.

Energy Needs

A relatively large portion of the feeds consumed by beef cattle is used in meeting the energy needs, regardless of whether animals are merely being maintained (as in wintering) or fed for growth, finishing, or reproduction.

The first and most important function of feeds is that of meeting the maintenance needs. If there is not sufficient feed, as is frequently true during periods of droughts or when the winter rations are skimpy, the energy needs of the body are met by the breaking down of tissues. This results in loss in condition and body weight.

After the energy needs for body maintenance have been met, any surplus energy may be used for growth or finishing. With the present practice of finishing cattle at early ages, growth and finishing are in most instances simultaneous and, therefore, not easily separated.

In the finishing process, the percentage of protein, ash, and water steadily decreases as the animal matures and fattens, whereas the percentage of fat increases. Thus, the body of a calf at birth many contain about 70 per cent water and 4 per cent fat, whereas the body of a fat two-year-old steer may contain only 45 to 50 per cent water but from 30 to 35 per cent fat. This storage of fat requires a liberal allowance of energy feeds.

Through bacterial action in the rumen, cattle are able to utilize a considerable proportion of roughages as sources of energy. Yet it must be realized that with extremely bulky rations the animal may not be able to consume sufficient quantities to produce the maximum amount of fat. For this reason, finishing rations contain a considerable proportion of concentrated feeds, mostly cereal grains. On the other hand, when the energy requirements are primarily for maintenance, roughages are usually the most economical sources of energy for beef cattle.

Mineral Needs[2]

Beef cattle are liable to the usual inefficiencies and ailments when exposed to (1) prolonged and severe mineral deficiencies or (2) excesses of fluorine, selenium, or molybdenum.

Although acute mineral-deficiency diseases and actual death losses are relatively rare, inadequate supplies of any one of the essential mineral elements may result in lack of thrift, poor gains, inefficient feed utilization, lowered reproduction, and decreased production of milk.

Needed minerals may be incorporated in beef cattle rations or in the water. In addition, it is recommended that all classes and ages of cattle be allowed free access to a two-compartment mineral box, with (1) salt (iodized salt in iodine-deficient areas) in one side and (2) a suitable mineral mixture in the other side. Free-choice feeding is in the nature of cheap insurance, with the animals consuming the minerals if they are needed.

SALT

Salt should be available at all times. It may be fed in the form of granulated, half-ground, or block salt; but because of weathering losses, flake salt is not satisfactory for feeding in the open. If block salt is used, the softer types should be selected.

Most ranchers compute the yearly salt requirements on the basis of about 25 pounds per cow.[3] Mature animals will consume 3 to 5 pounds of salt per

---

[2] Generally speaking, the recommendations given herein can be followed on a nation-wide basis. However, it is recognized that area differences do exist. Therefore, for more specific recommendations the stockman should always secure the counsel of his county agricultural agent or state college of agriculture.

[3] Ensminger, M. E., M. W. Galgan, and W. L. Slocum, Wash. Agri. Expt. Sta. Bul. 562, p. 43.

month when pastures are lush and succulent and 1 to 1½ pounds per month during the balance of the season.

Salt deficiency in cattle is manifested by intense craving for this mineral. High producing milk cows may even collapse and die when the salt deficiency has been of long duration.

Excessive salt intake can result in toxicity. However, as much as 3 pounds of salt can be consumed daily by cows without deleterious effects provided animals have free access to an abundant supply of drinking water.

The careful location of the salt supply is recognized as an important adjunct in proper range management. Through judicious scattering of the salt supply and the moving of it at proper intervals, the animals can be distributed more properly, and over-grazing of certain areas can be minimized.

CALCIUM

In contrast to phosphorus deficiency, calcium deficiency in beef cattle is relatively rare and mild and the symptoms much less conspicuous. In general, when the forage of cattle consists of at least one-third legume (legume hay, pasture, or silage), ample calcium will be provided. But even non-legume forages contain more calcium than cereal grains. This indicates that a mineral source of calcium is less necessary when large quantities of roughage are being consumed. Also, plants grown on calcium-rich soils contain a higher content of this element.

As finishing cattle consume a high proportion of grains to roughages—and the grains are low in calcium—they have a greater need for a calcium supplement than do beef cattle that are being fed largely on roughages. This is especially true of younger cattle and where a long feeding period is involved.

When the ration of beef cattle is suspected of being low in calcium, the animals should be given free access to a calcium supplement, with salt provided separately; or a calcium supplement may be added to the daily ration in keeping with nutrient requirements.

PHOSPHORUS

In some sections of this and other countries, the soils are so deficient in phosphorus that the feeds produced thereon do not provide enough of this mineral for cattle or other classes of stock. As a result, the cattle produced in these areas may have depraved appetites, may fail to breed regularly, and may produce markedly less milk. Growth and development are slow, and the animals become emaciated and fail to reach normal adult size. Death losses are abnormally high.

In range areas where the soils are either known or suspected to be deficient in phosphorus, cattle should always be given free access to a suitable phosphorus supplement. The need for phosphorus in such areas is strikingly illustrated by the following observations made on the King Ranch in Texas:

Analysis of records for two calving seasons showed that 85 per cent of the cows receiving phosphorus supplement produced calves, as compared with 64 per cent for the other cows. Calves from the phosphorus supplement-fed cows averaged 69 pounds more at weaning, and 126 pounds more at 18 months of age than the others. After deduction of the cost of the supplement, the value of the weaned calves averaged $5.78 more. In further tests, phosphorus was supplied (1) in the form of bone meal placed in self-feeders, (2) by dissolving disodium phosphate in the drinking water, and (3) by applying a superphosphate fertilizer to the pasture. All methods were satisfactory, the last giving the best results.[4]

To be on the safe side, the general recommendation for beef cattle on both the range and in the finishing lot is to allow free choice of a suitable phosphorus supplement in a mineral box or to add phosphorus supplement to the ration in keeping with nutrient requirements.

TRACE ELEMENTS

There is renewed interest in trace elements, and a general recognition of the importance of many of them in beef cattle rations. Unfortunately, there is a paucity of experimental work upon which to make recommendations.

Cobalt deficiencies in cattle are costly, for the affected animals become weak and emaciated and eventually die. Florida is without doubt the most serious cobalt-deficient area in the U.S., but similar deficiencies of a lesser order have been observed in Michigan, Wisconsin, New Hampshire, North Carolina, and New York. Cattle in these affected areas should have access to a cobaltized mineral mixture, made by mixing 0.2 ounce of cobalt chloride, cobalt sulfate, cobalt oxide, or cobalt carbonate per 100 pounds of either (1) salt or (2) mineral mix.

Iodized salt should always be fed to cattle in iodine-deficient areas (such as the northwestern states and the Great Lakes region). This can be easily and cheaply accomplished by providing stabilized iodized salt containing 0.01 per cent potassium iodide (0.0076 per cent iodine). Under some conditions, organic iodine appears to be an effective aid in the prevention and treatment of foot rot and lumpy jaw (soft tissues) in cattle.

Copper is sometimes deficient in the soils of certain areas, notably in the state of Florida. In such areas, 0.25 to 0.5 per cent of copper sulfate or copper oxide should be incorporated in the salt or mineral mixture. In addition to being an area disease, copper deficiencies have occurred in beef calves kept on nurse cows for periods extending beyond normal weaning age.

Under usual feeding practices, magnesium deficiencies are unlikely. However, a deficiency of this mineral may occur when milk feeding of calves is prolonged without grain or hay, for milk is rather low in magnesium.

---

[4] *Research Achievement Sheet*, USDA. This work was cooperative between the Texas Agri. Expt. Sta. and the USDA.

Recent research indicates that molybdenum is an essential mineral nutrient, being an integral part of an important enzyme system of the body. Although the requirement is unknown, it must be extremely small because 10 to 20 ppm in forage results in toxic symptoms. Thus, it is not recommended that molybdenum additions be made to beef cattle rations under most conditions pending more information on requirements.

A deficiency of manganese exists in some areas of northwestern U.S., where it has been shown to be one cause of "crooked calves."

High zinc intake has been shown to increase the rate and efficiency of gains by feedlot cattle in certain areas. This may be due to the relationship between (1) phytic acid and zinc and (2) calcium and zinc, which creates a need for supplemental zinc.

Vitamin Needs

The absence of one or more vitamins in the ration may lead to a failure in growth or reproduction, or to characteristic disorders known as deficiency diseases. In severe cases, death may follow. Although the occasional deficiency symptoms are the most striking result of vitamin deficiencies, it must be emphasized that in practice mild deficiencies probably cause higher total economic losses than do severe deficiencies. It is relatively uncommon for a ration, or diet, to contain so little of a vitamin that obvious symptoms of a deficiency occur. When one such case does appear, it is reasonable to suppose that there must be several cases that are too mild to produce characteristic symptoms but which are sufficiently severe to lower the state of health and the efficiency of production.

It is also recognized that vitamin deficiencies may occur as a result of lack of availability of vitamins or because of the presence of anti-metabolites. Both are important concepts. For example, analyses show corn to be adequate in niacin. Yet, due either to an anti-metabolite or unavailability, there may be niacin deficiencies when corn is fed—deficiencies which can be remedied by niacin supplementation.

Vitamin A is the vitamin most likely to be deficient in beef cattle rations. True vitamin A is a chemically formed compound, which does not occur in plants. It is furnished in most beef cattle rations in the form of its precursor, carotene. However, plants are a variable, and often undependable, source of carotene due to oxidation. Also, cattle are relatively inefficient as convertors of carotene to vitamin A. For these reasons, vitamin A is added to beef cattle rations by many stockmen.

The vitamin A needs of beef cattle are being re-evaluated. Previously recommended allowances are not adequate for optimum nutrition under some conditions, and it is now apparent that borderline to severe deficiencies of vitamin A in cattle are widespread. Although the picture is not entirely clear, higher vitamin A requirements than were formerly considered necessary are being attributed to (1) use of heavier applications of nitrogen fertilization, resulting in higher levels of nitrates (nitrites) in plants; (2) lower rate of con-

Fig. 14-2. Same bull before (left) and after (right) vitamin A (carotene) feeding. At the left, the bull shows advanced stages of vitamin A deficiency—note the dejected appearance and rough hair coat. At the right, the bull shows a general improvement in appearance and male characteristics following vitamin A feeding. (Courtesy, USDA)

version of carotene to vitamin A by cattle than previously estimated; (3) increased feeding of high concentrate-low roughage rations, which contain less carotene; (4) subjecting cattle to greater stress (such as shipping, more forced production, high feedlot temperatures with increased summer feeding); (5) storage of yellow corn for longer periods of time, with consequent loss of carotene; (6) changed thyroid activity due to feed, iodine level, breeding, weather, etc., and consequent decrease in its conversion of carotene to vitamin A; (7) feeding out more cattle during the summer, especially after they have been wintered on silage; (8) feeding of younger cattle, which are fed for longer periods of time; and/or (9) a lack of vitamin E affecting utilization and protection of vitamin A.

A severe deficiency of vitamin A may result in a low conception rate; a small calf crop; many calves weak or stillborn, with some calves born blind or without eyeballs; more cows with retained afterbirth; low gains; greater susceptibility to calf scours; and more respiratory troubles. Severe vitamin A deficiency in bulls may result in decreased sexual activity and lowered semen quality. On dry range or when poor quality roughage is fed, therefore, it is recommended that 20,000 to 30,000 I.U. of vitamin A be added to the ration of brood cows and bulls. This amount can be furnished at a cost of about one-fourth cent per head per day.

Where feedlot cattle receive insufficient vitamin A, it takes longer to get them on feed and the rate and efficiency of gain are lowered. Accordingly, it is recommended (1) that heavily-stressed cattle coming into the feedlot be given high vitamin A, either orally (100,000 I.U. daily for first week) or by injection (250,000 I.U., or more, injected intramuscular or intraruminal), and (2) that 20,000 to 30,000 I.U. of vitamin A be added to the daily ration, with even higher levels (up to 50,000 I.U.) in hot weather.

Detection of vitamin A deficiency can be confirmed by carotene and vitamin A analysis of blood and liver tissues of cattle.

When vitamin A deficiency symptoms appear, it is recommended that there be added to the ration either (1) dehydrated alfalfa or grass or (2) a stabilized vitamin A product.

When exposed to enough direct sunlight, beef cattle normally acquire their vitamin D needs, for the ultraviolet rays in sunlight penetrate the skin and produce vitamin D from traces of sterols in the tissues. Also, cattle obtain vitamin D from sun-cured roughages. However, the addition of vitamin D to the ration is important where cattle, especially calves, are kept in a barn most of the day, where there is limited sunshine, where the calcium-phosphorus ratio leaves much to be desired, and/or where little or no sun-cured hay is fed. Vitamin D helps build strong bones and sturdy frames. It is usually added at a level of about one-seventh the level of added vitamin A.

Added vitamin E may be necessary under certain conditions because of its relationship to vitamin A utilization and the prevention of white muscle disease. Through rumen synthesis, under most conditions, it is most likely that all necessary quantities of the B vitamins and vitamin K are manufactured.

Water Needs

Water is cheap but essential. Beef cattle should have an abundant supply of it before them at all times. Mature cattle will consume an average of about 12

Fig. 14-3. Watering facilities on C. K. Ranch, Brookville, Kan. (Courtesy, American Hereford Association.)

gallons of water per head daily, with younger animals requiring proportionally less. In the northern latitudes, heaters should be provided to make the water available, but they are not needed to warm the water further.

FEEDS FOR BEEF CATTLE

The principal function of beef cattle is to harvest vast acreages of forages and, with or without supplementation, to convert these feeds into more nutritious and palatable products for human consumption.

Beef cattle feeding practices vary according to the relative availability of grasses and grains. Where grasses are abundant and grain is limited, as in the western range states, cattle are primarily grown out or finished on roughages. On the other hand, where grain is abundant, as in the Corn Belt states, finishing with concentrates is common.

Pastures for Beef Cattle

Good pasture is the cornerstone of successful beef cattle production. In fact, there has never been a great beef cattle country or area which did not produce good grass. It has also been said that a good farmer or rancher can be recognized by the character of his pastures and that good cattle graze good pastures. Thus, the three go hand in hand—good farmers, good pastures, and good cattle. The relationship and importance of cattle and pastures has been further extolled in an old Flemish proverb which says "No grass, no cattle; no cattle, no manure; no manure, no crops."

Approximately 49.4 per cent of the total land area of the United States is devoted to pasture and grazing lands. Much of this area, especially in the far West, can be utilized only by beef cattle or sheep. Although the term pasture usually suggests growing plants, it is correct to speak of pasturing stalk and stubble fields. In fact, in the broad sense, pastures include all crops that are harvested directly by animals.

The type of pasture, as well as its carrying capacity and seasonable use, varies according to topography, soil, and climate. There is hardly any limit to the number of plants that are utilized as beef cattle pastures throughout the United States. In general, regardless of species or mixtures, pastures may be classified as permanent, rotation, or temporary and supplemental. As the name indicates, permanent pastures are those which, with proper care, last for many years. They are most commonly found on land that cannot be profitably used for cultivated crops, mainly because of topography, moisture, or fertility. Rotation pastures are of diverse character but include all crops used as pastures as a part of established crop rotations, generally two to seven years before plowing. Among temporary and supplemental pastures are such crops as Sudan grass or millet, which are seeded for the purpose of providing supplemental grazing during the season when the regular permanent or rotation pastures are relatively unproductive. Because of the hundreds of species of grasses and legumes that are used as beef cattle pastures, each with its own best adaptation, no attempt is made to discuss the respective virtues of each variety. Instead, it is recommended that the farmer or rancher seek the advice of his local county agricultural agent or write to his state agricultural college.

No method of harvesting has yet been devised that is as cheap as that which can be accomplished through grazing by animals. Accordingly, successful beef cattle management necessitates as nearly year-round grazing as possible. In the northern latitudes of the United States, the grazing season is usually of about six months' duration, whereas in the deep South year-long grazing is approached. In many range areas of the West, the breeding herds get prac-

Fig. 14-4. Shorthorn cattle on pasture. (Courtesy, American Shorthorn Association)

tically all their feed the year round from the range forage, being given supplemental feed only if the grass or browse is buried deep in snow.

In some instances, cattle on pasture fail to make the proper growth or gain in condition because the soil is seriously deficient in fertility or the pasture has not been well managed. In such instances, striking improvement will result from proper fertilization and management.

Hays and Other Dry Roughages for Beef Cattle

Hay is the most important harvested roughage fed to beef cattle, although many other dry roughages can be and are utilized.

The dry roughages are all high in fiber and therefore lower than concentrates in total digestible nutrients. Hay averages about 28 per cent fiber and straw approximately 38 per cent, whereas such concentrates as corn and wheat contain only 2 to 3 per cent fiber. Fortunately, cattle are equipped to handle large quantities of roughages. In the first place, the paunch of a mature cow has a capacity of three to five bushels, thus providing ample storage for large quantities of less concentrated feeds. Secondly, the billions of microorganisms in the rumen attack the cellulose and pentosans of the fibrous roughages, such as hay, breaking them down into available and useful nutrients. In addition to providing nutrients at low cost, the roughages add needed bulk to cattle rations.

Roughages, like concentrates, may be classified as carbonaceous or nitrogenous, depending on their protein content. The principal dry carbonaceous roughages used by cattle include hay from the grasses, the straws and hays from cereal grains, and the stalks and leaves of corn and the grain sorghums. Cured nitrogenous roughages include the various legume hays such as alfalfa, the clover hays, peanut hay, soybean hay, cowpea hay, and velvet bean hay.

Although leguminous roughages are preferable, it must be remembered that weather conditions and soils often make it more practical to produce the non-legumes. Also, in many areas, such feeds as dry grass cured on stalks, cereal straws, corncobs, and cottonseed hulls are abundantly available and cheap. Under such conditions, these feeds had best be used as part of the ration for wintering beef cows, for wintering stockers that are more than one year of age, or for finishing beef cattle.

In comparison with good quality legume hays, the carbonaceous roughages are lower in protein content and in quality of proteins, lower in calcium, and generally deficient in carotene (provitamin A). Thus, where nonlegume roughages are used for extended periods, these nutritive deficiencies should receive consideration. This is especially important with the gestating-lactating cow or the young, growing calf. For these reasons, where dry and bleached pastures are grazed for an extended period of time or when there is an unusually long winter, it is important that at least a part of the roughage be a legume, either silage or hay. It is also more necessary that careful consideration be given to providing suitable protein and mineral supplements.

Silages and Roots for Beef Cattle

Silage is an important adjunct to pastures in beef cattle production, it being possible to use a combination of the two forages in furnishing green, succulent feeds on a year-round basis. Extensive use of silage for beef cattle only dates back to about 1910. Prior to that time, it was generally thought of as a feed for dairy cows. Even today, only a relatively small percentage of the beef cattle of the United States are fed silage.

Where silage has been used, it has proved very popular. Some of the more important reasons advanced in favor of silage are as follows:

1. On most beef cattle producing farms, silage is the cheapest form in which a good succulent winter feed can be provided.

2. It is the cheapest form in which the whole stalk of an acre of corn or sorghum can be processed and stored.

3. Good silage can be made during times of rainy weather when it would be impossible to cure hay or fodder properly.

4. It helps to control weeds, which are often spread through hay or fodder.

5. Grass silage is a better source of vitamins, especially carotene and perhaps some of the unknown factors, than dried forages.

6. There is no danger of fire loss to silage.

7. Silage is a very palatable feed and a mild laxative.

8. Converting the crop into silage clears the land earlier than would otherwise be possible.

9. Silage makes for less waste, the entire plant being eaten with relish.

10. The removal of corn stalks, as is required in making silage, is one of the best methods of controlling the European corn borer.

11. Silage increases the number of animals that can be fed from the produce of a given area of land.

Corn was first and still remains the principal crop used in the making of silage, but many other crops are ensiled in various sections of the country. The sorghums are the leading ensilage crop in the Southwest, sunflowers are ensiled in the Northwest, and grasses and legumes are the leading ensilage crops in the Northeast. In fact, most any green or succulent crop may be ensiled. In addition to those crops already mentioned, in different sections of the country to which they are adapted, the following feeds are ensiled: cereal grains, field peas, cowpeas, soybeans, potatoes, and numerous fruit and vegetable refuse products.

In feeding silage to cattle, it must be remembered that, because of its high moisture content, about 3 pounds of silage are generally considered equivalent to 1 pound of dry roughage of comparable quality. Fifty-five to 60 pounds of corn silage plus ½ to ¾ pounds of protein concentrate daily will carry a dry cow through the winter. The ration may be improved, however, by replacing one-third to one-half of the silage with an equivalent amount of a dry roughage, adding 1 pound of dry roughage for each 3 pounds of silage replaced.

Silage may also be successfully used for finishing steers. Two-year-old steers will eat 30 to 45 pounds a day at the beginning of the feeding period, the larger amounts being consumed when no hay is fed with it. Better results are secured, however, if hay is included in the ration. The amount of silage is gradually decreased as the concentrates are increased. At the end of the feeding period, the cattle should be getting around 6 to 8 pounds of silage and

Fig. 14-5. Silage conveyed mechanically to a bunk feeder from two upright silos. On many beef cattle establishments, silage is the cheapest form in which a good succulent winter feed can be provided. (Courtesy, National Silo Assn., Glenview, Ill.)

2 or 3 pounds of hay. Because of the more limited digestive capacity, the allowance of silage fed to calves or yearlings should be correspondingly less.

Usually, silage provides a much cheaper succulent feed for beef cattle than roots. For this reason, the use of roots for beef cattle is very limited, being confined almost entirely to the northern areas.

Concentrates for Beef Cattle

The concentrates include those feeds which are low in fiber and high in nutritive value. For purposes of convenience, concentrates are often further classified as (1) carbonaceous feeds and (2) nitrogenous feeds. The chief carbonaceous feeds used for beef cattle are the cereal grains and such processed feeds as hominy feed, beet pulp, and molasses. The leading nitrogenous or high protein feeds utilized by beef cattle in this country are cottonseed meal or cake, linseed meal or cake, peanut meal, soybean meal or cake, soybeans, peas, wheat bran, corn-gluten meal and feed, urea, and commercial feed supplements.

In general, the use of concentrates for beef cattle is limited to (1) the finishing of cattle, (2) the development of young stock, and (3) use as limited supplements in the wintering ration. Over most of the United States the cereal grains are the chief concentrates fed to beef cattle, these grains being combined, if necessary, with protein supplements to balance the ration. The choice of the particular grain or grains is usually determined by price and availability.

For best results, the feeder should correct the nutritive deficiencies of the cereal grains. All of these feeds are low in protein, low in calcium, and lacking in vitamin D. All except yellow corn are also deficient in carotene. Regardless of whether the cereal grains are fed to growing, breeding, or finishing animals, their nutritive deficiencies can be corrected in a very effective and practical way by either adding (1) a good quality of legume hay to the ration or (2) a protein concentrate plus suitable minerals.

It is now known that a considerable portion of the protein consumed by cattle may be built into new nitrogenous compounds in the body of the microorganisms in the paunch, which in turn are digested and utilized by the cattle. Consequently, the use of more expensive and complete protein supplements of animal origin is not necessary in feeding cattle. But even the protein concentrates of plant origin are usually more expensive than home-grown legume hays as a source of proteins. Moreover, they lack the calcium and vitamins of the latter.

Where home-grown legume hays are not available, the selection of a protein concentrate should be determined largely by price and availability. Because protein feeds are usually higher in price than carbonaceous feeds, normally one should include in the ration only sufficient protein concentrates to balance the ration. Naturally, the amount will vary, especially according to the age of the animals and the kind and amounts of other feeds available.

SELF-FEEDING SALT-FEED MIXTURES
TO RANGE CATTLE[5]

In this country the practice of self-feeding a mixture of salt and protein supplement appears to have originated with range sheepmen in Texas, beginning about 1934. These ingenious operators devised the method to alleviate plant poisoning in sheep. Since then, the practice has become widespread among cattlemen, and to a lesser extent among sheepmen, receiving its greatest impetus with the labor shortage during World War II.

Early reports of cattlemen and sheepmen self-feeding controlled amounts of protein supplement on the range by regulating the amount of salt mixed with the meal were often dismissed as incredible, if not just a lazy man's way of supplemental feeding on the range. Some ranchers and scientists were skeptical, fearing salt poisoning and other hazards. Nevertheless, the practice grew in popularity, even after the war-time labor shortage was over. Today, more salt-feed mixtures are being self-fed than ever before; approximately 30 per cent of the range cattlemen follow this practice.

The proportion of salt to feed varies anywhere from 5 to 40 per cent (with 30 to 33⅓ per cent salt content being most common), the amount depending on the feed intake desired.

Fig. 14-6. The practice of self-feeding mixtures appears to be well adapted to inaccessible and rough areas, where daily feeding is difficult. In no case, however, should it be an excuse to accord neglect to animals, for herds and flocks need to be checked often. (Drawing by R. F. Johnson)

---

[5] Additional facts and instructions relative to self-feeding salt-feed mixtures to cattle are presented in *Beef Cattle Science*, a book by the same author and publisher as *Animal Science*.

Feed Additives

Most cattlemen are familiar with, or have used, one or more of the hormones, antibiotics, or other accessory ration ingredients. While the results have been variable, there is general agreement (1) that, when properly used and under most conditions, they will increase both rate and efficiency of gain at a profit to the feeder, and (2) that they are here to stay. It is beyond the scope of this book, however, to present details pertaining to each of the many feed additives.[6]

FEEDING THE HERD BULLS

The feeding program for the herd bull should be such as to keep him in a thrifty, vigorous condition at all times. He should neither be overfitted nor in a thin, run-down condition. In season, the nutritive requirements for the mature herd bull can usually be met through good pastures. With the young bull, during the breeding season or winter months, adequate grain and roughage should be provided. Usually, the bull is kept separate from the cow herd except during the breeding season.

FEEDING THE BEEF BREEDING COWS

Heavy grain feeding is uneconomical and unnecessary for the beef breeding herd. The nutrient requirements should merely be adequate to provide for maintenance, growth (if the animals are immature), and reproduction. Fortunately, these requirements can largely be met through the feeding of cheap roughages.

Feeding the Dry and Pregnant Cows

Breeding cows should be permitted to get neither overfat nor in a thin, run-down condition. The best calf crop is secured from cows that are kept in vigorous breeding condition. Usually, the pregnant cow should gain in weight sufficient to account for the growth of the fetus (60 to 90 pounds). In addition, she should slightly increase her body weight to carry her through the suckling period. In total, they should gain 100 to 150 pounds during the pregnancy period. Most of the feed of brood cows should consist of pasturage and other home-grown roughages such as silage or root crops and hay.

Except during the winter months, there is no finer place for breeding cows than the run of a pasture or range. Aside from supplying the necessary nutrients at low cost, this system provides much valuable exercise. Should the pasture become very short—because of droughts, deep snow, or over-grazing— a supplemental feed of silage, dry forage crops, or concentrates should be provided.

---

[6]For further discussion of this subject, the reader is referred to *The Stockman's Handbook*, a book by the same author and publisher as *Animal Science*.

Fig. 14-7. Wyoming Herefords on snow-covered range being fed hay from a horse-drawn wagon. (Courtesy, E. G. Reed, Union Pacific Railroad)

The winter feeding period is the most expensive, necessitating good management in order to hold down the cost. The cheaper home-grown roughages should constitute the bulk of the winter ration for dry or pregnant cows. Most of the grain and the higher class roughages then may be used by other classes of livestock. A practical ration may consist of silage or root crops and dry roughages (legume or grass hays) combined with a small quantity of protein-rich concentrates (such as linseed meal or cottonseed meal). With the use of a leguminous roughage, the protein-rich concentrate may be omitted. Dusty or moldy feed and frozen silage should be avoided in feeding all cattle but especially in the case of the pregnant cow, for such feed may produce complications and possible abortion. Feeding in the fall should not be delayed so long that the cows begin to lose weight. Furthermore, the herd should be fed in the spring until the grass has attained sufficient growth and substance.

Proper developing of the fetus requires adequate minerals. Although the mineral requirements of pregnant cows are much the same everywhere, it is recognized that age makes a difference. Additionally, there are area and feed differences. Thus, the informed cattleman will supply the specific minerals that are deficient in the ration, and in the quantities necessary. Excesses and mineral imbalances will be avoided.

Feeding at Calving Time

Proper feeding at calving time is very important. If the calves are dropped out on a pasture or range where both forage and water are reasonably accessible, cows will satisfactorily regulate their own needs. On the other hand, when inclement weather or other conditions make it necessary to confine the cow at calving time, the skill and good judgment of the caretaker become a matter of importance. Under such unnatural conditions of confinement, the cow may be watered at frequent intervals immediately before and after calving, but in no case should she be allowed to gorge. It is also a good plan to take some of the chill off the water in the wintertime. It is considered good practice to feed lightly and with laxative feeds during this period. A satisfactory ration at calving time may consist of a mixture of bran and oats, together with a generous allowance of hay. The quantity of feed given should be governed by the milk flow, the condition of the udder, the demands of the calf, and the appetite and condition of the cow.

Feeding the Lactating Cows

Up until weaning time, at approximately six months of age, the growth of the calf is chiefly determined by the amount of milk available from its dam. The principal part of the calf's ration, therefore, may be cheaply and safely provided by giving its mother the proper feed for the production of milk. In season, green, succulent pastures afford the most effective and practical way in which to stimulate lactation. When pastures are scanty or during the winter months, grain and protein supplement feeding of both the dam and the calf may be essential.

Dual-purpose cows that are producing market milk as well as calves should receive feeds nearly identical to those provided for dairy cows in the same area. Generally speaking, they should be fed 1 pound of concentrates for every 3 to 4

Fig. 14-8. Hereford cow and calf on pasture at C. K. Ranch, Brookville, Kan. (Courtesy, American Hereford Association)

pounds of milk produced, the exact amount depending upon the fat content of the milk.

FEEDING GRAIN TO SUCKLING CALVES

The vast majority of calves are raised on their mother's milk plus whatever pasture or other feed they share with their dams. If calves are to be marketed at weaning time or soon thereafter, if they are to be finished as baby beeves, or if they are to be sold as purebred stock, liberal grain feeding should be started at the earliest possible age. Calves handled in this manner will have a greater selling weight and more finish when they are marketed. Even when calves are not to be marketed at an early age—when finished over a longer feeding period or when carried as stockers—they should be taught to eat grain and hay so that the transition during weaning will not result in loss of flesh. Likewise, calves from dual-purpose cows from which market milk is to be produced should be taught to eat supplemental feeds within a few weeks after birth. Calves may be fed grain in a creep in the pasture, or they may be kept and fed separate from their mothers and allowed to nurse twice daily. Since the latter practice involves more labor, creep feeding is usually resorted to for feeding calves on pasture.

Creep Feeding Calves

A creep is an enclosure for feeding purposes made accessible to the calves but through which the cows cannot pass. This allows for the feeding of the calves but not the dams. For best use, the creep should be built at a spot where the herd is inclined to loiter. The ideal location is on high ground, well drained,

Fig. 14-9. A calf creep in use on the Malone Polled Hereford Ranch, Meridian, Mississippi. This arrangement allows for the grain feeding of the calves but not the dams. (Courtesy, National Cottonseed Products Association, Inc.)

in the shade, and near the place of watering. Keeping the salt supply nearby will be helpful in holding the cow herd near the creep.

It is important that calves be started on feed very carefully. At first only a small amount of feed should be placed in the troughs each day, any surplus feed being removed and given to the cows. In this manner, the feed will be kept clean and fresh, and the calves will not be consuming any moldy or sour feed. When calves are on luxuriant pasture and their mothers are milking well, difficulty may be experienced in getting them to eat.

In experiments at Sni-A-Bar Farms comparing creep-fed calves with calves allowed to nurse the cows without grain, it was found that Shorthorn calves fed $8.97 worth of grain in a creep on pasture during the nursing period, averaged 100 pounds heavier at weaning time than similar calves allowed to nurse the cows without grain. In addition, these creep-fed calves were worth $2.00 per hundred pounds or $17.88 per head more than the calves that received no grain.[7]

FEEDING STOCKERS

Stockers are young heifer replacements or steers and heifers that are intended for market and which are being fed and cared for in such manner that growth rather than finishing may be realized. Because of the very nature of the operation, the successful feeding of stockers requires the maximum of economy consistent with normal growth and development. This necessitates cheap feed—either pasture or range grazing or such cheap harvested roughages as hay, straw, fodder, and silage. In general, the winter feeds for stockers consist of the less desirable and less marketable roughages.

The feed consumption of stockers will vary somewhat with the quality of the roughage available, the age of the cattle, and the rate of gain desired. Usually, the daily gains should range from ¾ to 2 pounds. If a young, rapidly-growing stocker calf is not gaining at least ¾ of a pound daily, he may lose too much in condition.

FEEDING FINISHING CATTLE

The finishing of cattle is what the term implies, the laying on of fat. The ultimate aim of the finishing process is to produce meat that will best answer the requirements and desires of the consumer. This is accomplished through an improvement in the flavor, tenderness, and quality of the lean meat which results from marbling. Also, fat adds to the digestibility and nutritive value of the product.

In a general way, there are two methods of finishing cattle for market: (1) dry-lot finishing and (2) pasture finishing. Prior to 1900, the majority of

[7] Experiments conducted by the USDA and the Missouri Expt. Sta. in cooperation with Sni-A-Bar Farms of Grain Valley, Missouri.

slaughter cattle sent to the market were four- to six-year-old steers that had been finished primarily on grass. Even today, the utilization of pastures continues to play an important part in all types of cattle-feeding operations.

Dry-lot Finishing

As implied, dry-lot finishing refers to finishing cattle in the dry lot. Such operations vary all the way from small, mostly hand labor, barnyard enterprises— usually conducted during the winter months for the purpose of marketing home-grown feeds and obtaining the manure—to large and highly mechanized year-round business enterprises that grow little or none of the feed that is utilized. Many of the latter operations custom feed.

Cattle finishing has greatly expanded in recent years. Since 1930, it has increased from 3 million to 11.3 million head (1967). The primary reasons and transitions back of this increase are:

1. Increased human population, from 122 million in 1930 to 200 million in 1968.

2. Increased per capita beef consumption, from about 53 pounds in the 1930's to 100 pounds in the 1960's.

3. Increased per cent of consumer's income spent for beef, from $2\frac{1}{4}$ per cent in the 1930's to $2\frac{2}{3}$ per cent in the 1960's.

4. Improved cattle feeding methods and mechanization.

5. Shorter feeding periods, and a tendency to feed to Good and Choice grades, rather than Prime.

6. Increased cattle feeding in the West, where six to seven times more cattle are now being fed than in the 1930's.

For the inexperienced feeder or the "in-and-outer," this type of production is surrounded by many hazards. When feeders have the opinion that profits are due largely to clever buying and selling, the enterprise is often a gamble. However, for the man who follows cattle feeding year after year, and who practices skillful feeding and management, this system will give good returns over a period of years.

In dry-lot feeding, the selection of the roughage varies from area to area. Among the most common roughages used in finishing rations are: legume hays, silages, grass-legume mixed or grass hays, various stovers and fodders, corn-cobs, and cottonseed hulls. Where good legume hays are home-grown or are available at a reasonable cost, they make a very satisfactory forage, supplying the necessary proteins, calcium, and vitamin A for the dry-lot ration. The maximum use of silage can best be obtained early in the finishing period or with more mature steers that possess a larger digestive capacity. Whenever either a nonlegume dry forage or silage is used in finishing steers, a protein supplement should be added to the ration.

Generally speaking, the choice of a protein supplement should be determined by the comparative prices of a pound of protein in the available supplements. The leading protein supplements for finishing cattle are linseed meal, cottonseed meal, and soybean meal. Additionally, a considerable quantity of urea

Fig. 14-10. Feeding dry-lot finishing cattle by means of a mechanical feeder. (Courtesy, Massey-Ferguson)

is fed to finishing cattle. Where a good quality legume roughage is used, it may not be necessary to add a protein supplement to the ration of finishing cattle or even to that of calves. When nonlegume roughages are used, however, a protein supplement should be added to the ration—usually somewhere between ½ to 1½ pounds of supplement per head daily—the exact amount depending upon the kind of roughage and grain and the age of the cattle. Naturally, calves have a higher protein requirement. As protein concentrates are usually expensive, it is not economical to add more than is required to balance the ration.

Although corn is by far the most common grain used in finishing cattle, such cereal grains as barley, rye, oats, and wheat are used in many sections of the northern and Pacific Coast states. In the Southwest, the grain sorghums predominate, both as grain and silage. In the sugar-beet areas, beet pulp (dry or wet), beet tops, and molasses are used extensively; whereas in the Cotton Belt, cottonseed meal and hulls make up the standard cattle-finishing ration. Rye may be used if limited to not more than one-third of the grain ration. Because of the bulk, oats and dried beet pulp should not make up more than one-half of the ration and preferably not more than one-third. Wheat and oats are frequently too expensive to include in the cattle-finishing ration.

Barley seems to cause more bloat than most concentrates. For this reason, it is well that the other grains and the roughages be carefully selected when it seems desirable to include considerable barley in the ration. A mixture of barley, dried beet pulp, and oats is commonly used in the West. It is best not to use a straight legume hay along with a grain ration high in barley, because of bloat.

Fig. 14-11. Dry-lot steers eating field cured dry beet tops. (Courtesy, The Great Western Sugar Co., Denver)

Beet by-products are notoriously low in phosphorus. For best results, therefore, a suitable phosphorus mineral supplement should be provided where these feeds are used extensively.

Cottonseed meal and hulls are very deficient in vitamin A. When cattle are fed heavily on these products, they may develop serious deficiency symptoms, formerly known as cottonseed meal poisoning. This condition may be averted by adding stabilized vitamin A or a good source of carotene—such as green, leafy alfalfa hay or yellow corn—to rations high in cottonseed by-products.

In the final analysis, the choice of the concentrate ration should be determined largely by the availability and price of feeds. The experienced Corn Belt cattle feeder generally figures that it will take about 40 bushels of corn (or an equivalent amount of another grain) and one-third ton of good quality legume hay to finish a beef steer to Choice grade regardless of its age. Younger animals require a longer time in which to consume this feed and reach approximately the same degree of finish. When silage is used, it may be assumed that about 3 pounds of silage will replace 1 pound of hay.

Cattle finishing in the dry lot should have free access to salt. Other minerals should also be incorporated in the ration and/or cattle should have free access to a suitable mineral mixture.

Vitamin A (and in some cases vitamin D) should be added to feedlot rations. A common guideline on the level of vitamin A for feedlot cattle is to use 3,000 I.U. per 100 pounds body weight, or 1,000 I.U. for each pound of total feed. One million units of vitamin A cost less than 10 cents.

When vitamin D is needed and added to the ration, it is recommended that 4,000 to 6,000 I.U. be given per head per day. This is approximately one-sixth to one-seventh the recommended level of vitamin A. Of course, vitamin D is produced in the skin of animals that are exposed to direct sunlight; but during cloudy, winter weather, or when cattle are confined, it should be added to the ration.

Fig. 14-12. Hereford steers on bromegrass pasture near Lincoln, Neb. (Courtesy, C. B. & Q. Railroad Co.)

Normally, the rumen organisms synthesize adequate B vitamins and vitamin K, and nothing is gained by adding these to feedlot rations of healthy cattle. Likewise, no benefit has been reported from supplemental vitamin E or vitamin C.

Pasture Finishing

Where grazing land is extensive and not too high in price, pastures no doubt will continue to be utilized in finishing cattle for market. Cattle finished on grass may not make quite such rapid gains or reach the same high degree or quality of finish as cattle finished on grain. Moreover, grass-finished cattle do not command the values of grain-finished cattle. Yet when grass is plentiful and cheap, one can usually afford to sacrifice in gain, finish, and selling price because of the much lower cost of production.

In farming districts where there is much rough wasteland unsuited to tillage and where high grain prices prevail (because of shipment from distant areas), the finishing of cattle on grass (with or without supplements) is common, for pastures are then utilized to the maximum. On the other hand, in districts where there is but little untillable land, where more feed can be produced on an acre of tilled crops than on an acre of pasture, or where land is high in price, dry-lot finishing is more common. Even in the so-called dairy sections of the United States, there are many cheap, isolated pasture areas that are not now being effectively utilized for dairy production or other enterprises but which seem admirably adapted to a system of beef production in which pastures may be utilized to the maximum.

Generally speaking, no cheaper method of harvesting forage crops has been devised than is afforded by harvesting directly by grazing animals. Moreover, even most seeded pastures last several years; thus seeding costs may be distributed over the entire period. Naturally the cash income to be derived from pastures will vary from year to year and from place to place depending upon such factors as market price levels, class of animals, soil, season, and the use of adapted varieties.

REDUCING BLOAT ON PASTURES

There is always a possibility that bloat will occur when appreciable amounts of legumes are grazed. Even so, the high productivity of grass-legume mixtures usually makes their use profitable—especially for commercial cattle—provided that proper precautions are taken to minimize the danger from bloat.

The following practices will be helpful in reducing the bloat hazard:

1. In order to prevent the animals from filling up too rapidly on the green material, give a full feed of hay or other dry roughage before the animals are turned to legume pastures.

2. If possible, after the animals are once turned to pasture, they should be left there continuously. If they must be removed overnight or for longer periods, they should be filled with dry roughage before being returned to the pasture.

3. Mixtures that contain approximately half grasses and half legumes should be used.

4. Water and salt should be conveniently accessible at all times.

5. The animals should not be allowed to become empty when they congregate in a dry lot for shade or insect protection and then be allowed to gorge themselves suddenly on the green forage.

6. Many practical cattlemen feel that the bloat hazard is reduced by mowing alternate strips through the pasture, thus allowing the animals to consume the dry forage along with the pasture. Others keep in the pasture a rack well filled with dry hay or straw.

7. Because of the many serrations on the leaves, Sudan hay appears especially effective in preventing bloat when fed to cattle on legume pastures.

8. Consider the use of poloxalene, a non-ionic surfactant, developed through research at Kansas State University, for the control of legume bloat in cattle. One such product is manufactured by Smith Kline & French Laboratories and marketed under the trade name Bloat Guard. Always use such products according to the manufacturer's directions. Bloat Guard is a granular product containing 53 per cent active ingredient (poloxalene). It is cleared by the Food and Drug Administration for use as a top dressing on feed; it is fed at the rate of ⅔ ounce daily for animals under 1,000 pounds; and it costs 5 to 10 cents per head per day.

The Feeder's Margin

By margin is meant the difference between the cost per hundredweight of the feeder animals and the selling price per hundredweight of the same animal when finished. Gains made in the feedlot are expensive. They generally cost more per pound to produce than the selling price per pound obtained at marketing time. In order to cover this loss and secure a profit on the operations, the cattle must sell at a higher price per pound than was paid for them. This spread in price is commonly referred to as the necessary margin.

FACTORS DETERMINING THE NECESSARY MARGIN

The cost of feed and the cost of cattle are the two major capital expenses in any cattle feeding venture. Likewise, these same two factors are the most important ones in determining profits and losses. How the cost of feed and the cost of cattle influence the necessary margin for the feeder to break even on his operations is indicated in Figure 14-13.

Generally speaking, about 80 per cent of the cost of finishing cattle (exclusive of the initial purchase price for animals) is for feed. Another 6 per cent is usually absorbed by interest on the purchase price of the cattle. Then labor costs, taxes, purchasing and marketing charges, shrinkage losses, and death losses (about 2 per cent of the animals) make up most of the remaining expenses. Of course, the value of the manure compensates for part of these costs.

In summary form, the factors that determine the necessary margin are as follows:

1. The better the grade of cattle and the younger the animals, the smaller the necessary margin. This is so because better grades and younger cattle generally bring a higher selling price, and, therefore, a higher price is obtained on their gains made in the feedlot. This point is well illustrated in Figure 14-13.

2. The higher the cost of feed, the greater the necessary margin. This is so because of the high cost of gains as compared to their selling price. This point is also well illustrated in Figure 14-13.

3. The heavier the initial weight of the cattle, the smaller the necessary margin, provided the efficiency of feed utilization of the two groups is approximatly the same. Thus, a $2.00 margin on an initial weight of 800 pounds totals $16.00 per head, while a $2.00 margin on an initial weight of 400 pounds totals only $8.00 per head.

4. The longer the feeding period and the greater the gains necessary to get the cattle in a finished condition, the greater the margin. This is also due to the fact that gains made in the feedlot are expensive, generally costing more to produce than can be realized in selling on the market.

Considering all these factors collectively, it may be understood why less margin is necessary in the case of heavy, mature steers carrying considerable flesh when purchased as compared with thin, lightweight yearlings. Calves usually require the smallest margin of all because of their efficiency of gains and their higher value per hundredweight.

The computations upon which Figure 14-13 is based may best be illustrated by the following example, keeping in mind that a reading of the vertical price scale at the point of intersection between a given cost line for cattle and a given cost line for feed indicates the necessary margin required to break even on the

BREAK-EVEN MARGINS

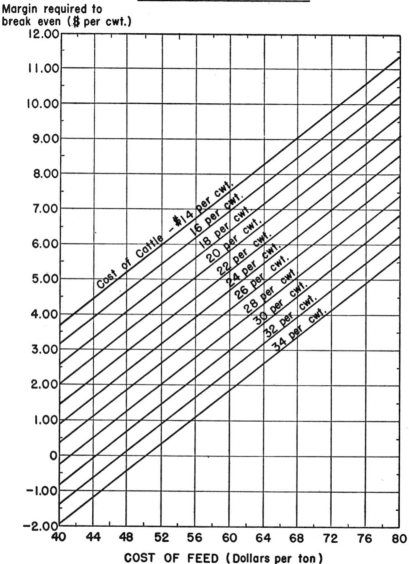

Fig. 14-13. This chart indicates the relation of the cost of feed and the cost of feeder cattle to the necessary margin required to break even on the feeding operation. It is based upon a 700-pound feeder steer fed to a slaughter weight of 1,000 pounds in 150 days, with an average weight of 850 pounds during the feeding period and an average daily feed consumption of 3 pounds per cwt. The costs include interest at 6% on the purchase price of cattle (for 5 months) but no other production costs. A reading of the vertical scale at the point of intersection between a given cost line for cattle and a given cost line for feed indicates the necessary margin required to break even on the feeding operations.

feeding operation under the conditions previously indicated. *If feeder cattle cost $20.00 per cwt. and feed costs $50.00 per ton, what margin is necessary in order to break even?* The computations required to answer this question are given below (but of course, the answer may be obtained directly from the left side of the chart, at the point of intersection between the cost lines for cattle and feed).

Step by step, the detailed computations are as follows:

1. Cost of each steer (700 lbs. @ $20. per cwt.)...= $140.00
2. Cost of feed:
   The amount of feed consumed is calculated by multiplying the average weight of the steer during the feeding period (850 lbs.) by the daily feed consumption (3 lbs. per cwt.) which is then multiplied by the length of the feeding period (150 days). (In this case 1.9125 tons @ $50. per ton).......=   95.625
3. Interest (6% on $140. for 150 days)...=   3.50
                                                                                                                              _____
4.   Total cost.............................. $239.125
5. Thus, a sale price of $23.91 per cwt., or a margin of $3.91 per cwt., is required in order to break even (1,000 lbs. at $23.91 per cwt.)................=   239.10

Finishing Cattle of the Various Market Grades

The most profitable grade of cattle to feed will generally be that kind of cattle in which there is the greatest spread of margin between their purchase price as feeders and their selling price as slaughter cattle. As can be readily understood, one cannot arrive at this decision by merely comparing the existing price between the various grades at the time of purchase. Rather, it is necessary to project the differences that will probably exist, based on past records, when the animals are finished and ready for market.

The length of the feeding period and the type of feed available should also receive consideration in determining the grade of cattle to feed. Thus, for a long feed and when a liberal allowance of grain is to be fed, only the better grades of feeders should be purchased. On the other hand, when a maximum quantity of coarse roughage is to be utilized and a short feed is planned, cattle of the medium or lower grades are most suitable.

Cattle of the lower grades should be selected with very special care in order to make certain that only thrifty animals are bought. Ordinarily, death losses are much higher among low-grade feeder cattle, especially when the low-grade animals are calves. The death loss in handling average or high-grade feeders seldom exceeds 1 per cent; whereas with "cull" or "dogie" cattle, it frequently is two or three times this amount. Many low-grade cattle are horned, and dehorning further increases the death risk—in addition to the added labor and shrinkage resulting therefrom.

No given set of rules is applicable under any and all conditions in arriving at the particular grade of cattle to feed, but the following factors should receive consideration.

1. The feeding of high-grade cattle is favored when:
   a. The feeder is more experienced.
   b. A long feed with a maximum of grain in the ration is planned.
   c. Conditions point to a wide spread in price between grades at marketing time.

2. The feeding of average or low-grade cattle is favored when:

   a. The feeder is less experienced.[8]

   b. A short feed with a maximum of roughage or cheap by-products is planned.

   c. Conditions point to a narrow spread in price between grades at marketing time.

3. In addition to the profit factors enumerated above, it should be pointed out that with well-bred cattle the following conditions prevail:

   a. Well-bred beef cattle possess greater capacity for consuming large quantities of feed than beef steers of a more common grade, especially during the latter part of the feeding period.

   b. The higher the grade of cattle, the higher the dressing percentage and the greater the proportionate development of the high-priced cuts.

   c. The higher the grade of cattle, the greater the opportunities for both profit and loss.

   d. There is a greater sense of pride and satisfaction in feeding well-bred cattle. To top the market with a load of Prime steers is frequently more gratifying and means more to the experienced and self-respecting feeder than any greater profits that might be derived from feeding low-grade cattle.

Certainly the producer who raises his own feeder cattle should always strive to breed high-grade cattle regardless of whether he finishes them out himself or sells them as feeders. On the other hand, the purchaser of feeder steers can well afford to appraise fully the situation prior to purchasing any particular grade.

The Value of Breeding and Type in Finishing Cattle

Although the supporting data is rather limited, it is fully realized that there is considerable difference between individual animals insofar as rate and economy of gain are concerned. It is to be emphasized that these differences are greater within breeds than between breeds.

In studies at the Wisconsin Experiment Station, feeding trials were conducted with purebred Angus, purebred Holsteins, and crossbred Angus-Holstein calves of approximately the same age. The Wisconsin investigators found that the particular Holsteins used produced slightly more rapid and economical gains than were obtained with the purebred Angus, with the crossbreds intermediate between the two. However, the beef-type animals had a higher dressing percentage and a more desirable quality of carcass, with a greater proportion of valuable cuts of meat. Thus, the animals of beef type and breeding brought a higher market price. The average selling price for the Angus steers was $13.00

---

[8] In general, the inexperienced feeder should stick to the middle kind and leave the extremes—the prime and the plain cattle—to the man with experience.

per cwt. in comparison with $12.16 for the crossbreds and $10.08 for the Holsteins.[9]

The Wisconsin studies would lend credence to the statement that the breeders should always strive to produce beef-type cattle of good breeding. On the other hand, where replacement calves are not needed in the dairy herd, it may often be advantageous to use a beef-type bull as a cow freshener—thus securing a calf which is more valuable either as a veal or as a potential feeder. There may, however, be sufficient spread in price between the grades to warrant that the purchaser of feeder steers shop about when considering the particular grade of cattle to choose.

Age as a Factor in Finishing Cattle

A generation ago the term feeder steer signified to both the rancher and the Corn Belt feeder a two-and-one-half to three-year-old animal weighing approximately 1,000 pounds. Today, feeder steers are referred to by ages as feeder calves, yearlings, and two-year-olds. This shift to younger cattle has been brought about primarily by the consumer demand for smaller and lighter cuts of meat.

The particular age of cattle to feed is one of the most important questions to be decided upon by every practical cattleman. The following factors should be considered in reaching an intelligent decision on this point:

1. **Rate of gain.**—When cattle are fed liberally from the time they are calves, the daily gains will reach their maximum the first year and decline with each succeeding year thereafter. On the other hand, when in comparable condition, thin but healthy two-year-old steers will make more rapid gains in the feedlot than yearlings, and likewise yearlings will make more rapid gains than calves.

2. **Economy of gain.**—Calves require less feed to produce 100 pounds of beef than do older cattle. This may be explained as follows:

   (a) The increase in body weight of older cattle is largely due to the deposition of high-energy fat, whereas the increase in body weight of young animals is due, in part at least, to the growth of muscles, bones, and vital organs. Thus, the body of a calf at birth usually consists of more than 70 per cent water, whereas the body of a fat two-year-old steer will only contain 45 per cent moisture. In the latter case, a considerable part of the water has been replaced by fat deposition.

   (b) Calves consume a larger proportion of feed in relation to their body weight than do older cattle.

   (c) Calves masticate and digest their feed more thoroughly than do older cattle. Despite the fact that calves require less feed per 100 pounds gain—because of the high-energy value of fat—older cattle store as much energy in their bodies for each 100 pounds of total digestible nutrients consumed as do younger animals.

---

[9] J. G. Fuller, Wis. Agr. Expt. Buls. Nos. 396, 405, and 410; see also Fuller, J. G., *Soc. Anim. Prod., Proc.* 1930.

3. **Flexibility in marketing.**—Calves will continue to make satisfactory gains at the end of the ordinary feeding period, whereas the efficiency of feed utilization decreases very sharply when mature steers are held past the time that they are finished. Therefore, under unfavorable market conditions, calves can be successfully held for a reasonable length of time, whereas prolonging the finishing period of older cattle is usually unprofitable.

4. **Length of feeding period.**—Calves require a somewhat longer feeding period than older cattle to reach comparable finish. In order to reach Choice condition, steer calves must be full fed from eight to nine months, yearlings five to six months, and two-year-olds only about four months. The longer finishing period required for calves is due to the fact that they are growing as well as finishing.

5. **Total gain required to finish.**—In general, calves must put on slightly more total gain in the feedlot than older animals in order to attain the same degree of finish. In terms of initial weight, calves practically double their weight in the feedlot, yearlings put on about 400 pounds weight, and two-year-olds about 300 pounds.

6. **Total feed consumed.**—The daily feed consumption of calves is considerably less than for older cattle, but as calves must be fed for a slightly longer feeding period, the total feed requirement for the entire finishing period is approximately the same for cattle of different ages.

7. **Experience of the feeder.**—Young cattle are bovine "babies." As such, they must be fed more expertly. Thus, the amateur feeder had best feed older cattle.

8. **Kind and quality of feed.**—Because calves are growing, it is necessary that they have more protein in the ration. Normally, protein supplements are higher in price than carbonaceous feeds, thus making for a more expensive ration. Also, because of the smaller digestive capacity, calves cannot utilize as much coarse roughage, pasture, or cheap by-product feeds as older cattle.

Calves also are more likely to develop peculiar eating habits than older cattle. They may reject coarse, stemmy roughages or moldy or damaged feeds that would be eaten readily by older cattle. Calves also require more elaborate preparation of the ration and attention to other small details designed to increase their appetite.

9. **Pigs following cattle.**—Because calves masticate and digest their feed more thoroughly than older cattle, the amount of pork secured from pigs following finishing cattle varies directly with the age of the cattle.

10. **Comparative costs and selling price.**—Calves usually cost more per 100 pounds as feeders than do older cattle. They also usually sell for a higher price per hundredweight as finished cattle.

11. **Dressing percentage and quality of beef.**—Older cattle have a slightly higher dressing percentage than calves or baby beef. Moreover, many consumers have a decided preference for the greater flavor of beef obtained from older animals.

From this discussion, it should be perfectly clear that there is no best age of cattle to feed under any and all conditions. Rather, each situation requires individual study and all factors must be weighed and balanced out.

Heifers Versus Steers

On the market, cattle are divided into five sex classes: steers, heifers, cows, bulls, and stags. The sex of feeder cattle is important to the producer from the standpoint of cost and selling price (or margin), the contemplated length of feeding period, quality of feeds available, and ease of handling. The consumer is conscious of sex differences in cattle and is of the impression that it affects the quality, finish, and conformation of the carcass.

Steers are by far the most important of any of the sex classes on the market, both from the standpoint of numbers and their availability throughout the year, whereas heifers are second.

The relative merits of steers versus heifers, both from the standpoint of feed-lot performance and the quality of carcass produced, has long been a controversial issue. Based on experiments[10] and practical observations, the following conclusions and deductions seem to be warranted relative to this question:

1. **Length of feeding period.**—Heifers mature earlier than steers and finish sooner, thus making for a shorter feeding period. In general, heifers may be ready for the market 30 to 40 days earlier than steers of the same age started on feed at the same time. Usually a short feed of 60 to 120 days is preferable with heifers.

2. **Market weight.**—The most attractive heifer carcasses are obtained from animals weighing 650 to 900 pounds on foot, showing good condition and finish but not so fat as to be patchy and wasty.

3. **Rate and economy of gain.**—Because of their slower rate of growth, the feedlot gains made by heifers are usually somewhat smaller and more costly than those made by steers of the same age. Steers generally gain about 0.3 pound more per head per day than heifers of similar age.

4. **Price.**—Because of existing prejudices, feeder heifers can be purchased at a lower price per pound than steers, but they also bring a lower price when marketed. Thus, the net return per head may or may not be greater with heifers.

5. **Carcass quality.**—In England there is no discrimination in price against well-finished heifers. In fact, the English argue that the grain of meat in heifer carcasses is finer and the quality superior. On the other hand, the hotels, clubs, and elite butcher shops in the United States hold a decided prejudice against heifer beef.

Carefully controlled experiments have now shown conclusively that when heifers are marketed at the proper weight and degree of finish, sex makes no

---

[10] Bull, Sleeter, F. C. Olson, and John H. Longwell, *Effect of Sex, Length of Feeding Period, and a Ration of Ear Corn Silage on the Quality of Baby Beef,* Ill. Agri. Expt. Sta. Bul. No. 355, 1930.

appreciable difference in the dressing percentage, in the retail value of the carcasses; or in the color, tenderness, and palatability of the meat.

6. **Ease of handling in the feedlot.**—Because of disturbances at heat periods, many feeders do not like to handle heifers in the feedlot.

7. **Flexibility in marketing.**—If the market is unfavorable, it is usually less advisable to carry heifers on feed for a longer period than planned because of (a) possible pregnancies and (b) the fact that animals become too patchy and wasty.

8. **Effect of pregnancy.**—Packer buyers have long insisted that they are justified in buying heifers at a lower price than steers of comparable quality and finish because: (a) most heifers are pregnant and have a lower dressing percentage, and (b) pregnant heifers yield less desirable carcasses. In realization that the packer will lower the price anyway, many feeders make it a regular practice to turn a bull with heifers about three to four months before the market period. Such feeders contend that the animals are then quieter and will make better feedlot gains.

In a carefully controlled experiment designed to ferret out the facts of this controversy, the Illinois Experiment Station[11] compared open and bred heifers in a five-month feeding period with the following pertinent results:

a. The bred heifers were quieter and easier to handle in the feedlot.
b. The bred heifers possessed keener appetites.
c. The young pregnant heifers grew less and put on more fat.
d. When kept at the same level of feed consumption, pregnancy had no appreciable effect on average daily gain.
e. Pregnancy did not affect dressing percentage. This was probably due to the higher finish and the lighter hides, heads, shanks, stomach, and smaller fill of the pregnant heifers. These factors were sufficient to overcome the weight of the three to four months fetus which averaged 30 pounds.
f. The carcasses of the bred heifers were noticeably better finished.
g. The flank, loin-end, and round were lighter in the bred than in the open heifers, but the other wholesale cuts were practically the same in each group.

The results of the Illinois experiment would indicate that the producer is entirely justified in breeding full-fed heifers three to four months prior to the time of marketing. It would also seem that packers are not justified in buying such bred heifers at a lower price because of any alleged lower dressing percentage or difference in carcass quality.

Spayed heifers may bring a slightly higher market price, but the difference is usually not sufficient to overcome the loss in weight, risk of operation, and the slower gains.

The trade in feeder cows and heifers assumes considerable volume only in

---

[11] Snapp, R. R. and Sleeter Bull, *Effect of Pregnancy on Quality of Beef*, Ill. Expt. Sta. Bul. No. 508, 1944.

the fall and early winter—at the close of the grazing season when the farmer or rancher is culling his herd and prior to the start of the wintering operations. When market conditions are favorable and an abundance of cheap roughage is available, cows may often be fed at a profit.

When there is considerable demand for cheap meats, the feeder may find it profitable to finish bulls and stags. Usually it is difficult to purchase such animals in large numbers. Here, as with the finishing of cows, the feeder should plan to utilize the maximum of cheap roughage.

Buildings and Equipment for Finishing Cattle

The equipment for feedlot cattle should be adequate and durable, but in no case should it be elaborate, expensive, or of such type as to contribute to high overhead or lack of operating capital.

Currently, there is much interest in confinement feeding and slotted floors for finishing cattle.

Confinement feeding refers to limited quarters of about 20 to 25 square feet per yearling animal; which is about one-eighth the space normally allotted to a yearling in an unsurfaced lot, or one-third that of a paved lot. The confinement may be with or without shelter; and the shelter may range all the way from an open shed to a completely enclosed building with air circulation, and temperature and humidity control.

Slotted floors are steel or concrete slats (wood may be used, but it is less durable) approximately 5 to 6 inches wide and spaced about 1½ to 1¾ inches apart.

Confinement feeding and slotted floors have been used in Iceland and Norway for many years. In these countries, it is not the purpose of the floors to save bedding, for they have never had bedding material. Rather, they claim that they make for more animal comfort, reduce labor, and increase stocking per farm. In recent years, the British have used confinement feeding and slotted floors in the production of their "barley beef"—young animals of dairy breeding finished at early ages. Also, the thrifty Scots have used confinement feeding.

In this country, interest in confinement feeding and slotted floors is prompted in an effort to (1) lessen mud, dust, odor, and fly problems; (2) cut down on bedding and facilitate manure management; (3) automate and lessen labor; and (4) increase gains and save on feed.

Every knowledgeable cattle feeder knows that winter mud is costly. Excess mud may (1) lower gains ¼ pound, or more, per head daily; (2) increase feed requirements by 75 pounds, or more, per 100 pounds gains; and (3) result in 5- to 30-pounds, or more, mud dock at marketing.

Unfortunately, there is a paucity of experimental work on which to make a final judgment on confinement feeding and slotted floors; and, too, such facilities are costly. Accordingly, unless the owner is (1) in a strong financial position or (2) able to charge off a good part of such costs against inquisitiveness or experimental, rather than rely on amortization through increased returns, he is admonished to wait and follow the results of experimental work now in progress. In the meantime, the following basic facilities will suffice for most cattle feedlots:

1. Well drained dirt lots, which, during wet weather, are mounded and bedded heavily with such materials as straw, corncobs, gin trash, sawdust, shavings, peanut hulls, or other absorbent material.

2. An open shed, or a suitable windbreak, for wintering calves in the colder areas.

3. Shades in areas subjected to very warm weather.

4. Concrete aprons and bunks.

5. Fences; scales; feed processing and storage facilities; water tanks; and facilities for restraining, sorting, loading, and handling constructed of conventional materials.

Excess Finishing

Excessive finishing is undesirable, both from the standpoint of the producer and the consumer. Experienced cattle feeders are fully aware of the fact that to carry finishing cattle to an unnecessarily high finish is usually prohibitive from a profit standpoint. This is true because the gains in weight then consist chiefly of fat and contain but little water. In addition, a very fat animal eats less heartily, with the result that a small proportion of the nutrients, over and above the maintenance requirement, is available for making body tissue.

Beef should carry ample finish to make the meat attractive, juicy, and well flavored; but any fat in excess of these requirements is usually trimmed off. Because of this situation, one of the real challenges to the beef cattle producer of the future is to produce animals which, from a genetic standpoint, are predisposed to produce marbling without excessive exterior fat.

Hogs Following Cattle

Cattle feeders who have a convenient source of feeder pigs, who are not "allergic" to keeping hogs, and whose cattle lots are fenced hog-tight, can add to their net income by having hogs follow cattle. The following hog-cattle ratio is recommended, using 75-to 150-pound pigs:

	If whole shelled corn is fed	If ground or rolled grain is fed
	(pig-steer ratio)	(pig-steer ratio)
Calves..................	1:3	1:5
Yearlings.............	1:2	1:4
Two-year-olds.......	1:1½	1:3

For every 50 bushels of whole corn fed to yearling cattle, approximately 50 pounds of pork will be produced. Allowing 20 cents for hogs, and subtracting $3.00 per pig for protein and other costs, that's $7.00 per pig.

Fig. 14-14. Hogs following cattle. Sometimes the only profit obtained is in the gains made by pigs following cattle. (Courtesy, American Feed Manufacturers)

Because pigs sometimes inflict injury on heifers (injuring the vulva when they are lying down), their use is generally limited to steers.

Sows may be used, but because of their size they may create problems by getting into the feed and water facilities.

Contract (or Custom) Feeding Cattle[12]

Contact feeding is not new. It increases in importance (1) during periods of financial stress, (2) when animals and feed are high in price, and (3) when feeders do not wish to take the risk of ownership. But these three factors alone do not explain the magnitude of today's contract feeding of cattle. Two additional factors generally accompany large contract feed yards and are primarily responsible for their expansion since World War II; namely, increased mechanization and know-how. Also, increased integration has made for more contract feeding.

The contract feeding of both cattle and lambs made rapid development after 1929, reaching a maximum during the severe drought of 1934. From this time to World War II, contract feeding declined with improved feed conditions on the western range, higher prices for feeder animals, and the availability of more credit to both the producer and the feeder through federal and private loan agencies.

In recent years (during and since World War II), some feeders have developed highly mechanized and most efficient plants, with capacities ranging up to 50,000, or more, cattle at one time. Through contract feeding, they sell the use of their facilities and their services to cattle owners, usually with profit to each party.

---

[12] The common types of contracts are discussed in *Beef Cattle Science*, a book by the same author and publisher as *Animal Science*.

The experience of owners and feeders with contract feeding and the difficulties encountered suggest opportunities for improvement in methods and practices along the following three principal lines, which, if carried out, would make for greater success in the handling of feeder cattle under contract:

1. Use of contracts that are fair to both owner and feeders.
2. Utilization of proper feeding methods and rations.
3. Employment of experienced and efficient help.

FEED ALLOWANCE AND SOME SUGGESTED RATIONS FOR BEEF CATTLE[13]

Some general rules of feeding may be given, but it must be remembered that "the eye of the master fattens his cattle." Nevertheless, the beginner may well profit from the experience of successful feeders. It is with this hope that the following general rules for feeding cattle are presented.

Table 14-1 is a Handy Beef Cattle Feeding Guide for different classes and ages of cattle. Also, some fitting rations follow. All of these are merely intended as general guides. Variations can and should be made in the rations used. The feeder should give consideration to (1) the supply of home-grown feeds, (2) the availability and price of purchased feeds, (3) the class and age of cattle, (4) the health and condition of the animals, and (5) the length of the grazing season.

In using Table 14-1 as a guide, it is to be recognized that feeds of similar nutritive properties can and should be interchanged as price relationships warrant. Thus, (1) the cereal grains may consist of corn, barley, wheat, oats, and/or sorghum; (2) the protein supplement may consist of soybean, cottonseed, peanut, and/or linseed meal or cake; (3) the roughage may include many varieties of hays and silages; and (4) a vast array of by-product feeds may be utilized.

Fitting Rations for Cattle[14]

All animals intended for show purposes, including both breeding animals and steers, must be placed in proper condition. To accomplish this, a suitable ration must be selected and the animal or animals must be fed with care over a sufficiently long period. The rations listed are ones that have been used by successful showmen. They are higher in protein content than rations used in commercial-finishing operations, but most experienced herdsmen feel that by such means they get more bloom. In general, when show animals are being forced fed on any one of these concentrate mixtures, experienced herdsmen prefer to feed a grass hay or a grass-legume mixed hay to a straight legume, because of the laxative effect and possible bloat hazard of the latter.

---

[13] Where possible, these rations were computed from the requirements as reported by the National Research Council and adapted by the author.

[14] Further information on selecting, fitting, and showing beef cattle is presented in *Beef Cattle Science*, a book by the same author and publisher as *Animal Science*.

TABLE 14—1

SUGGESTED RATIONS With all rations and for all classes and ages of cattle, provide free access in separate containers to (1) salt (iodized salt in iodine-deficient areas) and (2) a suitable mineral mixture.	Wintering mature beef breeding cows (av. wt. 1,100 lbs.) (per day)		Wintering replacement heifers (weighing 400 to 500 lbs. start of wintering). (per day)	
	(lbs.)	(kg)	(lbs.)	(kg)
1. Legume hay or grass-legume mixed hay, good quality	18-26	8-12	12-18[3]	5-8
Grain	....		2-4	1-2
Protein supplement	....	....	....	......
2. Grass hay or other nonlegume dry roughage	18-28	8-13	12-18[3]	5-8
Grain	....	......	2½-4½	1-2
Protein supplement	½-1	.2-.5	1¼-1½	.6-.7
3. Legume hay or grass-legume mixed hay, good quality	7-11	3-5	8-12[3]	4-5
Grass hay or other nonlegume dry roughage	11-17	5-8	4-6	2-3
Grain	....	....	2½-4	1-2
Protein supplement	....	....	½-1	.2-.5
4. Silage	55-60	25-27	25-40[4]	11-18
Grain	....	....	....	....
Protein supplement	½-1½	.2-.7	1½-1¾	.7-.8
5. Silage	40-45	18-20	16-28	7-13
Legume hay or grass-legume mixed hay, good quality	5-6	2-3	3-4	1-2
Grain	....	....	....	....
Protein supplement	....	....	1¼-1½	.6-.7
6. Silage	40-45	18-20	16-28	7-13
Grass hay or other nonlegume dry roughage	5-6	2-3	3-4	1-2
Grain	....	....	....	....
Protein supplement	½-1	.2-.5	1¾-2	.8-1

[1]If stocker calves are late or the roughage is fair to poor in quality, it may be desirable to add 2 to 4 pounds of grain per head daily. If farm scales are available, monthly weights may be used as the criterion for grain feeding. Keep in mind that the calves should gain ¾ to 1 pound daily.

[2]In general, the experienced feeder plans that cattle on full feed shall consume (1) feeds in amounts (daily; air-dry basis) equal to about 2.5 per cent of their live weight, (2) 70 to 75 per cent concentrates, and (3) a minimum of 0.5 to 0.8 lbs. roughage for each 100 lbs. live weight. In areas where roughage is more abundant and comparatively cheaper than grain, as in the irrigated valleys of the West, the proportions of roughage to grain should be somewhat higher than indicated. In computing roughage consumption, three pounds of silage are considered equivalent to one pound of hay.

Rations 1 to 5 are bulky. They are recommended for use (1) by the inexperienced feeder and (2) in starting prospective show animals on feed.

Ration No. 1	(lbs.)	(kg)
Ground barley	50	22.7
Crushed oats	20	9.1
Wheat bran	20	9.1
Protein supplement[1]	10	4.5

Ration No. 2		
Ground corn	20	9.1
Ground barley	30	13.6
Crushed oats	20	9.1
Wheat bran	20	9.1
Protein supplement[1]	10	4.5

Ration No. 3		
Ground corn	40	18.2
Crushed oats	30	13.6
Wheat bran	20	9.1
Protein supplement[1]	10	4.5

Ration No. 4	(lbs.)	(kg)
Crushed oats	30	13.6
Ground barley	30	13.6
Ground corn	10	4.5
Wheat bran	20	9.1
Protein supplement[1]	10	4.5

Ration No. 5		
Crushed oats	30	13.6
Ground corn	60	27.2
Protein supplement[1]	10	4.5

[1] See footnote below ration No. 11 on p. 462.

HANDY BEEF CATTLE FEEDING GUIDE

Wintering stocker calves; roughed through the winter, and generally grazed the following summer. Fed for winter gains of 3/4 to 1 lb. per head daily (weighing 400 to 500 lbs. start of wintering).[1] (per day)		Finishing calves in dry lot, generally in winter. (Weighing 400 to 500 lbs. start of feeding, and 750 to 850 lbs. at marketing.)[2] (per day)		Wintering yearlings; roughed through the winter, and generally pasture finished the following summer. Fed for winter gains of 1 to 1 1/4 lbs. per head daily (weighing about 600 lbs. start of wintering). (per day)		Finishing yearlings in dry lot, generally in winter (weighing about 600 lbs. start of feeding and 850 to 1000 lbs. at marketing).[2] (per day)		Finishing two-year-old steers in dry lot, generally in winter (weighing about 800 lbs. start of feeding and 1,100 lbs. at marketing).[2] (per day)	
(lbs.)	(kg)	(lbs.)	(kg)	(lbs.)	(kg)	(lbs.)	(kg)	(lbs.)	(kg)
12-18[3]	5-8	4-6	2-3	16-24	.7-11	4-8	2-4	6-12	3-5
....	....	12-15	5-7	....	....	15-19½	7-9	16-22	7-10
....	....	1-1½	.5-.7	....	....	1-1½	.5-.7	....	....
12-18[3]	5-8	4-5	2-2.3	16-24	7-11	4-8	2-4	6-12	3-5
....	....	12-15	5-7	....	....	15-20	7-9	16½-22¾	7-10
1¼-1½	.6-.7	1¼-2	.8-1	1½-1¾	.7-.8	1½-2½	.7-1	1½-1¾	.7-.8
8-12[3]	5-8	2-3	1-1.4	6-8	3-4	2-4	1-2	3-6	1-3
4-6	2-3	2-3	1-1.4	10-16	5-7	2-4	1-2	3-6	1-3
....	....	12-15	5-7	....	....	15-19¾	7-9	16-22	3-10
¼-1	.1-.5	1½-1¼	.7-.8	1-1½	.5-.7	1¼-1¼	.6-.8	½-¾	.2-.3
25-40[3]	11-18	12-15	5-7	45-55	20-25	18-24	8-11	24-36	11-16
....	....	8-12	4-5	....	....	11-16	5-7	15-21	7-10
1-1¼	.5-.6	2-2¼	.9-1	1¼-1½	.6-.7	2-2½	1-1.1	1¼-1½	.6-.7
20-30	9-14	6-8	3-4	40-50	18-23	12-18	5-8	16-24	3-11
2-4	1-2	2-3	1-1.4	2-4	1-2	2-3	1-1.4	3-4	1-2
....	....	8-12	4-5	....	....	11-16	5-7	15-21	7-10
¾-1[5]	.3-.5	1¼-2	.8-1	¾-1	.3-.5	¼-1¼	.3-.8	1-1½	.1-.2
20-30	9-14	6-8	3-4	40-50	18-23	12-18	5-8	16-24	3-11
2-4	1-2	2-3	1-1.4	2-4	1-2	2-3	1-1.4	3-4	1-2
....	....	8-12	5-8	....	....	11-16	5-7	15-21	7-10
1¼-1½	.6-.7	2-2¼	.9-1	1¼-1½	.6-.7	1¼-2	.6-1	1-1¼	.5-.6

[3] With calves (both replacement heifers and stockers) an extra 2 lbs. of hay daily over and above requirements are herewith indicated in order to allow for wastage. Practical operators generally feed stemmy or other hay left over by calves to the cow herd.

[4] Practical operators report scouring and unsatisfactory gains where grass or legume silage only is fed to young stock. On the other hand, corn or sorghum silage properly balanced with a protein supplement appear to be entirely satisfactory for young animals.

[5] A protein supplement is not necessary for wintering stocker and feeder calves when good quality silage and good quality legume hay are fed free choice.

Rations 6 to 11 are less bulky and higher in energy. They are recommended for use (1) by the experienced feeder and (2) during the latter part of the fitting period.

Ration No. 6	(lbs.)	(kg)
Ground corn or sorghum chop	50	22.7
Ground barley	40	18.2
Protein supplement[1]	10	4.5

Ration No. 7		
Ground corn	60	27.2
Crushed oats	20	9.1
Dry beet pulp	10	4.5
Protein supplement[1]	10	4.5

Ration No. 8		
Ground corn	40	18.2
Ground barley	20	9.1
Crushed oats	10	4.5
Dried beet pulp	10	4.5
Wheat bran	10	4.5
Protein supplement[1]	10	4.5

Ration No. 9	(lbs.)	(kg)
Crushed oats	25	11.4
Ground barley	20	9.1
Ground wheat	20	9.1
Ground corn	20	9.1
Wheat bran	10	4.5
Protein supplement[1]	5	2.3

Ration No. 10		
Ground barley	35	15.9
Crushed oats	20	9.1
Ground wheat	20	9.1
Dry beet pulp	15	6.8
Protein supplement[1]	10	4.5

[1] See footnote below ration No. 11 on p. 462.

Ration No. 11	(lbs.)	(kg)		(lbs.)	(kg)
Rolled barley	20	9.1	Beet pulp, dried molasses	4	1.8
Rolled corn	20	9.1	Wheat bran	6	2.7
Rolled oats	20	9.1	Commercial supplement	8	3.6
Whole barley (dry wt. basis,			Linseed meal (pellets)	8	3.6
but cooked before feeding)	13	5.9	Salt	1	.5

[1] The protein supplement may consist of linseed, cottonseed, peanut, or soybean cake or meal; with pea-sized cake preferred to meal. With most herdsmen, linseed meal is the preferred protein supplement. It gives the animal a sleek hair coat and a pliable hide. Because it is a laxative feed, however, caution should be used in feeding it. Although it is true that an animal getting good clover or alfalfa hay needs less protein supplement than does one eating nonleguminous roughage, it is not possible to supply all the needed protein with hay and still get enough grain into young animals to finish them quickly.

Ration 11 is used in fitting show steers at Washington State University. The whole barley is prepared by (1) adding water in the proportion of 2 to 2½ gallons to each gallon of dry barley and (2) cooking until the kernels are thoroughly swelled and can be easily squashed between the thumb and forefinger. Then it is mixed with the balance of the ration in about the proportions (on a dry basis) indicated. Each steer also receives 4 pounds daily of a nurse cow replacer (or milk replacer). As the animal approaches show finish, the ration is changed by decreasing the rolled barley by 7 pounds and increasing the rolled oats by 5 pounds and the wheat bran by 2 pounds.

Rules of Feeding Show Cattle

As previously indicated, the selection of the particular fitting ration should be determined largely by the availability and price of feeds. Make the maximum use of home-grown feeds. Other important points in compounding the show ration and feeding the animal are:

1. Use care in getting the animal on feed. Avoid digestive disturbances and setbacks. A safe plan consists in feeding not more than 1 pound of grain at the first feed, or 2 pounds for the day. This may be increased approximately by ¼ to ½ pound daily until the animal is on full feed three to four weeks later.

From the beginning, it is safe to full-feed grass hay or the hay to which the animal is accustomed. Oats are the best concentrate for the beginning ration. As the grain feed is increased according to the directions given above, gradually (a) replace the oats with the mixed ration selected, and (b) decrease the hay, until the animal is eating only 3 to 6 pounds of hay daily at the end of the feeding period.

2. When on full feed, the average animal will eat from 1½ to 2½ pounds of grain for each 100 pounds of live weight. Feed only as much grain as the animal will clean up in one-half to one hour's time.

3. Feeds used in fitting rations should be coarsely ground or crushed. Most herdsmen prefer steamed rolled grains.

4. Provide needed minerals (see earlier section entitled "Mineral Needs").

5. If the droppings are too thin or there is scouring, (a) cut down on the grain allowance and (b) clean up the quarters. If trouble still persists, cut down on the legume roughage and the protein supplement (especially linseed

meal). Many experienced herdsmen prefer feeding grass or grass-legume mixed hay to a straight legume hay, because of some difficulty in keeping forced fed animals on feed when a legume is fed.

6. The palatability of the ration may be enhanced by adding blackstrap molasses. Make it by diluting one-half to one pint of molasses with an equal volume of water and mixing it with each grain ration just before feeding. Although blackstrap molasses is preferable, beet molasses is satisfactory.

7. Nurse cows are costly, but they are used by most successful herdsmen in fitting young animals, especially animals under 15 months of age. Satisfactory milk replacers, which alleviate the need for nurse cows, are now on the market.

QUESTIONS FOR STUDY AND DISCUSSION

1. Why is knowledge of beef cattle feeding so important?
2. Use Fig. 14-13 to estimate the necessary margin on cattle that you have bought or sold this year, or on cattle sales with which you are acquainted.
3. What age, grade, and sex of cattle should you feed on your farm or ranch? Justify your answer.
4. Is the cattle feeder justified in breeding heifers 3 to 4 months prior to marketing? Is the packer justified in buying such bred heifers at a discount?
5. In Washington Experiment Station Bulletin 562, it is reported that 78.3 per cent of the cattlemen fed a commercial mineral mix. Is this good, bad, and/or economical? Why do so many use a commercial mineral rather than a home-mixed mineral?
6. For beef cattle, list the vitamins most apt to be deficient; then (a) list some of the deficiency symptoms and (b) give practical sources of each vitamin for use on your farm or ranch.
7. When would you use each (a) stilbestrol, (b) antibiotics, and/or (c) other feed additives in the beef cattle ration; when wouldn't you?

SELECTED REFERENCES

In addition to the Selected References listed in Chapter III, the following are recommended for Chapter XIV:

Title of Publication	Author(s)	Publisher
Beef Cattle in Florida	L. H. Lewis T. J. Cunha	Florida Department of Agriculture, Tallahassee, Fla., 1958.
Beef Cattle Production	K. A. Wagnon Reuben Albaugh G. H. Hart	The Macmillan Company, New York, N. Y., 1960.
Feed Formulations Handbook	Tilden Wayne Perry	The Interstate Printers and Publishers, Inc., Danville, Ill., 1966.
Feeding Cattle for Beef	Farmers' Bul. 1549	U.S. Department of Agriculture, Washington, D.C.
Nutrient Requirements of Beef Cattle, Pub. No. 1137	Wise Burroughs et al.	National Academy of Sciences, National Research Council, Washington, D.C., 1963.
Problems and Practices of American Cattlemen	M. E. Ensminger M. W. Galgan W. L. Slocum	Wash. Agri. Exp. Sta. Bul. 562, Washington State University, Pullman, Wash., 1955.
Stockman's Handbook, The	M. E. Ensminger	Interstate Printers and Publishers, Danville, Ill., 1969.

Chapter XV

MARKETING AND SLAUGHTERING CATTLE AND CALVES

Contents   Page

Leading Terminal Cattle Markets	466
Leading Terminal Calf Markets	467
Leading Terminal Feeder Cattle Markets	467
Market Classes and Grades of Cattle	469
Factors Determining Market Classes of Cattle	469
Cattle and Calves	469
Use Selection of Cattle and Calves	469
The Sex Classes	471
Age Groups	471
Weight Divisions	472
The Market Grades of Cattle	472
Other Cattle Market Terms and Factors	476
Native and Western Cattle	476
Grassers and Fed Cattle	476
Baby Beef	477
Butcher Stock	477
Bologna Bulls	477
Packer Slaughtering and Dressing of Beef Cattle	477
Steps in Slaughtering and Dressing Cattle	478
How Slaughtering of Veal Calves Differs	479
Kosher Slaughter	479
The Dressing Percentage	479
Aging Beef	481
Disposition of the Beef Carcass	482
The Beef Carcass and Its Cuts	482
The Veal Carcass and Its Cuts	483
Questions for Study and Discussion	485
Selected References	485

In the general chapter devoted to marketing livestock (Chapter VI), it was pointed out that livestock are sold through the following avenues: (1) on terminal markets, (2) through auctions, (3) in the country, (4) on the basis of carcass grade and weight, and (5) as purebreds.

Some cattle are marketed through each of these channels, with the seller selecting the method which he feels will be most remunerative for the particular kind and quality of animals being marketed. Except for those animals that are sold as purebreds or stockers and feeders, the vast majority of cattle are bought for immediate slaughter; and, even with purebreds or stockers and feeders, the ultimate objective is meat over the block.

Of the total livestock slaughtered in the United States in 1967, 83 per cent of the cattle, 53 per cent of the calves, 84 per cent of the hogs, and 89 per cent of the sheep and lambs were slaughtered under federal inspection. The balance of slaughtering, that which is not under federal inspection, consists of farm slaughter and slaughter at local plants.

Fig. 15-1. Cattle buying scene on the Chicago market. (Courtesy, Swift and Company)

LEADING TERMINAL CATTLE MARKETS

With the development of the Corn Belt and western range cattle industry,

TABLE 15—1

CATTLE RECEIPTS (EXCLUDING CALVES) OF TEN LEADING
TERMINAL CATTLE MARKETS, BY RANK, 1966[1]

Market	1966
Omaha, Nebraska	1,872,425
Chicago, Illinois	1,372,747
Sioux City, Iowa	1,231,420
South St. Paul, Minnesota	1,070,450
Kansas City, Missouri	709,690
St. Joseph, Missouri	694,487
Oklahoma City, Oklahoma	638,627
St. Louis, N.S.Y	601,393
Sioux Falls, South Dakota	529,003
West Fargo, N.D	360,806
Total of 53 public markets	14,316,914

[1]*Livestock and Meat Statistics*, USDA, Supp. for 1966 to Statistical Bul. No. 333, p. 38.

the markets established at various points on the Great Lakes and along the Mississippi and Missouri Rivers became important. It is logical that these should have remained leading cattle markets because of their proximity to both producers and consumers. About 70 per cent of the cattle and calves are raised west of the Mississippi, while about 70 per cent of the beef is consumed east of this geographical location.

Although the central markets vary from year to year in their total receipts, Table 15-1 shows the largest cattle markets and their receipts of cattle, in 1966.

LEADING TERMINAL CALF MARKETS

Cattle under approximately 400 pounds in weight are designated as calves. As would be expected, many of these animals are of dairy breeding, especially the surplus bull calves that are not needed for breeding purposes. Of the remainder, a considerable number are culled out from beef herds because of undesirable type or breeding from the standpoint of future development. It can be expected, therefore, that the leading calf markets would not coincide with the leading cattle markets. Table 15-2 shows the 10 leading terminal calf markets in the United States.

TABLE 15—2

CALF RECEIPTS OF TEN LEADING TERMINAL CALF
MARKETS, BY RANK, 1966[1]

Market	1966
South St. Paul, Minnesota.............................	247,107
Milwaukee, Wisconsin	206,093
Sioux City, Iowa	150,295
Fort Worth, Texas	97,296
Oklahoma City, Oklahoma.............................	97,224
Houston, Texas	93,667
Springfield, Missouri.................................	90,338
Omaha, Nebraska....................................	71,658
West Fargo, N.D.	59,687
Louisville, Ky.	57,525
Total of 53 public markets.....................	1,803,117

[1]*Livestock and Meat Statistics*, USDA, Supp. for 1966 to Statistical Bul. No. 333, p. 38.

LEADING TERMINAL FEEDER CATTLE MARKETS

Cattle feeding often involves a two-phase type of operation. Thus, the western range area is well adapted to a cow-and-calf proposition, and, because of the abundance of relatively cheap forage, many of the steers are grown out and marketed as yearlings or two-year-olds. On the other hand, the Corn Belt produces a great surplus of grain and is noted as a cattle feeding center. It is but natural that the leading feeder cattle markets should be conveniently located between the range producing area and the Corn Belt feeding area. Table 15-3

Fig. 15-2. Portion of the cattle pens of the Kansas City market. (Courtesy, University of Missouri)

gives the 10 leading terminal feeder cattle markets by rank, whereas Table 15-4 shows the state destination of feeder cattle.

Table 15-3 shows the central markets upon which most feeder cattle are handled, whereas Table 15-4 indicates the states which acquire the greatest numbers of market feeder cattle from outside sources for finishing purposes.

In recent years, there has been an increasing tendency to market feeder cattle direct, without passing them through the central market. A considerable and increasing number of western producers also are arranging to have their feeders fed out on contract. Despite these other methods of handling, over six million head of feeder cattle pass through United States central markets each year.

TABLE 15—3

FEEDER CATTLE SHIPPED FROM TEN LEADING FEDERALLY INSPECTED PUBLIC STOCKYARDS, BY RANK, 1966[1]

Market	1966
Oklahoma City, Oklahoma	605,451
Sioux City, Iowa	462,212
Ft. Worth, Texas area	436,059
Kansas City, Missouri	313,708
Clovis, New Mexico area	311,075
West Fargo, North Dakota	306,187
Omaha, Nebraska	280,896
Springfield, Missouri	266,166
San Antonio, Texas	248,063
Greeley, Colo	175,627
Total feeder cattle received at 42 U.S. markets	6,175,280

[1]*Livestock and Meat Statistics*, USDA, Supp. for 1966 to Statistical Bul. No. 333, p. 41.

TABLE 15—4

TEN LEADING STATE-DESTINATIONS OF MARKET FEEDER
CATTLE (NOT INCLUDING "DIRECT" SHIPMENTS),
BY RANK, 1966[1]

State	No. Shipped Into
Iowa	1,053,924
Texas	796,021
Nebraska	472,121
Kansas	471,830
Colorado	377,655
Missouri	358,218
Oklahoma	346,260
Illinois	296,297
Idaho	291,019
Minnesota	230,739
Total 50 states	6,175,280

[1]*Livestock and Meat Statistics*, USDA, Supp. for 1966 to Statistical Bul. No. 333, p. 41.

MARKET CLASSES AND GRADES OF CATTLE[1]

The generally accepted market classes and grades of live cattle are summarized in Table 15-5. The first five divisions and subdivisions include those factors that determine the class of the animal or the use to which it will be put. The grades indicate how well the cattle fulfill the requirements to which they are put.

Factors Determining Market Classes of Cattle

The market class of cattle is determined by (1) use selection, (2) sex, (3) age, and (4) weight.

CATTLE AND CALVES

All members of the bovine family are designated as calves until they are one year of age, after which they are known as cattle. On the average, about 21 per cent is calves and 79 per cent cattle.

USE SELECTION OF CATTLE AND CALVES

The cattle group is further divided into three use divisions, each indicating something of the purpose to which the animals will be put. These divisions are: (1) slaughter cattle, (2) feeder cattle, and (3) milkers and springers. Slaughter cattle include those which are considered suitable for immediate slaughter; feeders are those which are to be taken back to the country and grown for a time or finished; and milkers and springers include those cows recently freshened or soon due to calve and which are sold for milk purposes.

The calf group is also subdivided into three classes: (1) vealers, including

---

[1] This section was authoritatively reviewed by Mr. John C. Pierce, Director, Livestock Division, Consumer and Marketing Service, USDA.

TABLE 15—5

THE MARKET CLASSES AND GRADES OF CATTLE

Cattle or Calves	Use Selection	Sex Classes	Age Wt. (Group)	Weight Divisions			Commonly Used Grades
					(lbs.)	(kg)	
Cattle	Slaughter Cattle	Steers	Yearlings — Light Medium Heavy		750 down 750-950 950 up	340.5 down 340.5-431.3 431.3 up	Prime, Choice, Good, Standard, Commercial, Utility, Cutter, Canner
			2-year-old and over — Light Medium Heavy		1100 down 1100-1300 1300 up	499.4 down 499.4-590.2 590.2 up	Prime, Choice, Good, Standard, Commercial, Utility, Cutter, Canner
		Heifers	Yearlings — Light Medium Heavy		750 down 750-900 900 up	340.5 down 340.5-408.6 408.6 up	Prime, Choice, Good, Standard, Utility, Cutter, Canner
			2-year-old and over — Light Medium Heavy		900 down 900-1050 1050 up	408.6 down 408.6-476.7 476.6 up	Prime, Choice, Good, Standard, Commercial, Utility, Cutter, Canner
		Cows	All ages	All weights			Choice, Good, Standard, Commercial, Utility, Cutter, Canner
		Bulls (choice & good grade bulls often called "beef" or "butcher" bulls & lower grades bologna bulls)	Yearlings	All weights			Choice, Good, Commercial, Utility, Cutter, Canner
			2-year-old and over — Light Medium Heavy		1300 down 1300-1500 1500 up	590.2 down 590.2-681.0 681.0 up	Choice, Good, Commercial, Utility, Cutter, Canner
		Stags	All ages	All weights			Choice, Good, Commercial, Utility, Cutter, Canner
	Feeder Cattle	Steers	Yearlings — Light Medium Heavy Mixed				Prime, Choice, Good, Standard, Utility, Inferior
			2-year-old and over — Light Medium Heavy Mixed				Prime, Choice, Good, Standard, Commercial, Utility, Inferior
		Heifers	Yearlings — Light Medium Heavy Mixed				Prime, Choice, Good, Standard, Utility, Inferior
			2-year-old and over — Light Medium Heavy Mixed				Prime, Choice, Good, Standard, Commercial, Utility, Inferior
		Cows	All ages	All weights			Choice, Good, Commercial, Utility, Inferior
		Bulls	All ages	All weights			None
		Stags	All ages	All weights			None
	Milkers & Springers	Cows (milkers or springers)	All ages	All weights			None
Calves	Vealers	No Sex Class (Sex characteristics of no importance at this age)	Under 3 months — Light Medium Heavy		110 down 110-180 180 up	49.9 down 49.9-81.7 81.7 up	Prime, Choice, Good, Standard, Utility, Cull
	Slaughter Calves	Steers Heifers Bulls	3 months to 1 year — Light Medium Heavy		200 down 200-300 300 up	90.8 down 90.8-136.2 136.2 up	Prime, Choice, Good, Standard, Utility, Cull
	Feeder Calves	Steers Heifers Bulls	Usually 6 mo. to 1 year — Light Medium Heavy Mixed				Prime, Choice, Good, Standard, Utility, Inferior

[1] In addition to the above quality grades, there are the following yield grades: Yield Grade 1, Yield Grade 2, Yield Grade 3, Yield Grade 4, and Yield Grade 5. Thus, slaughter cattle may be graded for (1) quality alone, (2) yield grade alone, or (3) both quality and yield grades.

milk-fat animals under three months of age which are sold for immediate slaughter; (2) slaughter calves that are between the ages of three months and one year, which have usually received grain in addition to milk, and which are fat enough for slaughter; and (3) feeder calves which are of weaning age and are sold to go back into the country for further growing or finishing.

In the selection of feeder cattle or calves, the sex, age, weight, and grade are of importance. In addition, consideration should be given to the following factors: (1) constitution and thrift, (2) natural fleshing, (3) breeding, (4) uniformity, (5) absence of horns, and (6) temperament and disposition.

As can be readily understood, the use to which animals are put is not always clear-cut and definite. Thus, when feed is abundant and factors are favorable for cattle finishing, feeders may outbid packer buyers for some of the animals that would normally go for slaughter purposes. On the other hand, slaughterers frequently outbid feeders for some of those animals that would normally go the feeder route.

THE SEX CLASSES

Cattle are divided into five sex classes: steers, heifers, cows, bulls, and stags. Each of these groups has rather definite and easily distinguishable characteristics that are related to the commercial value of the carcass—especially in the cattle group—and which are important in determining the suitability of animals as feeders. In older cattle, sex is an important factor affecting carcass quality, finish, and conformation. The definition of each sex class follows:

Steer.—A steer is a male bovine animal that was castrated at an early age, before reaching sexual maturity and before developing the physical characteristics peculiar to bulls.

Heifer.—A heifer is a female bovine animal that has not had a calf or has not reached the stage of advanced pregnancy or has not developed the mature form of a cow.

Cow.—A cow is a female bovine animal that has had one or more calves or that has reached the stage of advanced pregnancy. Barren female bovine animals that have reached maturity and have developed the predominating physical characteristics peculiar to cows also are so classified.

Bull.—A bull is an uncastrated male bovine animal of any age.

Stag.—A stag, as applied to cattle, is a male bovine animal that was castrated after it had developed the physical characteristics of a mature bull.

Calves are merely divided into three sex classes: steers, heifers, or bulls. Because the secondary sex characteristics are not very pronounced in this group, the sex classes are of less importance for slaughter purposes than in older cattle. On the other hand, bull calves are not preferred as feeders because castration involves extra trouble and risk of loss.

AGE GROUPS

Because the age of cattle does affect certain carcass characteristics, it is logical that age groups should exist in market classifications. The terms used to indicate approximate age ranges for cattle are: vealers, calves, yearlings, two-year-old, and older cattle. As previously indicated, vealers are under three months of age,[2] whereas calves are young cattle between the vealer and yearling stage. Yearlings range from 12 to 24 months in age, and 2-year-olds from 24 to 36 months. Older cattle are usually grouped along with the two-year-olds as "two-year-old and over."

WEIGHT DIVISIONS

It is common to have three weight divisions: light, medium, and heavy. When several weight divisions are included together, they are referred to as mixed weight. The usual practice is to group animals by rather narrow weight divisions because purchasers are frequently rather choosey about weights, and market values often vary quite sharply with variations in weights.

The Market Grades of Cattle

While no official grading of live animals is done by the U.S. Department of Agriculture, market grades do form a basis for uniform reporting of livestock marketing. The grade is the final step in classifying any kind of market livestock. It indicates the relative degree of excellence of an animal or group of animals. The three factors of primary importance in determining cattle grades—conformation, finish, and quality—apply to all classes of market animals. Since they have been discussed in the general chapter on marketing livestock, no repetition will be necessary.

Table 15-5 lists the commonly used grades of cattle by classes. As noted, the number of grades varies somewhat between classes chiefly because certain groups of animals present a wider range of variations in conformation, finish, and quality than do other groups.

Slaughter steers and heifers are divided into eight grades: Prime, Choice, Good, Standard, Commercial, Utility, Cutter, and Canner. However, only seven grades apply to slaughter cows, and six grades to bulls and stags—the grade Prime being deleted chiefly because of deficient conformation, finish, and quality in these classes. Also, there is no standard grade for bulls and stags; and, as in carcasses, bulls and stags on foot are always designated as slaughter bulls and slaughter stags, since meat obtained from these respective classes is never interchanged (1) with each other or (2) with meat carrying the same grade name from steers, heifers, and cows.

The terms "Cutter" or "Canner" are applied to the two lowest grades of slaughter cattle. Cutter cattle are so poor in form and lacking in muscle and fat covering that only such wholesale cuts as the loin and round are cut out and sold over the block. The balance of the carcass is boned out and used in sausage and canned-meat products. Canners are almost entirely processed as ground and canned meats.

---

[2]Vealers must also be over 21 days of age for slaughter. Underage veal calves are called "deacons" or "bob veal."

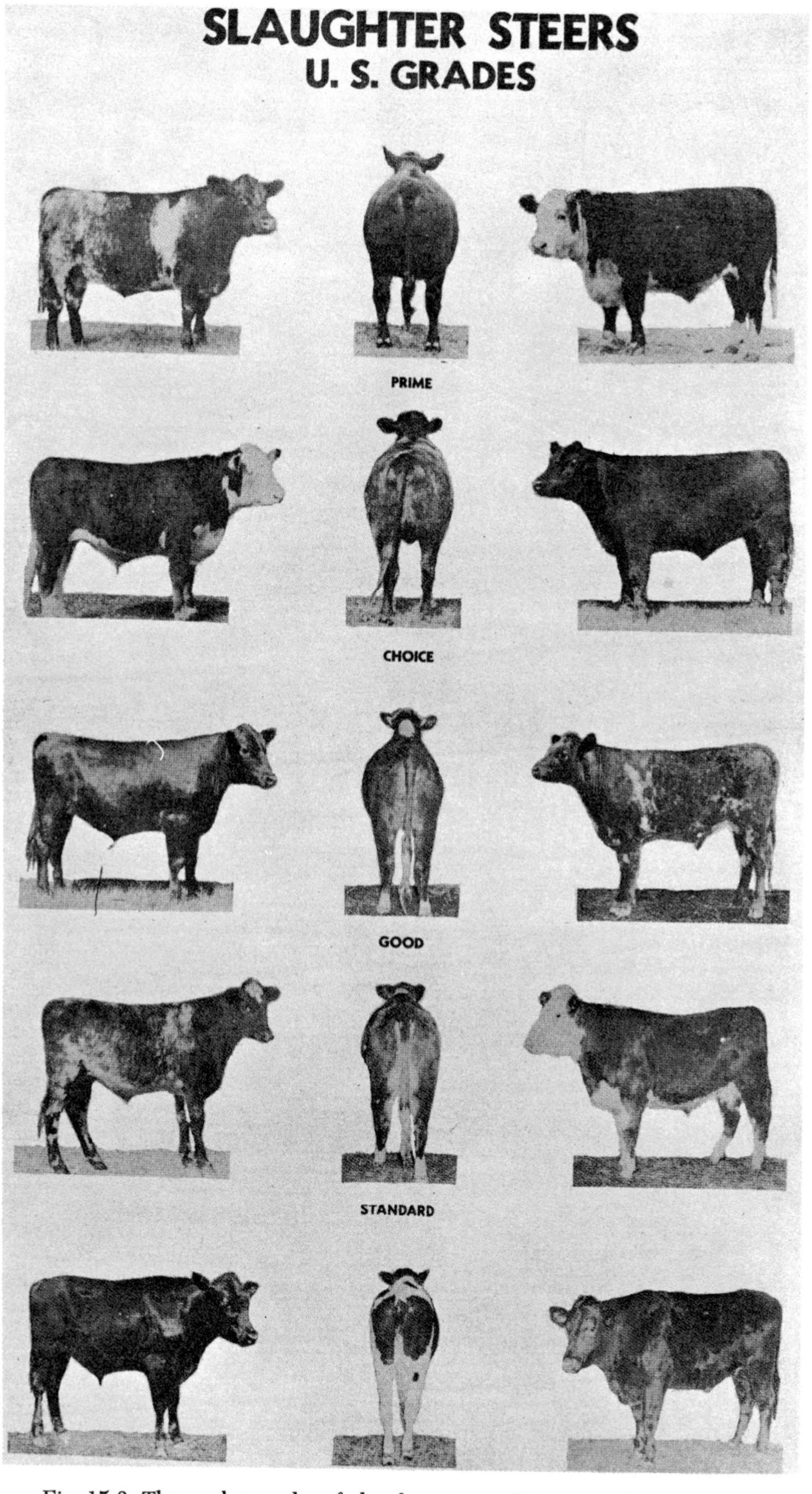

SLAUGHTER STEERS
U. S. GRADES

PRIME

CHOICE

GOOD

STANDARD

Fig. 15-3. The market grades of slaughter steers. (Courtesy, USDA, Agricultural Marketing Service)

PRIME

CHOICE

GOOD

STANDARD

UTILITY

Fig. 15-4. The market grades of feeder steers. (Courtesy, Consumer and Marketing Service, USDA)

The grades of feeder cattle are: Prime, Choice, Good, Standard, Commercial, Utility, and Inferior. These grades are based on two value-determining characteristics—logical slaughter potential and thriftiness. The logical slaughter potential of an animal is the slaughter grade at the time the animal's carcass quality grade and carcass conformation grade become equal.

Thriftiness in feeder cattle refers to the ability of the animal to gain weight and finish rapidly and efficiently.

There are no U.S. grades for feeder bulls and stags, although these animals are infrequently used as feeders.

As would be expected, the higher grades of slaughter cattle usually carry more weight, and the lower grades are lighter and usually underfinished. Figure 15-5 shows the relationship of the weight of beef steers to the grade.

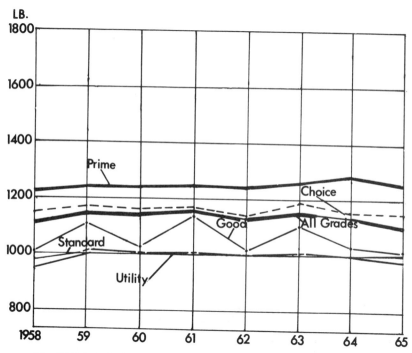

Fig. 15-5. Weight by grade of beef steers at Chicago, 1958-1965. This shows that the higher grades of fat cattle usually carry more weight, and the lower grades are lighter and usually underfinished. (Data provided by Mr. John C. Pierce, Director, Livestock Division, Consumer and Marketing Service, USDA; chart by R. F. Johnson)

Because the production of the better grades of cattle usually involves more expenditure in the breeding operations (due to the need for superior animals) and feeding to a higher degree of finish, there must be a spread in market grades in order to make the production of the top grades profitable. Figure 15-6 shows the eight-year average price per hundredweight of beef steers, by grades, on the Chicago market from 1958 to 1965.

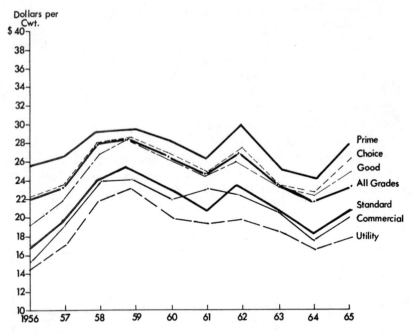

Fig. 15-6. Prices of beef steers sold out of first hands, by grades, at Chicago, 1956-1965. This shows that there is a rather uniform difference in the selling price of the different grades of cattle, with a slightly greater spread between the lower grades. (Data from *Livestock and Meat Statistics*, 1962, Statistical Bul. No. 333, pp. 216-19, and from Market News Branch, Livestock Division, Consumer and Marketing Service, USDA; chart by R. F. Johnson)

OTHER CATTLE MARKET TERMS AND FACTORS

In addition to the more or less general terminology used in cattle dealing and reporting, the following terms and factors are significant.

Native and Western Cattle

Native cattle are those coming from the farms of the Corn Belt, East, and South; whereas western cattle are the branded cattle coming from the western ranges. Not so long ago, western cattle lacked the breeding and quality of native cattle. But this condition no longer prevails. Today, many of the champion steers at the major shows throughout the country come from range herds, and, in general, range shipments possess far more uniformity than native cattle.

Grassers and Fed Cattle

The term grassers designates animals that have not been grain fed and which come direct from the pasture or range. Fed cattle are those that have been fed grain. Short-fed cattle are those which have been grain fed for 60 to 120 days, whereas long-fed cattle have been grain fed for more than 120 days.

Baby Beef

The term baby beef is frequently applied to Good to Prime animals (either steers or heifers) from 12 to 18 months of age and weighing 700 to 1,200 pounds on foot. For the most part, these animals have never been allowed to lose their milk fat.

Butcher Stock

On many markets the term butcher stock is used to designate heifers, cows, bulls, and stags marketed for slaughter and suitable to be sold in the carcass as block beef. These carcasses are largely sold to city and country retail dealers or butchers.

Bologna Bulls

Bologna bulls are bulls that are muscular but not sufficiently fat for block beef purposes. The meat from such carcasses is usually used in the manufacture of bologna sausage.

PACKER SLAUGHTERING AND DRESSING OF BEEF CATTLE

Table 15-6 shows the proportion of cattle and calves slaughtered commercially (meaning that they were slaughtered in federally inspected and other wholesale and retail establishments) and the proportion slaughtered on farms. The total figure refers to the number dressed in all establishments and on farms. Although farm slaughter procedure may differ somewhat, the ultimate

TABLE 15—6

PROPORTION OF CATTLE AND CALVES SLAUGHTERED
COMMERCIALLY 1955 TO 1964[1]

Year	Cattle			Calves	
	Total Number Slaughtered (Commercially and Non-commercially)	Number Slaughtered Commercially	Per Cent Slaughtered Commercially	Total Number Slaughtered (Commercially and Non-commercially)	Number Slaughtered Commercially
	(1,000 head)	(1,000 head)	(%)	(1,000 head)	(1,000 head)
1955.....	26,587	25,722	96.75	12,864	12,377
1956.....	27,754	26,862	96.79	12,999	12,512
1957.....	27,089	26,232	96.84	12,353	11,904
1958.....	24,396	23,555	96.55	9,738	9,315
1959.....	23,722	22,931	96.67	8,072	7,683
1960.....	26,026	25,224	96.92	8,611	8,225
1961.....	26,467	25,635	96.86	8,081	7,701
1962.....	26,905	26,083	96.94	7,854	7,494
1963.....	28,064	27,232	97.04	7,198	6,833
1964.....	31,666	30,818	97.32	7,625	7,254

[1]*Livestock and Meat Statistics,* Sept. 1965, USDA, Supp. for 1964 to Statistical Bul. No. 333, p. 64.

objective is always the same. Because of the greater total numbers of cattle involved in this system of handling, only packer slaughtering and dressing—the kind that is done commercially—will be discussed.

Cattle intended for slaughter purposes are bought primarily on the basis of projected quality of carcass and dressing percentage. Upon reaching the packing house, they rapidly pass through the operations of killing and dressing. Unlike most manufacturing, meat packing is primarily a disassembly process wherein the manufacturing operation starts with a complete unit that is progressively broken down into its component parts. The various parts then are subjected to divergent processing operations. Because of their size and other physical characteristics, cattle cannot be processed with the endless chain method of dressing that is used in the dressing of hogs, calves, and sheep.

Steps in Slaughtering and Dressing Cattle

The slaughtering and dressing procedure differs somewhat between plants, but in general the process consists of the steps that follow. It is noteworthy, however, that the continuous line system, including a hide puller, is being installed in most of the new plants.

1. **Rendering insensible.**—The cattle are rendered insensible.[3] The following methods are accepted as humane for cattle and calves: captive bolt stunners, gunshot, or electric current. Carbon dioxide may also be used for calves.

2. **Shackling, hoisting, sticking, and bleeding.**—The animal is next shackled, hoisted by the hind legs, stuck, and bled. The head is then skinned and removed.

3. **Lowering to floor and partial skinning.**—The carcass is next lowered to the floor (in some of the newer plants, carcasses are no longer lowered to the floor); the shanks are skinned and removed at the knees and hocks; the hide is opened along the median line on the belly and is removed from the belly and sides; and the breast and aitch (rump) bones are split by sawing.

4. **Raising to half-hoist position and further skinning.**—Beef hooks are inserted on the gam cord and the carcass is partially raised to a position known as half-hoist. In this position, the skinning of the shanks is completed and the round and rump are skinned out.

5. **Hoisting carcass to overhead track, completing skinning, removing viscera.**—All internal organs are removed except the kidneys. If the plant is under federal inspection, the carcass and viscera are examined at this stage in the slaughtering process.

6. **Splitting carcass and removing tail.**—The carcass is then split through the center of the backbone and the tail is removed.

7. **Washing and drying.**—The split carcass or sides are washed with warm water under pressure.

_____

[3]By federal law (known as the Humane Slaughter Act) passed in 1958 and effective June 30, 1960, unless a packer uses humane slaughter methods, he forfeits the right to sell meat to the government. The law lists the following methods as humane: 1. By rendering insensible to pain by a single blow or gunshot or an electrical, chemical, or other means that is rapid and effective, before being shackled, hoisted, thrown, cast, or cut. 2. By slaughtering in accordance with the ritual requirements of the Jewish faith or any other religious faith.

8. **Shrouding.**—The better carcasses are shrouded tightly with cloth so that they may have a smoother appearance following chilling.

9. **Sending to coolers.**—Following slaughtering, the sides are sent to the coolers where they are kept at a temperature of about 34° F. for a minimum period of 24 hours before ribbing.

How Slaughtering of Veal Calves Differs

Because of their smaller size, calves may be dressed by the endless-chain method. A wheel hoist is used in lifting the shackled calves to the rail. They are then stuck, bled, dressed, and washed. Because of the high moisture content of veal, the hide is usually left on for the purpose of reducing evaporation. This also produces a more desirable carcass color. When the hide is left on, it is thoroughly washed before the carcass is sent to the cooler.

Kosher Slaughter

Meat for the Jewish trade must come from animals slaughtered according to the rules of *Shehitah* (the ancient dietary rules). Although we usually think in terms of cattle when kosher slaughtering is mentioned, calves, sheep, lambs, goats, and poultry are slaughtered in a similar manner.

The killing is performed by a rabbi of the Jewish Synagogue or a specially trained representative; a person called the *shohet* or *shocket*, meaning slaughterer.

In kosher slaughter, the animal is hoisted without stunning and is cut across the throat with a special razor-sharp knife, known as a *chalaf*. With one quick, clean stroke the throat is cut; through the jugular vein and other large vessels, together with the gullet and windpipe. Two reasons are given for using this method of killing instead of the more conventional method of stunning and sticking; namely, (1) it produces more instant death with less pain and (2) it results in more rapid and complete bleeding, which Orthodox Hebrews consider essential for sanitary reasons.

The shohet also makes an inspection of the lungs, stomach, and other organs while dressing. If the carcass is acceptable, it is marked on the brisket with a cross inside a circle. The mark also gives the date of slaughter and the name of the inspector.

Since neither packers nor meat retailers can hold kosher meat longer than 216 hours (and even then it must be washed at 72-hour intervals; see section under "Kosher Meats"), rapid handling is imperative. This fact, plus the heavy concentration of Jewish folks in the eastern cities results in large numbers of live cattle being shipped from the markets farther west to be slaughtered in or near the eastern consuming areas.

The Dressing Percentage

Dressing percentage may be defined as the percentage yield of chilled carcass in relation to the weight of the animal on foot. For example, a steer which weighed 1,200 pounds on foot and yielded a carcass weighing 720 pounds may be said to have a dressing percentage of 60. The offal—so-called because formerly (with the exception of the hide, tallow, and tongue) the offal (waste) was thrown away—consists of the blood, head, shanks, tail, hide, viscera, and loose fat.

A high carcass yield is desirable because the carcass is much more valuable than the by-products. Although the packers have done a marvelous job in utilizing by-products, about 90.5 per cent of the income from cattle and calves is derived from the sale of the carcass and only 9.5 per cent from the by-products. Thus, the estimated dressing percentage of slaughter cattle is justifiably a major factor in determining the price or value of the live animal.

The chief factors determining the dressing percentage of cattle are: (1) the amount of fill, (2) the finish or degree of fatness, (3) the general quality and refinement (refinement of head, bone, hide, etc.), and (4) the size of udder. The better grades of steers have the highest dressing percentage, with thin canner cows showing the lowest yield. Table 15-7 gives the dressing percentages that may be expected for different grades of cattle and calves.

The highest dressing percentage on record was a yield of 76¾ per cent made by a spayed Angus heifer at the Smithfield Fat Stock Show in England. It is estimated that market cattle and calves in the United States dress about 56 per cent.

TABLE 15—7

DRESSING PER CENT OF CATTLE AND CALVES, BY GRADE[1]

Cattle			Calves and Vealers		
Grade	Range	Average	Grade	Range	Average
Prime	60-67	63	Prime	60-66	62
Choice	57-63	60	Choice	56-62	58
Good	56-60	58	Good	54-58	56
Standard	53-58	55	Standard	50-55	53
Commercial	52-60	55	Utility	46-52	49
Utility	47-55	51	Cull	40-46	44
Cutter	43-52	47			
Canner	38-46	43			

[1]Data from Mr. John C. Pierce, Director, Livestock Division, Consumer and Marketing Service, USDA.

TABLE 15—8

AVERAGE LIVE WEIGHT, CARCASS YIELD, AND DRESSING PERCENTAGES OF ALL CATTLE AND CALVES COMMERCIALLY SLAUGHTERED IN THE U.S. IN 1965[1]

	Average Live Weight		Dressed Weight		Dressing Percentage
	(lb)	(kg)	(lb)	(kg)	(%)
Cattle	999	454	568	258	56.8
Calves	227	103	127	58	55.9

[1]Data from Mr. John C. Pierce, Director, Livestock Division, Consumer and Marketing Service, USDA.

The average live weights of cattle and calves dressed by commercial meat packing plants, and their percentage yields in meats, for the year 1965 is given in Table 15-8.

AGING BEEF

Except for veal, fresh beef is not at optimum tenderness immediately after slaughter. It must undergo an aging or ripening process before it really becomes tender. This process consists of the dissolution of the connective tissue (collagen) by the action of enzymes. Beef should be aged from two to six weeks at temperatures ranging from 34° to 38° F., but only the better grades can be

Fig. 15-7. Aging beef in a cooler. Beef should be aged from two to six weeks at temperatures ranging from 34° to 38° F. (Courtesy, *Meat Magazine*)

aged for the longer periods. Beef must have a fat covering to protect the meat from bacterial action by sealing it from the air. With well-finished beef, some trimming is necessary anyway and the removal of the mold does not constitute any additional loss. The aging process may be hastened by the use of ultraviolet lights in high temperature coolers with controlled humidity.

DISPOSITION OF THE BEEF CARCASS

Beef carcasses are of two types; namely, those suitable for (1) block beef and (2) processed meats.

1. **Block beef.**—Block beef refers to beef that is suitable for sale over the block. Such beef is purchased by the retailer in sides, quarters, or wholesale cuts. Block beef may enter regular channels of trade either as fresh chilled or fresh frozen. Fresh chilled beef is chilled at temperatures ranging from 34° to 38°F. for a minimum of 24 hours before moving out to the retail trade, or it may be held longer if aging is desired. Frozen beef is subjected to temperatures of 0° F. or below and is frozen solid, in which form it can be kept for a period of several months. United States consumers prefer fresh chilled beef, although the consumption of frozen beef is increasing. The bulk of the export beef is frozen.

2. **Processed meats.**—Beef that is not suitable for sale over the block is boned out and disposed of as boneless cuts, is canned, is made into sausage, or is cured by drying and smoking. It is estimated that about one-fifth of all slaughter cattle are disposed of as processed meats.

THE BEEF CARCASS AND ITS CUTS

The methods of cutting beef are more varied than are found in the cutting of veal, lamb, or pork. Each area has its traditional cuts of beef. In the Midwest and West most cutting is according to the Chicago style in which the wholesale cut known as the rib has the seven last ribs on the front quarter, thus leaving five ribs on the chuck. On the other hand, the eastern seaboard states adhere mostly to the New York style in which the rib cut includes eight ribs, and the short chuck four ribs.

In quartering beef, all 13 ribs are left on the forequarter for the Brooklyn and Philadelphia markets; whereas three ribs are included on the hindquarter for the Boston market. Most other markets cut one rib on the hindquarter. Naturally, the number of ribs left on the hindquarter affects the percentage weight of fores and hinds. Thus, a three-rib hindquarter represents about 50 per cent of the side; one-rib hinds represent about 48 per cent of the side; whereas a hind without any ribs represents only 46 to 47 per cent of the side.

Although considerable beef is shipped to retail shops as sides and quarters, most retailers like to handle a considerable quantity of wholesale cuts because of the flexibility afforded. If steaks are in greater demand, therefore, steak-yielding cuts may be obtained without getting an oversupply of cuts better adapted for other purposes (roasts, stews, etc.).

When cut Chicago style, the forequarter yields five wholesale cuts: chuck, rib, plate, brisket, and shank. The hindquarter is divided into five wholesale cuts: round, rump, loin end, short loin, and flank. Figure 15-8 shows the wholesale cuts of a side of beef and some of the common retail cuts, when cut according to the Chicago style.

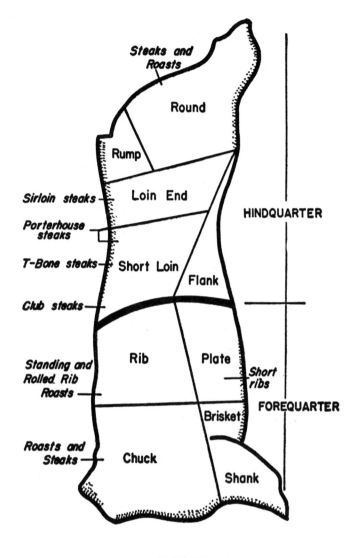

BEEF

Fig. 15-8. Wholesale cuts of beef, and some of the common retail cuts, when cut Chicago style. (Drawing by R. F. Johnson)

THE VEAL CARCASS AND ITS CUTS

Because veal has very little protective fat covering and is high in moisture, it does not lend itself to aging or ripening. It is necessary, therefore, that veal be moved into retail channels fairly rapidly.

The size of the veal carcass will determine the method of cutting. The larger carcasses (calf rather than veal carcasses) are generally halved and then quartered much like beef carcasses, whereas practically all of the younger veal carcasses are cut into fore and hind saddles.

The fore saddle consists of that part of the carcass anterior to the twelfth rib or the two unsplit forequarters. The hind saddle consists of the two unsplit hindquarters posterior to the twelfth rib.

When the veal carcass is further divided, the common wholesale cuts from the hindquarter are the leg and loin; and from the forequarter, the rib, shoulder, breast, and shank. Figure 15-9 shows the common wholesale cuts of veal and some of the common retail cuts. The veal carcass is generally sold with the liver and sweetbread attached.

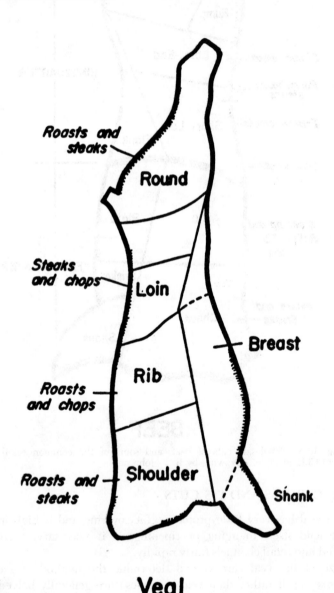

Veal

Fig. 15-9. Wholesale cuts of veal and some of the common retail cuts. (Drawing by R. F. Johnson)

QUESTIONS FOR STUDY AND DISCUSSION

1. Why is cattle marketing important?
2. In recent years, many top authorities have said that cattle marketing is the cattlemen's number one problem. Why do they feel this way?
3. What method of marketing (what market channel) do you consider most advantageous for the cattle sold off your home farm or ranch, and why?
4. How do you account for the fact that the leading cattle markets (Table 15-1), the leading calf markets (Table 15-2) and the leading feeder cattle markets (Table 15-3) do not coincide?
5. Why is it important that a cattleman know the leading markets for each class of cattle?
6. Since there is a rather uniform difference in the selling price of the different grades of cattle, with the top grades bringing the higher prices, why do not more cattlemen produce the top grades?
7. Studies indicate the following transitions in consumer preference of beef:
   a. Greater demand for more red meat and less fat.
   b. Increased consumption of more highly processed meat; that is, more boning out, more packaging, etc.
   c. Sale of more frozen meat.
   Discuss the impact of each of these trends from the standpoint of the producer, the processor, and the consumer.
8. Define on-foot market (a) classes and (b) grades of cattle and tell of their value.
9. Why is it important that a cattleman know the market classes and grades of cattle and what each implies?
10. What prompted the addition of the Standard grade of beef in 1956?

SELECTED REFERENCES

In addition to the Selected References listed in Chapter VI, the following are recommended for Chapter XV:

Title of Publication	Author(s)	Publisher
Beef Cattle in Florida	L. H. Lewis T. J. Cunha	Florida Department of Agriculture, Tallahassee, Fla., 1958
Beef on the Farm—Slaughtering, Cutting, Curing	Farmers' Bul. 1415	U.S. Department of Agriculture, Washington, D.C.
Beef Production and Distribution	Herrell DeGraff	University of Oklahoma Press, Norman, Okla., 1960.
Marketing Cattle and Calves Through Southern Auctions	R. G. Stout	Southern Coop. Series, Bul. 48, Agri. Expt. Stations of Ala., Ark., Ga., Ky., La., Miss., N. C., Okla., S. C., Tenn., Va., West Va.
Marketing Feeder Cattle and Sheep in the North Central Region	V. J. Bernsike	North Central Regional Pub. 25, University of Nebraska, Lincoln, Nebr., 1952.
Marketing Slaughter Cattle by Carcass Weight and Grade	A. A. Dowell G. Engelman E. F. Ferrin P. A. Anderson	Agri. Expt. Sta. Techn. Bull. 181, University of Minnesota, St. Paul, Minn., 1949.
Marketing Western Feeder Cattle	I. M. Stevens R. T. Burdick H. G. Mason H. P. Gazaway	Wyo. Agri. Expt. Sta. Bul. 317, University of Wyoming, Laramie, Wyo., 1952.

CHAPTER XVI

THE DAIRY INDUSTRY[1]

Contents   **Page**

Importance and Uses of Milk 488
World Distribution and Production of Dairy Cattle 489
Magnitude of the U.S. Dairy Industry 490
Leading States in Milk Production and Cow Numbers 491
Production per Cow, Milk Cow Numbers, and Human Population 491
Kinds and Sizes of Dairy Farms 492
The Business Aspects 494
Factors Favorable to Dairy Production 494
Factors Unfavorable to Dairy Production 495
Future of Dairying 496
Questions for Study and Discussion 497
Selected References 497

Under natural conditions, wild mammals produce only enough milk for their offspring. However, long before recorded history, man found that milk was good—and good for him—with the result that he domesticated milk-producing animals and began using and selecting them for higher production for his own use. For the most part, this included the cow, the buffalo, and the goat—although the ewe, the mare, the sow, and other animals have been used for producing milk for human consumption in different parts of the world. The importance of the cow in milk production is attested to by her well-earned designation as, "the foster mother of the human race."

Records exist of cows being milked as early as 9000 B.C. The Bible contains many references to milk; one of the best remembered of which is from Exodus 3:8—"milk and honey." Also, Sanskrit writings, thousands of years old, relate that milk was one of the most essential of all foods. Hippocrates recommended milk as a medicine five centuries before Christ.

When Christopher Columbus came to America, there were no cows on the American continent. But on his second voyage, in 1493, he brought cattle and other farm animals to the West Indies.

The Pilgrims did not bring any cows with them. As a result, lack of milk is said to have contributed to the high death rate of the colonists, particularly of the children.

The first cows in the U.S. were brought over to Jamestown in 1611, and the first cows arrived at the Plymouth Colony in 1624.

---

[1] The author acknowledges with thanks the authoritative review accorded the entire dairy section—Chapters XVI through XXII—by the following persons: Dr. J. L. Albright, Department of Animal Sciences, Dairy Section, Purdue University, Lafayette, Indiana; Dr. H. A. Herman, Executive Secretary, National Association of Animal Breeders, Columbia, Missouri; and Professor Lyle Sasser, Assistant Professor of Dairy Science, Fresno State College, Fresno, California.

Throughout the colonial period, and until past the middle of the 19th century, dairying was limited to a few cows cared for by family labor. Management practices were poor when compared with today's standards. Also, the perishable nature of milk and the difficulty in transporting it made large-scale dairy operations impractical.

Starting soon after 1850, the following developments paved the way for the modern U.S. dairy industry of today: Cattle which were the foundation of our present-day breeds were brought to this country; milk was pooled by neighboring farm families in a cooperative effort to make cheese; condensed milk was developed by Borden in 1856; the centrifugal cream separator was invented in 1878; the Babcock test for fat evolved in 1892, followed by the adaptation of pasteurization to milk, mechanical refrigeration, homogenization, and modern packaging and transportation.

IMPORTANCE AND USES OF MILK

Milk is an important constituent of the American diet in terms of (1) per capita consumption (Table 16-1) and (2) a rich source of needed nutrients (Table 16-2).

TABLE 16—1

PER CAPITA CONSUMPTION OF FLUID MILK AND
MANUFACTURED DAIRY PRODUCTS, 1965[1]

	Qt.		Lb.
Fluid Milk Products, Total...	142.1	**Manufactured Products:**	
Fresh whole milk...........	120.9	Condensed whole milk.....	2.2
Cream...........................	3.5	Evaporated whole milk....	7.8
Skim milk......................	17.7	Butter.............................	5.4
		Cheese:	
		American..................	6.3
		Other.......................	3.6
		Cottage....................	4.6
		Dry whole milk..............	0.3
		Nonfat dry milk..............	5.9
		Evaporated and condensed skim milk.....................	5.1
		Frozen desserts:	
		Net milk used............	53.4
		Ice cream product......	18.2

[1]*Milk Facts*, Milk Industry Foundation, 1967 ed., p. 14.

In 1965, the total milk equivalent consumption of all dairy products was 620 pounds, a 16 per cent decline from 1950. But the growth in human population offset per capita decline, with the result that total consumption increased.

Table 16-3 shows the quantity of milk going into different channels, and Fig. 16-1 shows the relative importance of each outlet.

Almost half (45.7 per cent) of the milk marketed by farmers in 1966 was consumed in fluid form. In the 1930's, 54 per cent of the milk supply was used

TABLE 16—2

PERCENTAGE OF TOTAL NUTRIENTS CONTRIBUTED BY
DAIRY FOODS TO THE U.S. DIET[1]

Nutrient	Contributed by Dairy Foods
	(%)
Protein	24
Energy	13
Calcium	77
Phosphorus	38
Riboflavin	45
Vitamin A value	12
Thiamine	10

[1]*Organization and Competition in the Dairy Industry*, Tech. Study No. 3, National Commission on Food Marketing, June 1966, pp. 3 and 4.

TABLE 16—3

HOW THE U.S. MILK SUPPLY WAS USED IN 1966[1,2]

Product	Milk Equivalent
	(*Mil. lb.*)
Fluid milk and cream:	
Sold by dealers (25 billion qts.)	53,857
Sold by producers directly to consumers (811 million qts.)	1,743
Creamery butter	23,828
Cheese	16,791
Frozen dairy products[3]	10,621
Evaporated and condensed milk	4,766
Used on farms where produced	5,494
Other uses	4,501

[1]*Milk Facts*, Milk Industry Foundation, 1967 ed., p. 11.
[2]Includes Alaska and Hawaii.
[3]Only that milk used directly in making frozen dairy products. Does not include approximately 1,978,000,000 pounds of milk derived from other manufactured dairy products which, when added, give a total of 12,599,000 pounds of milk used in the production of frozen dairy products in 1966.

for butter, compared to 19.6 per cent in 1966. However, the proportion of milk marketed by dairy farmers which was used in making butter has remained relatively stable since World War II; and butter continues to be the second most important use of milk.

WORLD DISTRIBUTION AND PRODUCTION OF DAIRY CATTLE

Table 16-4 shows the number of milk cows and their proficiency in the principal countries of the world.

Some countries produce more dairy products than they can use, whereas others are importers. The United Kingdom is an especially heavy importer of butter, cheese, and condensed milk.

Among the factors that determine the present development of the dairy industry in different countries are: the character and preferences of the people; the adaptation of the country to dairying—dairying is not adaptable to areas

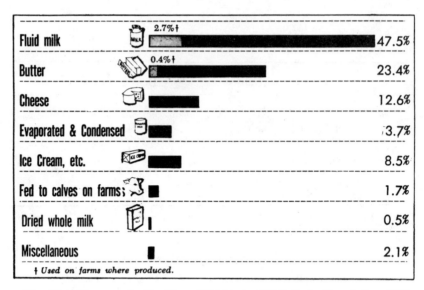

Fluid milk	2.7%†	47.5%
Butter	0.4%†	23.4%
Cheese		12.6%
Evaporated & Condensed		3.7%
Ice Cream, etc.		8.5%
Fed to calves on farms;		1.7%
Dried whole milk		0.5%
Miscellaneous		2.1%

† Used on farms where produced.

Fig. 16-1. The uses of milk. (From *Milk Facts*, Milk Industry Foundation, 1967 ed., p. 11)

TABLE 16—4

TEN LEADING COUNTRIES IN (1) MILK COWS ON FARMS
AND (2) MILK PRODUCTION PER COW, 1966[1]

Country	No. Milk Cows on Farms	Country	Average Milk Production/ Cow
	(1,000 head)		(lb.)
United States	15,477	Netherlands	9,303
France	8,954	Denmark	8,735
Germany, West	5,816	Belgium	8,630
United Kingdom	4,204	United States	8,080
Italy	3,250	Germany, West	8,029
Australia	3,012	Sweden	8,000
Canada	2,885	Switzerland	7,416
New Zealand	2,068	Finland	7,388
Netherlands	1,692	Norway	7,139
Ireland	1,547	France	6,465

[1]*Agricultural Statistics, 1966*, USDA, Table 564, p. 387.

that are excessively hot or cold, or where soils are poor; the relative size of urban and rural population; and the extent and effectiveness of dairy research and education.

MAGNITUDE OF THE U.S. DAIRY INDUSTRY

Table 16-5 shows the importance of the U.S. dairy industry. As noted, the farm income from milk totals more than $5 billion and represents 13 per cent of the total farm cash income.

Table 1-3, Chapter I of this book, shows the cash income of dairy prod-

TABLE 16—5

U.S. DAIRY FARM DATA, 1966[1]

Milk cows on farms (not including heifers not fresh).....................................(no.)....	14,123,000
Value of cows and heifers on farms (1966)...........($).......	3,761,252,000
Farm milk production...................................(lb.).....	120,230,000,000
Average production per cow.............................(lb.).....	8,513
Cash farm income from milk:	
Value...($).......	5,513,080,000
Income from milk as percentage of total	
farm income.......................................(%)......	12.8

[1] *Milk Facts*, Milk Industry Foundation, 1967 ed., p. 19.

ucts compared with other leading sources of farm and ranch income. Dairy products rank second only to cattle and calves in per cent of income of farmers and ranchers.

In addition to the income derived from milk, the sale of cows, heifers, steers, and veal calves from dairy herds accounts for an additional 3 per cent of farm cash receipts, or a total of approximately $1.2 billion annually.

Another indication of the magnitude and importance of the diary industry is that consumers spent $13.5 billion for dairy products in 1963, which represented about 16 per cent of their total expenditures for food.

LEADING STATES IN MILK PRODUCTION
AND COW NUMBERS

Milk is produced in every state of the Union. However, the greatest concentration of dairy cows is found in those areas with the most dense human population. This is as one would expect from the standpoint of the demand for and the marketing of fresh milk.

Table 16-6 gives the 10 leading states in dairy cattle numbers, by rank (see left half of table). Human population centers, which provide a large market for milk, have been a major factor in determining the intensity of dairying. Also, climate, land, and feed exert a considerable influence.

Some states have a well-managed dairy industry, but, because of their small size, they do not have a large total dairy cattle population. Therefore, proficiency of dairy management is best indicated by average annual production per cow, as shown in Table 16-6 (see right half of table).

PRODUCTION PER COW, MILK COW NUMBERS,
AND HUMAN POPULATION

The average production per cow has steadily increased, from 3,138 lb. in 1920 to 8,513 lb. per cow in 1966; simultaneously, cow numbers have declined and human population has spiraled (Table 16-7). This increase in average production per cow represents progress in improved breeding, feeding, disease control, and management. Also, increased milk production has made for greater efficiency.

TABLE 16—6

TEN LEADING STATES IN (1) MILK COWS ON FARMS
AND (2) MILK PRODUCTION PER COW, 1965[1]

State	No. Milk Cows on Farms	State	Average Milk Production/ Cow
	(1,000/head)		(lb.)
Wisconsin	2,078	California	10,840
Minnesota	1,231	Arizona	10,370
New York	1,173	Massachusetts	10,100
Pennsylvania	787	Hawaii	10,090
California	783	New Jersey	10,050
Iowa	734	Rhode Island	9,900
Michigan	604	Connecticut	9,900
Ohio	568	Nevada	9,570
Missouri	544	New York	9,420
Texas	459	Michigan	9,390

[1]Agricultural Statistics, 1966, USDA, Table 561, p. 384.

TABLE 16—7

U.S. MILK PRODUCTION PER COW, MILK COW NUMBERS,
AND HUMAN POPULATION, 1920-1965

Year	Milk Production Per Cow[1]	Number of Milk Cows[2]	Human Population[3]	Ratio of Milk Cows to People
	(lb.)			(no. cows to no. people)
1920	3,138	21,455,000	105,710,620	1 - 4.9
1930	4,508	23,032,000	122,775,046	1 - 5.5
1940	4,625	24,940,000	131,669,275	1 - 5.6
1950	5,314	23,853,000	150,697,361	1 - 6.6
1960	7,002	19,527,000	180,684,000	1 - 9.3
1965	8,080	17,592,000	194,600,000	1 -11.1

[1]Agricultural Statistics, USDA.
[2]Livestock and Meat Statistics, 1957, Stat. Bul. Nos. 230 and 333.
[3]Statistical Abstract of the United States, 1949, and The World Almanac and Book of Facts, 1966.

The cows which were in record-keeping dairy herd improvement associations, and which obviously were the more efficient ones, produced an average
of 12,127 pounds of milk and 462 pounds of butterfat in 1966.

KINDS AND SIZES OF DAIRY FARMS

Through the years, dairy farms have become more specialized and larger.
Separating cream, making butter, processing market milk, growing and mixing
concentrates, and keeping bulls have largely disappeared from the average dairy
farm; and this trend will continue.

The Walker-Gordon Laboratory of Plainsboro, New Jersey, has long obtained its milk supply from cows owned and cared for by individual contractors. Today, many California cattlemen neither raise replacement heifers
nor produce any feed. They have just enough corral space and facilities for
their cows. Others specialize in raising dairy heifer replacements. Also, in dif-

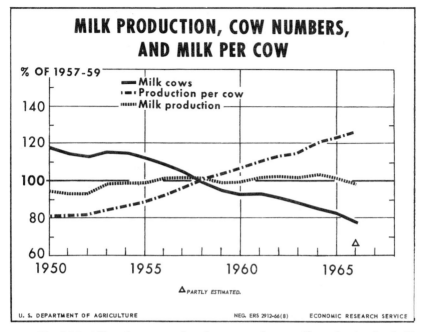

Fig. 16-2. Although cow numbers have gone down, milk production has held relatively stable due to higher production per cow.

Fig. 16-3. Corral system of dairying, in California. (Courtesy, Babson Bros. Co., Chicago, Ill.)

ferent sections of the country there is much interest in cow pools and cooperatives, and in vertical integration with the feed manufacturing facilities, the
dairy herd, and/or the milk processing and distributing plant under one ownership.

Larger, but fewer, enterprises have been ushered in with specialized enterprises. This is evident in Table 16-8. It is expected that the trend to bigness will continue.

TABLE 16—8

NUMBER OF FARMS REPORTING MILK COWS[1]

Size of Herd	1950	1954	1959
1 to 49 head	3,631,584	2,933,152	1,801,630
50 to 99 head	13,080	19,026	27,940
100 or more	3,593	4,722	6,551
Total dairy farms	3,648,257	2,956,900	1,836,121

[1]*Milk Facts*, Milk Industry Foundation, 1966 ed., p. 11.

THE BUSINESS ASPECTS

On a typical dairy farm, the business may consist of one or more of the
following enterprises: (1) the milking herd, (2) raising heifers for replacement purposes, (3) production of forage, and (4) production of cash crops.

As can be seen, dairy farm businesses are seldom comparable to one another, because the proportions of the enterprises vary. Hence, from the standpoint of records and analyses, it is important that each enterprise of the dairy
farm be considered separately. Only by doing so, is it possible to determine which
enterprises are most profitable, and which are least profitable. Such information
makes it feasible for the owner to make important managerial decisions as to
the future course—how much and what feed crop to grow, whether to enlarge
or reduce the number of cows in the milking herd, whether to raise replacement
heifers, and what to do to reduce costs or improve income in each enterprise
in the dairy farm business.

FACTORS FAVORABLE TO DAIRY PRODUCTION

Some of the special advantages to dairy production as compared to other
livestock on the farm are:

1. **Dairying is a stable business.**—Total milk production does not vary from
year to year as much as the output of most other agricultural products; the change
is often less than 1 per cent, and usually not more than 2 per cent. Nor does
milk consumption vary widely. As a result, milk and other dairy products are not
subject to as wide daily, seasonal, or yearly price fluctuations as are many
other agricultural products.

2. **The dairy cow is unequaled as an efficient producer of human food.**—

A cow producing 10,000 lb. of milk per year supplies as many food nutrients as are produced by two 1,250 lb. steers. Additionally, she is still available for more productive years. See Table 3-6 of this book for the feed to food efficiency rating of the dairy cow compared to other species of animals.

3. **Steady income is assured.**—A grain farmer, a fruit producer, or a vegetable grower receive income only when products are sold, usually once per year. Likewise, a beef cow-calf man secures most of his income when the calf crop is marketed, and, here again, this is generally once per year. On the other hand, a dairyman receives a regular milk check at frequent intervals (bi-weekly or monthly) throughout the year.

4. **Steady employment is provided for labor.**—Many types of agricultural work are highly seasonable, with the result that a labor force must be increased and decreased at such intervals as necessary, particularly during harvest. In the dairy enterprise, however, fairly uniform labor needs exist throughout the year. This makes it possible to keep better quality employees on a permanent basis.

5. **Dairy cows use much unsalable roughage.**—Each year, considerable amounts of roughages are produced on the farms and ranches of America which would have little value if not used by dairy cattle and other ruminants. Also, much of the rolling land on which such feeds are grown is unsuited to the production of grain or other crops.

6. **Soil fertility is maintained.**—By returning the manure to the land, the fertility and physical condition of the soil are preserved.

FACTORS UNFAVORABLE TO DAIRY PRODUCTION

Among the factors which, under certain conditions, may be unfavorable to dairy production are:

1. **Considerable capital is required.**—The investment for land, buildings, and equipment may run as high as $2,000 per cow, which is double, or more, what is normally required in investment per cow in a beef cow-calf enterprise.

2. **Successful dairy management necessitates superior training.**—The larger the dairy enterprise, the more important this becomes. A superior manager must be knowledgeable in the basic sciences, business administration, animal physiology, and nutrition; and he must possess the necessary personality and ability to weld this knowledge into a smooth-functioning, efficient production unit.

3. **The bewildering number and kinds of regulatory programs.**—The federal, state, and local regulatory programs necessitate that the dairyman be familiar with, and follow, those that are applicable to him. No matter how noble the objectives of these regulatory programs, this takes considerable time, and often it is a frustrating experience.

4. **Dairying is confining.**—Unlike many agricultural endeavors, dairying must be done regularly, and without fail, particularly where it is a market milk enterprise. Thus, an owner or a manager who is interested in vacation time, short

work weeks, or even short days, should not enter into a one-man dairy enterprise.

5. **Hourly returns are low.**—Hourly returns to dairy farmers have, on the average, been below returns in many other types of farming, and well below the average for all U.S. manufacturing industries (see Table 16-9).

TABLE 16—9

RETURNS PER HOUR OF WORK ON FARMS AND IN ALL
MANUFACTURING INDUSTRIES, 1964[1]

Item	Return/hour
	($)
Dairy farms..	0.61
Egg-producing farms, New Jersey....................	0.15
Broiler farms, Maine......................................	1.19
Hog-dairy, Corn Belt.....................................	1.14
Hog-beef finishing, Corn Belt.........................	0.99
Cash grain, Corn Belt....................................	2.13
All U.S. manufacturing industries....................	2.53

[1]*Organization and Competition in the Dairy Industry*, Tech. Study No. 3, National Commission on Food Marketing, June 1966, Table 2-8, p. 31.

6. **The threat of imitations**—Milk—long extolled as the "perfect food"—is being threatened by imitations.

FUTURE OF DAIRYING

Two factors, above all others, assure U.S. dairy production a bright future: (1) our expanding human population, and (2) the efficiency of the dairy cow from the standpoint of transforming plant materials into animal food products for humans (see Table 3-6).

The following developments will likely characterize the dairy production of the future:

1. **Larger units and increased automation.**—Table 16-8 shows that units have become bigger and fewer. This trend will continue, and with it there will be more automation.

2. **New and useful products.**—Intensive research attempts are being made to provide products (a) with the characteristics of fresh milk, but which will last longer in storage and (b) which can be transported at lower cost. Sterile milk and concentrated milk are receiving the most attention.

3. **More dairy beef.**—The dairy industry provides one-fourth to one-third of the beef consumed in this country; with these animals marketed as veal calves, cull dairy cows and bulls, and finished dairy heifers and steers. Improvements in the science and technology of feeding and processing favor the growing and finishing of more dairy beef, which will lessen the slaughter of veal calves.

4. **Higher production and greater efficiency per cow.**—It is evident that,

as profit margins narrow and knowledge becomes greater, we shall continue to move, at an accelerated pace, to higher production and greater efficiency per cow. This will be achieved through the application of modern breeding, feeding, milking, management, and marketing.

5. **More training, experience, and business acumen.**—The successful dairy manager of the larger and more highly specialized units of the future must have more know-how and experience, and the ability to operate the dairy establishment as a big business.

QUESTIONS FOR STUDY AND DISCUSSION

1. Why are some mammals other than milk cows—such as water buffaloes, goats, and mares—used for milk production in different parts of the world?
2. What characteristics should a successful dairyman possess?
3. What conditions have prompted the present trend toward the production of more beef from animals of dairy breeding?
4. In the future, how is dairy production likely to fare in comparison with beef production, sheep production, swine production, and poultry production from the standpoints of (a) increasing or decreasing as our population increases and (b) continuing to use cereal grains as they become scarcer and higher?
5. Why is accessibility to a market so important in selecting a dairy farm?
6. What factors have caused dairy farms to increase in size?
7. What factors have prompted the trend toward more and more specialization in the dairy enterprise, in contrast to diversification?
8. What factors should be considered in determining whether to raise dairy heifers where one is milking cows?
9. How do (a) federal milk orders, (b) state milk orders, (c) state trade practice laws, and (d) sanitary regulations affect the dairy farmer?
10. How may a dairyman keep abreast of new developments?

SELECTED REFERENCES

Title of Publication	Author(s)	Publisher
Dairy Cattle and Milk Production	C. H. Eckles E. L. Anthony	The Macmillan Co., New York, N. Y., 1956.
Dairy Cattle Feeding and Management	P. M. Reaves H. O. Henderson	John Wiley & Sons, Inc., New York, N. Y., 1966.
Dairy Cattle in American Agriculture	A. R. Porter J. A. Sims C. F. Foreman	The Iowa State University Press, Ames, Iowa, 1965.
Dairy Cattle Management	J. M. Wing	Reinhold Pub. Corp., New York, N. Y., 1963.
Dairy Cattle Selection, Feeding and Management	W. W. Yapp W. B. Nevens	John Wiley & Sons, Inc., New York, N. Y., 1955.
Dairy Science	W. E. Peterson	J. B. Lippincott Co., Philadelphia, Pa., 1950.
Milk Production and Processing	H. F. Judkins H. A. Keener	John Wiley & Sons, Inc., New York, N. Y., 1963.
Modern Dairy Cattle Management	R. F. Davis	Prentice-Hall, Inc., Englewood Cliffs, N. J., 1962.

CHAPTER XVII

BREEDS OF DAIRY CATTLE

Contents

Page

Popularity of Breeds..499
Characteristics of Breeds...499
Milk and Butterfat Production of Breeds..501
Programs of the Registry Associations..502
Questions for Study and Discussion...504
Selected References 504

There are five major breeds of dairy cattle in the U.S.; all developed in Europe, and all of which have proven satisfactory in different sections of the U.S.

POPULARITY OF BREEDS

Table 17-1 shows (1) when each of the five principal breed registries was formed and (2) the 1966 and total registrations to date of the major breeds of dairy cattle. Even though data for one year only fail to show trends, the recent annual figures reflect the current popularity and numbers of the respective breeds more than total registrations since establishing the breed registry.

TABLE 17—1

DAIRY BREEDS: (1) YEAR IN WHICH BREED REGISTRY WAS FORMED AND (2) 1966 AND TOTAL REGISTRATIONS

Breed	Breed Association Formed		1966 Registrations	Total Registrations
	in Europe	in U.S.		
Ayrshire..............	1877	1875	14,310	810,740
Brown Swiss	1911	1880	17,460	663,238
Guernsey	1814	1877	47,196	2,948,789
Holstein	1873	1871	270,377	8,164,281
Jersey	1833	1868	64,960	3,297,261

CHARACTERISTICS OF BREEDS

Table 17-2 gives in summary form the place of origin and the characteristics of each of the breeds of dairy cattle.

TABLE 17—2

BREEDS OF DAIRY CATTLE AND THEIR CHARACTERISTICS

Breed	Place of Origin	Color	Distinctive Head Characteristics	Other Distinguishing Characteristics	Disqualifications
Ayrshire	County of Ayr, in south-western Scotland.	Light to deep cherry red, mahogany, brown, or a combination of these colors, with white. or white alone. Black or brindle are objectionable.	Horns are widespread and tend to curve upward and outward. However, there is a polled strain.	The udders are especially symmetrical and well attached to the body. The breed is noted for its style and animation, good feet and legs, and grazing ability.	
Brown Swiss	The Alps of Switzerland.	Solid brown varying from very light to dark. White markings are objectionable.	The nose and tongue are black, and there is a characteristic light-colored band around the muzzle. Medium length horns.	Strong and rugged, with some tendency toward the heavy muscling characteristic of the beef breeds. Calm and unexcitable.	
Guernsey	Isle of Guernsey.	Fawn with white markings clearly defined; preferably a clear (buff) muzzle.	Good length of head; horns incline forward, are refined and medium in length, and taper toward the tips.	The milk is especially yellow in color; golden yellow skin pigmentation; the unhaired portions of the body are light or pinkish in color (whereas in the Jersey they are near black); calves are relatively small at birth.	
Holstein-Friesian	Netherlands and Northern Germany.	Black and white markings, clearly defined.	Clean-cut, broad muzzle, open nostrils, strong jaw, broad and moderately dished forehead, straight bridged nose.	Large angular animal; females should weigh 1,500 lbs. (mature); males in breeding condition 2,200 lbs.	Colors which bar registry: all black or all white, black in switch, black belly, black circling leg and touching hoof, black from hoof to knee or hock, black and white intermixed to give color other than distinct black and white.
Jersey	Island of Jersey.	Jerseys vary greatly in color, but the characteristic color is some shade of fawn, with or without white markings.	Forehead, broad and moderately dished with large, bright eyes. Clean-cut and proportionate to body.	Jerseys are especially known for their well-shaped udders and strong udder attachments. They are also very angular and refined.	Total blindness, permanent lameness that interferes with normal function, blind quarter, freemartin heifers, and animals showing signs of being operated upon or tampered with.

Fig. 17-1. Hammond's Top Primrose, Ayrshire cow. Her production through 1966 was 149,754 lb. of milk and 6,057 lb. of fat, with an average butterfat test of 4.0. (Courtesy, Ayrshire Breeders' Assn.)

Fig. 17-2. Lee's Hill Keeper's Raven 171673, Brown Swiss holder of the breed's highest milk record (see Table 17-4). Classified "Excellent." (Courtesy, The Brown Swiss Cattle Breeders' Assn.)

Fig. 17-3. Ideals Beacon's Nora, lifetime milk and butterfat champion of the Guernsey breed 4,328 days: 225,287 lb. of milk; 11,740 lb. of fat. Individual milk and fat record: 305 days-3x, 25,063 lb. of milk; 1,301 lb. of fat, AR. (Courtesy, The American Guernsey Cattle Club)

Fig. 17-4. Princess Breezewood R A Patsy, Holstein-Friesian holder of U.S. butterfat production 305-day, twice-a-day milking. (Courtesy, Holstein-Friesian Assn. of America)

Fig. 17-5. Beacon Bas Patience, Grand Champion female in 1964 All American Jersey Show. (Courtesy, The American Jersey Cattle Club)

MILK AND BUTTERFAT PRODUCTION OF BREEDS

There are breed differences in milk and butterfat production. Table 17-3 summarizes the averages by breeds. On the basis of milk production, they rank in the following order: Holstein, Brown Swiss, Ayrshire, Guernsey, and Jersey. However, on the basis of butterfat test they rank: Jersey, Guernsey, Ayrshire, Brown Swiss, and Holstein.

The U.S. milk and butterfat record holders for each of the breeds are given in Table 17-4.

TABLE 17—3

HERD IMPROVEMENT AVERAGES FOR EACH BREED

Breed	Year	Milk Production	Butterfat Test	Butterfat Production
Ayrshire	1966	12,472	4.1	506
Brown Swiss	1966	12,728.5	4.07	517.49
Guernsey	1966	10,490	4.83	507
Holstein	1966	15,039	3.66	551
Jersey	1966	9,267	5.2	480

TABLE 17—4

U.S. PRODUCTION RECORDS FOR EACH BREED

Breed	Name of Cow	Year	Milk Production	Butterfat Test	Butterfat Production
Milk Production:					
Ayrshire[1]	Middle Brook Fancy Madge	1967	27,360	3.9	1,058
Brown Swiss[2]	Lee's Hill Keeper's Raven	1958	34,850.9	4.53	1,579.28
Guernsey[2]	Nill Farm Poppy	1961	29,665	4.0	1,190
Holstein[1]	King View Francy Allegra	1958	34,124	3.2	1,106
Jersey[3]	Etta's Sparkle	1967-68	28,260	4.74	1,340
Butterfat Production:					
Ayrshire[1]	Bob's Pansy Girl	1963	20,240	6.0	1,213
Brown Swiss[2]	Letha Irene Pride	1959	34,810.9	4.98	1,733.13
Guernsey[1]	Longmeadow Minnie	1957	26,695	5.5	1,461
Holstein[1]	Princess Breezewood R A Patsy	1959	31,788	4.9	1,562
Jersey[3]	Victory S.C.		23,500	6.5	1,536

[1]305-day, 2x
[2]365-day, 3x
[3]365-day, 2x

PROGRAMS OF THE REGISTRY ASSOCIATIONS

In addition to registering animals, most of the breed associations promote the following programs:

1. **Production testing in Dairy Herd Improvement Registry (DHIR).**—Each breed registry association has a program for testing registered cows under the Unified Rules for Official Testing as adopted by the Purebred Dairy Cattle Association and the American Dairy Science Association. This program is conducted cooperatively by the breed association and the Division of Dairy Herd Improvement Investigations of the USDA (the division which, in cooperation with the states, is responsible for DHIR records). Records recognized as official by both groups are included in one program.

Under DHIR, milk testing is conducted once each month, with the tester obtaining a 24-hour milk weight and butterfat test. Also, the tester secures data on each cow that has freshened, feed consumption and quality, labor, price of milk, etc. All this data is sent to a central laboratory for analysis, with many states cooperating on a regional basis in the Electronic Data Processing Method (EDPM). The machine-processed records are then returned to the dairyman, giving him current information on milk yield, income over feed costs, milk produced per cow, and other pertinent information to help him in making culling and managerial decisions.

In 1966-67, two breed registry production testing programs—(a) Advanced Registry (AR) and (b) Herd Improvement Registry (HIR)—were discontinued, and the Dairy Herd Improvement Registry (DHIR) became the official milk recording program of all the breeds.

2. **Type classification.**—Since many animals are not exhibited at cattle shows,

the associations started a voluntary program of herd classification whereby a qualified classifier, selected by the association, at the request of the owner and on a nominal charge basis, comes to the farm and classifies for type or conformation each milking animal in the herd. Each animal is rated according to the score card and placed in the corresponding category, as shown in Table 17-5.

TABLE 17—5

TYPE CLASSIFICATION BY BREEDS

Nomenclature	Ayrshire	Brown Swiss	Guernsey	Holstein	Jersey
	← score in points →				

E-Excellent
VG-Very Good
GP-Good Plus
    (D-Desirable in
    Guernseys)
	90 & over
	85-89
	80-84
		90 & over
		85-89
		80-84
			90 & over
			85-89
			80-84
				90 & over
				85-89
				80-84
					90 & over
					85-89
					80-84

G-Good
    (A-Acceptable in
    Guernseys)
	75-79	70-79	75-79	75-79	75-79

F-Fair P-Poor	70-74 Under 70	60-69 Under 60	70-74 Under 70	65-74 Under 65	70-74 ————
Year when initiated	1941	1942	1947	1929	1932

The program has been increasingly utilized by breeders, and it has been highly effective in the general improvement of conformation and in merchandizing cattle.

3. **Recognition awards.**—Some of the breed associations have established certain programs and recognition awards for breeders, cows, and bulls; and two of them have special milk merchandizing programs. These are summarized in Table 17-6.

TABLE 17—6

BREED RECOGNITION AWARDS

Breed	Breeder Award	Sire Award	Dam Award	Milking Merchandising Program
Ayrshire	Constructive Breeder	Approved Sire	Approved Dam	
Guernsey	Gold Star Breeder Gold Star Herd	Gold Star Sire A.I. Gold Star Sire A.I. Silver Star Prod. Sire	Gold Star Dam	Golden Guernsey Milk (started in 1923)
Holstein- Friesian	Progressive Breeder Registry	Silver Medal Produc- tion Sire Silver Medal Type Sire Gold Medal Sire (Type and Production)	Gold Medal Dam (Type & Produc- tion)	
Jersey	Constructive Breeder Gold Star Herd	Star Bull Selective Registration Silver Medal Bull Gold Medal Bull Medal of Merit Bull A.J.C.C. Tested Sire Superior Sire Senior Superior Sire Century Sire	Silver Medal Cow Gold Medal Cow Medal of Merit Cow Tested Dam Ton-of-Gold Certif- icate	All Jersey Milk
Milking Shorthorn	Progressive Breeder	Advanced Registry of Production Sire (ARP)	ARP Dam	

These awards vary somewhat between breeds, and they are revised upward from time to time so as to maintain them as worth-while goals. For breeder recognition, the general factors taken into account are: ownership of a certain minimum number of (a) registered females and (b) animals bred by owner, meeting established minimum production requirements under one of the breed testing programs, meeting established minimum type classification requirements, and evidence of a healthy herd, especially with respect to tuberculosis and brucellosis. Sire and dam awards are based on their apparent ability to transmit a high level of production and/or type to a specified number and percentage of offspring.

QUESTIONS FOR STUDY AND DISCUSSION

1. Of what importance are the (a) distinguishing characteristics and (b) disqualifications of the breeds of dairy cattle?
2. Justify any preference or bias that you may have for one particular breed of dairy cattle.
3. Is there a need for more breeds of dairy cattle than we now have in the U.S.?
4. Are breeds of dairy cattle likely to decline in importance as happened in the poultry industry?
5. How do you account for the difference between breeds in milk and butterfat production?
6. Obtain breed registry association literature of one breed of dairy cattle. Evaluate the soundness and value of the material that you receive.

SELECTED REFERENCES

Title of Publication	Author(s)	Publisher
Breeds of Livestock in America	H. W. Vaughan	R. G. Adams and Co., Columbus, Ohio, 1937.
Modern Breeds of Livestock	H. M. Briggs	The Macmillan Co., New York, N. Y., 1949.
Types and Breeds of Farm Animals	C. S. Plumb	Ginn and Co., Boston, Mass., 1920.
World Dictionary of Breeds, Types and Varieties of Livestock	I. L. Mason	Commonwealth Agric. Bureau, Farnham House, Farnham Royal, Slough, Bucks, England.

CHAPTER XVIII

ESTABLISHING THE DAIRY HERD;
SELECTING AND JUDGING

Contents   Page

Factors to Consider in Establishing the Herd..............................505
Purebred Business 507
  Requisites of a Purebred Herd.....................................507
  Requisites of a Registered Breeder................................507
Selecting Herd Replacements...507
Culling Dairy Cattle..508
Judging Dairy Cattle 509
  Parts of a Cow...510
  Dairy Type; Breed Type...510
  Unified Score Cards..510
Questions for Study and Discussion....................................513
Selected References 513

Whether establishing a new herd or maintaining an old one, a dairyman must constantly appraise or evaluate his animals—he must buy, sell, retain, and cull.

FACTORS TO CONSIDER IN ESTABLISHING THE HERD

In establishing a dairy herd, the following factors must be considered:

1. **Dairy or dual-purpose type.**—Approximately one-third of the cows of the U.S. are kept for milk production. Of these, about 70 per cent belong to the five major dairy breeds, and the remainder to the dual-purpose breeds, beef cattle, or nondescript breeding. Where dairying is highly specialized, most milk cows are of strictly dairy breeding, rather than of dual-purpose type.

2. **Grades or purebreds.**—Technically, a purebred animal is one that can meet ancestry requirements in one of the breed registry associations, whereas a registered animal is a purebred which has been recorded in one of the registry books. Grade animals are those that are not registered or eligible for registry; however, such animals frequently approach purebred status as a result of several generations of breeding up by using sires of one breed. Thus, if a registered sire is used successively for seven generations, the final offspring will, mathematically speaking, consist of 99 per cent registered parentage. From this, it can be reasoned that, from an inherited production potential, the gap between registered and grade animals is often very small.

In general, the man who is inexperienced in handling dairy animals, or who has a limited amount of capital, should start with grade animals, then improve them by the use of good purebred sires through artificial insemination programs

505

However, the man who is experienced, and who has adequate capital, may well consider the purebred business.

3. **Choice of a breed.**—The choice of a breed is usually made on the basis of personal preference, prior association with the breed and the breeders, and the availability of the breed in the immediate area. Perhaps it is well to add that the choice of a breed is likely of less importance than the choice of good individuals within the breed, simply because there is more difference within breeds than between breeds.

4. **Buying cows, heifers, or calves.**—In starting a herd, three methods are available: buying cows, buying heifers, or buying calves. Also, cows and heifers of breeding age may be either open or bred at the time of purchase. The choice between the alternatives should be determined primarily by (a) the time when it is desired to be in production, (b) available capital, and (c) experience.

Where there is no question pertaining to the honesty and integrity of the seller, and good cows with production records back of them can be acquired at what is considered to be a fair and reasonable price, usually this constitutes the best buy. In acquiring cows, it is well to keep in mind that, on the average, they remain in the milking herd for only four to five years, and, for the most part, they are culled from, or leave, the herd before they are seven years of age.

The purchase of heifers at breeding age or as "springers" to start a herd is a very popular method. When buying heifers, consideration should be given to the caliber of their dams and the record of their sires.

The purchase of calves requires the least initial capital of any of the methods, but it also takes more time to get into production. In many ways, however, the purchase of calves offers the best opportunity to get high quality breeding animals.

5. **Production records.**—Production records should be used in selecting individual animals, with proper consideration given to the environmental factors under which the records were made.

6. **The disease problem.**—In establishing a herd, one should take every possible precaution to avoid bringing in a disease, especially such diseases as tuberculosis, brucellosis, leptospirosis, trichomoniasis, and mastitis. Despite all precautions, however, it is well that newly acquired animals be isolated for a period of 30 to 60 days, and that they be re-tested at the end of that period before being placed in the herd.

Of course, there are other factors to consider in establishing a herd, among them longevity. Since it normally takes the profit from the first lactation plus about one-half of the second lactation to cover the initial investment in the animal before she freshens, it becomes crystal clear that longevity is important to the owner. Other factors of importance are: uniformity, condition, reproductive ability, temperament, size, and price.

PUREBRED BUSINESS

It is estimated that approximately 10 per cent of the dairy cattle of the U.S. are purebred. However, these animals exert a powerful influence through supplying seedstock to the dairy industry—to other purebred breeders and to those who have grade dairy cattle.

Requisites of a Purebred Herd

The primary requisites of a purebred herd are:

1. **High production.**—If purebred animals are to bring about further improvement through the dissemination of seedstock, it is imperative that they be top producers.

2. **Good type.**—There is much controversy over the value of type and its relationship, or lack thereof, to production. Nevertheless, no one has proved that, on the average, cattle with good conformation produce less than cattle with poor conformation. Further, it is generally acknowledged that, among top producers, one can select animals with superior type. Also, people instinctively desire and appreciate beauty, no matter what the object; and usually they are willing to pay extra for it. It follows, therefore, that good type is important in the purebred herd because animals must be sold.

3. **Attractive surroundings.**—Although it is not necessary that the physical plant of a purebred herd be elaborate, it should be neat and attractive.

Requisites of a Registered Breeder

As is true of the commercial dairymen with grade cows, to be successful the purebred breeder must possess a love for the dairy business and the necessary knowledge and experience in the production, handling, and marketing of milk. Additionally, the registered breeder should (1) have knowledge of breeding and pedigrees, (2) pay attention to details, (3) be able to promote and sell, (4) be able to withstand disappointment, and (5) practice honesty and integrity in all dealings.

SELECTING HERD REPLACEMENTS

The average dairy cow in the U.S. remains in the milking herd about four years. This means that about 25 per cent of the average milking herd must be replaced each year. These replacement animals must be either raised or purchased. In either event, the animals brought in should be of herd-improving kind.

In this section, selection of herd replacements will be limited to females. Bull selection is covered in the chapter on "Breeding Dairy Cattle."

When the major source of income is from the sale of milk, selection is simplified. The cows can be ranked from high to low on the basis of milk production, and the most profitable ones used as replacements. Where purebred breeding stock is involved, the breeder usually invokes an additional point—type or conformation.

Where heifers are being selected for eventual replacement purposes, pedigree information is very important.

CULLING DAIRY CATTLE

The successful dairyman is constantly checking his herd and evaluating individual cows, then culling those that do not make money. With high milk prices and low salvage prices, he often finds it difficult to decide which cows to cull from the herd, and how many he should cull. Tables 18-1 and 18-2 are designed to assist in this regard. Such forms facilitate establishing minimum standards in each area of concern and importance.

TABLE 18—1

CULLING GUIDE (based on 305-day butterfat production)[1]

	A	B	C	D	E	F	G	H	I	J	K	L
Pounds of Butterfat	Under 350	350-374	375-399	400-424	425-449	450-474	475-499	500-524	525-549	550-574	575-599	600-Over
Mature cows (3rd lactation or more)												
Pounds of butterfat	Under 310	310-331	332-353	354-375	376-397	398-419	420-441	442-464	465-486	487-508	509-530	531-Over
Second-lactation cows												
Pounds of butterfat	Under 280	280-299	300-319	320-339	340-359	360-379	380-399	400-419	420-439	440-459	460-479	480-Over
First-lactation cows												
Herd Total												

[1]From *A Guide to Culling Dairy Cows*, AXT-11, by Robert D. Appleman, University of California Agricultural Extension Service.

Table 18-1, "Culling Guide," is simply a form on which the butterfat production of each cow can be listed (list each cow by number in the proper category), with provision for first lactation cows, second lactation cows, and mature cows. By using this form, culling decisions can be made without having to compute age-conversion factors. After listing cows in the proper columns, the dairyman can decide where to draw the line. For example, if he decides to cull all mature cows that are below the 425-pound level, he will take out all cows in columns A, B, C, and D. Similarly, he might decide to draw the line on second lactation cows at 376 pounds, and on first lactation cows at 340 pounds.

After culling on the basis of productivity, the dairyman must also cull for other reasons. The cow evaluation form, Table 18-2, is designed for this purpose. It can be applied, and those that do not measure up can be culled.

TABLE 18—2

COW EVALUATION[1]

Production	Retain		Cull
	High	Average	Low
Mature cows	10% above mature herd average	Within 10% of mature herd average	10% or more below mature herd average
Second-lactation cows	Above mature herd average	Within 20% of mature herd average	20% or more below mature herd average
First-lactation cows	Above or within 10% of mature herd average	10 to 30% below mature herd average	30% or more below mature herd average
Miscellaneous Factors: Expected dry period	2 months	3-5 months	6 months or more
Health and injuries	Good	Temporary	Chronic
Milking qualities	Fast	Medium	Slow and hard
Disposition	Quiet	Not easily excitable	Nervous or dull
Type, particularly udder conformation	Highly desirable	Sound	Undesirable

[1]From *A Guide to Culling Dairy Cows*, AXT-11, by Robert D. Appleman, University of California Agricultural Extension Service.

JUDGING DAIRY CATTLE

It appears that only about 19 per cent of the cows in lactation are tested to determine their milk-yielding capacity. Even fewer dairy animals are subjected to the scrutiny of an experienced judge in the show ring. Thus, the only method, other than pedigree, available to evaluate the great bulk of dairy animals is by what is commonly known as judging.

Judging—as practiced in shows, in contests, or on the farm—is an attempt to place or rank animals in the order of their excellence in body type. Scoring, or type classifying, an animal accomplishes the same thing, in that the individual being scored is classified and compared to an animal that is theoretically perfect, and a rating is assigned on this basis.

Admittedly, there is considerable question as to the degree of correlation between type and production. Yet, it is generally recognized that desirable type in no way negates functional value. Moreover, it is generally recognized that attractiveness, and what we think of as desirable type, enhances the market value of purebred animals. Also, well-attached udders are less subject to injury and mastitis infection, and strong legs hold up longer than weak legs and feet.

It is noteworthy that good and successful owners and managers are generally good judges of dairy cattle.

Parts of a Cow

One of the characteristics of a good judge is that he possesses a thorough knowledge of animals. In speaking of the characteristics of a dairy animal, we usually refer to parts rather than to the individual as a whole. It is important, therefore, to become familiar with the names of the parts. Figures 18-1 and 18-2 show animals in outline form and identify by name the various parts of animals. These figures should be studied until each part of the animal can be easily and quickly identified by location and name. Nothing so quickly sets a real "cow man" apart from a novice as a thorough knowledge of the parts and the language commonly used in describing them.

Dairy Type; Breed Type

Webster defines type as, "the combination of characters appropriate to a special kind of use." Certainly, this definition is adequate for distinguishing beef type from dairy-type cattle, or perhaps even for distinguishing Jersey type from Holstein type. However, it lacks the necessary specificity for those desiring to differentiate type within a breed. Hence, the following definition is proposed:

Type refers to an ideal or standard of perfection combining the physical characteristics which contribute to an animal's usefulness for a specific purpose.

Additionally, to practical dairymen, the word "type" has come to express the kind of cow that is adapted to modern herd management, with emphasis placed on profitability.

Type has become more meaningful in dairy cattle since the establishment of the type classification program, first introduced in the Holstein breed in 1929. Today, each of the major dairy breed associations has an active committee on dairy types.

There is no conflict between dairy type and breed type; the latter merely adds certain distinctive breed characteristics. The breed registry associations promulgate breed type through shows, type classification programs, and models and paintings.

A monetary value is placed on type by most dairymen, particularly by purebred breeders; hence, type may be said to be of market importance.

Unified Score Cards

A score card is a listing of the different parts of an animal, with a numerical value assigned to each according to its relative importance. Fortunately, there was a common meeting ground by the purebred dairy cattle associations in the development of the Unified Score Cards herewith reproduced as Figures 18-1

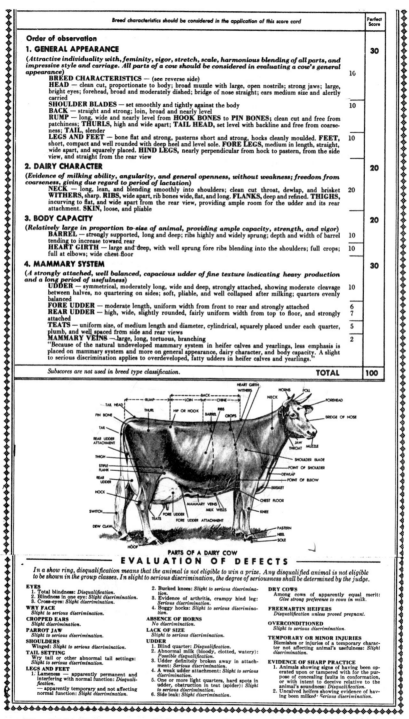

Breed characteristics should be considered in the application of this score card	Perfect Score

Order of observation

1. GENERAL APPEARANCE — **30**

(Attractive individuality with, feminity, vigor, stretch, scale, harmonious blending of all parts, and impressive style and carriage. All parts of a cow should be considered in evaluating a cow's general appearance)

BREED CHARACTERISTICS — (see reverse side) ... 16

HEAD — clean cut, proportionate to body; broad muzzle with large, open nostrils; strong jaws; large, bright eyes; forehead, broad and moderately dished; bridge of nose straight; ears medium size and alertly carried

SHOULDER BLADES — set smoothly and tightly against the body ... 10

BACK — straight and strong; loin, broad and nearly level

RUMP — long, wide and nearly level from HOOK BONES to PIN BONES; clean cut and free from patchiness; THURLS, high and wide apart; TAIL HEAD, set level with backline and free from coarseness; TAIL, slender

LEGS AND FEET — bone flat and strong, pasterns short and strong, hocks cleanly moulded. FEET, ... 10
short, compact and well rounded with deep heel and level sole. FORE LEGS, medium in length, straight, wide apart, and squarely placed. HIND LEGS, nearly perpendicular from hock to pastern, from the side view, and straight from the rear view

2. DAIRY CHARACTER — **20**

(Evidence of milking ability, angularity, and general openness, without weakness; freedom from coarseness, giving due regard to period of lactation)

NECK — long, lean, and blending smoothly into shoulders; clean cut throat, dewlap, and brisket ... 20
WITHERS, sharp. RIBS, wide apart, rib bones wide, flat, and long. FLANKS, deep and refined. THIGHS, incurving to flat, and wide apart from the rear view, providing ample room for the udder and its rear attachment. SKIN, loose, and pliable

3. BODY CAPACITY — **20**

(Relatively large in proportion to size of animal, providing ample capacity, strength, and vigor)

BARREL — strongly supported, long and deep; ribs highly and widely sprung; depth and width of barrel ... 10
tending to increase toward rear

HEART GIRTH — large and deep, with well sprung fore ribs blending into the shoulders; full crops; ... 10
full at elbows; wide chest floor

4. MAMMARY SYSTEM — **30**

(A strongly attached, well balanced, capacious udder of fine texture indicating heavy production and a long period of usefulness)

UDDER — symmetrical, moderately long, wide and deep, strongly attached, showing moderate cleavage ... 10
between halves, no quartering on sides; soft, pliable, and well collapsed after milking; quarters evenly balanced

FORE UDDER — moderate length, uniform width from front to rear and strongly attached ... 6

REAR UDDER — high, wide, slightly rounded, fairly uniform width from top to floor, and strongly ... 7
attached

TEATS — uniform size, of medium length and diameter, cylindrical, squarely placed under each quarter, ... 5
plumb, and well spaced from side and rear views

MAMMARY VEINS — large, long, tortuous, branching ... 2

"Because of the natural undeveloped mammary system in heifer calves and yearlings, less emphasis is placed on mammary system and more on general appearance, dairy character, and body capacity. A slight to serious discrimination applies to overdeveloped, fatty udders in heifer calves and yearlings."

Subscores are not used in breed type classification.

TOTAL | **100**

PARTS OF A DAIRY COW

EVALUATION OF DEFECTS

In a show ring, disqualification means that the animal is not eligible to win a prize. Any disqualified animal is not eligible to be shown in the group classes. In slight to serious discrimination, the degree of seriousness shall be determined by the judge.

EYES
1. Total blindness: *Disqualification.*
2. Blindness in one eye: *Slight discrimination.*
3. Cross-eyes: *Slight discrimination.*

WRY FACE
Slight to serious discrimination.

CROPPED EARS
Slight discrimination.

PARROT JAW
Slight to serious discrimination.

SHOULDERS
Winged: *Slight to serious discrimination.*

TAIL SETTING
Wry tail or other abnormal tail settings: *Slight to serious discrimination.*

LEGS AND FEET
1. Lameness — apparently permanent and interfering with normal function: *Disqualification.*
— apparently temporary and not affecting normal function: *Slight discrimination.*

2. Bucked knees: *Slight to serious discrimination.*
3. Evidence of arthritis, crampy hind leg: *Serious discrimination.*
4. Boggy hocks: *Slight to serious discrimination.*

ABSENCE OF HORNS
No discrimination.

LACK OF SIZE
Slight to serious discrimination.

UDDER
1. Blind quarter: *Disqualification.*
2. Abnormal milk (bloody, clotted, watery): *Possible disqualification.*
3. Udder definitely broken away in attachment: *Serious discrimination.*
4. A weak udder attachment: *Slight to serious discrimination.*
5. One or more light quarters, hard spots in udder, obstruction in teat (spider): *Slight to serious discrimination.*
6. Side leak: *Slight discrimination.*

DRY COWS
Among cows of apparently equal merit: *Give strong preference to cows in milk.*

FREEMARTIN HEIFERS
Disqualification unless proved pregnant.

OVERCONDITIONED
Slight to serious discrimination.

TEMPORARY OR MINOR INJURIES
Blemishes or injuries of a temporary character not affecting animal's usefulness: *Slight discrimination.*

EVIDENCE OF SHARP PRACTICE
1. Animals showing signs of having been operated upon or tampered with for the purpose of concealing faults in conformation, or with intent to deceive relative to the animal's soundness: *Disqualification.*
2. Uncalved heifers showing evidence of having been milked: *Serious discrimination.*

Fig. 18-1. Dairy cow unified score card. (Copyrighted by The Purebred Dairy Cattle Association, 1943; revised, and copyrighted 1957; approved—The American Dairy Science Association, 1957)

Breed characteristics should be considered in the application of this score card	Perfect Score

Order of observation

1. GENERAL APPEARANCE — 45

(Attractive individuality, with masculinity, vigor, stretch, and scale, harmonious blending of all parts, and impressive style and carriage. All parts of a bull should be considered in evaluating a bull's general appearance)

BREED CHARACTERISTICS — (see reverse side) — 15

HEAD — clean cut, proportionate to body; broad muzzle with large, open nostrils; strong jaws; large, bright eyes; forehead, broad and moderately dished; bridge of nose straight; ears medium size and alertly carried

SHOULDER BLADES — set smoothly and tightly against the body — 15

BACK — straight and strong; loin, broad and nearly level

RUMP — long, wide, and nearly level from **HOOK BONES** to **PIN BONES**; clean cut and free from patchiness; **THURLS**, high and wide apart; **TAIL HEAD**, set level with backline and free from coarseness; **TAIL**, slender

LEGS AND FEET — bone flat and strong, pasterns short and strong, hocks cleanly moulded. **FEET**, short, compact, and well rounded with deep heel and level sole. **FORE LEGS**, medium in length, straight and wide apart, squarely placed. **HIND LEGS**, nearly perpendicular from hock to pastern from the side view, and straight from the rear view — 15

2. DAIRY CHARACTER — 30

(Angularity and general openness, without weakness; freedom from coarseness)

NECK — long, with medium crest and blending smoothly into shoulders; clean cut throat, dewlap, and brisket. **WITHERS**, sharp. **RIBS**, wide apart, rib bones wide, flat, and long. **FLANKS**, deep and refined. **THIGHS**, incurving to flat, and wide apart from the rear view. **SKIN**, loose, and pliable

3. BODY CAPACITY — 25

(Relatively large in proportion to size of animal, providing ample capacity, strength, and vigor)

BARREL — strongly supported, long, and deep; ribs highly and widely sprung; depth and width of barrel tending to increase toward rear — 12

HEART GIRTH — large and deep, with well sprung fore ribs blending into the shoulders; full crops; full at elbows; wide chest floor — 13

Subscores are not used in breed type classification.   **TOTAL** — 100

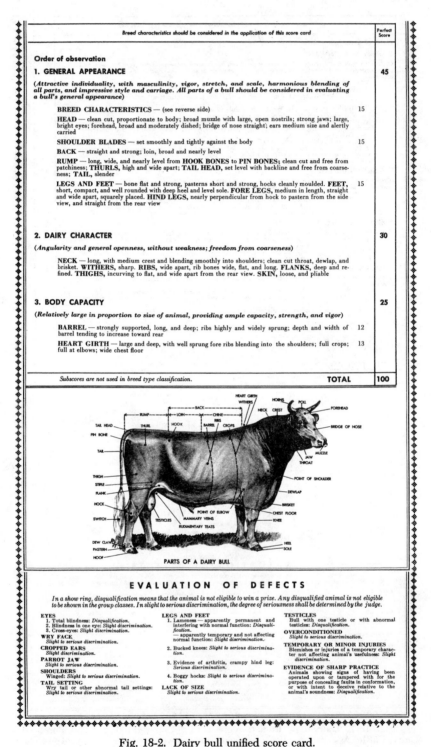

PARTS OF A DAIRY BULL

EVALUATION OF DEFECTS

In a show ring, disqualification means that the animal is not eligible to win a prize. Any disqualified animal is not eligible to be shown in the group classes. In slight to serious discrimination, the degree of seriousness shall be determined by the judge.

EYES
1. Total blindness: *Disqualification.*
2. Blindness in one eye: *Slight discrimination.*
3. Cross-eyes: *Slight discrimination.*

WRY FACE
Slight to serious discrimination.

CROPPED EARS
Slight discrimination.

PARROT JAW
Slight to serious discrimination.

SHOULDERS
Winged: *Slight to serious discrimination.*

TAIL SETTING
Wry tail or other abnormal tail settings: *Slight to serious discrimination.*

LEGS AND FEET
1. Lameness — apparently permanent and interfering with normal function: *Disqualification.*
— apparently temporary and not affecting normal function: *Slight discrimination.*

2. Bucked knees: *Slight to serious discrimination.*

3. Evidence of arthritis, crampy hind leg: *Serious discrimination.*

4. Boggy hocks: *Slight to serious discrimination.*

LACK OF SIZE
Slight to serious discrimination.

TESTICLES
Bull with one testicle or with abnormal testicles: *Disqualification.*

OVERCONDITIONED
Slight to serious discrimination.

TEMPORARY OR MINOR INJURIES
Blemishes or injuries of a temporary character not affecting animal's usefulness: *Slight discrimination.*

EVIDENCE OF SHARP PRACTICE
Animals showing signs of having been operated upon or tampered with for the purpose of concealing faults in conformation, or with intent to deceive relative to the animal's soundness: *Disqualification.*

Fig. 18-2. Dairy bull unified score card.

and 18-2. Breed characteristics may be, and are, considered in the use of the Unified Score Card, among them the picturesque style of the Ayrshire; the traditional strength and ruggedness of the Brown Swiss; the tractable disposition and milk color of the Guernsey; the size, scale, and color markings of the Holstein; and the refinement of the Jersey.

The score card for dairy cattle has considerable value in acquainting students and beginners with the various parts of an animal and the relative importance of each. It also has the advantage of listing the various parts of an animal under functional relationship—such as dairy character, body capacity, mammary system, etc.; and it promotes systematic observation and analysis of the points of strength and weakness in the animal being examined. The major weakness in any score card is that the user may not recognize that the failure of an important part of an animal may bring about the functional failure of the entire animal, and not just the part involved.

QUESTIONS FOR STUDY AND DISCUSSION

1. Were you to enter the dairy business, what breed would you select? Would you start with (a) grades or purebreds or (b) cows, heifers, or calves? Justify your choices.
2. Is it important that a modern dairyman be a good judge of dairy cattle?
3. Why is longevity important in dairy cattle?
4. Of what value is (a) dairy type and (b) breed type?
5. Should production records replace body type evaluations?
6. Under what circumstance would you evaluate an animal by (a) use of the score card, (b) show-ring record, and (c) type classification sponsored by the breed registry?

SELECTED REFERENCES

Title of Publication	Author(s)	Publisher
Dairy Cattle Judging and Selection	W. W. Yapp	John Wiley & Sons, Inc., New York, N. Y., 1959.
Selecting, Fitting and Showing Dairy Cattle	J. E. Nordby H. E. Lattig	The Interstate Printers & Publishers, Inc., Danville, Ill., 1961.

CHAPTER XIX

BREEDING DAIRY CATTLE

Contents   **Page**

Physiology of Reproduction..516
  Reproductive Organs of the Bull...517
  Reproductive Organs of the Cow...517
  Fertilization 518
  Sterility and Delayed Breeding...518
  Reproductive Diseases 520
  Normal Heat and Gestation Periods..520
Genetics of Dairy Cattle Breeding...521
  Heritability of Characters...522
  Number of Characters Selected for Simultaneously.....................522
Records Are Necessary...523
  Kind of Records; Choosing a System...523
    Milk and Butterfat Records...523
    Breeding Records..523
    Lifetime Record of Individual Cow...524
    Sire Selection Records...524
  Records Affected by Environment...528
  Correction Factors 530
    Times Milked Per Day..531
    Days Milked 531
    Age of Cow...531
    Fat Corrected Milk (FCM)..532
Selecting Breeding Stock...532
  Bases of Selection...533
  Methods of Selection...533
  Selecting Cows 534
  Selecting Replacement Heifers..534
  Selecting Sires 534
    Proved Sires 535
    Young Sires..535
Systems of Breeding...535
Develop and Follow a Breeding Program..536
Artificial Insemination of Dairy Cattle...537
Sex Control...537
Questions for Study and Discussion..537
Selected References 538

The objective of dairy cattle breeding is to mate individuals whose offspring will possess the necessary heritability to (1) produce the maximum amount of milk of the desired composition and (2) develop the desired body type; then to feed and manage these animals so that their maximum genetic potential will be expressed. This recognizes the fact that dairy cattle are products of heredity and environment, as are all other animals.

The economic justification for improved breeding is that good cows pay more. This fact is clearly illustrated in Fig. 19-1. There are two main explanations for the increase in rate of production per dairy animal shown in this figure: (1) the productive ability of milk cows has been increased through the selection of better producing animals, and they have been better fed and managed, and (2) with the decline in milk cow numbers in recent years, most of the decrease has come about in the marginal herds and among the low producers, with the results that the cows that remain are among the higher producers.

As noted in Fig. 19-1, feed costs increase with milk production, but labor and other costs increase very little with the higher production, with result that net profit increases. Thus, a cow producing 14,000 lb. of milk will make for a net profit of about two and one-half times that of an 8,000 lb. cow—the national average.

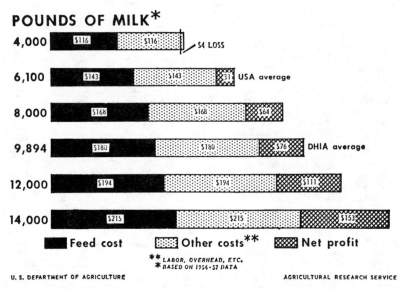

Fig. 19-1. Good cows pay more.

Today, all dairy cattle breeding may be classed as two kinds: (1) breed improvement and (2) herd improvement. Of course, the country as a whole is greatly interested in breed improvement. However, each individual dairy farmer is primarily interested in herd improvement. Naturally, if he is able to improve his herd so that he gets a greater net return, it means more to his own welfare. Also, any permanent herd improvement made by an individual dairyman inevitably contributes to permanent breed improvement. In fact, breed improvement through the years has largely come about through the progress made by master breeders in their own herd improvement programs.

It is important, therefore, that modern dairy breeders understand and follow a constructive breeding program.

PHYSIOLOGY OF REPRODUCTION

Dairymen encounter many reproductive problems, a reduction of which calls for a full understanding of physiology and the application of scientific practices therein. In fact, it may be said that reproduction is the first and most important requisite of dairy cattle breeding, for if animals fail to reproduce the breeder is soon out of business. Simply stated, milk production is a by-product of the reproductive process.

Reproductive Organs of the Bull

The reproductive organs of the bull are designed to produce semen and to convey it to the female at the time of mating. Semen consists of two parts: (1) the sperm (genetic portion) which are produced by the testes and (2) the liquid (energy portion), or semen plasma, which is secreted from the seminiferous tubules, the epididymis, the vas deferens, the seminal vesicles, the prostate,

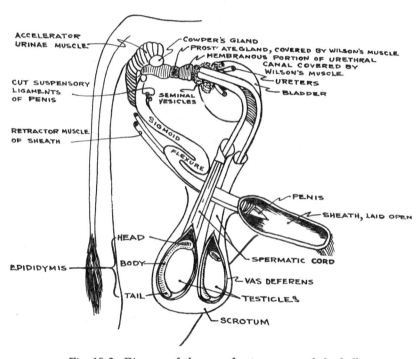

Fig. 19-2. Diagram of the reproductive organs of the bull.

and the Cowper's glands. Actually, the sperm make up only a small portion of the ejaculate. On the average, at the time of each service, a bull ejaculates 4 to 7 cubic centimeters of semen, containing about 6 to 10 billion sperms. The sperm concentration is about 1½ billion per cubic centimeter.

Reproductive Organs of the Cow

The cow's functions in reproduction are: (1) to produce the female reproductive cells, the eggs or ova; (2) to develop the new individual, the embryo, in the uterus; (3) to expel the fully developed young at time of birth or parturition; and (4) to produce milk for the nourishment of the young. Actually,

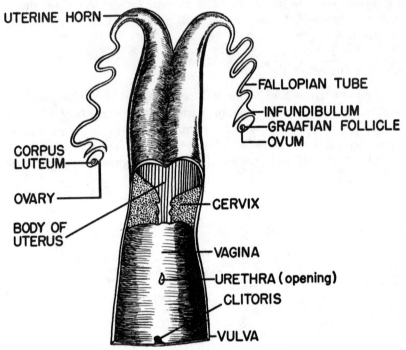

Fig. 19-3. The reproductive organs of the cow.

the part played by the cow in the generative process is much more complicated than that of the bull. It is imperative, therefore, that the modern dairy producer have a full understanding of the anatomy of the reproductive organs of the cow and the functions of each part.

Fertilization

Fertilization is the union of the male and female germ cells, sperm and ovum. The sperm are deposited in the vagina at the time of service and from there ascend the female reproductive tract. Under favorable conditions, they meet the egg and one of them fertilizes it in the upper part of the oviduct near the ovary.

In cows, fertilization is an all or none phenomenon, since only one ovum is ordinarily involved. Thus, the breeder's problem is to synchronize ovulation and insemination; to insure that large numbers of vigorous, fresh sperm will be present in the fallopian tubes at the time of ovulation.

Standing to be mounted by another cow appears to be the best single characteristic of the heat period. Using this as a guide, it is recommended that cows be bred during the final 10 hours of standing heat, or during the first 10 hours after the end of standing heat. This is illustrated in Fig. 19-4.

Sterility and Delayed Breeding

It has been estimated that sterility and delayed breeding in dairy cattle

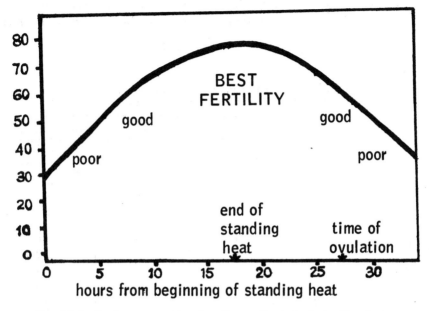

Fig. 19-4. For best conception, breed near the end of standing heat.

make for an expected yearly loss of $40 per cow, for a national total loss of $600 million, and that one-half of these losses could be prevented.[1] Thus, on the average, sterility and infertility may be expected to cause losses of the magnitude indicated in Table 19-1 (center column), one-half of which could be prevented (right column).

Another noteworthy statistic is that, nationally, including both beef and

TABLE 19—1

HERD SIZE DETERMINES THE SAVINGS POSSIBLE
BY MINIMIZING STERILITY

Herd Size	Expected Yearly Loss	Possible Yearly Saving
	($)	($)
30	1,200	600
40	1,600	800
50	2,000	1,000
60	2,400	1,200
70	2,800	1,400
100	4,000	2,000

[1] *Dairy Cattle Sterility*, Pub. by Hoard's Dairyman, 1964, p. 3.

dairy herds, only an 86 per cent calf crop is produced—the other 14 per cent of the cows are sterile, temporarily or permanently.

Of course, the causes of infertility are many, and they vary from herd to herd. Table 19-2 lists some of these common causes and gives the relative importance of each.

TABLE 19—2

COMMON CAUSES OF INFERTILITY IN CATTLE AND THE
RELATIVE IMPORTANCE OF EACH[1]

Cause	Percentage of Infertile Cattle Affected By	Percentage of Affected Animals Having Lowered Fertility	Percentage of All Infertility Which It Accounts for
Vibriosis	25	60	15
Purulent metritis	10	100	10[2]
Glandular vaginitis	50	10	5
Leptospirosis	15	20	3
Brucellosis	3	50	1.5
Trichomoniasis	1	100	1.0
Silent heats	20	36	7.2
Nymphomania	5	100	5.0
Anestrus	10	30	3.0
Ovulation failure	3	30	0.9
Genetic defects			10
Nutritional deficiencies			10
Improper care at calving			10[2]
Lack of observation			2
Breeding too soon after calving			2
Total			75.6[2]

[1]Olds, Durward, D.V.M. and Ph.D., University of Kentucky, in *The Allied Veterinarian*, March-April, 1958. The percentage figures in column 1 total more than 100 because of the fact that simultaneous infections occur in many cases.
[2]The 10 per cent due to purulent metritis is also listed as improper care at calving.

REPRODUCTIVE DISEASES

Brucellosis, leptospirosis, trichomoniasis, and vibriosis are the most troublesome specific genital diseases of dairy cows. In summary form, Table 19-3 gives the pertinent facts about each of them from the standpoint of sterility and delayed breeding.

Normal Heat and Gestation Periods

After heifers reach puberty, the normal heat period recurs at approximately 21 day intervals, but it may vary from 19 to 23 days.

The normal gestation period of the dairy cow is 283 days. Based on studies made by the Ohio Experiment Station, however, it is evident that there is variation between breeds. The following figures give the gestation period by breeds, as found in this experiment: Ayrshire, 278 days; Brown Swiss, 288 days; Guernsey, 283 days; Holstein, 279 days; and Jersey, 278 days.

The Ohio station also reported (1) that the gestation period of first calf

TABLE 19—3

FOUR MAIN REPRODUCTIVE DISEASES OF DAIRY CATTLE

Disease	Annual Losses Caused By[1]	Symptoms	Prevention
Brucellosis	$32,840,000 (dairy cows and milk)	Abortion last third of pregnancy. Retained afterbirth. Several services per conception. Uterine infections.	Calfhood vaccination. Use artificial insemination.
Leptospirosis	$12,189,000 (dairy cows and milk)	High fever (103° to 107° F). Poor appetite. Abortion any time. Bloody urine. Anemia. Ropy milk.	Periodic vaccination. Keep different classes of livestock separated. Purchase clean animals, isolate for 30 days, and retest.
Trichomoniasis	$8,040,000 (beef and dairy)	Abortion in first third of pregnancy. Uterine infections. Irregular heat periods. Several services per conception.	Use artificial insemination and semen treated with antibiotics.
Vibriosis	$104,194,000 (beef only; dairy figures not available)	Abortion in middle third of pregnancy. Several services per conception. Irregular heat periods.	Use artificial insemination and semen treated with antibiotics. Use vaccine as directed.

[1]*Losses in Agriculture*, Agricultural Handbook, No. 291, ARS, USDA, 1965.

heifers is about two days less than that of older cows of the respective breeds, and (2) that the gestation period where bull calves are born is about one day longer than that where females are born.

GENETICS OF DAIRY CATTLE BREEDING

In all animal breeding, and dairy cattle are no exception, no new genetic material is created. Rather, it is simply a matter of sorting or rearranging the many factors already present in the male and female gametes. These factors are referred to as genes. They are contained in the chromosomes of the sperm of the male and the egg of the female.

Dairy animals have 30 pairs of chromosomes in each cell. The number of genes per chromosome is not definitely known; estimates are that there may be as many as 30,000 genes for dairy cattle. These genes are responsible for how the animal looks and produces.

When the sperm and egg unite, the new cell formed contains 30 pairs of chromosomes, or a total of 60 chromosomes; half of which came from the sperm (male) and half from the egg (female). What determines which genes and which chromosomes are to be passed on to the new cell is still a relatively dark secret.

Heritability of Characters

The expression of a trait, such as milk production, depends upon two factors: (1) inheritance, or the ability to produce and (2) environment, or the opportunity to express the inborn ability. Heritability is 100 per cent when the expression of the trait varies solely because of inheritance. A trait that varies solely because of environment has a heritability of zero. Variations in most traits are neither wholly environmental nor completely hereditary. The heritability of some common dairy cattle traits is given in Table 19-4.

TABLE 19—4

HERITABILITY ESTIMATES FOR SOME
DAIRY CATTLE TRAITS

Trait	Heritability
	(%)
Milk yield	25
Fat percentage	50
Fat yield	25
Solids not fat	50
Milking rate	30
Longevity (length of life)	5
Type (final rating)	20
Breeding efficiency	5

As shown in Table 19-4, milk yield is about 25 per cent heritable, whereas fat percentage is 50 per cent heritable.

The following example will show how heritability can be computed: Let us assume that we have a herd that averages 440 lb. of butterfat on a mature level. Further, let us select a young sire that we estimate is capable of transmitting inheritance for 500 lb. of butterfat production. He is mated to select cows in the herd with production records averaging 500 lb. of butterfat in a normal 305-day lactation period. Because heritability is 25 per cent, we expect only one-fourth of the apparent superiority of the parents expressed in the offspring. The selected parents averaged 60 lb. of butterfat higher than the herd. One-fourth of the 60 equal 15 lb. of butterfat. Thus, the offspring would be expected to average 455 lb. of butterfat in this herd when given the same opportunity as the parents. The additional butterfat of the parents resulted from influences such as better feeding and management.

Number of Characters Selected for Simultaneously

Most rapid progress can be made in a breeding program by selecting for one trait only. However, when two characteristics are inherited in close relationship, considerable progress may be achieved in both of them. This is true, for example, in total milk production and total production of fat. On the other hand, body type and high production of milk are not closely associated in inheritance, with the result that selection for both of them will result in relatively slow progress in either one. Under these circumstances, the herd owner must decide which of the traits in the herd need most improvement and make his decision on the characteristics to be emphasized in selection accordingly. If good type will bring more monetary return than increased milk production, it should be emphasized. On the other hand, if higher production will increase income to a greater degree than improved body type, then it should be given greater importance in selection.

In many herds, particularly purebred herds, both type and production are important and selection for both should be made. In other words, selection for either type or production should not be made at the expense of serious loss in the other.

As a general rule, milk production and butterfat percentage are the characters usually considered in the breeding of dairy cattle, but other characters should also be considered as many of them have economic value.

RECORDS ARE NECESSARY

The foundation for a good breeding program is production records on every cow in the herd, year after year. Additionally, for the purebred breeder, type evaluation is important. Use of these two tools—production records and type evaluation—through a careful culling and selection program tends to get rid of the undesirable genes and concentrate on those which are superior. Also, milk and butterfat records are the key to scientific dairy cattle feeding.

Kind of Records; Choosing a System

As is true in bookkeeping or cost accounting, a number of different systems and forms are available. The important thing is to choose that system, or systems, which will give the desired information, then stick to it.

MILK AND BUTTERFAT RECORDS

A number of production record systems have been developed (see Chapter 20, "Feeding and Management of Dairy Cattle," and Chapter 17, "Breeds of Dairy Cattle").

BREEDING RECORDS

Breeding records are as essential as milk production records. Among other things, they are the only way in which to diagnose and reduce infertility.

Surveys show that about 5 per cent of the dairy cows in the U.S. become infertile each year. Further, about half of these represent a serious threat to the reproductive health of the rest of the herd, simply because they are "spreaders" of whatever trouble exists.

With proper records, here are some reasonable goals for which to strive:

1. At least 70 per cent of the cows should conceive at first breeding.

2. At any given time, there should be no more than 10 per cent of the cows with reproductive difficulties.

3. At the end of a year, the herds should average no more than 1.3 services per conception.

But to achieve these goals, or to be able to diagnose and reduce infertility, good records are essential. The breeding records should serve the following purposes:

1. Indicate when to start breeding.
2. Aid the feeding program.
3. Indicate breeding efficiency.
4. Suggest disease problems or the need for veterinary services.
5. Suggest infertility of the bull being used.
6. Indicate when to turn the cow dry.
7. Indicate approximate date of calving.
8. Show parentage and disposal of calf.

An example of a good breeding form is given in Fig. 19-5.

LIFETIME RECORD OF INDIVIDUAL COW

In addition to the monthly record provided by a testing program, for genetic progress it is important to have complete information on each individual cow. A record book containing forms similar to the one shown in Fig. 19-6 is recommended for this purpose.

The Lifetime Record of Individual Cow should provide for (1) complete identification of the individual animal, (2) test-day milk weights, (3) lactation production summary, (4) calving record, (5) breeding record, and (6) health and veterinary record. With this information available, each cow may be evaluated.

SIRE SELECTION RECORDS

With proved sires, the production records of the daughters are the most important single criterion for evaluating.

Most sires are proved by the Division of Dairy Herd Improvement Investigations of the U.S. Department of Agriculture, on the basis of DHIA records. Official proofs are issued whenever a bull in artificial breeding has 25 or more daughter-dam comparisons or a bull in natural service has 10 or more daughter-dam comparisons. A desirable proof is one in which the average production of the bull's daughters is well above the average for their dams and for the breed.

The three most common methods of evaluating proved sires, from a production standpoint, are:

1. **Daughter average.**—The average production of the daughters of a bull

DAIRY BREEDING RECORD

Name or Ear Tag	Date Fresh	Heat Dates		Date Bred	Bull	Days Since Service	Date Rebred	Bull	Days Since Service	Date Rebred	Bull	Days Since Service	Date Rebred	Bull	Due to Calve	Calved	Sex	Remarks
		1st	2nd															

1. BREED COWS FROM MIDDLE TO END OF HEAT
2. WAIT AT LEAST 60 DAYS AFTER FRESHENING BEFORE BREEDING
3. LEAVE MONEY AND REGISTRATION CERTIFICATE FOR TECHNICIAN
4. MARK COW TO BE INSEMINATED

Fig. 19-5. An example of a good breeding record form.

BARN NAME							TATTOO NUMBER	EARTAG NUMBER

REGISTRATION NAME		REGISTRATION NUMBER

BREED	DATE OF BIRTH	OFFICIAL TYPE CLASSIFICATION	CHECK IF COW IS PROGENY OF ARTIFICIAL INSEMINATION ☐

SIRE		REGISTRATION NUMBER OF SIRE

DAM	INDEX NUMBER	EARTAG OR REGISTRATION NUMBER OF DAM

TEST DAY MILK WEIGHTS

LACT NO.	DATE FRESH			MONTH OF LACTATION											
	MO.	DAY	YEAR	1	2	3	4	5	6	7	8	9	10	11	12
1															
2															
3															
4															
5															
6															
7															
8															
9															
10															

LACTATION PRODUCTION SUMMARY

LACT NO.	TYPE OF RECORD	AGE OF FRESHENING (Months)	WEIGHT WHEN FRESH	DAYS DRY BEFORE CALVING	FIRST 305 DAYS					COMPLETE LACTATION				
					DAYS CARRIED CALF	DAYS MILKED 3 TIMES	MILK	%	BUTTER FAT	DAYS IN MILK	LACTATION/LIFETIME TOTALS			SUPVR'S INITIALS
											MILK	B.F.	INCOME ABOVE F.C.	
1														
2														
3														
4														
5														
6														
7														
8														
9														
10														

DHIA Form 1057
Jan 1959

Fig. 19-6a. Lifetime history of individual cow, USDA Form 1057 (front side. See Fig. 19-6b for reverse side).

are a valuable indication of his breeding value, provided (a) the daughters are unselected and (b) there are enough of them. Most breeders desire that there be a minimum of 100 daughters for an AI proved sire and 15 to 20 for a naturally proved sire.

BARN NAME   INDEX NUMBER

CALVING RECORD

LACT NO.	DATE OF CALVING			CALF'S NAME & EAR TAG NUMBER	SEX OF CALF	SIRE OF CALF	DISPOSAL OF CALF
	MO.	DAY	YEAR				
1							
2							
3							
4							
5							
6							
7							
8							
9							
10							

BREEDING RECORD

LACT NO.	DATE OF CALVING			DATE BRED	SIRE USED	DATE BRED	SIRE USED	DATE BRED	SIRE USED	DATE BRED	SIRE USED	REMARKS
	MO.	DAY	YEAR									
1												
2												
3												
4												
5												
6												
7												
8												
9												
10												

HEALTH AND VETERINARY RECORD MAINTAINED BY OWNER

DATE	DISEASE, AILMENT, OR TEST	TREATMENT AND REMARKS

Fig. 19-6b. Lifetime history of individual cow, USDA Form 1057 (reverse side of 19-6a).

2. **Daughter-dam comparison.**—This is one of the oldest methods of evaluating a proved sire, and it is still used today. It consists in comparing the production of a bull's daughters with that of their dams. The disadvantages of a daughter-dam comparison are: (a) the dams and daughters may not be milking at the same time, which means that there are inevitably environmental differences; (b) comparisons are usually made in one, or only a few herds, which means that only a limited range of environmental conditions prevail; and (c) many dams do not have records, with the result that there is nothing with which to compare their daughters.

3. **Herdmate-daughter comparison.**—This is the newest and soundest method of sire evaluation, having come into existence about 1960. By herdmates reference is made to other cows in the herd that were calved in the same year and season as the daughters of the sire being compared. This method of sire evaluation has two objectives: (a) to compare performance of one animal with another which is not paternally related, with the records being made at the same time, and (b) to compare records made under the same environment. Under this system, all records are converted to twice-a-day milking 305 days, and six years of age. All animals in the herd, regardless of age, which freshen three months before or three months after a daughter of the particular sire in question freshens are included in the comparison.

Despite the fact that the milk production records of the progeny of a proved sire are most important, the pedigree of the sire and the body type of his offspring, including their freedom from defects, must be considered.

Records Affected by Environment

Recently, the effect of environment on dairy cattle was clearly demonstrated in an experiment in New Zealand. It involved the selection of 20 calves from low-producing herds and 20 calves from high-producing herds. All of them were sired artificially by outstanding bulls. The 40 head were assembled at the Rurakura Experiment Station, raised and milked together for the first lactation. Under these conditions, no significant difference between the production of the two groups was observed. Then, they were sent back to the respective herds from whence they came, whereupon their production was comparable to that of the cows with which they were being milked. Then, for a second time, they were returned to the Rurakura Experiment Station, where again there was no significant difference in their production. The Rurakura station then went one step further; they confirmed these results by using identical twins, with both twins milked at the Rurakura station, and then later divided between high and low producing herds for subsequent lactation.

The New Zealand experiment points up the importance of management. No matter how good the genetics, a good environment is essential to obtain high production.

Among the environmental factors affecting milk production records are the following:

Fig. 19-7. Production records are affected by environment, the most important factor of which is feed.

1. **Feeding.**—This is the most important factor of all from the standpoint of determining the productivity of a cow.

2. **Milking practices.**—Good milking practices result in increased production as compared to poor milking practices.

3. **Age of animal.**—On the average, production increases each year from the time the first calf is born until the cow reaches six to seven years of age; after which it declines.

4. **Size of animal.**—Within the same breed and age group, the larger animals, as measured by their capacity to consume more feed, usually produce more milk than the smaller animals.

5. **Season of freshening.**—Cows that freshen in the spring and summer months usually produce less than cows freshening in the winter months. Of course, this variation differs between herds and areas.

6. **Calving interval.**—Cows that calve within 12 to 15 months from last calving produce more for that lactation than cows calving within 10 and 12 months, without an adequate dry period.

7. **Length of dry period.**—Cows with a dry period of six to eight weeks produce more during the following lactation than those cows with a dry period of less than four weeks duration.

8. **Freedom from disease, parasites, and injury.**—Any one of these may de-

press production, with the degree of depression determined by the severity of the ailment.

9. **Rate of maturity.**—Some strains or families of cows mature at a slower rate than others.

10. **Yearly differences.**—There are important yearly differences within a given area, primarily due to weather conditions and the general quality of feed available.

Research conducted at the University of Wisconsin showed that certain environmental factors affected production (see Table 19-5).

TABLE 19—5

ENVIRONMENTAL INFLUENCES (OVER ALL HERDS)

Factor	Yearly Production Change for Each Unit Change of Environment
1. Milking practices (poor, fair, good, excellent)	(lb. butterfat) + 33
2. Feeding practices (poor, fair, good, excellent)	+ 24
3. Calving interval (range 10 to 14 months)	+ 20
4. Pounds of TDN (energy fed daily per 1,000 pounds of body weight (ranging from 14 to 22 pounds)	+ 12
5. Previous dry period (range 3 to 9 weeks)	+ 2
6. Herd size (22, 28, 34, 40, and 46)	- 7

Table 19-5 suggests, for example, if a herd were producing 300 lb. of butterfat per cow yearly and poor milking practices were being followed, the herd could be expected to average 333 lb., if milking practices could be improved one step—from poor to fair. There is, of course, an interaction of these different environmental factors which makes it difficult for the dairyman to evaluate the effect of each one on his particular farm. Nevertheless, when an attempt is being made to evaluate the breeding worth of an individual animal, all of these factors may be playing an important part in the production records.

Correction Factors

It is frequently desirable to compare the performance of a group of animals. To do so, it is necessary to correct all records to a comparable basis. For this purpose, correction factors have been developed. Some of the common correction factors follow.

TIMES MILKED PER DAY

To convert three times a day milking to two times a day basis, multiply by 83 per cent (.83). For purposes of illustrating how this works, let's assume that we have a four-year-old Holstein cow that has a three times a day 305-day record of 14,000 pounds of milk and 610 pounds of fat; and that it is desired to convert it to two times a day basis. Simply multiply the cow's record by 0.83. Hence—

$$14,000 \text{ lb. milk} \times 0.83 = 11,620 \text{ lb. milk on } 2 \times \text{basis}$$
$$610 \text{ lb. fat} \times 0.83 = 506.3 \text{ lb. fat on } 2 \times \text{basis}$$

DAYS MILKED

Normally, records not exceeding 305 days are used for comparative purposes. If the cow goes dry before the full 305 days, she gets credit only for the days she actually milked. On the other hand, if this is an incomplete record, an adjustment may be made. The factors commonly used for this adjustment are:

Days Milked	Factor
95	2.82
125	2.16
155	1.77
185	1.51
215	1.32
245	1.18
275	1.08

For comparing a 365-day record, it can be reduced to a 305-day record equivalent by taking 85 per cent of it.

AGE OF COW

The age of a cow is always based on her age when she calved, which is when her record begins. It is estimated, as a general rule, that at two years of age a cow produces approximately 70 per cent of her mature production; at three years, 80 per cent; at four years, 90 per cent; five years, 95 per cent; and at six years, her mature record. To equalize for age, there has been developed "age correction factors." The actual record is multiplied by the factor for the age when the record was made. This is known as the "mature equivalent" (ME record). Since the breeds mature at varying rates, there are different factors for different breeds. These were developed from breed registry association and DHIA records. They are used by the USDA, DHIA Sire Proving Work, and by the breed registry associations and their various programs. Table 19-6 gives the age conversion factors by breeds.

Here is how to use the age conversion factor: Let's assume that we have a Guernsey cow that was three years old when she began her lactation record;

TABLE 19—6

AGE CONVERSION FACTORS[1]
(Based on age when production record began
and 305-day production)

Age	Ayrshire	Brown Swiss	Guernsey	Holstein	Jersey	Milking Shorthorn
Yr. Mo.						
1 - 10	1.34	1.47	1.28	1.35	1.30	1.46
2 - 0	1.30	1.45	1.24	1.31	1.27	1.42
2 - 6	1.24	1.35	1.18	1.24	1.21	1.30
3 - 0	1.18	1.23	1.12	1.18	1.15	1.24
3 - 6	1.13	1.16	1.08	1.12	1.09	1.18
4 - 0	1.10	1.10	1.06	1.08	1.06	1.13
4 - 6	1.06	1.07	1.04	1.04	1.03	1.10
5 - 0	1.03	1.04	1.02	1.02	1.02	1.07
5 - 6	1.02	1.02	1.01	1.02	1.01	1.04
6 - 0	1.00	1.00	1.00	1.00	1.00	1.01
7 - 0	1.00	1.00	1.00	1.00	1.00	1.00
8 - 0	1.00	1.00	1.01	1.00	1.01	1.01
9 - 0	1.02	1.01	1.02	1.02	1.02	1.02
10 - 0	1.03	1.02	1.04	1.04	1.04	1.04
11 - 0	1.04	1.04	1.06	1.06	1.06	1.06
12 - 0	1.06	1.06	1.08	1.09	1.08	1.08
13 - 0	1.07	1.08	1.10	1.12	1.10	1.10
14 - 0	1.09	1.10	1.12	1.15	1.12	1.12

[1]Standardizing DHIA Records in Proving Sires, USDA, ARS, BDI-Inf.-162, Oct. 1953, by J. F. Kendrick.

that she was milked two times daily; and that her 305-day record was 11,510 pounds of milk and 508 pounds of fat. By referring to Table 19-6, it is observed that the age conversion factor for a four-year-old Guernsey cow is 1.06. Hence—

11,510 lb. milk $\times$ 1.06 = 12,200 lb. milk on ME basis

508 lb. fat $\times$ 1.06 = 538 lb. fat on ME basis

FAT CORRECTED MILK (FCM)

For comparative purposes, production records are sometimes standardized on an energy basis known as the Fat Corrected Milk method. It is based on calculating the production to a 4.0 per cent FCM equivalent by using the following formula:

4.0% FCM = (0.4 $\times$ milk production in lb.) + (15 $\times$ fat production in lb.)

SELECTING BREEDING STOCK

For most rapid progress, the dairyman should have an organized program of selecting and breeding. The first step in such a program consists in (1) establishing goals—goals in milk production, milk composition, body conformation, longevity, freedom from hereditary defects, etc.; (2) determining where you are now—recording the pertinent information on each animal; and (3) determining how you will get from "hither to yon"—from where you are now to the goals that you have set.

Bases of Selection

The success of any breeding program depends primarily on the ability of the breeder to select properly the animals that are to be parents of the next generation. Three methods of selecting such animals are recommended:

1. **Individual merit.**—This consists in selecting cows on the basis of their record of production and/or body type. It must be recognized that this basis of selection is materially affected by environment. For this reason, it is most effective if based on more than one lactation period, or even on the basis of a lifetime average, although, admittedly, the latter is too slow for most conditions.

2. **Pedigree.**—The usefulness of a pedigree depends to a large extent on its completeness, and upon the understanding of the descriptive material available. There is no accepted method of reporting information on a pedigree. However, a trend is rapidly developing toward reporting information on twice-a-day milking for a 305-day lactation, and either listing the actual age at time of freshening of each lactation or figuring all records to a mature equivalent basis of six years of age. When the actual cow age for each record is listed, it permits an appraisal of the frequency of calving, calving interval, and to some extent, the breeding efficiency.

Of course, the ancestors close-up in the pedigree are the most important ones in attempting to evaluate the breeding worth of an animal from its pedigree.

It is generally agreed that pedigree selection should be used as an accessory to individual selection. It is particularly useful when selecting young animals for traits that are sex-limited or that are exhibited only after sexual maturity; for example, udder shape and attachment, milk production, etc.

3. **Progeny testing.**—This method of selecting involves a study of the individual's offspring. Progeny testing is particularly valuable for selecting for such quantitative characters as milk production and milk constituents. When properly used, progeny tests prevent the breeder from being deceived by the effects of environment. It is emphasized, however, that progeny testing should be used to supplement, rather than replace, the other two bases of selection.

Methods of Selection

In addition to arriving at a basis of selection (usually a combination of individuality, pedigree, and progeny test), and the traits for which selection is to be made, the dairy cattle breeder must determine what method of selection shall be used. The following three general methods are available to him:

1. **Cull simultaneously, but independently, for each character.**—This means that culling levels are established for each trait, below which all individuals are culled, no matter how good they may be in other respects.

2. **Tandem method of selection.**—In this method, one characteristic is selected for at a time until it is improved, then selection is made for a second

trait, and later a third, and so on and so on. Tandem selection will result in improving one trait faster than can be achieved through any other method, but while that is being done other traits may deteriorate.

3. **Establish a selection index.**—This consists in totaling the animal's score for its merits in each characteristic, then retaining those with the highest total score. The selection index is looked upon more favorably than the tandem method because it permitts unusually high merit in one characteristic to make up for deficiencies in some other trait.

In practice, a combination of all three methods of selection is usually most desirable and effective.

Selecting Cows

When milk is the major source of income, selection is simplified. Cows in production are ranked from high to low on the basis of milk production, and the most profitable milk cows are retained and the least profitable ones sold.

A purebred breeder usually finds it desirable and profitable to select animals for type as well as production.

Where grade cows are involved, and replacement heifers are not being raised, cows can be selected or culled primarily on the basis of milk production. Where breeding animals are involved—that is, where replacement heifers or bulls are being selected for retaining in the herd or for sale purposes—cows should be selected on the bases of their milk production, pedigree, and progeny, provided all three are available.

Selecting Replacement Heifers

The number of heifer replacements needed each year to maintain herd size will depend upon the number of cows eliminated from the herd because of disease, injury, low production, or poor type. Normal turnover in DHIA herds is about 25 per cent each year. To meet this, and to allow some opportunity for culling undesirable first calf heifers, it is necessary to raise approximately one-third as many heifer calves each year as there are milking animals in the herd.

The dairyman who raises his replacements is in a better position to evaluate the animals genetically than the operator who buys replacements, simply because their dams and close relatives are available in the same herd under similar feed and management conditions.

Selecting Sires

The selection of a sire is extremely important because he becomes the parent of many more offspring than any individual cow. Generally speaking, the dairyman has three sources of herd sires: (1) artificial insemination service, (2) purchase of a herd sire, or (3) raising a herd sire. In any event, the problem is to select the herd sire that will maintain a higher level of production than the current herd average. This is essential if there is to be improvement in the herd.

Sires should be selected largely on a production basis. They may also be selected by pedigree (line of breeding, production records of ancestry, etc.), type (individual, ancestors and offspring type), and family or blood lines.

The dairyman must also decide between a proved sire and a young sire.

PROVED SIRES

The three common methods of evaluating proved sires, based on production records, are: (1) daughter average, (2) daughter-dam comparison, and (3) herdmate comparison, all of which were covered earlier in this chapter.

YOUNG SIRES

Generally speaking, an individual dairyman can avail himself of the use of a proved sire through artificial insemination. However, good proved sires are not always available at a price that the individual breeder can afford to pay, particularly when he wishes to use them in natural service. Further, they are even expensive for artificial insemination associations to purchase. Additionally, it is recognized that proved sires are generally six to eight years old, and that they have a remaining life expectancy of only two to three years. For these reasons, there is increasing interest in young sires.

Young sires are generally selected on the basis of pedigree information, but with consideration given to type and freedom from defects.

Until the young sire is proved, it is good procedure to use him one season, then let him remain idle until his first daughters are in production and tested. For young sires that are going to be used in artificial insemination, it is recommended that 50 to 100 daughters be tested before proceeding with further use, whereas in natural service there should be some 10 to 15 tested daughters at the very minimum. With this system of testing—that is, using the young sire one season, and then letting him idle until his first daughters are tested, he can be proved by the time he is five years of age. This means that a young sire, tested in this manner, will have two to three years longer life of usefulness than is possible with the proved sire program previously described.

SYSTEMS OF BREEDING

In dairy cattle breeding, one of the following accepted systems of breeding is generally followed: (1) inbreeding, which embraces (a) close breeding or (b) line breeding; (2) outcrossing; or (3) crossbreeding.

Close breeding (the mating of animals that are closely related) is usually limited to those dairymen who are particularly good students of their animals, who recognize their weak and strong points, and who cull ruthlessly when the situation demands such action. When successful, it concentrates the most desirable traits and produces some outstanding individuals who transmit fairly uniformly. Close breeding is best left to the dairyman who has complete records of production and type, and whose herd is at a high average level of production, and has been so for a number of years.

Line breeding is practiced much more extensively by dairymen than close breeding. It is a conservative type of breeding program which the vast majority of average and small dairy breeders can safely follow to their advantage.

Outcrossing (the mating of unrelated animals) is the most widely used system of breeding by the majority of dairymen. It offers considerable opportunity to introduce new genes into the herd, simply because a wide choice of animals can be made. It often results in producing animals which are highly desirable within themselves, but they may not transmit uniformly. However, this system does not carry the dangers that often go with inbreeding, such as possible reduction in size and scale, lack of vigor, development of possible recessive factors which may become undesirable, and a greater concentration of any undesirable trait.

Crossbreeding cannot be practiced in registered herds because the offspring cannot be registered. For those dairymen who have no preference as to color and general appearance, crossbreeding may be followed with good results provided good proved sires are used. The aims of this system of breeding are to use the best sires available regardless of breed, and to gain hybrid vigor in the offspring (reduced calfhood mortality) and possibly more economical milk production.

DEVELOP AND FOLLOW A BREEDING PROGRAM

Where replacement animals are raised, in either a purebred or a grade herd, a breeding program must be developed and followed if herd progress and breed progress are to be made. The following steps are pertinent to such a program:

1. Choose a suitable breed of cattle.

2. Select or purchase the best cows available, based primarily upon their production record, but with due consideration given to type and pedigrees.

3. Decide on the breeding system—inbreeding, versus outcrossing, versus crossbreeding—that shall be followed.

4. Evaluate the strong points and the weak points of the cows in the herd.

5. Obtain the services of the sire(s) which offers the greatest promise of further improvement in production and in type; but with due consideration given to the price of the sire, along with the age and health of the individual if he is to be used in natural service.

6. Enroll in the particular testing program which best meets the breeding and management programs that will be followed.

7. Follow that program of type evaluation which best meets the needs of the breeding program.

8. Arrive at the method(s) of selection that shall be followed; choosing between individual culling levels, the tandem method, or a selection index.

9. Establish and maintain reasonable standards for freedom from disease,

temperament, fertility and sterility, ease and completeness of milking, and such other factors as are considered important.

10. Follow a feeding and management program which will permit the animals in the herd to express the maximum genetic potential which they possess.

ARTIFICIAL INSEMINATION OF DAIRY CATTLE

Artificial insemination, as a means of dairy cattle improvement, is now accepted and utilized world-wide. The increased use of outstanding sires to enhance production potential, control certain genital diseases transmitted through natural service, and encourage general mass improvement is well recognized. In 1966, 7,286,580 head, or 48 per cent, of the dairy cows and heifers of the U.S. were bred by artificial insemination. Also, it is noteworthy that, in 1966, an average of 3,322 cows were bred per bull used in artificial insemination, or approximately 100 times more cows per bull than in natural service.

SEX CONTROL

Sex ratios of dairy calves at birth show that there is a slight deficiency in heifers; out of each 100 calves, on the average, 49 are heifer calves and 51 are bull calves.

Many unsuccessful attempts have been made to control sex; including attempts to use electrophoretic, mechanical, and chemical methods of separation of the two types of sperm cells. Obviously, some method of controlling sex of offspring would have tremendous significance in the dairy field. However, to date, no practical solution has been found. Until there is adequate experimental evidence, any method or theory that purports to control sex should be regarded with skepticism. Of course, research is being continued because the stakes are high if any workable method can be found.

QUESTIONS FOR STUDY AND DISCUSSION

1. What determines the limit of a cow's ability to produce milk and butterfat?
2. How are chromosome numbers maintained constant from one generation to the next?
3. Which is most important in a dairy cow, heredity or environment?
4. At what period in the heat cycle should a cow be bred in order to get the highest conception rate?
5. How would you go about selecting cows or dairy heifer replacements?
6. Under what circumstances might it be desirable to use a young sire rather than a proved sire?
7. Explain the differences between, and the advantages of, (a) inbreeding, (b) outcrossing, and (c) crossbreeding. Under what circumstances would you use each?
8. Outline a sound breeding program for a dairy herd.
9. Would you use artificial insemination or natural service in a dairy herd?
10. What is a pedigree, and how would you recommend that it be used?
11. What system(s) would you use in evaluating a proved sire?

SELECTED REFERENCES

Title of Publication	Author(s)	Publisher
Animal Breeding	A. L. Hagedoorn	Crosby Lockwood & Son, Ltd., London, England, 1950.
Animal Breeding	L. M. Winters	John Wiley & Sons, Inc., New York, N. Y., 1948.
Animal Breeding Plans	J. L. Lush	Collegiate Press, Inc., Ames, Iowa, 1965.
Artificial Insemination of Dairy and Beef Cattle	H. A. Herman F. W. Madden	Lucas Brothers, Pub., Columbia, Mo., 1963.
Artificial Insemination of Farm Animals, The	E. J. Perry	Rutgers University Press, New Brunswick, N.J., 1968.
Breeding and Improvement of Farm Animals	V. A. Rice F. N. Andrews E. J. Warwick J. E. Legates	McGraw-Hill Book Co., Inc., New York, N. Y., 1957
Breeding Better Livestock	V. A. Rice F. N. Andrews E. J. Warwick	McGraw-Hill Book Co., Inc., New York, N. Y., 1953.
Breeding Livestock Adapted to Unfavorable Environments	R. W. Phillips	Food and Agriculture Organization of the United Nations, Washington, D. C., 1949.
Dairy Cattle Breeding	L. O. Gilmore	J. B. Lippincott Co., Philadelphia, Pa., 1951.
Dairy Cattle Sterility	H. D. Hafs L. J. Boyd	W. D. Hoard and Sons Co., Fort Atkinson, Wisc.
Elements of Genetics, The	C. D. Carlington K. Mather	The Macmillan Co., New York, N. Y., 1950.
Farm Animals	John Hammond	Edward Arnold & Co., London, England, 1952.
Gene . . . The Universal Calf	L. N. Hazel L. E. Johnson	Fred Hahne Printing Co., Webster City, Iowa, 1956.
Genetic Resistance to Disease in Domestic Animals	F. B. Hutt	Comstock Publishing Assn., Cornell University Press, Ithaca, N. Y., 1958.
Genetics of Livestock Improvement	J. F. Lasley	Prentice-Hall, Inc., Englewood Cliffs, N. Y., 1963.
Highlight of Breeding Systems	V. A. Rice	Holstein-Friesian Assn. of America, Brattleboro, Vt.
Improvement of Livestock	Ralph Bogart	The Macmillan Co., New York, N. Y., 1959.
Robert Bakewell— Pioneer Livestock Breeder	H. C. Pawson	Crosby Lockwood & Son, Ltd., London, England.
Tables for Coefficients of Inbreeding in Animals	C. D. Mueller	Agri. Expt. Sta. Tech. Bul. 80, Kansas State College (now University), Manhattan, Kansas.

Chapter XX

FEEDING AND MANAGEMENT
OF DAIRY CATTLE

Contents
	Page
The Digestive System	540
Parts and Functions of the Ruminant Stomach	541
Calf's Stomach	543
Nutritive Requirements	543
Energy	543
Protein	545
Minerals	545
Vitamins	546
Water	547
Other Feed Requirements	547
Feeds for Dairy Cows	548
Roughages (Forages)	548
Rules of Thumb for Roughage Consumption	550
Concentrates (Grains)	551
Special Feeds	551
Commercial Dairy Feeds	553
How to Select a Commercial Feed	553
Feeding Concentrates to Dairy Cows	554
Suggested Concentrate Rations for Lactating Cows	555
How to Balance a Dairy Ration	556
Amount of Concentrate to Feed; "Challenge" or "Lead" Feed	560
Feeding on Pasture	563
Special Feeding Programs	563
Dry Cows	563
Feeding at Calving Time	564
Show and Sale Animals	564
Dairy Calves	565
Dairy Heifer Replacements	567
Normal Growth of Calves and Heifers	568
Dairy Bulls	569
Milk and Butterfat Records; Testing Programs	569
Dairy Herd Improvement Association (DHIA)	569
Owner-Sampler Records (OS)	569
Weigh-a-day-a-month (WADAM)	570
Other Feed and Management Pointers	570
Common Dairy Health Problems	571
Bloat	571
Calf Scours	571
Milk Fever	571
Nitrate Poisoning	572
Beware of Pesticide Residues	572
Feeds Affecting Milk Flavor	573
Marketing Dairy Herd Replacement Stock	574
Dairy Beef Production	574
Some Management Recommendations	575
Management of Dry and Milking Cows	575
Management of Dairy Calves	577
Management of Replacement Heifers	577
Feed Terms; Conversions	578
Questions for Study and Discussion	580
Selected References	580

Feed, more than any other one factor, determines the productivity and profitableness of dairy cows. Within a herd, approximately 25 per cent of the difference in milk production between cows is due to heredity; the remaining 75 per cent is determined by environmental factors, with feed making up the largest portion. Feed accounts for about 50 per cent (with a range of from 40 to 65 per cent) of the cost of milk production. Therefore, a good feeding program is necessary for profitable milk production.

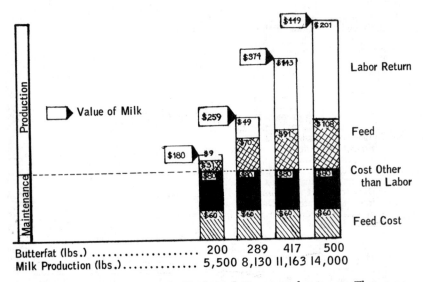

Fig. 20-1. It costs more to feed high producing cows—but it pays. The reason: feed and overhead costs for maintenance are practically the same, regardless of level of production.

THE DIGESTIVE SYSTEM

An understanding of the principal parts and functions of the digestive system is essential to intelligent feeding of dairy cattle. Fig. 20-2 shows the location of the parts of the ruminant's stomach and the route of digestion followed by most feed. Table 20-1 gives capacity figures.

To be useful to animals, nutrients must enter the blood stream for transport to various parts of the body. The process whereby the animal releases feed nutrients from feed is termed digestion. As commonly used, the process also includes absorption of food from the digestive tract into the blood stream. Most of the unused portion of the feed is eliminated in the feces, although a considerable proportion is also given off as gas through the mouth and nose.

Dairy cattle belong to the ruminant or cud-chewing group of animals (which includes cattle and sheep), whereas swine and chickens are monogastric animals (those having only one stomach).

The primary nutritional difference between cows, or ruminants, and simple-stomached animals comes about through the normal functioning of the rumen and its trillions of micro-organisms—the bacteria and protozoa. These micro-organisms

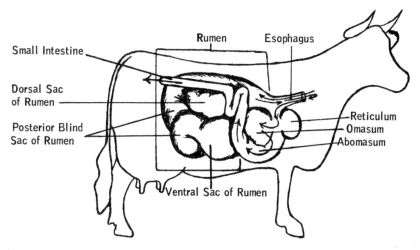

Fig. 20-2. Location and parts of the ruminant stomach (four compartments), with pathway of feeds indicated by arrows. (Drawing by Caren Carney)

TABLE 20—1

PARTS AND CAPACITIES OF DIGESTIVE TRACTS

Parts	Cow	Horse	Pig
	—(Qts. capacity)—		
Stomach:	(200)	8-16	6-8
Rumen (paunch)	160		
Reticulum (honeycomb).....................	10		
Omasum (manyplies)	15		
Abomasum (true stomach)	15		
Small intestine..	62	48	9
Cecum...		28-32	
Large intestine..	40	80	10

live on the food material supplied in the cow's diet. The rumen provides a highly desirable environment in which they can grow and reproduce themselves every half-hour or so. In turn, they release to the cow during life and from their bodies as protoplasm upon death, many of the cow's required nutrients. This is how the cow gets many nutrients needed for milk production that are not supplied in the diet.

Parts and Functions of the Ruminant Stomach

The feed taken in by cows is mixed with a heavy flow of saliva, which is needed to help in chewing and swallowing of dry materials. This saliva of ruminants, unlike that of nonruminants, does not contain enzymes to aid in the digestion of starches. However, the saliva of cows, estimated to be about 120 pounds per day in a mature animal, does have enough buffers (sodium bicarbonate) to neutralize the fatty acids produced in the rumen and maintain the rumen contents at approximately a neutral pH (7.0).

The ruminant stomach consists of four distinct compartments—(1) the rumen, or "paunch," as it is commonly called; (2) the reticulum, or "honeycomb"; (3) the omasum, or "manyplies" (so called because of the plies or folds); and (4) the abomasum, or "true stomach." When feeds are ingested, the normal pathway they follow is in the order just listed, with portions being returned to the mouth for chewing before they enter the omasum. These four compartments do not lie in a straight arrangement; rather, they are bunched and joined together to form a compact structure. A discussion of each of the parts of the ruminant's stomach follows:

1. **Rumen.**—In large, mature cows, the rumen has a capacity of about 40 gallons, or as much as 300 pounds of material. The functions of the rumen are: (a) to act as a storage place (it holds the feed which the cow gathers during her feeding period; later, when she rests, she regurgitates the larger particles back to the mouth, to grind them more completely); (b) to refine the coarser pieces of feed so that the bacteria, and later the digestive juices, can have a larger surface upon which to act; and (c) to provide a place for fermentation—there is a continual flow of feed material into and out of the rumen, constant introduction of saliva which controls the pH, absorption of the end products of the microbial action, and a population of micro-organisms—bacteria and yeasts, both of which are plants, and one-celled animals called protozoa—which develop in accordance with the amount and type of feed consumed. These organisms in the paunch (a) helps digest the crude fiber, (b) form essential amino acids and build up complete proteins, and (c) manufacture the B-complex vitamins.

The fermentation process produces large amounts of carbon dioxide, methane, and ammonia; smaller amounts of hydrogen, hydrogen sulfide, and carbon monoxide; and probably trace amounts of other gases. Normally, these gases are passed off by the reflex action of belching. However, sometimes a cow is unable to get rid of this gas, and bloating results.

2. **Reticulum.**—The reticulum lies directly in front of the rumen. Actually, the rumen and the reticulum are not completely separated; hence, food particles pass freely from one to the other. The interior of the reticulum is lined like a honeycomb; hence, the popular name.

The main function of the reticulum is its action as a screening device. Heavy objects, such as nails or wire eaten with the feed, have a tendency to settle out into this compartment. Therefore, it is sometimes referred to by dairymen as the "hardware stomach."

3. **Omasum.**—The third compartment is lined with plies or folds of tissue; hence, it is sometimes called the "manyplies." Less is known about the functions of the omasum than of any of the other compartments of the ruminant stomach. It is generally believed, however, that the primary functions of this compartment are (a) to reduce the water content of the feedstuffs, and (b) to exert a regrinding and squeezing action on the material.

4. **Abomasum.**—The abomasum is often referred to as the "true stomach"

because its action is similar to the stomach action in monogastric animals. As in the monogastric stomach, digestive juices are added and the moisture content of the feed material is increased. The digestive juices contain enzymes, resulting in protein digestion in the abomasum. Little or no digestion of fat, cellulose, or starch occurs in this organ.

The feed material leaving the abomasum is highly fluid in nature. It is then passed out of the stomach through the small intestine, where additional digestion occurs, and the unabsorbed material is then excreted by way of the large intestine.

CALF'S STOMACH

When the calf is born, the rumen is small and the fourth stomach is by far the largest of the compartments. Thus, digestion in the young calf is more like that of a single-stomached animal than that of a ruminant. The milk which the calf normally consumes by-passes the first two compartments and goes almost directly to the fourth stomach in which the rennin and other compounds for the digestion of milk are produced. If the calf gulps too rapidly, or gorges itself, the milk may go into the rumen where it is not digested properly and may cause upset of the calf's digestive system. As the calf nibbles at hay, small amounts of material get into the rumen. When certain bacteria become established, the rumen develops and the calf gradually becomes a full-fledged ruminant.

NUTRITIVE REQUIREMENTS

A nutrient is any substance that aids in the support of life. The first consideration in any dairy feeding program, therefore, is to determine the nutritive need. Dairy cattle require nutrients for growth, body maintenance, pregnancy or reproduction, and milk production.

The nutritive needs for growth, body maintenance, and pregnancy generally are provided for before milk production can take place in quantity. For this reason, it does not pay to underfeed. A cow produces most economically when worked near full capacity.

The nutritive requirements for dairy cattle have been established by the National Research Council (NRC Pub. 1349, 1966). Table 20-2 is a summary of some of the needs. It is to be emphasized, however, that the nutritive requirements set forth in Table 20-2 do not allow for any margin of safety; that is, for animal differences, feed differences, and losses of certain nutrients in storage. Accordingly, in the formulation of rations, certain margins of safety should be provided.

Energy

Lack of energy (total digestible nutrients, or TDN) is the most common deficiency of dairy rations. Cows cannot produce milk at peak levels if their rations are too low in energy.

TABLE 20—2

DAILY NUTRIENT REQUIREMENTS OF DAIRY CATTLE[1]

	Body Weight		Daily Gain		Feed[2]		Protein Total		Protein Digestible		Energy TDN		Energy DE[3]	Energy ME[3]	Ca	P	Carotene	Vitamin A	Vitamin D[4]
	(kg)	(lb.)	(g)	(lb.)	(kg)	(lb.)	(g)	(lb.)	(g)	(lb.)	(kg)	(lb.)	(Mcal)	(Mcal)	(g)	(g)	(mg)	(1000 I.U.)	(I.U.)
Growing Heifers:	50	110	500	1.1	1.0	2.2	200	.44	180	.39	1.00	2.205	4.4	3.6	4.0	3.0	5.3	2.1	300
	100	220	650	1.4	2.8	6.2	430	.94	280	.61	1.90	4.189	8.4	6.9	9.6	8.4	10.6	4.2	660
	200	441	700	1.5	5.2	11.5	520	1.13	380	.83	3.15	6.945	13.9	11.4	13.0	12.0	21.2	8.5	1300
	300	662	600	1.3	7.2	15.9	660	1.44	410	.90	4.10	9.040	18.0	14.8	15.0	14.0	31.8	12.7	
	400	882	600	1.3	8.8	19.4	700	1.53	420	.92	4.60	10.143	20.2	16.7	16.0	15.0	42.4	17.0	
	500	1103	400	.9	9.6	21.2	750	1.64	450	.98	4.80	10.584	21.1	17.3	16.0	15.0	53.0	21.2	
Maintenance of Mature Cows:	450	992			6.2	13.7	450	.98	270	.59	3.20	7.056	14.1	11.6	12.0	12.0	48.0	19.2	
	550	1213			7.8	17.2	533	1.16	330	.72	3.80	8.379	16.7	13.7	15.0	15.0	58.0	23.2	
	650	1433			8.6	19.0	608	1.33	365	.80	4.20	9.261	18.5	15.2	17.0	17.0	69.0	27.6	
	750	1654			9.8	21.6	692	1.51	415	.91	4.65	10.253	20.5	16.8	20.0	20.0	80.0	32.0	
Reproduction (add to maintenance last 2 to 3 months)	400	882			4.0	8.8	400	.88	240	.53	2.4	5.292	10.6	8.7	10.0	8.0	22.0	8.8	
	550	1213			5.0	11.0	460	1.01	275	.60	3.0	6.615	13.2	10.8	13.0	11.0	30.0	12.0	
	700	1544			6.0	13.2	550	1.20	330	.72	3.6	7.938	15.8	13.0	16.0	14.0	38.0	15.2	
Lactation (add to maintenance) for cows producing following amounts of milk (4% fat) daily: ← per kg (2.2046 lbs.) milk produced →																			
More than 35 kg (77 lb.)							88	.19	56	.12	4.20	.93	1.85	1.52	2.8	2.0			
20 to 35 kg (44 to 77 lb.)							78	.17	51	.11	3.70	.81	1.63	1.34	2.4	1.8			
Less than 20 kg (44 lb.)							70	.15	46	.10	3.30	.73	1.46	1.20	2.2	1.6			

[1]From NRC Pub. 1349, with avoirdupois system added by author of *Animal Science*. Thiamine, riboflavin, niacin, pyridoxine, pantothenic acid, folic acid, vitamin B_{12}, and vitamin K are synthesized by bacteria in the rumen, and it appears that adequate amounts of these vitamins are furnished by a combination of rumen synthesis and natural feedstuffs.

[2]Based on air-dry feed containing 90% dry matter. These figures are only rough estimations since the amount depends on the composition of the ration.

[3]ME (metabolizable energy) has been estimated on the basis that 1 gm of TDN has 4.4 kcal of DE (digestible energy) (4.4 Mcal per kg) and that 82% of the DE is available as ME. The ME values can be converted to DE by multiplying them by 122.

[4]While vitamin D is known to be required, quantitative data are not available for growing animals above 200 kg in body weight and for maintenance and reproduction. Animals exposed to direct sunlight or fed sun-cured forages do not need supplemental vitamin D.

Most of the energy required is supplied by carbohydrates and fats in forage and grain. All cows, except low producing ones—those producing less than 15 to 20 pounds of milk per day, need some grain if they are to yield at top levels.

Protein

Proteins are essential for growth, repair of old tissue, milk production, and development of the unborn calf.

For dairy cattle, it's the total amount of protein that counts, not the source. This is so because cattle have micro-organisms in the rumen which build up most of the amino acids needed.

Protein requirements are usually calculated on the basis of digestible protein. However, in the feed industry, protein levels are usually shown in terms of total crude protein. To convert the figure on the tag to approximate digestible protein, take 80 per cent of it (multiply by 4/5). Thus, a 16 per cent crude protein contains 12.8 per cent digestible protein.

The amount of protein needed in the grain mix depends on the kind and quality of roughage. As the amount of legume increases, the percentage protein in the grain mix can be lowered.

When more protein is fed than needed, it is used as a source of energy. Because protein concentrates are more expensive than carbohydrate feeds, it usually is more economical to feed only the amount needed.

Minerals

Minerals make up about 5 per cent of the weight of the dairy cow. This is mostly calcium and phosphorus, found chiefly in the skeleton.

But the lactating cow has additional mineral requirements, over and above those needed for her own body or for the developing fetus.

Milk contains about 0.7 per cent minerals. Thus, one cow producing 15,000 lb. of milk gives 105 lb. of mineral per year. By way of comparison, it is noteworthy that 3 steers produce only 120 lb. of minerals by the time they reach 1,000 lb. in weight (at 18 months of age). This means that in one lactation a cow produces in her milk nearly as much mineral as three steers store in their bodies in 54 months (3 x 18). Additionally, a milk cow needs minerals for body maintenance (which requirements are about the same as those of a steer), for development of the unborn calf, and for growth if she is a young cow.

Dairy cattle of all ages and stages of production are more apt to suffer from a lack of phosphorus in their feed than from a deficiency of any other mineral element. Major changes in dairy cattle feeding have accentuated the phosphorus deficiency in recent years. Among these changes are: (1) increased crop yields as a result of improved varieties and heavy nitrogen fertilization, which have depleted the phosphorus of the soil; (2) alfalfa constituting more of the roughage component, and alfalfa is always a rich source of calcium (in alfalfa, calcium-phosphorus ratios of 6 to 8:1 are not uncommon); (3) more

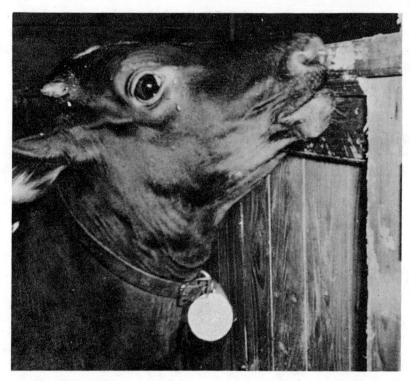

Fig. 20-3. Phosphorus deficient calf chewing wood, a manifestation of depraved appetite. (Courtesy, Dr. S. E. Smith, Department of Animal Science, Cornell University)

urea is being fed (and urea does not contain any minerals), whereas protein-rich oil meal supplements are a valuable source of phosphorus; and (4) high-level feeding and increased milk production, which carries with it a built-in stress factor that tends to emphasize any difficulty that may be encountered if any nutrient is deficient or supplied in excess. Generally speaking, the calcium-phosphorus ratio of the total ration should not be wider than 2:1.

It is also good business to guard against any trace mineral deficiencies by providing iodine, cobalt, copper, manganese, and zinc. These trace minerals may be provided in the mineral mix, in trace-mineralized salt, or in the ration itself.

Salt and other minerals may be added to the concentrate mix; usually at the rate of about 1 per cent salt and 1 per cent other minerals. Even so, they should always be available free choice.

Vitamins

Dairy cattle, like other animals, require vitamins. Of the known vitamins, only A and D are likely to be lacking in the average dairy ration. Vitamin K and the B-complex vitamins are synthesized by the body tissues. Vitamin E is abundant in most feeds.

Lack of vitamin A causes a breakdown of the nervous system, skin, and body linings. Calves may be born weak, dead, or partially blind. Vitamin A deficiency is most likely to occur when hays which are bleached or badly weathered, and low in carotene, are fed. Thus, where average or poor quality hay is fed, a rich source of carotene or synthetic vitamin A should be added to the ration. The addition of about 5 per cent dehydrated alfalfa or dehydrated grass to the grain ration will usually suffice, or one may add vitamin A at the rate of about 1,000 I.U. per pound of concentrate.

Dairy calves kept indoors may suffer from rickets, a vitamin D deficiency. Because it is difficult to predict the vitamin D content of forage, since it depends on the length of time forage is exposed to the sun's rays while growing and other factors, it is usually well to add vitamin D to most calf rations. Vitamin D may be added at the rate of 150 I.U. per pound of concentrate.

Water

Large amounts of water are essential if a cow is to produce to her maximum capacity. Cows drink an average of 100 to 200 lb. of water per day, with heavy producers drinking up to 300 lb. per day. The amount of water a cow will drink depends on her size and milk yield, the temperature and relative humidity of the air, the temperature of the water, and the amount of moisture in her feed.

In extremely cold weather, it is a good idea to have a tank heater to keep the water from freezing. Also, frequency of watering is important. Cows stabled in a stanchion-type barn produce 3½ to 4 per cent more milk if they have drinking cups available than if they are watered twice daily. Contrary to some opinions, cows do not produce more milk from softened than from normal hard water.

Other Feed Requirements

In addition to being nutritionally complete, the following factors should receive consideration in dairy cattle rations:

1. **Palatability.**—If they don't eat it, they won't produce. Hence, palatability is important. The feeder should avoid mature, moldy, musty, coarse, or weed-infested hay; finely ground hay or grain; and silages which are moldy, slimy, or too mature.

2. **Preparation.**—Grain for dairy cows should either be steam rolled or medium ground. Calves under six months of age can be fed whole corn.

Pelleted concentrates are more compact and less dusty than flaked or ground grains. Also, cows will consume pelleted feeds faster than ground or flaked feeds. Cows fed pelleted grain produce slightly more milk, with a slightly lower fat content, than those fed unpelleted grain.

Cows produce as well on long hay as on chopped or ground hay. Finely ground, pelleted hay affects the amount and proportions of volatile fatty acids in the ruminant, with the result that the percentage fat content of the milk is lowered. Wafering, on the other hand, has no effect on either milk production or fat tests. Both pelleting and wafering lessen the transportation, storage, and handling charges on hay in comparison with long hay.

3. **Variety.**—Some variety in the ration is desirable, but palatability and nutritive content of individual feeds are more important than number of ingredients. Cows crave some dry forage in their rations.

4. **Bulk.**—Some bulk in the feed is desirable. However, in modern dairy cattle feeding, more grain and less roughage is being fed.

5. **Laxativeness.**—Cows that receive average amounts of legume hay and/or silage seldom become constipated. But grass hay or straw may cause some trouble. Constipation can be corrected by feeding such feeds as alfalfa, wheat bran, linseed meal, or molasses.

6. **Cost.**—Cost is important. But even more important is net returns; hence, it may well be said that it's net returns rather than cost per ton, or per bag, that counts.

FEEDS FOR DAIRY COWS

For convenience, the commonly used dairy cattle feeds are herewith classified as (1) roughages, (2) concentrates, and (3) special feeds.

Fig. 20-4. Fenceline feeding, with a tractor-drawn, automated wagon. (Courtesy, Allis-Chalmers Mfg. Co., Milwaukee, Wisc.)

Roughages (Forages)

Cows can produce up to 70 per cent of their ability when fed good quality roughage alone. But with high-producing cows, a greater percentage of the total feed intake must be in the form of concentrates. Even so, large amounts of high quality roughage should be the basis for feeding on most dairy farms.

In using any kind of roughage, three important points should be kept in mind: (1) to obtain the most nutrients from roughage, it must be of good quality; (2) the better the roughage, the smaller the requirement for grains; (3) the cow is, by nature, a good consumer of forage.

A high-quality roughage is one that possesses the physical and chemical characteristics commonly associated with palatability and an abundance of feed nutrients. The most important physical factors of quality that may be gauged in a practical way are (1) stage of maturity when cut, (2) percentage of leaves, (3) green color, (4) amount of heating, spoilage, etc., (5) pliability of stems, (6) aroma, and (7) freedom from foreign material.

1. **Hay.**—Legumes make the best hay for dairy cattle. For best quality, alfalfa should be cut before one-tenth bloom. Table 20-3 data (from experiments conducted by the USDA) shows the relationship of maturity to nutritive value. This table shows that protein decreases as hay matures, and that cows produce considerably less milk when fed too mature hay.

TABLE 20—3

ALFALFA MATURITY AND NUTRITIVE VALUE[1]

	Initial Bloom	Half Bloom	Full Bloom
	←---lb. per acre ---→		
Dry matter	7,896	7,778	6,061
Total digestible nutrients	4,660	4,413	3,269
Digestible protein	1,106	1,016	722
Production of 4% fat-corrected milk	6,330	5,254	3,970

[1] U.S. Department of Agriculture data.

Dairymen can afford to pay a higher price for good hay. Calculations show that if hay cut at full bloom is worth $20 per ton, hay cut at 1/10 bloom is worth $35 per ton.

2. **Silage.**—The feeding value of silage is no better than the material put in the silo. Good silage is easy to make if the crop is cut at the proper stage of growth, cut fine and ensiled as rapidly as possible at 65 to 70 per cent moisture, evenly and well-packed, and stored in a silo free of air leaks.

In regions where rainy weather frequently makes hay making difficult, it is wise to harvest forage as silage. This especially applies to the first cutting of grasses and/or legumes, which may normally be used as hay.

Usually, it is possible to produce more milk per acre of land when the crops are harvested as silage rather than as hay. Also, silage helps alleviate the week to week variation that often goes with pastures or green chop.

Many forages can be, and are, successfully used as silage for dairy cows, including corn silage, grass silage, oat silage, sorghum silage, and many others.

Adding high calcium limestone (20 lb./ton) to corn silage will improve the quality of the silage. When this is done, however, dairymen who are feeding alfalfa hay (high in calcium) will need to balance out the calcium-phosphorus ratio of the total ration. Otherwise, they may encounter a high incidence of milk fever, and perhaps other troubles.

If *carefully mixed*, urea can be added to corn silage, at the rate of 10 pounds of urea per ton of silage. Corn silage of 70 per cent moisture content contains about 2.5 per cent protein, or 7.5 per cent protein on an air-dry (90 per cent dry matter) basis. By adding 10 pounds of urea per ton of silage, the protein content is increased to 3.8 per cent on a wet basis or 11.4 per cent on an air-dry basis.

3. **Haylage (low-moisture silage).**—Haylage is made from grass and/or legume that is wilted to 40 to 45 per cent moisture content before ensiling. Properly made haylage is good smelling, palatable, high-quality feed. Cows usually receive more dry matter and net feed value in haylage than in silage made from the same cut.

Haylage is easy to prepare and preserve in a gas-type silo where air is excluded. But it can be made in a conventional silo provided certain precautions are taken—precautions designed to keep out the air.

Haylage is growing in popularity. Its feed value depends on the stage of the growth of the crop when filled and the percentage of dry matter in the silage.

4. **Green chop (silage).**—Many dairymen harvest and feed green chop daily. It reduces wastage as compared to pasture. With tall growing chops, 50 per cent more feed value may be realized from a given area. However, green chop requires special equipment and harvesting every day. Also, there are harvesting problems in wet weather, and there is inevitable change in feed quality as the season progresses. Thus, this system is gradually giving way to stored feeding.

5. **Pasture.**—Good pastures provide a highly nutritious feed that milk cows relish, especially when fresh growth is maintained; and the cows do their own harvesting. However, pasturing results in considerable waste of the crop through trampling, with lower yield of nutrients per acre than from harvested crops. Also, it is sometimes difficult to maintain growth of even feed value because of variable weather conditions. This results in fluctuation in milk production. Additionally, in areas of high-priced land and where grain crops yield well, pastures must be exceedingly well managed to compete with other crops. For the latter reason, especially in the more fertile areas, dairymen are shifting from pasture to continuous feeding of stored feed.

In recent years, the old system of continuous grazing on one field all season has been largely abandoned. The new systems of pasture management include rotation grazing, strip grazing (or daily rotation grazing), and zero grazing.

RULES OF THUMB FOR ROUGHAGE CONSUMPTION

The common rules of thumb for forage consumption of dairy cows are as follow:

1. A cow will eat 2 to 3 pounds of hay per 100 pounds of body weight if fed hay alone.

2. Three pounds of silage are equal to (and will replace) 1 pound of hay; the lower feeding value of silage being due to its high moisture content.

3. It takes about 3 pounds of good hay to supply the same amount of usable energy as 2 pounds of grain.

4. Cows will consume 100 to 200 pounds of pasture per day; since pasture normally contains 70 to 85 per cent moisture, that's 15 to 60 pounds of dry matter per day.

If roughage is of very high quality, cows will eat more of it, with the result that the grain requirement will be lessened. However, over and above meeting the minimum roughage requirement, the proportion of roughage to concentrate should be determined primarily by the economics of the situation— that is, it should be decided on the basis of the relative price of available roughage and concentrate, the milk production, and the net returns.

Concentrates (Grains)

Concentrate feeds are those which are high in energy and low in fiber. They are usually classed, according to total crude protein content, as (1) low protein, (2) medium protein, and (3) high protein feeds. The chemical analysis of feeds can be obtained from feed composition tables (such as those shown in *The Stockman's Handbook*, 4th ed., and in NRC Pub. 1349).

Many different kinds of concentrate feeds can be, and are, used in dairy cattle feeding.

Three factors besides chemical composition are important in evaluating concentrates for milk cows—palatability, quality of milk produced, and cost.

The most infallible way in which to appraise the first two factors is through actual feeding trials. Consideration of the third factor necessitates that the dairyman be a keen student of values. He must change the formulations of his ration(s) in keeping with comparative feed prices.

Special Feeds

Among the special feeds used by dairymen are the following:

1. **Urea.**—Due to the increasing shortage and higher price of oil seed proteins, more and more urea is being fed to dairy cows. Urea is manufactured synthetically from the nitrogen of the air. When properly used, it is a safe, low-cost source of protein for dairy cattle; when improperly used, it becomes a hazard. It is recommended that urea in a concentrate mixture not exceed 2 per cent, and that it not exceed 1 per cent of the total hay and grain ration. It is further recommended that not more than one-third of the protein requirements be met through urea. Under experimental conditions, much higher quantities of urea have been fed to dairy cows. For example, beginning in 1958, Dr. A. I. Virtanen, the Finnish Nobel prize winner, successfully fed dairy cows on a protein-free diet, utilizing small amounts of ammonium salts combined with urea

as practically the sole source of nitrogen.[1] Yet, it is emphasized that this was done under carefully controlled experimental conditions. Further, most state laws limit the amount of urea that can be put in commercial feeds.

One pound of urea provides as much protein value as 6.4 lb. of 41 per cent soybean meal or cottonseed meal. Each percent added to a feed mixture increases the potential protein content by 2.6 per cent. However, urea does not provide either energy, minerals, or vitamins; with the result that these must be provided through other sources when urea is substituted for protein meals.

When added to the dairy cattle ration, urea must be mixed thoroughly to insure even distribution, and used according to directions. It may be toxic when improperly used, or when fed in too large amounts. Also, the long-time effect of urea feeding upon the health and well-being of dairy cows is not known.

Normally, dairymen limit urea to 1.5 to 2.0 per cent of the concentrate ration. Higher levels (up to 2.75 per cent of the concentrate) are unpalatable and depress appetite. However, the unpalatability may be alleviated by pelleting the urea with alfalfa.

2. **Antibiotics.**—Antibiotics are not nutrients; they are classified as additives.

Research studies have given variable and inconsistent results on the effect of feeding antibiotics from the standpoint of increasing milk production. Until additional information showing the value of antibiotics from the standpoint of increased and economical milk production is available, there is no reason for recommending their use for feeding lactating cows. Research has shown that low-level antibiotics (10 milligrams per 100 pounds body weight per day) will not result in antibiotics appearing in the milk.

Antibiotics do lessen the incidence of diarrhea in calves and result in increased rate of gain in dairy calves. For this reason, they are usually included in milk replacers and calf starters.

3. **Thyroprotein (protamone).**—When treated in a special way with iodine, dried milk protein yields a product that has a similar activity in the body as the thyroid hormone. When added to the feed at certain levels (usually about 15 grams/head/day) and under certain conditions, thyroprotein stimulates the cow to produce more milk (up to 20 per cent more) of a higher fat (up to 30 per cent more) content. However, to be effective, this product must be added at a specific time during the lactation period and it must be withdrawn very gradually before the end of lactation. Also, cows must be given additional feed to produce the extra milk. Not all cows will respond to thyroprotein. Because of the problems involved in feeding the product, it is not generally recommended in feeding practice. Also, since thyroprotein is classified as a drug, milk and butterfat production records of cows fed thyroprotein are not acceptable under DHIA rules.

4. **Sprouted grain (hydroponics).**—Oats and other cereal grains are sometimes sprouted in incubators, and the green vegetation produced fed to cows. Research has not shown that dairy cows fed sprouted grains produced any better

---

[1] *Science*, Sept. 30, 1966, Vol. 153, No. 3744, pp. 1603-1614.

than those receiving an equal amount of dry matter from grain. Thus, considering equipment costs, mold growth in the units, and the loss of dry matter in the sprouting process, it does not appear to be economical to feed sprouted grain to milk cows. There is need for additional experimental work, however.

5. **Sodium propionate, sodium and calcium lactate, and propylene glycol.**—Sodium propionate and sodium and calcium lactate powder have some value in preventing ketosis in dairy cows when fed at levels of one-fourth to one-half pound per cow per day, beginning one week before calving and extending six weeks after calving. Propylene glycol, a liquid, fed at levels of ¼ to ½ pint per cow per day, can be used in a similar manner. Since these products are not palatable, they should be added to the ration gradually or used as a drench.

6. **Irradiated yeast.**—Yeast contains considerable ergosterol, which, when exposed to ultraviolet light, produces vitamin D. This high potency vitamin D-containing yeast is helpful in preventing milk fever in dairy cows, when fed at a level of 20 million units of vitamin D daily, in the form of irradiated yeast, for seven days just before calving. It should not be fed longer than the seven-day period, as it may result in detriment to the cow's health.

Commercial Dairy Feeds

Commercial dairy feeds are just what the name implies—feeds mixed by commercial manufacturers who specialize in the business, rather than farm mixed. Today, about 60 million tons of commercial feeds are marketed in the U.S. each year, slightly over one-fifth (21.8 per cent in 1964) of which are used by dairy cattle.

The commercial feed manufacturer has the distinct advantages of (1) purchase of feed in quantity lots, making possible price advantages; (2) economical and controlled mixing; (3) the hiring of scientifically trained personnel for use in determining the rations; and (4) quality control. Most dairymen have neither the know-how nor the quantity of business to provide these services on their own. Because of these advantages, commercial feeds are finding a place of increasing importance in dairy cattle feeding. Also, it is to the everlasting credit of reputable feed dealers that they have been good teachers; often getting dairymen started in the feeding of balanced rations.

Several different types of commercial feeds are available for dairy cattle, among them (1) complete dairy concentrates, (2) dry cow rations, (3) fitting rations, (4) growing or young stock rations, (5) calf starters, (6) milk replacer feeds, and (7) protein supplements.

HOW TO SELECT A COMMERCIAL FEED

An enlightened dairyman will know how to determine what constitutes the best in commercial feeds for his specific needs. He will not rely solely on how the feed looks and smells. The most important factors to look for in buying a commercial feed are:

1. **The reputation of the manufacturer.**—This may be determined by (a)

checking on who is back of it, (b) conferring with other dairymen who have used the particular product, and (c) checking on whether or not the commercial feed under consideration has consistently met its guarantees (samples of each commercial feed are taken each year, and analyzed in the state laboratories to determine if the manufacturer lived up to his guarantee).

2. **The specific needs.**—Feed needs vary according to (a) whether they are being fed to lactating cows, dry cows, replacement heifers, etc. and (b) the other available feeds on the farm with which they are being combined.

3. **Feeds with flexible formulas.**—Feeds with flexible formulas are usually the best buy. This is because the price of feed ingredient in different source feeds varies considerably from time to time. Thus, a good feed manufacturer will shift his formula as prices change in order to give the dairyman the most for his money. This is as it should be, for there is no one best ingredient, and if substitutions are made wisely, the prices of feed can be kept down and the dairyman will continue to get equally good results. Flexible formulas are particularly desirable where linear programming and electronic computers are used, for they will cause feed grains to enter the ration when prices to the feed manufacturer change by as little as 10 cents per ton.

4. **What's on the tag?**—A dairyman should be able to study and interpret what's on the feed tag. State laws vary somewhat, but, generally speaking, the commercial feed manufacturer is required to give (a) the brand or name of the feed; (b) the net weight; (c) the guaranteed analysis (each stated in per cent) in minimum crude protein and crude fat, maximum crude fiber, ash, and mineral, minimum and maximum calcium, and minimum phosphorus, maximum salt, and minimum TDN; (d) the ingredients, usually listed in descending order of amounts, by weights; (e) the name, address, and phone number of the manufacturer; and (f) the feeding directions.

By studying the feed tag, a knowledgeable dairyman can, readily and easily, see what's in the feed and determine if it meets the nutritive requirements of his animals. Of course, guaranteed analysis, within itself, will not suffice. For example, on the basis of chemical composition, soft coal and coffee grounds are comparable to many commonly used grains; yet, no one would be so foolish as to feed these products to dairy cows.

FEEDING CONCENTRATES TO DAIRY COWS

Cows fed an all-forage ration produce about 30 per cent less milk than cows fed concentrates in average amounts. This is because a cow's stomach simply isn't big enough to hold all the roughage necessary to get the amount of energy needed. To provide the needed energy, grain must be added. Grain provides energy in concentrated form. For example, 5 lb. of barley contain as much TDN as 8 lb. of hay or 25 lb. of silage.

Grain rations also supply protein. The percentage total protein needed in the grain ration depends upon the type of roughage fed. Some guides are given in Table 20-4.

As shown in Table 20-4, with high quality legume roughage, a 10 per cent

TABLE 20—4

PER CENT PROTEIN NEEDED IN GRAIN MIX

Roughage Fed	Per Cent Protein in Grain Mix
	(%)
All legume	10-14
Mixed (part legume and part grass)	14-18
All grass	18-20

protein grain mix will suffice. With a low quality grass roughage, however, the protein level of the grain mix should be much higher, up to 18 to 20 per cent.

Since proteins are always the most expensive part of a ration, for practical reasons the dairyman should not feed more of them than necessary. For this reason, the protein content of the grain mix should always be balanced out on the basis of the roughage being fed.

Suggested Concentrate Rations for Lactating Cows

The concentrate ration needed to supplement the available roughage on the dairy farm may either be home-mixed or a commercial concentrate. About 30 per cent of all concentrates fed to dairy cattle in the U.S. are commercially mixed. Commercially mixed dairy concentrates have largely taken over, and replaced home-mixed grains, in dairy herds operating in grain deficit areas and among those highly specialized dairy enterprises on which little or no grains are produced. This trend will continue.

On the smaller dairies, and particularly where grain is home-grown or abundantly available locally, home-mixing of dairy concentrates will continue.

Table 20-5, "Handy Lactating Cow Feeding Guide," will serve as a useful guide for the dairyman who wishes to mix his own concentrate, with the ingredients therein based on the kind of roughage available. Of course, variations can and should be made in the rations listed in Table 20-5. The dairyman should give consideration to the supply of home-grown feeds, and to the availability and price of ingredients. Feeds of similar nutritive properties can and should be interchanged as price relationships warrant. Thus, the cereal grains may consist of corn, barley, wheat, oats, and/or sorghum; the protein supplements may consist of soybean, cottonseed, peanut and/or linseed meal; and a vast array of by-product feeds may be utilized.

Here is how to use Table 20-5: Let's assume that a dairyman has (1) a medium quality forage and (2) both low and medium-high protein concentrates from which to choose. How many pounds each of the low and medium-high protein concentrates will be required in a 1,000 pound concentrate mix? Step by step, here is the answer:

1. Look under "medium roughage-medium protein forage" (column to the left).

2. Mix No. 2-m, containing 650 pounds of low protein concentrates (7 to

12 per cent protein) and 350 pounds of medium-high protein concentrates (18 to 26 per cent protein), will meet the needs. The concentrates may be chosen from among those listed at the top of the respective columns of Table 20-5—the low protein concentrates from column 2 (7 to 12 per cent) and the medium-high protein concentrates from column 4 (18 to 26 per cent).

How to Balance a Dairy Ration

A balanced ration is one which provides an animal the proper proportions and amounts of all the required nutrients for a period of 24 hours.

Generally speaking, the rations given in Table 20-5 will suffice. But it is recognized that rations should vary with conditions, and that many times they should be formulated to meet the conditions of a specific dairy farm. Also, a good dairyman should know how to balance a ration. Then, if the occasion demands, he can do it. Perhaps of even greater importance, he will be able more intelligently to select and buy rations with informed appraisal, to check on how well his feed supplier and nutritionist are doing, and to evaluate the results.

Before attempting to balance a ration, the following points should be considered:

1. **Availability and cost of different feed ingredients.**—Preferably, cost of ingredients should be based on delivery where fed and after processing, because delivery and processing costs are quite variable.

2. **Feed composition tables.**—This information for the commonly used dairy feeds can be obtained from *The Stockman's Handbook,* 4th ed., or NRC Pubs. 1349 and 1684. or other similar sources.

3. **The nutrient requirements.**—Table 20-2 of this book will suffice as a source of nutrient requirements for most herds. If needed, additional categories can be obtained from NRC Pub. 1349. In using such a table, it must be recognized that it is just what the designation implies—requirements, and *not allowances.* No margins of safety are provided to allow for variations in feed composition (due to soils on which grown, stage of maturity, weathering, and processing and storage), environment and stress, individuality, etc. Hence, some overage should be provided in the rations formulated.

Rations are commonly formulated by one of the following three methods:

1. **The Square (or Pearson Square) Method,** in which protein content alone receives major consideration (see *The Stockman's Handbook* for instruction on balancing rations by this method).

2. **The Trial and Error Method,** in which consideration is given to meeting whatever nutritive allowances one cares to list—TDN, protein, fiber, minerals, vitamins; all or any part of them.

3. **The Computer Method,** in which the procedure is essentially like the Trial and Error Method, but a lot faster and with all possible combinations checked.

In the example that follows, the Trial and Error Method is used, with consideration given to energy and protein. Also, crude protein rather than digest-

TABLE 20—5

HANDY LACTATING COW FEEDING GUIDE

Suggested Grain Mix, Based on Kind of Roughage Available	(7% to 12%) Concentrates	Low-Medium Protein (12% to 18%) Concentrates	Medium-High Protein (18% to 26%) Concentrates	High Protein (32% to 34%) Concentrates
FEEDS:	(% protein) Corn & cob meal...... 7.4 Molasses*.............. 8.4 Corn.................. 8.9 Dried beet pulp....... 8.9 Sorghum (milo)....... 11.0 Hominy feed.......... 11.1 Barley............... 11.7 Oats................. 11.8 Rye*................. 11.9 12% dairy feed....... 12.0 Wheat*.............. 12.1	(% protein) 16% dairy feed...........16.0 Wheat bran.............16.0 Wheat middlings........17.2	(% protein) 18-24% dairy feed...18-24 Copra (coconut) meal*.. 21.3 Peas*................ 22.5 Corn gluten feed.... 25.3 Brewer's dried grains*.. 25.9 Malt sprouts........ 26.2 Distillers dried grains.. 27.1	(% protein) 32-34% dairy feed.....32-34 Linseed meal......... 35.3 Cottonseed meal*.... 41.4 Corn gluten meal.... 42.9 Soybean meal........ 45.8 Peanut meal......... 47.4
Excellent Roughage—High Protein Forage: (1) legume or (2) legume and nonlegume mixed forages of *high quality*; consisting of dry forages and/or silage.	*(lb.)*	*(lb.)*	*(lb.)*	*(lb.)*
Mix No. 1-e	1000			
" " 2-e	900			100
" " 3-e	800		200	
" " 4-e	850	100		50
Medium Roughage—Medium protein forage: (1) legume or (2) legume and nonlegume mixed forages of *medium quality*, consisting of dry forages and/or silage.				
Mix No. 1-m	800			200
" " 2-m	650		350	
" " 3-m	700	100	100	100
" " 4-m	Straight 16% dairy feed, or ½ Mix No. 1-p & ½ 16% dairy feed			

Footnote at end of table.

(Continued)

TABLE 20—5 (Continued).

Suggested Grain Mix, Based on Kind of Roughage Available	Low Protein (7% to 12%) Concentrates	Low-Medium Protein (12% to 18%) Concentrates	Medium-High Protein (18% to 26%) Concentrates	High Protein (32% to 34%) Concentrates
	(lb.)	(lb.)	(lb.)	(lb.)
Poor Roughage—Low protein forage: nonlegume forage; consisting of dry forages and/or silage.				
Mix No. 1-p	700	300		
,, ,, 2-p	600		200	200
,, ,, 3-p	600			200
,, ,, 4-p	500	100	100	
		and 500 lbs. 32% Dairy Feed		

COMMENTS:

Add—To all rations (1) 1 per cent iodized or trace-mineralized salt; (2) 1 per cent steamed bone meal, dicalcium phosphate, or the equivalent (use monosodium phosphate or a high-phosphorus commercial mineral where alfalfa is fed liberally); (3) 1,000 I.U. of vitamin A/lb. of concentrate and, unless cows are in sunlight, add 150 I.U. of vitamin D/lb. of concentrate.

Limitations—Wheat, not more than 50 per cent of the ration; dried molasses beet pulp, 20 per cent; molasses, 15 per cent; peas and brewer's dried grains, 30 per cent; rye, 10 per cent; and cottonseed meal, 20 per cent of the mix for calves, but as needed for mature cows.

ible protein is used because (1) this is what the feed manufacturer wants to know as he plans a feed formula, and (2) this is what the dairyman sees on the feed tag when he purchases feed. As stated earlier in this chapter, in most mixed dairy feeds approximately 80 per cent of the total protein is digestible.

Example:

Let's assume that we have a 1,433 pound cow producing 60 pounds of milk testing 4.0 per cent fat. The dairyman is feeding 15 pounds of alfalfa hay and 45 pounds of corn silage per day. Corn, oats, and soybean meal are available. What concentrate mix shall he use to meet the needs of this lactating cow, from the standpoint of energy and protein?

Before proceeding further, here are some general rules that we shall follow:

a. The TDN of the complete ration of lactating cows should be 70 per cent or better, preferable 74 to 75 per cent.

b. One per cent (1%) salt and 1 per cent (1%) of a low-calcium high phosphorus mineral (including trace minerals) are to be added to the grain ration. Also, salt and a mineral mix will be self-fed in a two-compartment mineral box.

c. Vitamin A and vitamin D will be added to the ration at a level of 1,000 I.U. of vitamin A and 150 I.U. of vitamin D per pound of concentrate, respectively.

d. The feed compositions used in the following example were taken from *The Stockman's Handbook,* 4th ed., and NRC Pub. 1349:

	TDN (%)	Crude Protein (%)
Alfalfa hay	51	15.2
Corn	81	8.9
Corn silage	19	2.3
Oats	68	11.8
Soybean meal	73	45.8

Here are the steps in balancing this ration:

Step No. 1—The daily TDN and crude protein requirements of this cow (1,433 lb. body weight, 60 lb. milk) are (see Table 20-2):

		TDN (lb.)	Crude Protein (lb.)
Requirements of cow for—			
	Maintenance	9.3	1.33
	Milk production	22.0	4.62
	Total	31.3	5.95

Step No. 2—The roughage (15 lb. alfalfa hay, 45 lb. corn silage) is supplying:

		TDN	Crude Protein
	Alfalfa hay, 15 lb.	7.6	2.28
	Corn silage, 45 lb.	8.6	1.04
	Total from forage	16.2	3.32

Step No. 3—Remainder, to be supplied by concentrate | | 15.1 | 2.63 |

Step No. 4—Let's try out (that's why it is called the "trial and error method") a grain mix of 700 lb. corn, 280 lb. oats, 10 lb. monosodium phosphate, and 10 lb. salt; and see how much TDN and crude protein is in 1,000 lb. of the grain mix

	TDN	Crude Protein
	(lb.)	(lb.)
Corn, 700 lb.	567.0	62.3
Oats, 280 lb.	190.4	33.0
Monosodium phosphate, 10 lb.	—	—
Salt, 10 lb.	—	—
Total	757.4	95.3
or in per cent	75.7%	9.5%

Step No. 5—Divide the TDN needed from concentrate (15.1 lb.) by the per cent TDN in the mixture (75.7%). Thus, feeding 19.9 lb. of the concentrate will meet the energy needs.

Step No. 6—Will this level of grain mix (19.9 lb.) also meet the crude protein needs? By multiplying the lb. concentrate mixture by the per cent crude protein (19.9 x 9.5%) we find that the proposed concentrate would supply 1.89 lb. of crude protein, whereas 2.63 lb. are needed. Therefore, a high protein supplement must be substituted for some of the home-grown grain.

Step No. 7—Let's substitute 100 lb. of soybean meal for 100 lb. of corn. Hence, the ration as now proposed will consist of—

Corn, 600 lb.	486.0	53.4
Oats, 280 lb.	190.4	33.0
Soybean meal, 100 lb.	73.0	45.8
Monosodium phosphate, 10 lb.	—	—
Salt, 10 lb.	—	—
Total	749.4	132.2
or in per cent	74.9	13.2

Step No. 8—By referring back to Step No. 3, we can divide the lb. of TDN and crude protein needed from the concentrate, by the percentage of TDN and crude protein found in the grain mix in Step No. 7. We find that 15.1 + 74.9 = 20.2 lbs. needed to supply ... 15.1

and 2.63 + 13.2 = 19.9 lb. needed to supply 2.63

Thus, we find that the following ration will supply the needed TDN and crude protein for a 1433-pound lactating cow producing 60 pounds of milk testing 4 per cent fat:

Alfalfa hay, 15 lb.	7.6	2.28
Corn silage, 45 lb.	8.6	1.04
Concentrate mix (Step No. 7) 20.2 lb.	15.1	2.67
Total	31.3	5.99

In many sections of the country, especially in grain deficit areas and on highly specialized dairies where little or no grain is grown, the dairyman may find it most economical to purchase a commercial dairy feed to balance out the roughage that is being fed.

Amount of Concentrate to Feed; "Challenge" or "Lead" Feed

Today, rules of thumb for use as grain feeding guides are in disrepute. Actually, the old thumb rules of feeding proved to be stumbling blocks to wise grain feeding. With cows not capable of high production, or those on very good roughage, some rules can lead to wasteful overfeeding. On the other hand, some rules can lead to underfeeding the high-producing cows. It can be concluded, therefore, that no simple set of thumb rules can replace experience and dairy intuition. The current rule of the expert feeder is to increase grain so long as the cow responds with extra milk at a profit. Michigan reports (Ext. Bul. E-423, 1963): "Generally throughout Michigan the cost of grain per pound is only ½ to ¾ the price received for milk. Studies have shown that high-producing cows will return $4.00 to $7.00 worth of milk per 100 pounds of grain fed up to the productive capacity of the cow."

After calving, each cow should be allowed to consume energy to the limit of her ability in order to respond with higher milk yield. This concept is called "challenge" or "lead" feeding. A high level energy intake from soon after calving until a cow reaches her peak of production has the following effects: (1) it lessens ketosis, (2) it helps maintain body weight, (3) it produces a higher yield of milk at the peak of lactation, which tends to persist throughout the production cycle, and (4) it prevents uneconomical feeding since the input of energy is determined by the ability of the cow to respond.

Some dairymen report that they have increased milk production by 2,000 pounds per cow by challenge feeding—by using less roughage and more concentrates properly fortified, fed to the right animals at the right time. And increases of over 5,000 pounds of milk per lactation have been achieved.

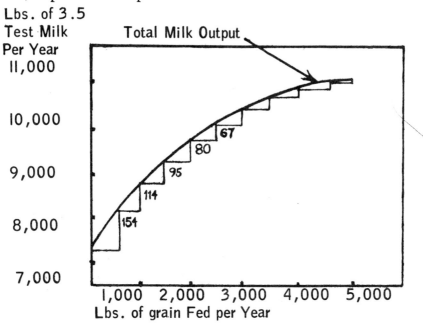

Fig. 20-5. Challenge feed (stair-step feed) "for production," rather than "according to production." The cow charted above has the ability to produce 10,000 pounds of milk per year when fed 1 pound grain for every 4 pounds of milk produced. Production on roughage alone is around 7,500 pounds of milk per year. With added grain, milk production increases. The first 500 pounds of grain give 154 pounds of milk for each 100 pounds of grain. The second 500 pounds result in somewhat less milk and so on until very little additional milk is obtained with the last 500 pounds. (From Washington State University Ext. Bul. 486)

The amount of grain that it will pay to feed milking cows depends upon several factors: (1) quality of roughage, (2) price of roughage, (3) price and quality of concentrates, (4) price of milk, and (5) inherent producing ability of cows. Of these, the most important is the inherent milk producing ability of the cow. This necessitates (1) using milk and fat production records of each cow and (2) weighing and feeding the concentrate to each individual cow. The feeder keeps adding grain by one pound increases until the value of the added milk produced no longer pays for the cost of the grain. This "stair-step" method of feeding, as it is sometimes called, is illustrated in Fig. 20-5.

Cows respond best to challenge grain feeding early in the lactation period when the lactation drive is greatest. As the lactation period progresses, the grain feeding schedule should be checked with care, at least once per month, and adjusted to the most economical feeding level. As would be expected, some cows respond to extra grain feeding more than others. Those which do not respond should be cut back until the grain feeding level is such that the intake of feed pays off in added milk.

With loose housing and milking parlors, cows generally do not have time to consume over 10 to 15 pounds of grain per day while in the milking parlor. Thus, high-producing cows should be fed additional concentrate away from the parlor.

Where cows cannot be fed grain on an individual basis, or where high producers need more grain than they have time to eat in the parlor, the next best procedure is to segregate them into two or more production groups; with the highest producing group fed the most grain. This is not as effective as feeding cows individually, but it is much more economical than feeding all cows in the herd the same level of grain, regardless of production.

Fig. 20-6. Cows on pasture. (Courtesy, Holstein-Friesian Assn. of America)

FEEDING ON PASTURE

Problems of milk production are at a minimum during the early pasture season, when plant growth is lush. However, when the weather gets hot, it is a different story; this is the period known as the "summer slump." High temperatures actually affect pasture growth more than the well being of the cows.

The following summer feeding program is recommended for most dairy cows:

1. Have good pastures and follow good pasture management.

2. Consider ensiling the early pasture growth, thereby avoiding wasted grass early in the season.

3. Bunk feed hay with pasture, regardless of pasture quality. If the quality of the pasture is comparable to the roughage that was used in the winter ration, continue with the concentrate mix that was used in the winter. On the other hand, if summer pastures are considerably better or considerably poorer than the quality of the winter roughages, the grain mix should be changed accordingly. In other words, the grain mix used when cows are on pasture should be formulated so as to balance out the deficiencies of the grass, just the same as the winter concentrate balances out the deficiencies of the winter roughages.

4. When pastures are poor and/or the weather is very hot, feed more grain and limit the hay; thereby providing needed added energy and avoiding the excess heat of high fiber rations. But do not restrict roughage to the point that butterfat test drops.

5. Provide adequate shade for cows on summer pasture.

6. Consider supplementing summer pastures with silage.

SPECIAL FEEDING PROGRAMS

The nutritive requirements of dairy cattle vary according to age, and according to whether they are lactating or dry. For this reason, more than one ration is necessary.

Dry Cows

Dry cows have three important jobs: (1) recovering from a heavy milk producing period and resting the mammary glands, (2) developing the unborn calf (more than half the fetal growth occurs during the last two months of lactation), and (3) storing up body reserves for the next milking period. This necessitates that they be properly fed.

The following routine is recommended for dry cows:

1. Turn first and second lactation heifers dry 60 to 65 days before expected calving. Turn cows more than four years of age dry 50 to 60 days before freshening.

2. Stop grain feeding and milking abruptly to hasten drying off. Examine the udder at intervals, and rub oil (such as camphorated oil or a mixture of lard and spirits of camphor) on it at intervals, but do not milk it out. At the end of five to seven days, when the udder is soft and flabby, milk out what little secretion remains.

3. Feed only good quality roughage during the first two to three weeks of the dry period. Beginning five to six weeks before expected calving, start feeding concentrates twice daily. The amount of concentrate to feed should be determined primarily by the cow's condition and the quality of the roughage. It may vary from 4 to 20 pounds per head daily. A guide to desirable gains follows:

Weight of Cows	Pounds Gain
800–1,000	75–150
1,000–1,200	100–200
1,200–1,400	125–250

4. A special dry cow concentrate mix can be fed during this period. The dry cow mix may contain 2 to 4 per cent less protein than the grain mixture normally fed to the milking herd. Also, if milk fever is a problem, as it is in most herds, it is desirable that the dry cow ration (a) be balanced out for calcium and phosphorus (a 1:1 ratio preferably, and not to exceed a 2:1 calcium to phosphorus ratio) and (b) contain added vitamin D.

Many successful dairymen make it a practice of reaching a feeding level of 1 to 1½ pounds of grain to each 100 pounds of live weight about one week before freshening, and continuing at this rate right up to freshening. This pre-calf feeding gets the rumen, and the cow's appetite and eating habits, adjusted to liberal feeding before freshening. Also, a cow freshening in good condition starts off better and maintains a higher level of production; her milk is usually higher in total solids; and the incidence of milk fever and ketosis is usually reduced.

Feeding at Calving Time

Until recent years, cows were not fed much grain prior to freshening; and, immediately after calving, they were given all the roughage they wanted but the grain allowance was sharply reduced. Today, dairymen feed appreciably more grain to cows prior to calving—from 12 to 20 pounds per day before freshening; and feed is not withheld at calving. Instead, on the first day after calving, cows are fed the same amount of grain that they were used to before calving, followed by an increase of 2 to 3 pounds per day according to the cow's appetite. The experienced caretaker is in the best position to determine how much, and what, to feed each individual cow at calving time.

The colostrum milk should be used for calf feeding or discarded until it is normal and can be marketed (about five days following freshening).

Show and Sale Animals

Dairy animals intended for show or sale should be fed so as to achieve a certain amount of finish or bloom, but they should not be too fat. Linseed meal, beet pulp, oats, barley, and wheat bran are popular feeds in a fitting and showing ration. Likewise, good roughages are always very important.

Dairy Calves

One of the most important phases of dairy production is that of feeding and managing the dairy calves raised for replacement purposes. Statistics reveal that more than 20 per cent of the dairy calves die of sickness or disease before reaching maturity. Many of these deaths are caused by faulty nutrition.

Fig. 20-7. Group of 10 dairy calves in a partially-shaded pen, with a feed bunk along the front. (Courtesy, Babson Bros. Co., Chicago)

Regardless of the calf-feeding system followed later, all calves should receive the first milk—colostrum. It contains antibodies which protect calves against disease. Also, colostrum is high in protein and in vitamins and minerals. Surplus colostrum can be frozen and stored for a period of one year or longer. It may then be thawed and warmed to about 100° F. and fed as needed. Colostrum is a valuable feed for calves, regardless of their age; hence, it can be fed to them at any time with no ill effects.

All calf-feeding systems make use of colostrum for the first two to three days following birth. At this time, cleanliness and sanitation are especially important.

Basically, calves are fed according to one of three systems: (1) the whole milk system, (2) the combination whole milk-milk replacer system, or (3) the combination whole milk-calf starter system. Of course, various combinations of these three systems are used, also. A suggested schedule for each of these three systems is given in Table 20-6.

The whole milk method costs the most, but it produces the fastest gains, the best appearing calves, and requires the least skill of any system.

Milk replacers are composed of sizeable amounts of milk by-products, such

TABLE 20—6

SCHEDULE FOR FEEDING DAIRY CALVES BY THREE DIFFERENT SYSTEMS[1]

Age of Calf	Whole Milk System	Whole Milk-Milk Replacer System	Whole Milk-Calf Starter System
0 to 3 days	Calf should receive colostrum during first three days.	Calf should receive colostrum during first three days.	Calf should receive colostrum during first three days.
3 days	Start feeding whole milk at the rate of 1 pound milk to 10 pounds body weight.[2]	Start feeding whole milk at the rate of 1 pound milk to 10 pounds body weight.[2]	Start feeding whole milk at the rate of 1 pound milk to 10 pounds body weight.[2]
7 days	Make grain available in box in pen.	Make calf starter available in box in pen.	Make calf starter available in box in pen.
7 to 10 days		Start replacing whole milk with fluid milk replacer. Replace 1 to 2 pounds milk daily with fluid milk replacer until change is completed.	
14 days		Transition to milk replacer should be completed.	
21 days	Make good quality hay available in rack in pen.	Make good quality hay available in rack in pen.	Make good quality hay available in rack in pen.
60 days		Discontinue milk replacer.	Discontinue feeding whole milk. Larger, more vigorous calves may have whole milk stopped as early as 42 days.
60 to 120 days	Permit calves to consume grain free-choice, up to 4 or 5 pounds daily. Rest of nourishment should be obtained from hay.	Permit calves to consume calf starter-free-choice, up to 4 to 5 pounds daily. Rest of nourishment should be obtained from hay.	Permit calves to consume calf starter-free-choice up to 4 or 5 pounds daily. Rest of nourishment should be obtained from hay.
90 days	Discontinue whole milk.		

[1]From Washington State University Ext. Bul. 486.
[2]For economic reasons, it is never advisable to feed calves more than 12 pounds whole milk daily during the entire whole milk feeding period.

as dry skim milk, buttermilk, or whey; and they are generally fortified by antibiotics, vitamins, and minerals. They can be fed as the only feed immediately following the colostrum period; or, as shown in Table 20-6, they may replace whole milk beginning on about the seventh day.

There is hardly any limit to the number of calf starters on the market. Most of them are mixed commercially. It might well be added that because of the difficulty in formulating a home-mixed calf starter ration, the purchase of a good commercial feed usually represents a wise investment.

Two suggested calf starter rations are given in Table 20-7.

Starter Ration A, of Table 20-7, is designed for feeding anytime after the

TABLE 20—7

CALF STARTER RATIONS

Ingredients	Starter Ration A[1] (for feeding about first 45 days, along with liquid skim milk)	Starter Ration B[1] (for feeding after first 45 days, with dry skim milk there-in)
	(lbs.)	(lbs.)
Dried skim milk............................		400
Soybean or cottonseed meal (41%)......	560	450
Barley...	1,000	750
Wheat bran....................................	200	150
Dicalcium phosphate........................	20	20
Trace mineralized salt......................	20	20
Antibiotic (follow mfg.'s directions)	10	10
Vitamin A......................................	10,000 I.U./lb.	2,000 I.U./lb.
Vitamin D (not needed if calf is in sunlight).....................................	2,000 I.U./lb.	400 I.U./lb.
Molasses..	200	200
Total......................	2,000	2,000
PROXIMATE ANALYSIS:	(%)	(%)
Crude protein............................	17.8	20.7
Fiber..	6.6	4.1
Fat..	2.3	1.4
Calcium....................................	.43	.69
Phosphorus................................	.77	.74
T.D.N.......................................	69.9	74.7

[1]In 1/8- or 3/16-inch pellets.

first day following birth. Starter Ration B is designed for feeding beginning about 45 days of age. As is true in any ration change, the transition from Ration A to Ration B should be made gradually by blending the feeds over a period of two to three days.

Good quality hay for young calves is essential; it provides an economical source of nutrients, helps maintain rate of gain, and speeds up the development of the rumen.

Many dairymen make the mistake of placing calves on pasture at too early an age. Unless pastures are properly supplemented, young calves simply cannot hold enough grass, or other pasturage, to obtain sufficient nutrients for their growing bodies. Accordingly, growth will be retarded.

Veal calf production is also becoming an important part of the dairy industry. Whether or not it is profitable, will depend on the price of veal, the price of feeds used to produce the veal, and the skill of the operator to maintain healthy calves and a low death loss.

Dairy Heifer Replacements

Without doubt, dairy heifers are more commonly neglected than any other animals on the dairy farm. This is especially true during the period from six months of age until freshening. Since growing heifers are the nucleus of the future dairy herd, it is important that they be given every opportunity to grow and develop into large, deep-bodied two-year-olds at the time of freshening.

When the feeding of milk, or other special calf meals is discontinued, heifers should have an abundance of other feeds, especially of good quality roughage, so that their growth will not be retarded. Whether receiving dry roughage or on pasture, young heifers need a supplemental feeding of concentrates. The amount of grain fed, in addition to forage, will vary according to the age of the animal and the quality of the forage, but usually it ranges from 3 to 5 pounds per head per day; but, with poor roughage, 6 to 8 pounds may be necessary. In any event, replacement heifers should neither be overfed nor underfed. Heifers that are underfed do not come in heat at an early date and they may be too small to breed. On the other hand, hiefers that are too fat do not conceive easily, and they do not produce as well as heifers that are fed properly.

Well-grown heifers can be bred at 14 to 16 months of age. Table 20-8 can be used as a guide to determine if the heifers have obtained sufficient growth to permit breeding at the age indicated.

NORMAL GROWTH OF CALVES AND HEIFERS

Table 20-8 shows the weight and heart girth measurements of dairy calves or heifers at monthly intervals up to two years of age. If the dairyman does not

TABLE 20—8

NORMAL HEART GIRTH MEASUREMENT AND WEIGHT OF CALVES
AND HEIFERS DURING THE GROWING PERIOD[1]

Age in Months	Holstein		Ayrshire		Guernsey		Jersey	
	(inches)	(pounds)	(inches)	(pounds)	(inches)	(pounds)	(inches)	(pounds)
Birth	31	96	29½	72	29	66	24½	56
1	33½	118	32	98	31½	90	29½	72
2	37	161	35½	132	34½	122	32½	102
3	40¼	213	38¾	179	38	164	32¼	138
4	43½	272	42¾	236	41¼	217	38¼	181
5	47	335	45½	291	44¼	265	41½	228
6	50	396	48¼	340	47	304	44½	277
7	52½	455	51¼	408	49¾	362	47¼	325
8	54¾	508	53	447	51¾	410	49¾	369
9	57	559	55	485	53¾	448	51¾	409
10	58¾	609	57	526	55	486	53¼	446
11	60½	658	58	563	56¾	521	55	481
12	62½	714	59	583	58¼	549	56½	520
13	63¼	740	60¾	630	59¼	587	57½	540
14	64¼	774	62	666	60½	615	58½	565
15	65¼	805	63	703	61¾	640	59	585
16	66¼	841	64	731	62½	674	59¾	611
17	67¼	874	65¼	758	63½	696	60½	635
18	68½	912	66	781	65	727	61½	660
19	69¼	946	66½	813	65½	752	62½	687
20	70½	985	67½	841	66¼	780	63	712
21	71½	1,025	68½	885	67½	816	64	740

[1]Body weights for Holsteins and Jerseys from USDA Technical Bulletins 1098 and 1099. Heart girth measurements for these weights taken from Research Bulletin 194 (1960), Nebraska Agricultural Experiment Station. Weights and heart girth measurements for Ayrshires and Guernseys calculated from data furnished by Professor H.P. Davis, University of Nebraska.

have scales, he can measure the heart girth with a tape to estimate (within 95 per cent accuracy) weight. In any event, weight for age is important from the standpoint of determining the growth progress made in herd replacements.

Dairy Bulls

Bull calves raised for breeding purposes should be fed and handled much the same as heifers. Older bulls should be kept in thrifty, vigorous condition, but they should not be permitted to get too fat. Mature bulls can be fed the same grain ration as the lactating cows. Depending on the quality of the roughage, usually about ½ pound of grain per 100 pounds of body weight will suffice for the mature bull. Also, individual differences must be considered, for some bulls are easier keepers than others.

In addition to the grain and roughage ration, the bull should have free access to a double compartment mineral box, with ground salt in one side and a suitable mineral mixture in the other.

MILK AND BUTTERFAT RECORDS; TESTING PROGRAMS

Individual cow records are a must in any progressive dairy production program. Dairymen use records as a guide for feeding, for locating and culling out the least profitable cows, and for maintaining a permanent, detailed record of each cow. Records necessitate that each cow be individually identified, and that there be milk and butterfat production records.

The three testing programs sponsored by federal and state research extension services follow.

Dairy Herd Improvement Association (DHIA)

In this program, a supervisor or tester, employed by the local testing association, visits the herd one day each month. He identifies all cows in the herd, and he weighs and takes representative samples of the milk from all animals in the herd for two consecutive milkings (three milkings on herds on three times daily milkings). He then combines the milk samples and tests them for butterfat. Records are also obtained on the amount of grain fed each cow, and roughage consumption is calculated on a herd basis. Additional information on breeding dates, calving dates, dry dates, and other factors affecting cow productivity, is recorded. Costs, or value data, are obtained on feed used and milk or other products sold.

Owner-Sampler Records (OS)

Under the owner-sampler plan, the owner himself, rather than the supervisor, weighs and samples the milk. The samples are then tested at a central laboratory.

MONTHLY REPORT DHIA-200 7-64 — **DAIRY HERD IMPROVEMENT RECORD**

UNITED STATES DEPARTMENT OF AGRICULTURE
AGRICULTURAL RESEARCH SERVICE
DAIRY CATTLE RESEARCH BRANCH AND
STATE AGRICULTURAL EXTENSION SERVICES COOPERATING

Type of Record and Herd Code	St.	Co.	Herd No.	Center	Date Tested Mo.	Day	Page No.	Name and Address		Number Assoc.	Supervisor	Processing Center Received Mo.	Day	Mailed Mo.	Day	Test Period From Mo.	Day	To Mo.	Day	Yr.
DHIA	55	27	0001	02	2	3	1	JOE DOKES / ROUTE 1 / ANYWHERE N C	15 / 27364	12	100	2	4	2	7	1	18	2	14	65

BREED CODE: 1. Ayrshire 2. Guernsey 3. Holstein 4. Jersey 5. Brown Swiss 6. Milking Shorthorn 7. Red Dane 8. Other 9. Red Poll

STATUS CODE: 1. In Milk 2. Calved 3. Dry 4. Bred 5. Left Herd 6. First Calf Heifer 7. Entered Herd 8. Aborted

* MILKED 3X THIS TEST PERIOD

* COWS NEED TO BE DRIED OFF AT 220 DAYS OF PREGNANCY IN ORDER TO HAVE A 60-DAY DRY PERIOD.

* COW IN MILK MORE THAN 60 DAYS. BREED COWS 60 TO 90 DAYS AFTER FRESHENING FOR NORMAL (12 TO 13 MONTH) CALVING INTERVAL.

* MILKED 3X THIS LACTATION

CONDITION AFFECTING RECORD: 1-Estimated 2-Sold for Dairy 3-Died or Sold for Beef 4-Injury 5-Mastitis 6-Ketosis 7-Other Sickness 8-Abortion 9-Nurse Cow R-305 Day lactation C-Complete lactation X-305 DAY RECORD HAS BEEN COMPUTED OR WILL NOT BE COMPUTED THIS LACTATION IF AGE AT CALVING IS BLANK

Breed	Registration or Eartag Number	Status Code	Date Change Mo.	Date Change Day	Daily Milk Wt. (Lbs.)	% Fat	% PLM	Concentrates Lbs. Fed	Concentrates Lbs. Indicated	Barn Name	Cow Index Number	Current Days in Milk	Current Milk Lbs.	Current Fat Lbs.	Age at Calving (Mos.)	Body Weight 10 Lbs.	Days Dry	Days Carried Calf	Days in Milk	Milk Pounds	% Fat	Fat Pounds	% PLM	Pounds PLM	Value Product $	Income over Feed Cost $	Cond. Aff. Recd.
2	52A887158									1	0001				77	106	35	6	305	10240	5.22	537	8.29	868			R
		1			197	65	92	9	8			28	550	36	77	106	35	47	346	11090	5.23	592	8.16	949	732	408	X
3	52XAK5454	3	2	01				3	6	2	0002	14	280	11	73	132	14	229	351	14100	3.22	446	7.18	1100	729	352	X
3	52XAD5125									3	0003				71	133	107		162	9030	4.20	361	8.14	759			3 R
		5	1	13								- 4	180	7	71	133	107		162	9030	4.20	361	8.14	759	503	256	3XC
3	52ACX6062	1			350	37	83	13	10	4	0004	28	980	36	73	133	38		207*	10640	3.16	385	8.15	908	567	288	
3	52XAD5468	2	1	18						5	0005				56	175	32	258	413	20390	3.16	725	8.13	1689	1098	541	XC
		2	1	18	651	53	91	22	35			25	1630	86	71	175	32		25	1630	5.23	86	9.11	148	112	71	
3	52ACX6642	3						5	6	9	0009				48	133	67	227	410	17690	3.18	670	8.18	1557	984	459	X
3	52XAL7574	1			256	42	87	8	6	10	0010	28	720	30	63	131	40		205*	8600	4.11	351	9.17	837	486	233	
3	52ADV8873	4	2	01	404	44	96	13	15	12	0012	28	1130	50	46	129	32	14	178	7830	4.13	333	10.15	821	451	233	
3	52ADZ4660	1			423	37	86	15	14	16	0016	28	1180	44	27	122		87	400	18720	3.17	698	9.12	1730	1036	588	X
3	52XAM1938	1			413	30	87	12	12	17	0017	28	1160	35	31	106			180*	8170	3.12	263	9.14	771	414	214	
3	52XAM1939	1			433	40	92	15	15	18	0018	28	1210	48	31	127			128*	5410	4.11	222	10.19	592	309	138	
3	3947443	7	1	19				5	5	19	0019					110	27			0						→ 19	
3	5661335	7	1	21	345	45	94	12	12	20	0020	25	860	39	31	118			158*	6360	3.19	245	10.14	663	344	168	
3	52ADZ4654	6	1	23	522	35	77	18	19	21	0021	20	1040	36	41	134			20	1040	3.15	36	7.17	80	59	33	

Herd Data	Average Calving Interval / Age / Br. Body Wt.	Number of Cows On Test (Cow-Months / Cow-Days / Cow-Years)	In Milk (% / Cow-Days / %)	Milk	Butterfat %	Fat	% PLM	PLM	Concentrates Consumed		Dry Forage Consumed		Succulents Consumed		Pasture		Feed Index	Rate of Forage Feeding	Value of Product	Feed Cost Concentrate	Feed Cost Total	Income over Feed Cost	Feed Cost per Cwt. Milk / No. Workers	Milk Price Information	
Daily Avg. per Cow This Mo.	15	12	79	30.35	4.12	1.26	8.28	2.67	11	70	9	34	60	14			94	2.10	1.87	.40	1.00	.87	3.30	5.77	3.7
12 Mo. Herd Totals	51	7658	6821	2754		1057		2088	1299		14		107		394				1551	457	776	775	.9		
12 Mo. Herd Avg.	3 127	21.0	89	13114	3.8	503	7.6	994	62	56	13	7	103	23	187	14	109	1.16	739	218	370	369	2.81	306	86

Fig. 20-8. Monthly report DHIA-200. (Courtesy, Victor H. Lytton, Extension Dairy Husbandry Specialist, North Carolina State University, Raleigh)

Weigh-a-day-a-month (WADAM)

In this program, the owner weighs the milk from each cow one day each month, and enters the weight and feeding information on the forms provided. He mails the information and forms to the supervisor, or a central office, where calculations are completed, following which summaries are returned to him.

As can be surmised, DHIA records are considered much more "official" than the other two, for the reasons that the tester represents an independent agency. Certainly, the other two programs are less costly than the DHIA program; and, if well kept, they can be equally as valuable. However, because there is no one solely responsible for the testing and record, the hazard in the owner-sampler and weigh-a-day-a-month plan, is that they will be neglected.

OTHER FEED AND MANAGEMENT POINTERS

There are innumerable other feed and management matters of great importance to dairy production. When disregarded, many of them will materially lessen production and make the enterprise unprofitable, no matter how good the breeding of the animals or the feed being used. Still others are important tools from the standpoint of enhancing good management. Some of these pointers will be discussed in the sections that follow.

Common Dairy Health Problems

In this book, it is not possible to discuss all of the diseases and parasites affecting dairy cattle, for there are a very considerable number of them. Moreover, it is generally recognized that good nutrition and good health will alleviate many disease and parasite problems. In particular, dairymen recognize the importance of proper nutrition from the standpoint of lessening the following ailments: bloat, calf scours, mastitis, and milk fever. (See Chapter 21, "Milk Secretion and Handling," for a discussion of mastitis.)

BLOAT

Bloat causes losses in dairy cattle (including losses in milk) totaling $48,228,-000 annually (*Losses in Agriculture,* Agric. Handbook 291, USDA, p. 73, 1965).

Dairymen have long known that some families of animals are more susceptible to bloat than others—that is, there is a genetic factor involved. Also, it is generally recognized that certain feeds, particularly legume pastures, cause a higher incidence of bloat than others.

Bloat may be lessened by (1) avoiding straight legume pastures, (2) feeding dry forage along with pasture, (3) avoiding a rapid fill from an empty start, (4) keeping animals continuously on pasture after they are once turned out, (5) keeping salt and water conveniently accessible at all times, and (6) avoiding frosted pastures. Based on recent and limited experimental work and use in the field, Poloxalene—a non-ionic surfactant—appears to be very effective in controlling bloat in cattle fed lush pastures or green chop. The product should be used according to the manufacturer's directions. As a top dressing, it is recommended that Poloxalene be used at the rate of ¾ oz. daily for animals under 1,000 pound weight, with additional quantities for heavier animals. It costs 5 to 10¢ per head per day.

CALF SCOURS

It is generally recognized that calf scours cause heavier losses in dairy calves than any other disease.

Proper feeding, along with strict sanitation, appears to be the best method of preventing and controlling calf scours. The use of colostrum and the feeding or injecting of an antibiotic appear to be quite effective in the control of this disease.

MILK FEVER

Milk fever causes average annual losses in dairy cattle (including milk) of $10,619,000 (*Losses in Agriculture,* Agric. Handbook 291, USDA, p. 73, 1965).

Through increasing the phosphorus and achieving a more desirable calcium-phosphorus ratio, milk fever is lessened. The University of California (*Journal of Dairy Science*, Vol. 37, No. 4, 1954, p. 360) lowered the incidence of milk fever from 30 per cent to none by changing the calcium-phosphorus (Ca:P) ratio from 6:1 to 1:3.3 during the last month of the dry period. Similar evidence that a high calcium-low phosphorus ratio increases milk fever has been reported by the University of Arizona (*Journal of Dairy Science*, Vol 46, No. 6, 1963, p. 635), and by Ender, *et al.* of Norway (*Journal of Dairy Science*, Vol. 49, No. 2, 1966, p. 244).

There is also evidence that high vitamin D immediately before freshening is effective in lessening milk fever. It is recommended that cows be fed 20 million units of vitamin D daily in the form of irradiated yeast for four to seven days before calving (never longer than seven days). It is emphasized, however, that such high levels of vitamin D cannot be fed for a longer period than seven days. Since calving time cannot be predicted with certainty, the use of high levels of vitamin D for this purpose is not without difficulty.

A recent report (Kendall, K. A., University of Illinois) indicates that high grain feeding three weeks prior to calving will lower the incidence of milk fever.

In summary, therefore, the most effective preventive for milk fever appears to be that of having the correct calcium-phosphorus ratio in the ration and feeding more concentrate three weeks prior to calving.

NITRATE POISONING

Sometimes cows are poisoned by nitrate (NO_3), which accumulates in plants and is converted to nitrite (NO_2) when consumed through the feed or water by ruminants. Upon absorption into the blood stream, nitrite reacts with the red oxygen-transporting pigment, hemoglobin, to form a chocolate-brown pigment, methemoglobin, that cannot carry oxygen. Prevention of nitrite poisoning consists in avoiding high nitrate feeds and water.

Beware of Pesticide Residues

Pesticides are chemicals that are used to kill pests—insects, weeds, and rodents. These products are very necessary for food and milk production. Our abundant supply of wholesome foods would not have been available without their use. Yet, it is important that they be properly used, and that certain precautions be taken. The following points are pertinent to their proper use:

1. **Pesticides that have been associated with milk contamination.**—This includes the chlorinated hydrocarbons, aldrin, dieldrin, heptachlor epoxide, DDT and its isomers, toxaphene, and lindane. Of course, other pesticides may become a problem in the future.

2. **How pesticides contaminate milk.**—They are absorbed by animal fat. Since milk contains fat, it is one channel through which the animal eliminates pesticides from its body.

3. **Length of time that a contaminated cow may give contaminated milk.**—Cases are known where residues have been detected in milk for four to eight months after discontinuing the feeding of contaminated feeds.

4. **Ways that milk may become contaminated.**—Milk becomes contaminated (a) by spraying animals and non-recommended pesticides, (b) by using these materials in back-rubbers and vaporizers, (c) by feeding forages and concentrates which have been contaminated with these materials, (d) by allowing cows to drink pesticide-contaminated water, and (e) by using milk utensils that have become contaminated through their use for chores other than handling milk or in milk production. Hence, milk contamination can be prevented by avoiding any of these avenues of contamination.

5. **The meaning of the word "tolerance" as applied to a chemical residue.** —A given tolerance is that amount of chemical residue, usually expressed in ppm (parts per million) set by the FDA (Food & Drug Administration), that remain on or in a commodity at harvest and which is at least 100 times less than that amount of the chemical known to be toxic to experimental animals.

A zero tolerance, as applied to chemical residue, means that no amount of the pesticide chemical may remain on or in the raw agricultural commodity when it is offered for shipment. Recently, the FDA raised the tolerance level for pesticides in milk from 0 to 1.25 ppm on a fat basis. This means that there must be less than 1.25 parts of the pesticide (DDT, for example) to one million parts of milk fat figured on a weight basis.

Feeds Affecting Milk Flavor

Consumers want milk to taste like milk—not like silage, grass, or weeds.

Although feeds are not the only cause of milk flavors, they are major contributors. Feed flavors enter the milk through the digestive system, respiratory system, and by direct absorption. Research indicates that most feed flavors are detectable in the milk 20 minutes after the feed is consumed, and that they are usually most pronounced at the end of two hours.

Feed flavors that enter the milk through the respiratory system can usually be detected much sooner than those entering through the digestive system. For example, if a cow breathes air reeking with silage odors, these flavors can be detected in the milk almost immediately. Flavors that are directly absorbed by milk are less common, but they appear if the milk is left exposed for a long enough period.

The following control measures are recommended to alleviate feed flavors:

1. **Avoid sudden change to fresh, lush pasture.**—Cows should be shifted from winter feeding, or old pasture, to new and lush pastures on a gradual basis. Also, cows should be taken out of such pastures two to three hours before milking. For the same reasons, freshly cut grass should not be fed immediately before milking.

2. **Control and avoid undesirable weeds.**—Many weeds when eaten by cows will impart a strong flavor to milk, among them are: wild onions, skunk

cabbage, some members of the mustard family, bitterweed, carrot weed, ragweed, and others. It is easier to get rid of these weeds today than formerly, so they should be eliminated from pasture and hay fields utilized by milk cows.

3. **Silage flavor.**—Silage flavor is both common and objectionable. It can be avoided by feeding all silages after milking, never before or during milking. Usually one will be safe if silage is not fed within two to four hours of milking time, but it's safer to feed it shortly after milking. This permits the flavor-causing material to pass through the cow's digestive system before the next milking.

If cows breathe the odor of silage, it will appear as flavor in the milk. Thus, silage should never be left in the mangers or feed alleys. In fact, it is preferable that it be fed in the corral, and not in the area where the cows are being milked.

Marketing Dairy Herd Replacement Stock

Most established dairymen have surplus animals to sell—replacement heifers, cull cows and bulls, veal calves, and feeder animals for growing and finishing. Those establishing new herds, and to a more limited extent those maintaining herds, are on the buying end of the business. Dairy animals intended for slaughter are marketed through the same channels as beef animals sold for slaughter.

Dealers are the major outlet for dairy replacement stock, with most of their purchases made on the farm. Dealers resell replacement stock by either private treaty or auction. In addition to dealers, with some variation from area to area, replacement heifers are marketed through breed registry association sponsored sales (usually state or local sponsorship), cooperatives, artificial insemination associations, and dairy cattle sales associations.

In most areas, the following improvements would benefit both the seller and the buyer of replacement heifers:

1. Establishing and using uniform grades.

2. Reporting market information on prices.

3. Maintaining high health standards, and getting uniform health regulations from state to state.

4. Keeping production records on all cows from which replacement heifers will be sold.

5. Lowering the stress and disease losses which accompany the transportation of heifers.

Dairy Beef Production

Marketing dairy animals—cows, heifers, steers, and veal calves—for slaughter accounts for 3 per cent of farm cash income, which amounted to $1.2 billion in 1965. The importance of dairy beef production will increase.

The results of earlier experiments in which steers of dairy breeding were compared with one of the established beef breeds were unfavorable to the use of dairy beef. Generally speaking, animals of dairy breeding gained slightly more rapidly and on somewhat less feed than animals of beef breeding. However, the dairy animals generally yielded 2 to 3 per cent less carcass and the carcasses graded lower, primarily because of some deficiencies in conformation and finish. They did produce more lean.

Today, the accent in beef production is on rapid gains, efficiency of feed utilization, and high cut-out value with a minimum of "bark" or outside fat, and a maximum of lean meat; factors which place animals of dairy breeding in a more favorable position. This shift in consumer preference, along with our rapidly expanding population and increased per capita consumption of beef, will result in the production of increased quantities of dairy beef.

For the most part, increased dairy beef is, and will continue to be, produced by feeding out more dairy steers, rather than destroying or selling them as veal. For such an enterprise to be profitable, it is necessary to raise dairy steers to the finishing stage and age—600 to 700 pounds—on a minimum of marketable milk and a maximum of roughage.

Some Management Recommendations

Successful dairymen pay close attention to the details of management. Without attempting to cover all dairy management practices, the following will supplement those made throughout this chapter.

MANAGEMENT OF DRY AND MILKING COWS

1. **Lot and Housing Facilities:**
   - Provide the following minimum lot space per head:

Kind of Lot	Sq. Ft./Animal
All paved	100
Paved and dirt	150
Dirt	200

   - Slope paved lots 1/4 to 1/2 inch/foot, and slope dirt lots 1/2 inch or more per foot.
   - Pave (rough finish) a 15 to 20 foot area around waterers, feed bunks and racks, and entrances to sheds.
   - Open sheds may be used under a loose housing system. Free stall housing saves bedding, keeps the cows cleaner, and saves labor. For small breeds, use 7 x 4 ft. stalls; for large breeds, 7½ x 4 ft.
   - Keep the temperature in stall barns 40° F. or more; and in milking parlors 50° to 60° F. during the winter.
   - Provide for proper ventilation—changing of air—in cold climates and during the winter months; with care taken to avoid direct drafts and coldness. A fan system installed according to manufacturers directions is best. For each 1,000 pounds of animal weight in a well-insulated barn, the fan should be capable of removing a minimum of 100 cubic feet per minute (CFM).

Fig. 20-9. Environmental-controlled barn, in Oregon. Note (1) free stalls down the center and (2) feed bunks around the outside of the building, with hay stored conveniently to bunks. (Babson Bros. Co., Chicago)

- Bed all cows except in dry climates.
- Provide for efficient manure disposal, selecting the system best adapted for the particular dairy and area.

2. **Feed and Water Facilities:**
   - Provide 24 to 30 inches per head of manger space for roughage feeding.
   - Make bunks and roughage racks 24 to 30 inches wide when cattle are fed from one side; 36 inches wide when feeding from both sides.
   - Provide adequate water space: (a) one linear foot of open tank per 8 to 10 head, or (b) one automatic bowl per 15 head.
   - Keep water temperature within the range of 35° to 80° F.; warm it to 50° F. in the winter.

3. **General Management:**
   - Worm cows if they need it, especially during the dry period. If worming is done during the lactation period, it should be under the direction of the veterinarian.
   - Treat for external parasites if necessary, using approved insecticides and application.
   - Develop a written-down herd health program in cooperation with the local veterinarian, then follow it.
   - Do not rebreed cows until at least 60 days after calving.
   - Strive for a 10-month lactation period, a 60-day dry period, and a 12-month calving interval.
   - Examine herd for pregnancy at regular intervals.

MANAGEMENT OF DAIRY CALVES

1. **Housing:**
   - House calves separately (in individual pens or tie stalls)—from birth until at least one week after milk or milk substitute is discontinued. Thereafter, they may be raised in groups, with (a) a maximum of 10 head per group (preferably 6 to 8 per group) and (b) a maximum age difference of two months between calves.
   - Provide a minimum of 24 sq. ft. pen space for individual calves; 2½ x 4 ft. tie stalls; 30 sq. ft. for calves in groups without outside runs.
   - Solid partitions between individual pens reduce drafts and chilling. Front of pens should be wire or slatted.
   - Preferred pen temperature is within the range of 50° to 75° F.

2. **Feed and Water:**
   - Feed boxes for individual calves should be 8″ x 10″ x 6″ deep, and they should be removable so as to facilitate cleaning. Troughs for group feeding should be 10″ x 6″ deep, with two linear feet per calf; provide stanchions. Top of feed containers should be 20″ from the floor; and feed containers should be located in corner of pen away from water.
   - Feed calves at least twice daily.
   - Automatic drinking cups are preferred for both individual quarters and group pens (one cup/5 to 8 calves). Where pails or tanks are used, keep them clean. Top of drinking cups for calves should be 20″ from the floor.
   - Always locate water facilities at a corner away from the feed.

3. **General Management:**
   - Dehorn anytime after 10 days of age, using an electric dehorner or caustic potash.
   - Remove extra teats before heifers are six months old; cut them off with clean scissors and disinfect area with iodine.
   - Check for scours.

MANAGEMENT OF REPLACEMENT HEIFERS

1. **Lots and Housing:**
   - Provide the following lot space per head:

Kind of Lot	Sq. Ft./Animal
All paved	50-75
Paved and dirt	75-100
Dirt	100-150

   - Slope paved (rough finish) lots ¼ to ½ inch/foot, and dirt lots ½ inch or more per foot.
   - Pave (rough finish) a 15 to 20 foot area around waterers, feed bunks and racks, and entrances to sheds.

- Provide an open shed; allow 20 to 30 sq. ft. per head for small cattle, and 30 to 40 sq. ft. per head for large cattle. Bed sheds as needed.
- Provide artificial shade in hot climates if natural shade is not available. Allow 20 to 30 sq. ft. per animal, and build shade 8 to 10 ft. high.

2. **Feed and Water Facilities:**
- Provide feed bunks that are 24″ to 30″ above the ground (to top of bunk; with height determined by size of cattle); 8″ to 12″ deep (12″ deep for silage); and 18″ to 24″ wide when feeding from one side, 36″ wide when feeding from two sides.
- Allow the following amount of feeder space per head:

	Grain	Roughage
Small cattle	12″	18″
Large cattle	18″	24″

- Allow one linear foot of tank space for each 10 animals and one automatic watering bowl for each 25 animals. Water temperature may range from 35° to 80° F.; warming to 50° F. in the winter is desirable.

3. **General Management:**
- Separate bulls and heifers before six months of age; do not have over three months difference in age of animals within a given group.
- Treat for worms when the need is demonstrated.
- Breed heifers at 15 to 18 months of age, but also consider weight and size.
- Accustom bred heifers to milking barn procedure beginning about one month prior to calving.

FEED TERMS; CONVERSIONS

The following terms are generally used in analyzing dairy feed costs and practices:

1. **Net energy (NE)**—is the net portion of the feed available for production. It is expressed as megacalories (a megacalorie is 1,000,000 small calories. The term "megacalorie" is preferable to the term "therm," although both equal 1,000,000 small calories).

2. **Animal Unit Month (AUM)**—is the amount of feed required for one mature cow for one month. It is equivalent in nutrients to 0.4 tons of average hay, or 320 mcal of energy.

3. **Hay equivalent (HE)**—is the energy equivalent of 1 ton of hay which, on the average, contains 800 mcal of net energy. With an AUM being equivalent to 320 mcal of net energy, 2.5 AUM are required to furnish the same amount of energy as 1 ton of hay.

4. **Fat Corrected Milk (FCM)**—is a term used to compare milks of different composition on a standard energy basis. Four per cent FCM is calculated by multiplying the actual milk yield by 0.4, then adding to this product the

actual fat yield multiplied by 15. For example, if a cow produces 60 pounds of 3.5 per cent milk (60 x 3.5%) or 2.1 pounds fat, her Fat Corrected Milk production is (60 x .4) plus (2.1 x 15), or 55.5 pounds of 4 per cent milk.

5. **Estimating TDN from chemical analysis**—frequently, dairymen have a chemical analysis made of a mixed feed. The results thereof are usually reported in terms of crude protein, crude fat (ether extract), crude fiber, ash, moisture, and N.F.E. Such a reading needs to be augmented by TDN, or energy, values. Where a mixed feed is involved, this poses a very difficult question because digestibility is affected by many things—level of feed intake, particle size, condition of animal, and individuality.

If the formulation of a mixed feed is known, the TDN values can be calculated as follows:

a. Obtain the digestible nutrients of each ingredient by multiplying the percentage of each nutrient by the digestion coefficient. For example, dent corn contains 8.9 per cent protein of which 77 per cent is digestible. Therefore, the per cent of digestible protein is 6.9. This same procedure is applied to each ingredient and each nutrient.

b. Then, the TDN is the sum of all the digestible organic nutrients—protein, fiber, nitrogen free extract, and fat (x 2.25).

This procedure is rather tedious and laborious.

A simple and quick rule-of-thumb method for arriving at the TDN of a mixed ration follows:

(1) 70% of the crude protein, plus
(2) fat times 2-1/4, plus
(3) N.F.E.

This rule-of-thumb method for determining TDN is close enough for most purposes. However, it is not recommended where considerable amounts of such by-product feeds as almond hulls, raisin stems, or grape seeds are included in the ration.

6. **Converting crude protein to digestible protein**—in most good mixed dairy feeds, approximately 80 per cent of the total protein is digestible. Hence, where the crude protein value is given, the digestible protein can be estimated by simply taking 80 per cent of the crude protein. Where the digestible protein is given, and it is desired to convert it to crude protein, this may be done by dividing the digestible protein by 80 and then multiplying by 100.

7. **Converting TDN to therms**—TDN vs. therms—a full discussion of the calorie system vs. the TDN system is contained in *The Stockman's Handbook*, 4th ed. Since it seems likely that energy values will replace TDN as a means of expressing the energy requirements of dairy cattle, and other animals, the following approximate conversion factor may be used:

One pound of TDN = 2,000 Calories (large C), or 2 therms

It is recognized, however, that the roughage component in a ration affects its energy value. Thus, when converting all-roughage rations from TDN to Calories, some scientists figure that one pound of TDN = 1,500 Calories, instead of 2,000.

QUESTIONS FOR STUDY AND DISCUSSION

1. Name the parts of the ruminant stomach, and describe the functions of each.
2. In practical dairy cattle rations, what are the chief sources of energy, protein, minerals, and vitamins?
3. What factors should determine the proportion of roughage to grain fed to lactating cows?
4. What factors should be considered in arriving at a decision between (a) home-mixing and (b) buying a commercial concentrate?
5. Select a cow of a certain body weight and milk production, then balance a ration for her from the standpoint of TDN and protein; using available feeds and the Trial and Error Method.
6. What is meant by challenge or lead feeding, and how is it done?
7. Give the pertinent considerations for feeding (a) dry cows, (b) cows at calving time, (c) show and sale animals, (d) calves, (e) replacement heifers, and (f) bulls.
8. Name and describe the different milk and butterfat testing programs, and give the advantages and disadvantages of each.
9. How would you lessen bloat, calf scours, and milk fever?
10. Why and how would you alleviate (a) pesticide residues and (b) feed flavors in milk?
11. Define the following terms: (a) net energy, (b) TDN, (c) Animal Unit Month, (d) Hay equivalent, (e) Fat Corrected Milk. Illustrate how each may be used.
12. How would you convert (a) proximate analysis to TDN, (b) crude protein to digestible protein, and (c) TDN to therms?

SELECTED REFERENCES

Title of Publication	Author(s)	Publisher
Animal Nutrition	L. A. Maynard J. K. Loosli	McGraw-Hill Book Co., New York, N. Y., 1962.
Applied Animal Nutrition	E. W. Crampton L. E. Harris	W. H. Freeman and Co., San Francisco, Calif., 1969.
Energy Metabolism of Ruminants, The	K. L. Blaxter	Hutchinson & Co., Ltd., London, England, 1962.
Feed Composition, Tables of	Pub. 1684	National Academy of Sciences, National Research Council, Washington, D. C., 1969.
Feed Formulations Handbook	T. W. Perry	The Interstate Printers & Publishers, Inc., Danville, Ill., 1966.
Feeds and Feeding, 22nd edition	F. B. Morrison	Morrison Publishing Co., Ithaca, N. Y., 1956.
Fundamentals of Nutrition	E. W. Crampton L. E. Lloyd	W. H. Freeman and Co., San Francisco, Calif., 1959.
Nutrient Requirements of Dairy Cattle	Pub. 1349	National Academy of Sciences, National Research Council, Washington, D. C., 1966.
Physiology of Digestion in the Ruminant	Dougharty, et al.	Butterworth, Inc., 7300 Pearl St., Washington, D. C., 1964.
Stockman's Handbook, The	M. E. Ensminger	The Interstate Printers & Publishers, Inc., Danville, Ill., 1969.

CHAPTER XXI

MILK SECRETION AND HANDLING

Contents

	Page
Chemical Composition	581
Udder Development	582
Structure of the Udder	582
Milk Secretion	584
Milk Ejection or "Let Down"	586
Disturbances or "Hold Up"	586
Milking the Cow; Managed Milking	586
Milking Equipment	589
Can and Bulk Systems of Handling	589
Produce Quality Milk	589
Physiological Factors Affecting Amount and Composition of Milk	590
Environmental Factors Affecting Amount and Composition of Milk	592
Mastitis	596
Milk Flavor	597
Drying Off Cows	598
Questions for Study and Discussion	599
Selected References	599

Zoologically, cattle belong to the class Mammalia; and all mammalia are warmblooded, hairy animals that produce their young alive and suckle them for a variable period on a secretion from the mammary glands called milk.

The number of mammary glands and their position on the body is peculiar to each species. For example, the cow has four glands (quarters), each with a passage way (teat) to the outside; whereas in the sow and the bitch there are generally 10 or more mammary glands.

The ability of dairy cattle to produce large amounts of milk is the principal reason why they are accorded a prominent place in American agriculture. It is important, therefore, that the physiology of milk production and the methods of "milk harvesting" be fully understood.

CHEMICAL COMPOSITION

Contrary to popular belief, all milk is not alike. Chemically, it varies in composition by species (see Table 21-1).

Also, the composition of milk differs according to breeds. Table 21-2 shows the average composition of milk of each of the five major dairy breeds. It is not claimed that these figures are true breed averages; rather, they give some indication of the levels of each component for each breed and the differences between breeds.

Also, the composition of milk is greatly affected by both physiological and environmental factors, which will be discussed later in this chapter.

The first secretion of the mammary gland following parturition is known as

TABLE 21—1

THE CHEMICAL COMPOSITION OF MILK[1]

Animal	Water	Total Solids	Fat	Protein	Lactose	Ash
	← — — — — — — — — — — — — — — (%) — — — — — — — — — — — — — →					
Cow..........	86.2	13.8	4.4	3.8	4.9	0.7
Goat..........	87.1	12.9	4.1	3.7	4.2	0.8
Human......	88.0	12.0	3.8	1.2	7.0	0.21
Horse	90.1	9.9	1.0	2.6	6.9	0.35
Pig.............	82.8	17.2	5.1	7.1	3.7	1.1
Sheep........	82.0	18.0	6.4	5.6	4.7	0.91

[1]*Story of Milk Production*, published by Chas. Pfizer & Co., Inc., Vol. 3, No. 2, 1959, Table 2, p. 16.

TABLE 21—2

MILK COMPOSITION BY BREEDS[1]

Breed	Total Solids	Butterfat	Solids—Not Fat	Protein
	(%)	(%)	(%)	(%)
Ayrshire	12.77	4.10	8.67	3.36
Brown Swiss	13.20	4.20	9.00	3.55
Guernsey	13.97	4.90	9.07	3.53
Holstein	12.27	3.80	8.47	3.19
Jersey	14.55	5.30	9.25	3.77

[1]*Causes of Variation in Protein and Solids-not-fat Content of Milk*, by Robert H. Benson, University of Connecticut report of Oct. 24, 1962. Figures from a Massachusetts study of 1,000 cows in 27 herds over a 20-month period.

colostrum. Colostrum is Nature's product, designed to give young a good start in life. It is higher than milk in dry matter, protein, vitamins, and minerals. Additionally, it contains antibodies that give newborn animals protection against certain diseases.

UDDER DEVELOPMENT

The development of the udder starts early in the growth of the fetus. At birth the udder consists of the teats, teat cisterns, gland cisterns, and structures which will later develop to form the duct system. From birth to puberty, little mammary change takes place, although there may be some deposition of fat in well-fed animals.

After puberty, there is some growth of the duct system with each recurrence of the estrus cycle. This growth is stimulated by estrogen, a hormone secreted by the ovarian follicle. The secretory tissue develops under the influence of another hormone, progesterone, from the corpus luteum of the ovary. However, there is little apparent enlargement of the udder until the secretion of colostrum begins, a short time before the birth of the calf.

STRUCTURE OF THE UDDER

Mammary glands vary considerably among species in arrangement of glands and nipples. Udders also vary among cows—in sizes, shapes, quality, and udder attachments.

The udder consists of the following parts:

1. **Suspension.**—On a mature cow, the udder weighs from 25 to 60 lbs., and it may hold 50 or more pounds of milk; thus, good suspension is imperative. The main supporting structures of the udder are the median and lateral suspensory ligaments, and the skin.

A well-attached udder fits snugly against the abdominal wall in front and on the sides, and extends high between the thighs in the rear. "Breaking away" of the udder from the body occurs when the supporting ligaments weaken or stretch.

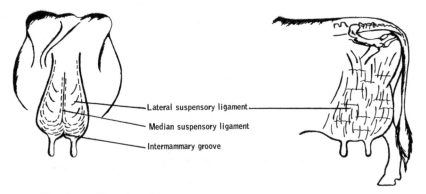

Lateral suspensory ligament
Median suspensory ligament
Intermammary groove

Fig. 21-1. How the udder is suspended. (Drawing by Caren Carney)

2. **Four glands.**—The cow's udder consists of four separate quarters; and there is no way for the milk to move from one half to the other, or from one quarter to the other. The left and right halves are separated by distinct membrane and the main supporting ligaments. The front and rear quarters are also completely separated, but the division is less marked.

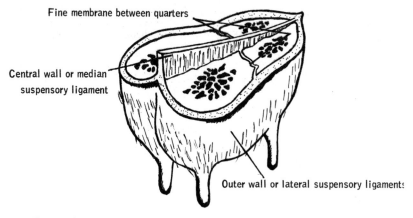

Fine membrane between quarters

Central wall or median suspensory ligament

Outer wall or lateral suspensory ligaments

Fig. 21-2. Cross section of the udder. (Drawing by Caren Carney)

Because of their greater depth, the rear quarters usually produce about 60 per cent of the milk. This partially explains why the forequarters often are milked out before the rear quarters.

3. **Teats.**—The teat is a tube of skin which hangs down from the udder. It is hollow and more or less closed at the top and at the bottom. The bottom of the teat is closed by a circular (sphincter) muscle. If this muscle is tight, the cow may be a "hard" milker. If it is loose, the cow is an "easy" milker.

The opening in the lower end of each teat is known as the teat canal.

4. **Milk collecting system.**—The duct system of the udder consists of the teat cistern, the gland cistern, and many collecting ducts. The udder also contains the nerve and lymph system and tissues that support and connect the basic parts.

5. **Alveolus.**—The basic milk-producing unit in the udder is a very small bulb-shaped structure with a hollow center called the alveolus. It is estimated that each cubic inch of udder tissue contains one million alveoli; hence, in total

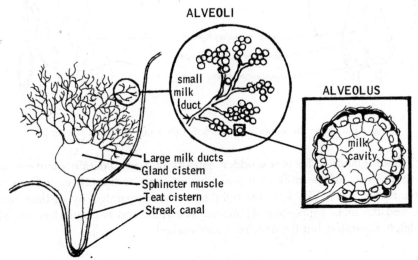

Fig. 21-3. Milk is produced and stored in the alveoli. By action on the muscle-like cells surrounding the alveoli, the hormone, oxytocin, forces milk into the large ducts and cisterns of the udder. At milking time, it passes through the streak canal. (Drawing by Caren Carney)

there are billions of alveoli in the udder. The alveoli are lined with epithelial cells which manufacture milk from the blood circulating through the udder. The milk is then stored in the alveoli until it is forced out by hormone action on small muscle tissues around the alveoli. When this forcing action takes place, the milk enters small ducts, passes through the larger ducts, and collects in the milk cistern just above the teat.

MILK SECRETION

The phenomenon of milk secretion is very complex. The tiny epithelial cells in the alveoli are the "factories" in which the constituents carried by the blood are taken out of the blood capillaries and synthesized (when necessary) into the component parts of milk—fat, lactose, protein, minerals, vitamins, and the other constituents of milk. These cells have the unique ability of changing or manufacturing materials entirely different from those from which they came. Further, it is believed that each cell in the alveoli can manufacture all the milk constituents, and that there are no specialized cells for each type of compound.

The efficiency of milk secretion becomes apparent when it is realized that a cow that produces 10,500 pounds of milk during one year manufactures 370 pounds of milk fat, 500 pounds of milk sugar, 365 pounds of milk protein, and 65 pounds of minerals and vitamins, or a total of over 1,300 pounds of food. (Since milk contains approximately 87 per cent water and 13 per cent solids, 10,500 pounds of milk contains 1,365 pounds of solids—13 per cent of 10,500.) That's as much edible food as two steers produce in 18 months time. Moreover, the cow is still alive and can repeat the productivity again and again, whereas the two steers must be slaughtered or "spent."

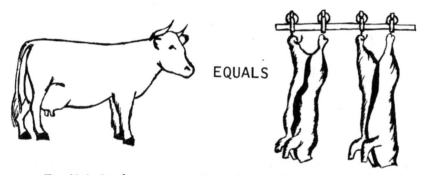

EQUALS

Fig. 21-4. It takes two steers 18 months time (for each steer) to produce as much food as one milk cow produces in one year. And the cow remains alive to do it over again! (Drawing by Caren Carney)

Approximately 400 pounds of blood must pass through the udder to supply the raw materials for 1 pound of milk. This means that a cow making 80 pounds of milk in a day pumps 32,000 pounds, or 16 tons, of blood through her udder daily. Hence, the blood supply to the udder is extremely important. In fact, milk production may be limited by the nutrients in the blood and the amount of blood available to milk-secreting cells of the udder.

Onset of milk production, shortly before parturition, is brought about by the action of the hormone, prolactin, secreted by the anterior pituitary. Other hormones are necessary for the maintenance of milk production; specifically, the thyroxin, secreted by the thyroid gland, and the adrenal gland secretions.

Milk secretion takes place more or less continuously until stopped by the mounting pressure within the alveoli.

Milk Ejection or "Let Down"

As has already been noted, the milk is stored in the alveoli. Before it is available to the calf or milker, it has to be forced from the alveoli into the larger ducts and cisterns. This process is known as the "let down" of the milk. Here is how it works (see Fig. 21-5): When the udder (especially the teats) is stimulated by a calf or a milker (1) impulses are conducted along the nerves to the posterior pituitary at the base of the cow's brain; (2) the posterior pituitary stores and releases the hormone oxytocin into the blood stream; (3) the blood transports oxytocin back to the udder; and (4) the oxytocin causes the smooth, muscle-like cells surrounding each alveolus to contract, thereby forcing the milk out of them into the large ducts and cisterns of the udder.

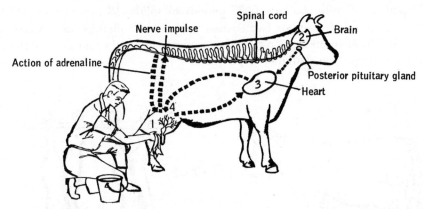

Fig. 21-5. Steps in milk let down. See narrative for details. (Drawing by Caren Carney)

The stimulation of the udder lasts for a limited time only; less than one minute in a "fresh" cow, since oxytocin is destroyed in the blood stream. Hence, once the "let down" has occurred, it is important that the milk be removed within approximately five minutes to obtain the greatest amount. This is so because a second stimulation cannot be obtained soon after the first.

Disturbances or "Hold Up"

When a cow is frightened or angry (from being hit, chased, shouted at, barked at, or for other reasons), she may not let down her milk. This is because of an overriding hormone action. Upon such occasions, another hormone, adrenalin, is released into the blood stream. This hormone interferes with the action of oxytocin by reducing blood circulation to the alveoli.

Hold up of milk may also be the result from a poorly operated milking machine or from a poor hand-milker.

MILKING THE COW; MANAGED MILKING

Milking is the act of removing milk from the udder. The calf sucks milk, and, simultaneously, massages the teat. In hand milking, the teat is grasped between the thumb and forefinger; then, by applying pressure with the other fingers, milk is forced from the teat cistern through the streak canal. In machine milking, the milk is drawn out by vacuum in much the same way that a nursing calf does.

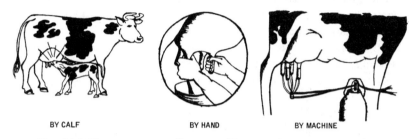

BY CALF   BY HAND   BY MACHINE

Fig. 21-6. Three ways to milk a cow. (Drawing by Caren Carney)

Milking is the most important single job to be done on the dairy farm. Some individuals are excellent milkers, others are very poor—and this statement applies to both machine milking and hand milking. Also, it is important that the cow be milked at regular times, preferably by the same milker; and that each milking be a pleasant experience. Cows like to be milked—if it is done properly.

The physiology of the discharge of milk is a delicate process, and it requires the close cooperation of the man and the cow if it is to be successful. A managed milking program is made up of the following coordinated steps:

1. **Preparing the equipment.**—Prior to milking, the equipment to be used in the milking process should be assembled and sanitized. Also, it should be checked and adjusted if necessary.

2. **Preparing the cow.**—Under natural conditions, the cow is primed or stimulated by the suckling of the calf. This process can be simulated by washing the cow's teats and udder with warm water (120° to 130° F.), then massaging and drying them with a paper towel. Following this process, remove two or three streams of milk from each quarter into a strip cup (never strip milk onto the floor) and examine for visible evidence of mastitis. Also, this (a) washes out any debris adhering to the end of the teat, and (b) enhances the let down effect.

About 45 seconds after the priming stimulus, the udder becomes full and firm (especially in early lactation), and milk occasionally will leak from the teats. This is evidence that the cow has let down her milk and is ready for the next step.

3. **Attaching the teat cup and beginning.**—About 1 minute after washing the udder, and not more than 1½ minutes, the teat cups should be attached and milking should begin. Most cows will milk out in three to six minutes, depending upon the amount of milk and the characteristics of the cow. Also, and most important, each quarter should be milked individually, because some quarters milk out faster than others.

4. **Stripping by machine.**—When it is apparent that the cow is about milked

out, she should be machine stripped. This consists of pulling down on the teat cups with one hand, and massaging the udder downward with the other. This process should not take over about 20 seconds.

5. **Removing the teat cups.**—Both incomplete and over-milking should be avoided. The greatest cause of machine injury is leaving the teat cups on too long. Incomplete milking usually results because one or more quarters are more difficult to milk than the others.

As soon as the udder is empty, and before the teat cups crawl up, they should be removed, properly and gently. Then, dip the teats with a fresh disinfected solution (100 ppm idophor or chlorine, or other sanitizing agent). This will remove the milk from the ends of the teats and prevent the invasion of bacteria into the udder. Also, it will avoid attracting flies.

As soon as the teat cups have been removed from the udder of the cow, they should be cleaned. First, dip them in clean, cold water to remove milk inside the liners; then put them in a clean, warm, approved sanitizing solution. Change the solution after each five to.seven cows.

6. **Cleaning up equipment**—After milking the last cow, all milking equipment should be thoroughly cleaned and put away.

7. **Milking time.**—The true, or actual milking time per cow will range from 3 to 6 minutes, with an average time of 3-1/2 minutes for cows in mid-lactation. But additional time must be allowed for let-down, adjustments, and interval between cows.

The number of machines one man can manage successfully depends upon the type of barn, the type of milking equipment, the ability of the milker, and the jobs he has other than milking.

One man should handle no more (preferable less) than the following number of units:

Type Milker	Units per man
Stanchion barns:	
Bucket	2
Pipeline	3
Milking parlor:	
Walk-through	3
Side-opening	3
Herringbone	4

With a three-in-line elevated parlor, one man will average 18 to 25 cows per hour. With a four-in-line parlor, one man will average 25 to 30 cows per hour. However, additional time must be allowed to bring the cows in from the outside, setting up, cleaning up, as well as milking problem cows.

8. **Milking order.**—Cows that have mastitis or a history of chronic mastitis are a source of infection to non-infected cows. Hence, it is well to milk "clean" cows first. A desirable milking order in stanchion barns is:

a. First calf heifers that have been free of mastitis.
b. Older cows that have been free of mastitis.
c. Cows that have a previous history of mastitis, but which no longer show symptoms.
d. Cows with quarters producing abnormal milk.

Milking Equipment

Basically, there are two types of milking equipment: (1) the bucket system and (2) the pipeline system.

In the bucket system, the milk is received directly into a nearby vacuumized portable bucket.

Conventional pipeline systems use a rigid heat-resistant glass or stainless sanitary pipe for carrying vacuum from the milk receiver to the individual milking units, and for carrying the milk from the units to the receiver.

Regardless of make, the mechanical milking systems can be separated broadly into four major parts: (1) vacuum supply, (2) milk flow, (3) pulsation, and (4) milking unit.

Can and Bulk Systems of Handling

There are two characteristics of milk which make it ideal for the development of bacteria: (1) it is a well balanced food in which bacteria thrive, and (2) as it comes from the cow, the temperature is ideal for bacterial growth. For these reasons, milk must be cooled to at least 50° F. (preferably to 40° F.) as soon as possible in order to inhibit bacterial growth.

Milk may be handled by either of two systems: the can system or the bulk system. Until 1939, when the bulk system was first introduced in California, all milk was handled in cans. Today, the trend is to more and more bulk tanks. Although the initial cost is greater than where cans are used, the greater returns over a period of time seem to justify the expense. Further, many dairymen are facing the situation of being forced into going to bulk tanks if they are to retain a market outlet.

Generally speaking, the following advantages accrue to the use of bulk tanks, in comparison with cans: (1) a saving in labor, (2) less loss in milk, (3) alleviating 10 gallon cans, (4) higher butterfat tests (due to butterfat being left on lids of cans), (5) a saving in hauling costs, and (6) a premium paid by the plant.

PRODUCE QUALITY MILK

Consumers and health departments all have a distinct interest in the quality of milk.

Quality milk can be produced only when the dairyman pays special attention to a number of factors:

1. **Health of the herd.**—The herd should be free from diseases that might be spread to human beings through the milk. Bacteria in milk coming from cows

must be eliminated. Mastitis is the most important herd-health problem at the present time.

2. **Clean animals.**—The milker should clean the flanks and udders of cows just prior to milking to prevent dirt from getting into the milk. Clean floors and bedding and well-drained yard make the cleaning job easier.

3. **Clean equipment.**—All milking equipment should be kept as clean and free from bacteria as possible. Bacteria grow in cracks and rough spots on equipment if it is not washed properly.

4. **Cool and store milk properly.**—Proper cooling and storage of milk on the dairy farm require facilities which will cool the milk promptly from the in-the-pail temperature of about 90° F. down to 40° F., and then hold it at that temperature until it is collected. Bacteria will reproduce (divide) once every 30 minutes in 70 to 90 degree temperature; thus, in 12 hours, one bacterium can reproduce 16 million. Cooling will control this growth.

5. **Keep barn and milk house clean.**—The milking barn should be clean and should have a concrete floor. Barn odors may be eliminated by having a building well ventilated.

A milk room is important to the convenience of the operator, and an aid to the production of high quality milk.

6. **Control flies.**—Fly control measures are important to dairymen. Flies add to the bacterial count of milk; cases are on record of flies carrying as many as 1,250,000,000 bacteria. They can carry typhoid, dysentery, and other contagious diseases.

Breeding places for flies, such as manure piles and mud holes, should be eliminated.

7. **Control bacteria.**—In summary, here is how the bacterial count in milk can be kept down:

  a. Rinse the utensils and equipment with hot water after cleaning so they dry off quickly.
  b. Remove all milkstone[1] from the equipment as bacteria must have food.
  c. Cool the milk as quickly as possible to 40° F. as bacteria like high temperatures.
  d. Wash and sanitize with proper cleaning and sterilizing material.
  e. Have a well-lighted barn and milkhouse as bacteria like darkness rather than light.

PHYSIOLOGICAL FACTORS AFFECTING AMOUNT AND COMPOSITION OF MILK

The variation in the butterfat composition of milk at the plant has puzzled

---

[1] Milkstone is a complex mixture of milk and water minerals with entrapped fat, protein, soil particles, and micro-organisms, plus cleaner and sanitizer residues. This film adheres tightly to the surface of milk-handling equipment and requires special acid treatment for removal.

dairymen. And since the fat content of the milk has a bearing on the paycheck, it's an economic factor, too.

A number of physiological factors affect the amount and composition of milk:

1. **Breed and individual inheritance.**—Variation in the ability of cows to produce total milk, fat, and solids-not-fat is an inherited characteristic. There is both a breed difference (see Table 21-2) and an individual difference. In general, total milk production increases and butterfat content decreases by breeds in the following order: Holstein, Brown Swiss, Ayrshire, Guernsey, and Jersey.

Within the Holstein breed, a range in butterfat from 2.6 to 6.0 per cent has been reported; and within the Jersey breed from 3.3 to 8.4 per cent. Similar variation between breeds and individuals exists in total milk production.

2. **Stage of lactation.**—The greatest variation in the composition of milk takes place immediately following parturition, within the first five days after freshening. The secretory product known as colostrum, found in the udder at the time of calving and produced for a short time thereafter, is not milk as such. It contains more globulins, vitamins A and D, iron, calcium, magnesium, chlorine, and phosphorus than does milk; but it contains less lactose and potassium than milk.

Total milk production generally increases for the first month following freshening, then it decreases gradually thereafter. Conversely, the butterfat test is usually higher toward the end of the lactation period than soon after freshening.

3. **Persistency.**—This refers to the level at which milk production is maintained as lactation progresses. Generally speaking, following the peak lactation period, about a month after freshening, the total milk production each month is approximately 90 per cent of that of the previous month (see Fig. 21-7).

4. **Estrus; pregnancy.**—Milk and butterfat production may fluctuate, usually downward, on the day of or the day following the heat period. Pregnancy seems to have little effect on milk composition. However, beginning about the fifth month of pregnancy, total production of gestating cows declines more rapidly than that of non-pregnant cows. It has been estimated that the energy requirement of the fetus are equivalent to about 400 to 600 lb. of milk.

5. **Calving interval.**—Research indicates that it is most profitable for cows to calve at 12-month, rather than longer, intervals. With an 8-week dry period, this means a lactation period of 10 months.

6. **First-and last-drawn milk.**—The percentage of fat in last-drawn milk is higher than that in first-drawn milk. The reasons for this are not known.

7. **Age.**—The age of a cow has a definite effect on production. Most cows reach maturity and maximum milk production at about six years of age, following which there is a decline in production. Records indicate that cows produce approximately 25 per cent more milk at maturity than they do as two-year-olds. Also, after passing their prime—after six years of age—butterfat gradually decreases with advancing age.

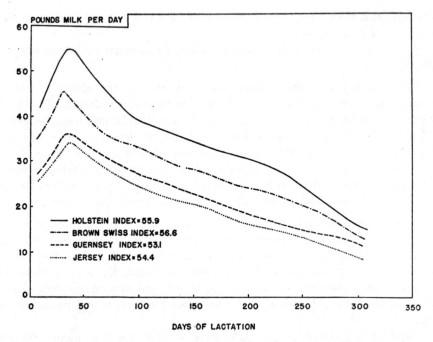

Fig. 21-7. Average lactation curves of four breeds of dairy cattle under Arkansas conditions. (From Arkansas Experiment Station Bulletin 678, Nov. 1963)

Conversion tables are available for adjusting the records of immature cows to expected mature production or *mature equivalent* (ME). The conversion factors given in Table 21-3 were developed from the Cooperative Dairy Herd Improvement Program for converting production records to the mature equivalent (ME) basis.

8. **Size.**—Within a breed, large cows usually produce more milk than small cows. However, according to Brody of the Missouri station, for each 100 lb. increase in body weight, production only increases 70 per cent of the proportional increase in body size.

ENVIRONMENTAL FACTORS AFFECTING AMOUNT AND COMPOSITION OF MILK

All animals, including dairy animals, are the result of two forces—heredity and environment. Because of this, the maximum development of dairy cattle characteristics of economic importance—particularly total milk production—cannot be achieved unless there are optimum conditions of environment. Among the environmental factors affecting amount and composition of milk are the following:

1. **Feed.**—If milk cows are not fed, or if they do not eat, they will not produce. There are a number of ways in which feed may affect the quantity and/or composition of milk. Among them—

TABLE 21—3

FACTORS FOR CONVERSION OF RECORDS OF MILK
AND FAT PRODUCTION TO THE MATURE EQUIVALENT BASIS[1]

Factor	Ayrshire	Brown Swiss	Guernsey	Holstein	Jersey
	(yrs. & mos.)	(yrs. & mos.)	(yrs. & mos.)	(yrs. & mos.)	(yrs. & mos.)
1.48		1— 9			
1.47		1—10			
1.46		1—11			
1.45		2— 0			
1.44		2— 1			
1.43		2— 2			
1.41		2— 3			
1.39		2— 4			
1.37		2— 5		1— 9	
1.36	1— 9				
1.35		2— 6		1—10	
1.34	1—10				
1.33		2— 7		1—11	
1.32	1—11				1— 9
1.31		2— 8	1— 9	2— 0	
1.30	2— 0			2— 1	1—10
1.29	2— 1	2— 9		2— 2	
1.28	2— 2		1—10	2— 3	1—11
1.27	2— 3	2—10			2— 0
1.26	2— 4		1—11	2— 4	2— 1
1.25	2— 5	2—11		2— 5	2— 2
1.24	2— 6		2— 0	2— 6	2— 3
1.23	2— 7	3— 0	2— 1	2— 7	2— 4
1.22	2— 8		2— 2	2— 8	2— 5
1.21	2— 9	3— 1	2— 3	2— 9	2— 6
1.20	2—10	3— 2	2— 4	2—10	2— 7
1.19	2—11	3— 3	2— 5	2—11	2— 8
1.18	3— 0	3— 4	2— 6	3— 0	2— 9
1.17	3— 1	3— 5	2— 7	3— 1	2—10
1.16	3— 2	3— 6	2— 8	3— 2	2—11
1.15	3— 3	3— 7	2— 9	3— 3	3— 0
1.14	3— 4-5	3— 8	2—10	3— 4	3— 1
1.13	3— 6-7	3— 9	2—11	3— 5	3— 2
1.12	3— 8-9	3—10	3— 0	3— 6-7	3— 3
1.11	3—10-11	3—11	3— 1	3— 8	3— 4
1.10	4— 0-1	4— 0	3— 2	3— 9-10	3— 5
1.09	4— 2	4— 1-2	3— 3-5	3—11	3— 6-7
1.08	4— 3-4	4— 3-4	3— 6-8	4— 0	3— 8-9
1.07	4— 5	4— 5-6	3— 9-11	4— 1	3— 10-11
1.06	4— 6-7	4— 7-8	4— 0-2	4— 2	4— 0-1
1.05	4— 8-9	4— 9-10	4— 3-5	4— 3-4	5— 1
1.04	4—10-11	4—11- 5— 1	4— 6-8	4— 5-6	5— 2-6
1.03	5— 0-1	5— 2-4	4— 9-11	4— 7-11	4— 2-3
1.02	5— 2-6	5— 5-7	5— 0-2	5— 0-6	4— 4-5 / 4— 6-9
1.01	5— 7-11	5— 8-11	5— 3-6	5— 7-11	4—10-
1.00	6— 0- / 8— 0	6— 0- / 8— 0	5— 7- / 7— 5	6— 0- / 8— 5	5— 7- / 7— 5
1.01	8— 1-11	8— 1-	7— 6-	8— 6-8	7— 6-

Footnotes at end of table.

(Continued)

TABLE 21—3 (Continued)

Factor	Ayrshire	Brown Swiss	Guernsey	Holstein	Jersey
	(yrs. & mos.)	(yrs. & mos.)	(yrs. & mos.)	(yrs. & mos.)	(yrs. & mos.)
1.02	9— 0-11	9— 5 9— 6- 10— 5	8— 0 8— 1- 9— 0	3— 9- 9— 2	8— 0 8— 1- 9— 0
1.03	10— 0- 11—11	10— 6-11	9— 1-11	9— 3-8	9— 1- 9—11
1.04	11— 0- 11— 5	11— 0-5	10— 0-5	9— 9- 10— 2	10— 0-5
1.05	11— 6-11	11— 6-11	10— 6-11	10— 3-8	10— 6-11
1.06	12— 0-5	12— 0-5	11— 0-5	10— 9- 11— 2	11— 0-5
1.07	12— 6- 13— 2	12— 6-11	11— 6-11	11— 3-6	11— 6-11
1.08	13— 3- 13—11	13— 0-5	12— 0-5	11— 7-10	12— 0-5
1.09	14— 0	13— 6-11	12— 6-11	11—11- 12— 2	12— 6-11
1.10		14— 0	13— 0-5	12— 3-6	13— 0-5
1.11			13— 6-11	12— 7-10	13— 6-11
1.12			14— 0	12—11- 13— 2	14— 0
1.13				13— 3-6	
1.14				13— 7-11	
1.15				14— 0	

[1]From Kendrick, J.F., "Standardizing and Improving Dairy-Herd Improvement-Association Records in Proving Sires." U.S. Department of Agriculture, ARS-52-1. 1955.

a. **Underfeeding.**—By underfeeding we usually refer to not providing sufficient energy. The degree of milk reduction therefrom is related to the extent of underfeeding and the length of time it exists.

b. **Challenge or lead feeding in early lactation.**—One of the most critical periods for proper feeding is immediately following freshening. It is very difficult for high-producing cows to consume enough feed to supply the energy needs for production at this time. As a result, most cows lose weight during this period. The current system of bringing cows to full feed as rapidly as possible after calving and maintaining energy intake as close as possible to their total needs is known as challenge or lead feeding. In this method, cows are fed to their inherited capacity for milk production as determined by profitability; in other words, at the point where the added milk produced does not pay for the added feed, it is time to discontinue further feed increases.

c. **Deficiency of nutrient(s).**—A deficiency of any essential nutrient required by the cow will lower milk production and feed efficiency, rather than make for significant changes in the composition of milk.

d. **Some feed ingredients and rations influence feed composition.**—Some feeds reduce the fat percentage of milk. Among such feeds are: cod-liver oil and other fish oils, certain pasturages (especially lush spring pastures), and pearl millet. Also, fine grinding of forage, too small an amount of roughage, or heated starch will lower the butterfat content of milk. On the other hand, such feeds as whole cottonseed, soybeans, and coconut oil result in a temporary increase in the fat content of milk.

The amounts of fat-soluble vitamins A, D, and E in milk are influenced by the amounts of these particular vitamins in the ration, and in the case of vitamin D, exposure to sunlight is a factor, also.

2. **Length of dry period.**—A dry period of approximately 60 days is recommended following each lactation period. This is important because it permits the cow's body to store up reserves so as to meet the rigorous demand of the next lactation, and it permits proper involution and conditioning of the udder. A short dry period usually results in lower milk production.

3. **Condition at calving time.**—Cows that are in a thin, run-down condition at calving time produce less milk than cows in good condition. Excessive condition will also lower milk production after freshening, but it should be added that this seldom happens in good producing dairy cows.

Cows in good flesh at calving time have been observed to start their lactation with 25 per cent more milk production than those calving in poor condition. Generous feeding of thin cows following freshening may eliminate some of this difference, but it is questionable that thin, high-producing cows can ever consume enough to catch up.

4. **Frequency of milking.**—Frequency of milking does result in more total milk produced; cows milked three times a day consistently produce more milk than those milked twice a day, and cows milked four times a day produce more milk than those milked three times daily. It has also been observed that cows milked more frequently are more persistent in their production throughout the lactation; that is, milk production declines less rapidly as lactation progresses. Of course, a decision as to whether or not it pays to milk more than twice daily will depend on whether the additional milk more than covers the added labor and other costs of obtaining it. In a limited number of herds, managed for intensive production, three daily milkings have been possible.

Frequency of milking has no effect on butterfat percentage.

5. **Irregular feeding and milking.**—Unequal interval between milkings affects both quantity and composition of milk; more milk of slightly lower fat content is obtained following the longer intervals.

6. **Change of milkers.**—High-producing dairy cows may be under stress, with the result that they are usually very sensitive to any changes, including that of the caretaker. Creating a pleasant, quiet, and comfortable environment causes a cow to perform more efficiently.

7. **Environmental temperature; season.**—Butterfat percentage of milk varies with the season, being higher in the fall and winter and lower in the spring and summer. It may vary up and down seasonally by an average of .3 to .5 per cent. Solids-not-fat also show a seasonable variation, with the low point in the spring

and summer. The reasons for these changes are not known; it may be due to temperature and humidity, changes in body weight, or kinds and amounts of feeds may be reflected.

Severe weather conditions usually decrease the amount of total milk produced and may influence the fat test either up or down. Temperatures above 85° F. greatly affect cows and the situation is accentuated when high temperatures are accompanied by high humidity.

It is also noteworthy that cows calving in the fall months consistently produce more than those calving at other times of the year. Cows calving in the spring produce the least. This difference may be as much as 10 to 15 per cent. This phenomena may be due in part to temperature, but more than likely available feeds, including spring pastures to which fall-calving cows respond so well, may be a factor.

8. **Day-to-day variation.**—Research has shown that day-to-day butterfat tests vary from 0.1 to 2.0 per cent.

9. **Disease.**—Disease does affect milk secretion, in both total production and composition; with the degree of the affect determined by the kind and severity of disease. Mastitis will, for example, lower both the total production of milk and the composition thereof.

10. **Drugs.**—Many types of drugs have been used in an effort to increase milk production and affect its composition. Most of them have no effect, so it is questionable that they can be used on a practical basis.

When added to the feed at certain levels, thyroprotein (Thyroxine) stimulates the cow to produce more milk of a higher percentage fat. However, to be effective, it must be added at a specific time during the lactation period and cows must be fed more when they are receiving the drug.

Oxytocin will, on a temporary basis, increase yields of both milk and fat. This is because it permits greater release of milk from the udder. But it must be administered just after each milking in order to get the residual milk which makes its administration both expensive and time consuming. Hence it is not considered a practical procedure.

11. **Prepartum milking.**—Prepartum milking is the practice of milking cows 10 days to 2 weeks before they are due to freshen. Those who follow this practice usually do so because they believe it will lessen congestion and swelling of the udder and belly of the cow. Among some, the feeling also persists that it will lessen the incidence of both mastitis and udder edema. It is known that prepartum milking will result in cows producing normal milk at the time of freshening, rather than colostrum. Thus, where prepartum milking is done, it is necessary to save (freeze) the early milk in order to have colostrum available for the newborn calf.

MASTITIS

Mastitis refers to an inflammation of the udder. The term *mastitis* is from the Greek word *mastos,* for breast, and *itis* refers to inflammation of.

Mastitis causes estimated average annual losses in dairy cattle (including milk) of $411,090,000 (*Losses in Agriculture*, Agric. Handbook, 291, USDA, 1965, p. 73). It has been said that dairymen themselves are responsible directly, or indirectly, for 90 per cent of their mastitis troubles; however, most dairymen blame their milking machine. The three main routes through which mastitis comes are: (1) dirty, or poorly adjusted, milking equipment; (2) poor milking practices; and (3) injuries to cows because of their surroundings.

Several species or groups of micro-organisms may cause mastitis, but over 95 per cent of all cases are caused by the following species of streptocci and staphylococci: *Streptococcus agalactiae, Streptococcus dysgalactiae, Streptococcus uberis,* and *Staphylococcus aureus.* Infection with any of these organisms is usually chronic, with flair-ups occurring at regular intervals. No amount of drugs given to cows today can prevent another attack next month under the same conditions.

Although mastitis is usually apparent, it may be a "hidden" disease. Therefore, several different tests have been developed for detecting the presence of the causative micro-organisms: (1) *screening tests,* or *presumptive tests,* made either at the side of the cow or at the bulk tank, of which the California Mastitis Test (CMT) is the most widely used one, and (2) *specific laboratory tests* designed to detect the causative organism. A reasonable goal, based on using the CMT test, is to have at least 75 per cent of the bucket milk samples score negative or trace; less than 75 per cent negative (-) and trace (T) bucket readings indicates a milking management problem. On an individual quarter basis, 90 per cent of the samples scoring negative or trace indicates a well-managed herd.

Through the years, many different kinds of drug therapy have been used—including dyes, chemicals, sulfas, antibiotics, and nitrofurans. Many times such drugs have been effective, at least temporarily; in any event, acute cases of mastitis should be treated by a veterinarian.

In summary, it may be said that the dairymen themselves are unwittingly setting the stage for mastitis flair-ups in their herds, by providing the ideal conditions—poor milking practices, poor milking equipment, and improper surroundings. By rectifying these shortcomings—through managed milking and sanitation—dairymen can reduce or eliminate mastitis.

MILK FLAVOR

Most consumers base the quality of any product on its flavor; and milk is no exception. They want milk that "tastes good." The flavors most often found in milk, and their cause and prevention, are:

1. **Feed and weed flavors.**—These have been covered under the section on "Feeds Affecting Milk Flavor" in the chapter on "Feeding and Management of Dairy Cattle," so repetition is unnecessary.

2. **Oxidized flavors.**—This has been described as a cardboard flavor. Some causes of oxidized flavor are: (a) metallic contamination from copper and iron, which may be alleviated by using stainless steel; (b) exposure to sunlight or

just daylight; (c) foaming; and (d) dry-lot feeding. Feeding vitamin E to the milking herd will reduce or eliminate oxidized flavors.

3. **Rancid flavors.**—This flavor is caused by a breakdown of the butterfat which releases strong-flavored acids. This action is caused by the enzyme lipase, which is present in all milk. The primary causes of rancid milk are (a) stripper cows (those well advanced in lactation); (b) excessive agitation of milk, due to high lifts and sharp turns in pipeline milking; and (c) slow cooling with foaming.

4. **Barney.**—This flavor(s) is caused by dirty stables, poor ventilation, unclean milking, and unclean cows—all of which can be alleviated.

5. **Salty.**—This flavor, which masks the slightly sweet flavor of milk, is caused by mastitis, stripper cows, or certain individual cows. Milk from cows that have mastitis, or from strippers, should not be marketed.

6. **Malty.**—Malty flavor is primarily due to high bacteria count. The remedy is to keep bacteria out of milk as much as possible, and to prevent growth of those that do get into it. Clean and cold milk will practically eliminate malty flavor. Also, milk handlers should pick up all the milk and not leave any of it in the farm bulk tank.

7. **High acid, sour milk.**—This is due to very high bacterial count. In these days of mechanical refrigeration, there is no excuse for sour milk; simply cool it as rapidly as possible from the 90° F. temperature of the milk pail to 40° F.

8. **Unnatural or foreign.**—This refers to flavors that come from medicinal agents and disinfectants. The control of such off-flavors consists in (a) handling medicines and disinfectants so that the flavor or odor from them will not get into the milk, and (b) using chemical sanitizers only in the concentrations indicated by the directions. Do not market milk from drug-treated cows for at least 72 hours after last treatment, or longer if so prescribed on the drug label or by the veterinarian.

For good-tasting milk, the dairyman should keep it clean, keep it cold, feed silage after milking (not before), use good quality feed, and not ship milk from problem cows.

DRYING OFF COWS

There are several methods of drying off cows, ranging from complete cessation of milking (see Chapter XX, under section on "Dry Cows") to intermittent milking. Perhaps in the final analysis each dairyman will do best by following his own procedure. Regardless of the method used, however, the grain should be reduced when it is decided to turn cows dry, with the tapering off of the grain beginning about a week before starting the actual drying off. Also, it is well to take cows off lush pastures or silage at that time, but they may be fed hay.

QUESTIONS FOR STUDY AND DISCUSSION

1. How do you account for breed differences in milk composition?
2. Scientists have been able to make milk replacers. In fact, it is claimed that many such products are superior to milk, because the synthetic products are fortified with minerals, vitamins, and/or antibiotics. Despite this achievement, scientists have not been able to make colostrum in the laboratory. Why?
3. What are the main parts of the udder and the functions of each part?
4. How is milk formed in the cow's udder?
5. Why is a rapid milker likely to get more milk from a cow than a slow milker?
6. Outline the steps of a good milking routine.
7. On the whole, what three physiological factors have the most effect on the amount and composition of milk?
8. For the U.S. as a whole, what three environmental factors have the greatest effect on the amount and composition of milk?
9. Of the 3 methods of milking—via the calf, by hand, or by machine—which will result in the highest milk yield?
10. Why do some cows inherit the ability to produce more milk than others?

SELECTED REFERENCES

Title of Publication	Author(s)	Publisher
Dairy Science	W. E. Petersen	J. B. Lippincott Co., Philadelphia, Pa., 1950.
Harvesting Your Milk Crop	C. W. Turner	Babson Bros. Co., Chicago, Ill., 1954-1955.
Mammary Gland, The	C. W. Turner	Lucas Bros., Columbia, Mo., 1952.
Milker's Manual, The	W. R. Van Sant	University of Arizona, Bul. A-37, 1965.
Milking Management	R. D. Appleman, et al.	University of California Agricultural Ext. Serv., Pub. Axt-94, 1963.
Principles of Milk Production	W. B. Nevens	McGraw-Hill Book Co., New York, N. Y., 1951.
Secretion of Milk	D. Espe V. R. Smith	The Iowa State College Press, Ames, Iowa, 1952.

CHAPTER XXII

MARKETING MILK AND DAIRY PRODUCTS

Contents   Page

Market Importance of Milk and Dairy Products.............................601
Farm Production and Handling of Milk...602
  How Milk Is Sold by Dairymen..602
How Milk Is Used..603
  Per Capita Consumption...606
Market Channels for Milk and Dairy Products............................606
How Milk Is Priced and Regulated..607
  Federal Milk Marketing Orders...607
  State Milk Control..607
  Cooperatives 608
  Other Regulatory Programs..608
    Sanitary Regulations...608
    Standards and Grades..609
    State Trade Practice Laws..609
  Methods of Pricing or Paying for Fluid Milk........................609
  The Price Support Program..611
Profitability of Dairy Processing Firms..612
Manufactured Milk Products..612
  Number and Size of Plants..612
  Uses of Milk...613
    Cream 613
    Ice Cream and Similiar Frozen Desserts..........................613
    Butter 613
    Nonfat Dry Milk...613
    Cheese 614
    Condensed and Evaporated Milk.......................................615
Imports and Exports..615
Outlook 616
Questions for Study and Discussion..616
Selected References 617

Marketing is that all-important end of the line; it's that which gives point and purpose to all that has gone before.

In our present system, the marketing of milk and dairy products is handled largely by specialists, usually under a multitude of regulations and controls. However, a successful milk producer must understand milk markets and the factors affecting them if he is to take full advantage of his opportunities.

MARKET IMPORTANCE OF MILK AND DAIRY PRODUCTS

The farm value of dairy products (including the value of farm consumption) in 1963 was $5.1 billion. After processing, the value of shipments was $11.2 billion, and, upon being retailed, consumers spent $13.5 billion for dairy products (Table 22-1). Other noteworthy statistics are: (1) dairy products accounted for

TABLE 22—1

FARM VALUE, VALUE OF SHIPMENTS OF PROCESSED PRODUCTS,
AND RETAIL VALUE OF DAIRY PRODUCTS, 1963[1]

Item	Value
	(billions)
Farm value[2]..................	$ 5.1
Value of shipments........	11.2
Retail value..................	13.5

[1]*Organization and Competition in the Dairy Industry,* Technical Study No. 3, National Commission on Food Marketing, June 1966, Table 1-4, p. 4.
[2]Includes the value of farm consumption.

13.6 per cent[1] of the cash income of the nation's farmers in 1964 (Table 1-3 of this book) and (2) consumers spent 16 per cent of their food dollar for dairy products in 1964.

FARM PRODUCTION AND HANDLING OF MILK

Satisfactory milk marketing necessitates one basic ingredient—quality milk; and, ultimately, this means more income for the dairyman.

The difference in price between Grade A milk and the lower grades is considerable. But it goes beyond this; quality can mean increased consumer demand.

Buyers, consumers, and health departments, all have a distinct interest in the quality of milk marketed and used for manufacturing.

Quality milk can be produced only when dairymen pay special attention to a number of factors; among them herd health, the layout and structure of the barn and milk house, clean cows, care of the utensils, cooling and storage of milk, and transportation of milk to market.

How Milk Is Sold by Dairymen

Dairymen sell most of their product in the form of whole milk (Fig. 22-1).

At one time, dairymen marketed a considerable amount of their product as farm-separated cream, but the proportion of this product has been declining. In 1965, farm-separated cream was equivalent to only 3 per cent of total marketing, compared to 38 per cent in 1940.

Whole milk production in the U.S. increased by 8.5 billion pounds between 1950 and 1965, while marketing by farmers increased by 20 billion pounds during this same period of time. This difference was primarily the result of less milk being used on dairy farms. In 1965, only 5 per cent of the total production was used on farms, compared with 15 per cent in 1950. Obviously, the point has been reached where little additional marketing of milk by farmers can be

[1]Sale of dairy cattle and calves accounts for an added 3% of farm cash receipts; hence, in total, dairying accounts for 16.6% (13.6 + 3.0) of farm cash receipts, which ranks it second to the 18% farm income derived by farmers from top ranking beef cattle and calves.

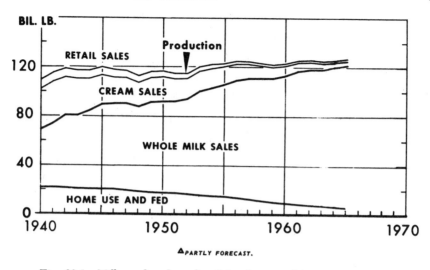

BIL. LB.

Fig. 22-1. Milk used and marketed by farmers. (From *Organization and Competition in the Dairy Industry,* Tech. Study No. 3, National Commission on Food Marketing, June 1966, Fig. 1, p. 5)

expected through decreased use on the farm. Future increases in milk marketings will have to come from increased production.

HOW MILK IS USED

Almost half of the milk marketed by dairy farmers today is consumed in fluid form, and the proportion has been gradually increasing (Table 22-2). Fluid

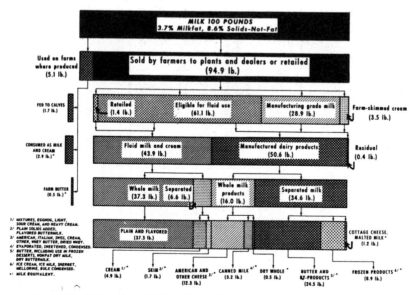

Fig. 22-2. Utilization of U.S. milk production, 1964. (From *Organization and Competition in the Dairy Industry,* Tech. Study No. 3, National Commission on Food Marketing, June 1966, Fig. 2, p. 8)

TABLE 22—2
USE OF MILK SOLD BY FARMERS, MAJOR COMMODITIES, SELECTED YEARS, 1935-65[1]

Year	Fluid use (millions of pounds)	(per cent)	Butter[2] (millions of pounds)	(per cent)	Cheese[3] (millions of pounds)	(per cent)	Condensed products[4] (millions of pounds)	(per cent)	Frozen products (millions of pounds)	(per cent)	Total manufactured products[5] (millions of pounds)	(per cent)	Total milk sold[6] (millions of pounds)	(per cent)
1935	26,696	35.5	33,452	44.5	6,310	8.4	4,550	6.0	2,565	3.4	48,498	64.5	75,188	100
1945	40,459	41.2	27,015	27.8	11,122	11.3	10,613	10.8	5,176	5.3	57,824	58.8	98,373	100
1950	42,392	43.1	27,803	28.3	11,855	12.0	7,894	8.1	6,894	7.0	55,956	56.9	98,348	100
1955	49,386	45.6	28,003	25.9	13,553	12.5	7,124	6.6	8,171	7.5	58,934	54.4	108,320	100
1960[7]	53,178	46.8	29,374	25.9	13,364	11.7	6,182	5.4	9,453	8.3	60,578	53.2	113,756	100
1964	55,507	46.1	31,296	25.9	15,635	13.0	5,692	4.7	10,250	8.5	65,024	53.9	120,531	100
1965[8]	56,045	47.0	28,903	24.3	15,750	13.2	5,295	4.4	10,576	8.9	63,082	53.0	119,127	100

[1] U.S. Department of Agriculture, Economic Research Service, Dairy Situation, DS—310, May 1966, p. 16.
[2] Includes butter made from farm-separated cream.
[3] Includes American and other varieties.
[4] Evaporated milk, condensed whole milk, and dry whole milk.
[5] Includes miscellaneous manufactured products and a small amount of unclassifiable milk and milk products.
[6] Milk sold by farmers, excluding farm-made butter.
[7] Includes Alaska and Hawaii beginning in 1960.
[8] Preliminary.

TABLE 22—3

DAIRY PRODUCTS: PER CAPITA CIVILIAN CONSUMPTION, UNITED STATES, 1950-65

(pounds)

Year	Fluid Whole Milk	Cream[1]	Low Fat Milk[2]	Total Product Weight	Total Whole Milk Equivalent[3]	Butter	American	Other	Cottage Cheese	Evaporated Whole Milk	Condensed Whole Milk	Evaporated and Condensed Skim Milk	Ice Cream	Ice Milk	Sherbet	Other Frozen Dairy Products	Mellorine	Dry Whole Milk	Nonfat Dry Milk	Dry Butter Milk	Dry Whey	Malted Milk
1950	297	11.8	33.6	342	349	10.7	5.5	2.2	3.1	18.1	2.0	5.1	17.2	1.2	0.7	0.3	—	0.3	3.7	0.2	0.2	0.2
1951	303	11.5	33.0	348	352	9.6	5.1	2.1	3.3	16.3	2.0	4.8	17.4	1.5	.9	.4	—	.3	4.2	.1	.1	.2
1952	306	10.8	32.8	350	352	8.6	5.3	2.3	3.4	15.7	1.9	4.7	17.9	1.8	1.1	.4	0.4	.5	4.6	.2	.2	.2
1953	303	10.5	31.5	345	347	8.5	5.1	2.4	3.6	15.4	2.0	4.8	18.0	2.1	1.3	.4	.7	.2	4.2	.2	.2	.2
1954	304	10.1	28.1	342	348	8.9	5.5	2.4	3.8	14.8	2.0	4.9	17.4	2.6	1.4	.2	.9	.2	4.5	.2	.2	.2
1955	306	9.9	28.5	344	348	9.0	5.4	2.5	3.9	14.2	2.0	4.7	18.0	2.9	1.5	.1	1.0	.2	5.5	.3	.2	.2
1956	308	9.9	27.8	346	348	8.7	5.1	2.6	4.5	13.6	2.2	4.5	18.0	3.3	1.4	.1	1.0	.2	5.2	.3	.3	.2
1957	304	9.7	26.4	340	343	8.3	5.5	2.6	4.6	13.1	2.3	4.6	18.0	3.6	1.4	.1	1.1	.3	5.3	.4	.3	.2
1958	298	9.3	26.7	334	335	8.3	5.5	2.6	4.7	12.3	2.5	4.2	17.8	3.8	1.4	.2	1.2	.3	5.6	.4	.3	.2
1959	292	9.1	27.1	328	328	7.9	5.4	2.8	4.6	11.9	2.5	4.5	18.7	4.2	1.5	.2	1.2	.3	6.2	.4	.3	.1
1960	286	9.1	27.1	322	322	7.5	5.7	2.9	4.7	11.2	2.5	4.5	18.3	4.5	1.5	.1	1.3	.3	6.2	.4	.3	.1
1961	276	8.7	27.9	313	310	7.4	6.1	2.9	4.6	10.7	2.4	4.8	18.0	5.0	1.4	.2	1.3	.3	6.1	.4	.3	.1
1962	275	8.5	29.0	312	308	7.3	6.1	3.1	4.6	10.1	2.6	4.8	17.9	5.6	1.4	.2	1.3	.3	5.8	.4	.3	.1
1963	275	8.1	30.4	314	307	6.9	6.2	3.1	4.6	9.4	2.3	4.5	18.0	6.0	1.5	.2	1.3	.3	6.0	.4	.4	.1
1964[5]	273	7.8	33.1	314	305	6.8	6.2	3.3	4.6	9.0	2.3	4.7	18.2	6.4	1.5	.2	1.3	.3	6.0	.4	.4	.1
1965[6]	270	7.5	34.7	312	302	6.6	6.2	3.3	4.6	8.5	2.4	4.7	18.3	6.7	1.5	.2	1.3	.3	6.0	.4	.4	.1
Percentage change, 1950-65[7]	-9	-36	+3	-9	-14	-38	+13	+50	+48	-53	+20	-8	+6	+458	+114	-337	+225	0	+62	+100	+100	-50

Column group headings: Fluid milk and cream (Fluid Whole Milk, Cream[1], Low Fat Milk[2], Total: Product Weight, Whole Milk Equivalent[3]); Butter; Cheese — Whole and Part Skim Milk Cheese[4] (American, Other), Cottage Cheese; Evaporated and Condensed (Evaporated Whole Milk, Condensed Whole Milk, Evaporated and Condensed Skim Milk); Frozen products (Ice Cream, Ice Milk, Sherbet, Other Frozen Dairy Products, Mellorine); Dry Milk Products (Dry Whole Milk, Nonfat Dry Milk, Dry Butter Milk, Dry Whey, Malted Milk).

[1]Includes milk and cream mixtures.
[2]Includes skim milk, buttermilk, and flavored milk drinks.
[3]Fat solids basis.
[4]Excludes cottage cheese.
[5]Preliminary.
[6]Partly forecast.
[7]1962 to 1965.

Source: U.S. Department of Agriculture, Economic Research Service, Dairy Situation, DS-308, November 1965, p. 22.

milk is retailed as pasteurized milk, homogenized milk, fortified milk (vitamin D), skim milk, flavored milk (whole milk with flavoring added), or flavored milk drink (skim milk with flavor added).

Table 22-2 shows that in 1935, 44.5 per cent of the milk supply was used for butter, whereas only 24.3 per cent was so used in 1965. However, it is noteworthy that the use of milk for butter has decreased very little since 1945.

In 1964, farmers sold almost 95 out of every 100 pounds of milk they produced. Sixty-one pounds were eligible for fluid use (Class I or Grade A), 29 pounds were manufacturing grade milk (sometimes called Class II or Grade B), and 5 pounds were retailed from the farm or sold as farm-separated cream.

The major end products of milk in 1964 were as shown in Fig. 22-2.

Per Capita Consumption

Table 22-3 (p. 605) shows the per capita consumption of individual dairy products and the changes that have occurred in each during the past 15 years.

It is noteworthy that declines in per capita consumption from 1950 to 1965 were registered in the following products: evaporated milk, down 53%; butter, down 38%; fluid cream products, down 36%; and fluid whole milk, down 9%. The largest gains were made in low fat products. Ice milk was up, 458%; sherbet, up 114%; nonfat dry milk, up 62%; and cottage cheese, up 48%.

MARKET CHANNELS FOR MILK AND DAIRY PRODUCTS

Milk moves from the farm to the consumer in the following three stages:

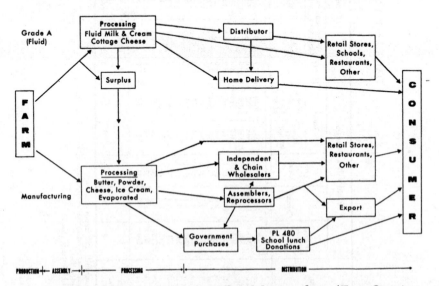

Fig. 22-3. Marketing channels for milk and dairy products. (From *Organization and Competition in the Dairy Industry*, Tech. Study No. 3, National Commission on Food Marketing, June 1966, Fig. 7, p. 17)

1. Assembly and transportation of milk from farms to processing plants.
2. Processed and packaged or manufactured into various dairy products.
3. Packaged milk and manufactured milk products distributed to consumers.

Also, dairymen market their milk as (1) Grade A milk or (2) manufacturing milk (Grade B).

The market channels for milk and dairy products are shown in Fig. 22-3.

HOW MILK IS PRICED AND REGULATED

Chaotic conditions in milk marketing, resulting from the breakdown of private controls and the serious economic plight of farmers during the depression years of the early 1930's, brought requests from organized producers and distributors for government control. Out of this evolved two forms of government controls—those established by the federal government, and those established by state governments; both designed to bring more stability into the marketing of milk. Today, federal and state agencies, directly or indirectly, affect the pricing of all milk marketed by dairy farmers in the U.S. It has been estimated that nearly two-thirds of all milk eligible for fluid markets is affected by milk orders.

Federal Milk Marketing Orders

Federal milk marketing orders are established and administered by the Secretary of Agriculture under Acts of Congress passed in 1933 and 1937. They are legal instruments, and they are very complex. However, stated in simple terms, they are designed to stabilize the marketing of fluid milk and to assist farmers in negotiating with distributors for the sale of their milk. Prices paid to farmers are controlled, but there is no direct control of retail prices.

Federal orders are not concerned with sanitary regulations. These are administered by state and local health authorities.

On January 1, 1966, there were 74 different federal milk market orders, each with a market administrator and provision for setting minimum farm prices and regulating transactions between farmers and milk dealers.

Prices in other Grade A markets were influenced by prices established under federal orders or state control programs. Additionally, dairy support programs directly affected the price of 35 billion pounds of manufacturing grade milk marketed by farmers and the 4 billion pounds of milk farmers sold as farm-separated cream.

State Milk Control

In 1965, 20 states had authority to set minimum farm prices and/or retail prices at the wholesale and retail level. Most of these states were in the northeastern, southeastern, and the western parts of the United States. Of the 20 states, 19 set minimum farm prices, and 12 also set prices at the wholesale and/or retail level.

In setting minimum farm prices, state control agencies often operate in a manner similar to federal milk orders. Classified pricing principles are used, and prices are set for a particular market and not necessarily for the whole state. Retail prices are based on cost of processing and distribution. It is noteworthy that fewer and fewer state milk commissions set retail milk prices; once there were 29 states setting retail prices, now there are only 12. The foes of retail pricing point out that, on the average, retail price setting results in a lower price to the farmer than where retail prices are not tampered with.

Because of their inability to cope with out-of-state milk, state milk controls will likely decline in importance in the future; they will be replaced by federal milk orders.

Cooperatives

The practice of dealing separately with a large number of producers led to dissatisfaction in a number of cases. To rectify this situation, cooperatives were organized. These cooperative associations are of two general types:

1. Bargaining associations which do not handle any milk, but make all business arrangements.

2. Associations which process and distribute milk or assemble it for fluid use.

In 1964, about 66 per cent of the total deliveries of milk to plants and dealers in the United States was handled by cooperatives.

Other Regulatory Programs

Because of the essential nature of milk, plus the fact that it is easily contaminated and a favorable medium for bacterial growth, it is inevitable that numerous regulatory programs have evolved around it—federal, state, and local: some designed to control prices and assure a reasonably uniform flow of milk, and others for sanitary reasons.

SANITARY REGULATIONS

The sanitation of milk and dairy products is assured by the enforcement of sanitary regulations by federal, state, and local authorities.

All major cities and states have sanitary regulations governing the production, transportation, processing, and delivery of milk. Unfortunately, from area to area, there are a bewildering number of different regulations, with the result that milk going to more than one city market is often subjected to duplication and confusion in inspection. Also, sanitary and health regulations have sometimes been used as barriers to keep milk out of a certain area for competitive reasons.

In 1923, the U.S. Public Health Service (USPHS) established an Office of Milk Investigations, and, in 1924, the USPHS published its first Grade A pasteurized milk ordinance. Subsequently, this regulation has been revised 13 times.

The U.S. Public Health Service evolved with the "Grade 'A' Pasteurized Milk Ordinance—1965 Recommendations of the USPHS" as a means of alleviating duplication of effort and confusion. Among its provisions are that milk shall not contain over 100,000 bacteria per ml on delivery and a maximum temperature of 50° F. This is, without a doubt, the most complete set of sanitary milk rules available, and it is being adopted by more and more regulatory officials.

The Food and Drug Administration (FDA) is charged with inspecting dairy products and processing plants for contamination and adulteration.

In an attempt to improve the quality of milk, on April 6, 1967, a National Conference of Interstate Milk Shippers passed a resolution calling for milk to contain not more than 1,500,000 leucocytes per ml on herd milk (leucocytes in milk are an indirect measure of mastitis in cows).

STANDARDS AND GRADES

The U.S. Department of Agriculture has responsibility for the development of standards and grades for milk and dairy products. Milk is graded as Certified, Class I (Grade A), or Class II.

The major dairy products for which the USDA has established grades and the proportion graded in 1965 are shown in Table 22-4.

It is expected that more and more dairy products will be federally graded.

TABLE 22—4

SELECTED DAIRY PRODUCTS GRADED BY USDA IN 1965

Product	Volume	Share of U.S. Production
	(million lb)	*(%)*
Butter...........................	880	62
Cheese (Cheddar and processed)........	113	10
Nonfat dry milk	1,254	59

STATE TRADE PRACTICE LAWS

For more than 20 years, there has been considerable concern about competitive practices in the sale of fluid milk products and ice cream. Among the unfair trade practices sometimes observed or suspected in the marketing of milk are: discriminatory price cutting, secret rebates, loans, advertising rebates, furnishing and servicing equipment, and the giving of gifts and free signs.

In January 1966, 30 states had laws concerned with the marketing and/or pricing of milk and dairy products. Without doubt, more states will enact dairy fair trade practice laws, and this approach will be used by the state as a substitute for complete milk control.

Methods of Pricing or Paying for Fluid Milk

The economist refers to the different systems of paying for milk as "price plans." These plans, which in actual practice generally involve two or more plans (for example, pricing based on (1) class, (2) grade, and (3) base-surplus), are:

1. **Flat price plan.**—This was the common method up to World War I. The milk producer was paid a uniform price for all milk sold, regardless of quality or the use made of it.

2. **Use classification plan.**—Most marketing orders established two use classes —Class I and Class II.

Class I milk generally includes milk used in fluid form such as whole fluid milk, or milk for creamed drinks which must be made from milk approved by local health authorities. Generally speaking, Class I prices are 35 to 100 per cent higher than Class II prices.

Class II milk usually includes milk in excess of fluid needs used to make manufactured dairy products—primarily butter, nonfat dry milk, and cheese.

On some markets, a further division is made, primarily for milk going into cottage cheese, with the result that there are three classes of milk—Class I, Class II, and Class III.

3. **Blend price.**—When dealers buy according to classification prices, they may pay producers a blend price. The blend is an average of class prices weighted by the volume of milk in each class, usually quoted at a specific point and for a specific test of milk.

4. **Quality grade plan.**—Frequently, the terms Grade A and Grade B (usually called Manufacturing Grade Milk) are encountered in milk marketing. Although there may be some local variations in their use, Grade A usually refers to milk produced under conditions which make it acceptable for fluid use in a given market. Grade B often refers to milk produced under conditions which do not make it acceptable for fluid milk use; it's manufacturing milk.

The production of Grade A milk relative to that of Manufacturing Grade Milk has been increasing in recent years. In 1965, 69 per cent of the milk sold by farmers to plants and dealers was Grade A.

5. **Base-surplus plan.**—The base surplus plan (or base rating plan) is designed to encourage that a uniform supply of milk is available. It compensates the dairyman who maintains a high fall production, when more milk is needed. The base period is established during the lowest production months, usually over a period of three to six months. Then, a dairyman's base is established by the average amount of milk delivered during the base period. His base may be modified from time to time.

6. **Butterfat test price plan.**—The butterfat test of milk affects the price. The common practice is to establish a price for 100 lb. of milk of a specified butterfat test. Usually 3.5 per cent butterfat is the basis for pricing, although several markets have established their base at as high as 4.0 per cent butterfat. Then, a price differential (per point or 0.1 per cent) is set up for milk testing above or below this amount.

7. **Solids-not-fat price plan.**—Today, the emphasis on the food value of

milk is shifting from fat content to the other solids, especially protein. This is feasible because tests for solids-not-fat have been devised, and these are proving practical for field use. It is anticipated that this system of pricing milk will expand in the future.

On the average, whole milk contains about 2¼ pounds of solids-not-fat for each pound of milk fat. Thus, milk testing 4 per cent butterfat contains approximately 9 pounds of solids-not-fat, to a total of 13 pounds of solids per hundredweight.

8. **Gallon or quart plan.**—Occasionally a producer supplies milk to a distributor on a per gallon or per quart basis. Since average milk weighs 2.15 lb. to the quart and 8.6 lb. to the gallon, 100 lb. of milk would be equivalent to 46.5 quarts or 11.6 gallons. Thus, one can easily compute the possible returns from selling milk by different methods.

9. **Special milks.**—Certain milks are sold under special labels. Among them are:

    a. **Certified milk.**—This is milk that is produced under special sanitary conditions prescribed by the American Association of Medical Commissioners. It is sold at a higher price than ordinary milk.

    b. **Golden Guernsey milk.**—Golden Guernsey milk is produced by owners of purebred Guernsey herds who comply with the regulations of the American Guernsey Cattle Club. Such milk is sold under the trade name "Golden Guernsey," at a premium price.

    c. **All-Jersey milk.**—This is produced by registered Jersey herds whose owners comply with the regulations of the American Jersey Cattle Club. It is sold at a premium price under the trademark of "All Jersey."

The Price Support Program

Some of the price-support programs pertaining to surpluses since World War II had their origin in wartime programs designed to increase production. Following the war, the demand for dairy products for military and foreign use declined sharply. Thereupon, the Agricultural Act of 1948 extended the price support authorization at 90 per cent of parity for milk and butterfat; and, beginning the following year, the Agricultural Act of 1949 authorized and directed the Secretary of Agriculture to support prices to producers of milk and butterfat at between 75 and 90 per cent of parity. Annually, the Secretary of Agriculture announces a support price for the ensuing marketing year starting April 1. In making this decision, the Secretary arrives at a support price which, in his judgment, and all factors considered, will assure an adequate supply of milk. For the marketing year 1966-67, the support price for manufacturing milk was $3.50 per hundredweight, which was 78 per cent of parity as of March 31, 1966.

In several of the postwar years, the government has made substantial purchases of dairy products—through CCC and other purchase programs—to support prices at announced levels. Annual expenditures for dairy support pro-grams, except special milk, averaged $330 million per year from 1955 to 1964.

PROFITABILITY OF DAIRY PROCESSING FIRMS

Like most businesses, dairy processing firms are owned by people; and most people want to make money, which is quite proper.

There are two ways of gauging the profitability of dairy firms: (1) Net Returns Per Dollar of Sales and (2) Return on Net Worth.

In 1964, the net profits after taxes as a per cent of sales of 14 major companies processing and manufacturing dairy products was 3.0 per cent, and as a per cent of stockholder's equity it was 12.2 per cent. For a 10-year average, the net returns per dollar of sales were within the range of 2.5 to 3.0 per cent and the returns on net worth were within the range of 10.5 to 12.4 per cent. (From *Organization and Competition in the Dairy Industry*, Tech. Study No. 3, National Commission on Food Marketing, June 1966, Table 14-7, p. 202.)

MANUFACTURED MILK PRODUCTS

The production of manufacturing grade milk is primarily centered in the Midwest and the Great Lakes area. Thus, with the exception of ice cream making, the processing of manufactured dairy products—butter, nonfat dry milk powder, cheese, evaporated and condensed milk, and minor other prod-ucts—is concentrated near those areas of production.

Number and Size of Plants

During the past two decades, the number of milk manufacturing plants in the U.S. has been decreasing while the output per plant has been in-creasing (Table 22-5).

TABLE 22—5

TOTAL MILK MANUFACTURED, NUMBER OF PLANTS MANUFACTURING MILK AND AVERAGE ANNUAL VOLUME OF MILK PROCESSED PER PLANT, 1944 and 1961[1]

Item	1944	1961	Percentage Change 1944 to 1961
Total milk manufactured (million lbs.)[2]	54,749	63,063	+15
Number of plants	9,739	6,134	-37
Average annual volume per plant (thousand lbs.)[2]	5,622	10,281	+83

[1]Carley, D.H. and Cryer, T.L., *Flexibility of Operation in Dairy Manufacturing Plants—Changes 1944-1961*, U.S. Department of Agriculture, Economic Research Service and Statistical Reporting Service, Agri-cultural Economics Report 61, October 1964. USDA, *Production of Manufactured Dairy Products*, CS-40, November 1949, and DA 2-1 (64), July 1964.

[2]In terms of whole milk equivalent.

Uses of Milk

The uses of milk have already been covered (see Tables 22-2 and Fig. 22-2). However, a few pertinent points relative to each of the manufacturing products will be presented in the sections which follow.

CREAM

Cream is made by concentrating the fat portion of milk. Prior to the advent of the cream separator, this was accomplished by gravity separation. Today, it is done by passing milk through a cream separator. In commerce, whipping cream contains about 40 per cent fat, coffee or table cream 18 to 20 per cent, and half-and-half, 12 per cent fat.

ICE CREAM AND SIMILAR FROZEN DESSERTS

In 1964, 96 per cent of all frozen desserts in the U.S. consisted of ice cream, sherbet, ice milk, and mellorine (made with a vegetable fat base). Other frozen desserts include frozen custard, frosted malted milk, artificially sweetened ice cream and ice milk, and water ices.

BUTTER

Butter is made from cream. As marketed, it consists of about 80 per cent milk fat. The remainder is water, salt, and traces of other substances.

Butter is sometimes referred to as the "balance wheel" of the dairy industry. This designation comes from the fact that milk is not used for butter until all other demands have been met, with the result that butter manufacture increases or decreases as necessary to balance out total milk production with utilization.

Table 22-6 shows the per capita consumption of butter and margarine, from 1909 to 1965. As noted, the per capita consumption of margarine surpassed butter in 1957. In 1965, the per capita consumption of butter was 6.5 pounds, whereas the per capita consumption of margarine was 9.8 pounds.

State and national laws and regulations bar additives to or changes in butter. Nevertheless, experiments are being conducted on low butterfat spreads. Besides their appeal to homemakers, these products would be better able to compete with oleomargarine.

NONFAT DRY MILK

Among the dried products produced from milk are roller and spray dried nonfat milk, dried skim milk for animal feed, dried whole milk, dried cream, dried whey, dried buttermilk, and malted milk powder. Of these, the production of nonfat dry milk is by far the most important; in 1964, it totaled more than four times that of the production of all other dried products combined.

Nonfat dried milk has many uses, principally as an ingredient in other dairy and food products, although its use in the home has grown considerably

TABLE 22—6

PER CAPITA CONSUMPTION OF BUTTER AND MARGARINE, 1909-65[1]

Year	Per Capita Consumption		Year	Per Capita Consumption	
	Butter	Margarine		Butter	Margarine
	(pounds)			*(pounds)*	
1909.........	17.8	1.2	1938............	16.6	3.0
1910.........	18.3	1.6	1939............	17.4	2.3
1911.........	18.6	1.1	1940............	17.0	2.4
1912.........	16.6	1.5	1941............	16.1	2.8
1913.........	16.5	1.5	1942............	15.9	2.8
1914.........	17.0	1.4	1943............	11.8	3.9
1915.........	17.2	1.4	1944............	11.9	3.9
1916.........	17.3	1.8	1945............	10.9	4.1
1917.........	15.7	2.7	1946............	10.5	3.9
1918.........	14.1	3.3	1947............	11.2	5.0
1919.........	15.2	3.4	1948............	10.0	6.1
1920.........	14.9	3.4	1949............	10.5	5.8
1921.........	16.3	2.0	1950............	10.7	6.1
1922.........	17.1	1.7	1951............	9.6	6.6
1923.........	17.8	2.0	1952............	8.6	7.9
1924.........	17.8	2.0	1953............	8.5	8.1
1925.........	18.1	2.0	1954............	8.9	8.5
1926.........	18.3	2.0	1955............	9.0	8.2
1927.........	18.3	2.3	1956............	8.7	8.2
1928.........	17.6	2.8	1957............	8.3	8.6
1929.........	17.6	2.9	1958............	8.3	9.0
1930.........	17.6	2.6	1959............	7.9	9.2
1931.........	18.3	1.9	1960............	7.5	9.4
1932.........	18.5	1.6	1961............	7.4	9.4
1933.........	18.2	1.9	1962............	7.3	9.3
1934.........	18.6	2.1	1963............	6.9	9.6
1935.........	17.6	3.0	1964............	6.8	9.7
1936.........	16.8	3.1	1965............	6.5	9.8
1937.........	16.8	3.1			

[1]U.S. Department of Agriculture, Economic Research Service, *Dairy Statistics Through 1960,* Statistical Bulletin 303 and supplement for 1963-64; and USDA, ERS, *National Food Situation,* February 1966.

in recent years. Despite its wide variety of uses, nonfat dry milk has been in surplus much of the time.

CHEESE

Cheese is made by (1) exposing milk to specific bacterial fermentation or (2) treating with enzymes, or both, to coagulate some of the proteins.

Milk can be, and is, processed into many different varieties of cheese. Some are made from whole milk, others from milk that has had part of the fat removed, and still others are made from skim milk. The major whole milk cheeses are American (Cheddar) and Colby. The most important variety produced from skim milk is cottage cheese. Other important types of cheese are Swiss, munster, brick, limburger, cream, neufchatel, and blue mould. American cheese (cheddar type) accounts for approximately 65 per cent of the cheese sold in the United States.

In 1964, 24 per cent of all the milk used in manufactured dairy products was processed into cheese, and about 13 per cent of the total milk marketed was used in cheese.

The leading states in the production of cheese, by rank, are: Wisconsin (with 44 per cent of the total production), New York, Missouri, Illinois, and Iowa.

CONDENSED AND EVAPORATED MILK

The primary products within this category are evaporated milk and condensed milk packed in cans for consumer use, and condensed whole and skim milk shipped in bulk. Condensed and evaporated milk are manufactured by removing a major portion of the water from the whole milk in a machine called a vacuum pan. Condensed milk is further treated by the addition of large amounts of sugar.

Candy manufacturers, especially bakers and ice cream processors, are large users of condensed milk.

The production of evaporated whole milk is declining. In 1950, about 6.3 per cent of milk marketings of the U.S. were used in evaporated milk, compared with only 2.9 per cent in 1965.

IMPORTS AND EXPORTS

A number of dairy products, including several types of cheese, butter, malted milk, butteroil, and dried milk are covered by specific import quotas. Although not formally restricted, certain other dairy products may be limited by agreement between the U.S. and the exporting country. Total imports on a milk equivalent basis have been very small. In 1965, imports were just over 900 million pounds, when total production was more than 125 billion pounds.

As long as domestic prices are above world prices, and world supplies are ample, exporting countries will look to the U.S. as a possible market. As a result, import pressure will persist; yet, imports of many commodities probably will continue to be limited by quotas.

Likewise, exports are rather small. From 1955 to 1965, exports of dairy products ranged from less than 1 per cent to more than 5 per cent of the total supply. However, it is noteworthy that on a milk equivalent or solid-not-fat basis, export volume has been much larger than import volume (Fig. 22-4).

Exports of dairy products will continue to be influenced by the availability of surplus products and the demand for dairy products in foreign policy. A more active role in meeting food deficiencies in the less developed countries of the world could increase total demand for dairy products and demand for export products.

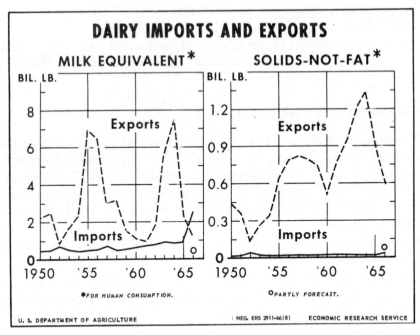

Fig. 22-4. Dairy imports and exports.

OUTLOOK

Per capita consumption of milk and most dairy products appears to have reached a rather stable stage. The most important factors affecting the future demand for dairy products will continue to be changes in population, income, consumer preferences, and new products.

It is expected that per capita consumption of various dairy products will follow the trend of recent years; products high in fat will decline in per capita consumption, while those low in fat will increase. The proportion of milk consumed in fluid form will increase; per capita consumption of butter and evaporated milk will likely decline on a gradual basis; and low-fat fluid milk, nonfat dry milk, low-fat frozen desserts, cheese, and sour cream dressings are likely to increase in per capita consumption.

Without doubt, new low-fat dairy products and nondairy substitutes will replace some of the consumption of similar products higher in fat. The use of man-made milk will increase.

An increasing number of dairy heifer replacements will be raised and marketed by specialists in the business; and more dairy beef will be produced.

QUESTIONS FOR STUDY AND DISCUSSION

1. In 1963, the dairy farmer received $5.1 billion for his milk, but this product retailed at $13.5 billion. Is such a wide spread justified?

2. Why has "home use and fed" milk declined in recent years?

3. On a per capita basis, what dairy products will likely increase in the future? What ones will decrease?

4. What will determine the per capita consumption of butter vs. margarine in the future?

5. Should we have a "free market" for milk?

6. Should the states regulate milk prices, or should this be handled only through federal milk marketing orders?

7. Discuss the advantages and disadvantages of each plan for paying for milk.

8. Analyze the profitability of dairy processing firms based on (a) net returns per dollar of sales and (b) return on net worth. Are they doing all right?

9. Why are milk manufacturing plants becoming fewer and larger?

10. How will the bulk of dairy herd replacements be produced in the future?

11. Will more dairy beef be produced in the future? If so, where and how will it be produced?

12. Will U.S. dairymen be plagued by imports in the next 10 years?

13. Are you optimistic or pessimistic about the future of the U.S. dairy industry?

SELECTED REFERENCES

Title of Publication	Author(s)	Publisher
Federal Milk Marketing Order Program, The Market Bul. 27	USDA	Supt. of Documents, U.S. Government Printing Office, Washington, D. C., 1963.
Fluid Milk Marketing	G. M. Beal H. H. Bakken	Mimir Publishers, Madison, Wisc., 1956.
Grade "A" Pasteurized Milk Ordinance, Pub. Health Service Pub. 229	U.S. Pub. Health Service	Supt. of Documents, U.S. Govt. Printing Office, Washington, D. C. 1965.
Organization and Competition in the Dairy Industry, Tech. Study No. 3	National Commission on Food Marketing	Supt. of Documents, U.S. Govt. Printing Office, Washington, D. C. 1966.

Chapter XXIII

THE SHEEP AND GOAT INDUSTRY[1]

Contents   Page

Origin and Domestication of Sheep..620
    The Moufflon..621
    The Asiatic Urial...622
Origin and Domestication of Goats..623
Position of Sheep in the Zoological Scheme..623
Wool; Precious Fiber Through the Ages...623
Bakewell's Improvement of English Sheep..626
Early Importations and Improvements of Sheep in the U.S.......................626
The Westward Movement of Sheep..628
Growth, Decline, and Transition of the U.S. Sheep Industry....................629
World Distribution of Sheep..630
World Wool Production...632
    Sheep Raising in Australia..633
    Sheep Raising in New Zealand..635
    Sheep Raising in South America..635
    Sheep Raising in South Africa...636
Sheep and Wool Production in the United States.......................................636
    Areas of Sheep Production...637
        The Range Sheep States..637
        The Farm Flock Sheep States..638
    Leading States in Sheep Production...639
Factors Favorable to Sheep Production..640
Factors Unfavorable to Sheep Production..640
Present Position; Future Outlook..640
Questions for Study and Discussion...642
Selected References 643

Sheep and goats were first domesticated in the New Stone Age. The first Egyptian portrayal of sheep appears on one of the earliest sculptures known. dating back to 4000 B.C. Some subsequent sculptures showed one of the early uses of sheep—that of being driven across the freshly sown fields in the Nile Valley to tread in the grain. Other historical records show that sheep provided primitive pastoral peoples with meat, wool, tallow, skins, and milk.

Sheep belong to the genus *Ovis*, and goats and their wild relatives make up the genus *Capra*. These two genera of the family Bovidae are closely related; so closely related, in fact, that a naturalist never speaks lightly of "separating the sheep from the goats." Goats may be distinguished from sheep, however, by the presence of a beard, by the absence of the foot glands (which sheep have). by the strong smell of the bucks, and by differences in horns and skeleton. Goats also are more intelligent, independent, and possess greater ability to fight and fend for themselves.

---

[1] Many helpful suggestions relative to Chapters XXIII through XXXI were made by the following competent sheep specialist: Dr. Clair E. Terrill, Chief, Sheep and Fur Animal Research Branch, U.S. Department of Agriculture, Beltsville, Md.

ORIGIN AND DOMESTICATION OF SHEEP

There is more confusion and disagreement about the ancestry and classification of sheep than with any other animal. This difficulty arises from the bewildering number of breeds and the marked changes produced by domestication. There are more than 200 distinct breeds of sheep scattered throughout the world. Although differing widely in body form and wool character, domestic sheep of all breeds are universally timid and defenseless and the least intelligent and the least teachable of all the domestic four-footed animals. These traits are plainly the result of selection by man and are connected with the herding of sheep in large bands where independence of behavior is a disadvantage. As a result, domestic sheep have become completely dependent on man. Unlike other farm animals, they are unable to return to a wild life, which we refer to as becoming feral. Though this dependence is a logical final result of domestication, it does

Fig. 23-1. Man has herded sheep and woven wool fibers since the Stone Age. Sheep have played an important part in world history. (A copper engraving from a 17th century edition of Vergil's "Bucolica." Photo obtained through the courtesy of The Wool Bureau, Inc.)

appear that the evolution of the sheep in this direction may have gone too far, for they are pitifully helpless in emergencies.

It is certain that domestic sheep came from the wild sheep of Europe and Asia. The confusion and disagreement is over the number of species and the identity of the wild stocks mixed up in their ancestry. One of the chief difficulties in the way of tracing the ancestry of our domestic sheep lies in the fact that most of them are long tailed, whereas all of the wild species from whence they came are short tailed. It appears, however, that lengthening of the tail is a characteristic which appeared with domestication.

Domestic sheep are thought to descend mainly from two wild stocks: (1) the moufflons (*Ovis musimon* and *Ovis orientalis*), and (2) the Asiatic urial (*Ovis vignei*). There is, however, considerable evidence to indicate that the wild big-horned sheep of Asia may be at least partial progenitors of the fat-rumped sheep of central Asia. Perhaps, too, some modern breeds trace back to other wild stocks than those herein indicated.

The Moufflon

There are two wild stocks of the Moufflon, the Asiatic Moufflon (*O. orientalis*), a wild sheep still found in Asia Minor and the Caucasus, and the European Moufflon (*O. musimon*), which is native to Europe and still found in Sardinia

Fig. 23-2. The European Moufflon (*Ovis musimon*), one of the ancestors of domestic sheep. Like all the wild species from which sheep descended, the Moufflon is short tailed. It appears, therefore, that lengthening of the tail is a characteristic which came with domestication. (Courtesy, New York Zoological Society)

and Corsica. These two relatives are closely allied, but the Asiatic Moufflon is redder and has a somewhat different twist to the horns. Both of the moufflon stocks are considered as ancestors of domestic sheep.

Even today relatively unimproved moufflon-like, short-tailed domestic sheep exist in different sections of northern Europe. The least modified of these primitive types is the semi-feral race of sheep on the uninhabited island of Soay, northwest of Scotland. The only essential difference between the Moufflon and the feral Soay sheep is the shorter wool of the latter. The island of Soay is visited once or twice each year by the residents of St. Kilda who hunt down the Soay sheep with dogs and shear them.

The Asiatic Urial

The Asiatic Urial (*O. vignei*), which is a smaller race of sheep than the Moufflon, is native to the grassy open plains of central Asia. It lives in large flocks and is much less a mountain animal than the Moufflon. Most of our familiar breeds of sheep are thought to be descendants of this wild stock. For example, the Merino seems to have originated in Asia Minor about the eighth

Fig. 23-3. A wild sheep (*Ovis Vignei*), native to the province of Punjab in northern India. This is a member of the Asiatic Urial, the smaller of the two wild ancestors of domestic sheep. Most of our familiar U.S. breeds of sheep are thought to have descended chiefly, if not entirely, from the Asiatic Urial. (Courtesy, New York Zoological Society)

century B.C., and to have been spread by the Phoenicians into North Africa and Spain. Likewise, the fat-tailed sheep in western Asia and Africa, the long-tailed African and Arabian breeds, and perhaps the fat-rumped sheep of central Asia, are descendants of the Asiatic urial.

ORIGIN AND DOMESTICATION OF GOATS

The ancestry of the goat is far less confused than is that of the sheep, but a report on the wild relatives of this genus will not be given here. Suffice it to say that goats have not produced nearly so many breeds nor, except for some of the milk-producing types, such extremely modified breeds. Unlike sheep, goats easily return to a wild state if given the opportunity. In fact, only the domestic cat can equal the goat in returning promptly and successfully to the independent life of a wild creature.

Like sheep, goats were probably among the first animals to be domesticated. Goat-like remains are found in the Swiss Lake dwellings of the New Stone Age, and the goat was well known in Biblical days.

POSITION OF SHEEP IN THE ZOOLOGICAL SCHEME

The following outline shows the basic position of the domesticated sheep in the zoological scheme:

Kingdom *Animalia:* Animals collectively; the Animal Kingdom.

Phylum *Chordata:* One of approximately 21 phyla of the animal kingdom, in which there is either a backbone (in the vertebrates) or the rudiment of a backbone, the chorda.

Class *Mammalia:* Mammals or warm-blooded, hairy animals that produce their young alive and suckle them for a variable period on a secretion from the mammary glands.

Order *Artiodactyla:* Even-toed, hoofed mammals.

Family *Bovidae:* Ruminants having polycotyledonary placenta; hollow, non-deciduous, unbranched horns; and nearly universal presence of a gall bladder.

Genus *Ovis:* The genus consisting of the domestic sheep and the majority of wild sheep. The horns form a lateral spiral.

Species *Ovis aries:* Domesticated sheep.

WOOL; PRECIOUS FIBER THROUGH THE AGES

Wool was first spun and made into cloth many years before the beginning of recorded history. According to historians, fabrics of wool have been discovered in the ruins of the Swiss Lake villages, which were inhabited during the Neanderthal Age, between 10,000 and 20,000 years ago. Moreover, wool was used as a clothing material by the Babylonians about 4000 B.C., and sheep are pictured on the earliest Egyptian monuments, which date some time between 5000 and 4000 B.C.

The ancient Egyptians, Babylonians, Greeks, and Hebrews did hand spinning and weaving in the home. The wool industry, like most others, first developed as a household craft, rather than as a primitive factory system.

Fig. 23-4. Ancient Babylonian loom in operation. Wool was first used as a clothing material by the Babylonians beginning about 4000 B.C. (Courtesy, The Bettmann Archive)

Sheep raising was known as the earliest pastoral industry, and reference is frequently made to it in Old Testament literature. For example, we are told that Abraham, the patriarch of the Old Testament, thrived and prospered through his great flocks and herds. Subjects of the King of Israel were taxed according to the number of their rams. The Bible also refers to Eve's son, Abel, as a "keeper of sheep"; and it was shepherds watching over their flocks by night who first saw the star over Bethlehem. Sheep raising was recognized as an early agricultural pursuit, and the early herds and flocks served as a medium of ,exchange.

Sheep were treated with marked respect in Greece.· Individual names were given to them and shepherds would proudly call out their favorites. To protect their fleeces from inclement weather, skins were spread over the animals, while the keeper of the flock had to content himself with a loin cloth.

When Rome was in her glory, her wealthy and refined citizens boasted of their achievement in producing the finest quality wool in the world. Sheep were given extraordinary care, and they were even blanketed so that a luster and

Fig. 23-5. Ancient Egyptian spinning and weaving. As a household craft, the wool industry had its simple beginning among the Egyptians some time between 5000 and 4000 B.C. (Courtesy, The Metropolitan Museum of Art)

gloss might be imparted to the wool. At frequent intervals, the fleece was parted, combed, and moistened with the rarest oils, oftentimes with wine. Surplus stock was usually killed at two years of age, for the Romans believed that the fleece was in its best condition at that period. The distinctive toga, a loose outer garment which was worn by officials of ancient Rome when appearing in public in time of peace, was made from woolen fabrics.

Before the year 1000, both Spain and England attached great importance to their flocks; and, by the year 1500, they were recognized as the two greatest sheep-producing countries of the world. Although the Spanish wools were much finer, for several hundred years Spain and England were regarded as competitors on the great wool markets of Flanders.

In Spain, the powerful nobility and clergy engaged in the lucrative sheep industry. In an attempt to produce the finest staple possible, the early Spanish flockmasters drove their sheep from southern to northern pastures in the spring and returned them in the fall. In this manner, it was possible to secure the most favorable grazing and climatic conditions for the flock. The early laws of the kingdom stipulated that the owners of large flocks should be allowed a path 90 paces wide through all enclosed lands. In the migration process, any animal that failed to keep with the band was left by the wayside. Presumably, this accounts for the flocking or gregarious instinct of the Merino sheep as well as their hardiness. With the repeal of the migration laws and consequent prohibition of seasonal migration, the Spanish shepherd blanketed his sheep through the colder months—his object being that of keeping an equitable temperature, thus producing a more uniform and higher quality product.

During the Middle Ages (500 to 1500) in England, sheep were the sheet anchor of farming. Their chief product was not meat, milk, nor hides, but wool. Unlike the flocks of Spain, those in England were small; the sheep were not in the hands of a very few powerful owners as they were in Spain, and they were not compelled to travel across the country. The great problem of the English sheep farmer, therefore, was to procure sheep that were adapted to his particular locality. This largely accounts for the development of the many types and breeds in that country. The cold winters, scarcity of winter feed, and the presence of scab and rot made the early sheep raising of England a risky venture. The shepherd's position was highly respected, and lame shepherds were in great demand because a lame man was not so likely to overdrive his sheep. None of the wools from the English breeds was as fine as that of the Merino. Nevertheless, there was a ready market for the English wools because they were more suitable for a variety of uses than those from Spain.

BAKEWELL'S IMPROVEMENT OF ENGLISH SHEEP

By the time Robert Bakewell of Dishley (1726 to 1795) entered the live-stock-breeding business of England, wool had declined in price until—with the rapidly advancing values of English lands—it alone would no longer justify the keeping of sheep. Bakewell, however, had the foresight to picture the future needs of a growing population in terms of meat, and he set about improving the Leicestershire sheep of the day. He was successful in creating a low-set, blocky, quick-maturing type of animal. He paid little or no attention to fancy points; no animal met with his favor unless it had utility value, as measured by meat over the block. Bakewell gradually transformed the large, heavy-boned and heavy-framed sheep, that had little or no propensity to finish quickly, to a shorter-legged, blocky form with finer bone and quick-finishing propensities. Other breeders followed suit.

EARLY IMPORTATIONS AND IMPROVEMENTS
OF SHEEP IN THE U.S.

The Big Horn or Rocky Mountain sheep, prevalent in the Rocky Mountain region from Alaska to California, were native to this continent, but the ancestors of our present-day domestic sheep were imported. The Spanish explorer, Columbus, brought sheep and goats to the West Indies on his second voyage in 1493. Cortez brought Merino sheep into Mexico in 1519. The Spaniards who founded old Santa Fe, New Mexico, were thought to have brought in the multi-colored sheep from which the flocks of the Navajo Indians have descended. If, as is generally supposed, these early importations were of Spanish Merino extraction, special permission to take them out of Spain must have been granted by the king.

The first sheep of the British breeds to be introduced in this country are

Fig. 23-6. Hairy, multi-colored, unimproved Navajo sheep on the Navajo Reservation, New Mexico. It is thought that the ancestors of these sheep were brought to America from Spain by the Spaniards who founded old Santa Fe. (Courtesy, Southwestern Range and Sheep Breeding Laboratory, Fort Wingate, N. M.)

said to have been brought into Virginia by the London Company in 1609.[2] Two decades later, there were as many as 400 sheep in Charleston, now a part of Boston. We are told that these early importations represented very poor specimens of British sheep, the imperfections of which were generally acknowledged. Furthermore, because of the lack of care, inadequate shelter, and promiscuous breeding, the sheep yielded a wool that had lost all pretense to fineness. Predatory animals played havoc with the flocks, and for this reason many of the early sheep were herded on small islands off the coast. Even today, sheep are found on the islands off the coast of Maine and Massachusetts, especially on Martha's Vineyard and Nantucket.

Sheep husbandry was promoted by the colonist primarily in order to furnish wool rather than for purposes of increasing the food supply. In addition to the demand for wool in most new countries, the product is well adapted to marketing in an undeveloped area—being (1) light in weight, value considered and (2) imperishable with respect to time involved in getting it to market.

As early as 1662, there was a woolen mill at Watertown, Massachusetts. At about this same time, the exportation of ewes or lambs, except to other colonies, was forbidden. In 1670, in order to encourage sheep growing, Connecticut re-

---

[2] In 1607, a shipment of sheep came over in the *Susan Constant* but these were consumed during the famine of the ensuing winter, thus having no permanent effect.

quired every person to labor for one day each year at clearing the underwood to make pasturage. Drastic legislation was passed by all the New England colonies to protect the sheep from dogs. A dog that bit or killed a sheep was often hanged as though he were a human malefactor. The execution was usually carried out in some nearby swamp, whence comes the name "Hang-Dog Swamp," given to several localities in colonial Massachusetts and Connecticut.

The town common was open to all kinds of livestock, but because sheep were the most defenseless of domestic animals, and the hardest to raise, the town regulations concerning their care were numerous. Moreover, each town had one or more shepherds who were considered very important persons.

Owners identified their stock by marks or brands (ear-notches or ear-holes were the most common means of marking)—a Medieval European device revived in the New World. These marks were registered with the town clerk, and sometimes the description was embellished with a crude picture.

In due time, early importation to America and the improvements made by the colonists were to become the sturdy basis for some of our great American flocks. Breeding stock was imported from some of the foreign countries; and the early flock owners practiced rigid selection in order to improve the quality of wool produced, employing sight and touch, ordinary scales for weighing the fleeces, and in some instances a ruler for measuring fiber length. These empirical methods served well, however, and remarkable improvements in wool were brought about. Fleeces became heavier, and the fibers were longer and more uniform. It is also interesting to note that in the year 1836 fleeces produced in this country averaged only about 2 pounds in weight and were satisfactory only for the coarser woolen fabrics. Half a century later the average weight had been increased to 5½ pounds. Almost simultaneously, the growing importance of the lamb and mutton trade changed the character of the sheep from one with a small carcass and with a short, fine fleece to a heavier and larger animal growing a longer-stapled and coarser-grade wool. Thus, a dual-purpose type of animal was developed.

THE WESTWARD MOVEMENT OF SHEEP

In 1810, the census figures clearly indicated that the northeastern part of the United States—New England and New York—was the sheep-producing center of the nation. At this date, there were an estimated seven million head of sheep in the United States. By 1840, sheep numbers in the United States had increased to 19 million head. At that time there were no appreciable numbers of sheep in the Far West except those owned by the Navajo Indians in northern New Mexico. In fact, the only state west of the Mississippi having sheep in considerable numbers was Missouri. Ten years later, the densest sheep population was centered in the Ohio Valley and Great Lakes region. When this area became somewhat thickly settled and land values rose, many sheepmen, desiring to operate on a large scale, moved farther west where range was cheap and extensive. It must be remembered that during this period sheep were maintained primarily for wool production and that the market-lamb business, as we know it to-

Fig. 23-7 Three Merinos, two ewes and one ram, were imported to the United States from Spain in 1793, but these animals were butchered. Don Pedro (above) was then imported in 1801, by Dupont deNemours at a cost of $1,000. It is claimed that this ram left a larger impression on the sheep of America than any other sheep ever imported. Don Pedro was acclaimed the father of the fine-wool industry in the United States. He weighed 138 pounds. After careful washing in cold water, his fleece weighed 8½ pounds, and it had a staple length of 1¾ inches. (Courtesy, The National Wool Grower)

day, was practically unknown. It was not at all surprising, therefore, to find that with the opening up of cheaper rangelands in the West there was also an immediate and marked shift of the sheep population from east to west.

Like other wars, the Civil War caused sharply increased sheep numbers as a result of the demand for and the high price of wool. Following the war, wool prices fell because of lower demand and increased competition from cotton and imported wool. Yet the westward expansion and the opening up of cheap lands continued.

GROWTH, DECLINE, AND TRANSITION OF THE U.S. SHEEP INDUSTRY

Fig. 23-8 shows that sheep numbers have fluctuated rather widely from time to time. Although it is not shown in Fig. 23-8, they peaked in 1884; and they near-peaked again in 1942 during World War II, when they reached 56 million head. On January 1, 1968, there were 19,184,000 stock sheep, plus an additional 2,938,000 sheep and lambs on feed, in the United States—the lowest number since records were started in 1867.

Several factors contributed to the decline in sheep numbers since 1942, including (1) lower returns and higher risks from sheep than from cattle and some crops in many areas; (2) scarcity and high wages of competent sheep herders; (3) uncertainties in tariff levels and imports, wool incentive payments,

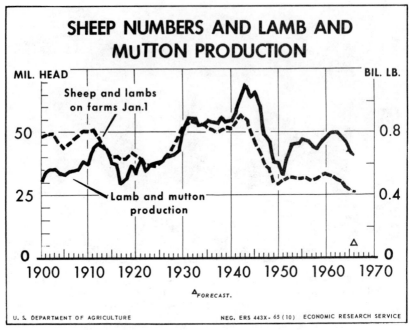

Fig. 23-8. Growth and decline of the U.S. sheep industry. (Courtesy, Economic Research Service, USDA)

and grazing allotments on public domain; and (4) application of more science and technology in competing meat and fiber industries.

Also, the geography of sheep production has shifted. The Rocky Mountain region had become the dominant sheep section of the country by 1900, but sheep numbers declined more sharply in the range states than in the native states during the Forties. Since 1950, sheep numbers have declined proportionally in both farm flock and range band areas; at that time (1950), the 11 western states and Texas had 68.17 per cent of the nation's stock sheep and lambs, and in 1967, these same 12 states still had 67.98 per cent of the breeding sheep.

WORLD DISTRIBUTION OF SHEEP

Despite the obscurity surrounding their domestication and the disagreement about their ancestry and classification, it is known that sheep raising followed the conquest and colonization of the Western Hemisphere to Australia, New Zealand, South Africa, and other countries. Today, the sheep industry is world-wide, with numerous breeds providing needed adaptation. Like other industries, sheep raising is affected by wars; national and international policies and politics; supply and demand; wool substitutes; competition for land, labor, and capital; and many other factors.

As will be noted in Table 23-1, the United States is now excelled in sheep

TABLE 23—1

SIZE AND DENSITY OF SHEEP POPULATION OF TEN LEADING SHEEP-AND WOOL-PRODUCING COUNTRIES OF THE WORLD, BY RANK

Country	Sheep[1]		Human Population[2]		Size of Country		Sheep per Capita[3]	Sheep per	
	Number	When Estimated	Number	When Estimated	(sq. mi.)	(sq. km)		(sq. mi.)	(sq. km)
Australia..........	164,980,000	1964	11,185,167	1964	2,971,081	7,695,100	14.74	55.52	21.43
U.S.S.R...........	133,900,000	1964	229,100,000	1965	8,655,890	22,418,755	.58	15.47	5.97
China.............	55,134,000	1956-60 av.	750,000,000	1964	2,279,134	5,902,957	.07	24.19	9.34
New Zealand......	51,290,000	1964	2,627,488	1965	103,736	268,676	19.52	494.42	190.89
Argentina.........	47,500,000	1964	22,045,000	1964	1,072,700	2,778,293	2.15	44.28	17.09
India.............	40,900,000	1964	471,627,000	1964	1,261,597	3,267,536	.09	32.45	12.51
Republic of So. Africa..........	38,100,000	1956-60 av.	17,474,000	1964	472,359	1,223,410	2.18	80.66	31.14
Turkey...........	32,279,000	1964	31,118,000	1964	296,500	767,935	1.04	108.87	42.03
United States.....	28,021,000	1965	194,600,000	1965	3,548,974	9,191,843	.14	7.90	3.04
Ethiopia..........	24,634,000	1964	22,200,000	1964	398,350	1,031,727	1.11	61.84	23.87
World total.......	989,000,000	1964	3,220,000,000	1964	52,403,746	135,725,702	.31	18.87	7.28

[1]Agricultural Statistics, 1965, USDA, p. 335.
[2]World Almanac, 1966, New York World-Telegram.
[3]Sheep per capita computed from most recent sheep and human census figures reported; in some cases, this necessitated using data for different years.

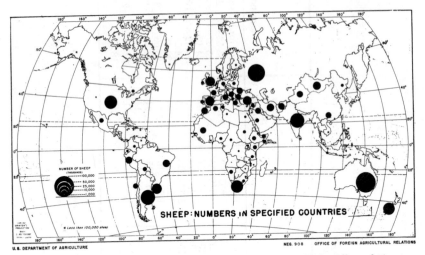

Fig. 23-9. World distribution of sheep. (Courtesy, USDA, Office of Foreign Agricultural Relations)

numbers by Australia, U.S.S.R., China, New Zealand, Argentina, India, Republic of South Africa, and Turkey. The majority of the world's sheep are concentrated in a relatively small number of countries; the 10 leading countries have over 72.5 per cent of the world's sheep. Australia and the U.S.S.R. account for 30 per cent of the world total. Although the industry is world-wide, it is of greatest importance in those countries which have (1) vast frontier-land areas that are sparsely settled and (2) temperate climates. These conditions prevail in the Southern Hemisphere, and it is there that most of the world's sheep are located. On the other hand, there are areas within countries of the Northern Hemisphere with many great flocks and numerous small ones.

Since World War II, sheep numbers have increased in most countries. From 1942 to 1964, world sheep numbers increased from 782,000,000 head to 989,000,000. By contrast, since World War II, sheep declined in the United States. This difference can be attributed to (1) the world's rising aggregate demand for food and fiber in relation to U.S. demands, and (2) the fact that sheep are an excellent subsistence occupation for people in nations with a high proportion of nonarable land and relatively low living standards.

Favorable prices for wool and lambs and satisfactory grazing and weather conditions usually make for stable or increased sheep numbers in those countries to which they are adapted. Historically, wars have always played a prominent part in stimulating the sheep business.

WORLD WOOL PRODUCTION

Inspection of Table 23-2 reveals that, generally speaking, there is quite a close correlation between sheep numbers and wool production. It is noteworthy, however, that the U.S.S.R. has a very low wool production per sheep; only

TABLE 23—2

WOOL (GREASY BASIS) PRODUCTION IN TEN LEADING
COUNTRIES OF THE WORLD, BY RANK, 1966[1]

Country	Wool Production		Number of Sheep	Wool Produced/Sheep	
	(million)		(thousands)		
	(lbs.)	(kg)		(lbs.)	(kg)
Australia	1712.2	777.3	157,563	10.87	4.93
U.S.S.R.	826.7	375.3	129,800	6.37	2.89
New Zealand	730.0	331.4	57,340	12.73	5.78
Argentina[2]	440.0	199.8	49,000	8.98	4.08
Republic of So. Africa	342.0	155.3	42,760	8.00	3.63
United States	250.0	113.5	24,734	10.11	4.59
United Kingdom	128.0	58.1	21,818	5.87	2.66
Uruguay	189.6	86.1	21,800	8.70	3.95
Turkey	99.2	45.0	33,382	2.97	1.35
Spain	84.4	36.3	17,073	4.94	2.24
World Total	5938.3	2696.0	1013,800	5.86	2.66

[1]*Agricultural Statistics*, 1967, USDA, pp. 412 and 397.
[2]Argentina sheep numbers are for 1965.

6.37 pounds in comparison with 12.73 pounds in New Zealand. Australia produces nearly one-third of the world's wool at the present time.

The Southern Hemisphere countries of Australia, New Zealand, Union of South Africa, and the South American countries of Argentina and Uruguay are the main wool surplus producing areas. As would be expected, with the declining sheep numbers in the United States, the production of wool has been correspondingly lowered in this country.

Wool production is definitely a frontier industry, thriving in those areas where there is an abundance of cheap range area and where the human population is sparse. On the other hand, wool consumption is greatest in centers of dense population, especially the temperate zone of the Northern Hemisphere. Prior to World War II, the leading importing countries were the United Kingdom, France, Germany, United States, Belgium, and Japan.

Sheep Raising in Australia

Australia holds undisputed claim to being the leading sheep country of the world, having about one-sixth of the world's sheep and producing nearly one-third of the world's wool. It is a large country which is best suited to a pastoral type of agriculture and in which sheep seem to have been the animals best adapted to her grazing lands.

Although sheep existed in Australia at an early date, the Merino was first introduced in 1789. Other Merino importations followed, most of which came from Saxony in Germany. The early sheep industry of Australia was financed with English capital, the original aim being to render that country independent of Spanish, German, and other foreign sources of supply. The wool from the Australian Merino flocks met with a ready demand on the part of English manu-

Fig. 23-10. Mustering (called herding in the United States) sheep for shearing in Australia. Note that horses and dogs are used. Australia has wide, flat
grasslands. (Courtesy, Australian News and Information Bureau)

facturers, thus giving great encouragement to the further expansion of the sheep
industry of Australia.

Merino blood still predominates in Australian flocks, although the mutton
breeds are gradually increasing in favor and greater attention is being given to
the mutton qualities of the Merino. Most of the wool is marketed in England.
Likewise, Australia disposes of most of her surplus mutton by shipping frozen
carcasses to England.

Most of the flocks of Australia are kept in fenced holdings, rather than being
herded as is the most common practice on the western ranges of the United
States. The Australian owners prefer ranging on enclosed lands, contending:
(1) that the sheep make better use of the range under this system, the animals
scattering out in contrast to each sheep regularly maintaining a fairly definite
position in the band as happens in herding; (2) that less driving is required, as,
in herding, the animals must be rounded into camp at night, driven to water,
and kept from other bands of sheep; (3) that the fences cost less than the
added labor in herding; and (4) that the fences give considerable protection
against predatory animals and help protect the forage from the ravages of
rabbits (the fences being rabbit proof). Experienced operators contend that
handling sheep in fenced holdings is satisfactory provided that the band can be
kept under these conditions the year round but that it will not work if the animals
must be removed from fenced range at intervals and herded, for the band will
then be untrained and unmanageable.

Sheep Raising in New Zealand

New Zealand is a small country, less than twice the area of the state of Illinois. However, there are over 50 million sheep in New Zealand, or 494 sheep per square mile; the densest sheep population of any country of the world. The sheep of this country run more to the mutton type than do the animals of Australia. Practically all the flocks are kept in fenced holdings without herders, in

Fig. 23-11. Sheep raising in New Zealand. Note the musterers and dogs to the right. (Courtesy, New Zealand Embassy, Washington, D.C.)

a manner similar to the method followed in Australia. Year-round grazing is available. Cattle and sheep share many areas, to the advantage of each other; with cattle utilizing the coarser vegetation and sheep the finer grasses and legumes. The best lambs in New Zealand are produced by using Southdown rams on Romney ewes.

Sheep Raising in South America

There is a considerable sheep industry in Argentina, Chile, Uruguay, Brazil, and Peru.

Without doubt, the finest sheep country in South America, and one of the finest in the world, is the La Plata River area of Argentina and Uruguay, where sheep compete with cattle for the lush pastures of the Pampas region. Predatory animals are few, winter feeding is seldom necessary, and diseases are rare. In brief, it has been said that there is probably no other comparable area in the world where the shepherd's life is easier than in this particular territory. Sheep raising in other areas and countries of South America does not compare with the La Plata River section, either in terms of favorable conditions or quality of flocks.

In all the South American countries, Merino breeding was used as a foundation and in effecting improvement, but many subsequent importations of the mutton breeds have been made, especially the long-wooled breeds. Much of the coarse wools produced in South America are used in the manufacture of rugs.

Sheep Raising in South Africa

The Republic of South Africa's chief claim to fame as a sheep country is in terms of wool production. Merino blood predominates, although a considerable number of representatives of the mutton breeds have been introduced in more recent years. The major handicaps to sheep production in South Africa are: (1)

Fig. 23-12. Sheep scene in the Republic of South Africa. Note that the sheep show fine wool breeding. (Courtesy, Embassy of the Republic of South Africa, Washington, D.C.)

prevalence of diseases and parasites, especially sheep scab; (2) unreliable labor; (3) predatory animals, especially jackals; and (4) frequent droughts.

SHEEP AND WOOL PRODUCTION
IN THE UNITED STATES

Table 23-3 gives the numbers and value of sheep and goats in the U.S. As shown, sheep numbers totaled 22,122,000 in 1968. This was only 40 per cent of the 56 million head of the peak wartime year of 1942.

TABLE 23—3

NUMBERS AND VALUE (TOTAL VALUE AND VALUE/HEAD) OF
SHEEP AND GOATS ON UNITED STATES FARMS

Class	Number	Farm Value	
		Value	Total Value
		(Dollars/head)	(Thousands dollars)
Sheep (1968)[1]	22,122,000	19.23	425,444
Goats and kids (1966)[2]	3,691,000	4.90	18,100

[1]From *Livestock and Poultry Inventory*, January 1, Release of February 13, 1968, USDA, p. 16.
[2]*Ibid.*, p. 5, No. and value, Texas farms.

The United States is not a great sheep- and wool-producing nation. We rank ninth in world sheep numbers and sixth in world wool production. In terms of total farm value, both cattle and swine exceed sheep by a considerable sum.

The vast majority of U.S. sheep are still in the western range area, where most of them graze on arid and semi-arid pastures. For the most part, farm flocks utilize untillable areas and waste feeds.

Although the range area still dominates U.S. sheep production, many range operators either retired or switched to cattle, and few young men entered the business.

The U.S. does not produce enough lamb or wool to meet its requirements; it is an importer. By 1966, lamb and mutton imports were equivalent to 11.6 per cent of our production and about 75 per cent of our wool requirements came from abroad.

Areas of Sheep Production

Sheep raising in the United States may be divided into two areas: (1) the range sheep states and (2) the farm flock sheep states. Each of these areas will be discussed separately.

THE RANGE SHEEP STATES

About 68 per cent of the breeding or stock sheep of the nation is in the 11 western range states and Texas. For the most part, this type of sheep husbandry is characterized by large bands of from 1,000 to 1,500 ewes under the care of a herder. In general, these bands are run on unenclosed land. As more than half of the ranges of the West are publicly owned and are likely to continue so, fences will not be built simply because it is not wise to go to so much expense on other than private holdings. On the other hand, scarcity and high cost of labor have resulted in fencing a considerable amount of private holdings in southwestern United States. As most of these ranges are used the year round and the bands are not herded on mountain ranges during the summer months, fenced range has been satisfactory.

Within the western range, there are great variations in topography, rainfall, and vegetation. Thus, in most cases, the sheep production of this territory is a migratory type of enterprise, in which deserts, plains, foothills, and mountains may be used during different seasons of the year in such manner as to obtain as nearly year-round foraging as possible. In general, the ranges of the southwestern states do not afford sufficiently good grazing to produce milk-fat market lambs. Wool production with Rambouillet type sheep, therefore, is of comparatively greater importance in this area than it is in the Northwest. On the better ranges of the Northwest, however, the objective is always that of producing a fat market lamb at weaning time, and feeder lambs result only because the ranges proved inadequate (perhaps through lack of moisture) or because of the usual rejects in culling. Because the vegetation is more abundant in the Northwest, a larger, crossbred type of sheep predominates in this area. This type produces a coarser fleece than the Rambouillet type ewes of the Southwest and yields lambs of more desirable type and quality.

Most of the better range operators provide supplemental feeding during a part of the year, especially in the lambing season and during times when the range is covered with snow. Alfalfa from the irrigated areas is the chief hay crop; and corn, oats, barley, and various protein supplements may be used on occasion. In the trade, wools produced in the range states are known as territory wools.

THE FARM FLOCK SHEEP STATES

This includes the sheep production throughout the U.S., except in the western range states. It embraces the farm flocks, ranging from a few head to a thousand or more, which are kept on the farms of the East, South, and Midwest. In the trade, the wool coming from farm flocks is known as native wool.

Many of the smaller farm flocks of this area are primarily kept as scavengers, and, unfortunately, they are often accorded the neglect of a minor enterprise. In general, the lambs from farm flocks are sold directly for slaughter, only a few finding their way to feedlots for further finishing. Farm flocks carry a heavier infestation of parasites than do range bands, and the fleeces lack the care and uniformity accorded to range wool production. Also, some lambs coming from farm flocks are not docked or castrated, a neglect which is a rarity on the western range where sheep production is more of a specialty.

Purebred flocks as well as commercial enterprises characterize the farm sheep flocks. The purebred producer markets his surplus stock (1) to other purebred breeders and (2) as breeding stock for commercial enterprises.

Leading States in Sheep Production

Some idea of the relative importance of sheep production in the leading states may be obtained through studying Table 23-4.

As will be noted, Texas has a substantial lead in sheep numbers, a position

Fig. 23-13.   A farm flock of sheep. (Courtesy, Dr. Clair E. Terrill, Chief, Sheep and Fur Animal Research, U.S. Department of Agriculture)

which it also holds in cattle, horse, and goat numbers. In fact, the leading sheep states are predominantly in the range sheep area of the United States.

TABLE 23—4

TEN LEADING STATES IN SHEEP AND LAMB NUMBERS,
BY RANK, 1968[1]

	1968
Texas	4,206,000
Wyoming	1,847,000
California	1,535,000
Colorado	1,384,000
South Dakota	1,382,000
Montana	1,275,000
Utah	1,074,000
Iowa	947,000
New Mexico	873,000
Idaho	834,000
U.S. total	22,122,000

[1]*Livestock and Poultry Inventory*, January 1, Release of February 13, 1968, USDA.

FACTORS FAVORABLE TO SHEEP PRODUCTION

As compared to other classes of livestock, sheep possess the following natural advantages:

1. They are unexcelled in the utilization of the more arid type of grazing.

2. In the farm flock states, they frequently utilize what would otherwise be wasteland. They are also excellent scavengers, gleaning fields and destroying weeds.

3. Compared to cattle, they produce more liberally in proportion to what they consume.

4. They produce two products, lamb and wool, which are available for market at two different periods of the year; and it seldom happens that both products sell at bottom prices the same year.

5. Their returns come quickly; lambs may be marketed eight months after the ewes are bred.

6. Their habit of bedding down on the highest areas of the field or range leaves the larger part of the droppings at the places where they are most needed. Moreover, the form in which sheep manure is dropped and the way it is tramped into the soil insures a smaller waste than is possible under any other system of stock farming.

7. Their wool clip is easily stored and shipped, thus making wool production ideally suited to a frontier type of agriculture.

FACTORS UNFAVORABLE TO SHEEP PRODUCTION

There are, however, many factors which are quite unfavorable to sheep production, as many sheepmen will testify to their regret. Some of these are:

1. Wool has always been in politics, and it is apt so to remain. It is rather difficult, therefore, to predict prices over a long period of time.

2. Consumption of lamb has declined to the point where it is a minor product, with the result that both on-foot and retail marketing problems have increased.

3. Sheep are very much subject to attack from numerous predatory animals, including dogs.

4. When disease or injury strikes, they have less resistance than other classes of livestock.

5. Herding is not a particularly attractive profession, thus resulting in a scarcity of satisfactory herders.

6. Sheep are quite susceptible to a number of very devastating parasites.

7. The increasing competition from synthetic fibers affects the demand for wool.

PRESENT POSITION; FUTURE OUTLOOK

The *present position* of the sheep industry is herewith summarized:

1. **U.S. sheep population has not kept pace with world trends.**—World sheep numbers have increased by about 22 per cent during the past 10 years. However, during this same period of time, U.S. sheep numbers have gone down from an average of 31,761,000 head in 1956-60 to 22,122,000 in 1968.

2. **Per capita consumption of lamb and mutton has declined.**—Prior to 1945, U.S. per capita consumption of lamb and mutton—and most of it was lamb—was about 7 pounds per year. In 1966, it was 4.0 pounds.

3. **Synthetic fibers have increased.**—In the period 1946 to 1966, U.S. per capita

consumption of scoured wool declined from 5.2 to 1.9 pounds. During this same twenty-year period, per capita consumption of man-made fibers increased from 6.6 pounds to 17.4 pounds.

4. Imports of lamb and mutton increased; wool imports exceed domestic production.—Prior to 1957, imports represented less than 1 per cent of this nation's lamb and yearling production; but by 1966 this figure had increased to 11.6 per cent. In 1960, 55.5 per cent of U.S. wool consumption was imported. By 1966, three-fourths (74.9%) of our wool was imported.

5. Fewer sheep on national forests.—In 1944, approximately 4.3 million sheep and goats grazed on national forests. By 1965, this number had been cut to less than half—to 2.1 million.

The *future outlook* for the U.S. sheep and wool industry, based on all available facts and figures and the considered judgment of the author, follows:

1. Per capita consumption of lamb may decline slightly.—The future of lamb will be determined primarily on how well producers (a) meet consumer preference—and in a greater number of stores, (b) provide larger and year-round supplies of uniform quality, and (c) apply more science and technology.

2. Per capita consumption of wool faces stiff competition.—Synthetic fiber producers will continue to invest large sums in research and promotion; and there is every reason to believe that these efforts will be as effective and productive as in the past.

3. Imports of lamb and wool may increase.—A number of factors, especially improved transportation for carcass meat and the impact of the European Common Market, point to greater importation of lamb in the years ahead. If properly controlled, increased importation of lamb could be a help, thereby assuring year-round availability and stimulating consumption.

Domestic synthetic fiber production and imported fabrics (rather than fiber) will continue to constitute more of a threat to domestic wool production than foreign imports of wool.

4. Continued shift in the geography of production.—It is expected that sheep production will continue, gradually, to shift from range bands to farm flocks —from west to east; primarily because of economics of production. Large range bands will, for the most part, be limited to those grazing areas that are not well suited to cattle and which are marginal or submarginal for most other agricultural products.

5. Producer profits will be dependent on management.—As in all agriculture, increased production costs appear inevitable, but no comparable long-time rise in the price of lamb and wool is in the offing. Thus, superior management holds the key to profits in the years ahead.

6. Science and technology will increase.—It is predicted that the sheep and wool industry will accelerate experimental work and the application of science and technology. Although those competing meat and fiber producers with a head

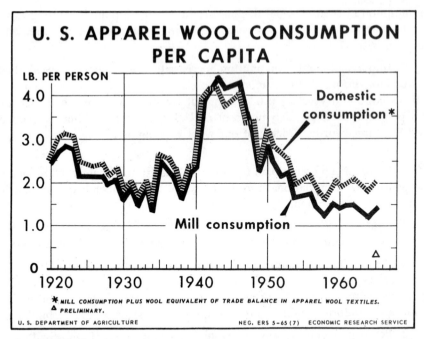

Fig. 23-14.   Per capita consumption of apparel wool increased during World War II, primarily because of meeting military needs. Since then, it has declined due to competition from synthetic fibers. (Courtesy, USDA)

start will not pull up the reins of progress, it is inevitable that, percentage-wise the sheep and wool industry can make greater scientific and technological strides in the immediate future. For example, considerable encouragement can be derived from recent advances in parasite control, thus lessening one of the major handicaps to sheep production. Also, from the standpoint of producing and marketing quality products, it appears that the U.S. sheep industry will emulate, in part, Australian wool production and New Zealand lamb production.

In brief, the future of the sheep business in America is largely dependent upon the industry itself. Significant breakthroughs are needed (1) in increased efficiency—in lambs raised and wool production per ewe, (2) in quality, merchandizing, and promotion of lamb, and (3) in marketing and processing of wool.

QUESTIONS FOR STUDY AND DISCUSSION

1. There are more than 200 distinct breeds of sheep scattered throughout the world. How do you explain the fact that there are more breeds of sheep than there are of cattle and swine?

2. Apparently the wild stocks of sheep were short-tailed and the lengthening of the tail followed domestication. How can you explain the selection of long-tailed sheep?

3. The great plague, or Black Death of 1348 to 1349, served as a great impetus to the sheep industry of England because laborers were scarce and the landlords were forced to do less cultivating and more pasturing. Would such circumstances apply in this era of mechanization?

4. Christmas cards and other Biblical scenes depicting shepherds, watching over their flocks by night, usually show more than one shepherd because the shepherds brought their flocks together at night. Why did they get together at night?

5. Why have sheep numbers increased in many parts of the world since World War II but, simultaneously, declined in the United States?

6. What factors account for Australia holding undisputed claim to being the leading sheep country of the world?

7. Some all-weather bands are being maintained in southwestern United States currently, why?

8. Discuss the future of U.S. lamb and wool imports and production.

9. Where, and under what circumstances, would you recommend (a) that one enter sheep production or (b) that one discontinue sheep production?

SELECTED REFERENCES

Title of Publication	Author(s)	Publisher
America's Sheep Trails	E. N. Wentworth	The Iowa State Press, Ames, Iowa, 1945.
Encyclopaedia Britannica		Encyclopaedia Britannica, Inc., Chicago, Ill.
History of Livestock Raising in the United States, 1607-1860	J. W. Thompson	Agric. History Series No. 5, U.S. Department of Agriculture, Washington, D. C., Nov. 1942.
Our Friendly Animals and Whence They Came	K. P. Schmidt	M. A. Donohue & Co., Chicago, Ill., 1937.
Productive Sheep Husbandry	W. C. Coffey	J. B. Lippincott Co., New York, N. Y., 1937.
Profitable Sheep	S. B. Collins	The Macmillan Company, New York, N. Y., 1956.
Program for Improving Returns of Domestic Sheep Producers, A	McKinsey & Co., Inc., Management Consultants	Report prepared for Sheep Producers, June 1962.
Sheep Book, The	John McKinney	John Wiley & Sons, Inc., New York, N. Y., 1959.
Sheep Production	R. V. Diggins C. E. Bundy	Prentice-Hall, Inc., Englewood Cliffs, N. J., 1958.
Sheep Science	W. G. Kammlade, Sr. W. G. Kammlade, Jr.	J. B. Lippincott Co., New York, N. Y., 1955.

Chapter XXIV

TYPES AND BREEDS OF SHEEP[1]

Contents   **Page**

Classes of Sheep 645
Fine-wool Breeds 646
Medium-wool Breeds 646
Long-wool Breeds 647
Crossbred Wool Breeds 647
Carpet-wool Breeds 648
Fur Sheep Breeds 648
Popularity of Breeds 650
Characteristics of Breeds 650
Questions for Study and Discussion 660
Selected References 660

In no other class of farm animals have so many types and breeds evolved as in sheep. As domestic sheep were improved in various parts of the world, the producers within different geographical areas soon became convinced that the animals under their care possessed special attributes not found in more distant flocks. Out of this thinking has arisen the approximately 200 different breeds of sheep that exist today. Many of these breeds are of little importance in commercial production, with more than three-fourths of the industry of the world based on the use of not more than six breeds. Even so, breed enthusiasts are usually vociferous about the relative merits of their particular breed, no matter how small the numbers.

CLASSES OF SHEEP

Breeds of sheep may be and are classified on several different bases, including (1) their degree of suitability for mutton or wool production (mutton or wool type), (2) color of face (white or black face), (3) presence or absence of horns (horned or polled), (4) topography of the area in which they originated (mountain, upland, or lowland), and (5) type of wool produced. Each system of classification has its special merits, but perhaps a classification based on type of wool produced is as good as any. The following summary shows the

---

[1] Sometimes folks construe the write-up of a breed of livestock in a book or in a U.S. Department of Agriculture bulletin as an official recognition of the breed. Nothing could be further from the truth, for no person or office has authority to approve a breed. The only legal basis for recognizing a breed is contained in the Tariff Act of 1930, which provides for the duty-free admission of purebred breeding stock provided they are registered in the country of origin. But the latter stipulation applies to imported animals only.

In this book, no *official* recognition of any breed is intended or implied. Rather, the author has tried, earnestly and without favoritism, to present the factual story of the breeds in narrative and picture. In particular, such information relative to the new and/or less widely distributed breeds is needed, and often difficult to come by.

most common United States breeds of sheep classed according to type of wool produced:

Fine-Wool Type	Medium Wool Type	Long-Wool Type	Crossbred Wool Type	Carpet-Wool Type	Fur Type
American Merino	Cheviot	Cotswold	Columbia	Black-faced Highland	Karakul
Debouillet	Dorset	Leicester	Corriedale		
Delaine Merino	Hampshire	Lincoln	Panama		
Rambouillet	Montadale	Romney	Tailless or No Tail		
	North Country Cheviot		Targhee		
	Oxford				
	Shropshire				
	Southdown				
	Suffolk				
	Tunis				

In general, all of the breeds listed within each of the six wool-type categories produce wool of a similar character, especially from the standpoint of diameter and length of fibers.

FINE-WOOL BREEDS

The common fine-wool breeds of the United States are the American Merino, Debouillet, Delaine Merino, and Rambouillet. All of these breeds are of Spanish Merino extraction and really represent different types or ideals of Merinos brought about through selection. Because of their common ancestry, therefore, the four breeds still possess many characteristics in common. All of them are noted for fineness of wool and a great amount of yolk; the fleece sometimes loses over 70 per cent in weight in scouring. In general, modern purebred animals of these breeds are of more acceptable mutton conformation than formerly, although they are not equal to the mutton breeds in this respect. The fine-wool breeds are hardy, gregarious, long-lived, and well suited to production under range management methods throughout the world. Also, like the Dorset and Tunis breeds, ewes of the fine-wool breeds will conceive out of season.

MEDIUM-WOOL BREEDS

The Southdown, Shropshire, Oxford, Hampshire, and Suffolk breeds are collectively referred to as the "down" breeds, because of the nature of the country in which they were developed. This area in southern England is a country of hills or downs. The down breeds came into prominence during Bakewell's time. From the beginning, they were bred primarily for mutton, with special emphasis on those characteristics considered important to the nature of the particular grazing lands and climatic conditions as well as on the market demands of the regions in which they were developed. The face and leg color of all the down breeds is some shade of brown or black, and the fleece occupies a middle position between the length and coarseness of the long wools and the extreme fineness and density of the fine wools.

The medium-wool breeds have been popular in the farm-flock regions of the United States, and rams of the larger breeds have been extensively used in market-lamb production on the western ranges.

LONG-WOOL BREEDS

The long-wool breeds, bred chiefly for mutton, are the largest of all sheep. They originated in Great Britain in an era when producers and consumers regarded with favor a large, coarse, slow-maturing sheep that produced long, coarse wool, and which when liberally fed would become very fat. These conditions gave rise to such important breeds as the Cotswold, Leicester, Lincoln, and Romney. All of the long-wool breeds are large framed, have square bodies, and are somewhat rangy in build with conspicuously broad backs. As compared with the fleeces of the fine- or medium-wool breeds, those of the long-wool sheep are open, coarse, and very long.

As their size would indicate, these breeds were developed in level-lying country where feeds were abundant and could be obtained without too much travel.

At the present time, most purebred sheep of the long-wool breeds are considered too slow maturing and big to satisfy the demands of the lamb market. Moreover, their carcasses are quite coarse and overlaid with fat. They are, however, of great value in crossbreeding to improve the weight of wool in other breeds, to increase the size of little sheep, and to increase the finishing qualities of some breeds. It is claimed that the long-wool breeds, especially the Romney, will thrive in regions of excessive rainfall, as the long wool carries the water off the body and does not soak it up as a more dense fleece will do. It is noteworthy, however, that most practical sheepmen caution against keeping sheep on marshy ground.

CROSSBRED WOOL BREEDS[2]

The crossbred breeds, which are descended from a long-wool X fine-wool foundation, produce medium-fine wool and are therefore often classed with the medium-wool breeds. In general, however, the crossbred wool breeds are better adapted to the western range than are their respective parent stocks or any of the medium-wool breeds. Under range conditions, they produce better market lambs and heavier fleeces than the Rambouillet, and they are more active and have superior herding tendencies in comparison with either the long-wool or medium-wool breeds.

---

[2] The listing of the crosses which produced each of the crossbred wool breeds is given in Table 24-2 for purposes of breed history. In no sense does it imply any lack of purity of the respective breeds, or that all of them are new breeds.

For many years, commercial ranchers have been crossing long-wool rams on grade fine-wool ewes in an effort to secure larger ewes that would yield more wool and produce heavier and superior market lambs. The results were often variable. Sometimes the mutton qualities would be improved but the wool would be coarse; whereas at other times the wool yield would be greater, but the mutton qualities would be disappointing.

Despite the lack of uniformity, most commercial sheepmen of the West preferred this method to the system of alternating in the use of black-faced and fine-wool rams. Topping the band with black-faced rams produced an excellent market lamb; but because of lack of the herding instinct, poor fleeces, and other deficiencies, the resulting crossbred ewe lambs were not suitable for flock replacements. In order to get desirable replacements, therefore, fine-wool rams had to be used at intervals, with the result that the wether lambs of this breeding did not meet market demands. Thus, the need was for a type of sheep which would eliminate the ram problem that invariably plagued sheepmen in the alternative use of black-faced and fine-wool rams and which would produce lambs suitable for either market or replacement purposes. Such was the need, and out of this need arose the Columbia, Corriedale, Panama, and Targhee breeds of sheep—all descended from long-wool X fine-wool foundations.

CARPET-WOOL BREEDS

Wools used in the manufacture of carpets and rugs in the United States are imported from New Zealand and Argentina, where the native sheep possess a coarse, wiry, tough fleece. Most American wools are too fine to be used in carpets. If so used, they would mat down and wear very rapidly. Carpet wools are quite variable, ranging from 1 to 13 inches in length and from 15 to 70 microns in diameter. In addition, carpet wools show a tremendous range of luster, strength, crimp, and resilience. Although several foreign breeds of sheep produce carpet wools, the only carpet-wool breeds known to most people in this country are the Black-faced Highland and the Karakul; and the latter breed is primarily kept for fur production (the production of carpet wool being somewhat incidental from mature breeding stock). The Karakul is herein discussed as a fur sheep.

FUR SHEEP BREEDS

New processes have resulted in the use for fur of pelts obtained from many breeds of sheep. Except for the Karakul, however, all the other breeds of sheep are still kept primarily for lamb and wool production; and any fur production is secondary.

Karakul sheep are bred primarily because of the suitability of the lamb pelts for fur production. The majority of Karakul lambskins are produced in Bokhara (U.S.S.R.), Afghanistan (Herat), Southwest Africa, Bessarabia, Shiraz (Iran), Baghdad and Salzfelle (Iraq), and India. The best-grade lambskins come from Bokhara, the country in which the Karakul breed originated.

In order of their value, the pelts are classified as follows:

1. **Broadtail.**—This is the most valuable, although its production is comparatively small. It is produced from prematurely born or stillborn lambs, and in some instances from those killed within a few hours after birth. The hair is undeveloped, grows in different directions, and reflects light, giving the pelt its moire appearance (moire means watery design).

Such premature deaths are not forced but are the result of accidents, such as abortions.

2. **Persian lamb.**—This type of fur is next in value and comes from Karakul lambs 3 to 10 days old. It has a tight lustrous curl that must be watched carefully from the time the lamb is born, for the curl is likely to open rapidly after the fifth day; and while the value of the pelt increases with size, it is essential that the curl remain tight.

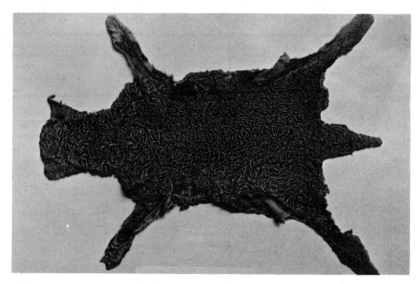

Fig. 24-1. A Persian lamb pelt properly dried (not shaped) and cleaned for shipment and sale. (Courtesy, Lowry Hagerman, Santa Fe, New Mexico)

3. **Caracul.**—Caracul, spelled with a "C," is a trade name given to the lustrous open-type of fur that shows a wavy moire pattern free from close curls.

Caracul skins are light in weight and are best if removed when lambs are not more than two weeks old. But this type of pelt does not deteriorate so rapidly with growth as do those of either the broadtail or Persian lamb types. Caracul is the least valuable of the three types of pelts.

Within each of these three groups, there are different grades of pelts, depending upon quality, tightness of curl, luster, pattern, color, and general appearance. As would be expected, the price varies with the type and quality of the fur and with the supply and demand.

As is true in making any fur garment when the smaller furs are involved, large numbers of pelts are required for proper matching. For this reason, it is often difficult to sell small numbers of pelts to advantage.

POPULARITY OF BREEDS

Table 24-1 shows the 1965 and total registrations to date of the common breeds of sheep. Although the annual figures for 1965 are probably more meaningful at the present time than the all-time registrations, it is recognized that one year's data fail to show trends.

TABLE 24—1

1965 AND TOTAL REGISTRATIONS OF SHEEP IN
U.S. BREED ASSOCIATIONS

Breed	1965 Registrations	Total Registrations
Suffolk[1]	31,852	531,359
Hampshire	25,901	1,231,535
Corriedale	13,071	357,036
Southdown	9,193	356,222
Columbia	7,260	165,000
Dorset	6,390	166,367
Shropshire	6,333	1,287,121
Rambouillet	5,252	658,792
Cheviot	3,356	131,766
Montadale	2,832	49,800
Oxford	1,582	228,252
Delaine Merino[2]	1,407	79,806
Romney	1,135	60,369
Debouillet	747	13,911
Targhee	701	5,133
Lincoln	341	73,994
Cotswold	135	
Tunis	128	9,000

[1]Includes: National Suffolk Sheep Assn., 1965=21,372 and total=298,722 registrations; American Suffolk Sheep Soc., 1965=10,480 and total=232,637 registrations.
[2]Includes: Texas Delaine-Merino Assn., 1965=1,111 and total=71,177, and American and Delaine Merino Record, 1965= 296 and total=8,629 registrations.

CHARACTERISTICS OF BREEDS

The characteristics of the different breeds of sheep are summarized in Table 24-2.

TABLE 24—2

BREEDS OF SHEEP AND THEIR CHARACTERISTICS

Breed	Place of Origin	Color; Face, Ears, and Legs	Head Characteristics	Other Distinguishing Characteristics	Disqualifications
(Classified by type of wool produced)[1]					
Fine-Wool Breeds:					
American Merino	Spain	White. Reddish-brown spots may occasion-ally appear on lips, ears, and pasterns.	Most rams have horns, but there are some polled strains.	Distinguished from the Delaine Merinos by more skin wrinkles; the more wrinkled American Merinos being the "A" and "B" types. Strong flocking instinct. Ewes will breed out of season.	
Debouillet	On the Amos Dee Jones ranches of Roswell and Tatum, New Mexico. Ass'n organized in 1954.	White	Rams may have horns, but there are also polled strains; open face.	Comparatively smooth body; long staple.	Failure to pass inspection.
Delaine Merino	Spain	White. Reddish-brown spots may occasion-ally appear on lips, ears, and pasterns.	Most rams have horns, but there are some polled strains.	Comparatively smooth bodied; of the "C" type. Strong flocking instinct. Ewes will breed out of season.	
Rambouillet	France	White, brownish, or black spots are sometimes present, but discriminated against.	Most rams have horns, but there are some polled strains. Ewes are hornless.	The largest fine wool breed. Strong flocking instinct. Ewes will breed out of season.	Less than 2 normal sized testicles descended in the scrotum, short or long jaws, rolled eyelids, inverted teats, black spots or black fibers in the fleece, excess pigmentation in the hooves, broken-down pasterns, any serious bone deformity, or any other defect which will limit the animal's usefulness.
Medium-Wool Breeds:					
Cheviot	Scotland; in the Cheviot Hills between Scotland and England.	White face with a black nose. Often black spots are on the ears.	Both sexes are polled.	Stylish, alert, and active. Head and legs free from wool.	Black spots other than ears. Overshot or undershot jaw.
Dorset	England; especially in the southern countries of Dorset and Sumerset.	White and practically free from wool.	There are horned and polled strains, both of which are registered by The Continental Dorset Club. Except for the presence or absence of horns, the two strains are identical.	Ewes will breed out of season.	Black spots on body, legs, and face.
Hampshire	England; in the south-central county of Hampshire.	Rich deep brown, approaching black.	Both sexes are hornless, although rams sometimes have scurs.	Large size; early maturity.	Horns; short or long jaw; abnormal testicles; inverted eyelids.

Footnote at end of table.

(Continued)

TABLE 24—2 (Continued)

Breed	Place of Origin	Color; Face, Ears, and Legs	Head Characteristics	Other Distinguishing Characteristics	Disqualifications
Montadale (Columbia X Cheviot)	U.S.; by E.H. Mattingly, St. Louis, Missouri.	White	Both sexes are polled.	Face and legs free from wool.	Horns. Brown hair or spots on face, ears or legs. Black spots in the wool.
North Country Cheviot	In Scotland, from the old Long Hill sheep, but with infusion of Merino, Ryeland, and Southdown blood in formative period.	White	Nose straight to slightly Roman. Rams are sometimes horned.	Wool grades 50's to 56's mature rams weigh up to 300 pounds and mature ewes up to 200 pounds.	
Oxford	England; in the south-central county of Oxford.	Variable, from gray to brown.	Both sexes are polled. Topknot of wool.	Largest of the Down breeds.	Black fiber; stub horns.
Shropshire	England; in the central western counties of Shropshire and Stafford.	Dark face, but a gray nose is not objectionable.	Both sexes are polled, although rams frequently have scurs.	Covering of dense wool well over the poll.	Such lack of type as to render the identity of the breed doubtful; horns or stubs (not scurs); overshot or undershot jaws.
Southdown	England; in the south-eastern county of Sussex.	Light or mouse brown color preferred.	Both sexes are polled, although rams sometimes have scurs.	Superior conformation and quality of carcass.	Horns; dark poll; speckled markings on face, ears, and legs; one testicle only; black or brown fleece.
Suffolk	England; in the south-eastern counties of Suffolk, Essex, and Norfolk.	Very black head, ears, and legs.	Both sexes are polled, although rams frequently have scurs.	The head and ears are entirely free from wool.	
Tunis (or American Tunis)	Asia; in Tunis.	Reddish brown to bright tan.	Both sexes are polled; long, drooping ears; head free from wool.	Originally, it was a fat-tailed sheep, which means that the tail was distinctly broad and fat. However, breeders have selected away from this trait. Pendulous ears. Will mate almost any season of the year.	Horns; red or black wool; one testicle; undershot or overshot jaw.
Long-Wool Breeds:					
Cotswold	England; in the Cotswold hills of Gloucestershire.	White, although grayish specks and bluish tinge are common.	Both sexes are polled, although rams frequently have scurs.	The natural wavy ringlets or curls in which the fleece hangs all over the body. The tuft of wool on the forehead. Second only to the Lincoln in size.	
Leicester	England; in the central county of Leicester.	White, but may have a bluish tinge or black spots.	Both sexes are polled.		
Lincoln	England; along the eastern coast of England and bordering the North Sea, in Lincolnshire.	White. Black spots may be present but are discriminated against.	Both sexes are polled.	The largest of all breeds of sheep. Produces the heaviest fleece of any mutton breed.	

Footnote at end of table.

(Continued)

TABLE 24—2 (Continued)

Breed	Place of Origin	Color; Face, Ears, and Legs	Head Characteristics	Other Distinguishing Characteristics	Disqualifications
Romney	England; in the Romney Marsh region of the County of Kent.	White	Both sexes are polled.	In comparison with other long-wool breeds; the Romney is shorter legged, more rugged, and its fleece is shorter, finer, and less open.	
Crossbred Wool Breeds[1]					
Columbia (Lincoln rams, Rambouillet ewes)	United States; in Wyoming and Idaho.	White	Both sexes are polled.	Open-faced, with no tendency to wool blindness.	Horns or scurs; wool blindness; uneven or light fleece; overshot or undershot jaw; colored wool; excessive folds.
Corriedale (Lincoln and Leicester rams, Merino ewes)	New Zealand	White, although black spots are sometimes present.	Both sexes are polled.		Black or brown spots. Wool blindness. Malformed mouth. Horns.
Panama (Rambouillet rams, Lincoln ewes)	United States; by Laidlaw and Brockie of Muldoon, Idaho.	White	Both sexes are polled.		Horns, scurs, or knobs; overshot or undershot mouth; excessive folds or wrinkles; colored wool; colored spots larger than 3/4 in. in diameter on clear areas; any unsound hereditary factor.
Tailless (or No Tail)	South Dak. Agric. Expt. Sta.	White	Both sexes are polled.	Usually produce tailless offspring.	
Targhee (Rambouillet rams, Lincoln-Rambouillet-Corriedale ewes)	United States; by the USDA at Dubois, Idaho.	White	Both sexes are polled.	Open-faced.	Marked scurs or horns. Noticeable coarseness of wool on the britch or tail. Noticeable defects.
Carpet-Wool Breed:					
Black-faced Highland (or Scottish Black face)	Scotland; in the highland country.	Black or mottled.	Both sexes have horns.	Striking stylish appearance. Fleece consists of long coarse outer-coat and a finer inner-coat.	
Fur-Sheep Breed:					
Karakul	Asia; in the county of Bokhara (USSR).	Black or brown.	Rams have horns, but ewes are hornless.	Drooping ears. A fat-tailed sheep. Lamb pelts suitable for fur production.	

[1]The listing of the crosses which produced each of the "crossbred-wool breeds" is given for breed history purposes only, and does not imply any lack of purity of the respective breeds. Nor does it indicate that all of them are new breeds: for example, the Corriedale, which is an old breed, was originated in New Zealand about 1880.

Fig. 24-3. Debouillet sheep on the range. (Courtesy, Debouillet Sheep Breeders Assn.)

Fig. 24-2. Merino ewe of "C" type, sometimes referred to as the smooth or Delaine Merino. (Courtesy, USDA)

Fig. 24-4. This impressive Rambouillet ram weighed 275 pounds soon after dropping his lamb teeth. Bred by Miles Pierce, Alpine, Texas. (Courtesy, The American Rambouillet Sheep Breeders Assn.)

Fig. 24-5. A champion Cheviot ewe at the Royal Winter Fair, Toronto, Canada. The Cheviot is a beautiful and distinctive sheep, especially noted for its style and alertness. The face and legs are open and covered with soft, white hairs. (Courtesy, Canadian Sheep Breeders' Assn.)

Fig. 24-6. A champion Dorset ram. The face and legs are practically free from wool and white in color. (Courtesy, *Sheep Breeder and Sheepman*)

Fig. 24-7. A Polled Dorset ram, at two years of age. Except for the absence of horns, they are identical to the horned strain. (Courtesy, The Continental Dorset Club, Inc.)

Fig. 24-8. Grand Champion Hampshire ewe at the International Livestock Exposition, Chicago; bred and owned by Iowa State University, Ames, Iowa. (Courtesy, The American Hampshire Sheep Assn.)

Fig. 24-9. Grand Champion Montadale yearling ram. Bred by Audry Head, Snyder, Texas. Sold for $1,700 to D. H. Sutton, Delaware, Ohio. (Courtesy, Montadale Sheep Breeders' Assn., Inc.)

Fig. 24-10. Champion Oxford ewe at the Michigan State Fair. The most distinguishing characteristic of the Oxford is its great size; it is the largest of the medium-wool breeds. (Courtesy, American Oxford Down Record Assn.)

Fig. 24-11. Champion Shropshire ewe at the 1965 International Livestock Exposition, Chicago; bred and exhibited by Robert C. Thurman, Tipp City, Ohio. (Courtesy, The American Shropshire Registry Assn., Inc.)

Fig. 24-12. The Grand Champion Wether—a Southdown—over all breeds at the International Livestock Exposition, Chicago; bred and exhibited by Iowa State University, Ames, Iowa. (Courtesy, Iowa State University)

Fig. 24-13. Champion Suffolk ram. (Courtesy, American Suffolk Sheep Registry)

Fig. 24-14. Tunis yearling ram. First prize yearling ram at the New York State Fair. Exhibited by James McGuire, Oakfield, New York. The Tunis is characterized by pendulous ears. (Courtesy, James McGuire, Oakfield, N. Y.)

Fig. 24-15. A champion Cotswold ram at Royal Winter Fair, Toronto, Canada. The most distinctive characteristics of the Cotswold breed are the natural wavy ringlets or curls in which the fleece hangs all over the body and the tuft of wool on the forehead. (Courtesy, Canadian Sheep Breeders' Assn.)

Fig. 24-16. A yearling Border Leicester ram bred in Scotland. The Border Leicester is distinguished from the English Leicester in that there is no wool on any part of the head; the ears are more erect and alert; the face is cleaner cut and more refined; and the wool is shorter, denser, and has a purled or twisted tip. (Courtesy, Canadian Sheep Breeders' Assn.)

Fig. 24-17. Three times Champion Lincoln ram at the Chicago International. Owned by Ralph and Janice Shaffer, Fair Haven Farm, West Milton, Ohio. The Lincoln is reputed to be the heaviest breed of sheep in the world. (Courtesy, National Lincoln Sheep Breeders' Assn.)

Fig. 24-18. A Romney ram. Shorter legged and more rugged than the other long-wool breeds, the Romney is reputed to thrive in areas of heavy rainfall and on low, wet land. (Courtesy, American Romney Breeders' Assn.)

Fig. 24-19. Champion Columbia ram at the National Columbia Show and Sale; bred by Mark Bradford, Spanish Fork, Utah, and sold to Hartley Stock Farm, Page, North Dakota, for $3,525. The Columbia is an open, white-faced breed. It was developed primarily for the better ranges of the West, but its distribution is nation-wide. (Courtesy, Columbia Sheep Breeders Assn. of America)

Fig. 24-21. A Panama ram lamb, bred by Tom Bell, Rupert, Idaho. The Panama is a white, open-faced breed—closely resembling the Columbia. (Courtesy, University of Idaho)

Fig. 24-20. Grand Champion Corriedale ewe, International Livestock Exposition, Chicago; exhibited by the University of Wyoming, Laramie, Wyoming. (Courtesy, American Corriedale Assn., Inc.)

Fig. 24-22. Tailless or "no tail" sheep, developed by South Dakota State University. If this program is successful, as it now gives promise of being, it will eliminate the necessity of docking lambs of this breed. (Courtesy, South Dakota State College)

Fig. 24-23. Targhee ram, bred and owned by the U.S. Sheep Experiment Station, Dubois, Idaho. The Targhee is a white-faced, polled breed of intermediate size developed primarily for use on the intermediate ranges of the West. (Courtesy U.S. Sheep Experiment Station, Dubois, Idaho)

Fig. 24-24. Black-faced Highland ram. This animal was bred by David Provan, Gateside, Douglas, Lanark, Scotland; and sold by auction in the Lanark Ram sale to Messrs. Ben Wilson, John Lammie, and James Anderson for $9,000. Note the spiraled horns and style. (Courtesy, David Provan of Scotland)

Fig. 24-25. A yearling Karakul ram. Karakul lambs are eminently adapted for fur production, but the wool of mature animals is of low market quality—grading carpet wool—and the breed is of poor mutton type. (Courtesy, USDA)

QUESTIONS FOR STUDY AND DISCUSSION

1. List the (a) distinguishing characteristics and (b) disqualifications of each breed of sheep. Discuss the importance of each.
2. Obtain breed registry association literature and a sample copy of a magazine of your favorite breed of sheep. (See Appendix Tables VI and VII for addresses.) Evaluate the soundness and value of the material that you receive.
3. Justify any preference that you may have for one particular breed of sheep.
4. What need(s) prompted the development of the Columbia, Corriedale, Panama, and Targhee breeds of sheep?
5. How did the Polled Dorset breed evolve?

SELECTED REFERENCES

Title of Publication	Author(s)	Publisher
Breeds of Livestock, The	C. W. Gay	The Macmillan Company, New York, N. Y., 1918.
Breeds of Livestock in America	H. W. Vaughn	R. G. Adams Co., Columbus, Ohio, 1937.
British Purebred Sheep		Nat'l Sheep Breeders' Assn., 5 King St., London, W.C. 2, England.
Karakul Sheep	C. G. Potts V. L. Simmons	Farmer's Bul. 1632, U.S. Department of Agriculture, Washington, D. C., 1938.
Modern Breeds of Livestock	H. M. Briggs	The Macmillan Company, New York, N. Y., 1958.
Productive Sheep Husbandry	W. C. Coffey	J. B. Lippincott Co., New York, N. Y., 1937.
Sheep Production	R. V. Diggins C. E. Bundy	Prentice-Hall, Inc., Englewood Cliffs, N. J., 1958.
Sheep Production	L. J. Horlacher	McGraw-Hill Book Co., New York, N. Y., 1927.
Sheep Science	W. G. Kammlade, Sr. W. G. Kammlade, Jr.	J. B. Lippincott Co., New York, N. Y., 1955.
Stockman's Handbook The	M. E. Ensminger	The Interstate Printers & Publishers, Inc., Danville, Ill., 1969.
Study of Breeds in America, The	Thomas Shaw	Orange Judd Co., New York, N. Y., 1900.
Types and Breeds of Farm Animals	C. S. Plumb	Ginn and Co., Boston, Mass., 1920.
World Dictionary of Breeds, Types and Varieties of Livestock, A	I. L. Mason	Commonwealth Agric. Bureaux Slough, Bucks, England, 1951.

Also, breed literature pertaining to each breed may be secured by writing to the respective breed registry associations (see Sec. VI, Appendix. for the name and address of each association).

CHAPTER XXV

ESTABLISHING THE FLOCK; SELECTING AND JUDGING SHEEP

Contents   Page

Factors to Consider in Establishing the Flock....................661
  Purebreds, Crossbreds, or Grades..................662
  Native or Western Ewes...................662
  Selection of the Breed...................662
  Size of the Flock or Band...................663
  Time to Start...................663
  Uniformity 664
  Health 664
  Age 664
  Soundness of Udder...................664
  Size 664
  Price 665
Selection and Its Bases...................665
  Selection Based on Type or Individuality...................666
  Selection Based on Pedigree...................666
  Selection Based on Show-Ring Winnings...................667
  Selection Based on Production Testing...................667
Flock Improvement Through Selection...................667
Judging Sheep 668
  Parts of a Sheep...................668
  Ideal Mutton-type and Conformation...................668
  Ideal Fleece-type and Conformation...................670
  Recognizing and Evaluating Common Faults...................670
  Method of Examining...................670
  Catching and Handling Sheep...................672
  Determining the Age of Sheep...................672
Questions for Study and Discussion...................674
Selected References 675

Whether a large range operation or a small farm flock is being established or maintained, consideration must be given to certain factors if the venture is to be successful. In the final analysis, sheep are maintained for the production of market lambs and wool. This means that each individual in the flock should possess those characteristics making for maximum and efficient production of these two products. Furthermore, if progress is to be made in the breeding program, each succeeding generation must represent an improvement over the parent stock.

FACTORS TO CONSIDER IN ESTABLISHING THE FLOCK

The factors to consider in establishing a flock of sheep are not unlike those that the stockman must face in establishing a herd of cattle, hogs, or horses. They are, however, somewhat more confused because (1) two major products are involved—lamb and wool—instead of one, and (2) there are more breeds from which to select, and the practice of crossbreeding is more prevalent.

Purebreds, Crossbreds, or Grades

Generally speaking, only the experienced breeder should undertake the production of purebreds with the intent eventually of furnishing foundation or replacement stock to other purebred breeders or purebred rams to the commercial producer. Unless prices are unusually favorable, the beginner should start with crossbred or grade ewes and a purebred ram. The vast majority of range operators, most of whom are capable sheep specialists, elect to keep bands of high-grade ewes that are mated to purebred rams.

Native or Western Ewes

Native ewes are those that are produced outside of the western range area, and that show a predominance of mutton-type breeding. Western ewes are those that are produced in the range area, and that either show a predominance of fine-wool breeding or represent fine-wool X long-wool crossbred types.

In starting a farm flock, the question often arises as to whether native or western ewes should be purchased. Both types of ewes are found in flocks throughout the country and may well be considered by the beginner. In general, western ewes are more uniform, smaller in size, less costly, and less likely to be infested with parasites. On the other hand, native ewes are larger, and produce a larger lamb. If they are bought locally, a saving in price may be effected. In purchasing native ewes, however, the buyer should make very certain that he is not obtaining the cull ewes (shy breeders and ewes with unsound udders or other defects) from one or several flocks. From this standpoint, the purchase of yearlings affords the best protection.

For range operations, where a large number of animals are to be handled in one or more bands, grade ewes of fine-wool breeding or ewes of the fine-wool X long-wool crossbred type are essential.

Selection of the Breed

Within certain limitations, preference is usually the deciding factor in the selection of a breed. As already noted, however, there is good reason that most commercial bands of the West should carry considerable fine-wool breeding (chiefly because of the herding instinct in the animals). Except for this situation, sheep producers of this country have given little consideration to possible special-area adaptations of the different breeds. English sheep breeders, on the other hand, have long contended that some breeds are peculiarly adapted to certain conditions. This conviction springs from the fact that the several English breeds were developed in different geographical areas, each of which had different climatic, soil, and crop conditions.

According to English breeders, the small and more active breeds of sheep that were developed in the hill country of England are not adapted to the lowland region, whereas the large and more sluggish breeds developed in the fertile lowland areas will not thrive on the uplands. Moreover, the Romney breed is said to thrive better than any other breed in marsh areas similar to those of its native home in southern England.

Unfortunately, there is little experimental work either to substantiate or refute these contentions relative to environmental adaptations of breeds. It is interesting to note, however, that on the USDA Experiment Station at Dubois, Idaho, two crossbred breeds of sheep have been developed—the larger Columbias for the lush ranges of the West and the smaller Targhees for the average ranges. It is also a well-known fact that for the production of hothouse lambs, the ewes must breed out of season and milk well. This limits the production of hothouse lambs to ewes of Dorset, Tunis, Rambouillet, or Merino breeding.

In so large and variable a country as the United States, it would appear quite probable that some breeds would be better adapted to certain conditions than others. It is also quite likely that rather wide differences in environmental adaptations may exist within breeds. Perhaps there is need for experimental work to determine these differences, if any, but it must be recognized that (1) breed preference is, and should remain, a powerful factor in the selection of a breed and (2) it is difficult, if not impossible, to obtain a representative cross section of a widely disseminated breed of sheep for experimental study.

Size of the Flock or Band

The unit of sheep management varies all the way from a small farm flock consisting of a few head to a large range band with as many as 3,500 head. Usually, the farm flock is merely a part of a diversified type of farm enterprise, whereas several range bands may constitute a highly specialized type of operation with little or no diversification.

Small farm flocks are variable in size, ranging from a few head to as many as 300 to 500 or more. In determining the size of the farm flock, it is to be noted that the labor and equipment cost, except at lambing time, differs very little whether the flock numbers 12 or 50. The smaller flock will require the services of one ram and practically the same amount of fencing to provide rotation of pastures or suitable corrals away from dogs. Furthermore, fewer sheep are much more likely to receive the neglect often accorded a minor enterprise.

On the other hand, the beginner can acquire valuable, practical experience with a very small flock without subjecting a large flock to the possible hazards that frequently accompany inexperience. In range operations, the size of the band varies somewhat according to the method of management, the general character of the country, and the season of the year. The number of bands run by a given operator is usually determined by the amount of range and capital available.

Time to Start

Late summer, after the lambs have been weaned and before the ewes are bred, is usually the best time in which to start in the sheep business. At this season of the year, it is generally possible to buy some of the surplus ewes from neighboring farmers or ranchers or to obtain a wide selection of ewes from the terminal markets. Ewes can usually be purchased at reasonable prices at this period, and for the beginner there is a period of valuable training prior to lambing time. Also, there is usually an abundance of meadows, grain stubble land, and other forage available on the farm or ranch that will make it possible to get the ewes in good thrifty condition prior to breeding time. Then, too, the purchase of a uniform flock of ewes makes possible the intelligent selection of the ram and the production of lambs with uniformity of type and quality.

Uniformity

In order to produce uniform market lambs and wool, it is first desirable that the ewe flock selected be uniform—preferably from the standpoint of breeding, size, body conformation, and fleece grade and quality. Such uniformity is of decided advantage in the marketing of products at premium prices. Also, the constructive sheepman is able to select more wisely a ram or rams for most successful mating with a uniform flock or band of ewes.

Health

All ewes selected should be in a thrifty, vigorous condition. They should have every appearance of a life of usefulness ahead of them and give every evidence of being capable of producing a good fleece and raising strong, healthy lambs. Animals showing dark blue skins, paleness or lack of coloring in the lining of the nose and eyelids, listlessness or a lack of vigor, and a general run-down condition should be regarded with suspicion.

Age

The vast majority of sheepmen prefer to establish a flock by acquiring yearling ewes that are bred to lamb when approximately 24 months of age. When it can be made certain that culls are not being secured, however, older ewes are frequently the best buy. Sometimes it is to the advantage of a farmer to secure range ewes that have one to two years of usefulness left, provided that they are placed under conditions where (1) less traveling is required, (2) the pastures are more abundant, and (3) more attention is given to winter feed.

Soundness of Udder

In selecting ewes, particular attention should be given to the udder and teats. The udder should be soft and pliable and the teats normal. Ewes having hard or pendulous udders, teats that have been removed through careless shearing, or meaty or abnormally large teats should be rejected.

Size

There is great variation in the size of the different breeds of sheep, extending all the way from the small, refined Southdowns to the large, ponderous Lincolns. The rank and file of commercial sheep producers in this country prefer an animal with considerable size, because, based on experience, it has been found that such animals are more profitable from the standpoint of the net receipts derived from the usual combination of lamb and wool production. This is due to the fact that, in general, the cost of handling sheep is on a per-head rather than on a per-pound basis, and our markets are not sufficiently discriminating in the purchase of lamb and wool to warrant any great sacrifice in quantity in favor of quality production. On the other hand, an exception exists when a premium is paid for early-maturing, high-quality lambs, such as in hothouse lamb production. Under the latter conditions, it is preferable to use early-maturing, mutton-type rams on medium-sized ewes. Also, where feed is sparse and sheep are run with a minimum of care, smaller sheep may be preferable, as they often are more efficient than larger animals.

In an effort to secure more size on the lush ranges of northwestern United States, many commercial operators are keeping crossbred type ewes, based on long-wool X fine-wool crosses. Moreover, larger grade ewes of Rambouillet extraction have always been more popular on the western ranges than the smaller ewes of Merino breeding.

Price

The price of breeding sheep must be based upon the projected price of the products of production—lamb and wool. Although it is usually sound business to pay a premium for quality foundation stock, it must be remembered that the ultimate objective of all sheep production is profitable market-lamb and wool production; thus, the price should be governed accordingly.

SELECTION AND ITS BASES

The criteria used in selecting an individual or group of sheep or lambs will vary according to the use for which the animal or animals are intended. In general, commercial farmers or ranchers select sheep or lambs for the following purposes: (1) breeding sheep, with market lambs as the primary objective; (2) breeding sheep, with wool production as the chief objective; (3) feeder lambs for further finishing; or (4) finished lambs to send to the market. Thus, where market-lamb production is the main consideration, primary attention is given to those factors that will result in the production of a heavy, finished lamb of acceptable type and grade. When sheep are maintained chiefly for wool production, the clean weight and quality of fleece are of paramount importance. Feeder lambs are selected on the basis of desirable type and quality, health and thrift, and projected gains and finish with feeding. Slaughter lambs are selected out for the market, using finish, conformation, and quality as the criteria in determining value. The experienced operator can determine the degree of finish of sheep by touch, by rapidly applying the palm of the hand to the animals being examined as they file through a cutting chute.

Purebred breeders may add certain breed fancy points and highly prized pedigrees to the above considerations, and market specialists find it necessary to add other considerations in arriving at the rather imposing list of market classes and grades of sheep. It is not intended, therefore, that the amateur may become proficient as a sheep judge through merely reading about the subject. There is no shortcut or substitute for long years of patient practice.

In establishing a new flock or improving an old one, however, there are four bases of selection: (1) selection based on type or individuality, (2) selection based on pedigree, (3) selection based on show-ring winnings, and (4) selection based on production testing.

Selection Based on Type or Individuality

A vast majority of sheep, both purebred and commercial animals, are selected on the basis of type or individuality. In limited instances, three additional criteria may be available and invoked effectively; namely, pedigree, show ring, and production selection. Although production selection offers a new and modern approach to animal improvement and pedigree selection may be a valuable guide in certain instances, perhaps for many years to come selection will continue to be based largely on individuality. Without doubt, however, the progressive sheep producer of the future will at least make increased use of production-tested rams. Despite the greater certainty and more rapid progress afforded through selection based on production, it is well to note in retrospect that we have traveled a long way in sheep improvement—from the rather poor mutton type and average 2-pound clips of the sheep characteristic of General Washington's time to the modern sheep of today.

The judging of sheep—their selection based on individuality—differs materially from the judging of cattle, hogs, or horses because of the presence of the fleece. Not only must an additional characteristic of economic importance be considered, but the presence of the fleece makes it more difficult to determine the body type. This is especially true when the animal has been subjected to the blocking art of a clever shepherd, but the problem exists whenever there is any appreciable wool growth. Even though complete production records are not available, the progressive sheepman can arrive at sufficient evaluation to enable him to (1) cull the dry ewes, (2) remove wool-blind ewes and rams, and (3) sort out the light-fleeced animals by the "touch method" or according to actual fleece weights. This type of selection directly affects the income, even though it may not be very important genetically.

Selection Based on Pedigree

Without doubt, less attention is paid to pedigree selection and family names in sheep than in any other class of farm animals. It is a rare occurrence, indeed, to find a commercial sheepman who has any concern about the ancestry of the rams that he is contemplating purchasing. Although most purebred breeders are interested in the pedigree of stud rams, there is comparatively little interest in the ancestry of the flock ewes. In some respects, this relative lack of interest in pedigrees on the part of sheep breeders is fortunate, for breeding programs have not been subjected to the hazards of worshiping family names or of selecting a breeding animal chiefly because its ancestry traces to some noted ancestor many generations removed. On the other hand, it must be recognized that fancy pedigrees may have sales value from the standpoint of the purebred breeder.

Selection Based on Show-Ring Winnings

There can be no question that the great livestock shows of the land have been a profound influence in establishing type in the different breeds of sheep. It might well be added, however, that when utilitarian considerations have been ignored, their influence has not always been for the good. A prime example of the latter point is the face covering that has been bred into certain of the mutton breeds of sheep. This has caused the affected breeds to diminish in importance and numbers, because, through sad experience, the practical operator has found that ewes subject to wool blindness produce less market lamb and wool. Utility value, therefore, should always come first and breed fancy points, second.

Winning rams and ewes and their progeny are usually in great demand, with the result that they generally bring premium prices. Provided that the type has been established wisely and is based on utilitarian considerations, the purebred breeder may find it desirable and profitable to select some animals on the basis of show-ring winnings.

Selection Based on Production Testing

The relative merits of (1) performance testing and (2) progeny testing have been presented in Chapter II; and traits of importance in testing sheep and suggested records are given in Chapter XXVII. At this point, it may be well to emphasize that the importance attached to each trait will vary in different areas. For example, in southwestern United States, where wool production is relatively more important than lamb production, greater stress should be placed upon selecting animals whose progeny possess the maximum in fleece weight and quality. On the other hand, in those areas where feed is more abundant and approximately two-thirds of the annual income is derived from the sale of lamb, evaluations should be based largely on the market weight, type, and finish of the offspring.

Production selection should be given greater emphasis in animal improvement, for, in most instances, it is production—of which individuality or type is merely a part—that produces the income. Also, again and again, it should be emphasized that selection based on either performance testing or progeny testing is far more accurate than any other method of selection.

FLOCK IMPROVEMENT THROUGH SELECTION

Once the flock or band has been established, improvement can be obtained only through constant, rigid culling and careful selection of replacements. Such procedure makes the flock more profitable from the standpoint of quantity and quality lamb and wool production and affords a means of accomplishing genetic gain in the next generation.

JUDGING SHEEP

Since the general requisites in judging, which are similar with all classes of livestock, are fully covered in Chapter XI, repetition at this point is not necessary.

The judging of sheep differs from the judging of cattle or swine in that two products of economic importance are involved instead of one. That is, in addition to meat production, wool is a valuable product. The situation is made more difficult because body conformation is often difficult to determine because of the wool under which it is hidden. The latter situation is accentuated when sheep are subjected to the art of blocking by a clever shepherd.

Parts of a Sheep

The first step in preparation for judging sheep consists of mastering the language that describes and locates the different parts of the animal. Figure 25-1 sets forth this information.

Fig. 25-1. Parts of a sheep. The first step in preparation for judging sheep consists in mastering the language that describes and locates the different parts of the animal. (Drawing by R. F. Johnson)

1. Mouth	8. Breast	15. Thigh	22. Ribs
2. Nostril	9. Top of shoulder	16. Hock	23. Fore flank
3. Face	10. Back	17. Hind leg	24. Fore leg
4. Forehead	11. Loin	18. Dew claw	25. Shoulder
5. Eye	12. Hip	19. Foot	
6. Ear	13. Rump	20. Hind flank	
7. Neck	14. Dock	21. Belly	

Ideal Mutton-type and Conformation

The second requisite of a successful judge of any class of livestock is that he have clearly in mind an ideal or standard of perfection. Thus, the sheepman, regardless of whether he is producing purebred or commercial animals or whether he is a farm-flock or range-band operator, should have a type or ideal in mind and make his selections accordingly. For the mutton-type breeds, and when the production of market lambs is the primary objective, this ideal means plenty of size; good width; depth and compactness of body; a short, wide head

Hampshire ewe----mutton type

Rambouillet ram----fleece type

Fig. 25-2. The successful sheep judge must have clearly in mind an ideal or standard of perfection. The ideal mutton-type is more blocky and shorter legged than the ideal fleece-type. Also, when the production of wool is the main source of income, weight and quality of fleece are of the utmost importance.

with large, clear eyes; a short, thick neck; a wide, deep chest; good spring of rib; lowness in both fore and rear flank; a wide, strong back; width and thickness through the loin; length and levelness over the rump; a large leg of mutton; plenty of bone on which to stand; straight legs and closeness to the ground; a fleece of acceptable weight and quality; and a pink skin.

If purebred, the animals should show the characteristics of the breed represented. Rams should show boldness and masculinity, and ewes should be feminine.

Ideal Fleece-type and Conformation

When the production of wool is the main source of income, weight and quality of fleece are of the utmost importance. The fibers should be long, fine, of good crimp; and the fleece should be dense, clean, and bright. Animals with fleeces that show black fibers or any tendency of the fleece to be hairy, loose, or open should be rejected. From the standpoint of body form, the typical wool-type sheep is quite different from those animals representing the ultimate in mutton type. The former are more upstanding and angular, with considerably less width, depth, fullness, and smoothness throughout. It is to be noted, however, that the present-day smooth-bodied Rambouillet sheep are of much more acceptable mutton type than the ideal extreme wool-type of former years.

Recognizing and Evaluating Common Faults

No animal is perfect. In judging, therefore, one must be able to recognize and appraise the common faults. Likewise, credit must be given for the good points. Finally, the judge must be able to weigh and evaluate the relative importance of the characteristics that he has observed, and the degree to which they are good or bad. Skill and accuracy in this art can be achieved only through patient study and long experience. Figure 25-3 shows the ideal mutton type versus some common faults.

Method of Examining

As in examining any class of livestock, the examination of sheep should be systematic and thorough. This is especially true in selecting breeding animals or in close competitive judging such as is encountered in the show ring, but it is neither practical nor essential in handling the large numbers of sheep in a central market.

The sheep being examined should first be looked over from a distance, so that views from the front, side, and rear may be secured. It does not make any difference which view of the animal is noted first, but it is important that the same procedure be followed each time. This general inspection should furnish a good idea as to the size, balance, width, and depth of body; compactness; the make-up of the head; length of neck; straightness of lines; closeness to the ground; straightness of legs; and breed type and character of the animal. Next, the impression gained through distant inspection should be verified by handling

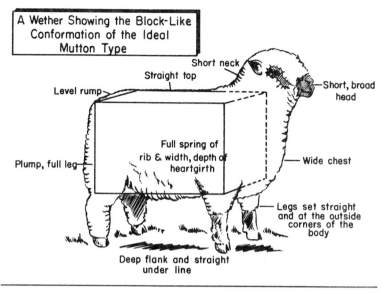

A Wether Showing the Block-Like Conformation of the Ideal Mutton Type

Short neck
Straight top
Level rump
Short, broad head
Full spring of rib & width, depth of heartgirth
Wide chest
Plump, full leg
Legs set straight and at the outside corners of the body
Deep flank and straight under line

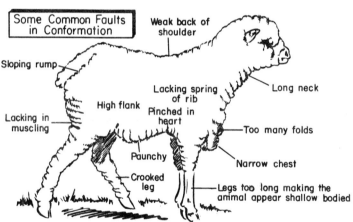

Some Common Faults in Conformation

Weak back of shoulder
Sloping rump
Lacking spring of rib
Long neck
High flank
Pinched in heart
Lacking in muscling
Too many folds
Paunchy
Narrow chest
Crooked leg
Legs too long making the animal appear shallow bodied

Fig. 25-3. Ideal mutton-type versus common faults. The successful sheep judge must know what he is looking for, and be able to recognize and appraise both the good points and the common faults.

with the hands, and the fleece should be examined. Good judges differ as to whether one should start handling the animal from the front or rear. Perhaps as good a method as any is illustrated in Figure 25-4.

With market sheep, most of the examining that is necessary in arriving at the market classes and grades is done by observation. Even so, these specialists usually like to get their hands on slaughter lambs; and when part of a drove of lambs is fat enough to go the slaughter route—whereas others must go as feeders— they will make the cut after handling each of them as they file through a cutting chute.

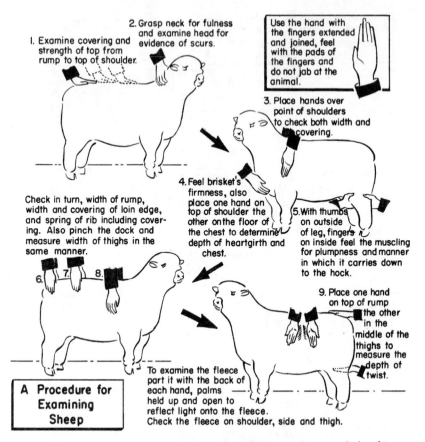

Fig. 25-4. A good procedure for examining sheep and some of the things for which to look.

Catching and Handling Sheep

If sheep are to be caught and handled for any reason, they should first be confined to a small corral or shed. Sheep may best be caught around the neck, by the hind leg, or by the rear flank. Never should they be caught by the wool. Such rough treatment results in badly injured skin and tissue, which may require weeks or even months to heal. As a result of such mishandling, market sheep will exhibit a damaged carcass, and the fleece of breeding animals will lack uniformity because of the disturbance in the injured area.

In handling sheep, the fingers should be kept together. In this way, the correct touch is obtained in the palm of the hand, and the wool is not disarranged. In observing the fleece and skin, the wool should be parted well down on the shoulder, side, and leg. Opening the fleece on the back should be avoided, as it will allow water to run in.

Determining the Age of Sheep

Until sheep are four years of age, the front teeth of the lower jaw furnish

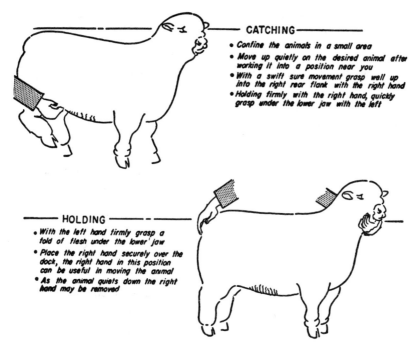

CATCHING

- Confine the animals in a small area
- Move up quietly on the desired animal after working it into a position near you
- With a swift sure movement grasp well up into the right rear flank with the right hand
- Holding firmly with the right hand, quickly grasp under the lower jaw with the left

HOLDING

- With the left hand firmly grasp a fold of flesh under the lower jaw
- Place the right hand securely over the dock, the right hand in this position can be useful in moving the animal
- As the animal quiets down the right hand may be removed

Fig. 25-5. Diagram showing the correct method of catching and holding a sheep. (Drawing by R. F. Johnson)

a fairly reliable guide as to their development. The lamb has small, narrow teeth that are known as milk teeth. At 12 to 14 months of age, the two center incisors are replaced by two large, broad, permanent teeth. Each succeeding year, an additional pair of permanent teeth appears, one on either side of the first pair, until four years of age, when there is a full mouth. It must be remembered, however, that teeth represent the degree of development rather than the exact age according to birth, and, therefore, they are not an infallible indication of age.

After the sheep has a solid mouth (at four years), it is impossible to tell the exact age. With more advanced age, the teeth merely wear down and spread apart, and the degree of wearing or spreading is an indication of age. The normal number of teeth may be retained until eight or nine years, but often some are lost after about the fifth or sixth year, resulting in a "broken mouth." When most of the teeth have disappeared, animals are known as "gummers."

Ewes of mutton breeding usually start on the decline at about five years of age, whereas ewes of the fine-wool breeds do not begin to decline until about a year later. Even so, outstanding producers should not be disposed of just because they have reached this age, especially in a purebred flock. Also, animals that have reached the age where it may no longer be wise to expose them to the rigors of range handling may often be retained satisfactorily and profitably in a farm flock for one to two years longer.

With market sheep, the break-joint or lamb-joint is also an important criterion

Determining the Age of Sheep By Their Teeth

1. Lamb's mouth with 8 incisors, these temporary teeth are called milk teeth

4. 3-yr. old mouth with 3 pairs of permanent incisors

2. Yearling mouth with I pair of permanent incisors

5. 4-yr. old mouth with 4 pairs of permanent incisors

3. 2-yr. old mouth with 2 pair of permanent incisors

6. Broken mouth condition which may begin to occur about 6 yrs. of age, a sheep that has lost all incisors is called a gummer

Fig. 25-6. Diagram showing how to determine the age of sheep by the teeth.

of age. For further information on this point, the reader is referred to Chapter XXIX.

QUESTIONS FOR STUDY AND DISCUSSION

1. In establishing a flock of sheep, wherein do the factors that should be considered differ from the factors to consider in establishing cattle, hogs, or horses?

2. Select a certain farm or ranch (either your home farm or ranch, or one with which you are familiar). Assume that there are no sheep on this establishment at the present time. Then outline, step by step, (a) how you would go about establishing a flock and (b) the factors that you would consider. Justify your decisions.

3. Discuss each of the four bases of selection of sheep.

4. Cite an example when utilitarian consideration in show-ring judging of sheep was ignored, to the detriment of a certain breed of sheep.

5. Why are stockmen more conscious about and familiar with the determination of the age of sheep by the teeth than they are in applying this method to cattle, hogs, or horses?

SELECTED REFERENCES

Title of Publication	Author(s)	Publisher
Breeding Better Livestock	V. A. Rice F. N. Andrews E. J. Warwick	McGraw-Hill Book Co., New York, N. Y., 1953.
Determining the Age of Farm Animals by Their Teeth	Farmer's Bul. 1721	U.S. Department of Agriculture, Washington, D. C.
Elements of Livestock Judging, The	W. W. Smith	J. B. Lippincott Co., Philadelphia, Pa., 1930.
Judging Sheep	Farmer's Bul. 1199	U.S. Department of Agriculture, Washington, D. C.
Livestock Judging Handbook	J. E. Nordby W. M. Beeson David L. Fourt	Interstate Printers and Publishers, Danville, Ill., 1962.
Stockman's Handbook, The	M. E. Ensminger	Interstate Printers and Publishers, Danville, Ill., 1962.

Chapter XXVI

SYSTEMS OF SHEEP PRODUCTION

Contents   Page

The Farm Flock Method..677
The Purebred Flock Method..678
The Range-Band Method..679
Lamb Feeding...680
Questions for Study and Discussion..681
Selected References 681

It is logical that different systems of sheep production should exist in a country so large and diverse as the United States. This is fortunate, both from the standpoint of (1) the most efficient utilization of production factors, especially feeds, and (2) the meeting of consumer needs. For purposes of convenience and discussion, the different systems of sheep production are herein grouped into the following categories: (1) the farm flock method, (2) the purebred flock method, (3) the range-band method, and (4) lamb feeding. Although the system of sheep production and the size of the enterprise may introduce new problems, the fundamental nature of sheep remains the same. For this reason, there is neither as much difference nor as many secrets to success in different systems of sheep production as some would have us believe. Essentially, success in any area or system depends upon maintaining a healthy and highly productive flock that is economically managed and upon the advantageous marketing of the lamb and wool crop.

THE FARM FLOCK METHOD

The farm flock method is the common system of sheep production in the humid farming areas of central, southern, and eastern United States. In general, it accompanies a diversified and intensive system of farming. Since it stresses market-lamb production, with wool production of secondary importance, most of the sheep in the farm flock states are of mutton-type. Farm flocks range in size from a few head to several hundred head. The commercial farm flock is not under the care of a special shepherd or herder, but its handling is entrusted to a farm worker who has other responsibilities. For this reason, it is often neglected as a minor enterprise, especially when the flock is very small and the caretaker has other assignments which are considered more important and remunerative.

During the grazing season, farm flocks usually compete with beef and dairy cattle for the use of permanent or seeded pastures. Because many of the soils of the humid region are subject to considerable erosion, there appears to be a tendency to seed increased acreages to pastures, thus providing more grasses.

Also, on many farms, sheep are considered scavengers, and as such they are given the assignment of keeping down the weeds and grass of fence rows, lanes, and draws. For best results, especially from the standpoint of greater efficiency of production and parasite control, however, the farm flock should be given better pastures, and a system of pasture rotation should be followed. Also, confinement or partial-confinement production should be considered.

Fig. 26-1. The farm flock method. A large flock of sheep in Kentucky. (Courtesy, The University of Kentucky)

THE PUREBRED FLOCK METHOD

For the most part, purebred flocks are comparatively small and the vast majority of purebred breeders are located in the farm flock states. There are, however, a sizeable number of purebred flocks in the range states, some of which are quite large and are handled by range-band methods.

In general, the purebred sheep breeder has as his objectives the sale of rams to commercial sheepmen and the sale of both rams and ewes to established or new purebred breeders. Over a period of years, the most successful purebred breeders are keen students of commercial sheep production, keeping ever in mind that the ultimate objective in all sheep production is the sale of market lambs and wool and gauging their type or ideal accordingly.

Most purebred flocks are given much closer attention than the average commercial flock. Frequently, a full-time caretaker is assigned. Also, in keeping with the general requirements for successful purebred production—regardless of the class or breed of farm animals—more attention is given to (1) the location of the farm, (2) individual records, (3) the careful study and selection of individual sheep rather than of flocks or bands, (4) matings that will produce

Fig. 26-2. The purebred flock method. (Courtesy, *Farmer and Stock-Breeder*, London)

animals with great inherent possibilities, (5) the maximum development of animals through feeding, and (6) different methods of advertising, including showing. In brief, the production of purebred sheep is a highly specialized business, and only a few sheepmen should attempt this system of production.

THE RANGE-BAND METHOD

Seventy per cent of the sheep of the United States are located on the western range, with the vast majority of these animals handled according to the range-band method. Each band is under the care of an experienced herder who moves the animals over a comparatively large area of unenclosed land. In southwestern United States, however—in Texas, Oklahoma, and much of northern New Mexico—nearly all of the range is fenced. Under the latter conditions, the management of sheep is very similar to that existing in Australia and New Zealand.

The relative emphasis on lamb and wool production in the range area varies according to the rainfall and vegetation. In the arid and semi-arid regions of the Southwest, where feed is not sufficient for satisfactory grass-finished lamb production, the production of wool is of greater relative importance than in those areas where the vegetation is more abundant. Even so, at the present time, lambs constitute the major source of income in these areas. In general, however, the sheep of this area are smaller, produce finer quality wool, and practically all the lambs go the feeder route for finishing in more distant areas where feeds are more abundant.

In the semi-arid and sub-humid areas of the West and Northwest, where the ranges are more lush, many of the lambs go the slaughter route at weaning time,

Fig. 26-3. The range-band method. A band of sheep that has sought shelter during a blizzard on the range. (Courtesy, Charles J. Belden, Pitchfork, Wyo.)

being finished entirely on milk and grass. Most operators in this area produce feeder lambs only because the range was poorer than normal. The main source of income, therefore, is derived from the sale of lambs, with the income from wool being of secondary importance. The sheep of this area are larger—large Rambouillets or long-wool X fine-wool crossbreds predominating—produce coarser wool, and yield lambs of more desirable shape and meat quality.

LAMB FEEDING

Lamb feeding is a highly specialized system of sheep production. In general,

Fig. 26-4. Good quality, crossbred, black-faced range lambs on feed in Montana. Note the feed equipment and the shelter. (Courtesy, Northern Pacific Railroad)

where pasture or range conditions are sufficiently good, the sheepman strives to produce grass-finished lambs at weaning time. When the vegetation is not good or if for other reasons the lambs lack finish at weaning time, they are usually sold for further finishing. Seldom does the producer attempt to finish out his own feeders. Most lamb feeders are large, specialized operators whose feedlots are located in close proximity to adequate and economical feed supplies, such as irrigated valleys, mill centers, or areas where winter wheat fields may be grazed. A full discussion of lamb-feeding methods and problems is contained in Chapter XXVIII.

QUESTIONS FOR STUDY AND DISCUSSION

1. Select a certain farm or ranch (your home farm or ranch, or one with which you are familiar). Assume that there are no sheep on this establishment at the present time. Which of the four systems of sheep production would you elect to follow? Justify your decision.

2. Why have range bands decreased in relative importance whereas farm flocks have increased in recent years?

SELECTED REFERENCES

Title of Publication	Author(s)	Publisher
Sheep Book, The	John McKinney	John Wiley & Sons, Inc., Publishers, New York, N. Y., 1959.
Sheep Production	R. V. Diggins C. E. Bundy	Prentice-Hall, Inc., Englewood Cliffs, N. J., 1958.
Sheep Science	W.G.Kammlade,Sr. W.G.Kammlade,Jr.	J. B. Lippincott Company, New York, N. Y., 1955.

Chapter XXVII

BREEDING SHEEP

Contents	Page
Normal Breeding Habits of Ewes	684
Age of Puberty	684
Age to Breed Ewes	685
Heat Periods	685
Gestation Period	685
Fertility and Prolificacy in Sheep	685
Flushing	686
Preparation of Ewes and Rams for Mating	687
Trimming and Tagging the Ewes	687
Preparation of the Ram for Mating	687
Marking the Ram	688
Care and Management of the Ram	689
Age and Service of the Ram	689
Care of the Pregnant Ewe	690
Feed and Water	690
Exercise	690
Shelter	691
Care of the Ewe at Lambing Season	691
The Lambing Pen	691
Normal Presentation	692
Taking the Lamb	692
Chilled and Weak Lambs	693
Disowned Lambs	693
The Orphan Lamb	694
Feed and Water After Lambing	694
Examination of the Udder	694
Factors Affecting Reproduction	695
Systems of Lamb Raising	695
Hothouse Lambs	696
Easter Lambs	696
Spring Lambs	696
Lambs Raised on Grass	697
Crossbreeding in Sheep	697
Lethals and Other Hereditary Abnormalities in Sheep	699
Production Testing Sheep	699
Hormonal Control of Reproduction in Ewes	703
Questions for Study and Discussion	703
Selected References	704

As with other classes of farm animals, sheep breeders are of two types: (1) commercial producers, and (2) purebred breeders. The commercial producers are primarily concerned with securing a high percentage lamb crop and with the utility features of the animals and their ability to make efficient use of feeds. These men direct most of their effort toward improvement through the selection of purebred rams.

The purebred breeders are interested in producing rams for sale to the commercial sheepmen and, at the same time, in further improving their own flock and selling both ewes and rams to other purebred breeders. Although breed fancy points are often given consideration, for success over a long period of

Fig. 27-1. Good breeding and wise management are essential for the successful production of sheep on the farm or range. This flock is grazing on Traver Ranch, Glenwood Springs, Colorado. (Courtesy, National Cottonseed Products Association, Inc.)

years the purebred breeders must be ever aware of the fact that the ultimate goal in sheep production is the sale of lambs and wool.

NORMAL BREEDING HABITS OF EWES

Perhaps there is as much scientific information about the normal breeding habits of the ewe as there is about any class of farm animals. Even so, not all of the phenomena are clear, and much work in the field of sheep breeding remains to be done.

Age of Puberty

Sheep reach puberty at five to seven months of age. As evidence of the fact that the sex organs of ram lambs become functional at this age, it might be pointed out that it is not unusual to find that they have bred a few of the ewes prior to the normal weaning time.

Ewe lambs are probably somewhat slower than ram lambs in reaching sexual maturity, but it must be realized that in sheep full development of the female may be reached before the onset of estrus or heat, for in sheep there are long periods (anestrus) when the female organs are not active. Generally, the first estrus in ewe lambs of the mutton breeds occurs during the fall of their first year, when they are 8 to 10 months of age; whereas in the more slow-maturing Merinos, it may be delayed until they are 16 to 20 months of age.

Age to Breed Ewes

Most ewes are bred during the first breeding season after they are one year of age, producing their first lambs when approximately 24 months old.

As a rule, ewe lambs are not used for breeding purposes. Range sheepmen almost never follow the practice, and only comparatively few farm flock owners breed ewe lambs so that they will drop their first lambs when approximately 12 months of age. Limited experimental work plus practical observations would indicate that the following results may be expected from the practice of breeding ewe lambs:

1. Growth of bred lambs is retarded temporarily, but is not stunted permanently.

2. Wool yield is not affected by early breeding.

3. Some ewe lambs do not conceive; birth weights of lambs born to ewe lambs are lighter; and more troubles are encountered at lambing time. (More ewes require assistance at lambing and more lambs are disowned.)

4. If computed on the basis of total lifetime production up to five or six years of age, ewes bred as ewe lambs will show more lambs and total pounds of lambs produced per ewe than ewes bred at the normal yearling age.

Many good sheepmen are of the opinion that Suffolk rams should be used if ewe lambs are bred to black-faced rams, for the reason that the smaller head and shoulders of the progeny will cause less difficulty at lambing time.

Heat Periods

The duration of estrus in ewes ranges from 20 to 42 hours, with an average of 30 hours. Unlike other farm animals, the ewe shows no visible external indications of heat, the acceptance of the ram (or teaser with an apron on) being the only method of external detection. Ovulation seems to occur late in the heat period, usually from about 24 to 30 hours after the onset of estrus. If the ewe is not bred, or if she fails to get in lamb, estrus recurs after an interval of 14 to 20 days, with an average of 16 to 17 days.

Gestation Period

The period of gestation of sheep varies between breeds and individuals, with the range from 144 to 152 days and the average 148 days. Medium-wool breeds, including the down breeds, have short gestation periods of from 144 to 148 days; whereas the fine-wool breeds, such as the Merino and Rambouillet, have long gestation periods ranging from 148 to 152 days. The long-wool breeds, such as the Lincoln and Romney, have gestation periods intermediate between the medium and fine wools, averaging 146 to 149 days. Individual gestation periods within a breed may vary up to a range of 15 days.

FERTILITY AND PROLIFICACY IN SHEEP

In a summary of all available data, two Swedish investigators, Johannson and Hansson, found that among all breeds of sheep and types of environment about 176 pairs of twins and 10 sets of triplets occur in every 1,000 births; and one set of quadruplet lambs is born in every 5,000 births.[1] This is a 119.6 per cent lamb crop.

In general, flockmasters have long considered that twinning is important. This is well illustrated in the following old English adage: "Ewes yearly by twinning rich masters do make; the lambs of such twinners for breeders go take." There is now substantial evidence to indicate that this adage was well founded.

Though twinning is inherited, it is not highly so in comparison with certain other traits. Experimental work has shown that the heritability of twinning ranges from 10 to 15 per cent; whereas the heritability of face covering is about 56 per cent.

Prolificacy in sheep is largely determined by the number of eggs liberated by the ovary at the heat period, and by the amount of fetal atrophy. If only one egg is released and fertilized, a single lamb will result unless this egg should divide so that twins are produced. Such division does not seem to occur with much frequency, it undoubtedly being true that most twins and triplets are due to the shedding of a like number of eggs, which are fertilized and complete their development.

Under natural conditions, the number of eggs shed depends on heredity, environment, and age. It is generally recognized that, because of heredity, some breeds and strains produce a higher percentage of twins and triplets than others. On the other hand, under certain conditions, the number of eggs shed may be increased by flushing; that is, through providing improved nutritive conditions prior to the breeding season. Practical observation would indicate that age is a factor in twinning, with middle-aged ewes producing a higher percentage lamb crop than either ewe lambs or very old ewes.

Twins are desirable, for they greatly increase the weight of lambs sold per ewe. The annual maintenance requirements of ewes are not far different, regardless of whether they are producing twins or singles.

In some localities, rams of at least some of the breeds go through a period of lowered semen volume and quality during the summer months. The reasons for this phenomenon are not fully understood, and limited experimental studies to date have given conflicting results. Nevertheless, there appears to be a definite seasonal difference in the fertility of rams. Where early lambs are desired, this factor may be of considerable economic importance.

FLUSHING

Flushing is that practice of feeding thin ewes more generously during the period of 2 to 8 weeks immediately prior to breeding. This may be accomplished either by providing more lush pasture or range or by grain feeding.

---

[1] Reeve, E. C. R. and F. W. Robertson, "Factors Affecting Multiple Births in Sheep," *Animal Breeding Abstracts*, Vol. 21, No. 3, 1953, pp. 211-224.

Fig. 27-2. A large percentage of twins is desirable. Apparently this factor is affected by heredity, environment, and age. (Courtesy, International Wool Secretariat, London)

Although it is not likely that all of the benefits ascribed to flushing will be fully realized under all conditions, the general feeling persists that the practice will result in a 15 to 20 per cent increase in the lamb crop and that the ewes will both breed earlier and more nearly at the same time. Fat ewes are best conditioned for breeding by increasing the exercise.

PREPARATION OF EWES AND RAMS FOR MATING

Several practices pertaining to both ewes and rams are important during the breeding season. Each of these points will now be discussed.

Trimming and Tagging the Ewes

Tagging is the removal of tags or locks of wool and dirt about the dock. It is important that this job be done prior to the breeding season in order to prevent the ewes from befouling themselves and to remove obstacles for the service of the ram.

Preparation of the Ram for Mating

As the weather is usually rather warm at the time of the breeding season, shearing the ram just prior to this will make him more active. This is especially true of old show or sale rams. Where rams are not sheared completely, they should at least have the wool clipped from the neck and from the belly in the region of the penis, for this will result in copulation with greater ease. It is also important to see that the hoofs of the ram are properly trimmed prior to the breeding season.

Marking the Ram

When several rams are turned in with a large band of ewes, it is impossible to detect individual rams that may be failing to settle ewes. Moreover, it is quite likely that a different ram will serve the ewe should there be a recurrence of heat, or perhaps more than one ram may serve the ewe at the time of estrus. When only one ram is being used on a small flock, however, it is important to know whether the ewes are getting with lamb. Then, too, with a purebred flock individual breeding records are rather important.

A breeding record can best be kept by using a marking harness (breeding harness), containing a crayon (different colored crayons are available), on the ram, or by smearing the breast of the ram and the area between his forelegs every day or two with a thick paste. Then, as the ram serves the ewe a mark will be left on her rump. Paint or tar should never be used for this purpose.

Fig. 27-3. Marking the ram. A breeding record can best be kept by smearing the breast of the ram and the area between his forelegs every day or two with a thick paste, or by using a marking harness. (Courtesy, Washington State University)

The color of the crayon or paste should be changed every 16 days (the approximate estrus cycle of the ewe) so that one can determine whether ewes that have been bred are returning in heat. For example, during the first 16-day interval, the thick paste used on the ram might well be a mixture of ordinary lubricating oil and yellow ochre; for the second 16-day interval, it might be lubricating oil and venetian red; and for the third 16-day interval (if there is still some question about some of the ewes having settled), it might be a paste made by using lubricating oil and lamp black (thus proceeding from light to dark colors).

Naturally, if a good percentage of the ewes are found coming in heat for a second time, the ram should be regarded with suspicion, and perhaps another ram should be obtained. The sterility in some instances may be temporary because of high condition and lack of exercise.

CARE AND MANAGEMENT OF THE RAM

If possible, the ram should be secured considerably in advance of the breeding season. At this time, better rams are available and the prices are more favorable. Then, too, the ram will have an opportunity to become acclimated before being placed in service. In case of show or sale rams, it may also be advisable to remove gradually some of their surplus flesh.

Stud rams are usually kept separate from the ewes except during the breeding season. Their quarters need not be elaborate or expensive. Usually, a dry shelter that will provide protection during times of inclement weather is all that is necessary. Plenty of exercise should be provided at all times.

Fig. 27-4. Stud rams on pasture. Shelter, shade, and pasture constitute a good combination for keeping breeding rams thrifty and virile. (Courtesy, *Sheep Breeder and Sheepman;* photo by Greg W. Hilton)

Rams may subsist largely on pasture and dry roughage. If the pasture has been scanty prior to the breeding season, the rams may be conditioned by feeding a little grain, usually not more than 1 pound daily. Rams are usually fed some grain when being fitted for show or sale, but it must be remembered that excess fat may actually be harmful from a breeding standpoint.

AGE AND SERVICE OF THE RAM

The number of ewes a ram will serve in a season depends on his age, vigor, and method of handling. Table 27-1 gives pertinent information relative to the

TABLE 27—1

HANDY RAM MATING GUIDE

Age	No. of Matings/Yr.		Comments
	Hand-mating	Pasture-mating	
Lamb..........................	20-25	——	Most range operators use 1 ram to 25 to 35 ewes.
Yearling or older..........	50-75	35-60	A ram should remain a vigorous and reliable breeder up to 6 to 8 years of age.

use of the ram, including consideration that should be given to age and method of mating.

Generally speaking, it is best not to use a ram lamb, but a vigorous, well-grown, early-maturing lamb may be used on 20 to 25 ewes with no apparent harm. Many good sheepmen believe that there is a definite breed difference in early reproductive capacity. A vigorous ram one to four years old that is run with the flock during the breeding season is sufficient for 35 to 60 ewes. When the ram is turned with the flock for only a limited period daily—perhaps an hour in the morning and an hour in the evening—or when a teaser is used for the purpose of locating ewes that are in heat, one mature ram may be sufficient for 50 to 75 ewes. Unless the ram becomes extremely nervous and restless when removed, his energy will be conserved through keeping him away from the flock; and he, therefore, will be available for heavier breeding service. Often he will remain contented if one or two wether lambs or bred ewes are kept with him. With a heavy ram and warm weather, a good plan is to allow him to run with the flock at night and to remove him to separate quarters during the day. Regardless of the system followed, the ewes should be checked daily and accurate records kept of the breeding dates. Though there is considerable variation, most range sheepmen usually plan to have three to four active mature rams with each hundred ewes.

CARE OF THE PREGNANT EWE

The requirements of the pregnant ewe are neither exacting nor difficult to meet. These needs are feed and water, exercise, and shelter.

Feed and Water

For successful sheep production, the ewes must be economically and properly fed and watered during the pregnancy period. As these requirements are fully covered in Chapter XXVIII, no further discussion is necessary at this point.

Exercise

During periods of inclement weather and when feed is brought into the barn, ewes quite often exercise entirely too little. As a result they become sluggish, and their blood circulation is poor. Forced exercise may be brought about by scattering a palatable roughage some distance from the shed or by driving the ewes at a moderate walk. Above all, overexertion, such as wading through a deep snow or being chased by dogs, should be avoided. With a good winter pasture and open weather conditions, no other arrangements for exercise will be necessary.

Shelter

The shelter should be of such nature as to protect the flock from becoming soaked with rain or wet snow. Dry snow or bitter cold has no harmful effect, and up until lambing time, a shelter open to the south on well-drained ground may be entirely satisfactory.

CARE OF THE EWE AT LAMBING SEASON

As previously stated (under the section on "Fertility and Prolificacy in Sheep"), there is an average lamb crop of 119.6 per cent. However, only 92 lambs are raised per 100 ewes one year old and over.[2] This means that there is an appalling death loss of 28 per cent from birth to weaning. Most of these losses occur in the first few days of life.

The careful and observant shepherd or herder realizes the importance of having everything in readiness for the lambing season. If pregnant ewes have been so fed and managed as to drop a crop of strong, vigorous lambs, the next problem is that of saving the newborn animals.

As lambing time approaches, unsheared ewes should be tagged (or crutched). This consists of shearing the wool from around the udder, flank, and dock. The ewe should also be placed where she has plenty of room, away from any jamming or crowding. The grain allowance should be materially reduced, but the roughage allowance may be continued, if it is certain that it is of good quality and palatable. Careless feeding at this time is likely to result in milk fever following parturition. At this time, the wool around the udder should be clipped short in order to allow the lamb to find the teats readily. If breeding records have not been kept, the signs of approaching parturition must be relied upon. A nervous, uneasy disposition; a sinking in front of the hips; and fullness of udder are such indications.

The Lambing Pen

Just before lambing, or immediately thereafter, the ewe should be placed in a lambing pen. These pens are usually 4 feet square and are made by placing together two hinged hurdles, which are then set against the walls of the sheep barn. Use of the lambing pen prevents other sheep from trampling on the newborn lamb, eliminates the possibility of the lamb wandering away and becoming chilled, and, through keeping the dam and offspring together, lessens the danger of disowned lambs.

---

[2] *Agricultural Statistics, 1965*, USDA, Table 497, p. 337.

Fig 27-5. A lambing pen (4' x 4') occupied by a ewe and her twin lambs. Use of lambing pens protects newborn lambs from trampling, decreases the hazard of chilling, and lessens the danger of disowned lambs. (Drawing by Steve Allured)

Lambing pens should be clean, dry, well bedded, and well ventilated and should be located so as to be free from drafts. During extremely cold weather, additional warmth may be provided for the first few hours after birth by throwing a blanket over the top of the pen.

Normal Presentation

A good rule for the shepherd to follow is to be near during parturition but not to disturb the ewe unless she needs help. Normal presentation of the lamb consists of having the forelegs extended with the head lying between them, although some lambs are delivered hind legs first. Even though the lambs are born in clean quarters, tincture of iodine should be applied to the navel soon after birth. The latter precaution may not be necessary when lambs are dropped on an uncontaminated pasture or range, though many range operators report that they have found it necessary to apply iodine to the navel of lambs born on the range as well as in the shed.

Taking the Lamb

If the ewe has labored for some time with little progress or is laboring rather infrequently, it is usually time to give assistance. If the lamb is not in the proper position, such assistance consists of inserting the hand and arm in the vulva and turning the lamb so that the forefeet and head are in position to be delivered first. Delivery may then be helped by pulling the young outward and downward as the ewe strains. Before doing this, however, the fingernails should be trimmed closely and the hands and arms should be thoroughly washed with soap and warm water, disinfected, and then lubricated with vaseline or linseed oil.

Chilled and Weak Lambs

Lambs arriving during cold weather may become chilled before they have dried. One of the most effective methods of reviving a chilled lamb is to immerse the body, except for the head, in water that is as warm as one's elbow can bear. The lamb should be kept in this for a few minutes and then removed and rubbed vigorously with cloths. It then should be wrapped in an old blanket, a sheepskin, or other heavy material and should be given some warm milk as soon as possible. Another convenient and effective method of drying and warming a chilled lamb consists of putting it into a box containing a light bulb or electric heater.

When strong, healthy ewes have been properly fed and cared for during pregnancy, there will be a minimum of weak lambs. The shepherd should first make certain that the membrane has been removed from the nostrils and that breathing has started. Blowing into the mouth, lifting the body and dropping it a short distance, working the legs, and pressing the sides are artificial methods of starting breathing that may revive lambs that at first appear lifeless.

After breathing has started and the navel cord has been painted with iodine, an attempt should be made to get the lamb to nurse. Quite often even a very weak lamb will nurse the ewe if it is held to the teat. If it refuses to nurse in this manner, some of the colostrum of the ewe should be milked into a sterilized bottle, and the lamb should be fed a few teaspoonsful each hour by means of the bottle and nipple, until it gains strength.

If the ewe has no milk, an attempt should be made to obtain milk from another ewe that has just lambed, and perhaps in a few hours the normal flow of milk will start.

Disowned Lambs

When lambing pens are used, the number of disowned lambs is kept to a minimum. For the most part, disowning of lambs is due to improper feeding during pregnancy or because of a poor milk supply, an inflamed udder, or a maternal instinct that is not sufficiently developed, as is often true in ewes with their first lambs.

For the first few days, a ewe seems to recognize her young by scent or sense of smell. When difficulty is encountered in getting a ewe to own her own lamb or when it is desired to transfer or "graft" a lamb (as may be necessary with the loss of a lamb or when there are twins on an old ewe), deception in the sense of smell is an effective approach. One of the most common practices is to milk some of the ewe's milk on the rump of the lamb and then to smear some of it on the nose of the ewe. Many good shepherds take some of the mucus from the mouth and nose of the newborn lamb and smear it over the nose of the ewe. If these methods fail and the ewe persists in fighting the lamb away, blindfold her so that she cannot see the lamb. As a last resort, and when all other methods have failed, tie a dog in an adjoining pen. Sometimes the latter method will cause latent maternal instincts to rise to a surprising degree.

Occasionally a ewe will fail to own one of a pair of twin lambs. When this condition exists, about all that can be done is that the shepherd be patient in training the disowned lamb to nurse at the same time as its mate. Both lambs are usually kept from the ewe and turned with her at intervals.

The Orphan Lamb

A lamb may be orphaned through the death of its mother or because of the inability of the mother to suckle it. The most satisfactory arrangement for the orphan is to provide a foster mother. The good shepherd will try to have every ewe raise a lamb. There may be a ewe that has just lost her lamb or a strong, healthy ewe with just one lamb. When a lamb dies at birth and it is desired to transfer or "graft" another lamb on the ewe, two procedures are common. Sometimes a ewe will accept another lamb provided that the lamb to be adopted is first rubbed with the body of the dead lamb that it is to replace. Though a bit more bothersome, a more effective approach consists of removing the skin from the dead lamb and tying it over the lamb to be adopted. After two or three days, the skin may be removed gradually, a piece at a time. The latter method is commonly used in the range bands of the West.

When it is impossible to transfer an orphan lamb to another ewe, it may be raised either on cow's milk or on milk replacer. Of course, the problem will be simplified if the lamb has received some colostrum (the first milk) from its mother or from another ewe.

If cow's milk is used, it should not be diluted, because cow's milk is lower in butterfat and total solids than ewe's milk. Milk replacer should be mixed according to the manufacturer's directions.

Both cow's milk and milk replacer should be warmed to 100° F. and fed in sterilized bottles. During the first few days, the orphan should be fed about one ounce of milk (or milk replacer) every two hours. Gradually, the quantity may be increased and the intervals spaced further apart.

Feed and Water After Lambing

Following parturition, the ewe is in a feverish condition and should be handled carefully. She may be watered immediately after lambing, and at frequent intervals thereafter, but she should never be allowed to gorge. It is also a good plan to take the chill off the water before giving it to her. In general, feeds of a bulky and laxative nature should be provided during the first few days. A mixture of equal parts of oats and wheat bran may be fed in very limited quantities, with all the hay that can be consumed. Heavy grain feeding at this time may cause udder trouble in the ewe and digestive disturbances in the lamb. The feed may be gradually increased until the ewe is on full feed in about a week.

Examination of the Udder

During the first two days following lambing, the udder should be examined night and morning. Sometimes a lamb will nurse one side only. If all the milk is not being taken by the lamb, the udder should be milked out and the ration lessened accordingly. If the udder becomes swollen and feverish, it should be milked out, bathed with warm water, and then dried. Following this, it should be painted with tincture of iodine. This treatment should be repeated once or twice daily, as necessary. Lambs should not be allowed to suckle their mothers when the udder is in such a condition. It is also a good plan to isolate the affected ewes from the rest of the flock.

FACTORS AFFECTING REPRODUCTION

Normally, ewes come in heat during late summer or early fall, though there is both an area and a breed difference. The breeding season is usually restricted to about four months. Among the factors that affect reproduction in sheep are:

1. **Daylight.**—The initiation of the breeding season is affected by the number of hours of light in the day. Sheep will generally begin cycling when the number of daylight hours drops below 14. This is the reason most breeds of sheep come into heat during the fall months. To initiate estrus, however, it does appear that the shorter days must be preceded by longer days. Ewes that come into heat before or after the normal breeding season demonstrate very erratic cycle lengths.

2. **Temperature.**—Most breeds of sheep begin cycling with the coming of cooler fall weather, when night temperatures drop to around 74° F. Some breeds, such as the dark-faced mutton breeds, are particularly sensitive to heat levels. Other breeds, such as the Dorset, Merino, and Tunis, will cycle the year around and appear to be affected little by higher temperatures.

There is increasing research evidence that more ewes cycle and conceive in hot weather than has been previously thought. However, there is a high rate of embryo mortality during this time, and lambs born from ewes pregnant during hot weather are generally weak and much smaller than those born in cool weather. Death loss from such lambs is high.

Temperature also affects the male reproductive system. High temperatures will cause lower semen quality in rams. During prolonged periods of excessive heat (temperatures of 100° F. or more), rams may become sterile. This damage is not permanent, however, and the ram usually becomes sexually sound after four to six weeks of cooler weather.

3. **Nutrition.**—Proper nutrition is necessary for good reproductive performance.

Energy, in the form of carbohydrates, is important. Thus, the practice of flushing induces the shedding of a larger number of ova and consequently higher fertility.

Vitamin A is of particular importance to the ewe, for the maintenance of the germinal epithelium of the ovary. This portion of the ovary gives rise to the egg or ovum of the female. Under prolonged drought conditions (low carotene intake), the ewe will cease to produce ova, so reproduction becomes impossible.

SYSTEMS OF LAMB RAISING

In general, four systems of lamb raising are practiced in the United States:

(1) hothouse lambs, (2) Easter lambs, (3) spring lambs, and (4) lambs raised on grass.

Hothouse Lambs

These are lambs produced out of season—principally for the Boston and New York markets—and sold from December to April. The lambs are dropped in the fall or early winter months and are ready for market in 6 to 12 weeks, weighing 30 to 60 pounds live weight. As the ewes must be bred out of season for this type of market lamb production, those individuals carrying a predominance of Dorset, Tunis, Rambouillet, or Merino breeding are usually used in the production of hothouse lambs. Generally, these ewes are mated to rams of the mutton breeds.

This system represents a highly specialized business, and the man entering it must, first of all, have assurance of his market. Then, in addition to having heavy milking ewes of the proper breeding, he must properly house and skillfully feed the lambs and ewes in order to produce the fancy carcass in demand. Hothouse lambs should be castrated; but, peculiarly enough, on certain markets, notably the Boston market, the consumer demand is for lambs that have not been docked. The usual explanation of the demand for undocked hothouse lambs is the fact that the city consumer associates the tailless condition with older sheep only, thus having considerable question about the age of a hothouse lamb should it be docked. Because of the high moisture content of the young carcass, the pelts are usually left on hothouse lambs until the carcass is ready for delivery to the consumer.

Easter Lambs

The Easter lamb trade has been a variable one, the demand being within a rather wide range both as to weight and quality of lambs. During the past several years, there has been a considerable Easter demand for light lambs, 20 to 30 pounds in weight and not carrying much finish. At the same time, there is always a rather constant demand for heavier lambs of higher quality for which good prices are paid.

Spring Lambs

Young lambs marketed in the spring of the year, and prior to July first, are referred to as *spring lambs*. This class is not to be confused with *lambs* born the previous year but which are marketed the following spring, perhaps following a period in the feedlot. The first spring lambs usually come from the southwestern states and California.

After July first, the market classification of spring lambs no longer exists, animals of similar birth simply being known as lambs. Likewise, after July first, those previously designated as lambs are yearlings (wethers) or yearling ewes.

Lambs Raised on Grass

The fourth general system of market-lamb production is that of having the lambs arrive in the spring and producing them to marketable weight entirely on milk and grass. This is the most common system of lamb production throughout the United States and the nearly universal method on the range. Lambs handled in this manner must have the benefit of lush pastures, otherwise it will be necessary to market them via the feeder route. They also are generally more subject to parasites than earlier lambs, and they sell on a somewhat lower market; but the cost of production is relatively low.

Fig. 27-6. Ewes and lambs on grass. This is the most common system of lamb production throughout the United States and the nearly universal method on the range. (Courtesy, Utah State University)

CROSSBREEDING IN SHEEP

Although the common systems used in breeding sheep are not unlike those applied to other classes of farm animals, there appears to be more crossbreeding among sheep because of (1) the fact that sheep are called upon to produce two products, lamb and wool; (2) the many diverse conditions under which they are produced; and (3) the conviction on the part of many sheepmen that the hybrid vigor of crossbreeding accounts for increased vigor and livability in the lamb crop. Crossbreeding, therefore, is extensively followed in the commercial sheep production on the western range. The ewe bands are predominantly of Rambouillet extraction; whereas, for market-lamb production, Hampshire or Suffolk rams are generally used. The Rambouillet ewe bands are desired because of their (1) gregarious or flocking instinct, (2) great hardiness, and (3) superior shearing qualities. On the other hand, lambs of this breeding are not so desirable for market lambs. Thus, mutton-type rams are used in order to get large, fast-growing lambs that will attain a good market finish on milk and range vegetation or that can be readily sold to go into feedlots for further finishing. As black-faced cross-bred lambs of this type are not suitable as flock replacements, both ewe and wether lambs are marketed. Replacement females are obtained by: (1) outright purchase from a sheepman who has used white-faced rams (Rambouillets, Columbias, Targhees, or Panamas) for purposes of raising animals for sale as replacements, (2) using white-faced rams on the band every third year and re-taining the ewe lambs (some sheepmen with several bands simply use certain bands for producing lambs for replacement purposes), or (3) using both white-faced and black-faced rams simultaneously on the same ewe band. In the latter type of program, the better white-faced ewe lambs—which are easily recognized as the offspring of the white-faced rams—are selected out for breeding purposes.

As can be readily surmised, crossbreeding in sheep does make for a con-siderable problem from the standpoint of producing or purchasing replacement animals. It also often makes the ram problem a difficult one. This practice, how-ever, was born of necessity, there being few or no existing breeds or types pos-sessing all the desirable features needed. In recent years, considerable effort has been made toward developing breeds of sheep better adapted to the needs, with the hope of alleviating the necessity of crossbreeding. The Columbia, Targhee, and Panama breeds evolved out of this need.

In addition to the crossbreeding common to the western range, most hot-house lambs are produced through using this system of breeding. Usually grade Merino or Dorset ewes are topped with a Southdown ram. Ewes of this extraction will breed out of season, and they are excellent milkers; whereas the Southdown rams impart to their progeny the ultimate in early maturity and mutton type. Crossbreeding has also gained in popularity in Kentucky where crossbred Hamp-

Fig. 27-7. Hothouse lambs produced from a three breed cross; Dorset X Merino ewes mated to a Southdown ram. (Courtesy, P. T. Ziegler, Pennsylvania State University)

shire-Rambouillet ewes are frequently bred to Southdown rams for the production of grass-fat lambs.

Crossbreeding in sheep is still extensively followed in England and New Zealand. Here again, this practice is attributed to the diverse areas in which sheep are produced and the great differences with respect to the demand for the products of sheep.

Regardless of the area or the objective in crossbreeding sheep, utility points rather than breed fancy points are of paramount importance. Thus, on the western range, mutton-type rams used in crossbreeding must possess size, scale, and ruggedness; there must be no tendency to wool blindness; and the head must not be so large as to cause excessive difficulty at lambing time.

LETHALS AND OTHER HEREDITARY ABNORMALITIES IN SHEEP

Lethal characters in sheep are caused by the presence of hereditary factors in the germ plasm that produce an effect so serious as to cause the death of the individual either at birth or later in life. Though strictly nonlethal, other hereditary abnormalities of practical importance in sheep include overshot and undershot jaws. *An overshot jaw is one in which the lower jaw is shorter than the upper;* whereas *in undershot jaw the lower jaw is longer than the upper.* Either condition is of practical significance because affected animals cannot graze well. Genetically, these conditions are thought to be due to the interaction of several gene pairs, possibly recessive in nature. Affected animals should be culled from the breeding flock.

Production Testing Sheep

In Chapter II, it was emphasized that: (1) to make breed improvement, either performance testing or progeny testing is imperative, and (2) to select intelligently on the basis of a testing program, the breeder must have adequate records and use them.

The following characteristics appear to be of greatest importance in evaluating the profitability of sheep:

1. **Prolificacy of ewes; regularity of lambing and twin production** (which has a heritability of 10 to 15 per cent[3]).—Where adequate feeds are available, twin lambs are desirable because (a) they greatly increase the weight of lambs sold per ewe, and (b) the annual maintenance requirements of ewes is not far different, whether they are producing twins or singles.

2. **Birth weight of lambs** (which has an approximate heritability of 33 per cent).—The larger lambs at birth are generally more vigorous and make faster gains.

---

[3] The rest is due to environment. The heritability figures given herein are averages based on large numbers; thus some variation from these may be expected in individual flocks.

3. **Weaning weight** (which has an approximate heritability of 30 per cent). —Heavy weaning weights are especially important in those areas where cost of production is largely on a per head rather than on a per pound basis, such as the western range.

4. **Type at weaning** (which has an approximate heritability of 13 per cent).—Type scores at weaning are difficult to make and are not highly heritable. Yet they are important because they are a major factor in reflecting market values.

5. **Finish or condition at weaning** (which has an approximate heritability of 4 per cent).—Finish at weaning is largely determined by available feed and is not highly heritable. Yet it is most important because milk-fat lambs suitable for slaughter at weaning time most always bring more per pound than thinner lambs that are sold as feeders. For the range area as a whole, about 25 per cent of the lambs lack sufficient finish for slaughter at weaning time.

6. **Wrinkles or skin folds** (which are heritable by approximately the following percentages: neck folds at weaning age, 39 per cent; and body folds at yearling age, 32 per cent).—Sheep with smooth bodies are preferred. Wrinkled sheep are difficult to shear and lack fiber uniformity.

7. **Face covering** (which has an approximate heritability of 56 per cent).— Wool-blind ewes do not graze well, require more labor if they are clipped around the eyes, and wean less pounds of lamb. At the Western Sheep Breeding Laboratory, ewes with open faces produced 11.1 pounds more of lamb per ewe bred than those with covered faces.

8. **Yearling grease fleece weight** (which has an approximate heritability of 28 per cent).—Grease wool is valued on the basis of its clean weight. Of course, the heavier fleeces bring more money, because wool is sold by the pound.

9. **Yearling clean fleece weight** (which has an approximate heritability of 38 per cent).—Clean fleece weight is most important, for the fiber is far more important than the materials scoured from grease wool.

10. **Staple length at weaning age** (which has an approximate heritability of 40 per cent).—Fiber length is important because it is a major factor in determining fleece weight, class, and grade.

The relative economic importance of lamb and wool production varies between breeds, areas, and years. But, for the nation as a whole, approximately two-thirds of the income comes from lamb and one-third from wool; hence, the emphasis is on market lamb production rather than on wool production.

Figures 27-8a and 27-8b show the individual ewe record form in use at Washington State University. Although it is expected that the record form devised will vary according to relative emphasis and importance of lamb and wool production and personal preference of the operator, some such form as this is very necessary.

Department of Animal Science

INDIVIDUAL EWE OR RAM RECORD   FLOCK NO. _____

Breed _____ Reg. No. _____ Ear Nick _____ Tattoo _____ Birth Date _____

Type of birth (Single, Twin) _____ Date _____

Sire _____ Bred by _____ Temperament _____ (Gentle, nervous)

Bought from _____

Address _____ Face Covering[6] (As a lamb) _____

Date Purchased _____

Type, Weaned[1] _____ Date _____ Face Covering[6] (As yearling) _____

Dam _____ Type, Yearling[2] _____ Date _____

Back[3] _____ Rump[4] _____ Leg[4] _____ Disposed to _____ Date _____

Defects & Abnormalities[5] _____ Why Disposed[11] _____

LAMBS (Use one line for each lamb for ewe's offspring; use one line for the average of a ram's progeny for each year)

Date of birth	Ear nick and No.	Vigor at birth	Type of birth	Type of rearing[4]	Sex	Birth Wt.	Defects and abnormalities[5]	Sire	Milking ability ewe[9]	Weaning age, days	120 Day Weight	Weaning condition[10]	Weaning type[8]	Disposition[11] or remarks

[1] Trueness to breed appearance and desired mutton conformation: "1" Excellent; "2" Medium; "3" Good.; "4" Fair; "5" Poor.

[2] Straightness, strength, and spring of rib.; width. "1" Excellent; "2" Good.; "3" Medium; "4" Fair; "5" Poor.

[3] Width and levelness: 1-2-3-4-5 as above.

[4] Plumpness of thigh: 1-2-3-4-5 as above.

[5] Including overshot or undershot jaw, scurs, black fiber, etc.

[6] "1" Not covered beyond poll; "2" Covered to eyes; "3" Covered slightly below eyes, but open faced; "4" Covered partially below eyes, but not subject to wool blindness; "5" Face covered and subject to wool blindness.

[7] S—Single; T—Twin; Tr—Triplet.

[8] S—Single; T—Twin; Tr—Triplet; Gr—Grafted on foster mother and give her number.

[9] Good, medium, poor.

[10] Condition or degree of fatness: "1" Excellent; "2" Good.; "3" Medium; "4" Fair; "5" Poor.

[11] Cause of death, reason for disposal, kept for breeding purposes, whom sold to.

(over)

Fig. 27-8a. Individual Ewe Record form in use at Washington State University. (See Fig. 27-8b for reverse side of record form.)

WEIGHT RECORD OF EWE OR RAM

Date	Age	Weight	Condition[1]	Remarks[2]

REMARKS

(For example: bad udder, poor mother, aborted, veterinary treatment and nature of ailment.)

Date: Remarks:

FLEECE
(Use one line for each year)

Length Side[3]	Fineness[4]			Date of Shearing	Days Growth	Grease Weight	Per cent of Yield	Clean Wt.	Color of Skin	Purity[5]	Remarks About Fleece
	Shoulders	Side	Thigh								

1. Condition or degree of fatness: "1" Excellent; "2" Good; "3" Medium; "4" Fair; "5" Poor.
2. Factors affecting weight: e.g. just shorn, soon lamb, etc.
3. Length of staple, middle at side, to nearest 0.2 cm., just before shearing.
4. Numerical grade as determined by U.S.D.A. samples, just before shearing.
5. Kemp, black fibers, etc.

Fig. 27-8b. Reverse side of Fig. 27-8a, Individual Ewe Record form.

HORMONAL CONTROL OF REPRODUCTION IN EWES

Hormones are being used on ewes with varying degrees of success for the following purposes:

1. To induce superovulation—the release of more than the normal number of eggs during one heat period.

2. To make ova transplantation (transfer from one female to another) practical.

3. To bring ewes in heat at will, followed by a high conception rate if bred.

4. To increase twinning.

Many obvious advantages would accrue from such scientific breakthroughs. For example, if under practical conditions one could bring ewes in heat at will and obtain a high conception rate, the following very real advantages would become reality:

1. Two lamb crops per year could be produced—by early weaning, or three crops could be produced every two years.

2. Artificial insemination would be facilitated.

3. Sheepmen could exchange help at lambing time.

4. A uniform lamb crop could be marketed.

5. Marketing of lambs could be distributed throughout the year, to the special benefit of consumers and packers.

6. Cost of production would be lowered, for it would take little more feed and labor to keep a ewe in more continuous production.

Indeed the stakes are high—the benefits to accrue would be great. Many scientists are of the opinion that such developments are imminent on a practical basis. But some stories to the contrary, such is not the case at the time of this writing. Among other things, we need to know more about the following:

1. The particular hormone or hormones to administer, how (oral or injection) and when to give them, in what dosage, and how to lower labor and product costs when administering hormones.

2. How to obtain a higher conception rate following hormone-induced heat.

In brief, we need more information before the hormonal control of reproduction in ewes can be considered practical. In the meantime, the sheepman is admonished to keep abreast of new developments and to rely on well-informed advisers.

QUESTIONS FOR STUDY AND DISCUSSION

1. Under what conditions would you recommend that ewe lambs be bred? Justify your answer.

2. What can a sheepman do to increase twinning in a flock?

3. What management techniques at breeding and parturition time are unique to sheep, and are not applied to cattle, hog, and horse breeding?

4. Discuss the experiment that caused Dr. John Hammond to postulate that the normal time of year at which ewes breed is controlled by seasonal changes in length of day, with ewes coming in heat 13 to 16 weeks after the longest day of the year.

5. List the essential factors for success in the production of hothouse lambs.

6. How do you explain the fact that crossbreeding is practiced more extensively with sheep than with other classes of livestock?

7. Based on (a) heritability and (b) dollars and cents value, what characteristics should receive greatest emphasis in a production testing program?

8. How would you go about production testing a flock of sheep? List and discuss each step.

SELECTED REFERENCES

In addition to the Selected References listed in Chapter II, the following are recommended for Chapter XXVII:

Title of Publication	Author(s)	Publisher
Genetics of Livestock Improvement	J. F. Lasley	Prentice-Hall, Inc., Englewood Cliffs, N. J., 1963.
Profitable Sheep	S. B. Collins	The Macmillan Company, New York, N. Y., 1956.
Robert Bakewell: Pioneer Livestock Breeder	H. C. Pawson	Crosby Lockwood & Son, Ltd., 26 Old Brampton Rd., London, SW 7, England.
Sheep Production	R. V. Diggins C. E. Bundy	Prentice-Hall, Inc., Englewood Cliffs, N. J., 1958.
Sheep Science	W.G.Kammlade,Sr. W.G.Kammlade,Jr.	J. B. Lippincott Co., New York, N. Y., 1955.

Chapter XXVIII

FEEDING SHEEP

Contents	Page

Specific Nutritive Needs of Sheep 706
  Protein Needs 706
  Energy Needs 707
  Mineral Needs 708
    Salt 708
    Calcium 708
    Phosphorus 709
    Cobalt 709
    Other Mineral Needs 709
  Vitamin Needs 709
  Water Needs 711
Feeds for Sheep 711
  Pastures for Sheep 711
  Hays and Other Dry Roughages for Sheep 712
  Silages and Root Crops for Sheep 713
  Concentrates for Sheep 714
  Feed Additives 715
Feeding the Ewes 715
  Flushing the Ewes 715
  Feeding the Pregnant Ewes 715
  Feeding at Lambing Time 717
  Feeding the Lactating Ewes 717
Feeding the Rams 718
Feeding Growing-Finishing Lambs 718
  Creep Feeding Lambs 719
Lamb Feeding 719
  Areas and Types of Lamb Feeding 720
  Field Finishing 720
  Dry-lot Feeding 722
    Shelter or Barn Feeding 722
    Open-yard Feeding 722
  Basic Considerations in Finishing Lambs 723
Feed Allowance and Some Suggested Rations for Sheep 724
  Fitting Rations for Sheep 727
Questions for Study and Discussion 728
Selected References 729

Sheep consume a higher proportion of forages than any other class of livestock, it being estimated that 89.8 per cent of the total feed supply of the United States sheep production is derived from roughages. Sheep are naturally adapted to grazing on pastures and ranges which supply a variety of forage plants, and they thrive best on forage that is short and fine rather than high and coarse. Although sheep will eat considerable quantities of weeds and brush, they prefer choice grasses and legumes.

Except at lambing season, sheep seldom receive much grain. In the northern latitudes, farm-flock ewes are frequently given from one-half to one pound daily of a grain ration in addition to the roughage allowance from about a month before lambing to the time that they are turned to spring pasture.

Fig. 28-1. Columbia sheep grazing on a ranch near Kalispell, Montana. (Soil Conservation Service photo. Courtesy, C. B. & Q. Railroad Co.)

Higher levels of grain are fed during the suckling period than during gestation. Many of the farm flocks of the South and range bands of the Southwest, however, are kept in good thrifty condition, and the lambs are raised to the marketing stages, without the feeding of any grain. In still other areas, the ewes are fed only during periods of deep snows or extended droughts. The range bands in the colder regions of the West are normally fed alfalfa hay and grain during the period of about three to four weeks that they are confined to the lambing camp.

In general, for practical reasons, the ration of ewes should consist of as nearly year-round pastures as possible, with well-cured hay and other forages available the balance of the year, plus a limited grain allowance under certain conditions. Good quality sun-cured hay and lush pastures will not only provide most of the necessary proteins but they also are excellent sources of calcium and the vitamins, especially vitamins A and D. As with finishing cattle, finishing lambs require a liberal allowance of grain.

SPECIFIC NUTRITIVE NEEDS OF SHEEP

As with other classes of livestock, the nutritive needs of sheep may be classified as (1) protein needs, (2) energy needs, (3) mineral needs, (4) vitamin needs, and (5) water needs. Each of these nutritive needs will be treated separately.

Protein Needs

Since wool is a protein product, sheep need feeds that contain a liberal supply of this nutrient in order to produce a good wool clip. Wool is especially rich in the sulfur-containing amino acid, cystine, but this requirement is usually amply met by the cystine of feeds or by methionine, another amino acid which is also rather widely distributed in natural sources and which is derived from rumen synthesis.

Growing lambs have a higher protein requirement than mature ewes. Also, ewes have both a high total nutrient and high protein requirement during the latter part of pregnancy and when suckling lambs. Though correspondingly less because of their smaller body size and lower milk production, the nutritive requirements of ewes that are nursing lambs are much like those of lactating cows.

Green pastures and legume hays (alfalfa, clover, soybeans, lespedeza, etc.) are excellent and practical sources of proteins for sheep in most areas. Where the ranges are bleached and dry for an extended period or legume hays cannot be produced for winter feeding, however, it may be desirable to provide sheep with such protein-rich supplements as linseed meal, cottonseed meal, soybean meal, or a commercial protein supplement at the rate of about one-quarter to one-third pound per ewe per day. As with other ruminants, where some of these essential amino acids are synthesized by micro-organisms in the paunch, the quality of proteins is of less importance in feeding sheep than in feeding swine. In general, if sheep have access to green grass or a reasonable quantity of legume hay, there will be no deficiency in either the quantity or quality of proteins.

Urea and other forms of non-protein nitrogen can be used to replace up to one-fourth to one-third of the protein equivalent of the total ration. Growing lambs and mature sheep seem to be able to utilize urea better than finishing lambs.

Insufficient protein intake results in reduced appetite, lowered feed intake, and poor feed efficiency. In turn, this makes for poor growth and muscular development, reduced reproductive efficiency, and reduced wool production. Under extreme conditions, there are severe digestive disturbances, nutritional anemia, and edema.

Energy Needs

Lack of energy—hunger—is probably the most common nutritional deficiency of sheep. It may result from lack of feed or from the consumption of poor quality feed.

Inadequate amounts of feed may result from drought, snow covering the feed, or from a low dry matter content of lush, washy feeds. Poor quality of feed is usually due to plants becoming too mature.

Inadequate energy may result in a slowing or cessation of growth, loss of weight, reproductive failure, increased mortality, and higher parasite infection due to lowered resistance.

The energy needs of sheep are largely met through the consumption and digestion of roughages. In general, sheep subsist on an even higher proportion of roughages to concentrates than do beef cattle, and this applies to finishing lambs. The bacterial action in the paunch of the sheep efficiently converts roughages into suitable sources of energy.

Mineral Needs[1]

The mineral requirements of sheep and beef cattle, both ruminants, are not far different. Moreover, these two classes of animals more or less compete with each other for much of the same land areas throughout the world. They are subjected, therefore, to many of the same nutritive deficiencies. (See Table 3-5 of this book for a summary of Nutritional Deficiency Diseases and Ailments of Animals.)

The mineral feeding recommendation for all classes and ages of sheep is to provide free access to a two-compartment mineral box, with (1) salt (iodized salt in iodine-deficient areas) in one side, and (2) a mixture of one-third salt (salt added for the purposes of palatability) and two-thirds bone meal (or other calcium-phosphorus supplement), or a good commercial mineral, in the other side. This will meet the needs for salt, and for calcium and/or phosphorus if the latter are needed. There will not be consumption if the minerals are not needed. In those areas where cobalt and/or copper deficiencies exist, add these minerals as recommended in Chapter III (see sections entitled, "Cobalt" and "Recommended Iron and Copper Supplements").

Minerals may also be incorporated in the ration in keeping with nutrient requirements.

SALT

Sheep are particularly fond of salt and consume considerably more per hundred pounds of live weight than do cattle. (Sheep consume about five times more salt/100 lbs. body wt. than do cattle.) The range man commonly estimates his salt needs for the year on the basis of 12 pounds per ewe. Breeding sheep may consume nearly one-half ounce per head daily and finishing lambs from one-fifth to one-fourth ounce. In the alkali districts of the West, sheep are allowed no salt other than that which they get in the alkali (alkali often runs 85 per cent or more salt). In iodine-deficient areas, stabilized iodized salt should always be provided.

When sheep are accustomed to salt, it is a good plan to let them have free access to this mineral at all times. It is to be noted, however, that death losses frequently occur if animals are given free access to salt when not accustomed to it.

CALCIUM

Since legumes are generally high in calcium, the requirements for this mineral are usually met when the winter forage for breeding ewes or the roughage for finishing lambs consists of one-third or more of a good quality legume hay. When nonlegume forages are fed (whether in the form of dry forages or

---

[1]Generally speaking, the recommendations given herein can be followed on a nationwide basis. However, it is recognized that area differences do exist. Therefore, for more specific recommendations the sheepman should always secure the counsel of his county agricultural agent or state college of agriculture.

pastures), there may be a decided lack of calcium in the ration, especially if the forage is produced on a soil low in this mineral. Under such conditions, the animals should be allowed free access to a calcium supplement (bone meal, ground limestone, or oyster shell flour are commonly used, preferably in mixtures with one-third salt) or a calcium supplement should be added to the ration in keeping with nutrient requirements.[2]

PHOSPHORUS

As is true with cattle, sheep will suffer from an acute phosphorus deficiency if they are forced to subsist entirely on feeds produced on phosphorus-deficient soils. Because of the high phosphorus content of the cereal grains, finishing lambs will usually secure an adequate allowance of this mineral, unless a high proportion of beet by-products or other low phosphorus feeds are used. Regardless of location and feeds or whether the breeding flock or finishing lambs are involved, it is good protection to (1) allow the animals access to a good phosphorus-containing supplement at all times, or (2) add a phosphorus supplement to the ration in keeping with nutrient requirements.[3]

COBALT

In cobalt-deficient areas, sheep should be provided a cobaltized mineral mixture prepared as directed in Chapter III (see section entitled "Cobalt").

OTHER MINERAL NEEDS

Iodine should always be fed to sheep in iodine-deficient areas, such as northwestern United States and the Great Lakes region. This can be easily and cheaply accomplished by providing stabilized iodized salt containing 0.01 per cent potassium iodide.

Copper deficiencies occur in Florida. It generally affects young lambs. In such areas, 0.25 to 0.5 per cent copper sulfate should be incorporated in the salt or mineral mixture.

Although thought to be essential, under natural conditions no evidence of deficiencies in sheep have been observed of the following mineral elements: manganese, zinc, sulfur, potassium, iron, and magnesium.

Vitamin Needs[4]

As with beef cattle, vitamin A is the only vitamin likely to be deficient in the normal feeding of sheep; and they receive plenty of this when they are on green pasture, or when they receive ample amounts of grass silage or of green

---

[2] For nutrient requirements, see *Nutrient Requirements of Sheep*, National Research Council, Pub. 1693; or Tables 2-3 and 2-4 of *The Stockman's Handbook*, 4th edition.

[3] For nutrient requirements see *Nutrient Requirements of Sheep*, National Research Council, Pub. 1693; or Tables 2-3 and 2-4 of *The Stockman's Handbook*, 4th edition.

[4] See Table 3-5 of this book for a summary of Nutritional Deficiency Diseases and Ailments of Animals.

hay not over one year old. Yellow corn and green peas are also good sources of vitamin A for sheep that are being grain fed. Sheep, especially lambs, may suffer from a deficiency of vitamin A where the range is dry and bleached or where the animals are forced to subsist on a winter feed consisting predominantly of cereal hay or straw, poor quality hay, or cottonseed hulls.

Vitamin A is fat soluble and is stored in the body. It takes about 200 days to deplete entirely the liver storage of vitamin A of lambs previously pastured on green feed. This explains why animals which graze green forage during the normal growing season are able to do reasonably well on a low carotene ration for periods of four to six months.

When vitamin A deficiency symptoms appear, it is recommended that there be added to the ration either (1) dehydrated alfalfa or grass or (2) a stabilized vitamin A product.

The fact that sheep are generally outdoors and exposed to the sunlight much of the time, even in winter, protects them from any deficiency of vitamin D. Also, hay and other sun-cured roughages are good sources of this factor. As all sheep, including finishing lambs, utilize considerable hay, they normally receive ample quantities of vitamin D in the ration. All forms of dietary vitamin D appear to be used equally well by sheep. Vitamin D is oxidized, but with greater difficulty than vitamin A. However, when mixed with minerals, especially calcium carbonate, its stability is poor.

In general, the feeds normally consumed by sheep, especially well-cured hays and green pastures, contain ample quantities of vitamin E. However, oxidation rapidly destroys it, with the result that old hay and ground feeds may be poor sources. It has been demonstrated that the incidence of stiff lamb disease can be reduced by (1) feeding one-fourth pound of linseed meal daily to ewes during the last two months of gestation (thought to be due to the selenium content of the linseed), and/or (2) the addition of vitamin E and selenium to the ration of lactating ewes. Also, alpha tocopherol (a stabilized form of vitamin E) is effective in the treatment of stiff lamb disease. Administer at first onset of symptoms (1) 500 mg. of alpha tocopherol acetate orally or (2) inject 300 mg. of pure alpha tocopherol. Continue every other day with one-fifth this amount until recovery is complete.

The B vitamins appear to be synthesized by micro-organisms in sufficient amounts in the functioning rumen of sheep, and thus these factors are removed as a dietary essential of mature sheep. However, young lambs with undeveloped rumens have a dietary need for thiamine, riboflavin, and folic acid. Other B complex vitamins may also be required by lambs.

Vitamin C is not an essential dietary constituent of sheep, since it is synthesized rapidly enough to meet needs.

Vitamins K_1 and K_2 are fat soluble and aid in the clotting of blood. All green, leafy materials (fresh or dry) are rich in vitamin K_1. Vitamin K_2 is normally synthesized in large amounts in the rumen, thus no supplementary dietary need for it has been demonstrated in sheep.

Water Needs

Contrary to frequent but unfounded opinions, sheep do require considerable water. Mature animals will consume an average of approximately a gallon per day; whereas feeder lambs require about half this amount. Like other classes of animals, the water consumption of sheep varies with the climate and type of feed. They consume more water in the summer than in the winter and more when on dry feeds than when eating considerable roots or other succulent feeds. Sheep will go for weeks without water when foraging on grasses and other feeds of high moisture content. This condition often prevails on desert ranges in the early spring and on many of the mountain ranges during the summer months.

FEEDS FOR SHEEP

Sheep are adapted to the consumption of a great variety of feeds. Most of the common feeds used by them are of plant origin and bulky in nature. The feeding of concentrates is usually limited to the finishing of lambs and for use by the breeding flock at such special periods as the lambing season or just before and during the breeding season. Roughages constitute 100 per cent of the ration of the vast majority of sheep during most seasons of the year. Most lambs are marketed as milk-fat lambs directly off pastures or ranges without having had any grain.

Pastures for Sheep

No other class of farm animals is so well adapted to the utilization of maximum quantities of pasture as sheep. Although cattle compete with sheep for many of the same grazing areas and are also ruminants, sheep are unique in that the vast majority of the young are marketed as milk-fat animals directly off pastures. Also, in their grazing habits, sheep differ from cattle in that (1) they show a decided preference for short, fine forages, and (2) they have the gregarious or flocking instinct.

Although there are great differences in plants, sheep are able to utilize the various grasses, legumes, weeds, forbs (broadleafed herbaceous plants commonly called weeds by sheepmen), and browse (broadleafed, woody plants, or shrubs, or bushes, or small trees) that grow on millions of acres of cultivated and uncultivated land in this and other countries. This characteristic, plus the imperishable nature of wool from the standpoint of storage and transportation, has made sheep raising a frontier industry throughout the world.

Sheep are adapted to the grazing of both fenced and unfenced holdings. In this country, most farm flocks and a limited number of range bands of the Southwest are confined to fenced areas with no herder being necessary. On the other hand, most of the range pastures of the West are utilized by migratory bands under the supervision of a herder.

Regardless of the location of the area, year-round grazing is desired. In order to obtain succulent and palatable pastures, the range bands of the West are frequently travelled to different altitudes at different seasons of the year. In the mountainous sections, the summer ranges are usually at high altitudes, the spring-fall grazing at intermediate altitudes, and much of the winter range is on the desert or lowland areas. On some ranges, such travelling is not possible, the ranges being used on a year-long basis.

During the winter months and following periods of extended drought, pastures usually become leached and bleached. Although sheep can and do utilize these forages, it must be realized that, in comparison with green growing grasses, they are lacking in nutrients, being especially low in protein and carotene (provitamin A) content. Consideration of these facts should be given when providing supplemental feeds.

Abundant and succulent pastures are ideal for stimulating milk production in ewes. Moreover, pastures of this type are desirable from the standpoint of the limited digestive capacity of the young lamb. Accordingly, the degree of finish carried by lambs at market time is an accurate reflection of the amount and quality of the forage available on the pasture or range.

Sheep may successfully utilize either permanent or cultivated pastures. In the range area, the vast majority of pastures are of a permanent type; whereas both types of pastures are used by native sheep.

Range sheep graze nearly all the year and receive most of their sustenance from native range plants. Pronounced deficiencies (singly or in combination) of range forages in protein, energy, phosphorus, and carotene (provitamin A) sometimes occur on ranges. These deficiencies are most apt to happen when the forage is mature or dormant, during over-grazing, or in periods of drought. Also, they are most marked in ewes during gestation or lactation.

Hays and Other Dry Roughages for Sheep

Inclement weather, extreme droughts, overstocked pastures and ranges, and leached and bleached pastures make it necessary that dry roughages be provided for sheep. They are fond of good roughage and make good use of it. In general, however, they cannot effectively use as much coarse roughage as cattle.

Hays are the standard winter feed for sheep when they cannot be out on the pasture or range or when the condition of the pastures is such as to require supplemental feeding. The choicest hay for sheep is a legume which has been produced on fertile soil, cut at the proper stage, and well cured. Such hay is palatable and rich in protein (and the quality of protein is good), calcium, and vitamins A and D. If legume hay cannot be secured, a high-quality grass-legume mixed hay will be entirely satisfactory and much superior to a straight grass hay. Sheep may do very well for a considerable period of time when fed no feed other than a good-quality legume hay, salt, and water.

Although legume hays are preferable for sheep, nonlegume hays are fed extensively in the sheep-raising and lamb-feeding areas. If straight grass hays must be fed, they should be cut at an early stage of maturity. Even then, they

Fig. 28-2.   Feeding hay to sheep. (Courtesy, *National Wool Grower*)

will be lower in protein, calcium, and vitamins than the legumes; and hence for best results, protein and mineral supplements should be provided.

Bright, early-cut corn, sorghum fodder, or stover and early-cut, green cereal hays, and straws of many kinds are fed to sheep in different areas. The feeding value of these coarser roughages varies considerably according to the stage of maturity at which they are cut, the amount of leaves, and the green coloration. Although these forages are not satisfactory as the sole roughage, especially during the latter part of gestation and in the suckling period, they may be successfully used when mixed with liberal quantities of good-quality legume hays.

Where nonlegume roughages are fed, special attention should be given to providing a suitable protein concentrate and minerals, especially calcium.

Silages and Root Crops for Sheep

Silage consists of green, succulent plants which are usually harvested at an early stage of maturity, chopped and compressed tightly into a silo, and allowed to ferment. During the fermentation, a part of the sugars in the plant are broken down, with the formation of organic acids—such as lactic, acetic, and butyric acids—and the release of carbon dioxide gas. The resulting product more closely approaches green pastures in nutritive value than dry roughages of comparable quality, being higher in carotene content and perhaps superior in other factors.

Silage for sheep may be made from a great variety of plants, including corn, sorghums, cereal grains, legumes, grasses, cannery refuse, pea vines, potatoes, beets, beet tops, sunflowers, and other materials. When properly preserved and fed, silages made from any of these materials are quite satisfactory.

Most practical sheepmen prefer to limit the silage allowance to about 4

Fig. 28-3. Ewes utilizing a root crop in New Zealand. For the most part, roots for sheep are stored and used as a winter feed in the United States. (Courtesy, Dept. of Scientific and Industrial Research, Wellington, New Zealand)

to 6 pounds per head per day, with the balance of the roughage ration consisting of hay. If a nonlegume silage is used, it is important that the hay be a legume. If for some unfortunate reason a legume hay cannot be provided when a nonlegume silage is fed, it is very necessary that a suitable protein concentrate and minerals should be provided.

Roots include all plants whose roots, tubers, bulbs, or other underground vegetative parts are used for feed. The important root crops for sheep are: mangels (stock beets), rutabagas (swedes), turnips, and carrots. These feeds are very succulent in nature, containing from 85 to 90 per cent or more of water. They are highly relished by sheep and have a peculiarly beneficial effect upon the digestion and general thrift of animals. The only objection to their general use is the cost and difficulty of growing, harvesting, and storing them. For the latter reason, roots are raised mainly by producers of purebred animals.

Roots are generally fed sliced, although some are fed whole. Where the teeth are good, practical sheepmen feel that little is gained by slicing roots. In this country, roots are usually limited to 5 to 6 pounds per head daily, but in other countries up to 12 to 14 pounds are often allowed daily per head.

Concentrates for Sheep

The concentrates include those feeds which are low in fiber and high in nutritive value. For purposes of convenience, concentrates are often further classified as (1) carbonaceous feeds and (2) nitrogenous feeds.

Ordinarily, sheep are fed few concentrates, except immediately before and after lambing, in conditioning ewes and rams for breeding, or when finishing lambs. During these periods, the most frequently used concentrates consist of the common farm grains: oats, corn, barley, wheat, rye, and the seeds of some of the grain sorghums. Numerous by-product feeds are also utilized for sheep, including those from the flour- and corn-milling industries, beet by-products, and oil meals or cake made from soybeans, flaxseed, and cottonseed.

Unless the seeds are unusually hard, none of the grains need to be ground when fed to sheep. The animals prefer to do their own grinding, and the feeds are no more efficiently utilized when ground.

Feed Additives

Antibiotics, hormones, and other feed additives, are being used less extensively by sheepmen than by cattlemen, but their use in lamb feeding is increasing. However, it is not within the scope of this book to discuss this area of sheep nutrition.[5]

FEEDING THE EWES

Success in the sheep business is largely measured by the percentage lamb crop raised and the pounds of lambs marketed per ewe. The most important factor affecting these criteria is the feed of the ewe. For purposes of convenience, the feeding of the ewes will be discussed under the following headings: (1) flushing the ewes, (2) feeding the pregnant ewes, (3) feeding at lambing time, and (4) feeding the lactating ewes.

Flushing the Ewes

The practice of conditioning or having thin ewes gain in weight just prior to breeding is known as "flushing." This may be accomplished by turning the ewes on a fresh, luxuriant pasture two to eight weeks before breeding time; or if such a pasture is not available, satisfactory results may be brought about by feeding a grain allowance of one-half to three-quarters of a pound daily over a like period of time. Oats alone are excellent, or a mixture of equal parts of oats and corn is very satisfactory. Pumpkins, broken and scattered over the pasture, are also relished and are excellent for flushing purposes. Some shepherds like to feed cabbage at this season.

In addition to any possible effect in increasing the percentage of lambs, flushing is said to result in the ewes breeding over a shorter period of time. The lamb crop will be more nearly uniform in size and easier to handle, and the ewes will be brought into good condition for winter.

Feeding the Pregnant Ewes

If a strong, healthy crop of lambs is to be expected, the ewes must be properly fed and cared for throughout the period of pregnancy. In general,

---

[5]For further information on the subject of feed additives for sheep, the reader is referred to Table 2-48 of *The Stockman's Handbook,* 4th edition, by the same author and publisher as *Animal Science.*

this means the feeding of a suitable and well-balanced ration, together with the necessary minerals and vitamins as required for maintenance (and growth, if the ewe is not fully mature), growth of the fleece, and development of the fetus. In addition, plenty of exercise must be provided. Suitable shelter should be made available during inclement weather, and the animals should be given access to an abundance of fresh air and sunshine at all times. Ewes should gain in weight during the entire period of pregnancy, making a total gain of 20 to 30 pounds for the period. They should enter the nursing period with some reserve flesh, because the lactation requirements are much more rigorous than those of the gestation period.

After the ewes are bred, they should have access to pastures as long as they are available and open. When the ground is firm, winter pasture or range, stalk, or stubble fields may be pastured to advantage. Green rye or wheat pastures furnish a very succulent feed and valuable exercise for the flock. Where winter pastures are either unavailable or inadequate, supplemental feeds must be provided. The most satisfactory forage is a good-quality legume hay—alfalfa, clover, lespedeza, or soybeans. The sheep producer, however, often seems to find it difficult to grow legumes on the farm or ranch and rather hard to buy such roughage at satisfactory prices. Where grass hay, such as native hays or timothy is used, every effort should be made to cut it at an early stage of maturity and to have it properly cured. Even then, a protein supplement should be provided, together with suitable minerals. Because of the known value of legumes from the standpoint of quality of proteins, minerals, and vitamins and the fact that grass hays are not recognized as too desirable for sheep, every effort should be made to supply at least a third of a good-quality legume roughage to pregnant ewes. A 150-pound ewe will eat about 4 pounds of hay daily. In order to prevent waste and protect the wool from chaff and hay seeds, suitable racks should be provided.

Such succulent feeds as roots and silage are desirable in keeping the ewes healthy and doing well. Of the root crops, turnips seem to be preferable for pregnant ewes. Silage made from corn, milo, legumes, or grasses, and which is not frozen, spoiled, nor moldy, may be fed quite safely and is excellent feed. Ordinarily, the daily ration of roots or silage should not exceed 5 pounds, which means that hay is usually fed in addition to the succulent feed.

About a month to six weeks before lambing time, the ewes are frequently given a concentrate allowance of one-half to three-fourths pound of grain daily, the amount depending upon the quality of roughage available and the condition of the ewes. At this time, the fetus is developing very rapidly and the demands being made upon the ewe are rather heavy. The concentrate given to the farm flock usually consists of home-grown grains, whereas range bands are often given pelleted or cubed protein supplements. Not only will good feeding result in stronger, and more vigorous lambs but the ewes will milk better.

On the western ranges, ewes are normally maintained on winter grazing areas, with or without supplemental feeds, as long as possible. Usually these ranges are located at the lower altitudes and the vegetation consists of rather mature and bleached grasses or brush and browse. When the vegetation is sparse or covered by deep snow, supplemental feeds of hays, preferably alfalfa, some other legume, or concentrates are provided. Often protein supplements in the form of pellets or cubes are used, for these may be scattered about the feeding grounds, neither being blown away nor difficult for the sheep to find. Usually such expensive protein supplements are fed only when native grass hays are being utilized, high quality alfalfa not requiring a protein supplement.

Feeding at Lambing Time

As lambing time approaches, or immediately after lambing, each ewe should be placed in an individual holding or lambing pen. At this time, the grain allowance should be materially reduced, but dry roughage may be fed free choice, when it is certain that it is of good quality and palatable. Usually, some five to seven days should elapse before ewes are placed on full feed following parturition. In general, feeds of a bulky and laxative nature should be provided during the first few days. A mixture of equal parts of oats and wheat bran is excellent. Soon after lambing, the ewe should be given water with the chill removed but should not be allowed to gorge.

Feeding the Lactating Ewes

Following lambing, the feed allowance of the ewe should be increased according to her capacity and needs. Although there is great individual and breed variation, ewes will yield from one to four quarts of milk per day. In comparison with cow's milk, ewe's milk is richer in protein and fat and higher in ash. It must also be borne in mind that, in addition to producing milk and maintaining her body, the ewe is growing wool, which is protein in character. Immature ewes are also growing. Under these circumstances, it is but natural and normal to expect ewes to lose in condition during the suckling period. The loss in weight is primarily determined by the inherent milking qualities of the individual and by the kind and amount of feed.

In general, it is considered good practice to feed lactating ewes rather liberally, for lambs make the most economical gains when suckling. It is a good plan to separate the ewes with twins from those with singles, giving the former more liberal rations or the benefit of the better pastures or ranges. In fact, some large sheep operators find this practice so advisable that they regularly separate out the twin bands.

Milk production can be greatly stimulated through the proper selection of feeds. If there is not sufficient high quality roughage for the entire winter, the most palatable and succulent portion should be reserved for use during the suckling period. Pastures should be provided as soon as possible, but in the meantime a high-quality legume hay or, better yet, a combination of hay and silage, will take care of the roughage needs. Though varying somewhat with the size and condition of the ewe and whether there are twins or merely a single, an adequate ration for lactating ewes may consist of approximately four pounds of high-quality alfalfa hay plus one to two pounds of grain daily. If neither a legume hay nor legume silage is available, a protein supplement should be included in the grain ration.

As soon as the spring range or pasture season has arrived, the use of harvested feeds should be discontinued, being both uneconomical and unnecessary.

FEEDING THE RAMS

The rams should be fed so as to remain in vigorous, active breeding condition. In general, rams should be fed the same kind of feeds as ewes but in slightly larger quantities. They need a generous allowance of relatively high-quality feed just before and during the breeding season, when pasture is not available. During the balance of the year, pasture is usually adequate when available; otherwise, the ration may be comparable to that of the ewes.

FEEDING GROWING-FINISHING LAMBS

The growing-finishing stage of lambs refers to that period extending from birth to weaning at four to six months of age. At no other period in the life of the sheep is the prevention of disease and the promotion of growth so important.

Where succulent pastures are available, most practical sheepmen, including producers with both farm flocks and range bands, consider that a combination of such green forage plus the ewe's milk is ample. In fact, lambs are unique among farm animals, inasmuch as they may be marketed at top prices off grass. Although young cattle may be sold off grass without having any other feed, they will usually fail to get sufficiently fat to bring top prices.

Frequently, farm-flock lambs are creep fed grain in addition to receiving their mother's milk and pastures. Usually creep feeding on the western range is too difficult. Should the range forages not be sufficiently abundant or lush to produce fat lambs, the range sheepman, therefore, usually elects to sell his animals as feeders at weaning time.

Good pastures for lambs are those that are rather succulent and that are composed of plants that are palatable and nutritious. This means green, actively growing pastures in contrast to dormant or dried forages.

Hothouse lambs are born out of season, in the fall or early winter, when pastures are usually unavailable. It is necessary that these animals be crowded for slaughter at two to four months of age, when they should weigh from 40 to 60 pounds. In addition to the right breeding for this specialty, therefore, hothouse lambs must be carefully fed. In the first place, the ewes should be given liberal quantities of a good succulent ration in order to stimulate the milk flow. Secondly, the lambs should be creep fed with a palatable and suitable ration from the time they are two weeks of age until marketing.

Creep Feeding Lambs

With farm flocks, creep feeding may be advantageous for the following reasons:

1. **To reach an early market and bring a higher price.**—April to June lamb prices are usually highest, following which prices decline very sharply. Normally, May and June lamb prices average $2.50 to $3.00 per hundred higher than August prices; $250 to $350 for 100 lambs. This means that lambs born in February have only about 100 days in which to reach the top market price of May and June. The following data point up this situation:

Lambing Date	Days to June 1
Jan. 1	151
Jan. 15	136
Feb. 1	120
Feb. 15	105
Mar. 1	92
Mar. 15	77
April 1	61

2. **To take advantage of extremely good feed conversion during the early life of the lamb.**—Two to 3 pounds of added creep feed will produce a pound of gain during this early period of growth. Therefore, if the creep ration costs $80 per ton, or $4 cwt., an 8¢ to 12¢ feed cost will return from 20¢ to 30¢ depending on market prices of top spring lambs.

3. **To maintain the finish of nursing lambs.**—Unless the pasture is good, top lambs will not be produced without creep feeding; that is, the lambs will not acquire sufficient finish and marketing will be delayed.

4. **To avoid added handling.**—Creep-fed lambs will go to market in 100 to 120 days, thus eliminating the need for worming, tagging, and handling lambs later in the season.

It is important that lambs be started on feed early and carefully. They will start eating at 10 to 14 days of age. At first, only a small amount of feed should be placed in the trough each day, any surplus feed being removed and fed to the ewes or to other livestock. In this manner, the feed will be kept clean and fresh, and the lambs will not be consuming any moldy or sour feed.

The creep ration selected is usually determined by (1) the availability and price of feed in the area and (2) the preference and judgment of the feeder. In addition to being reasonably economical and well balanced, it must be palatable. Such rations may be either commercially- or home-mixed. Rolled oats and wheat bran are especially palatable as a starting ration. A little later, grains may be added.

LAMB FEEDING

Prior to 1900, sheep feeding consisted of finishing the older animals, ewes, and wethers, chiefly on cheap and plentiful flour-mill by-products and prairie hay. As a result, the industry was centered near the flour-milling centers of St. Paul-Minneapolis and Chicago. In the early days, such feeding operations proved very lucrative. Huge yards were built, and thousands of sheep passed through these feeding plants. But gradually the competition for feeders increased, with the result that prices rose. Simultaneously, the by-products of the mills were found useful in feeding other classes of livestock, thus increasing in price. In the meantime, the Corn Belt farmers became interested in finishing sheep, and the market demand shifted to young lambs. All of these factors brought about the steady decline of the feed yards centered near the large flour mills, beginning about 1900. Moreover, the shift to lamb instead of mutton has been equally marked. Today, 90 to 95 per cent of the sheep slaughtered are lambs or yearlings.

The primary objective of the sheepman is that of producing milk-fat lambs suitable for slaughter at weaning time. Only when the range is inadequate are lambs sold via the feeder route. Almost all feeder lambs come from the range area. Some range areas produce only a small percentage of lambs which are classed as feeders; whereas in other areas almost all the lambs must be sold as feeders because the vegetation is not sufficient to promote rapid growth and finishing. It is estimated that, for the range area as a whole, an average of at least 25 per cent of all lambs produced in any one year receive additional feed after they are removed from the range and prior to slaughter.

Areas and Types of Lamb Feeding

Feeder lambs are generally sold to go into districts where grains and other concentrates are abundant or where fall and winter pastures are available. Such areas include: (1) the irrigated districts of the far West where the feeding of sugar beet by-products—beet pulp, beet tops, and molasses—predominates, (2) the wheat-raising sections of Oklahoma, Kansas, and Nebraska, where fall grazing of the wheat fields is practiced, and (3) the Corn Belt where stubble fields and meadows are gleaned and the corn crop may be harvested by lambs.

Colorado is the leading lamb-feeding state of the nation, finishing out one-sixth of the sheep and lambs fed in the United States. Here, locally grown alfalfa, sugar beet by-products, and barley are used extensively, along with considerable corn and protein supplements which are shipped in from outside areas.

Numerous feeding practices and a great variety of feeds are used in lamb-finishing operations. In general, however, all methods may be classified as (1) field finishing or (2) dry-lot finishing.

Field Finishing

This method of finishing lambs is somewhat comparable to the pasture finishing of cattle, except that a greater variety of feeds is used by lamb feeders. Field feeding requires relatively little labor and equipment, and the manure is dropped back on the land where it will do the most good. Death

Fig. 28-4. "Sheeping down" corn on an Iowa farm. First the crabgrass, weeds, and lower corn leaves are eaten. (Photo by A. M. Wettach, Mt. Pleasant, Iowa)

losses run higher than in dry-lot feeding because the feed consumption cannot be controlled.

The kind of field feeding varies from area to area and even between farms within the same locality. Most of the feeder lambs are shipped to these feeding areas in August and September at the time the lambs are normally weaned from range ewes. Usually these field-fed lambs are ready for market in November and early December, though it is not uncommon for a small

Fig. 28-5. Lambs finishing on winter wheat in western Kansas. (Courtesy, Rufus F. Cox, Kansas State University)

percentage of thin lambs to be held back for additional dry-lot finishing of 30 to 60 days.

Throughout the Corn Belt, feeder lambs are usually used as scavengers during the early part of the field-feeding process. Frequently, the lambs are pastured in the stubble fields or on the meadows until all these feeds are consumed, after which they are turned into cornfields.

In Kansas, Oklahoma, and Nebraska, thousands of lambs are finished primarily by fall pasturing of the wheat fields. In the Pacific Northwest, a limited number of lambs are finished by gleaning pea stubble.

Dry-lot Feeding

Dry-lot feeding is, as the name indicates, feeding under restricted conditions. This may either be (1) shelter or barn feeding or (2) open-yard feeding.

SHELTER OR BARN FEEDING

Because of inclement weather in the fall and early winter, many of the lamb-feeding operations in the central and eastern states are in dry lots which afford shelter. In some instances, the lambs are kept under cover without an exercising lot. These barns may consist of anything from open sheds to more costly and elaborate structures. In the vast majority of instances, the feeds are locally grown, corn being the chief concentrate used in these feeding operations. Lambs are finished as a means of marketing the grain, conserving the fertility of the soil, and furnishing gainful work during the winter months. Most of these lambs are finished by farmers who finish one or more carloads rather than by large operators who feed thousands of lambs. Practically all of the feeder lambs used in these operations come from the western ranges, either directly or via such markets as Denver, Omaha, Kansas City, St. Paul, or Chicago. After getting on full feed, these lambs are either hand-fed twice daily or self-fed.

OPEN-YARD FEEDING

Open-yard feeding is the common method of finishing lambs in the irrigated areas of the West, though a few eastern lamb-feeding operations are in open yards. In this system, equipment costs are kept to a minimum—the facilities merely consisting of an enclosed and well-drained yard which may or may not have a natural or constructed windbreak, and the necessary feed bunks. Open-yard feeding is often used by large operators who feed thousands of lambs.

Large quantities of alfalfa and sugar beet by-products are utilized in these yards. As it is often most economical to use a maximum of roughages, the feeding period may extend for as long as four to five months. Also, because of the desire to use a large proportion of roughage to grain, the lambs in these western feedlots are usually hand-fed twice daily rather than self-fed. In order to save labor, however, the practice of self-feeding is increasing. Lambs may be self-fed successfully, but it is recommended that the following precautions be

Fig. 28-6. Part of a flock of 1,750 lambs on feed. Note the square panel type feeders for alfalfa hay. (Courtesy, Great Northern Railway Company)

taken in order to lessen the incidence of overeating disease: (1) good management, (2) vaccination against enterotoxemia, and (3) more roughage and less concentrate be used.

Basic Considerations in Finishing Lambs

Although no rules of success are applicable to any and all conditions, the following basic considerations in finishing lambs are worth noting:

1. In lamb-feeding operations, the purchase price of the lambs represents 50 to 75 per cent of all costs. This indicates the importance of keeping death losses to a minimum.

2. Experienced feeders normally expect to lose about 2.5 per cent of lambs on feed. This is about twice the loss that occurs in commercial cattle-feeding operations.

3. Lamb feeding is seasonal in nature, usually extending from August to about the following May. This seasonal condition is due to the fact that (a) suitable feeder lambs are not available until the late summer and fall months, and (b) following the growing and harvesting seasons, the feeders have available quantities of marketable and unmarketable feeds which may be utilized by lambs.

4. As in cattle feeding, feedlot gains are expensive, usually costing more per pound than the selling price on the market. Thus, a reasonable margin or difference between the cost and selling price per hundredweight is necessary.

Under normal conditions, the necessary margin is estimated at $2.00 per hundred-weight.

5. Though the situation may vary according to the kind and comparative price of feeds available, it will require about 400 pounds of grain and 500 pounds of roughage to produce 100 pounds of gain. Thus, lambs utilize feeds more efficiently than cattle.

6. In a 250-mile shipment, lambs will shrink about 5 per cent. If properly fed, watered, and cared for enroute, lambs may be shipped 1,500 to 2,000 miles without much greater shrinkage than this.

7. Most feeder lambs weigh between 55 and 70 pounds when placed on feed and from 85 to 105 pounds following a 90- to 120-day feeding period.

8. Wool is of importance in selecting feeder lambs because it has a bearing on their market value, the pelt being the most valuable slaughter by-product.

9. Range feeder lambs are more plentiful than native feeders, thus allowing for greater selection; and usually they are more uniform and are less heavily infected with parasites.

10. Lambs are frequently fed on a contract basis, with many and varied agreements being used.

11. Wether lambs appear to make slightly more rapid gains but do not finish quite so early as ewe lambs.

12. Where western lambs have undergone a long shipment immediately after being taken from their mothers, special care is necessary in starting them on feed. After rest following shipment, lambs are usually started on grain by feeding about one-fourth pound per head daily. Gradually this allowance is increased so that the lambs are getting a full feed of about 2 pounds of grain per head daily and about the same amount of hay when on full feed four weeks later.

13. A great variety of feeds can be used in lamb feeding. In general, the successful feeder balances out the ration by selecting those feeds which are most readily available at the lowest possible price.

14. Unless such extremely hard seeds as millet are included in the ration, it does not pay to grind feeds for finishing lambs.

FEED ALLOWANCE AND SOME SUGGESTED RATIONS FOR SHEEP[6]

Sheep rations vary with the section of the country, depending chiefly on available local feeds. Fortunately, many feeds of similar nutritive properties can be interchanged in the ration as price relationships warrant. This makes it possible at all times to obtain a balanced ration at the lowest cost.

Except at lambing time or when emergencies occur as a result of drought or inclement weather, western bands receive little supplemental feed. Even with farm flocks, a minimum of grain is fed to breeding animals. Grain feeding

---

[6]Where possible, these rations were computed from the requirements as reported by the National Research Council and adapted by the author.

TABLE 28—1

HANDY EWE FEEDING GUIDE[1]

(Rams may be fed any of the rations listed for ewes, but they should receive
slightly more liberal allowances)

Type of Ration	First 100 Days of Gestation[2] (weighing 100 to 150 lbs.)		Last 6 Weeks of Gestation[2] (weighing 115 to 165 lbs.)	Ewes in Lactation (weighing 100 to 150 lbs.)
	(per day) (lbs.)	(kg)	(per day)	(per day)
1. Legume hay[3] or grass-legume mixed hay, good quality......................	3-5	1.4-2.3	To each ration listed in the first column add ½ to 1 lb. (.2-.3 kg) grain[6] daily.	To each ration listed in the first column, add ¾ to 2 lbs. (.3-.7 kg) grain[6] daily, plus ¼ lb. (.1 kg) protein supplement to each ration having less than 2 lbs. (.9 kg) legume.
2. Legume hay[3] or grass-legume mixed hay, good quality......................	1½-2½	.7-1.1		
Grass hay or other non-legume dry roughage......	1½-2½	.7-1.1		
3. Legume hay[3] or grass-legume mixed hay, good quality......................	1½-2	.7-.9		
Corn or sorghum silage.....	4-6	1.8-2.7		
4. Grass hay or other non-legume dry roughage......	3-5	1.4-2.3		
Protein supplement[4].........	¼-⅓	.1-.2		
5. Corn or other nonlegume silage.........................	8-11	3.6-5.0		
Protein supplement[4].........	¼-⅓	.1-.2		
6. Roots[5]............................	5-6	2.3-2.7		
Legume hay[3] or grass-legume mixed hay, good quality	2¼-3¼	1.0-1.5		
7. Grass hay or other non-legume dry roughage......	2-2½	.9-1.1		
Corn or sorghum silage.....	3-4	1.4-1.8		
Protein supplement[4].........	¼-⅓	.1-.2		

[1]The upper limits of hay given herein are higher than required because it is realized that ewes will refuse up to 30% of their forage allotment—the amount of waste varying according to the quality of the forage.
[2]Ewes should gain in weight during the entire pregnancy period, making a total gain of 15 to 25 pounds.
[3]The legume hay may consist of alfalfa, clover, soybean, lespedeza, etc.
[4]The protein supplement may consist of linseed, cottonseed, and/or soybean meal—with nutted (pea-size) products preferred.
[5]The important root crops for sheep are: mangels (stock beets), rutabagas (swedes), turnips, and carrots.
[6]The grain usually consists of whole corn, barley, wheat, oats, and/or sorghum; although other grains are used. Grain feeding the last six weeks of pregnancy will lessen pregnancy disease, increase the livability of lambs, and increase milk production.

usually is limited to the latter part of gestation and to the lactation period prior
to turning to pasture.

Tables 28-1 and 28-2 contain some handy feeding guides based on rations
that have been used by successful sheep operators in various sections of the
country. Also, some suggested show fitting rations follow. These are presented
as guides only. Sound judgment in their use should always prevail.

Some sheepmen, especially purebred and farm flock breeders, prefer to

TABLE 28—2

HANDY LAMB FEEDING GUIDE[1]

(Finishing lambs on full feed, weighing 55-105 pounds.
Many lamb feeders prefer to chop the hay and mix
and/or pellet it with the grain ration)

Type of Ration	Pounds/day	Kg/day
1. Legume hay	1¼-1¾	.57- .79
Grain[2]	1¼-1¾	.57- .79
2. Grass-legume mixed hay, good quality	1¼-1¾	.57- .79
Grain[2]	1¼-1¾	.57- .79
Protein supplement[3]	0.1-0.2	.05- .09
3. Legume hay[4]	1¼-1¾	.59- .79
Corn or sorghum silage	3¾-5¼	1.70-2.38
Protein supplement[3]	.15-0.2	.07- .09
4. Legume hay	¾-1	.34- .45
Corn or sorghum silage	1½-2½	.68-1.14
Grain[2]	1¼-1¾	.57- .79
Protein supplement[3]	0.1	.05
5. Corn or sorghum silage[4],[5]	2¾-4½	1.25-2.04
Grain[2]	1¼-1¾	.57- .79
Protein supplement[3]	0.2-0.3	.09- .14
6. Legume hay	1½-2½	.68-1.14
Grain[2]	¾	.34
Beet pulp, wet	2-3	.91-1.36

[1]Rations 3 and 6 are especially suited to starting lightweight lambs weighing 55 to 70 lbs., following which they should be switched to one of the other rations.
[2]Whole corn, barley, wheat, heavy oats, and/or sorghum.
[3]Linseed, cottonseed, and/or soybean meal.
[4]Although these rations are occasionally used, they are controversial. Most experienced sheep feeders prefer (1) a ration with some grain to ration No. 3 and (2) not to use silage for the only roughage as in ration No. 5.
[5]Ration No. 5 will be considerably improved by the addition of (1) ½ lb. of either dehydrated alfalfa or good legume hay and (2) 0.01 lb. of calcium carbonate.

feed grain mixtures rather than one grain only to ewes during the gestation and lactation periods. Then, any one of the following mixtures may be used:

Ration No. 1[1]	(lbs.)	(kg)
Oats	50	22.7
Barley	25	11.4
Wheat bran	10	4.5
Dry beet pulp	10	4.5
Linseed meal	5	2.3

Ration No. 2		
Corn or sorghum	50	22.7
Oats	20	9.1
Wheat bran	20	9.1
Protein supplement[2]	10	4.5

Ration No. 3		
Corn	60	27.2
Oats or wheat bran	30	13.6
Protein supplement[2]	10	4.5

Ration No. 4	(lbs.)	(kg)
Oats	30	13.6
Corn	20	9.1
Wheat bran	30	13.6
Protein supplement[2]	20	9.1

Ration No. 5		
Oats	60	27.2
Wheat bran	25	11.4
Protein supplement[2]	15	6.8

Ration No. 6		
Corn	90	40.9
Protein supplement[2]	10	4.5

[1]Ration 1 is used for gestating-lactating ewes at Washington State University. If the lactating ewes lose considerable flesh prior to turning to spring pasture, the shepherd adds a little corn to the ration.
[2]Linseed, cottonseed, and/or soybean meal.

Pound for pound, any of these mixed rations can replace the grain in any of the seven suggested rations of Table 28-1 but they are (1) slightly higher in protein and dry matter, and (2) slightly lower in TDN.

Fitting Rations for Sheep[7]

In addition to being reasonably economical (mostly home-grown) and well-balanced, the ration for show sheep must be palatable. Many feed combinations meet these specifications. The ration selected is usually determined by (1) the availability and price of feed in the area, and (2) the preference and judgment of the feeder.

Some suggested grain fitting rations follow. To each of these grain rations, good quality roughage—usually home-grown—should be added in about the proportions indicated in Table 28-2, Handy Lamb Feeding Guide:

A. Rations for lambs (either creep fed or weaned lambs that are being fitted for show). Show lambs on full feed will eat about 2½ pounds of grain per head daily:

Ration No. 1[1]	(lbs.)	(kg)	Ration No. 4	(lbs.)	(kg)
Oats	65	29.5	Oats	70	31.8
Wheat bran	17.5	7.9	Wheat bran	20	9.1
Linseed meal	17.5	7.9	Protein supplement[2]	10	4.5
Ration No. 2			**Ration No. 5**		
Corn	40	18.2	Oats	80	36.3
Oats	40	18.2	Wheat bran	20	9.1
Wheat bran	10	4.5			
Protein supplement[2]	10	4.5	**Ration No. 6**		
			Corn	45	20.4
Ration No. 3			Oats	45	20.4
Barley	20	9.1	Protein supplement[2]	10	4.5
Corn	20	9.1			
Oats	30	13.9	**Ration No. 7**		
Wheat bran	20	9.1	Corn, cracked	85	38.6
Protein supplement[2]	10	4.5	Soybean meal	15	6.8

[1]Beginning fitting ration used at Washington State University. Near the end of the fitting period, the shepherd adds 50 pounds of barley and 50 pounds of peas to each 100 pounds of Ration 1.
[2]Linseed, cottonseed, and/or soybean meal.

B. Rations for fitting yearlings and mature sheep. Show yearlings on full feed will eat about 3 pounds of grain per head daily, whereas mature sheep will eat about 3½ pounds of grain per head daily:

In general, these rations are higher in protein content than rations used in commercial fitting operations, but most experienced shepherds feel that by such means they get more bloom. Showmen prefer to feed steam rolled

---

[7]Further information on selecting, fitting, and showing sheep is presented in Chapter XVII of *Sheep and Wool Science,* a book by the same author and the same publisher as *Animal Science.*

Ration No. 1	(lbs.)	(kg)	Ration No. 3	(lbs.)	(kg)
Oats....................................	50	22.7	Corn....................................	40	18.2
Peas (split)...........................	40	18.2	Oats....................................	40	18.2
Wheat bran...........................	10	4.5	Wheat bran...........................	10	4.5
			Protein supplement[2]............	10	4.5
Ration No. 2					
Oats....................................	50	22.7	Ration No. 4		
Barley.................................	40	18.2	Oats....................................	60	27.2
Wheat bran...........................	10	4.5	Peas (split)...........................	10	4.5
			Barley.................................	10	4.5
			Wheat bran...........................	10	4.5
			Protein supplement[2]............	10	4.5

[2]Linseed, cottonseed, and/or soybean meal.

oats and barley and nutted (pea-sized) linseed meal.[8] Corn is usually cracked or coarsely ground, and peas are split or cracked. When pastures are not available, alfalfa is the most popular hay. But any good legume is quite satisfactory. The lighter types of lamb rations (A-1, 4, and 5) are usually used for summer feeding, especially when animals are being fitted for the late shows.

In fitting animals for show or sale, most successful shepherds feed a limited quantity of sliced carrots, cabbage, mangels (stock beets), rutabagas (swedes), or turnips. These succulent feeds are highly relished by sheep and appear to help their digestion and general thrift.

The following points also are pertinent in feeding sheep:

1. All classes and ages of sheep should be allowed free access to a double compartment mineral box, with loose salt in one compartment and a mixture of 1/3 salt and 2/3 steamed bone meal, or other suitable mineral, in the other.

2. Unless grains are unusually hard, they need not be ground for sheep. The animals prefer to do their own grinding, and the feeds are no more effectively utilized when ground.

QUESTIONS FOR STUDY AND DISCUSSION

1. In what ways may a stockman take practical advantage of the fact that sheep consume a higher proportion of forages than any other class of livestock?

2. What kind of feed was used in the Cornell experiment which showed one way in which stiff lamb disease may be reduced?

3. Most lambs are marketed as milk-fat lambs directly off pastures or ranges without having had any grain. What are the advantages of this, from an economic standpoint? Can this practice be applied to cattle or swine?

4. How do sheep differ from cattle in their grazing habits?

5. Lambs may be self-fed successfully, provided (a) they are vaccinated against enterotoxemia (overeating disease), and (b) considerable roughage and/or other bulky feeds are incorporated in the ration. What advantages does self-feeding have over hand-feeding?

6. Why is lamb feeding so seasonal in nature; more so than cattle feeding?

7. It requires about 400 pounds of grain and 500 pounds of roughage to produce 100 pounds of lamb. How does this efficiency of feed utilization compare with cattle and hogs?

[8]Among experienced shepherds, linseed meal is especially popular for fine wool sheep because of its reputed conditioning effect on the fleece.

8. In Table 28-2, the recommended pounds of hay and roughage are listed. How do these quantities compare with the recommended allowances for cattle on full feed?

9. Under what conditions might it be preferable that a feedlot operator feed lambs instead of cattle?

SELECTED REFERENCES

In addition to the Selected References listed in Chapter III, the following are recommended for Chapter XXVIII:

Title of Publication	Author(s)	Publisher
Fattening Lambs for Market	W. G. Kammlade	Circ. 523, University of Illinois, Urbana, Ill., Rev. 1950.
Feeding Range Lambs in Kansas	R. F. Cox T. D. Bell	Bul. 387, Agr. Exp. Sta., Kansas State University, Manhattan, Kan., 1957.
Lamb Feeding in Michigan	L. H. Blakeslee Graydon Blank R. E. Rust	Ext. Bul. 334, Michigan State University, East Lansing, Mich., 1955.
Nutrient Requirements of Sheep	No. V Pub. 1693	"Nutrient Requirements of Domestic Animals," Nat'l Academy of Sci. Nat'l Res. Council, Washington, D. C., 1968.

CHAPTER XXIX

MARKETING AND SLAUGHTERING SHEEP AND LAMBS[1]

Contents   Page

Leading Terminal Sheep and Lamb Markets..732
Leading Terminal Feeder Sheep Markets..732
Market Classes and Grades of Sheep..733
    Factors Determining Market Classes of Sheep................................733
        Sheep and Lambs..733
        Use Selection of Sheep and Lambs................................733
        The Sex Classes..735
        Age Groups..735
        Weight Divisions 737
    The Market Grades of Sheep and Lambs................................737
Other Sheep Market Terms and Factors..737
    Native and Western Sheep..737
    "Whiteface" and "Blackface" Sheep..738
    Discounting Long-tailed and Ram Lambs................................739
    Value of the Pelt in Market Sheep..739
Packer Slaughtering and Dressing of Sheep and Lambs................739
    Steps in Slaughtering and Dressing Sheep and Lambs................740
    The Break-joint or Lamb-joint..740
    The Dressing Percentage..741
Aging Lamb and Mutton..742
Disposition of the Lamb and Mutton Carcass................................742
The Lamb Carcass and Its Wholesale Cuts................................743
Goat Meat (Chevon)..743
Questions for Study and Discussion..744
Selected References 745

Although sheep are marketed through much the same media as cattle or hogs, the following differences exist:

1. In general, there is a greater transportation problem, because a preponderance of lambs are raised west of the Mississippi while most of the lamb is consumed east of the Mississippi.

2. Age is a greater factor in determining relative market values of sheep than it is in determining that of cattle and hogs; thus, 95 per cent of the sheep slaughter is from lambs and yearlings.

3. More sheep than cattle are sold in the country.

4. Because of the pelt, the by-products of sheep are more valuable than are the by-products obtained in cattle or hog slaughter.

5. More sheep and lambs than any other class of animals are slaughtered under federal inspection.

---

[1]The sections "Market Classes and Grades of Sheep," "Other Sheep Market Terms and Factors," and "Packer Slaughtering and Dressing of Sheep and Lambs" were authoritatively reviewed by John C. Pierce, Director, Livestock Division, Consumer and Marketing Service, USDA.

6. Sheepmen take more breeders back to the country than do cattle or hog producers.

LEADING TERMINAL SHEEP AND LAMB MARKETS

Sheep are marketed by much the same methods as cattle. As with stocker and feeder cattle, direct selling is increasing with stocker and feeder sheep. Denver is the leading sheep and lamb market. The nine largest sheep and lamb markets by rank and their receipts are given in Table 29-1.

TABLE 29—1

TOTAL RECEIPTS OF NINE LEADING TERMINAL SHEEP
AND LAMB MARKETS, BY RANK, 1966[1]

Market	1966
Denver, Colorado	758,000
South St. Paul, Minnesota	625,000
Fort Worth, Texas	424,000
Kansas City, Missouri	411,000
Omaha, Nebraska	401,000
Sioux City, Iowa	302,000
St. Joseph, Missouri	226,000
Chicago, Illinois	137,000
St. Louis National Stock Yards	111,000
United States total, public stockyards	6,424,000

[1]Agricultural Statistics, 1967, USDA, p. 403.

LEADING TERMINAL FEEDER SHEEP MARKETS

When the range or pasture is inadequate to produce a slaughter lamb, the animals must go the feeder route. Feeder lambs are finished out by various

TABLE 29—2

FEEDER SHIPMENTS FROM TEN LEADING TERMINAL FEEDER
SHEEP AND LAMB MARKETS, BY RANK, 1966[1]

Market	1966
Idaho Falls & Blackfoot, Idaho	168,000
South St. Paul, Minn.	126,000
Denver, Colo.	116,000
West Fargo, N.D.	113,000
Ogden, Utah	106,000
Sioux Falls, S.D.	52,000
Billings, Mont.	46,000
Sioux City, Iowa	36,000
Kansas City, Mo.	35,000
S. St. Joseph, Mo.	29,000
United States total, public stockyards	1,045,000

[1]Agricultural Statistics 1967, USDA p. 402.

methods and in various sections of the United States. Such feeder lambs are either sold direct or are consigned to terminal markets.

In-shipments of feeder sheep and lambs at central markets are not recorded, for the reason that it is difficult at the time of receipt of shipments to ascertain whether sheep will go the slaughter route or the feeder route. However, since most feeder sheep and lambs are eventually shipped out from terminal markets prior to being placed on feed, out-shipments from terminal markets are a satisfactory criterion of the rank of terminal markets in the handling of feeder sheep and lambs. On this basis, the 10 leading feeder sheep and lamb markets, by rank, are as indicated in Table 29-2.

MARKET CLASSES AND GRADES OF SHEEP

The market classes and grades of sheep follow closely the pattern for the classes and grades of cattle and swine (see Table 29-3). One notable difference is that a sizeable number of sheep are sold as breeders. For the most part, this class is made up of mature western ewes that are sold to country buyers for the purpose of producing one to two more crops of lambs before again being returned to the market. Usually such ewes can be acquired at a lower cost than ewe lambs. In certain sections of the country, many flock rams are acquired on the market, although no market quotation is given for such breeders and the practice is not considered too sound. Another difference between sheep and other species is found in the fact that one feeder class, namely the shearers, is based on wool value as well as adaptability for further feeding.

Factors Determining Market Classes of Sheep

The disposition or use to be made of sheep is determined by: (1) whether they are sheep or lambs, (2) the use selection, (3) sex, (4) age, and (5) weight.

SHEEP AND LAMBS

The first major market subdivision of the ovine species separates the animals into sheep and lambs. Lambs include those animals that are approximately one year old and under. When there is any question as to whether animals should be classified as sheep or lambs, a final decision is usually based upon an examination of the teeth. If the first pair of larger, broader permanent teeth is about fully developed, the animal is classified as a yearling; for this change in the teeth takes place at about 12 months of age.

At the present time, lambs and yearlings make up approximately 95 per cent of the total sheep slaughter.

USE SELECTION OF SHEEP AND LAMBS

Sheep and lambs are divided into six market groups based on the uses to be made of them or the purposes for which they are best suited: slaughter sheep, feeder sheep, breeding sheep, slaughter lambs, feeder lambs, and shearer lambs. A brief description of each of these classes follows:

TABLE 29—3

MARKET CLASSES AND GRADES OF SHEEP

Sheep or Lambs	Use Selection	Sex Classes	Age	Weight Division	(Pounds)	(Kilograms)	Commonly Used Grades
Sheep	Slaughter sheep	Ewes	Yearling	Light	90 down	40.9 down	Prime, Choice, Good, Utility, Cull[1]
				Medium	90 to 100	40.9-45.4	
				Heavy	100 up	45.4-up	
			Mature (2-year-old or older)	Light	120 down	54.5 down	Choice, Good, Utility, Cull[1]
				Medium	120-140	54.5-63.6	
				Heavy	140 up	63.6 up	
		Wethers	Yearling	Light	100 down	45.4 down	Prime, Choice, Good, Utility, Cull[1]
				Medium	100-110	45.4-49.9	
				Heavy	110 up	49.9 up	
			Mature (2-year-old or older)	Light	115 down	52.2 down	Choice, Good, Utility, Cull[1]
				Medium	115-130	52.2-59.0	
				Heavy	130 up	59.0 up	
		Rams	Yearling	All weights			Prime, Choice, Good, Utility, Cull[1]
			Mature (2-year-old or older)	All weights			Choice, Good, Utility, Cull[1]
	Feeder sheep	Ewes and wethers	Yearlings	All weights			Fancy, Choice, Good, Medium, Cull
		Ewes	Mature (2-year-old or older)	All weights			Choice, Good, Medium, Cull
	Breeding sheep	Ewes (rams occasionally purchased as breeders, but not listed in market reports)	Yearlings, 2, 3, or 4-yr.-olds and older	All weights			Fancy, Choice, Good, Medium, Cull
Lambs	Slaughter lambs	Ewes, wethers, and rams	Hothouse lambs	60 down			Prime, Choice, Good, Utility, Cull[1]
		Ewes, wethers, and rams	Spring lambs	Light	70 down	31.8 down	Prime, Choice, Good, Utility, Cull[1]
				Medium	70-90	31.8-40.9	
				Heavy	90 up	40.9 up	
		Ewes, wethers, and rams	Lambs	Light	75 down	34.0 down	Prime, Choice, Good, Utility, Cull[1]
				Medium	75-95	34.0-43.1	
				Heavy	95 up	43.1 up	
	Feeder lambs	Ewes and wethers	All ages	All weights			Fancy, Choice, Good, Medium, Cull
	Shearer lambs	Ewes and wethers	All ages	All weights			Choice, Good, Medium

[1] In addition to the above quality grades the following yield grades became effective March 1, 1969: Yield Grade 1, Yield Grade 2, Yield Grade 3, Yield Grade 4, and Yield Grade 5. Thus, slaughter sheep and lambs may be graded for (1) quality alone, (2) yield grade alone, or (3) both quality and yield grades.

Slaughter sheep.—Yearlings or older animals intended for immediate slaughter.

Feeder sheep.—Yearlings or older animals best suited for further finishing.

Breeding sheep.—Largely mature western ewes that are returned to the country for further reproduction. In addition to market grade in considering the suitability of ewes for breeding purposes, it is important that attention be given to the condition of the teeth and the breed, health, and general potentialities as a breeder.

Slaughter lambs.—Young animals under one year of age that are sufficiently fat for immediate slaughter.

Feeder lambs.—Young animals under one year of age that carry insufficient finish for slaughter purposes but which show indications of making good gains if placed on feed.

Shearer lambs.—Those intended for shearing and further finishing prior to slaughtering. This classification is of importance on certain markets during the late winter and early spring months. Typical shearer lambs carry nearly a full year's growth of wool, but they are not fat enough to be market-topping slaughter lambs. Such lambs are usually shorn out and finished before returning to the market. The term "shorn lamb" is used to designate those lambs that have had their fleece removed within 60 days prior to marketing. Those fed lambs that have not been shorn are usually differentiated from shorn lambs by adding the term "wooled" to the class name.

THE SEX CLASSES

The sex classes for sheep and lambs are: ewes, wethers, and rams. At the lamb and yearling stage, ewes and wethers are equally suitable for slaughter purposes. Ram lambs are usually somewhat discounted in price, and they are almost never used for feeder purposes. A definition of each sex class follows.

Ewe.—A female sheep or lamb.

Wether.—A male ovine animal that was castrated at an early age, before reaching sexual maturity and before developing the physical characteristics peculiar to rams.

Ram.—An uncastrated male ovine animal of any age. The term "buck" is sometimes applied to animals of this sex class.

AGE GROUPS

Each of the major age divisions is further separated into more exacting age groups. Thus, mature sheep may be designated as yearlings, two-year-olds, three-year-olds, four-year-olds, or mature sheep. Yearlings are much more acceptable for slaughter purposes than mature sheep.

In a general way, age groups in lambs are indicated by the terms "hothouse lambs," "spring lambs," and "lambs." Each of these age groups may be described briefly as follows:

Hothouse lambs.—Very young lambs—usually less than three months of age at slaughter—which are born and marketed out of season. Such milk-fat lambs are usually marketed during the period from Christmas to the Easter holidays at weights ranging from 30 to 60 pounds. Hothouse lambs may consist of ewe, wether, or ram lambs. Although sex class is unimportant, these lambs should be undocked if sold on the Boston market.

Fig. 29-1. Hothouse lambs "hog dressed" (meaning head and pelt on, but front feet and viscera removed). The method holds shrinkage to a minimum and maintains a pink carcass color in young lambs. The pluck is left in. (In this case, the pluck consists of the liver, heart, lungs, gullet, and windpipe.) (Courtesy, P. T. Ziegler, Pennsylvania State University)

Spring lambs.—New-crop lambs arriving at the market in the spring of the year. Usually these are lambs born in the late fall or the early winter and marketed prior to July 1. After July 1 animals of like birth are simply designated as lambs on the market. The most desirable spring lambs range from three to seven months in age and weigh from 70 to 90 pounds. Because of the young age, sex class is unimportant in spring lambs—they may be ewe, wether, or ram lambs.

Lambs.—All young ovine animals that do not classify as either hothouse or spring lambs. This is by far the most numerous class of market sheep under one year of age. These animals are usually born in the late winter or spring of the year and are marketed at 7 to 12 months of age. In general, they subsist on milk and grass. Lambs fed grain prior to marketing are designated as fed lambs in order to differentiate them from lambs.

Yearlings.—Young sheep between approximately one and two years of age.

They may be identified by the fact that they have cut their first pair of permanent incisor teeth but not the second pair.

Two-year-olds.—Sheep that are between 24 and 36 months old and which have cut their second pair of permanent incisor teeth.

Three-year-olds.—Sheep that are between 36 and 48 months old and which have cut their third pair of permanent incisor teeth.

Four-year-olds.—Sheep that are between 48 and 60 months old and which have a full set of permanent incisors.

Mature sheep.—Usually animals that are two-years-old or over. With further age and the loss of teeth, they are referred to as broken-mouthed. If all the incisors are missing or worn down to the gums, they are known as gummers. If the teeth are long and spread apart at the surface, the ewes are called spreaders. All gummers and broken-mouthed ewes should be rejected in buying breeding sheep, for such animals are not likely to hold up in flesh on winter feeds.

WEIGHT DIVISIONS

Weight is an especially important price factor in the case of lambs. As a rule, heavy lambs (90 pounds and up) are in less demand on the market than lighter-weight animals of similar grade. This is largely due to the consumer preference for small- or medium-sized cuts of lamb. Thus, weight is an important factor in both feeder and slaughter lambs. Heavy, fat ewes usually sell at a discount; they are not considered desirable for either slaughter or breeding purposes.

The Market Grades of Sheep and Lambs

Based on conformation, finish, and quality, slaughter sheep and lambs are graded as Prime, Choice, Good, Utility, or Cull. The corresponding grades of feeder sheep and lambs are: Fancy, Choice, Good, Medium, and Cull.

While no official grading of live animals is done by the U.S. Department of Agriculture, these grades do form a basis for uniform reporting of livestock marketing.

OTHER SHEEP MARKET TERMS AND FACTORS

In addition to the rather general terms used in designating the different market classes and grades of sheep, the following terms and factors are frequently of importance.

Native and Western Sheep

Native sheep are predominately of mutton breeding and are produced in the central, eastern, and southern states, in the mixed farming areas. Westerns are predominately of grade Rambouillet breeding or Rambouillet X mutton breed crossbreds that come from the western ranges. In the case of western sheep,

Fig. 29-2. Market grades of slaughter lambs. Names changed to conform to new USDA grades, as interpreted by the author. (Courtesy, USDA, Production and Marketing Administration)

their state of origin is frequently used as a designation rather than the broad classification as westerns.

"Whiteface" and "Blackface" Sheep

"Whiteface" and "blackface" are sometimes used to designate the general type and breeding of sheep and lambs. In general, whiteface sheep and lambs are predominately of fine-wool breeding and do not possess quite the blockiness and general excellent mutton conformation of the blackface sheep. Blackface sheep are either predominately of mutton breeding or are sired by a blackfaced ram of one of the mutton breeds.

Discounting Long-tailed and Ram Lambs

All market lambs from commercial flocks should be docked and castrated at an early age. Long-tailed and buck lambs are frequently docked up to $2 and $3 per hundredweight on a discriminating market. Thin lambs, which should go the feeder route, are discounted more than slaughter animals. Despite the dock in price of ram lambs that are subsequently culled out and marketed for slaughter, purebred breeders can often afford to retain all male lambs as rams until weaning age, at which time more intelligent selections may be made. Of course, this can only be justified when some of the ram lambs are valuable for breeding purposes.

Value of the Pelt in Market Sheep

When wool prices are good, the degree of desirability of the pelt is a factor of importance in determining the price of market sheep and lambs.

PACKER SLAUGHTERING AND DRESSING OF SHEEP AND LAMBS

Table 29-4 shows the proportion of sheep and lambs dressed commercially (meaning that they were slaughtered in federally inspected and other wholesale and retail establishments) and the proportion slaughtered on farms. The total figure refers to the number dressed in all establishments and on farms.

TABLE 29—4

PROPORTION OF SHEEP AND LAMBS SLAUGHTERED
COMMERCIALLY 1960 TO 1966[1]

Year	Sheep and Lambs		
	Total Number Slaughtered (Commercially and Non-commercially)	Number Slaughtered Commercially	Per Cent Slaughtered Commercially
	(1,000 head)	(1,000 head)	(%)
1960.....................	16,239	15,899	97.91
1961.....................	17,536	17,190	98.03
1962.....................	17,171	16,837	98.05
1963.....................	16,153	15,822	97.95
1964.....................	14,897	14,595	97.97
1965.....................	13,300	13,006	97.79
1966.....................	13,001	12,737	97.97

[1]Agricultural Statistics 1967, USDA. p. 404.

Whether sheep are slaughtered in a large federally inspected packing plant, in a small local slaughtering house, or on the farm, the slaughtering procedure is much the same. Because most sheep are slaughtered commercially rather than on farms, only packer slaughtering procedure will be discussed.

In order to avoid undue excitement and make for ease in handling, gregarious sheep and lambs are usually led to the packer's slaughtering pens by an old goat, commonly referred to as "Judas." A reasonable fast and quiet prior to slaughtering are especially important for sheep.

Steps in Slaughtering and Dressing Sheep and Lambs

The endless chain method is used in sheep slaughter. The steps in packing house slaughter procedure are as follows:

1. **Rendering insensible.**—The sheep are rendered insensible[2] by use of a captive bolt stunner, gunshot, electric current, or carbon dioxide; a shackle is placed around the hind leg just above the foot; and the animals are delivered to an overhead rail by means of a wheel hoist.

2. **Bleeding.**—A double-edged knife is inserted into the neck just below the ear so that it severs the large blood vessel in the neck.

3. **Removal of feet.**—After bleeding, the front feet are removed. Lambs and most yearlings will break at the break-joint or lamb-joint, a temporary joint characteristic of young sheep which is located immediately above the ankle. In dressing mature sheep, the front feet are removed at the ankle, leaving a round joint on the end of the shank bone.

4. **Removal of pelt.**—The pelt is next removed. Caution is taken to prevent damage to the fell (the thin, tough membrane covering the carcass immediately under the pelt).

5. **Removal of hind feet and head.**—Next the hind feet and head are removed.

6. **Opening of carcass and eviscerating.**—The carass is opened down the median line; the internal organs, windpipe, and gullet are removed; and the breast bone is split. The kidneys are left intact.

7. **Shaping.**—The forelegs are folded at the knees and are held in place by a skewer. A spread-stick is inserted in the belly to allow for proper chilling and to give shape to the carcass.

8. **Washed.**—Finally the carcass is washed, wiped, and promptly sent to the cooler. Some of the better-grade carcasses are wrapped in special coverings for marketing.

The Break-joint or Lamb-joint

In general, the packer classes as lamb all carcasses in which the forefeet are removed at the break-joint or lamb-joint. This point—which can be severed

---

[2] See footnote under "Steps in Slaughtering and Dressing Cattle," Chapter XV, relative to humane slaughter methods.

on all lambs, most yearling wethers, and some yearling ewes (ewes mature earlier than wethers or males)—is a temporary cartilage located just above the ankle. In lambs, the break-joint has four well-defined ridges that are smooth, moist, and red. In yearlings, the break-joint is more porous and dry. In mature sheep, the cartilage is knit or ossified and will no longer break, thus making it necessary to take the foot off at the ankle instead. This makes a round-joint (commonly called spool-joint). All carcasses possessing the round-joint are sold as mutton rather than lamb.

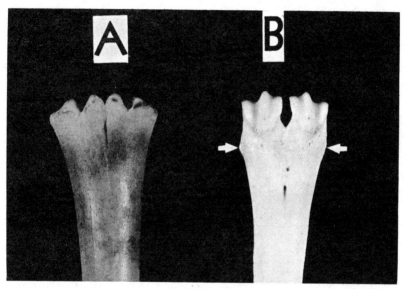

Fig. 29-3. The two types of joints of the foreleg of a sheep: A, the break-joint or lamb-joint, and B, the round-joint or spool-joint. Arrow indicates the location of the break-joint or ossification. All carcasses possessing the round-joint are sold as mutton rather than lamb. (Courtesy, Washington State University)

The Dressing Percentage

In order to yield a high percentage of carcass, sheep must be (1) light in pelt, (2) well finished and heavily muscled, and (3) free from paunchiness. Because of the higher value of the offal of sheep, especially the high value of the pelt, a high dressing percentage in sheep is not so important as in cattle or hogs. In fact, the wool is usually worth more per pound than the carcass of mutton or lamb. Wool yield, therefore, is usually an important item in slaughter return, and dressing return, and dressing percentage lowered by heavier wool yield may actually mean a greater total return. For this reason, the fleece should be as heavy as is consistent with the production of mutton or lamb of high quality.

Table 29-5 gives the dressing percentages that may be expected from the different grades of sheep and lambs. As would be expected, the highest dressing percentage is obtained when animals are slaughtered following shearing. Lambs of the mutton breeds yield a somewhat higher percentage of carcass than

TABLE 29—5

DRESSING PER CENT OF LAMBS AND SHEEP (MUTTON)
BY GRADE[1]

Lambs				Sheep (Mutton)		
Grade	Range	Average		Grade	Range	Average
Prime...........	47-53	50		Choice.........	47-53	50
Choice.........	45-50	47		Good...........	45-50	47
Good...........	43-47	45		Utility.........	42-46	44
Utility..........	41-45	43		Cull............	38-44	41
Cull..............	38-43	40				

[1]Provided by J.C. Pierce, Jr., Director, Livestock Division, Consumer and Marketing Service, USDA.

those of the so-called wool breeds. The offal and by-products from slaughter of sheep and lambs consist of the blood, pelt, feet, head, and viscera.

The average live weight of sheep and lambs dressed by federally inspected meat packing plants and their percentage yield in meat for the year 1966 was as shown in Table 29-6.

TABLE 29—6

AVERAGE LIVE WEIGHT, CARCASS YIELD AND DRESSING
PERCENTAGES OF ALL SHEEP AND LAMBS COMMERCIALLY
SLAUGHTERED IN THE U.S. IN 1966[1]

	Average Live Weight	Average Dressed Weight	Average Dressing Percentage
	(lbs.) (kg)	(lbs.) (kg)	(%)
Sheep and lambs............	102 46.3	50.6 23.0	49.6

[1]Livestock and Meat Statistics, USDA, Supp. for 1966 to Statistical Bul. No. 333, p. 85, 104.

AGING LAMB AND MUTTON

Prime and Choice lamb and mutton carcasses are best if aged two or three weeks. On the other hand, the medium and plain carcasses carrying less fat should be merchandised a few days after slaughter.

DISPOSITION OF THE LAMB AND MUTTON CARCASS

For the most part, lamb and mutton carcasses are sold to the retailers fresh and as entire carcasses rather than as wholesale cuts. On the other hand, some wholesale cuts are prepared in the packing plants, thus making it possible to meet the greater demands of certain areas for specific cuts.

A small amount of lamb and mutton is frozen and held for future market, but the consumers in this country have never accepted frozen lamb and mutton to the same degree as the British.

Lamb and mutton may be cured by the ordinary methods employed in curing pork. The curing of lamb and mutton requires somewhat less time because of the comparatively smaller cuts. Legs of lamb that have been cured and smoked—known as lamb hams—are very similar to pork hams in color and flavor. One of the main objections to cured and smoked lamb is that it dries out rapidly. For this reason, only a very small amount of lamb and mutton is cured in this country.

Carcasses or wholesale cuts that are not considered desirable for the trade, or for which there is not sufficient demand, are processed at the packing plant. Eventually they are sold as prepared meats and meat food products.

THE LAMB CARCASS AND ITS WHOLESALE CUTS

The two major wholesale cuts of lamb are the (1) hind saddle and (2) fore saddle. The division into hind and fore saddle is made between the twelfth and thirteenth ribs, with one pair of ribs remaining on the hind saddle. Each of these two larger cuts comprises about 50 per cent of the carcass weight.

The hind saddle is further subdivided into the legs and loins. The fore saddle is subdivided into the rack (or hotel rack), shoulder, and breast.

GOAT MEAT (CHEVON)

Goat meat is sold under the trade name of Chevon. However, most goat meat is put into processed meats. It is a perfectly wholesome food, though lacking in the blocky conformation and degree of finish possessed by the better grades of lamb and mutton. Chevon from older goats is likely to possess a strong flavor. Only a limited number of goats are slaughtered for meat.

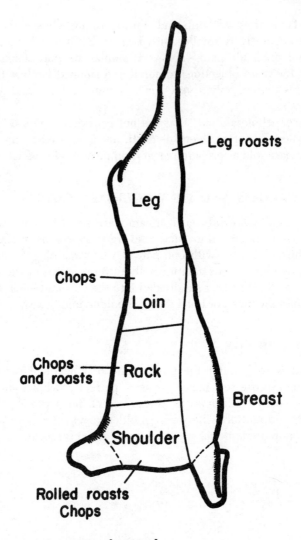

Lamb

Fig. 29-4. Wholesale cuts of lamb and some of the common retail cuts. Sometimes the carcass is divided between the twelfth and the thirteenth ribs into (1) the hind saddle (including the leg and loin) and (2) the fore saddle (including the rack, shoulder, and breast). (Drawing by R. F. Johnson)

QUESTIONS FOR STUDY AND DISCUSSION

1. Why is sheep marketing important?
2. What primary differences exist between the marketing of sheep and hogs?
3. What method of marketing (what market channel) do you consider most advantageous for the sheep sold out of your area, and why?
4. Why do not the leading sheep markets coincide with the leading cattle and the leading hog markets?
5. Why is it important that the sheepman know the leading sheep markets?

6. List the on-foot market (a) classes and (b) grades of sheep and lambs and tell of their value.
7. Why is it important that a sheepman know the market classes and grades of sheep and lambs and what each implies?
8. Define and give the special significance of the following sheep and lamb market terms:
   a. Breeding sheep
   b. Shearer lambs
   c. Hothouse lambs
   d. Spring lambs vs. lambs
   e. Native and western sheep
   f. Break-joint
   g. Fell
9. What is Chevon?

SELECTED REFERENCES

In addition to the Selected References listed in Chapter VI, the following are recommended for Chapter XXIX:

Title of Publication	Author(s)	Publisher
All About Lamb		National Livestock and Meat Board, 36 S. Wabash, Chicago, Ill.
Distribution of Lamb and Mutton for Consumption in the U.S.	H. O. Doty, Jr.	AMS-93m, Agricultural Marketing Service, USDA, Washington, D. C., Feb. 1956.
Killing and Cutting Lamb	R. W. Snyder	Extension Service B-106, Texas A and M College, College Station, Tex.
Lamb and Mutton on the Farm	Farmers' Bul. 1807	U.S. Department of Agriculture, Washington, D. C.
Lamb Cutting and Merchandising Manual		American Sheep Producers Council, 520 Railway Exchange Building, 909 17th St., Denver, Col.
Lamb Marketing Costs and Margins		Marketing Res. Report 159, U.S. Department of Agriculture, Washington, D. C.
Marketing Aspects of Fattening Lambs in the Mountain States 1954-55	L. H. Davis	Bul. 402, Ag. Exp. Sta., Utah State University, Logan, Utah.
Marketing Range Sheep and Lambs from New Mexico	Bul. 416	Ag. Exp. Sta., New Mexico State University, University Park, N. M.
Merchandising Heavy Lamb		National Livestock and Meat Board, 36 S. Wabash, Chicago, Ill.
Slaughtering, Cutting, and Processing Lamb and Mutton on the Farm	Farmers' Bul. 2152	U.S. Department of Agriculture, Washington, D. C.

Chapter XXX

WOOL AND MOHAIR

Contents   Page

Wool Is the Natural Clothing of Sheep..748
Virtues of Wool...749
Uses of Wool...750
Magnitude of the U.S. Wool and Textile Industry.............................750
The Wool Fiber...753
   The Three Cell Layers...753
   Chemical Composition of Wool..754
Some Fleece Characteristics..754
   Grease 755
   Length 755
   Density 755
   Diameter 756
Production and Handling of the Wool Clip..756
Requisites of Wool...760
Classes of Wool..760
   Combing or Staple Wool...760
   French Combing Wool...761
   Clothing Wool..761
   Carpet Wool 761
Wool Grading 762
   Grades of Wool..763
      The Blood System...765
      Numerical Count System..766
         Worsted Spinning Count...766
Wool Sorting...766
The Marketing of Wool...767
   International Trade in Wool...767
   Methods of Marketing Wool in the United States...........................768
The Manufacturing Processes...769
   Wool, from Fleece to Fabric...770
Mohair 770
   World Mohair Production...770
   U.S. Mohair Production and Consumption......................................771
   Mohair Characteristics 772
   Production, Handling, and Marketing of Mohair.............................773
   Classes and Grades of Mohair...773
   Uses of Mohair...775
The National Wool Act..775
Questions for Study and Discussion..776
Selected References 776

Sheep yield two products—lamb or mutton and wool, with the relative emphasis on each varying according to the remuneration derived therefrom. This same thinking applies wherever mutton and lamb are produced, which is throughout the world.

Despite the larger income from lamb under certain conditions, practical sheepmen everywhere recognize the fact that the fleece represents certain income, whether a lamb is produced or not. Accordingly, they select ewes and rams with long, dense fleeces of uniformly good quality and reject those individuals having fibers of any color other than white or those with hairy, loose, or extremely open fleeces.

No balance statement will ever alter the importance of wool as one of the world's greatest textile materials. Since the dawn of history, the wool of sheep, the natural function of which is to protect and conserve the warmth of the animal's body, has been used by the human race. Although its chief use has been, and still is, for clothing, it is widely used for blankets, upholstery, carpets, felts, and numerous other products in industry.

It is noteworthy that the income to U.S. sheep raisers from wool, including the value of pulled wool, amounts to about one-third of the total income from sheep, lambs, and wool. Thus, about two-thirds of the total income to sheepmen is derived from meat (chiefly lamb).

The discussion that follows is designed to bridge the gap between the wool producer and the manufacturer. Although each has his particular problems, both are working toward a common goal. The producer breeds, feeds, and manages his flock to supply the raw material; whereas the manufacturer scours, combs, spins, and weaves the fiber into cloth.

WOOL IS THE NATURAL CLOTHING OF SHEEP

With all the perfection and modification in the fleece that has been wrought through centuries of domestication, breeding, selection, and improved environmental conditions, it must not be forgotten that wool is the natural hair as well as clothing of sheep. A covering of hair or feathers performs a thermo-regulatory function for warm-blooded animals, the original intent being to protect the grower from heat or cold. As wool fibers are poor conductors of heat, they serve to prevent any abnormal loss of heat from the body.

In the wild state, sheep carried two distinct coats. The outer or protective coat consisted of long, coarse fibers, which today are classed as hairs (known as kemp). The undercoat of the wild sheep was soft and curly and provided the necessary warmth for the animal.

It is interesting to note that the relative development of these two coats varied with the climatic conditions under which the animals lived.

Unfortunately, up to the present time, breeding has not banished the coarse fibers entirely, for they are still evident in most breeds of sheep. This is particularly obvious in the Scotch Blackface sheep, one of the present breeds most closely related to the primitive type. However, since the days of mythology, when wool was rightfully called the Golden Fleece, sheep breeders everywhere have recognized that the elimination of black hairs, kemp, and other undesirable features must be accomplished in order to produce a fleece of the highest economic value and utility to mankind.

Domestication and proper cultivation have resulted almost exclusively in the production of true wool, with but little or none of the hairy fiber remaining. Even so, the exact character of the wool on the individual sheep varies considerably, according to its position on the body. For example, in the region of the lower britch, the wool becomes coarse and hairy; and near the feet, a short under-

Fig. 30-1. Wool is the natural clothing of sheep. The Merino ram pictured is a member of the breed that produces the world's finest wool. (Courtesy, The Wool Bureau, Inc.)

growth of stiff hair is found. Too many sheep seem to produce a limited number of short, stiff fibers or undergrowth over the entire body area. These short fibers have no value as textile fibers.

VIRTUES OF WOOL

It is noteworthy that the unique characteristics and virtues of wool have, through the years, enabled it to hold its position of prominence in competition with other animal fibers, products of plant origin, and the invasion of innumerable synthetic materials. Although certain other fibers may equal or even excel in one or several qualities, none can boast of the total qualities possessed by wool. The virtues of wool are as follows:

1. Wool is porous and will absorb water more readily than any other textile fiber. It can absorb as much as 18 per cent of its own weight in moisture without even feeling damp and up to 50 per cent of its weight without becoming saturated. This is an important health factor in clothing because body perspiration and outer dampness are prevented from clinging to the body in heat or cold, thus removing the chill line from the body.

2. Wool generates heat in itself.

3. Wool is a superior insulator, keeping the heat of the body from escaping and the cold air from entering. Because of this quality, wool is as effective as

a protection from tropical heat and sun as it is against the gale-driven storms of winter.

4. Wool is light.

5. Wool is very elastic; the average fiber will stretch 30 per cent of its normal length and still spring back in shape. Because of this resilience, wool garments resist wrinkling, stretching, or sagging during wear.

6. Wool transmits the health-giving ultraviolet rays.

7. Dyestuffs are less liable to fade and are faster on wool.

8. Wool is durable.

9. Wool is strong. Diameter for diameter, a wool fiber is stronger than steel.

10. Wool is almost nonflammable. It will stop burning almost as soon as it is taken away from a flame.

11. Wool can be felted or matted easily.

USES OF WOOL

About one-third of the raw wool consumed in the United States is carpet wool, and two-thirds is apparel wool.

The greater part of the carpet wool is used in the manufacture of floor coverings, although small quantities are used in the manufacture of press cloth, knit and felt boots, and heavy fulled lumbermen's socks.

About 2 per cent of the apparel wool is used in batting and in the manufacture of pressed felt, mostly for hat bodies. The other 98 per cent is consumed in the spinning of woolen and worsted yarn. About 15 per cent of the woolen and worsted yarn is used in the production of knit goods, including sweaters, hosiery, underwear, gloves, and mittens. The remainder is used in the weaving of fabrics, including such apparel fabrics as suitings, trouserings, dress fabrics, and coatings and such nonapparel fabrics as blanketing, upholstery, draperies, and woven industrial felts.

MAGNITUDE OF THE U.S. WOOL AND TEXTILE INDUSTRY

As shown in Table 30-1, the farmers and ranchers of the U.S. have long received over $100 million annually for their wool clip. This does not include additional pulled wool, nor does it tell the story relative to the huge imports. Table 30-2 gives the wool production, imports, and consumption; and per cent produced domestically. It is not expected that annual production plus annual imports will exactly equal annual consumption, due to stockpiling and certain other factors. However, among other things, the following noteworthy facts can be deducted from Table 30-2: (1) virtually all of our carpet wool is imported, (2) we produce about 40 per cent of our apparel wool, and (3) about 70 per cent of our total wool requirement (apparel and carpet) is imported and only 30 per cent is produced domestically.

It is noteworthy that expenditures for clothing consumed 6.7 per cent of the

Fig. 30-2. Approximately two-thirds of the wool consumed in the U.S. is apparel wool; and 98 per cent of the latter is used in the spinning of wool and worsted yarn. The picture shows a wool suit. (Courtesy, The Wool Bureau, Inc.)

TABLE 30—1

QUANTITY, PRICE PER POUND, AND TOTAL CASH VALUE OF
WOOL PRODUCED IN THE U.S., 1960 TO 1966[1]

Year	Shorn Wool Produced		Price per Pound	Cash Value
	(lbs.)	(kg)	(cents)	(dollars)
1960	265,480,000	120,527,920	42.0	111,496,000
1961	261,249,000	118,607,046	43.0	112,330,000
1962	249,065,000	113,075,510	47.7	118,709,000
1963	238,185,000	108,135,000	48.5	115,228,000
1964	221,897,000	100,741,238	53.2	117,941,000
1965	201,463,000	91,464,202	47.1	94,999,000
1966	194,149,000	88,143,646	52.1	100,741,000

[1] *Agricultural Statistics*, 1965, Table 510, p. 347, 1960-64 data; and *Statistical Abstracts*, 1967, p. 409, 1965-66 data.

TABLE 30—2

UNITED STATES PRODUCTION, IMPORTS AND CONSUMPTION OF WOOL; AND PER CENT PRODUCED DOMESTICALLY, CLEAN BASIS[1]

Year	Production[2]			Imports[3]			Consumption[4]			Domestic Production as Per Cent of Consumption			Imports as Per Cent of Consumption		
	Apparel	Carpet	Total	Apparel	Carpet	Total	Apparel	Carpet	Total	Apparel	Carpet	Total	Apparel	Carpet	Total
	(mil. lb.)	(mil. lb.)	(mil. lb.)	(mil. lb.)	(mil. lb.)	(mil. lb.)	(mil. lb.)	(mil. lb.)	(mil. lb.)	(%)	(%)	(%)	(%)	(%)	(%)
1960	151.1	——	151.1	74.3	153.9	228.2	246.4	164.6	411.0	61.3	——	61.3	30.2	93.6	55.5
1961	150.0	——	150.0	90.3	157.3	247.6	263.1	149.0	412.1	57.0	——	57.0	34.3	94.7	60.1
1962	140.6	——	140.6	125.8	143.4	269.2	280.2	148.8	429.0	50.2	——	50.2	44.9	96.4	62.8
1963	134.6	——	134.6	109.2	168.0	277.2	251.3	160.3	411.6	53.6	——	53.6	43.5	95.4	67.3
1964	124.1	——	124.1	98.4	114.0	212.4	233.6	121.8	355.4	53.1	——	53.1	42.1	93.6	59.8
1965[5]	113.1	——	113.1	162.6	108.9	271.5	274.7	112.3	387.0	41.2	——	41.2	59.2	97.0	70.2
1966[5]	101.2	——	101.2	162.5	114.6	277.1	266.6	103.6	370.2	38.0	——	38.0	61.0	110.0	74.9

[1] *Wool Statistics and Related Data*, 1920-1964, USDA, Statistical Bul. No. 363, July 1965, pp. 6, 39, and 87 and Supp. for 1966, p. 38.
[2] Reported on basis of clean fiber, using conversion factor of 47.7 per cent for shorn wool and 72.9 per cent for pulled wool.
[3] Imports for consumption. Apparel wool includes dutiable wool; carpet wool includes all duty-free wool.
[4] Consumption on the woolen and worsted systems. Apparel wool includes domestic and dutiable foreign wool. Carpet wool includes duty free foreign wool only.
[5] Supplement for 1966 to *Wool Statistics and Related Data*, 1920-64, p. 38, Table 82.

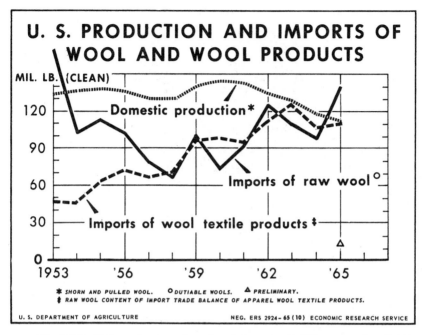

Fig. 30-3. U.S. production of wool and imports of (1) raw wool and (2) textile products. Our wool production is decreasing, while our imports of both wool and textile products are increasing.

income of the average American family in 1967.[1] In addition to the indispensability of its product, the wool textile industry is nationally important because it is one of the largest industries in the U.S.

THE WOOL FIBER

Wool is the natural protective covering of sheep. It differs from other animal fibers by having a serrated surface; a crimpy, wavy appearance; an excellent degree of elasticity; and an internal structure composed of numerous minute cells. In contrast, hair has a comparatively smooth surface, lacks in crimp or waviness, and will not stretch. As a product of the skin or cuticle of vertebrate animals, wool is similar in origin and general chemical composition to the various other skin tissues found in animals—horn, nails, and hoofs.

The Three Cell Layers

From the standpoint of structure, a microscope reveals that all wool fibers consist of two distinct cell layers, and some fibers have a third layer. According to their positions, these layers are known as (1) the epidermis or outer layer, (2) the cortex, and (3) the medulla. Although differing in characteristics, these same

---

[1]*Wool Statistics and Related Data 1920-1964*, Supplement for 1967, USDA, Statistical Bul. 363, May, 1968, Table 316, p. 104.

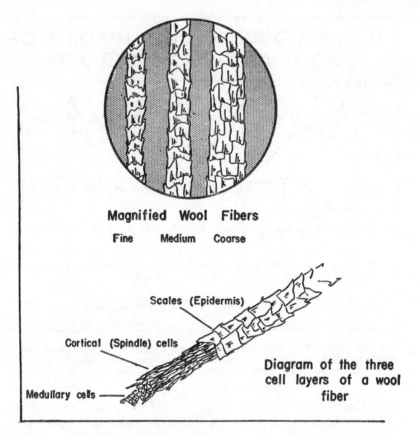

Fig. 30-4. Diagram showing the structure of wool fibers. Upper picture shows the epidermis—the outside cell layer—of fine, medium, and coarse fibers. Note that fine wool has a greater number of serrations. Bottom picture shows the three cell layers (1) the scales or epidermis, (2) the cortex, and (3) the medulla. (Drawing by R. F. Johnson)

three cell layers are found in most hair. The chief characteristics of these three layers in wool fibers will be discussed briefly.

Chemical Composition of Wool

Chemically, wool is chiefly keratin, which is also the primary constituent of hair, nails, hoofs, horns, and feathers. Keratin is a mixture of nitrogen and sulfur compounds and amino acids. A typical chemical breakdown of wool is as follows: carbon, 50 per cent; oxygen, 22 to 25 per cent; nitrogen, 16 to 17 per cent; hydrogen, 7 per cent; and sulfur, 3 to 4 per cent.

SOME FLEECE CHARACTERISTICS

The chief fleece characteristics of interest and importance to both the producer and manufacturer are: (1) grease, (2) length, (3) density, (4) diameter, and (5) variations of different body areas. It is well recognized that there are wide differences between breeds and individuals in such wool characters as fineness, length, density, and yield.

Grease

In a broad sense, grease refers to all the impurities found in unscoured wool, including the yolk, suint, and soluble foreign matter but not the vegetable matter. Shrinkage of fleeces varies widely, with many factors affecting it, but on the average and with all grades included, U.S. shorn grease wool shrinks about 55.5 per cent.[2] The following example shows how shrinkage is computed.

> 10 pounds grease wool before scouring
> 4.5 pounds clean wool after scouring
> 5.5 pounds loss in wool scouring
> 5.5 pounds = 55 per cent = shrinkage
> 4.5 pounds = 45 per cent = yield

The commercial value of a clip of wool is largely determined by the amount of clean wool fiber that it yields. Although a part of the impurities found in grease wool are essential for the growth and well-being of the fleece and the animal, the manufacturer is primarily concerned with securing the highest possible yield of clean wool of the finest quality.

Length

The length of the wool in a fleece is a matter of much importance to both the producer and the manufacturer. Together with quality, it constitutes the principal basis of classification and grading in buying and selling and largely determines the use to which wool will be put. The wool producer regards good length as a desirable attribute, for it gives a greater weight of wool. In judging sheep, fiber length is based on an appraisal of the annual growth as determined by parting the fleece at three body areas—the shoulder, side, and britch. Fiber length varies anywhere from 1 to 20 inches.

Density

Density refers to the closeness or compactness of the fibers in a fleece and is often defined as the number of fibers per unit area of skin. Experimental studies have revealed very clearly that density differences exist between breeds, individuals, and body areas. It has been estimated that the number of wool fibers per animal varies from a low of about 16,000,000 for some individuals of the medium or coarse-wool breeds to a high of 120,000,000 fibers for individuals of the Australian Merino breed. Fleece density is an attribute in determining

---

[2] Based on entire 1946 clip purchased by the Commodity Credit Corporation which included virtually all the domestic wool clip that year. These wools showed the following shrinkage by grades: Fine 56-65%; ½ Blood, 51-60%; ⅜ Blood, 41-50%; and ¼ Blood, 41-45%. (From *The Domestic Wool Clip*, USDA, Production and Marketing Administration, 1951, p. 14, Table I.)

fleece weight. In judging, fleece density is determined by grasping the wool of the side to feel its fullness and compactness and by parting the fleece to examine the apparent closeness of the fibers. Experimental evidence shows that often this method is misleading, apparently being affected by the grease and dirt content.

Diameter

The fineness of wool is very important because the character of the yarns and fabrics produced is determined to a very great extent by the variations in the diameter of fiber. Wool sorting is based on fineness of fiber, and this is considered to be the soundest basis on which wool and top qualities can be classified. In the trade, the experienced wool man is able to estimate the fineness by visual inspection and handling. It is a well-known fact, however, that an ordinary sample of wool that is estimated by a wool man as representing a certain fineness will, on close examination, usually show two or three other finenesses. That is, it is really a composite mixture. If placed under a microscope, it is also found that the shape or contour of fibers varies greatly. As a rule, fibers are irregular and possess varying degrees of ovality or ellipticity.

In judging sheep, the number of crimps is usually accepted as an index of fineness; that this is a good criterion is borne out by experiments in which more refined techniques have been used. The diameter of wool fibers varies anywhere from 0.0008 to 0.002 inch and the number of crimps from 5 to 36 per inch.

PRODUCTION AND HANDLING OF THE WOOL CLIP

If U.S. sheep producers are to survive the inroads of imports and synthetic fibers, it is imperative that they market a higher quality product—one that does not require unnecessary processing expenditures in the textile mills.

Despite remarkable improvement in wool wrought through improved breeding, handlers, buyers, and processors of the domestic wool clip are in general agreement that the overall quality of the nation's wool clip has declined in recent years, and that the primary reason for this decline is the generally poor preparation of the clip. The most common explanations or excuses back of this are: (1) carelessness and indifference on the part of sheep producers, and (2) lack of skilled and dedicated shearers. Whatever the cause, all are agreed that a change must be made if the domestic wool clip is to meet its increasing competition from imported wool and fabrics and from man-made fibers.

Observance of the following wool production and handling practices will result in marketing a higher quality product:

1. **Production.**—Augment improved breeding through (a) proper nourishment and thrift of sheep throughout the year; (b) protecting on-the-back fleeces from straw, trash, and burs; and (c) removing tags from time to time—none should be present at shearing time.

2. **Branding and identifying.**—Avoid the use of any branding fluid if possible. Where branding or identifying is necessary for practical reasons: (a) use proven scourable products, follow the directions on the label, and do not dilute or mix

with contaminating substitutes, and (b) consider the use of colored plastic ear tags.

3. **Management at shearing time.**—Shearing is the "harvesting" of one of the most valuable products, on a per pound basis, produced on American farms and ranches. Thus, its "harvesting" merits preparation commensurate with its value, including observance of the following management pointers at shearing time: (a) remove all weeds, hay, and other vegetative wastes from holding and shearing pens; (b) sprinkle shearing pens and corrals prior to bringing sheep into them, thereby alleviating dust; (c) shear only when the wool is perfectly dry; (d) keep lambs out of the shearing pens; (e) separate black sheep and shear them last, pack these fleeces separately and identify the wool bag accordingly; and (f) shear rams separately, pack these fleeces separately and identify the wool bag accordingly.

4. **Shearing.**—In the act of removing the natural clothing of sheep, by either machine or hand method, the following points should be observed: (a) shear in a clean place, and keep the shearing floor clean and dry at all times— keep brooms conveniently available, sweep the floor at intervals, place tags, dung locks, stained pieces, and other floor sweepings in a separate bag; (b) handle sheep carefully and without injury; (c) avoid "second cuts"—it's better

Fig. 30-5. Machine shearing. Modern sheep shearing equipment operates exactly like the clippers of a barber. The vast majority of the sheep in this country are now shorn by machine, rather than by hand shears. (Courtesy, Sunbeam Corp.)

to leave extra length on the sheep's back than to have second cuts in the bag; (d) keep the fleece unbroken—in one piece; (e) keep fleece free from straw, manure, and other extraneous matter; (f) avoid use of burlap in shearing operations for any purpose other than in packing; and (g) shear separately sheep with growths of 12-months, 6-months, 8-months, or lambs, pack separately and identify bags accordingly.

5. **Shearers.**—Those who do the shearing should be skilled, well informed, and careful. The following points are pertinent to shearers and shearing: (a) have a trained and well-informed man present to supervise the shearing operation; (b) use clean equipment, and provide clean oil for shearing heads; and (c) separate tags, dung locks, crutchings, face and leg wool, and stained pieces from the fleece while shearing and pack in separate bags and label accordingly.

6. **Rolling and tying.**—A well-rolled and properly-tied fleece creates a good impression with a buyer. To roll and tie correctly: (a) put the fleece flesh side (cut side) down on the floor, fold in each of the sides to meet the center, fold in the neck about as far as the shoulder, and start at the britch end and roll toward the neck—in this manner, the finest and best wool on the entire fleece will be on the outside of the bundle when it is finished; (b) use paper

Fig. 30-6. A properly rolled and tied fleece. Note that only one string of paper twine has been used. (Courtesy, USDA)

twine, with the string precut to appropriate length, to tie the fleece—never use cotton, jute, sisal string, or wire; and (c) do not tie 6-months, 8-months, or lamb wool.

7. **Packing.**—Proper packaging is paramount in modern marketing—in all products, and wool is no exception. To pack wool properly, the following "to do" list must be observed: (a) use new, regulation wool bags, preferably paper-lined—if a secondhand wool bag is used, make sure that it is clean, both inside and outside—avoid used grain and feed bags; (b) pack ewe, ram, yearling, burry and seedy, black, tags, and crutchings and floor sweepings separately and

Fig. 30-7. Packing wool in a regulation wool bag immediately after shearing. (Courtesy, The Wool Bureau, Inc., New York)

Fig. 30-8. Rejects—fleeces that are black, dead, gray, cotty, etc.—should be packed separately. (Courtesy, USDA)

mark each bag so as to identify its contents; (c) pack separately and identify 12-months, 6-months, 8-months, or lamb wool; (d) pack bags firmly to facilitate handling and reduce variations in core samples and test results; (e) mark bags or bales with approved marking materials—never use paint; and (f) keep bags off the ground and store under shelter.

8. **Shipping.**—When transporting wool (a) clean trucks or freight cars to eliminate contamination from foreign substances and materials and (b) keep bags dry—protect them from the elements.

REQUISITES OF WOOL

Good wool possesses character, purity, strength of fiber, good condition, cleanliness, low shrinkage, adequate but not excessive grease, uniformity, and a bright white color. These requisites apply to all wools, regardless of the class or grade.

CLASSES OF WOOL[3]

The wool trade recognizes two major classes of wool—apparel wool and carpet wool. As the names imply, most apparel wools are those suitable for manufacture into yarns and fabrics for human clothing, whereas most wools of the carpet class are used in making floor covering.

Apparel wools are further classified according to use as (1) combing wool or staple wool—the long-fibered wools within the class, (2) French combing wool—the wools of intermediate length, and (3) clothing wool—the short-fibered wools. Although these three classes are based largely on length of fiber, other factors—such as supply and demand, fiber diameter, purity, condition, etc.—are important in determining the use made of wools. Thus, many wools used by the woolen industry are longer than some used in worsted manufacture; and a considerable amount of wool classed as clothing is used in the worsted industry. In general, however, the manufacturer can realize the greatest profit by utilizing apparel wools according to their best adaptation as indicated by the three classes. Further, carpet wool is not suited for use as apparel wool.

Combing or Staple Wool

Combing or staple wools are usually referred to as the highest priced and best wool obtained from sheep. Both fineness and length are requisite. For example, a 64's combing wool should be 3 inches or more in length, with the length varying according to grade as shown in Table 30-3. By and large, combing wools are used for making worsted fabrics. They take their name from the fact that one of the main processes in worsted manufacturing is the combing operation, which separates the long fibers from the short ones. The long fibers are used to make

---

[3] The sections "Classes of Wool," "Wool Grading," and "Wool Sorting" were authoritatively reviewed by Dr. Elroy M. Pohle, in charge Livestock Division Wool Laboratory, Standardization Branch, Consumer and Marketing Service, USDA, Denver, Colo.

worsted cloths, and the short fibers (called noil) are used in the making of woolen cloths. In the former, the fibers are laid parallel to each other; whereas, in the latter, the shorter wool fibers that are used in making woolen cloths and felts are laid in every direction—in fact, the more mixing the better in woolens. These differences are of importance to the consumer. Among other things, they explain why "worsted suits" hold their press better than "woolen suits."

In the U.S., wools with sufficiently long fibers and otherwise adapted to the making of worsted cloth are commonly combed on the Noble or Bradford comb.

Prior to World War II, approximately 70 per cent of the apparel wool used in the U.S. was processed on the worsted system of manufacture. However, since that time there has been a gradual decline in the use of worsteds and an increase of woolens. In 1966, 64 per cent of the mill consumption of wool was processed on the worsted system and 36 per cent on the woolen system.

French Combing Wool

French combing wools are in between the combing wools and the clothing wools in length. These wools are manufactured on the French or Heilman comb, which is designed to use wools and still produce worsted fabrics. Thus, the French system utilizes much wool that is not long enough for manufacture on the regular worsted system known as Noble combing. This system of combing is becoming more popular.

Clothing Wool

Clothing wool is the name usually given to the shortest wool. This wool is too short to be manufactured on the worsted system, but it can be used successfully on the woolen system. Although longer fibers can be used in making woolens, they are usually more expensive than short fibers and hence are reserved for making worsteds which usually sell at a slightly higher price than woolens. The term "clothing wool," however, does not mean that the wool is suitable only for fabrics to be made into clothing. This type wool is also used to make felts.

Carpet Wool

Carpet wools, which are usually the coarsest wools, are of low quality because they (1) contain mixtures of very coarse, hairy fibers and finer fibers, and (2) vary markedly in fiber length. The chief requisite of carpet wool is resilience, the quality that makes it resistant to matting down and to wear under the constant scuffing of passing feet. Most of this wool comes from long-wooled sheep and from sheep that show lack of breeding. Most carpet wools are imported because our flocks, except the sheep kept by the Navajo Indians, have been improved to the point where the vast majority of wool grades as apparel wool. Carpet wools come chiefly from New Zealand and Argentina.

WOOL GRADING

Wool grading is based primarily on fiber diameter or fineness, but consideration is also given to length. Many manufacturers desire wool of certain finenesses only. This means that the wool must be separated at the warehouse and like fleeces must be piled by themselves. This process is called wool grading, and it is done by a highly trained wool man. As the best of daylight is needed for grading, it is better done on the north side of the building. It is carried out as follows: A grading board is set up near a door or window, and several baskets or boxes are placed in convenient positions about it. The bag of wool to be graded is brought up to one end of the board, and it is opened up along the seam by the grader's helper. The fleeces are thrown upon the table and are examined, one at a time, by the grader. He looks at the fleece as a whole and does not untie the twine. He considers the diameter, length, strength, color, and other factors and very quickly decides that the fleece is 60/62's combing wool or whatever it may be. He then throws the fleece into a special basket reserved for this particular fineness and length. As the baskets are filled, they are trucked away, and the wool therein is built into large piles on the floor or baled directly from the baskets. When a wool manufacturer desires wool, he can select it from the many large piles, each one of which contains fleeces of a different quality. Grading does not infer that the wool in a pile is all of one diameter. Any single fleece of wool as it comes from the sheep may possess several different grades of wool. Thus, a 60/62's combing wool simply means that the greater part of the

Fig. 30-9. Wool grading. Fleece grading consists of the grader examining the untied fleece, and, on the basis of its fineness, placing it into one of the boxes or crates containing wool of comparable grade. (Courtesy, USDA)

wool on the fleece is of that fineness and length. The manufacturer knows that some wool in these fleeces, especially on the shoulder part of the fleece, will be finer; and also that some wool, as on the britch, will be considerably coarser. Because of this, a further separation, known as sorting, follows. The ability to grade wool, which is acquired only with considerable experience, requires a keen sense of sight combined with the sense of touch and rare good judgment.

Grades of Wool

There are many factors which enter into the value of grease wool, but among the most important are diameter, length, and clean wool fiber present. The average diameter of fiber, and the limits for the variation in diameter for the various grades, are shown in Table 30-3. Maximum limits to the variation allowed for each grade are expressed by the statistical term—standard deviation. In application, if there is too much variation in fiber diameter, the wool is assigned to the next coarser grade. Wool can be separated roughly, after a little experience, into three broad market grades according to its diameter: (1) fine wool, (2) medium wool, and (3) coarse or braid wool. More accurately speaking, however, there are two distinct methods of grading wool according to diameter with several grades in each. The older method is called the blood system; the newer method is called the numerical count. A comparison of these two systems is contained in Table 30-3.

An experienced wool man determines the grade of wool by the senses of sight and touch. However, for use in more objective grade determination and for arbitration purposes where there may be a dispute as to grade before final settlement, there is a scientific method of test prescribed. A copy of this method of test, which explains micro-projector equipment recommended and also sampling and testing procedures, may be obtained from the USDA, Standardization Branch, Wool Laboratory, Denver, Colorado. Testers and research workers may also use calipers or photographic or air-flow equipment for grade determination.

The bulk of wools produced in this country is distributed by grades as follows:[4]

Blood Grade	Numerical Count	Per Cent of Total U.S. Production
Fine	64's and finer	54.5
½ Blood	58's-60's	13.4
⅜ Blood	56's	15.4
¼ Blood	48's-50's	10.3
Low ¼ Blood	46's and coarser	0.9
Common and Braid	36's-44's	0.2
Off wools		5.3

[4] Based on percentage distribution of shorn grease wool in the 1946 clip purchased by the Commodity Credit Corporation, which included virtually all the domestic wool clip that year. (From *The Domestic Wool Clip*, USDA, Production and Marketing Administration, 1951, Table 2, p. 15.)

TABLE 30—3

COMPARATIVE WOOL CHART

Type of Wool	Old Blood Grade	Standard Specifications[1]			Length Classes[2]							
		Numerical Count Grade	Limits for Average Fiber Diameter (Microns)[3]	Variability Limit for Standard Deviation Maximum (Microns)	Combing Wool		French Combing Wool				Clothing Wool	
					over						under	
					(in.)	(cm)	(in.)	(cm)	(in.)	(cm)	(in.)	(cm)
Fine	Fine	Finer than 80's	Under 17.70	3.59	----	----	1½	3.81	2½	6.35	1½	3.81
Fine	Fine	80's	17.70-19.14	4.09	2¾	6.99	1½	3.81	2½	6.35	1½	3.81
Fine	Fine	70's	19.15-20.59	4.59	2¾	6.99	1½	3.81	2½	6.35	1½	3.81
Fine	Fine	64's	20.60-22.04	5.19	3	7.62	1½	3.81	2½	6.35	1½	3.81
Medium	½ Blood	62's	22.05-23.49	5.89	3½	8.89	1½	3.81	3	7.62	1½	3.81
Medium	½ Blood	60's	23.50-24.94	6.49	3½	8.89	1½	3.81	3	7.62	1½	3.81
Medium	⅜ Blood	58's	24.95-26.39	7.09	3½	8.89	2½	6.35	3½	8.89	2½	6.35
Medium	⅜ Blood	56's	26.40-27.84	7.59	3½	8.89	2½	6.35	3½	8.89	2½	6.35
Medium	¼ Blood	54's	27.85-29.29	8.19	4	10.16	2½	6.35	4	10.16	4	10.16
Medium	¼ Blood	50's	29.30-30.99	8.69	4	10.16	2½	6.35	4	10.16	4	10.16
Coarse	Low ¼	48's	31.00-32.69	9.09	4½	11.43	----	----	----	----	4	11.43
Coarse	Low ¼	46's	32.70-34.39	9.59	4½	11.43	----	----	----	----	4	11.43
Coarse	Common	44's	34.40-36.19	10.09	5	12.70	----	----	----	----	5	12.70
Very Coarse	Braid	40's	36.20-38.09	10.69	5	12.70	----	----	----	----	5	12.70
Very Coarse	Braid	36's	38.10-40.20	11.19	5	12.70	----	----	----	----	----	----
Very Coarse	Braid	Coarser than 36's	Over 40.20		----	----	----	----	----	----	----	----

[1] Standards for grades of wool, as published by the U.S. Department of Agriculture, August 20, 1965, Federal Register (7 CFR Part 31). These standards became effective January 1, 1966.
[2] There are no USDA official lengths for the different classes. The lengths given herein are in keeping with trade practices and were provided for use in this book by Dr. Elroy M. Pohle, in charge, Livestock Division Wool Laboratory, Standardization Branch, USDA, Denver, Colorado 80225.
[3] A micron is 1/25,400 of an inch.

NOTE: Common and Braid are not classified according to length because these wools are practically always of combing length. Carpet wool includes all those not suited to the three classes listed.

Fig. 30-10. Grades of wool. Samples representative of the Official Standards of the U.S. for Grades of Wool are available at a nominal price from the Denver Wool Laboratory, Denver, Colorado. An application form should be requested before placing an order. (Courtesy, Consumer and Marketing Service, USDA)

The grades of wool produced vary widely between areas. Thus, about 90 per cent of the wool produced in Texas, New Mexico, Arizona, and Nevada, grades Fine; whereas, ⅜ Blood and ¼ Blood wool predominates in the North Atlantic, East North Central, West North Central, and South Atlantic states.

THE BLOOD SYSTEM

The blood system divides all wool, from finest to coarsest, into six market grades. These are: (1) Fine, (2) ½ Blood, (3) ⅜ Blood, (4) ¼ Blood, (5) Low ¼ Blood, and (6) Common and Braid. Originally, these fractional Blood names denoted the amount of Merino blood in the sheep producing the wool. At the present time, these names indicate wool of a certain diameter only and have no connection whatsoever with the amount of Merino blood in the sheep. As a matter of fact, it is possible to have ⅜ Blood wool from a sheep with no Merino blood at all. The blood grades, therefore, are merely trade names identifying the different grades of wool, without relationship to the breeding of the sheep and are rapidly being replaced with the numerical count.

NUMERICAL COUNT SYSTEM

The numerical count system divides all wool into 14 grades, and each grade is designated by a number. The numbers range from 80's for the finest wool down to 36's for the coarsest. This method gives more grades, and thus finer divisions can be made; and this is more satisfactory to the wool dealers and manufacturers. Table 30-3 shows the correlation between the two grade systems.

Worsted Spinning Count

Theoretically, the numerical count system is based on the number of hanks of yarn (each hank representing 560 yards) that can be spun from one pound of such wool in the form of top. Wool of 50's quality, therefore, should spin 50 x 560 yards per pound of top, if spun to the maximum on the worsted system of manufacture. Unfortunately, this is not always true; the lower grades will not spin up to their number. Moreover, it is noteworthy that, in actual practice, wools are rarely spun to their maximum limit. Furthermore, spinning count is not determined by diameter alone; such factors as fiber length, moisture conditions, and the skill of the workmen influence the count that may be spun. It may be concluded, therefore, that neither the blood system nor the numerical count system denote accurately what they are supposed to indicate according to derivation of the respective terms.

WOOL SORTING

Sorting is the operation of taking an individual fleece, untying the twine, opening the fleece, and separating the fleece into the various grades that it possesses in the different body areas. This operation is usually done in the mill, but occasionally it is done in a warehouse. The reason for this is that a mill knows exactly what qualities of wool it wishes to put into a fabric. The object of sorting is to obtain large lots of wool that are very even and uniform in diameter, length, strength, and other characteristics. It is easy for an inexperienced person to distinguish a very fine wool from a very coarse wool, but it takes considerable training to be able to separate two consecutive grades, such as 56's from 58's. Sorting is always done on the grease wool. The dusting and scouring operations break up the fleece into small pieces, so that sorting of scoured wool is impracticable. Sorting is necessary on wool if a uniform worsted yarn with high spinning count is desired. If the wool is not to be spun to the maximum count, then only a superficial sorting is necessary. The thoroughness of the sorting varies according to the type of fabric into which the wool is to be made.

THE MARKETING OF WOOL

Like most industries, the wool and textile business has progressed from the status of a family enterprise. In the early days of this country—and the same pattern held true in other nations—virtually every family owned a few sheep and produced sufficient wool to meet its own needs. Under the family system, carding, spinning, and weaving were carried on by members of the household for the purpose of supplying the family with clothing. Under these conditions, there was little or no marketing. With the concentration of population in the cities, the coming of artisans and craftsmen, and the bringing of wool from more distant points, however, markets were a necessity.

Fig. 30-11. Display of wool for prospective wool buyers. (Courtesy, Production and Marketing Administration, USDA)

Today, wool is one of the most important commodities of world commerce, and it might well be added that the marketing operations connected therewith are among the most intricate. In the first place, it is one of the most difficult items of commerce to classify and grade for the benefit of the trade. Secondly, few items have to be transported greater distances from producers to consumers. Wool production is a frontier type of industry, with the surplus-producing areas in those regions that are relatively undeveloped. On the other hand, wool consumption is greatest in the more populated regions.

International Trade in Wool

About two-thirds of the world's wool production is in the Southern Hemisphere, with the leading export countries consisting of Australia, Argentina, New

Zealand, Republic of South Africa, and Uruguay. On the other hand, the great wool-consuming nations are in the Northern Hemisphere, and, in 1965, included the United Kingdom, the United States, Japan, France, Italy, and Germany.

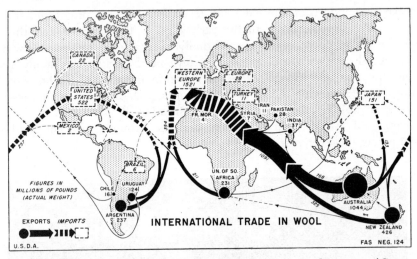

Fig. 30-12. The international trade in wool, exports and imports. (Courtesy, USDA)

London has been displaced as the greatest wool-marketing center of the world by Sydney, Australia. Today, Australia's wool auctions are the standard by which all others are judged.

Boston is the leading wool market of the United States. However, since the early 1950s, the market has moved nearer the production areas, with more shipments going directly to mills.

In order to protect American sheep producers, there is an import duty on apparel wool of the type generally grown in this country.[5] Wools of the type not grown in this country are imported free of duty when used for floor coverings, press cloths, knit or felt boots, or heavy fulled lumbermen's socks.

Methods of Marketing Wool in the United States

There are several differences between the marketing of animals on foot and the marketing of wool. In the first place, the average stockman is usually familiar with more than one of the several avenues through which live animals may be disposed; whereas, except for the larger wool growers, there is generally little knowledge concerning possible market outlets for wool. Also, practically all of the vast quantity of wool grown in the United States is bought and sold by private agreement, with no open- or auction-market arrangement to set values

---

[5] The Kennedy Round established downward rates as follows: On per pound of scoured wool, finer than 40s but not finer than 44s, 18 cents in 1968, graduated downward to 10 cents in 1972. Scoured wool finer than 44s, 21.5 cents in 1968, downward to 12 cents in 1972. Scoured mohair, 22 cents per pound in 1968, downward to 12.5 cents in 1972.

through competitive bidding. For this reason, it is difficult for the grower to know what his wool is worth. On the other hand, it must be recognized that an open market or auction would have its limitations in being informative to the grower for the reason that classes and grades of wool are so elusive and that it still is not practical to secure shrinkage determinations on small lots, even with the modern core system.

It is possible for the grower to sell his wool through several agencies—including both private enterprises and cooperative associations—the chief ones of which are: (1) local buyers, (2) wool merchants, (3) commission houses, (4) brokers or mill agents, and (5) cooperative associations.

THE MANUFACTURING PROCESSES

After wool is purchased by the manufacturer, it must pass through a number of intricate processes before the final product evolves. Wool fabrics are of two types—worsteds and woolens, each requiring different manufacturing and finishing processes. Woolens are made from the shorter wool fibers—carded but not combed—with the result that the little fibers in the yarn are in a criss-cross position, giving a soft, fuzzy yarn, as in broadcloth. The weave of a woolen

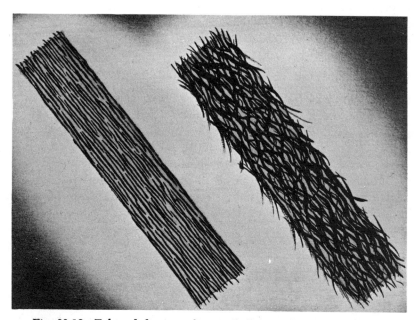

Fig. 30-13. Enlarged diagram of worsted (left) and woolen (right) yarns. The longer fibers are combed out parallel for worsteds, which explains why worsted suits hold their press better than woolen suits. (Courtesy, The Wool Bureau, Inc.)

cloth is more or less concealed by the fuzzy finish. A woolen also is usually softer and less firm than a worsted. Common worsted fabrics include serge, gabardine, rep, and coverts. Common woolen fabrics are cheviot, tweed, flannel, broadcloth, melton, kersey, cassimere, and mackinaw.

The longer fibers are used for worsteds, and they are combed in addition to being carded. The combing process places the fibers parallel, giving a yarn that is spun more tightly than the woolen yarns, as in serge. A worsted also has a clear-cut weave and a smoother surface than a woolen.

The steps in manufacturing worsteds and woolens vary according to the available equipment, kind of wool, and the finished product desired, but in general they consist of the following: (1) sorting; (2) dusting and opening; (3) scouring; (4) drying; (5) carbonizing or bur picking; (6) blending, oiling, and mixing; (7) carding; (8) combing; (9) spinning; (10) weaving or knitting; and (11) dyeing and finishing.

Wool, from Fleece to Fabric

Figure 30-14 shows the approximate amounts of grease wool required to make each of two common garments.

The numerous operations from fleece to fabric are responsible for the often considered elusive reasons why there is so much difference in the price of grease wool and a suit. To be more specific, it is estimated that, out of each dollar which the consumer spends for apparel and household goods made of wool, the wool producer gets 13.5 cents; wool merchandisers, 2.5 cents; manufacturers, 43.1 cents; wholesalers, 8.3 cents; and retailers, 32.6 cents.[6]

MOHAIR

Mohair, known as the most versatile of fibers, is produced by the Angora goat, one of the oldest animals known to man. Yet, few citizens in the United States are more than casually aware of the Angora goat or its existence, despite the fact that these animals graze millions of acres of land and the hard-wearing fabrics made from their lustrous coats are used and admired from coast to coast. Mohair possesses qualities all its own, found in no other animal fiber. It has less crimp and smoother surface scales than sheep's wool. These qualities add luster, softness, and dust resistance to the other fine qualities mohair shares with wool. Mohair has remarkable resistance to wrinkles, great strength, and unequalled affinity to brilliant, deep colors that resist time, the elements, and hard wear.

World Mohair Production

At the present time, the goat is bred on a commercial basis for fiber production in four countries: the United States, Turkey, the Republic of South Africa, and Lesotho. The goat population and mohair production of each of these nations are shown in Table 30-4.

---

[6] Figures for 1957 from *Changes in American Textile Industry*, Technical Bulletin 1210, USDA, Nov., 1959, Figures 7 and 8, pp. 24 and 25.

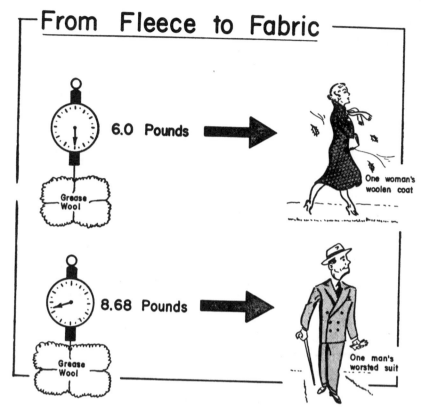

From Fleece to Fabric

6.0 Pounds

Grease Wool

One woman's woolen coat

8.68 Pounds

Grease Wool

One man's worsted suit

Fig. 30-14. Wool, from fleece to fabric. It requires 6 pounds of grease wool (nearly ¾ of an average fleece) to make one woman's woolen coat. It requires 8.68 pounds of grease wool (slightly more than one fleece) to make one man's worsted suit. (Drawing by R. F. Johnson)

TABLE 30—4

LEADING COUNTRIES, BY RANK, IN MOHAIR PRODUCTION, 1967[1]

Country	Mohair Production
	(lbs.)
United States	28,000,000
Turkey	19,800,000
Republic of South Africa	13,000,000
Lesotho	2,000,000
Total	62,800,000

[1]*World Mohair Production and Trade*, Foreign Agricultural Circular, FW 3-67, Nov. 1967.

U.S. Mohair Production and Consumption

Though goats are rather widely distributed throughout the United States, the production of goats and mohair is of economic importance in a comparatively few states only. Table 30-5 summarizes important data relative to the mohair industry of the United States. As may be noted, Texas is by far the leading state in Angora goat numbers and mohair production. In fact, about 97 per cent of the commercial mohair of this country is produced in the Lone Star State. It is also noteworthy that, during 1967, the farmers and ranchers of the U.S. received receipts aggregating $10.7 million. Thus, mohair production is a sizeable industry.

TABLE 30—5

LEADING STATES, BY RANK, IN MOHAIR PRODUCTION
AND INCOME, 1967[1]

State[2]	No. Goats Clipped	Ave. Clip per Goat		Total Production	Price per Pound	Cash Receipts
		(lbs.)	(kg)	(lbs.)	(cents)	(dollars)
Texas	3,928,000	6.5	2.9	25,514,000	41	10,461,000
Arizona	77,000	4.0	1.8	306,000	42	129,000
New Mexico	50,000	4.4	2.0	221,000	36	80,000
Missouri	25,000	4.8	2.2	120,000	35	42,000
Oregon	11,000	4.4	2.0	48,000	38	18,000
California	9,000	5.5	2.5	50,000	35	18,000
Utah	4,000	3.8	1.7	16,000	44	7,000
Total	4,104,000	6.4	2.9	26,275,000	40.9	10,755,000

[1]Wool and Mohair, USDA, Statistical Reporting Service, MtAN 5-3(3-68), p. 3.

In addition to being the largest producer of mohair, the U.S. is the largest user of this fiber. In 1966, the goat raisers of this country produced 29.6 million pounds of mohair,[7] and an additional 10.1 million pounds were imported.

Mohair Characteristics

As may be noted in Table 30-5, Angora goats, on the average, shear an annual clip of 3.8 to 6.5 pounds of unscoured fleece per animal. Purebred herds often clip double this amount. Much of the domestic mohair, especially that produced in the Southwest, is taken off in two clips per year, in the spring and fall, whereas Turkish mohair is usually allowed a full year's growth prior to shearing.

The three types of fleeces, based on the type of lock and ranked according to desirability are: the tight or spiral lock, the flat lock, and the fluffy fleece. The tight lock hangs from the body in ringlets and is associated with the finest fibers. The flat lock is usually more wavy and coarser, but it is associated with heavy shearing weight. The fluffy fleece is objectionable because it is easily broken and is torn out by brush to a greater extent than the other types.

The length of fiber averages about 12 inches for a full year's growth and 6 inches when the animals are shorn semi-annually. Sometimes, with animals that do not have a tendency to shed and when special attention is given to tying the fleece up, mohair up to 3 feet long is produced in a period of three years. Such exceptionally long fibers are used in making ladies' switches, dolls' hair, and theatrical wigs.

_____

[7]Wool Statistics and Related Data, 1920-64, Supplement for 1966; p. 112, Table 321; p. 113, Table 324.

In fineness, or diameter of fiber, mohair is somewhat coarser than wool. Length and luster are more sought than fineness. The fibers are usually very strong, high in luster, whitish in shade, fairly soft to the touch, and straight in staple appearance. Unfortunately, most mohair contains considerable kemp, which is highly undesirable from the standpoint of the manufacturer. Without doubt the amount of kemp can be lessened through breeding and selection.

Mohair shrinkage in scouring averages from 15 to 17 per cent and does not depend on fineness, as does wool, since adult mohair shrinks as much as does kid mohair.

Production, Handling, and Marketing of Mohair

Although mohair is usually accorded more neglect than wool, the principles involved in the economical production and advantageous marketing of a high quality product are the same with both fibers. For practical reasons, chiefly as a means of lessening fleece losses caused by shedding or brush, more goats are shorn twice per year than is the case with sheep. Also, in the Southwest, goats are shorn twice each year because of the warm weather. Except for this difference, and the fact that it is not recommended that the mohair fleece be tied at shearing time, the discussion already presented relative to the production, handling, and marketing of wool is equally applicable to mohair. The market channels and leading market centers for wool and mohair are identical.

It is unfortunate that a large amount of the mohair produced in this country continues to be marketed by placing all grades in a single bag, with little attention given to sorting. On most shearing floors, altogether too little attention is given to keeping the fleece intact and rolling it together in order that an intelligent job of grading and sorting may be done later. So long as these careless production methods are followed, mohair will neither meet the highest requirements of the manufacturer nor command a top price for the grower.

Most of the mohair is handled by the Boston market. It then may be sold to a mill in the original bag or on a sorted basis, or it may be combed and sold in the form of tops.

Classes and Grades of Mohair[8]

There appears to be somewhat less standardization in the classes and grades of mohair than for wool. Kid hair is finest and is especially sought by mills. The fleeces from adults—especially bucks and old wethers—are the coarsest; and that from yearlings is intermediate between the other classes. These classes can be recognized by the grower and should be packed separately at shearing time. In addition, those fleeces that are extremely coarse, weak, and shorter than 6 inches or those having an excess of kemp, burs, or other foreign matter should be kept separate from clean, strong fleeces of desirable length and fineness.

---

[8] The sections "Classes and Grades of Mohair," "Uses of Mohair," and "The National Wool Act" were authoritatively reviewed by Dr. Elroy M. Pohle, in charge Livestock Division Wool Laboratory, Standardization Branch, Consumer and Marketing Service, USDA, Denver, Colo.

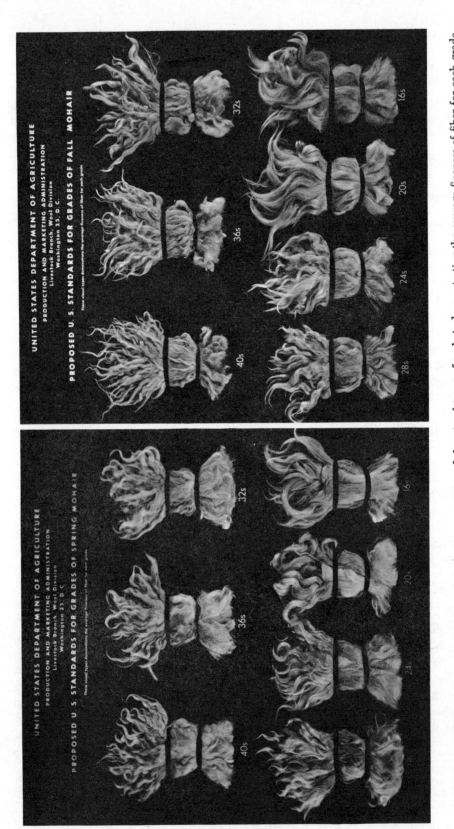

Fig. 30-15. Proposed grades of mohair. Samples representative of the visual types of mohair demonstrating the average fineness of fiber for each grade are available at a nominal price from the Denver Wool Laboratory, Denver, Colorado. (Courtesy, Consumer and Marketing Service, USDA)

The tentative grease mohair and mohair top grades and specifications proposed by the U. S. Department of Agriculture follow:

Current Trade Terminology	Grease Mohair Grades	Mohair Top Grades	Average Diameter Micron Range
No. 1 Kid............................	Finer than 40s 40s/36s	Finer than 40s 40s 36s	Under 23.55 23.55-25.54 25.55-27.54
No. 2 Kid	32s/30s	32s 30s	27.55-29.54 29.55-31.54
No. 1 Grown....................... & Yrlg.	28s/26s	28s 26s	31.55-33.54 33.55-35.54
No. 2 Grown.......................	24s/22s	24s 22s	35.55-37.54 37.55-39.54
No. 3 Grown.......................	20s/18s	20s 18s	39.55-41.54 41.55-43.54
	Coarser than 18s	Coarser than 18s	Over 43.54

As with wool, the grades of mohair are based primarily on the presumed spinning count obtainable on the Bradford system (or the number of 560-yard hanks to the pound). In practice, fineness is associated with softness and is recognized by the experienced touch when handled between the thumb and fingers.

Uses of Mohair

Mohair is used for car upholstery, portieres, robes, rugs, braids, and artificial furs; and there is considerable use of superior mohair in suit linings and for men's summer suitings. The long-fibered mohair is also in demand for use in manufacturing wigs and switches for theatrical purposes.

THE NATIONAL WOOL ACT

Through passage, and subsequent extension, of the National Wool Act (first passed in 1954), Congress continued to recognize wool as an essential and strategic commodity which is not produced in the U.S. in sufficient quantity to meet domestic needs.

The incentive payments are financed from the duties collected on the imports of wool. Also, the Act authorized an industry self-help program for the purpose of developing and conducting advertising and sales promotion programs for lamb and wool.

In the 1969 marketing year, the incentive price per pound of wool was 69 cents. For mohair, it was 77.4 cents per pound. Pulled wool, taken from sheep slaughtered for meat, was supported at a level comparable to the 69 cent price for shorn wool.

In order to secure the most benefit from this Act, the sheepman should (1) sell for the highest price possible and (2) obtain complete sale records. For example, let us assume that the national average wool price is 60 cents per pound. To bring the national average price of 60 cents to the incentive level of 69 cents, each producer's price would need to be increased by 15 per cent. Therefore, if you sell 1,000 pounds of wool for 60 cents per pound, you will get (1) $600 from the buyer and (2) $90 (or 15 per cent more) from the Department of Agriculture; making a total return of $690.

But if you sell your wool for 70 cents per pound, instead of 60 cents, the story is as follows: You will get (1) $700 from the buyer and (2) $105 (15 per cent of $700) from the Department of Agriculture; making a total return of $805. This shows how the returns on 1,000 pounds of wool could be increased by $155 through careful marketing.

QUESTIONS FOR STUDY AND DISCUSSION

1. Why is wool losing its position of prominence and being invaded by synthetic fibers?
2. Why do we not produce carpet wool in the U.S.?
3. Explain why worsted suits hold their press better than woolen suits.
4. May it be concluded that neither the blood system nor the numerical count system denote accurately what they are supposed to indicate according to derivation of the respective terms?
5. What are the classes of wool? How is wool graded and sorted?
6. It is estimated that, out of each dollar which the consumer spends for apparel and household goods made of wool, the wool producer gets only 13.5 cents. Why does he get so little?
7. For your farm or ranch, or one with which you are familiar, how and where would you market your wool clip?
8. It requires 6 pounds of grease wool (nearly ¾ of an average fleece) to make one woman's woolen coat. It requires 8.68 pounds of grease wool (slightly more than one fleece) to make one man's worsted suit. If grease wool is worth 69¢ per pound, why does it cost so much to buy a coat or a suit?
9. Compare mohair with wool, from the standpoint of characteristics and uses.
10. Discuss the National Wool Act.

SELECTED REFERENCES

Title of Publication	Author(s)	Publisher
American Wool Handbook	W. Von Bergen H. R. Mauersberger	Textile Book Pub., Inc., New York, N. Y., 1948.
California Wool Production	J. F. Wilson	Circ. 171, Calif. Ext. Ser., University of California, Davis, Calif., 1951.
Domestic Wool Clip, The		U.S. Department of Agriculture, Livestock Branch, Prod. & Marketing Adm., Washington, D. C.
Domestic Wools, Value-Determining Physical Properties and Characteristics of	Rept. # 211	U.S. Department of Agriculture, Agric. Mktg. Ser., Livestock Branch, Washington, D. C.
Domestic Wool Requirements and Sources of Supply		U.S. Department of Agriculture, Livestock Branch, Prod. & Mktg. Adm., Washington, D. C.
Mohair Report		U.S. Department of Agriculture, Livestock Branch, Prod. & Mktg. Adm., Washington, D. C.

Titles of Publication	Author(s)	Publisher
Physical Measurements and Their Application in Describing Wool	Rept. # 256	U.S. Department of Agriculture, Livestock Div., Agric. Mktg. Ser., Washington, D. C.
Sales Method Problems of Wool Cooperatives	W. L. Hodde	Rept. #6, U.S. Department of Agriculture, Farmer Co-Op Service, Washington, D. C.
Textiles	M. S. Woolman E. B. McGowan	The Macmillan Co., New York, N. Y., 1926.
Wool Handbook	Werner Von Bergen	Interscience Publishers, New York, 1963.
Wool Handling		Eavenson & Levering Co., Camden, N. J., 1936.
Wool Quality	S. G. Barker	His Majesty's Stationery Office, London, England, 1931.
Wool Science	Wm. D. McFadden	Pruett Press, Boulder, Colo., 1967.

Also, valuable reference material on wool and mohair may be obtained from the following sources:

American Sheep Producers Council, Inc.
Suite 520, Railway Exchange Building
909 Seventeenth St.
Denver, Colorado 80202

National Association of Wool Manufacturers
New York, New York

National Wool Growers Association
414 Pacific National Life Building
Salt Lake City, Utah

The Wool Bureau, Inc.
360 Lexington Ave
New York, New York 10017

Mohair Council of America
710 National Bank Bldg.
San Angelo, Texas 76901

Chapter XXXI

GOATS[1]

Contents

Page

The Angora Goat..779
  Distribution and Adaptation...780
  Characteristics 781
  Registration 782
  Management of Angora Goats..783
    Herding 783
    Breeding 783
    Feeding 784
    Shelter 784
    Care at Kidding Time..784
      The Toggle System...784
      The Pen (or Corral) System..786
  Goat Meat and Mohair..786
Milk Goats..787
  U.S. Breeds of Milk Goats..787
  Feeding Milk Goats..787
Questions for Study and Discussion..790
Selected References 790

Goats were probably among the first animals domesticated by man. Goat-like remains were found in the ruins of the Swiss lake dwellings of the New Stone Age; and, according to historical records, domestic goats and sheep were driven over the damp fields of the Nile Valley to trample the seed into the soil for the farmers of ancient Egypt. Also, according to Old Testament literature, goats were very versatile helpmates to man in Biblical days. They furnished milk for food, fiber for clothing, skin for bottles, and served as the object of many a sacrificial offering for Jehovah.

Although there are many breeds of goats in the Old World, only a few have been introduced into America. These are divided into two groups: (1) mohair-bearing goats and (2) milk goats.

THE ANGORA GOAT

The vast majority of the goats in America belong to the mohair-bearing Angora breed. Although there are more than 2 million head of these strange-looking, heavy-coated creatures in this country, few people outside the Angora goat districts know what they look like.

The breed derives its name from Angora, a province in Turkey, in which

---

[1] Since Texas is the leading state in Angora goat numbers, the author especially appreciated the authoritative review accorded this chapter by Professor J. M. Jones, Chief, Division of Range Animal Husbandry, Texas A&M University, College Station, Texas.

land they originated. Angora is a high plateau, lying from 1,000 to 4,000 feet above sea level. In 1881, the Sultan of Turkey passed an edict prohibiting the exportation of Angoras, expecting thereby to confine the mohair industry to Asia Minor and forever after hold a monopoly upon the mohair trade. Thirty years later, in 1910, South Africa followed suit, passing a law for the same purpose. Subsequent events proved that both Turkey and South Africa were too late in their efforts to hold a monopoly on the mohair trade, for some of the choicest Angora blood had already been brought to the United States.

The Angora goat was first introduced into this country by Dr. James B. Davis, of Columbia, South Carolina. Doctor Davis had been sent to Turkey by President Polk in answer to a request made by the Sultan for someone to experiment in the production of cotton in that country. Upon returning to the United States in 1849, 32 years before the Sultan's edict, Dr. Davis brought with him nine choice Angora goats, including seven does and two bucks. These and subsequent importations founded in the United States the Angora industry which continued to thrive in this new land despite later restrictions imposed by Turkey.

Distribution and Adaptation

Table 31-1 lists the seven leading goat states, by rank, and the total number of goats in the U.S.

TABLE 31—1

NUMBER OF GOATS AND KIDS IN SEVEN LEADING
GOAT-PRODUCING STATES, BY RANK, 1964[1]

State	Angora Goats and Kids	Other Goats[2] and Kids	Total Goats and Kids
	(number)	(number)	(number)
Texas	3,516,765	176,990	3,693,755
New Mexico	71,443	34,367	105,810
Arizona[3]	47,131	65,818	112,949
Missouri	32,737	37,261	69,998
Oregon	14,415	6,577	20,992
Oklahoma	8,009	11,811	19,820
California[3]	6,218	18,083	24,301
United States Total	3,696,718	350,907	4,047,625

[1]1964 Census of Agriculture.
[2]Milk goats and Spanish or common goats used for clearing brush and for meat.
[3]1959 Census of Agriculture.

It is noteworthy that in 1964 Texas alone accounted for the majority of the goats found in the United States. The huge goat population of Texas is due principally to the fact that the Lone Star State has a large area of rugged grazing land which is well adapted to utilization by this species. The center of goat raising in Texas is in the south central part of the state, a region generally known as the Edwards Plateau. The area is characterized by rolling hills, somewhat rough and broken, covered by grasses, cedar and oak trees, and a consider-

Fig. 31-1. Typical Angora flock on a west Texas ranch. Texas is the leading Angora state of the nation. (Courtesy, *Sheep and Goat Raiser*)

able amount of brush. The 'elevation is between 1,500 and 3,000 feet, and the rainfall varies from 15 to 25 inches per year.

Generally speaking, the densest Angora goat populations in this country are found in those areas in which the grazing is too scanty, rough, or brushy for cattle or sheep. On the other hand, a very large percentage of Texas Angora goats are handled on the same ranges that support cattle and sheep. The goats utilize browse which would be of little or no value to sheep and cattle and keep the brush from crowding out the natural grasses. On cut-over lands of the Pacific Coast states and in the Ozarks of the central states, Angora goats are frequently used for clearing land of brush; but if this end is to be accomplished, the area must be heavily stocked and closely grazed.

Characteristics

At the present time, the Angora goat of this country is considerably larger and more rugged than its Turkish ancestor. This transformation in type has been accomplished through long-continued selective breeding and some infusion of common or so-called Mexican goats. In range condition, mature bucks weigh from 125 to 175 pounds and does from 80 to 90 pounds. The breeders of this country prefer considerable size so long as it is not necessary to sacrifice fleece quality, because the added size gives a larger surface area upon which to produce a heavy fleece.

Angoras are almost always pure white, although a black one appears occasionally. Red kids will shed their hair and produce white mohair later, but it is recommended that these animals be culled out and sent to slaughter.

The outer coat of the animal is made up of long locks or strands of hair, known commercially as mohair, which covers the animal's body. The fleece should cover all parts of the body except the face and should be characterized by fine quality, a close curl, and high luster. It should be as free from kemp as possible.

Under range conditions, does and kids shear 5 to 6 pounds and wethers 6 to 7 pounds of mohair annually, which is usually removed in two clips.The best fleeces possess ample quantities of natural oil, and the best strains of Angoras show no tendency to shed.

Fig. 31-2. Angora buck. Winner of B-type yearling in the Texas Angora Goat Raisers Association Show and Sale. Bred and shown by Miss Nancy Haby, Leakey, Texas; purchased by Mr. Jack Richardson, Uvalde, Texas. (Courtesy, Miss Haby)

The body conformation should be symmetrical and denote a good constitution. Both sexes are usually horned, but polled individuals occur. The rather thin, long, and pendulous ears droop out of the hair.

Registration

The first United States breed registry association for Angora goats, known as the American Angora Goat Breeders' Association, was established in 1900. From that time until 1924, all animals registered by this association were either the original inspected stock and their progeny or goats subsequently imported. A second registry, known as the National Angora Record Association, was organized in 1918; but six years later, in 1924, it was merged with the American Angora Goat Breeders' Association. Today, the lineage of registered Angora goats in this country is recorded in the American Association only. In 1965, they registered 13,008 goats; which brought their total registrations to date to 379,600.

As in sheep production, the breeding of registered Angoras is considered a specialty business, and few large range goat operators engage therein. Yet, most practical commercial goat producers prefer to use registered bucks and patronize the purebred breeders in order to secure bucks of a type that they hope will improve their herds.

Management of Angora Goats

The proper care of goats differs little from that which should be accorded sheep under similar conditions. Like sheep, goats pay dividends for good management. It is unfortunate, therefore, that there is a widespread and common belief that goats will thrive despite neglect. This popular conception is not true. The successful goat raisers apply the same careful care and management to goat raising as is given to any other profitable livestock enterprise. Success with goats can be achieved in no other way. In the discussion which follows, particular attention is given to principles or systems of management wherein goats differ markedly from sheep. Needless repetition on such matters as fencing, castration, watering, etc., is omitted.

HERDING

A large number of Angora goats in the United States are maintained under range conditions, where they are grazed in herds much like range bands of sheep. These herds vary in numbers from a few hundred to over 2,000 head, with an average herd numbering about 1,200. On rough range or in thick brush, a larger number than 1,200 can seldom be properly controlled by a single herder.

The principles and practices of good herding with goats are almost identical to those with sheep. There is one distinct difference: Rarely do sheep herders work ahead of the band; whereas it is common practice for a goat herder to work in front, turning the lead goats back to avoid unnecessary travel.

At the present time, most of the goats of Texas and other southwestern states are "loose grazed" (unherded) in wolf-proof fenced ranges, in the same manner that sheep are handled in this area.

BREEDING

The normal breeding habits of goats and sheep are similar, with the former having a slightly longer estrus period and a gestation period one to two days longer (the gestation period of goats varies from 140 to 160 days, with an average of 151 days). The does are usually bred so that their first kids are dropped when they are approximately two years of age.

Like sheep, Angora does reproduce once each year, coming into heat in the late summer or early fall. The time of breeding is determined largely by the projected climatic conditions, feed supply, and shelter at kidding time. Most range goats of this country are bred to kid in March and April, for mild, settled weather and spring feed may normally be expected at this time.

FEEDING

Unfortunately, there is a widely prevailing popular belief that goats will eat and do well on anything from newspapers to rusty tin cans. This is erroneous. Like other animals that are hungry or suffering from mineral or vitamin deficiencies, they will develop depraved appetites and chew on many things; but they prefer good quality, wholesome feeds and will pay dividends when so fed.

Goats are naturally browse animals; but a good goat range, in addition to furnishing abundant palatable evergreen brush (not cedar or other coniferous vegetation), should provide a mixture of grasses and broadleaved herbs. On the most desirable goat ranges, this feed combination is available the year round, although browse is usually the principal winter feed. When supplemental feed is necessary, those feeds that are also suitable for sheep are used. The mineral (including salt) and water requirements for goats are similar to those of sheep.

SHELTER

It is essential that newly sheared goats be protected from cold rains and storms, no matter how simple the shelter may be; otherwise, losses are sometimes disastrous. Goat sheds are generally low structures, covered with a metal roof and boarded up on one or two sides. When well fed and not newly sheared, goats seldom succumb to cold and, therefore, do not need shelter.

CARE AT KIDDING TIME

Goats require much more care than sheep at the time the newborn are arriving. Young kids are much more delicate than young lambs—neither being able to endure so much cold or damp weather nor to follow their mothers to the range so early in life. It is not surprising, therefore, to discover that an 80 per cent kid crop is considered excellent for range bands.

If heavy losses of young kids are to be averted, a safe system of kidding must be followed. The two most common systems of kidding followed by progressive and successful goat raisers of today are: (1) the toggle (or staking) system and (2) the pen (or corral) system.

THE TOGGLE SYSTEM

Under the toggle system, the young kids are staked with about 15 inches of rope attached to a swivel on the stake end, with a loop on the other end being attached to the fetlock joint of the kid. This loop should be changed to another leg once daily. Each kid is provided with a box, usually a small A-

Fig. 31-3. A toggle camp in which the young kids are staked near small A-shaped boxes. (Courtesy, USDA)

shaped structure made of 12-inch boards, with one end open, which furnishes protection from the elements. The camp should have sufficient stakes and boxes to allow for as many kids as may be dropped within any 10-day period. Ten feet between stakes is considered about the right distance, providing sufficient space to avoid confusion, affording room for handling, and minimizing quarreling of the does. Whenever a kid is staked, it and its mother are branded with corresponding marks, thus avoiding any possibility of confusion in identity. Some ranchers clip the doe's tail and place the number there, whereas others place brand marks on similar body areas of the does and kids.

The ideal toggle camp should have a good slope for drainage. With such a slope, the older does will spend the night on the higher side; so their kids should be staked there, with the kids of the younger does being placed in the lower part of the camp. Disturbance will be avoided if the kids or does that fight or habitually overturn the kid boxes are placed at one end or corner of the camp. On cold rainy nights, the does should be confined or otherwise kept out of the toggle camp; for each time a doe passes through the yard to her kid, other kids will come out of their boxes and suffer possible exposure.

A doe that disowns her kid should be staked with it. Kids may usually be grafted if the foster mother and orphan kid are staked or penned together. The presence of "dogies," as orphan kids are known, is evidence that such details have not been given adequate attention around a kidding camp.

The careful herder passes through the toggle camp each morning and evening, ascertaining whether each kid has nursed. If a kid is gaunt or restless, its mother should be brought to the stake; if a doe has a distended udder, she should be taken to the kid or kids that carry the corresponding number or mark. Does with extra large teats may have to be hand-milked until the kids have learned to nurse the abnormally large teats.

Generally, kids should not be staked in the toggle camp for more than 10 days. At that time, they should be herded with their mothers. Some of the large operators, especially those in southwestern United States, release the kids directly from the toggle camp to the range with the does. These men insist that kids handled in this manner develop into better foragers and possess more muscle and bone. Others prefer to make the change from the toggle camp to the range more gradually. Usually the latter operators first transfer the does and their kids in small numbers from the toggle camp to a small field. The size of the field and herd is then gradually increased until the kid band may be turned on the range when the young average about six weeks of age. A modification of the latter system consists of confining the kids to a corral for a few weeks while the does depart via a "jump board" (a structure about 18 inches high) to forage on the range in the daytime.

The Pen (or Corral) System

The pen or corral system is gaining in popularity, because less work is involved in handling the animals and the results are as good as those obtained by using the toggle system. For a herd of 1,200 does, the pen system usually involves having about eight corrals of ample size to enclose 50 does and their kids, a dozen small pens each large enough to hold an individual doe and her kid, and one or two larger corrals that may be adequate for 400 to 500 does and their kids.

Even the toggle system should be supplemented with a few individual kidding pens, which may be used as "bum pens" to force does to accept disowned kids of their own or orphan kids that are to be grafted. In general, in the pen or corral system about 50 does and their kids of about the same age group are kept in one pen or corral for the first two or three weeks; the kids are confined to the corral, whereas the does are permitted to go out to the range in the daytime. As the kids get older, groups are combined and turned to larger areas, eventually to travel to the range in a kid herd consisting of 1,000 to 1,200 does and their kids.

Goat Meat and Mohair

Goat meat tastes much like mutton or lamb of similar finish and quality, and it is equally appetizing and nutritious. In general, however, goat carcasses are not so well finished and do not yield as high a dressing percentage as average sheep carcasses.

Reputable meat dealers sell goat meat under the trade name of chevon. Because of the unwarranted prejudice against goat meat by consumers, however, it may be true that some of this product is passed over the counter as mutton or lamb. There is no federal restriction against marketing it in the latter way, but in some cities and in the state of Oregon this practice is prohibited. Most Chevon is marketed in the West, as efforts to dispose of this product in the East have met with little enthusiasm. More than any other kind of meat, goat meat needs effective and deserved publicity.

The production, handling, and marketing of mohair have been fully covered in Chapter XXX.

MILK GOATS

The goat has long been a popular milk animal in the Old World, where it is often referred to as the poor man's cow. When travelling or vacationing, Asiatics frequently take their goats with them in order to be assured of a supply of milk. Thus, it is interesting to recall that the late Mahatma Ghandi of India took two milk goats with him on his last visit to England.

Milk goats were introduced to America in early times—the first settlers in the Virginia colonies bringing their milk goats from the mother country. However, improved strains were not imported until many years later, for the first pure-breds said to have been brought into the United States were four Toggenburgs imported to Ohio in 1893. Today, the milk goat industry is growing, and these small animals are supplying nature's finest food—milk—to many children who would otherwise be undernourished. They are especially well adapted for furnishing a milk supply for low-income families in small towns and the suburbs of large cities where there is not enough feed available for a cow. A doe can often secure much of her feed from lawn clippings or garden and kitchen waste or by grazing in vacant lots.

A good milking doe will average two quarts of milk per day over a lactation period of 10 months, with superior animals producing as much as four to five quarts. The highest official milk production on record in the U.S. was made by a Toggenburg doe that produced 5,750 pounds of milk in 305 days. The butter-fat record is also held by a Toggenburg that produced 202.5 pounds in 305 days.

In comparison with cow's milk, goat's milk has smaller fat globules, a higher mineral content, and a sweeter flavor. Goat's milk forms a fine, soft curd during digestion, thus making it more easily digestible than cow's milk for some children and for older people who cannot use cow's milk. If milked in clean quarters and away from the bucks, goat's milk will not have any unpleasant flavor or odor. The strong odor of the buck is quickly absorbed by warm milk.

U.S. Breeds of Milk Goats

There are many distinct breeds of milk goats in the Old World, but only those listed in Table 31-2 are important in the dairy business in America.

Feeding Milk Goats

The feed requirements of milk goats are similar to those for milk cows. These are set forth in Chapter XX. Although the allowance should vary according to production, the concentrates for lactating does may consist of 1½ to 2 pounds daily plus either (1) pasture in season or (2) hay and/or silage.

TABLE 31—2

BREEDS OF MILK GOATS AND THEIR CHARACTERISTICS[1]

Breed	Place of Origin	Color; Face, Ears, and Legs	Head Characteristics	Other Distinguishing Characteristics	Disqualification
French-Alpine	France; but from Swiss foundation stock.	Multicolored coats, with no standard markings.	Some have horns at birth and are dis-budded, others are hornless; erect ears; straight nose.		Pendulous ears.
La Mancha	Spain	Any color or combination of colors.	Short ears; straight nose; hornless or neatly disbudded.		Anything other than gopher ears in males. Ears other than true La Mancha type in females.
Nubian	Nubia, in northeastern Africa.	Black and whites, tan and whites, red and whites are common, but they may be any of these colors without white markings.	Some born with horns and disbudded, others are hornless. Long drooping ears. Roman nose and prominent fore-head. Does are beardless.		Upright ears.
Rock Alpine	United States.	Multicolored coats, with no standard markings.	Some have horns at birth and are dis-budded, others are hornless; erect ears; straight nose.		
Saanen	Switzerland, in the Saan-en Valley.	Pure white or creamy white.	Hornless animals pre-ferred; straight nose; erect ears.		Large (1½" di-ameter or more) dark spot in hair; pendu-lous ears.
Swiss Alpine	Switzerland.	Chamoise; solid brown, rang-ing from light to a deep-red bay. Black points.	Hornless or neatly disbudded. Erect ears.		
Toggenburg	Switzerland, in the Tog-genburg Valley.	Brown, with 2 white stripes on the face and white on the legs below the knees.	Hornless or debudded; straight or dished nose; erect ears.		Tricolor or pie-bald; large (1½" or more) white spot in males; pendulous ears.

[1]In addition to the specific breed disqualifications given in the right-hand column, the American Dairy Goat Associa-tion lists the following as disqualifications in any breed: total blindness; permanent lameness or difficulty in walking; blind or non-functioning half of udder; blind teat; double teats; extra teats that interfere with milking; hermaphrodism; navel hernia; crooked face in bucks; and extra teats, teats cut off, or double orifice in bucks.

Fig. 31-4. The French Alpine doe, Blue Bonnets La Merri, considered one of the great foundation animals of the breed. During her prime, she produced up to 9¾ quarts daily. (Courtesy, Allan L. Rogers, Caprice Farm, Burtonsville, Maryland)

Fig. 31-5. A Nubian doe. The Nubian is characterized by a Roman nose and drooping ears. Does are beardless. (Courtesy, American Milk Goat Record Association)

Fig. 31-6. Saanen doe, R3 Parford Frolic, B.S. 6812H. Bred by Miss J. Dupree, Chagford, Devon, England. Purchased and imported to the U. S. by Mr. Allan L. Rogers, Caprice Farm, Burtonsville, Maryland. This doe was a consistent show-ring winner in England. In the first 365 days of her first lactation, she produced 3,965 pounds of milk. The most approved color for the Saanen breed is pure white or creamy white. (Courtesy, Mr. Allan L. Rogers, Caprice Farm, Burtonsville, Maryland)

Fig. 31-7. A Toggenburg doe. The Toggenburg is brown in color with two white strips on the face and white on the legs below the knees. (Courtesy, American Milk Goat Record Association)

QUESTIONS FOR STUDY AND DISCUSSION

1. Discuss the adaptation of goats from the standpoint of (1) land use and (2) economy.
2. Discuss the similarities and differences in the management of Angora goats and sheep.
3. Can you tell the difference between chevon and lamb, when each is cooked and served?
4. Discuss the place of milk goats.

SELECTED REFERENCES

Title of Publication	Author(s)	Publisher
Angora Goat, The	Farmers' Bul. 1203	U.S. Department of Agriculture, Washington, D.C.
Dairy Goats	Colby, Byron E., *et al.*	University of Massachusetts, 1966.
Milk Goats	Farmers' Bul. 920	U.S. Department of Agriculture, Washington, D.C.
Modern Milk Goats	Irmagarde Richards	J. B. Lippincott Co., Philadelphia, Pa., 1921.

Also, breed literature pertaining to each breed of goats may be secured by writing to the respective breed registry associations (see Sec. VI, Appendix, for the name and address of each association).

Chapter XXXII

THE SWINE INDUSTRY

Contents   Page

Origin and Domestication of Swine 791
   European Wild Boar (*Sus scrofa*) 792
   East Indian Pig 793
Position of the Hog in the Zoological Scheme 794
Introduction of Swine to America 794
The Creation of American Breeds of Swine 795
Growth of the U.S. Swine Industry 796
World Distribution of Swine 797
Swine Production in the United States 799
   Leading States in Swine Production 800
Factors Favorable to Swine Production 800
Factors Unfavorable to Swine Production 802
The Future of the American Swine Industry 802
Questions for Study and Discussion 803
Selected References 804

Nomadic peoples could not move swine about with them as easily as they could cattle, sheep, or horses. Moreover, close confinement was invariably accompanied by the foul odors of the pig sty. For this reason, the early keepers of swine were often regarded with contempt. This may have been the origin of the Hebrew and Moslem dislike of swine, later fortified by religious precept. As swine do not migrate great distances under natural conditions and the early nomadic peoples could not move them about easily, there developed in these animals, more than in most stock, a differentiation into local races that varied from place to place. It also appears that swine were domesticated in several different regions and that each region or country developed a characteristic type of hog.

ORIGIN AND DOMESTICATION OF SWINE

Most authorities agree that two wild stocks contributed to American breeds of swine; namely, the European wild boar (*Sus scrofa*) and the East Indian pig (primarily *Sus vittatus*).[1] Both were gregarious, often forming large herds. Their feed consisted mostly of roots, mast (especially acorns and beechnuts), and such forage as they could glean from the fields and forests. Because of their roving nature, diseases and parasites were almost unknown.

In addition to these two stocks, there exist certain wild types of pig-like animals which, to this day, have never been domesticated. Included in the

---

[1] Some authorities now hold that the East Indian *Sus vittatus* is actually connected with *Sus scrofa* by a chain of intermediates.

latter group are the brightly colored tropical river pigs and the giant forest hog of Africa; the hideous wart hog of the African plains; the native American pigs (known as peccaries); and the babirussa of Celebes, whose tusks resemble horns more than they do teeth.

Pigs were first domesticated in China in Neolithic times, about 4900 B.C. Biblical writings mention them as early as 1500 B.C., and legendary and historical accounts refer to the keeping of swine in Great Britain as early as 800 B.C. Swine seem to have been especially variable under domestication and especially amenable to human selection. As evidence of this assertion, one need but observe the difference in length of snout and size of ears of modern breeds of hogs.

When given the opportunity, pigs promptly revert within only a few generations to a wild or feral state in which they acquire the body form and characteristics of their wild progenitors many generations removed. The self-sustaining razorback of the United States is an example of this reversion.

European Wild Boar (Sus scrofa)

The European wild boar (Sus scrofa) still lives in some of the forests of Europe. Although much reduced in numbers in the last few hundred years, it appears unlikely that the famous wild boar will become extinct like the Aurochs (the chief progenitor of domestic cattle). In comparison with the domestic

Fig. 32-1. European wild boar (Sus scrofa). Note the coarse hair, long head and snout, large feet, and long tusks. (Courtesy, New York Zoological Society)

pig, this race of hogs is characterized by its coarser hair (with an almost mane-like crest along the back), larger and longer head, larger feet, longer and stronger tusks, narrower body, and greater ability to run and fight. The color of mature animals is nearly black, with a mixture of gray and rusty brown on the body. Very young pigs are striped. The ears are short and erect.

These sturdy ancestors of domestic swine are extremely courageous and stubborn fighters and are able to drive off most of their enemies, except man. If attacked, they will use their tusks with deadly effect, although normally they are as shy as most wild animals and prefer to avoid man. The wild boar hunt has been regarded as a noble sport throughout history. Custom decrees that the hunt shall be on horseback and with dogs and that the quarry shall be killed with a spear.

The European wild boar will cross freely with domestic swine, and the offspring are fertile. It was domesticated somewhere around the Baltic sea in Neolithic times.

East Indian Pig

This broad classification includes a number of wild stocks of swine that were native to the East Indies and southeastern Asia. Though a bewildering number of domestic races are derived from the East Indian pig, including the domestic pig of China, all of them are smaller and more refined than the European wild boar. The East Indian pig is further distinguished by the absence of the crest of hair on the back and a white streak along the sides of the face. It is thought that *Sus vittatus* was the chief, if not the only, race or

Fig. 32-2. Malayan or Philippine pig (*Sus philippinensis*). This animal is rather typical of all East Indian pigs, the wild stock which, along with the European wild boar, contributed to American breeds of swine. In comparison with the European wild boar, East Indian pigs are smaller and more refined. (Courtesy, Chicago Natural History Museum)

species of the East Indian pig that was crossed with the descendants of the European wild boar in founding the American breeds of swine.

POSITION OF THE HOG IN THE ZOOLOGICAL SCHEME

The following outline shows the basic position of the domesticated hog in the zoological scheme:

Kingdom *Animalia*: Animals collectively; the animal kingdom.

Phylum *Chordata*: One of approximately 21 phyla of the animal kingdom, in which there is either backbone (in the vertebrates) or the rudiment of a backbone, the chorda.

Class *Mammalia*: Mammals, or warm-blooded, hairy animals that produce their young alive and suckle them for a variable period on a secretion from the mammary glands.

Order *Artiodactyla*: Even-toed, hoofed mammals.

Family *Suidae*: The family of nonruminant, artiodactyl ungulates, consisting of wild and domestic swine but, in modern classifications, excluding the peccaries.

Genus *Sus*: The typical genus of swine, formerly comprehensive but now restricted to the European wild board and its allies, with the domestic breeds derived from them.

Species *Sus scrofa* and *Sus uittatus*: *Sus scrofa* is a wild hog of continental Europe from which most domestic swine have been derived. *Sus vittatus* was the chief, if not the only, race or species of the East Indian pig that contributed to present-day domestic swine.

INTRODUCTION OF SWINE TO AMERICA

Although many wild animals were widely distributed over the North American continent prior to the coming of the white man, the wild boar was unknown to the native American Indian.

Columbus first brought hogs to the West Indies on his second voyage in 1493. According to historians, only eight head were landed as foundation stock. However, these hardy animals must have multiplied at a prodigious rate, for, 13 years later, the settlers of this same territory found it necessary to hunt the ferocious wild swine with dogs; they had grown so numerous that they were killing cattle.

Although swine were taken to other Spanish settlements following the early explorations of Columbus, pigs first saw America when crossing the continent with Hernando de Soto. The energetic Spanish explorer arrived in Tampa Bay (now Florida) in 1539. Upon his several vessels (between 7 and 10), he had 600 or more soldiers, some 200 or 300 horses, and 13 head of hogs.

This hardy herd of squealing, scampering pigs traveled with the army of

Fig. 32-3. De Soto discovers the Mississippi. When, in 1539, the Spanish explorer landed at Tampa Bay (now Florida) he brought with him 13 head of hogs. At the time of De Soto's death on the upper Mississippi, three years after the landing at Tampa, the hog herd had grown to 700. (Courtesy, The Bettmann Archive)

the brave Spanish explorer. The hazardous journey stretched from the Everglades of Florida to the Ozarks of Missouri. In spite of battles with hostile Indians, difficult travel, and other hardships, the herd thrived so well that at the time of De Soto's death on the upper Mississippi, three years after the landing at Tampa, the hog herd had grown to 700. De Soto's successor, Moscoso, then ordered that the swine be auctioned off among the men.

It is reasonable to assume, therefore, that the cross-country journey of De Soto's herd of pigs was the first swine enterprise in America. No doubt some of De Soto's herd escaped to the forest, and perhaps still others were traded to the Indians. At any rate, this sturdy stock served as foundation blood for some of our early American razorbacks.

THE CREATION OF AMERICAN BREEDS OF SWINE

The most thoroughly American domestic animal is the hog. In no other class of animals have so many truly American breeds been created. These facts probably result from (1) the suitability of native maize or Indian corn as a swine feed, (2) the ease with which pork could be cured and stored prior to the days of refrigeration, and (3) the need for fats and high-energy foods for laborers engaged in the heavy development work of a frontier country.

Unlike the beef and dairy stockmen, who sent their native cattle to slaughter and imported whole herds of blooded cattle from England, the American hog raiser was content to use the mongrel sow descended from colonial ancestry as a base, upon which he crossed imported Chinese, Neapolitan, Berkshire, Tamworth, Russian, Suffolk Black, Byfield, and Irish Grazier boars. These importations began as early as the second quarter of the nineteenth century. Out of the various crosses, which varied from area to area, were created the several genuinely American breeds of swine.

Structurally, the creation of the modern hog has been that of developing an animal that would put flesh on the sides and quarters, instead of running to bone and a big head. Physiologically, breed improvement has resulted in an elongation of the intestine of the hog, thus enabling him to consume more feed for conversion into meat. According to naturalists, the average length of the intestine of the wild boar compared with his body is in the proportion of 9 to 1; whereas, in the improved American breeds, it is in the proportion of 13.5 to 1.

Fig. 32-4. A typical Arkansas Razorback. This two-year-old sow weighed 180 pounds. (Courtesy, United Duroc Swine Registry)

GROWTH OF THE U.S. SWINE INDUSTRY

The growth of hog production has paralleled very closely the production of corn in the north central or Corn Belt states, as half of the United States corn crop is normally fed to hogs, and these states produce nearly three-fourths of the corn grown in the country. Thus, when corn yields are down, the price of feed is up and swine production decreases. The opposite occurs when corn yields are high.

As shown in Figure 32-5, hog numbers change sharply from year to year. Except for the sharp increase during the war years (with an all-time peak of 83,741,000 head on January 1, 1944), there has been a tendency to decline in numbers. This change has probably been the result, in part at least, of decreased export demands for pork and pork by-products and of the increased

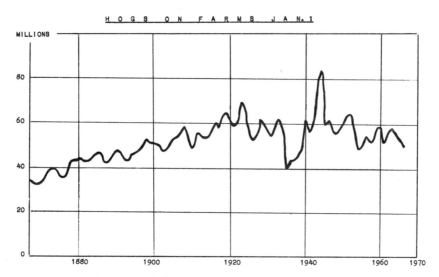

Fig. 32-5. Growth of the United States swine industry, 1867 to 1968.

competition that lard has encountered from vegetable oils. Also, beef has moved ahead of pork in per capita consumption.

WORLD DISTRIBUTION OF SWINE

Swine are produced most numerously in the temperate zones and in those areas where the population is relatively dense. There is reason to believe that these conditions will continue to prevail.

Table 32-1 gives data pertaining to the ten leading swine-producing countries of the world. China has long had the largest hog population, but, because

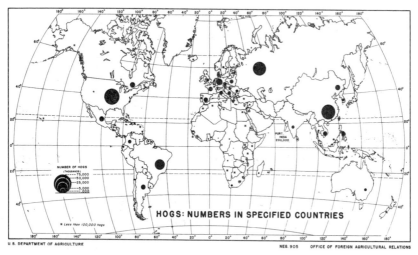

Fig. 32-6. World distribution of swine. (Courtesy, USDA, Office of Foreign Agricultural Relations)

TABLE 32—1

SIZE AND DENSITY OF HOG POPULATION OF TEN LEADING HOG PRODUCING COUNTRIES OF THE WORLD, BY RANK

Country	Hogs[1]		Human Population[3]		Size of Country		Hogs per Capita[4]	Hogs per	
	Number	When Estimated[2]	Number	When Estimated	(sq. mi.)	(sq. km)		(sq. mi.)	(sq. km)
China (Mainland)	69,000,000	1963	750,000,000	1964	2,279,134	5,902,957	.09	30.27	11.68
Brazil	57,669,000	1965	78,809,000	1964	3,286,270	8,511,439	.73	17.55	6.77
United States	53,052,000	1965	194,600,000	1965	3,548,974	9,191,843	.27	14.95	5.77
U.S.S.R.	52,800,000	1965	229,100,000	1965	8,655,890	22,418,755	.23	6.09	2.35
Germany (West)	18,169,000	1965	58,290,000	1964	95,931	248,613	.31	189.40	73.08
Poland	12,918,000	1964	31,161,000	1964	120,359	311,730	.41	107.33	41.43
Mexico	9,600,000	1965	39,643,000	1964	758,259	1,963,891	.24	12.61	4.88
Germany (East)	9,200,000	1964	17,011,000	1964	41,645	1,107,861	.54	220.91	85.29
France	9,087,000	1965	48,492,000	1965	212,659	550,789	.19	42.73	16.49
United Kingdom	7,958,000	1965	54,066,000	1964	94,209	244,001	.15	84.47	32.61
World total	459,460,000	1965	3,220,000,000	1964	52,403,746	135,725,702	.14	8.77	3.38

[1]*Foreign Agriculture Circular*, USDA, Livestock and Meats, FLM 3-65, May 1965.
[2]Preliminary for 1965.
[3]*World Almanac. 1966*, New York World-Telegram.

[4]Hogs per capita computed from most recent hog and human census figures reported; in some cases, this necessitated using data for different years.

of the large human population, production in that country is largely on a domestic basis, with very negligible quantities of pork entering into world trade. It must also be remembered that in China pigs are primarily scavengers and that the value of the manure produced is one of the main incentives for keeping them.

Hog production in the U.S.S.R. has risen sharply in recent years.

In general, in the European countries, hog numbers are closely related to the development of the dairy industry and the production of barley and potatoes—in much the same manner as the distribution of swine in the United States is closely related to the acreage of corn.

Corn is raised extensively in the La Plata region of South America and in the Danube Basin of southern Europe. In these corn-growing areas, hog production is a dominant type of farming.

Dairy by-products—skim milk, buttermilk, and whey—have long been important swine supplements in northeastern United States and also in Denmark, Holland, Canada, Ireland, Sweden, and Latvia. In Germany and Poland, potatoes have always been extensively used in swine feeding.

Since 1923, except for the increases occurring during World War II, there has been a downward trend in the exports of pork and lard from the United States. This has been due to a marked increase in production in Canada and in the European countries, particularly in Denmark, Germany, and Ireland and to various trade restrictions imposed by the importing countries. In no sense has this decrease been due to any lack of capacity to produce on the part of the American farmer.

Hog numbers fluctuate rather sharply on the basis of available feed supplies. Also, the annual per capita consumption of pork in different countries of the world varies directly with production and availability, cost, the taste preference of the people, and in some cases with the religious beliefs that bar the use of pork as a food.

SWINE PRODUCTION IN THE UNITED STATES

The contribution of the humble pig to American agriculture is expressed by his undisputed title as the "mortgage lifter." No other animal has been of such importance to the farmer. Hogs are produced on about two and one-half million American farms; and, upon these farms, 20 per cent of the world's supply of pork is produced.

On January 1, 1968, there were 54,263,000 head of hogs in the United States.[2] Hogs ranked second only to cattle in animal population. Hogs also rank as one of the most important sources of farm income, being exceeded only by cotton, dairy products, cattle, and wheat. The consumption of pork is higher in the United States than in any other country of the world.

The geographical distribution of swine in the United States closely coincides with the acreage of corn, the principal swine feed. Normally, one-half of

---

[2] *Livestock and Poultry Inventory*, January 1968, USDA, Feb. 13, 1968, p. 1.

the corn crop is fed to hogs. It is not surprising, therefore, to find that more than 60 per cent of the hog production is centered in the seven Corn Belt states: Iowa, Illinois, Indiana, Ohio, Missouri, Nebraska, and Kansas.[3] From this it should not be concluded that sections other than the Corn Belt are not well adapted to pork production. As a matter of fact, an area that produces dairy by-products, small grains, and forage is admirably adapted to the production of bacon of the highest quality.

Leading States in Swine Production

The state of Iowa has held undisputed lead in hog numbers since 1880, but the rank of the other states has shifted about considerably. A ranking of the 10 leading states, together with total numbers for the United States, is given in Table 32-2.

Growing corn and producing pork have contributed largely toward making the farmers of the upper Mississippi Valley the wealthiest agricultural people on the globe.

TABLE 32—2

TEN LEADING STATES IN HOG NUMBERS, BY RANK, 1968[1]

State	Number of Hogs
Iowa	13,740,000
Illinois	6,772,000
Missouri	4,174,000
Indiana	4,111,000
Minnesota	2,867,000
Nebraska	2,738,000
Ohio	2,340,000
South Dakota	1,615,000
Wisconsin	1,581,000
Kansas	1,541,000
U.S. total	54,263,000

[1]*Livestock and Poultry Inventory*, USDA, January 1, 1968.

FACTORS FAVORABLE TO SWINE PRODUCTION

The important position that the hog occupies in American agriculture is due to certain factors and economic conditions favorable to swine production. These may be enumerated as follows:

1. Swine excel all other farm animals in the economy with which they convert concentrated farm feed into meat and meat products.

At the Washington Agricultural Experiment Station, data taken from various experiments indicate that the feed required to produce gain in the dry lot during the market-finishing period of cattle, lambs, and pigs is about as shown in Table 32-3.

---

[3]*Agricultural Statistics, 1965*, Table 475, p. 322. For the period 1959-63, the seven Corn Belt states averaged 35,926,000 hogs out of the U.S. total of 57,656,000, which is 62 per cent.

TABLE 32—3

FEED EFFICIENCY OF CATTLE, SHEEP, AND SWINE

Age and Class of Animals	Days on Feed	Feed Required per 100 Lbs. (45.4 kg) Gain			
		Grain		Hay	
		(lbs.)	(kg)	(lbs.)	(kg)
Yearling steers......................	200	785	356.1	225	102.1
Feeder lambs	90	440	199.6	460	208.6
Growing-finishing pigs...........	90	400	181.4	---	---

2. Swine are prolific, commonly farrowing from six to twelve pigs, and producing two litters per year.

3. Swine excel in dressing percentage, yielding 65 to 80 per cent of their live weight when dressed packer style—with head, leaf fat, kidneys, and ham facings removed. On the other hand, cattle dress only 50 to 60 per cent, and sheep and lambs 45 to 55 per cent. Moreover, because of the small proportion of bone, the percentage of edible meat in the carcass of hogs is greater.

4. Pork is most nutritious. Because of the higher content of fat and the slightly lower content of water, the energy value of pork is usually higher than that of beef or lamb.

5. Hogs are efficient converters of wastes and by-products into pork. This includes grain wasted by finishing cattle, garbage, garden waste, and such dairy by-products as skim milk.

6. Since hogs are well adapted to the practice of self-feeding, labor is kept to a minimum.

7. Swine require a small investment for buildings and equipment.

8. The pig is adapted to both diversified and intensified agriculture.

9. The initial investment in getting into the business is small, and the returns come quickly. A gilt may be bred at eight months of age, and the pigs can be marketed six months after farrowing.

10. The spread in price in market hogs is relatively small—much smaller, for example, than the spread which usually exists between the price of Prime steers and Canner cows. Hogs may be sold at weights ranging from 150 to 300 pounds without any great penalty in price. Also, old sows that have outlived their usefulness in the breeding herd may be disposed of without difficulty.

11. Hogs are unexcelled as a source of farm meats. This is due to their ease of dressing and the superior curing and keeping qualities of pork.

12. The hog excels all other farm animals in fat storing ability, and pork fat is more valuable than fats produced by other domestic animals with the exception of the dairy cow.

FACTORS UNFAVORABLE TO SWINE PRODUCTION

It is not recommended that hogs be raised under any and all conditions. There are certain limitations that should receive consideration if the venture is to be successful. Some of these reservations are as follows:

1. Because of the nature of the digestive tract, the growing-finishing pig must be fed a maximum of concentrates and a minimum of roughages. Where or when grains are scarce and high in price, this may result in high production costs.

2. Because of the nature of their diet and their rapid growth rate, hogs are extremely sensitive to unfavorable rations and to careless management.

3. Swine are very susceptible to numerous diseases and parasites.

4. Fences of a more expensive kind are necessary in hog raising.

5. Sows should have skilled attention at farrowing time.

6. Because of their rooting and close-grazing habits, hogs are hard on pasture.

7. Hogs are not adapted to a frontier type of agriculture where grazing areas are extensive and vegetation is sparse. Neither are they best suited to the utilization of permanent-pasture areas.

THE FUTURE OF THE AMERICAN SWINE INDUSTRY

Some of the factors that will determine the future of the American swine industry are:

1. **Foreign competition.**—With the return of more abundant and cheaper feeds, several European and Scandinavian countries are again pork-exporting nations. Moreover, some of the South American countries are potential pork-producing and pork-exporting nations, an encouraging market being the only needed incentive. Canada is making great progress in swine production, in both quality and quantity. Only tariffs, quotas, and embargoes enacted by our federal government can prevent future and serious competition from foreign imports. However, with our huge corn production and improved swine-production methods, it is not anticipated that pork will ever have the potential foreign competition that exists with beef.

The potential pork-export situation is not encouraging.

2. **The lard situation.**—Lard was a "drug on the market" prior to 1941, and, soon after World War II, this status returned. Satisfactory vegetable oils can now be produced at lower cost. When processed lard sells for less than the price of hogs on foot, it should be perfectly evident that the product is lacking in demand. In order to alleviate the surplus lard situation, the soundest approach consists of: (a) breeding a type of hog that is less lardy in conformation, (b) feeding so as to produce less excess fat, (c) marketing at lighter weights, and (d) purchasing hogs on a quality basis (preferably rail-graded).

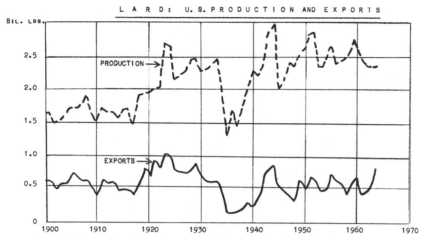

Fig. 32-7. Production and exports of lard from the United States, 1900 to 1965. Note that lard exports increased sharply during both World War I and World War II, but they were very small between 1935 and 1940. Most authorities agree that future lard exports will be negligible. (Courtesy, USDA Agricultural Marketing Service)

3. Increased human consumption.—Without doubt, some increased human consumption of pork could be brought about through the production of a higher quality product. Many folks, for example, would relish more high quality breakfast bacon. It is not anticipated, however, that any considerable opportunity for increased demand for hogs will come from any marked increase in per capita consumption of pork. Rather, such increases as occur will accrue from our expanding population.

4. Competition from other farm animals and between areas.—Despite the efficiency with which the pig converts grain to pork, he must continue to compete with all classes of animals for the available concentrates. For the nation as a whole, it appears, however, that there exists a fair balance of production with consumption of the several products of domestic animals. Thus, no immediate or sizeable shift that would be either favorable or unfavorable to increased pork production is anticipated. On the other hand, certain minor shifts in production from area to area may be expected.

Because of the year-round grazing, interest in diversification, the development of vertical integration and the diverse and comparatively cheap feeds in the southern states, increased swine production in this area is inevitable.

QUESTIONS FOR STUDY AND DISCUSSION

1. What prompted such early explorers as Columbus and De Soto to take swine with them?

2. More truly American breeds were created in swine than was the case with cattle, sheep, and horses. How do you explain this situation?

3. There has been a tendency for hog numbers to level off since 1923. Why has this been so?

4. Discuss the factors which account for each of the five leading swine producing countries (see Table 32-1) holding their respective ranks.

5. How do you account for the fact that over 60 per cent of the hog production is centered in the seven Corn Belt states?

6. Why does not swine production lend itself to two-phase production to the extent that cattle do; in the latter, cow-and-calf operations predominate on the range, and cattle are finished out primarily in Corn Belt feedlots or in irrigated valleys?

7. Select a certain farm or ranch (your home farm or ranch, or one with which you are familiar). Then, (a) discuss the relation of swine production on this farm or ranch to the type of agriculture, and (b) list the factors favorable and unfavorable to swine production on this particular farm or ranch.

8. When processed lard sells for less than the price of hogs on foot, it should be perfectly evident that the product is lacking in demand. How may we alleviate the surplus lard situation?

SELECTED REFERENCES

Titles of Publication	Author(s)	Publisher
Encyclopaedia Britannica		Encyclopaedia Britannica, Inc., Chicago, Ill.
History of Livestock Raising in the United States, 1607-1860	J. W. Thompson	Agricultural History Series No. 5, U.S. Department of Agriculture, Washington, D.C., November, 1942.
Natural History of the Pig, The	I. M. Mellen	Exposition Press, New York, N. Y., 1952.
Our Friendly Animals and Whence They Came	K. P. Schmidt	M. A. Donohue & Co., Chicago, Ill., 1938.
Pigs from Cave to Corn Belt	C. W. Towne E. N. Wentworth	University of Oklahoma Press, Norman, Okla., 1950.
Pork Production	W. W. Smith L. M. Hutchings, D.V.M.	The Macmillan Company, New York, N. Y., 1952.
Principles of Classification and a Classification of Mammals, The	G. G. Simpson	Bulletin of the American Museum of Natural History, Vol. 85, New York, N. Y., 1945.
Swine Production	C. E. Bundy R. V. Diggins	Prentice-Hall, Inc., Englewood Cliffs, N. J., 1956.

Chapter XXXIII

TYPES AND BREEDS OF SWINE[1]

Contents   **Page**

Types of Hogs..806
   The Lard Type..806
   The Bacon Type..807
   The Meat Type...808
Popularity of Breeds...808
Characteristics of Breeds..808
Questions for Study and Discussion...814
Selected References 815

In the hands of skilled livestock men, swine are the most plastic of any species of farm animals. This is due to their early maturity, multiple rate of reproduction, and short time between generations. A farmer who produces a total of 100 spring-farrowed pigs yearly needs only 14 gilts to raise a crop of the same size the following spring. There will be approximately 50 gilts from which he may select the 14 brood sows needed. He has a wide choice of keeping the lardy and more early maturing gilts or of picking others of a meaty form. Continued selection each year with emphasis upon the same characteristics and the purchase of boars of the same type can completely alter the conformation of the hogs in a herd in the short period of four to five years.

Despite this fact, progress in producing meat type hogs was often slow and painful throughout the thirties and forties. As a result, (1) pork gradually lost its place as the preferred meat, with beef taking the lead in the early fifties, and (2) a number of new American breeds of swine evolved, most of them carrying some Landrace breeding.

Pork may never regain the lead that it once enjoyed, and many of the newer breeds of swine may not survive. However, it is to the everlasting credit of the new breeds that they shook their older counterparts out of their lethargy. They more than justified the effort and cost back of them. Likewise, it is to the credit of the established breeds that they met the challenge and speeded up the transition in type. As a result, pork that satisfies consumer demands is once again being produced throughout America.

---

[1] Sometimes folks construe the write-up of a breed of livestock in a book or in a U.S. Department of Agriculture bulletin as an official recognition of the breed. Nothing could be further from the truth, for no person or office has authority to approve a breed. The only legal basis for recognizing a breed is contained in the Tariff Act of 1930, which provides for the duty-free admission of purebred breeding stock provided they are registered in the country of origin. But the latter stipulation applies to imported animals only.

In this book, no *official* recognition of any breed is intended or implied. Rather, the author has tried earnestly, and without favoritism, to present the factual story of the breeds in narrative and picture. In particular, such information relative to the new and/or less widely distributed breeds is needed, and often difficult to come by.

TYPES OF HOGS

Swine types are the result of three contributing factors: (1) the demands of the consumer, (2) the character of the available feeds, and (3) the breeding and pursuit of type fads by breeders.

Historically, three distinct types of hogs have been recognized: (1) lard type, (2) bacon type, and (3) meat type. At the present time, however, the goal for all U.S. swine breeds is for a meat-type hog, although it is obvious that some breeds have more nearly achieved this than others.

The Lard Type

Originally, breeders of hogs stressed immense size and scale and great finishing ability. This general type persisted until the latter part of the nineteenth century. Beginning about 1890, breeders turned their attention to the development of early maturity, great refinement, and a very thick finish. In order to obtain these desired qualities, animals were developed that were smaller in size, thick, compactly built, and very short of leg. In the Poland China breed, this fashionable fad was carried to the extreme. It finally culminated in the development of the "hot bloods." Hogs of this chuffy type were notoriously lacking in prolificacy. They often farrowed twins and triplets; and when they were carried to weights in excess of 200 pounds, their gains were very expensive. Small, refined animals of this type dominated the show ring from about 1890 to 1910.

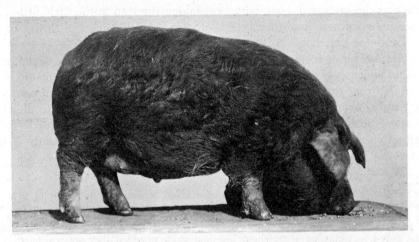

Fig. 33-1. A Poland China gilt of the chuffy type. Small, refined animals of this type dominated the American show ring from 1890 to 1910. (Courtesy, University of Illinois)

In order to secure increased utility qualities, breeders finally, about 1915,

Fig. 33-2. A Poland China boar pig of the rangy type. Long legged, weak-loined, "cat hammed" animals of this type dominated the American show ring from 1915 to 1925.

began the shift to the big-type strains. Before long, the craze swept across the nation, and again the pendulum swung too far. Breeders demanded great size, growthiness, length of body, and plenty of bone. The big-type animal was rangy in conformation and slow in maturity. Many champions of the show ring included as their attributes long legs, weak loins, and "cat hams." One popular champion of the day was advertised as being "so tall that it makes him dizzy to look down." Inasmuch as this type failed most miserably in meeting the require-ments of either the packer or the producer—being too slow to reach maturity and requiring a heavy weight in order to reach market finish—another shift in ideals became necessary.

The Bacon Type

Bacon-type hogs are more common in those areas where the available feeds consist of dairy by-products, peas, barley, wheat, oats, rye, and root crops. As compared with corn, such feeds are not so fattening. Thus, instead of producing a great amount of lard, they build sufficient muscle for desirable bacon. The countries of Denmark, Canada, and Ireland have long been noted for the production of high-quality bacon. In the past, the surplus pork produced in these countries has found a ready market in England, largely selling as Wiltshire sides.

In emphasizing the importance of character of feeds as a factor influencing the production of bacon-type hogs, it is not to be inferred that there is no heredi-tary difference. That is to say, when bacon-type hogs are taken into the Corn Belt and fed largely on corn, they never entirely lose their bacon qualities.

The Meat Type

Since about 1925, American swine breeders have been striving to produce meat-type hogs—animals that are intermediate between the lard and bacon types. The best specimens of the meat type combine muscling, length of body, balance, and the ability to reach market weight and finish without excess fat. In achieving the meat type, the selection and breeding programs of producers have been stoutly augmented by meat certification programs, livestock shows, and swine-type conferences.

POPULARITY OF BREEDS

Table 33-1 shows the 1965 and total registrations to date of the common breeds of hogs. Although trends are not shown in this table, it is noteworthy that the Hampshire took the lead from the Duroc in 1965.

TABLE 33-1
1965 AND TOTAL REGISTRATIONS OF SWINE IN
U.S. BREED ASSOCIATIONS

Breed	1965 Registrations	Total Registrations
Hampshire	51,587	1,817,320
Duroc	48,075	4,024,140
Yorkshire	27,663	435,000
Poland China	24,821	2,613,348
American Landrace	15,642	881,152
Chester White	15,624	989,624
Spotted	12,627	989,300
Berkshire	9,489	930,428
OIC	1,500	326,860
Tamworth	1,138	181,550
CPF No. 2[1]	130	207
Montana No. 1[1]	129	10,010
CPF No. 1[1]	128	254
Minnesota No. 3[1]	124	1,628
Beltsville No. 1[1]	97	4,536
Maryland No. 1[1]	84	1,299
Minnesota No. 2[1]	73	5,846
Palouse[1]	6	1,902
Hereford	—	109,198
Minnesota No. 1[1]	0	22,085
Incrosses[1]	0	3,581
Hybrids[1]	0	694

[1]Registered by the Inbred Livestock Registry Association, Augusta, Ill. Hybrids are crosses of two or more inbred lines or breeds of swine registered by the Inbred Livestock Registry Association.

CHARACTERISTICS OF BREEDS

With the exception of the American Landrace, Berkshire, Lacombe, Tamworth, Wessex Saddleback, and Yorkshire, the breeds of swine common to the United States are strictly American creations. This is interesting in view of the fact that none of our breeds of draft horses and few of our better known breeds

TABLE 33—2

BREEDS OF SWINE AND THEIR CHARACTERISTICS

Breed	Place of Origin	Color	Distinctive Head Characteristics	Other Distinguishing Characteristics	Disqualifications
American Landrace	Denmark	White, although small black skin spots are common.	Medium lop ears, straight snout, and trim jowl.	Very long side.	Black in the hair coat. Fewer than six teats on either side. Erect ears, with no forward break.
Beltsville No. 1 (75% Landrace & 25% Poland China)	United States; by the USDA at Beltsville, Maryland, beginning in 1934.	Black with white spots.	Fairly long, narrow head with trim, light jowl and moderately large, drooping ears.		
Berkshire	England; chiefly in the south central counties of Berkshire and Wiltshire.	Black with 6 white points, 4 white feet, some white on the face, and a white switch on the tail. Any or all white points may be missing.	Medium short nose, medium dished face, and erect ears.	Striking style and carriage.	A swirl on upper half of body. More than 10% white.
Chester White	United States; chiefly in Chester and Delaware counties of Pennsylvania.	White. Small bluish spots are sometimes found on the skin, but are discriminated against.			Not two-thirds big enough for age, upright ears, off colored hair, spots on hide larger than a silver dollar, cryptorchidism in males, hernia in males or females, or swirls on body above flanks.
CPF No. 1 (Developed from San Pierre X Beltsville No. 1)	Conner Prairie Farm, Noblesville, Ind.; beginning in 1956, accepted for registry in 1964.	Black and white.	Fairly long snout; trim jowl; moderate size, drooping ears.	Moderately long and well muscled.	
CPF No. 2 (25% Yorkshire, 25% Beltsville No. 1, 50% Maryland No. 1)	Conner Prairie Farm, Noblesville, Ind.; beginning in 1959, accepted for registry in 1964.	Black and white.	Fairly short snout, small ears that jut forward.	Fairly long body and length of leg, trim middle.	
Duroc	United States; chiefly in New York and New Jersey.	Red, varying from light to dark.	Medium size ear, tipping forward.		White feet or white spots on any part of body, any white on end of nose, black spots larger than 2 in. in diameter, swirls on upper half of the body or neck, ridgeling (one testicle) boars, or less than 6 udder sections on either side.
Hampshire	United States; in Boone County, Kentucky.	Black, with a white belt around the shoulders and body, including the front legs.	Longer and straighter in the face than most breeds; ears carried erect.		Any white on head other than front of snout, white on hind legs higher than bottom of ham, more than 2/3 of body white, solid black, white from belt running back on underline to meet white on hind quarters, an incomplete belt, one or both front legs black, a swirl, boar with one testicle, more than 2/3 undersize, or evidence of tampering to conceal faulty conformation or color markings.
Hereford	United States; by R. U. Webber of La Plata, Missouri.	Red body color, with white face, legs, and switch similar to Hereford cattle.			A white belt extending over shoulders, back, or rump; more than 2/3 white markings; no white markings on face; fewer than 2 white feet; a swirl; no marks or identification; boar with one testicle; or permanent deformities of any kind.

(Continued)

TABLE 33—2 (Continued)

Breed	Place of Origin	Color	Distinctive Head Characteristics	Other Distinguishing Characteristics	Disqualifications
Kentucky Red Berkshire	United States; in Kentucky.	Red	Short upturned nose, dished face, and erect ears.		
Lacombe (55% Landrace, 23% Berkshire, and 22% Chester White)	Canada; at the Experimental Farm Lacombe, Alberta, beginning in 1947.	White	Medium-sized flop ears and a medium length, slightly dished face.	Of the 3 parent breeds, it resembles the Landrace most closely.	
Maryland No. 1 (62% Landrace X 38% Berkshire)	United States; by the USDA and the U. of Maryland, beginning in 1941.	Black and white spotted.	The ears are erect or slightly drooping and intermediate in size.		
Minnesota No. 1 (48% Landrace X 52% Tamworth)	United States; by the USDA and the U. of Minnesota, beginning in 1936.	Red with occasional small black spots.	Long face, trim jowls, and fairly erect ears.	Long-bodied, short-legged, light shoulders, and a relatively straight back.	
Minnesota No. 2 (40% Yorkshire and 60% Poland China)	United States; by the U. of Minnesota, beginning in 1941.	Black and white.	Ears of medium size, with erect carriage. Snout is shorter than Minnesota No. 1.		
Minnesota No. 3 (From following 8 lines or breeds: Gloucester Old Spot, Welsh, Large White, C-Line Poland, Beltsville No. 2, Minnesota No. 1, Minnesota No. 2, and San Pierre)	Rosemount Experiment Station, Rosemount, Minn.; breeding stock first released in 1957.	Black and red spotted; or black and white.	Moderately dished face, trim jowl, ears tilted forward and slightly erect.	Noted for rapid growth and ruggedness.	
Montana No. 1 (55% Landrace X 45% Hampshire)	United States; in Montana, by the USDA and Montana State University, beginning in 1936.	Black	Drooping ears.		
OIC (Ohio Improved Chester)	United States; in Ohio, by L. B. Silver of Salem, Ohio.	White	Wide, short head and smooth dished face. Ears droop slightly.		Swirls on upper half of body, hernia, cryptorchidism, spots on skin with other than white hair, or inverted nipples.
Palouse (65% Landrace and 35% Chester White)	United States; by Washington State University, beginning in 1945.	White	Head is moderate in length; the ears are somewhat erect but inclined forward.		
Poland China	United States; in Ohio; in the Miami Valley of Warren and Butler Counties.	Black or black with white spots, with 6 white points—the feet, face, and tip of the tail.	Drooping ears.		Fewer than 6 teats on a side, a swirl on upper half of body, hernia, or cryptorchidism.
Spotted	United States, chiefly in Indiana.	Spotted black and white, 50% each.		Must have at least six prominent teats on each side to be eligible for show or sale.	Brown or sandy spots; less than 20% or more than 80% white on body; boar with a swirl; small upright ears; not over half normal size; cramped or deformed feet; seriously diseased, barren or blind; or if scoring fewer than 60 points.

(Continued)

TABLE 33—2 (Continued)

Breed	Place of Origin	Color	Distinctive Head Characteristics	Other Distinguishing Characteristics	Disqualifications
Tamworth	England; in the central counties of Stafford, Leicester, Warwick, and Northampton.	Red, varying from light to dark. Black spots may occur, but are objectionable.	Wide between the ears, snout moderately long and straight, neat jowl, and medium size, erect ears.		Swirls.
Wessex Saddleback	Hampshire, England.	Black, with a white belt around the shoulders and body including the front legs.	Fairly long snout, medium sized ears with forward pitch, trim jowl.		
Yorkshire (known as the Large White in England)	England	White, although black "freckles" appear.	Slightly dished face, and erect ears.		Swirls on upper third of body, hernia, hair color other than white, cryptorchidism, hermaphrodite, blind or inverted teats, total blindness, or fewer than 6 teats on each side.

of sheep and beef cattle were American creations. With the exception of the Hereford breed and some of the newer crossbred breeds of swine, the American breeds came into being in the period from 1800 to 1880—an era which was characterized by the production of an abundance of corn for utilization by hogs and by consumer demand for fat, heavy cuts of pork. The European breeds did not seem to meet these requirements.

It must be remembered, however, that the American breeds of swine were not developed without recourse to foreign stock. Prior to De Soto's importation, no hogs were found on the continent. The offspring of De Soto's sturdy razorbacks, together with subsequent importations of European and Oriental hogs, served as the foundation stock for the American breeds which followed. Out of these early-day multiple-colored and conglomerate types of swine, the swine producers of different areas of the United States, through the tools of selection and controlled matings, gradually molded uniform animals, later to be known as breeds. It is to be noted, however, that these foundation animals carried a variable genetic composition. This made them flexible in the hands of man

Fig. 33-3. Grand Champion American Landrace boar at the National Landrace Conference. Bred and exhibited by Makota Farm, Ames, Iowa; sold to James Kemp, Midlothian, Texas, for $2,000. (Courtesy, American Landrace Assn., Inc.)

Fig. 33-4. Beltsville No. 1. They are black with white spots. (Courtesy, Dr. T. C. Byerly, USDA)

Fig. 33-5. Champion Berkshire gilt at the National Berkshire Type Conference. Owned by Rahr Malting Co. Farm, Manitowoc, Wisconsin. (Courtesy American Berkshire Assn.)

Fig. 33-6. Iowa Junior Champion Chester White boar; bred by Clarence Williamson, Eagle Grove, Iowa; sold to KOK Farms, Sullivan, Illinois, for $2,200. (Courtesy, The Chester White Swine Record Assn., Rochester, Ind.)

Fig. 33-7. Royal Star CMS 35 SMS 2, 1958 Illinois Grand Champion Duroc boar, shown by Melvin Feik & Son, La Moille, Illinois, and presently owned by Oral W. Long, Elnora, Indiana. (Courtesy, United Duroc Swine Registry)

Fig. 33-8. All-American Senior Spring Hampshire boar; bred by Wilbert J. Meinhart, Hudson, Iowa; owned by J. W. Ralph and Dora Bishop, Tipton, Indiana. (Courtesy, Hampshire Swine Registry)

Fig. 33-9. A Champion Hereford gilt at the Iowa State Fair; bred and shown by Herbert Schulte, Norway, Iowa. (Courtesy, National Hereford Hog Record Assn.)

Fig. 33-10. A yearling Lacombe boar. (Courtesy, Department of Agriculture Experimental Farm, Lacombe, Alta.)

Fig. 33-11. Maryland No. 1 boar. They are black and white spotted. (Courtesy, Conner Prairie Farms)

Fig. 33-12. A Minnesota No. 1 gilt from the C. N. McMahan herd, Twin Hills Farm, Excelsior, Minnesota. (Courtesy, Inbred Livestock Registry Assn.)

Fig. 33-13. A Minnesota No. 2 boar. They are black and white in color. The ears are of medium size and carried erect, and the snout is shorter than that of the Minnesota No. 1. (Courtesy, Inbred Livestock Registry Assn.)

Fig. 33-14. A Montana No. 1 boar. They are black in color and have drooping ears. (Courtesy, Inbred Livestock Registry Assn.)

Fig. 33-15. Champion OIC sow at the Ohio and Indiana State Fairs; owned by W. W. Stutz, West Alexandria, Ohio. (Courtesy, OIC Swine Breeders' Assn., Inc.)

Fig. 33-16. A Palouse sow at 17 months of age. Note her deep, full ham; long, level rump; and high tail set. She has 14 teats. This great sow raised 11 pigs in her first litter, and 12 in the second. The second litter averaged 43.9 pounds at 56 days. (Courtesy, Washington State University)

Fig. 33-17. A Poland China gilt of approved type. (Courtesy, The Poland China Record Assn.)

Fig. 33-18. Spotted boar from a Certified Litter, sired by Bombshell. Bred by Sam Snyder, Byron, Illinois; sold to H. A. Melzer, Hanska, Minnesota. (Courtesy, National Spotted Poland China Record)

Fig. 33-19. Skyline Sam, Tamworth Certified Meat Sire No. 15. (Courtesy, The Tamworth Swine Assn., Inc.)

Fig. 33-20. Champion Gilt at Yorkshire Type Conference. (Courtesy, American Yorkshire Club, Inc.)

and accounted for the radical subsequent shifts in swine types that have been observed within the pure breeds.

Although there are many breed differences and most breed associations are constantly extolling the virtues of their respective breeds, it is perhaps fair to say that there is more difference within than between breeds from the standpoint of efficiency of production and carcass quality. Without doubt, the future and enduring popularity of each breed will depend upon how well it fulfills these two primary requisites.

QUESTIONS FOR STUDY AND DISCUSSION

1. Trace shifting of swine types throughout the years, including the factors that prompted such shifts.

2. Why have U.S. swine types shifted more rapidly and more radically than cattle and sheep types?

3. Most American-created breeds of swine evolved during two periods: (a) 1800 to 1880 and (b) since 1940. What is the explanation of this?

4. List the place of origin and distinguishing characteristics of each breed of swine. Discuss the importance of each.

5. Obtain breed registry association literature and a sample copy of a magazine of your favorite breed of swine. (See Appendix Sections VI and VII for addresses.) Evaluate the soundness and value of the material that you receive.

6. Justify any preference that you may have for one particular breed of swine.

SELECTED REFERENCES

Title of Publication	Author(s)	Publisher
Breeds of Livestock, The	Carl W. Gay	The Macmillan Company, New York, N. Y., 1918.
Breeds of Livestock In America	H. W. Vaughan	R. G. Adams and Company, Columbus, Ohio, 1937.
Breeds of Swine	J. H. Zeller	Farmers' Bul. No. 1263, U.S. Department of Agriculture, 1958.
Hog Annual, The 1952		The Farm Quarterly, Cincinnati, Ohio.
Hog Profits for Farmers	Dr. W. N. McMillen	Windsor Press, Vulcan Service Co., 403 Tuscaloosa Ave., Birmingham, Ala., 1952.
Meat Hog, The	C. H. Hinman	The Daily Sentinel, Grand Junction, Colo., 1955.
Modern Breeds of Livestock	H. M. Briggs	The Macmillan Company, New York, N. Y., 1958.
Pigs from Cave to Corn Belt	C. W. Towne E. N. Wentworth	University of Oklahoma Press, Norman, Okla., 1950.
Pork Production	W. W. Smith L. M. Hutchings	The Macmillan Company, New York, N. Y., 1952.
Raising Swine	G. P. Deyoe J. L. Krider	McGraw-Hill Book Company, New York, N. Y., 1952.
Stockman's Handbook, The	M. E. Ensminger	The Interstate Printers & Publishers, Danville, Ill., 1969.
Story of Durocs, The	B. R. Evans G. G. Evans	United Duroc Record Assoc., Peoria, Ill., 1946.
Study of Breeds, The	Thomas Shaw	Orange Judd Company, New York, N. Y., 1912.
Swine Production	C. E. Bundy R. V. Diggins	Prentice-Hall, Inc., Englewood Cliffs, N. J., 1956.
Swine Production	W. E. Carroll J. L. Krider	McGraw-Hill Book Company, Inc., New York, N. Y., 1956.
Types and Breeds of Farm Animals	C. S. Plumb	Ginn and Company, Boston, 1920.
Word Dictionary of Breeds, Types and Varieties of Livestock, The	I. L. Mason	Commonwealth Agricultural Bureaux, Farnham House, Farnham Royal, Slough, Bucks, England, 1951.

Also, breed literature pertaining to each breed may be secured by writing to the respective breed registry associations (see Sec. VI, Appendix, for the name and address of each association).

CHAPTER XXXIV

ESTABLISHING THE HERD; SELECTING AND JUDGING SWINE

Contents   **Page**

Factors to Consider in Establishing the Herd..817
    Type: Meat vs. Bacon; and Large, Medium, or Small...........................817
    Purebreds, Grades, or Crossbreds..818
    Selection of the Breed..819
    Size of Herd..819
    Uniformity 819
    Health 819
    Age 819
    Price 820
Selection and Its Bases...820
    Selection Based on Type or Individuality...820
    Selection Based on Pedigree...820
    Selection Based on Show-Ring Winnings...820
    Selection Based on Production Testing..821
Herd Improvement Through Selection..821
Judging Swine 821
    Parts of a Hog..822
    Ideal Type and Conformation..822
    Method of Examining...824
Questions for Study and Discussion...825
Selected References 825

The problems encountered and the principles employed in establishing the swine herd and in selecting and judging hogs are very similar to those outlined for beef cattle and sheep. In general, however, one can establish a swine herd at a lower cost and more quickly than is possible with other classes of farm animals. Until recently hog markets were less discriminating than cattle or sheep markets, with the result that the average commercial producer gave far less attention to becoming proficient in selecting and judging swine.

FACTORS TO CONSIDER IN ESTABLISHING THE HERD

At the outset, it should be recognized that the vast majority of the swine producers of this nation keeps hogs simply because they expect them to be profitable. That hogs have usually lived up to this expectation is attested by their undisputed claim to the title of "the mortgage lifter." For maximum profit and satisfaction, in establishing the herd the individual swine producer must give consideration to the type, breeding, and individual merit of each foundation animal, and to the size of the herd.

Type: Meat vs. Bacon; and Large, Medium, or Small

With reference to hogs, the word "type" is used in a dual capacity: (1) to denote whether breeds are of meat (or lard) type or bacon type, and (2) to denote the difference in form and general conformation within a breed on the basis of large, medium, or small type.

In the U.S., the difference in the general conformation and form between the modern meat and bacon types is less pronounced than formerly, primarily because of a shift of ideals within both types toward bred-in meat qualities. With lard becoming a "drug on the market," often selling for less per pound than the price of market hogs on foot, breeders of meat-type breeds are stressing the maximum cut-out value of primal cuts together with a minimum of lard. Likewise, breeders of bacon breeds are selecting for more muscling and thickness. Thus, the most desirable specimens of all U.S. breeds—the former (1) lard-type breeds and (2) bacon-type breeds—are now meat-type breeds, with similar goals; although some breeds more closely approach this objective than others. In Canada, on the other hand, bacon-type hogs prevail. Perhaps there is little difference in efficiency of production between the best specimens of the meat- and bacon-type breeds. Accordingly, consumer demand and market returns should be the determining factors as to the type of hogs produced.

As approximately 95 per cent of U.S. market hogs of the present day are of the so-called meat-type breeds, further discussion relative to possible variations of types within these breeds may be appropriate; for not all of these animals within breeds are of the true meat type. Over the years, most of these breeds have run the gauntlet in types, producing animals of the chuffy, rangy, and medium types. It is evident even today that these breeds possess the necessary store of genes through which such shift in types may be made by breeding and selection. Even so, most pork producers prefer the medium or intermediate type to either the chuffy or rangy types. Chuffy-type animals lack in prolificacy and rapidity of gains, whereas the rangy hog must be carried to too heavy a weight in order to reach market finish. The packer and consumer object to the chuffy animals because of their excess lardiness and to the rangy ones because of their large cuts that lack plumpness. It may be concluded, therefore, that most successful swine producers of the present day favor a medium- or meat-type hog.

Purebreds, Grades, or Crossbreds

Generally speaking, only the experienced breeder should undertake the production of purebreds with the intention of eventually furnishing foundation or replacement stock to other purebred breeders or purebred boars to the commercial producer. However, in many cases the spread in price between purebred and grade gilts is so small as to warrant the purchase of the former, even for commercial production. In any event, the use of a purebred boar is always to be advocated.

Crossbreeding of swine is fully discussed in Chapter XXXV. It is sufficient to say that this type of breeding program is more widely used in the production of hogs than with any other class of livestock, with the possible exception of sheep, and that under certain conditions it may be advantageous.

Selection of the Breed

No one breed of hogs can be said to excel others in all points of swine production and for all conditions. It is true, however, that particular breed characteristics may result in a certain breed being better adapted to given conditions; for example, hogs of light color are subject to sun scald in the deep South. Usually, however, there is a greater difference among individuals within the same breed than between the different breeds; this applies both to type and efficiency of production. In the end, therefore, the selection of a particular breed is most often a matter of personal preference, and usually the breed that the individual producer likes is the one with which he will have the greatest degree of success. Where no definite preference exists, however, it is well to choose the breed that is most popular in the community. This consideration allows for greater latitude in the choice of foundation stock and makes the problem of securing herd boars less difficult. The producer should also give some thought to the local market demands and initial costs.

Size of Herd

Hogs multiply more rapidly than any other class of farm animals. They also breed at an early age, produce twice each year, and bear litters. It does not take long, therefore, to get into the hog business.

The eventual size of the herd is best determined by the following factors: (1) size of farm, (2) available grains and pastures, (3) kind and amount of labor, (4) the disease and parasite situation, (5) the probable market, and (6) comparative profits from hogs and other types of enterprises.

Uniformity

Uniformity of type and ancestry gives assurance of the production of high-quality pigs that are alike and true to type. This applies both to the purebred and the grade herd. Uniform offspring sell at a premium at any age, whether they are sold as purebreds for foundation stock, as feeder pigs, or as fat hogs. With a uniform group of sows, it is also possible to make a more intelligent selection of the herd boar.

Health

Breeding animals that are in a thrifty, vigorous condition and that have been raised under a system of swine sanitation (by breeders who have exercised care in the control of disease and parasites) should have a decided preference. Tests should be made to make certain of freedom from swine brucellosis or contagious abortion. In fact, all purchases should be made subject to the animals being free from contagious diseases.

Age

In establishing the herd, the beginner may well purchase a few bred gilts that are well grown, uniform in type, and of good ancestry and that have been mated to a proved sire. Although less risk is involved in the purchase of tried sows, the cost is likely to be greater in relation to the ultimate value of the sows on the market.

Then, too, with limited capital, it may be necessary to consider the purchase of a younger boar. Usually a wider selection is afforded with this procedure, and in addition the younger animal has a longer life of usefulness ahead.

Price

The beginner should always start in a conservative way. However, this should never be cause for the purchase of poor individuals—animals that are high at any price.

SELECTION AND ITS BASES

Generally, the selection of foundation hogs is made on the basis of one or more of the following considerations: (1) type or individuality, (2) pedigree, (3) show-ring winnings, or (4) production testing.

Selection Based on Type or Individuality

In addition to choosing between (1) meat type and bacon type animals, and (2) rangy, medium, and chuffy type individuals, selection based on type or individuality implies the selection of those animals that approach the ideal or standard of perfection most closely and the culling out of those that fall short of these standards.

Selection Based on Pedigree

In the selection of breeding animals, the pedigree is a record of the individual's heredity or inheritance. If the ancestry is good, it lends confidence in projecting how well young animals may breed. It is to be emphasized, however, that mere names and registration numbers are meaningless. A pedigree may be considered as desirable only when the ancestors close up in the lineage—the parents and grandparents—were superior individuals and outstanding producers. Too often, purebred hog breeders are prone to play up one or two outstanding animals back in the third or fourth generation. If pedigree selection is to be of any help, one must be familiar with the individual animals listed therein.

The boar should always be purebred, which means that he is of known ancestry. This alone is not enough, for he should also be a good representative of the breed selected; and his pedigree should contain an impressive list of noted animals. Likewise, it is important that the sows be of good ancestry, regardless of whether they are purebreds, grades, or crossbreds. Such ancestry and breeding gives more assurance of the production of high-quality pigs that are uniform and true to type.

Selection Based on Show-Ring Winnings

Swine producers have long looked favorably upon using show-ring winnings as a basis of selection. Purebred breeders have been quick to recognize this appeal and to extol their champions through advertising. In most instances, the selection of foundation or replacement hogs on the basis of show-ring winnings and standards has been for the good. On many occasions, however, purebred and commercial breeders alike have come to regret selections based on show-ring winnings. This was especially true during the eras when the chuffy or rangy types were sweeping shows from one end of the country to the other. This would indicate that some scrutiny should be given to the type of animals winning in the show, especially to ascertain whether such animals are of a type that are efficient from the standpoint of the producer, and whether, over a period of years, they will command a premium on a discriminating market.

Perhaps the principal value of selections based on show-ring winnings lies in the fact that shows direct the attention of the amateur to those types and strains of hogs that at the moment are meeting with the approval of the better breeders and judges.

Selection Based on Production Testing

No criterion that can be used in selecting an animal is so accurate or important as past performance. It is recommended, therefore, that one purchase tried sows and a proved herd boar when such animals of the right kind can be secured at reasonable prices. Unfortunately, breeding animals of known merit are not usually available at a figure that a beginner can afford to pay. Sometimes, however, established breeders make the error of sacrificing brood sows of proved performance in favor of younger sows or find it necessary to sell proved boars because they can no longer be used in the breeding program. Animals of this kind constitute one of the soundest purchases that a young breeder can make.

Several of the purebred swine registry associations now have (1) production registry and/or (2) meat certification programs. Although these programs are not perfect, they do represent a progressive step in the right direction. Without doubt, both purebred and commercial swine producers of the future will make increasing use of such records as a basis for selection. (Production records in swine are discussed in Chapter XXXV.)

HERD IMPROVEMENT THROUGH SELECTION

Constructive breeders are those who effect improvement through breeding and selection, and this applies to both purebred and commercial producers. Such selection must be based on production factors of economic importance and market price as determined by carcass quality on a discriminating market.

JUDGING SWINE

Since the general requisites in judging, which are similar for all classes of livestock, are fully covered in Chapter XI, repetition at this point is unnecessary.

As previously indicated, until recently the small price spread in market classes and grades of swine offered little incentive to commercial swine producers to become proficient in judging. It is to the everlasting credit of purebred swine breeders, however, that they have been very progressive in this respect. The swine-type conferences sponsored by the various breed associations have made a unique contribution. Through bolstering live-animal work with a liberal amount of carcass data, these contests have soundly set fashions for both the producer and the packer.

Parts of a Hog

Most successful hog men, including both purebred and commercial producers, know the parts of a hog. In addition, they are aware of the possible merits of maximum development of these different parts from the standpoint of economical production and market value. Figure 34-1 shows the parts of a hog.

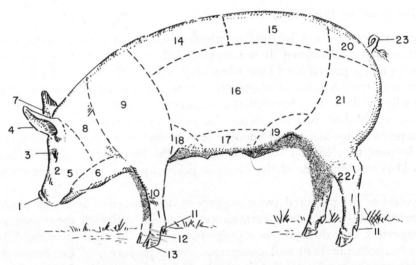

Fig. 34-1. Parts of a hog. The first step in preparation for judging hogs consists in mastering the language that describes and locates the different parts of the animal. (Drawing by R. F. Johnson)

1.	Snout	7.	Poll	13.	Toes	19.	Rear flank
2.	Face	8.	Neck	14.	Back	20.	Rump
3.	Eye	9.	Shoulder	15.	Loin	21.	Ham
4.	Ear	10.	Foreleg	16.	Side	22.	Rear leg
5.	Cheek	11.	Dew claw	17.	Belly	23.	Tail
6.	Jowl	12.	Pastern	18.	Foreflank		

Ideal Type and Conformation

The next requisite in judging or selection is to have clearly in mind a standard or ideal. Presumably, this ideal should be based on a combination of (1) the efficient performance of the animal from the standpoint of the producer, and (2) the desirable carcass characteristics of market animals as determined by the consumer.

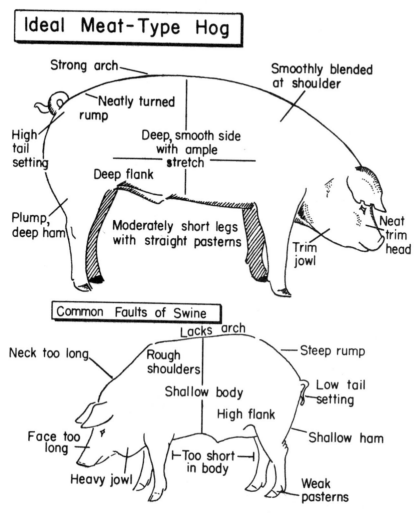

Fig. 34-2. Ideal meat type versus common faults. The successful hog judge must know what he is looking for and be able to recognize and appraise both the good points and the common faults. (Drawing by R. F. Johnson)

The most approved meat-type breeding animals combine size, smoothness, and quality, and the offspring possess the ability to finish during the growing period without producing an excessive amount of lard. The head and neck should be trim and neat; the back well arched and of ample width; the sides long, deep, and smooth; and the hams well developed and deep. The legs should be of medium length, straight, true, and squarely set; the pasterns should be short and strong; and the bone should be ample and show plenty of quality. With this splendid meat type, there should be style, balance, and symmetry and an abundance of quality and smoothness.

The most approved bacon-type breeding hogs differ from meat-type animals chiefly in that greater emphasis is placed on length of side and the maximum development of the primal cuts with the minimum of lard. Also, bacon-type hogs generally have less width over the back and have a squarer type of ham, and show more trimness throughout.

With both meat- and bacon-type animals, the brood sows should show great femininity and breediness; and the udder should be well developed, carrying from 10 to 12 teats. The herd boar should show great masculinity as indicated by strength and character in the head, a somewhat crested neck, well-developed but smooth shoulders, a general ruggedness throughout, and an energetic disposition. The reproductive organs of the boar should be clearly visible and well developed. A boar with one testicle should never be used.

Figure 34-2 shows the ideal meat-type hog versus some of the common faults. Since no animal is perfect, the proficient swine judge must be able to recognize, weigh, and evaluate both the good points and the common faults. In addition, he must be able to arrive at a decision as to the degree to which the given points are good or bad.

Method of Examining

Since a pig will neither stand still nor remain in the same vicinity long, it is not possible to arrive at a set procedure for examining swine. In this respect, the judging of hogs is made more difficult than the judging of other classes of livestock. Where feasible, however, the steps for examining as illustrated in Figure 34-3 are very satisfactory, and perhaps as good as any.

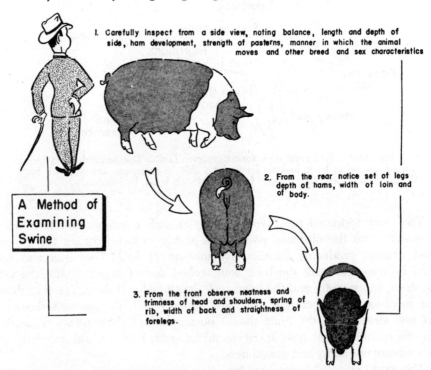

Fig. 34-3. A good procedure for examining a hog and some of the things for which to look. (Drawing by R. F. Johnson)

QUESTIONS FOR STUDY AND DISCUSSION

1. In establishing the herd, and in selecting and judging, what primary differences exist in swine as compared to beef cattle and sheep?
2. Select a certain farm or ranch (either your home farm or ranch, or one with which you are familiar). Assume that there are no hogs on this establishment at the present time. Then outline, step by step, (a) how you would go about establishing a herd, and (b) the factors that you would consider. Justify your decisions.
3. Discuss each of the four bases of selection of swine.
4. Cite examples of how purebred and commercial breeders alike have come to regret selections based on show-ring winnings.
5. Why is it difficult to arrive at a set procedure for examining a pig?

SELECTED REFERENCES

Title of Publication	Author(s)	Publisher
Breeding Better Livestock	V. A. Rice F. N. Andrews E. J. Warwick	McGraw-Hill Book Co., New York, N. Y., 1953.
Determining the Age of Farm Animals by Their Teeth	Farmers' Bul. 1721	U.S. Department of Agriculture, Washington, D. C.
Elements of Livestock Judging, The	W. W. Smith	J. B. Lippincott Co., Philadelphia, Pa., 1930.
Judging Livestock	E. T. Robbins	Cir. 579, Ext. Serv., University of Illinois, Urbana, Ill.
Livestock and Meat Manual, A	Ext. Misc. Pub. 40	Ext. Serv., Washington State University, Pullman, Wash.
Livestock Judging Handbook	J. E. Nordby W. M. Beeson D. L. Fourt	Interstate Printers & Publishers, Danville, Ill., 1962.
Pork Production	W. W. Smith L. M. Hutchings, D.V.M.	The Macmillan Company, New York, N. Y., 1952.
Selecting, Fitting and Showing Swine	J. E. Nordby H. E. Lattig	Interstate Printers & Publishers, Danville, Ill., 1961.
Stockman's Handbook, The	M. E. Ensminger	Interstate Printers & Publishers, Danville, Ill., 1969.

Chapter XXXV

BREEDING SWINE

Contents   Page

Normal Breeding Habits of Swine.....828
   Age of Puberty.....828
   Age to Breed Gilts.....828
   Heat Periods 828
   Gestation Period 829
   Breeding After Farrowing.....829
Fertility and Prolificacy in Swine.....829
Flushing Sows.....830
The Breeding Procedure; Hand Mating; The Breeding Crate.....830
Care and Management of the Boar.....831
   Feed, Shelter, and Exercise.....831
   Ranting 832
   Clipping the Tusks.....832
Age and Service of the Boar.....833
Care of the Pregnant Sow.....833
Care of the Sow at Farrowing Time.....834
   Signs of Approaching Parturition.....834
   Preparation for Farrowing.....834
      Sanitary Measures 834
      The Quarters.....835
      The Guard Rail.....835
      Bedding 836
   The Attendant.....836
   Chilled and Weak Pigs.....836
   Orphan Pigs 836
   Artificial Heat.....837
The Sow and Litter.....837
   The McLean County System of Swine Sanitation.....837
   The Needle Teeth.....837
   Ear Notching the Litters.....838
   Castration 840
   Exercise and Sunshine.....840
   Feed Requirements of the Nursing Sow.....840
Normal Breeding Season and Time of Farrowing.....840
   Show-yard Classifications May Determine Farrowing Dates.....841
Two Litters Versus One Litter a Year.....841
Multiple Farrowing 842
Gilts Versus Older Sows.....843
Crossbreeding Swine 843
Lethals and Other Hereditary Abnormalities in Swine.....845
Production Testing Swine.....845
   Production Testing by Swine Record Associations.....849
Questions for Study and Discussion.....849
Selected References 849

The laws of heredity apply to swine breeding exactly as they do to all classes of farm animals. But the breeding of swine is more flexible in the hands of man because: (1) hogs normally breed at an earlier age, thus making for a shorter interval between generations, and (2) they are litter-bearing animals. Because of these factors and because of the available feeds and the type of pork products demanded by the consumer, the American farmer has created more new breeds and made more rapid shifts in type in hogs than in any other class of farm animals.

NORMAL BREEDING HABITS OF SWINE

The pig lends itself very well to experimental study in confined conditions. It is reasonable to expect, therefore, that we should have a considerable store of knowledge relative to the normal breeding habits of swine, perhaps more than we have of any other class of farm animals.

Age of Puberty

The age of puberty in swine varies from four to seven months. This rather wide range is due to differences in breeds and lines, sex, and environment—especially nutrition. In general, boars do not reach puberty quite so early as gilts.

Age to Breed Gilts

Reasonably early breeding has the advantage of establishing regular and reliable breeding habits and reducing the cost of the pigs at birth.

Gilts that are well developed may, as a general rule, be bred to farrow at 12 to 14 months of age. It is to be emphasized, however, that this depends primarily upon development rather than age; thus, it is recommended that gilts weigh at least 225 pounds before breeding. Proper development is essential in order that animals may be able to withstand the strain of lactation, the demands of which are much more rigorous than gestation.

The breeding of show gilts is often delayed until after the show season. This practice frequently results in difficult conception and temporary, if not permanent, sterility. Perhaps this is due to the overfat condition in fitting.

Heat Periods

The heat period—the time during which the sow will accept the boar—lasts from one to five days, with an average of two to three days. Older sows generally remain in heat longer than gilts.

Ovulation probably occurs on the second day of heat, although evidence on the latter point is not too conclusive. As in females of all species, sows bred approximately at the time of ovulation are more likely to conceive than if bred at any other time. The first mating of gilts should be on the first day of estrus, and the first mating of sows on the second day. In each case, a second service should follow the first by 24 hours. If not bred, the heat period normally recurs at intervals of 18 to 24 days, with an average of 21 days.

The external signs of heat in the sow are restless activity, swelling or enlargement and discharge from the vulva (although these signs are not always present), frequent mounting of other sows, frequent urination, and occasional loud grunting.

Gestation Period

The average gestation period of sows is 114 days, although extremes of 98 to 124 days have been reported.

Breeding After Farrowing

Sows will often come in heat during the first few days after farrowing, but they rarely conceive if bred at this time—for the reason that they fail to ovulate.

Following the early postfarrowing heat period, sows normally will not come in heat again until near the end of the suckling period. However, they may be brought into heat during the lactation period by removing the pigs for several consecutive nights. Some producers follow this practice and rebreed about the fifth week after farrowing. Nevertheless, it is common practice first to wean the litter and let the animals have a few days rest before rebreeding. Normally, some will come in heat 3 to 10 days, with an average of about 7 days, after weaning.

When pigs are weaned under two weeks of age, it is recommended that sows be bred on the second heat period after weaning. However, when pigs are weaned at three or more weeks of age, it is generally satisfactory to breed on the first heat period following weaning.

The most natural breeding season for sows seems to be in the early summer and late autumn, although they will breed any time of the year.

FERTILITY AND PROLIFICACY IN SWINE

Under domestication and conditions of good care, a high degree of fertility is desired. The cost of carrying a litter of 10 pigs to weaning time is little greater than the cost of producing a litter of only 5 or 6. In other words, the maintenance costs on both the sow and the boar remain fairly constant. It must be remembered, however, that in the wild state high fertility may not have been characteristic of swine. Survival and natural selection were probably in the direction of smaller litters, but nature's plan has been reversed through planned matings and selection.

Low fertility in swine is most commonly attributed to hereditary and environmental factors. Maximum prolificacy depends upon having a large number of eggs shed at the time of estrus, upon adequate viable sperm present for fertilization at the proper time, and upon a minimum of fetal atrophy.

It is a well-known fact that some breeds and strains of swine are much more prolific than others. We are told that litters of 12 are considered normal rather than exceptional among Chinese swine. Also, through selection, more prolific strains of swine can be developed. Furthermore, the number of pigs produced increases with the age of the sow. It also appears that flushing or conditioning of sows exerts an influence on the number of eggs shed. All in all, it appears that more can be accomplished through proper management to increase litter size than can be done through selection.

Practical swine producers generally associate type with prolificacy. To substantiate their theory, they point out that the fat, chuffy hogs in vogue during the early part of the present century were not prolific but were prone to farrow twins and triplets. Experimental work substantiates this opinion.

Even though many eggs may be shed and fertilized, the size of the litter may be affected materially by fetal atrophy, which ranges from 5 to 30 per cent. This condition is usually attributed to (1) hereditary factors, perhaps recessive lethals; (2) overcrowding resulting from a large number of pigs and a consequent limited uterine surface area available for the nourishment of the individual embryos; (3) nutritionally incomplete rations prior to and during gestation; (4) excessive fatness or a thin run-down condition; (5) diseases or parasites; or (6) accidents or injuries. Additional studies need to be made relative to the cause and prevention of fetal atrophy.

Litter size is affected little, if any, by the boar. In fact, research work indicates that fertilization in swine is very much an all or none phenomenon. Perhaps an exception exists in boars that are on the borderline of sterility, when insufficient viable sperm are present to fertilize the eggs. Certainly, the boar cannot affect the number of eggs shed, and, therefore, cannot increase litter size. It has been observed that litter size may be slightly increased if two services are used instead of one. Also, it is recommended that, in advance of the regular breeding season, the boar be mated to a few market gilts; thereby providing for fresh viable sperm in the epididymis when the boar is placed in service in the breeding herd.

FLUSHING SOWS

The practice of feeding sows more liberally so that they gain in weight from 1 to 1½ pounds daily from about one to two weeks before the opening of the breeding season until they are safely in pig is known as flushing. Some of the beneficial effects attributed to this practice are: (1) more eggs are shed, and this results in larger litters; (2) the sows come in heat more promptly; and (3) conception is more certain.

If sows are already overfat, the best preparation for breeding consists of conditioning by providing plenty of exercise and access to a lush pasture, while decreasing the heavy grain ration.

THE BREEDING PROCEDURE;
HAND MATING; THE BREEDING CRATE

Hand mating is more generally practiced in swine than with either cattle or sheep. In fact, it is almost the universal procedure in purebred swine herds, and many commercial producers follow the same practice.

When a mature, heavy boar is to be bred to gilts or when a boar pig is to be bred to big, rangy sows, the use of a breeding crate is recommended. Animals that have formed the habit of breeding without the crate may be rather obstinate in accepting the new method, or may refuse service altogether. Com-

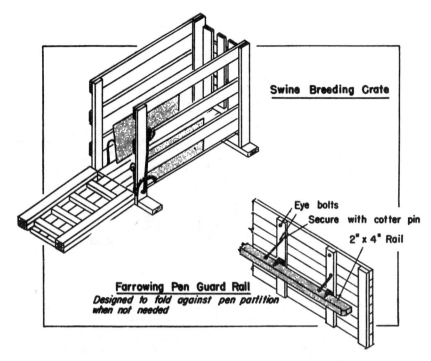

Fig. 35-1. Two handy pieces of swine equipment; the breeding crate (top) and the guard rail (bottom). (Drawing by R. F. Johnson)

mercial swine producers usually use active, young boars; in many instances they allow the boar to run with the sows to be bred.

CARE AND MANAGEMENT OF THE BOAR

Proper care and management of the herd boar is most essential for successful swine production. Too frequently the boar is looked upon as a necessary evil and is neglected. Under such conditions, he is usually confined to a small, filthy pen—a typical pig sty; exercise is discouraged; and the feeding practices are anything but intelligent.

Feed, Shelter, and Exercise

Outdoor exercise throughout the year is one of the first essentials in keeping the boar in a thrifty condition and virile. This may usually be accomplished by providing a well-fenced pasture. Even then, the herdsman may find it necessary to walk old boars or boars that are being fitted for the shows. In addition to the valuable exercise that is obtained in the pasture lot, green succulent pasture furnishes valuable nutrients for the herd boar. The amount of feed provided should be such as to keep the boar in a thrifty, vigorous condition at all times. He should be neither overfat nor in a thin, run-down condition. The concentrate allowance should be varied with the age, development, and tem-

Fig. 35-2. Diagram of a desirable arrangement for the herd boar; showing a good fence, a portable house, shade, water, and sufficient area for pasture and exercise. (Drawing by R. F. Johnson)

perament of the individual; breeding demands; roughage consumed; etc. Feeding the boar is more fully covered in Chapter XXXVI.

A satisfactory but inexpensive shelter should be provided for the boar, and he should be allowed to run in and out at choice.

Boars of the same age or size can be run together during the off-breeding season, but boars of different ages should not be kept together.

Ranting

Some boars pace back and forth along the fence, often chopping their jaws and slobbering. Such action is called ranting. Young boars that take to excessive ranting may go off feed, become "shieldy," and fail to develop properly. Although this condition will not affect their breeding ability, it is undesirable from the standpoint of appearance. Isolation from other boars or from the sow herd is usually an effective means of quieting such boars. Should the boar remain off feed, placing a barrow or a bred sow in the pen with him will help to get him back on feed.

Clipping the Tusks

It is never safe to allow the boar to have long tusks, for they may inflict injury upon other boars or even prove hazardous to the caretaker. Above all, such tusks should be removed well in advance of the breeding season, at which time it is necessary to handle the boar considerably. The common procedure in preparation for removing the tusks consists of drawing a strong rope over the upper jaw and tieing the other end securely to a post or other object. As the animal pulls back and the mouth opens, the tusks may be cut with a bolt clipper.

AGE AND SERVICE OF THE BOAR

The number of services allowed will vary with the age, development, temperament, health, breeding condition, distribution of services, and system of mating (hand coupling or pasture breeding). No standard number of services can be recommended for any and all conditions. Yet the practices followed by good swine producers are not far different. Such practices are summarized in Table 35-1.

For best results, the boar should be at least eight months old and well grown before being put into service. Even then, he should be limited to one service per day and a maximum total of two dozen services during his first breeding season, unless the mating period covers more than one month.

TABLE 35—1

HANDY BOAR MATING GUIDE

| Age | No. of Matings/Yr. | | Comments |
	Hand Mating	Pasture Mating	
8 to 12 mo. of age..................	24	12	Boar pigs should be limited to one service/day; older boars to two services/day.
Yearling or older	50	35-40	A boar should remain a vigorous and reliable breeder up to 6 to 8 years of age.

When fed and cared for by an experienced herdsman, a strong, vigorous boar from one to four years of age (the period of most active service) may serve two sows per day during the breeding season provided that a system of hand coupling is practiced. With pasture mating, fewer sows can be bred.

Excessive service will result in the release of a decreased concentration of sperm as well as immature sperm.

A boar should remain a vigorous and reliable breeder up to six or eight years of age or older, provided that he has been managed properly throughout his lifetime.

CARE OF THE PREGNANT SOW

Without attempting to review the discussion on feeding the gestating sow as found in Chapter XXXVI, it may be well to re-emphasize that there are two cardinal principles which the feeder should keep in mind when feeding sows during the pregnancy period. These are: to provide a ration which will insure the complete nourishment of the sow and her developing fetal litter, and to choose the feeds and adopt a method of feeding which will prove economical and adaptable to local farm conditions.

In addition to having proper nutrition, the pregnant sow should have regular and careful exercise. During periods of inclement weather and when feed is brought into the house, sows quite often exercise too little. As a result, they become sluggish; and the blood circulation is poor. Forced exercise may be brought about by feeding some distance from the house or by driving the animals at a moderate walk. Sows that have had plenty of exercise during the gestation period generally encounter less difficulty at farrowing time and produce stronger pigs.

The shelter for the bred sows should not be elaborate nor expensive. Less labor is involved when several sows of the same age, size, and condition are run together. The chief requirements are that the shelter be tight overhead, that it afford protection from inclement weather, that it is well drained and dry, and that it is of sufficient size to allow the animals to move about and lie down in comfort. Except during the most inclement weather, the sows should be encouraged to run outdoors where they will get exercise, fresh air, and sunshine.

But swine housing is changing. Today, an increasing number of producers are confining sows, individually or in groups, as a means of lessening labor and automating, freeing land for crops, and controlling environment.

CARE OF THE SOW AT FARROWING TIME

The careful and observant herdsman realizes the importance of having everything in readiness for farrowing time. If the pregnant sows have been so fed and managed as to give birth to a crop of strong, vigorous pigs, the next problem is that of saving the pigs at farrowing time.

It has been conservatively estimated that from 30 to 35 per cent of the pigs farrowed never reach weaning age, and an additional loss of 5 to 10 per cent occurs after weaning. This means that only 60 per cent of the pig crop reaches market age.

Signs of Approaching Parturition

The immediate indications that the sow is about to farrow are extreme nervousness and uneasiness, an enlarged vulva, and a possible mucus discharge. She usually makes a nest for her young, and milk is present in the teats.

Preparation for Farrowing

About three or four days prior to farrowing, the sow should be isolated from the rest of the herd. It is important, however, that moderate exercise be continued while the animal is in the farrowing quarters.

SANITARY MEASURES

Before being moved into the farrowing quarters, the sow should be thor-

Fig. 35-3. WSU's Swine Herdsman, Arvid Neibergs, washing a sow prior to moving her into the farrowing quarters. This removes adhering parasite eggs. (Courtesy, Washington State University)

oughly scrubbed with soap and warm water, especially in the region of the sides, udder, and undersurface of the body. This removes adhering parasite eggs (especially the eggs of the common roundworm) and disease germs.

The house should be thoroughly cleaned to reduce possible infection. This may be done by scrubbing the walls and floors with boiling-hot lye water made by mixing one can of lye to 15 gallons of water. If the farrowing house has dirt floors, the top 2 or 3 inches of soil should be replaced by an equal quantity of clean clay soil. The sow should then be placed in her new quarters.

THE QUARTERS

Hogs are sensitive to extremes of heat and cold and require more protection than any other class of farm animals. This is especially true at the time of parturition. It is recommended that the farrowing house temperature be maintained at 60° to 70° F., and that it not go below 40° F. or above 85° F. In the cold areas and during winter months, use heat lamps or pig brooders when the farrowing house temperature falls below 60° F. Along with this temperature there should be adequate ventilation at all times.

The main requirements for satisfactory housing are that the quarters be dry, sanitary, and well ventilated and that they provide good protection from heat, cold, and winds. The buildings should be economical and durable.

THE GUARD RAIL

A guard rail around the farrowing pen is an effective means of preventing sows from crushing their pigs. The importance of this simple protective measure may be emphasized best by pointing out that approximately half of the young pig losses are accounted for by those pigs that are overlaid by their mothers. The rail should be raised 8 to 10 inches from the floor and should be 8 to 12 inches from the walls. It may be constructed of 2 x 4's, 2 x 6's, strong poles, or steel pipe.

BEDDING

The farrowing quarters should be bedded lightly with clean, fresh material. Any good absorbent that is not too long and coarse is satisfactory. Wheat, barley, rye, or oat straw; short or chopped hay; ground corncobs; peanut hulls; cottonseed hulls; shredded corn fodder; and shavings are most commonly used.

The Attendant

The herdsman should be on the job, especially during times of inclement weather. It may be necessary to free the newborn pigs from the enveloping membrane and to help them reach the mother's teat. In cold weather the young should be dried off and other precautions taken to avoid chilling.

If the sow has labored for some time with little progress or is laboring rather infrequently, assistance should be given. This usually consists of inserting the hand and arm in the vulva and gently correcting the condition preventing delivery. Before doing this, the fingernails should be trimmed closely, and the hands and arms should be thoroughly washed with soap and warm water, disinfected, and then lubricated with vaseline or linseed oil.

As soon as the afterbirth is expelled, it should be removed from the pen and burned or buried in lime. This prevents the sow from eating the afterbirth and prevents the development of bacteria and foul odors. Many good swine producers are convinced that eating the afterbirth encourages the development of the pig-eating vice. Dead pigs should be removed for the same reason.

It is also well to work over the bedding; remove wet, stained, or soiled bedding and provide clean fresh material.

Chilled and Weak Pigs

Pigs arriving during cold weather are easily chilled. Under such conditions, it may be advisable to take the pigs from the mother as they are born and place them in a half-barrel or basket lined with straw or rags. In extremely cold weather, a few hot bricks or a jug of warm water (properly wrapped to prevent burns) may be placed in the barrel or basket; or the pigs may be taken to a warm room until they are dry and active.

One of the most effective methods of reviving a chilled pig is to immerse the body, except for the head, in water as warm as one's elbow can bear. The pig should be kept in this for a few minutes, then removed and rubbed vigorously with cloths.

Orphan Pigs

Pigs may be orphaned either through sickness or death of their mother. In either event, the most satisfactory arrangement for the orphan is to provide a foster mother. When it is impossible to transfer the pigs to another sow, they may be raised on cow's milk or milk replacer. The problem will be simplified if the pigs have received a small amount of colostrum (the first milk) from their mother.

If cow's milk is used, it is preferable that it be from a low-testing cow. Do not add cream or sugar; however, skim milk powder, at the rate of a tablespoonful to a pint of fluid milk may be added, if available. Milk replacer should be mixed according to the directions found on the container. The first two or three days the orphan should be fed regularly every two hours, and the milk should be at 100° F. Thereafter, the intervals may be spaced farther apart. All utensils (pan feeding or a bottle and nipple may be used) should be clean and sterilized.

Orphan pigs should be started on pre-starter or starter ration when they are one week old. Also, a source of iron should be provided (in keeping with instructions given in Chapter XXXVI).

Artificial Heat

During times of inclement weather, artificial heat usually must be provided, especially for pigs farrowed in the northern United States. Most large central hog houses are equipped with a heating unit for use in winter farrowing.

Individual houses may be insulated by banking with straw and other insulating materials. Then a lantern or oil burner may be suspended from the top of the house. It must be remembered, however, that there is considerable fire hazard from this practice. The electric pig brooder is a much safer heating unit for either the central or the movable hog houses. The principles involved are identical to those of the electric chick brooder.

THE SOW AND LITTER

The care and management given the sow and litter should be such as to get the pigs off to a good start. As is true of other young livestock, young pigs make more rapid and efficient gains than older hogs. Strict sanitation and intelligent feeding are especially important for the well being of the young pig.

The McLean County System of Swine Sanitation

The McLean County system of swine sanitation (see Fig. 35-4) was worked out especially for the purpose of preventing infestation of young pigs with the common roundworm. The application of these principles is usually effective in reducing trouble from other parasites and in disease control—thus making possible cheaper and more profitable pork production.

The Needle Teeth

Newborn pigs have eight small, tusk-like teeth (so-called needle or black teeth), two on each side of both the upper and lower jaw. As these are of no benefit to the pig, most swine producers prefer to cut them off soon after birth. This operation may be done with a small pair of pliers or with forceps made espe-

Fig. 35-4. The McLean County System of Swine Sanitation involves the four simple steps shown in the diagram: (1) cleaning and disinfecting the farrowing quarters, (2) washing the sow before placing her in the farrowing quarters, (3) hauling the sow and pigs to clean pasture, and (4) keeping the pigs on clean pasture until they are at least four months old. (Drawing by R. F. Johnson)

cially for the purpose. In removing the teeth, care should be taken to avoid injury to the jaw or gums, for injuries may provide an opening for germs. The needle teeth are very sharp and are often the cause of pain or injury to the sow, particularly if the udder is tender. Moreover, the pigs may bite or scratch each other, and infection may start and cause serious trouble.

Ear Notching the Litters

The common method of marking or identifying swine consists of ear notching the litters. Pigs are generally marked at the same time that the needle teeth are

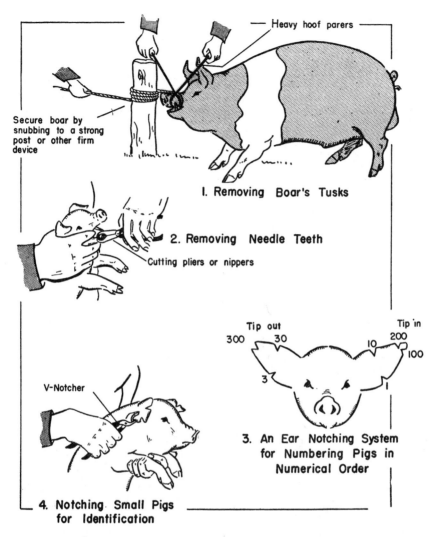

Heavy hoof parers

Secure boar by
snubbing to a strong
post or other firm
device

I. Removing Boar's Tusks

2. Removing Needle Teeth

Cutting pliers or nippers

Tip out   Tip in
300   30   200
                                        10   100

                     3   1

V-Notcher

3. An Ear Notching System
   for Numbering Pigs in
   Numerical Order

4. Notching Small Pigs
   for Identification

Fig. 35-5. Diagram showing some important swine management practices:
(1) removing boar's tusks, (2) removing needle teeth, (3) an ear notching
system for numbering pigs in numerical order, and (4) notching small pigs for
identification. (Drawing by R. F. Johnson)

removed. Purebred breeders find it necessary to employ a system of marking
so that they may determine the parentage of the individuals for purposes of
registration and herd records. Even in the grade herd, a system of identification
is necessary if the gilts are to be selected from the larger and more efficient
litters. The ear notches are usually made with a special ear marker or an ordinary harness punch. No universal system is employed; each individual
producer has his own ideas upon the subject. Most of the breed associations
are in a position to recommend a satisfactory marking system; some registry
associations even require a specific marking system.

Castration

All male pigs that are not to be used for breeding purposes should be castrated while they are still suckling their dam. They should be castrated early enough to allow plenty of time for the wounds to heal thoroughly before weaning. It should not be done at the same time that the pigs are vaccinated. In preparation for the operation, the pigs should be kept off feed 10 to 12 hours.

Before starting the castrating, the hands should be thoroughly washed with soap and water and rinsed in a good disinfectant. The knife should be disinfected both before and between operations; and the scrotum of the pig should be washed before and after making the incision. A coal tar dip, used according to the directions found on the container, will be satisfactory. The knife should be sharp, and the slit should extend well down so as to allow for proper drainage. In young pigs, the cord should be pulled out or broken off well forward.

Exercise and Sunshine

During seasons of the year when the weather is warm, the most natural and ideal place for the sow and litter is on a clean pasture, away from other livestock. Exercise, fresh air, and sunshine make for a good start in life.

The ideal arrangement is a movable hog house on clean pasture, preferably on land that has been plowed since hogs were last on the area.

Feed Requirements of the Nursing Sow

Until pigs are about three days old, limit the intake, and feed plenty of bran. Thereafter, gradually increase the feed allowance so as to arrive at full feeding 10 days to 2 weeks later. Throughout the lactation period, she should be fed liberally with feeds that will stimulate milk production. The most essential ingredients in the brood sow's ration during this period are an ample amount of protein, vitamin, and mineral substances.

NORMAL BREEDING SEASON AND TIME OF FARROWING

The season in which the sows are bred and the question of raising one or two litters a year or multiple farrowing, depend primarily on the facilities at hand. The location of the producer (particularly the weather conditions in the area), availability and price of feeds, condition and growth of the sows, equipment for handling pigs during the winter months, available labor, and the type of production (purebred or commercial) should be taken into consideration. No positive advice can be given, therefore, for any and all conditions. Sows will breed any time of the year; but, as in other farm animals, the conception rate is much higher during those seasons when the temperature is moderate and the nutritive conditions are good. For the country as a whole, spring pigs are preferred, as is shown by the size of the spring pig crop in comparison with the fall pig crop.

Show-yard Classifications May Determine Farrowing Dates

The purebred breeder who exhibits breeding hogs should plan the breeding program so that the maximum advantage will be taken of the various age groups.

TWO LITTERS VERSUS ONE LITTER A YEAR

Whether to have each sow farrow two litters or one litter per year is a problem that each individual swine producer must decide. Where climatic conditions, facilities, and feeds are favorable to the two-litter system, it has the following distinct **advantages:**

1. Maximum use is made of the capital invested in facilities and equipment.
2. More certain and rapid improvement can be effected in the breeding herd through maintaining outstanding tried sows throughout their useful lives. The two-litter system is conducive to retaining such sows.
3. There is a better distribution of labor.
4. Pigs are marketed at two different times of the year, thus distributing risks.
5. There is better distribution of farm income.

On the other hand, in the northern latitudes where suitable facilities and feeds may not always be available, the following **disadvantages** often apply to the two-littter system:

1. It is necessary that the spring-farrowed litter arrive reasonably early, often during inclement weather. Young pig losses, under such conditions, are higher than is usually encountered in a one-litter system.
2. Except in the South where nearly year-round pastures are available, fall farrowed pigs require more concentrates and high-priced protein supplements than pigs born earlier in the year and run on pastures. Because of inadequate nutrition, most fall pigs also are less thrifty and make slower gains than pigs run on pasture.

Because of the high cost in maintaining tried sows for a whole year to raise one litter of pigs, the one-litter system is usually based chiefly or entirely on the use of gilts that are finished and marketed soon after weaning their litters.

The **advantages** of the one-litter system are:

1. There are fewer management problems; it is easier to keep on schedule.
2. Less total capital is tied up in hog buildings and equipment.
3. Less grain storage is required.
4. The weather is usually more favorable at farrowing time.
5. Less labor and hard work are required.

The **disadvantages** of the one-litter system are:

1. Buildings and equipment are not used to the maximum.
2. It limits the rapidity of improvement that can be made in the breeding herd; sows are usually sold after one litter only, or if retained there is only one litter per year.
3. The labor requirements are not distributed throughout the year.
4. Farm income is not distributed throughout the year.

MULTIPLE FARROWING

Multiple farrowing refers to that type of program in which there is a scheduling of breeding so that the litters arrive in a greater number of farrowing periods throughout the year than is the case in the conventional one- and two-litter systems.

There is nothing mysterious or complicated about multiple farrowing. It does, however, entail some planning and close attention to management details. In practice, it generally means that the sow herd is split into either two or three groups, with each group farrowing twice each year. If two groups of sows are used, pigs are farrowed every three months. If three groups of sows are used, pigs can be farrowed every other month. Should a sow fail to conceive, she can be set back to another group.

As shown in Table 6-6, on the average, the highest price paid for market barrows and gilts occurs in June through August when the receipts are low, and the lowest price occurs during the months of November to May. Increased multiple farrowing will help alleviate these rather sharp fluctuations in hog receipts and prices, and prove beneficial both to producers and packers.

Among the factors **favorable** to multiple farrowing are:

1. It makes for a more stable hog market, with fewer high and low market receipts and price fluctuations.

2. It distributes the work load for the swine producer.

3. It makes for better use of existing buildings and equipment; for example, the farrowing house can accommodate more litters because of the longer farrowing season.

4. It provides a more sustained flow of hogs to market, which, from the standpoint of the packer, is desirable because—(a) it makes for more complete use of labor and plant capacity, and (b) it enables the processor more nearly to meet the demands of the retailer and consumer. Also, the producer's income is distributed throughout the year.

5. It provides retailers with a steady supply of pork for their trade.

6. It avoids sharp price rises, which the consumer dislikes.

Among the factors **unfavorable** to multiple farrowing are:

1. The swine enterprise is more confining for a longer period of time, for the reason that competent help must be available over a more prolonged farrowing season.

2. The possibility of a disease break may be increased because of the possible build-up of pathogenic organisms. That is, with multiple farrowing, it is not possible to clean-out and air-out for a long period of time.

No one expects the seasonal pattern of hog production to be completely eliminated, but, because of the several recognized advantages of multiple farrowing to both the processor and the producer, it is likely that it will be used sufficiently to make for a lessening of some of the market gluts of the past.

GILTS VERSUS OLDER SOWS

Controlled experiments[1] and practical observations, in which gilts have been compared with older (tried) sows, bear out the following facts: (1) gilts have fewer pigs in their litters than do older sows, and (2) the pigs from gilts average slightly smaller in weight at birth and also tend to make somewhat slower gains.

Despite these disadvantages, gilts have certain advantages, especially for the commercial pork producer. Their chief superiority lies in the fact that they continue to grow and increase in value while in reproduction. Although over-weight young sows bring less on the market than prime barrows, from this standpoint alone they generally return a handsome profit when the price of pork is sufficiently favorable. Many practical commercial producers, who probably are less close to the herd at farrowing time than purebred breeders, are of the opinion that the smaller gilts crush fewer pigs than do older and heavier sows.

In no case is it recommended that the purebred breeder rely only on gilts. Tried sows that are regular producers of large litters with a heavy weaning weight and that are good mothers and producers of progeny of the right type should be retained in the herd as long as they are fertile. This procedure is neces-sary to herd improvement.

CROSSBREEDING SWINE

Crossbreeding has been more widely applied in swine than in any other class of livestock, with the possible exception of sheep. Yet no system of breeding has been the object of greater controversy or of more heated arguments. In the discussion that follows, the author will merely attempt to explain the different methods and point out some of the advantages and disadvantages, with the hope that the reader may be better able to arrive at an independent evaluation of the merits or demerits of the system.

Crossbreeding is one of the three tools through which animal improve-ment may be brought about; the other two are selection and inbreeding. Genetically speaking, crossbreeding promotes the pairing of unlike genes by mating of animals that belong to different species (the horse and the ass cross produces mules or hinnys), to different breeds (a Duroc X Poland China cross), or to different families (crossing two families within a breed).

The four common crossbreeding systems followed in swine are:

1. **Crossing two different breeds.**—This consists of mating purebred boars to purebred or high-grade sows of another breed.

Where this system is held to first crosses only, the breeder is faced with the problem of sooner or later breeding the females back to a purebred boar of the same breed in order to secure replacement females. Under these conditions, he is prone to make little or no selection and to keep all of the females for re-

---

[1]Experiments of this type were conducted at the North Dakota and Wisconsin stations.

placement purposes. In such a program, it is usually found that the producer does well to maintain the quality of the female herd.

2. **Crisscrossing.**—In which selected crossbred gilts, produced by mating sows of breed A to a boar of breed B, are bred back to a boar belonging to one of the parent breeds (boar of breed A). Then selected offspring from this mating are next bred back to a boar of breed B.

3. **Triple crossing.**—In which first cross gilts are mated to a boar of a third breed. The program is then continued through rotating the sires among the three breeds.

4. **Type-crossing.**—This system involves the use of boars of several breeds, but, at such intervals as necessary to keep away from lardiness, boars of either the bacon or the Landrace crossbred strains are used. Both hybrid vigor and approved type are secured in this manner. This system of crossbreeding will increase when a greater premium is paid for pork carcasses with more red meat.

Although somewhat conflicting results have been reported, it seems reasonable to expect that crossbreds obtained through any of these methods possess some advantage over purebreds in terms of rate and efficiency of gains.

The chief **reasons for crossbreeding** in swine, or in any other class of farm animals, are:

1. It brings about an increase in vigor, commonly known as hybrid vigor or heterosis. In this connection, the term "vigor" is broadly used to cover such things as rate of gain, economy of gain, fertility, and general strength.

2. It constitutes the most rapid system of breeding through which new genes may be introduced in order to secure improved qualities. As undesirable qualities are generally recessive, crossbreeding offers the best way in which to improve certain characteristics merely by hiding them with dominants.

3. It creates new breeds. It must be remembered that there is nothing sacred about present existing purebreds. They will stand or fall on their own merits. There is no need to create a new breed, however, unless the combination of characters that the breed possesses fulfills a specific need better than any existing breed.

4. It may be used to produce market animals. It must be realized, however, that the continued improvement in any class of farm animals will always rest on superior purebreds.

Crossbreeding does, however, possess certain **disadvantages,** some of which follow:

1. Generally speaking, crossbred hogs lack the uniformity in color and general attractiveness of purebreds.

2. Desirable boars of the two or three breeds must be located and purchased.

3. Unless all the breeding is on a gilt basis, more than one boar must be maintained at all times.

4. If the young sows go to market after farrowing only one litter, little constructive selection can be practiced.

Before entering upon a crossbreeding program, the producer should become thoroughly acquainted with the advantages and disadvantages that may be expected therefrom. Also, crossbreeding should not be looked upon as a pana-cea for neglect of sound practices of breeding, feeding, management, and sanita-tion. Neither should it be assumed that the virtues of crossbreeding are sufficiently powerful to alleviate the necessity of selecting an outstanding boar rather than a scrub.

It should be understood that the disadvantages of crossing two breeds do not generally apply to the systems of crossbreeding between families or to the creation of a new breed when that seems desirable.

Fig. 35-6. Champion carload of crossbred barrows at the Pacific International, Portland; bred and exhibited by Washington State University. These meat-type barrows were descended from a Landrace X Chester White foundation. (Courtesy, Washington State University)

LETHALS AND OTHER HEREDITARY ABNORMALITIES IN SWINE

Lethal characters in swine, or in any class of animals, are caused by the presence of hereditary factors in the germ-plasm that produce an effect so serious as to cause the death of the individual either at birth or later in life. Breeding animals possessing hereditary lethals should be culled from the herd.

PRODUCTION TESTING SWINE

As pointed out in Chapter II, the effectiveness of selection can be increased provided that it is based upon carefully taken records rather than upon casual observation. Naturally, it would be illogical to expect upstanding, narrow-bodied, shallow sows and boars to beget well-balanced, deep, meat-type barrows that would be market toppers. Breeding animals of acceptable meat type can only transmit these qualities unfailingly to all their offspring when they themselves have been rendered relatively homozygous or pure for the necessary genes—a process that can be gradually accomplished through judgment by the eye

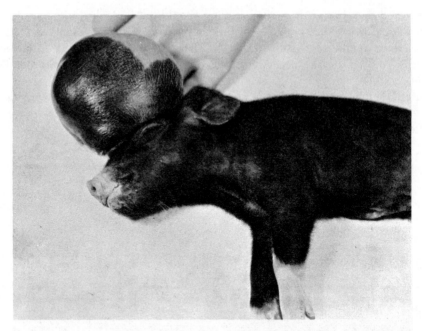

Fig. 35-7. Hydrocephalic (literally meaning water in the head) pig. Pigs affected with this condition die soon after birth. It is inherited as a simple recessive. (Courtesy, Purdue University)

method but which can be made more rapid and certain through securing and intelligently using production records.

The following characteristics in swine are relatively easy to recognize and measure and are a fairly accurate guide in estimating the economy of production:

1. **Litter size at birth** (which has a heritability of 15 per cent[2]).—On the average, a sow will have consumed a total of ¾ to 1 ton of feed during the period between breeding and the date her litter is weaned. Thus, if this quantity of feed must be charged against a litter of four or five pigs, the chance of eventual profit is small.

2. **Litter size at weaning** (which has an approximate heritability of 15 per cent).—Although greatly influenced by herdsmanship, litter survival to weaning is a measure of the mothering ability of the sow.

3. **Birth weight of pigs** (which has a heritability of 5 per cent).—Very light pigs usually lack vigor.

4. **Litter weight at weaning** (which has a heritability of 15 per cent).— Weaning weight is important, for it has been shown that the pigs that are heaviest at weaning time reach market weight more quickly. The low heritability of

_____
[2] The rest is due to environment. The heritability figures given herein are averages based on large numbers; thus, some variation from these may be expected in individual herds.

this factor indicates that it is largely a function of the nursing ability of the sow rather than genetic.

5. **Daily rate of gain from weaning to marketing** (which has a heritability of 30 per cent).—Daily rate of gain from weaning to marketing is important because (a) it is highly correlated with efficiency of gain, and (b) it makes for a shorter time in reaching market weight and condition, thus effecting a saving in labor, making less exposure to risk and disease, and allowing for a more rapid turnover in capital.

Rate of gain and lardiness may be correlated to some degree. Thus, one should not let this be the only factor upon which selection is based.

6. **Efficiency of feed utilization** (which has a heritability of 30 per cent).— Where convenient, accurate litter feed records should be kept, for the most profitable animals generally require less feed to make 100 pounds of gain.

7. **Conformation score** (which has a heritability of 27 per cent).—This heritability figure is likely to be considerably higher in a herd of low quality.

8. **Carcass characteristics:**
   a. **Length** (which has a heritability of 60 per cent).—Carcass length is perhaps the most highly hereditary trait in hogs. This accounts for the rapid shifts that frequently have been observed; for example, in changing from chuffy to rangy hogs.
   b. **Backfat thickness** (which has a heritability of 50 per cent).—The knife probe, Lean Meter, or ultrasonic equipment can be used to measure backfat thickness on prospective breeding animals.
   c. **Loin lean area** (which has a heritability of 40 per cent).—Loin area is an indication of muscling or red meat.

That swine show variations in these characteristics is generally recognized. The problem is to measure these differences from the standpoint of discovering the most desirable genes and then increasing their concentration and, at the same time, to purge the herd of the less desirable characters.

Finally, it should be recognized that swine are raised primarily for profit, and profit is dependent upon efficiency of production and market price. Fortunately, the factors making for efficiency of production—including litter size and survival, growth rate, and feed efficiency—do not change with type fads. For this reason, emphasis should be placed on a proper balance of the production factors. It might well be added that type changes, quite likely, would not be so radical as in the past if they were guided by market demands based on carcass values. These facts show clearly enough that production testing will lend stability to swine breeding operations, from the standpoint of both efficiency of production and type.

A prerequisite for any production data is that each animal be positively identified—by means of ear notches. For purebred breeders, who must use a system of animal identification anyway, this does not constitute an additional detail. But the taking of weights and grades does require additional time and labor—an expenditure which is highly worthwhile, however.

In order not to be burdensome, the record forms should be relatively simple. Figure 35-8 (lower half) is an Individual Pig Record, designed for use in recording the lifetime production record of one sow; whereas Fig. 35-8 (upper

WASHINGTON STATE UNIVERSITY
DEPARTMENT OF ANIMAL SCIENCE
Litter Record

Breed_____Litter No._____
                                        (notch, tattoo)

Data on Dam:
                                       (Sire)
  Pedigree:_____
           (name, reg. no., and ear notch)   (Dam)

  Birth date_____
                 (date and year)
  Litter mate carcass data, if any:
     No. carcasses_____; Av. back fat_____; loin eye_____; length_____
                                 (in.)   (sq. in.)   (in.)
  Sow's_____Litter.
           (1st, 2nd, etc.)

Data on Sire:
                                       (Sire)
  Pedigree:_____
           (name, reg. no., and ear notch)   (Dam)

  Birth date_____
  Litter mate carcass data, if any:
     No. carcasses_____; Av. back fat_____; loin eye_____; length_____
                                 (in.)   (sq. in.)   (in.)

Date of birth_____ Health Services:
No. pigs born: Date cholera vaccinated_____
  Alive_____   Date erysipelas vaccinated_____
  Dead_____   Date wormed_____
  Mummies_____   Other, including iron pills or shots (list)_____

  Total_____
No. pigs weaned_____

Individual Pig Record

Pig's No.	Sex	No. Teats	Birth Wt.	Off Color Markings	Defects & Abnormalities	Weaning Wt. _____days (fill in)	Date Castrated	Date & Cause of Death	Disposal Date & To Whom	Remarks

Fig. 35-8. Litter record form in use at Washington State University.

half) is a Litter Record Form for use in recording detailed information on one litter.

Production Testing by Swine Record Associations

Several U.S. swine registry associations are sponsoring production testing programs. Generally, these programs are known as Production Registry (P.R.).[3] Production Registry is designed to emphasize practical utility points and to enable breeders to coordinate outstanding individuality (type) with equally outstanding production ability.

The National Association of Swine Records adopted a uniform program of Certified Meat Hogs. This program adds carcass evaluation to Production Registry.

In addition to improving swine, participation in such programs furnishes valuable information for advertising purposes. For specific information relative to these programs, the swine producer should write to the registry association of the breed of his choice.

QUESTIONS FOR STUDY AND DISCUSSION

1. Why is swine breeding more flexible in the hands of man than cattle and sheep breeding?
2. What management techniques at breeding and parturition time are unique to swine, and are not applied to cattle, sheep, or horses?
3. Discuss each of the following points pertaining to the McLean County System of Swine Sanitation:
   a. What it was and is designed to accomplish.
   b. How it got the name "McLean County."
   c. The four steps which it embraces.
4. Discuss the advantages and disadvantages of the two-litter system.
5. Discuss the advantages and the disadvantages of gilts vs. older sows.
6. Which of the four common crossbreeding systems would you recommend, and why?
7. Discuss the advantages and the disadvantages of crossbreeding swine.
8. Based on (a) heritability and (b) dollars and cents value, what characteristics should receive greatest emphasis in a swine production testing program?

SELECTED REFERENCES

In addition to the selected references listed in Chapter II, the following are recommended for Chapter XXXV:

Title of Publication	Author(s)	Publisher
Fifty Years of Progress in Swine Breeding	W. A. Craft	*Journal of Animal Science,* Vol. 17 No. 4, November 1958.

---

[3] The stipulations of these programs are summarized in *Swine Science* and *The Stockman's Handbook,* books by the same author and publisher as *Animal Science.*
[4] Same as 3.

Title of Publication	Author(s)	Publisher
Hog Annual, The		*The Farm Quarterly,* Cincinnati, Ohio, 1952.
Hog Profits for Farmers	W. N. McMillen	Vulcan Service Co., 403 Tuscaloosa Ave., S.W., Birmingham, Ala., 1952.
Meat Hog, The	C. H. Hinman	The Daily Sentinel, Grand Junction, Colo., 1955.
Pork Production	W. W. Smith L. M. Hutchings, D.V.M.	The Macmillan Company, New York, N. Y., 1952.
Raising Swine	G. P. Deyoe J. L. Krider	McGraw-Hill Book Company, New York, N. Y., 1952.
Results of Swine Breeding Research	W. A. Craft	Circular No. 916, U.S. Department of Agriculture, Washington, D. C.
Robert Bakewell: Pioneer Livestock Breeder	H. C. Pawson	Crosby Lockwood & Son, Ltd., 26 Old Brompton Rd., London, SW 7, England.
Swine Production	C. E. Bundy R. V. Diggins	Prentice-Hall, Inc., Englewood Cliffs, N. J., 1956.
Swine Production	W. E. Carroll J. L. Krider F. N. Andrews	McGraw-Hill Book Company, New York, N. Y., 1962.
Swine Science	M. E. Ensminger	The Interstate Printers & Publishers, Danville, Ill., 1969.

Chapter XXXVI

FEEDING SWINE[1]

Contents	Page
Specific Nutritive Needs of Swine	852
Protein Needs	852
Energy Needs	854
Mineral Needs	855
Salt	855
Calcium and Phosphorus	856
Iodine	857
Iron and Copper	858
Zinc	859
Other Mineral Needs	859
Feeds as a Source of Minerals	859
Method of Feeding the Mineral Supplement	860
Vitamin Needs	861
Vitamin A	861
Vitamin D	861
The B Vitamins	861
Unknown Factor or Factors	862
Body Storage	862
Summary of Vitamin Needs of Swine	862
Water Needs	862
Feeds for Swine	863
Concentrates for Swine	863
Pastures for Swine	864
Dry Roughages for Swine	866
Silage for Swine	866
Hogging Down Crops	867
Advantages of Hogging Down Corn	867
Disadvantages of Hogging Down Corn	868
Garbage for Swine	868
Feed Additives	869
Creep Feeding Pigs	869
Feeding Growing-Finishing Pigs	870
Feeding Prospective Breeding Gilts and Boars	871
Feeding Herd Boars	872
Feeding the Brood Sows	872
Flushing Sows	872
The Gestation Period	873
Farrowing Time	874
The Lactation Period	874
The Corn-Hog Ratio	874
Soft Pork	875
Feed Allowances and Some Suggested Rations for Swine	876
Pointers in Formulating Rations and Feeding Swine	879
Fitting Rations for Show and Sale Swine	883
Questions for Study and Discussion	886
Selected References	886

---

[1] The author gratefully acknowledges the helpful suggestions of Dr. Wilton W. Heinemann, Washington State University, who reviewed this chapter.

In the natural state, the wild boar roved through the forests gleaning the feeds provided by nature; whereas on a modern farm the range is restricted and sometimes entirely devoid of vegetation. Domestic swine have less choice in their selection of feed than any other class of livestock. For the most part they are able to consume only what the caretaker provides. This consists largely of concentrated feeds with only a small proportion of roughage. These conditions are made more critical because hogs grow much faster in proportion to their body weight than the larger farm animals, and they produce young at an earlier age. Thus, a knowledge of the nutritional needs of swine is especially important.

Extensive surveys indicate that about 25 per cent of all pigs farrowed fail to live to weaning age. Although these heavy losses are due to many and variable factors, certainly nutritional deficiencies play a major role.

Knowledge of feeding swine is also important from an economic standpoint, because feed accounts for approximately 80 per cent of the total cost of producing pork.

SPECIFIC NUTRITIVE NEEDS OF SWINE

The feed requirements of swine vary according to the purpose for which the animals are kept. The ration for finishing hogs should be quite different from that supplied to prospective breeding animals, and the ration for brood sows should differ from both of these. There are, however, certain basic nutritive needs for all classes of swine. These nutritive requirements are:

1. An adequate supply of proteins of good quality for maintenance and the building of muscle tissue.

2. A certain amount of energy for maintenance and finishing.

3. The necessary minerals for the body framework and the normal physiological processes of the body.

4. Those vitamins that are recognized as essential for the growth and well being of the animal.

5. Water.

Protein Needs

Protein feeds are essential for maintenance and building of body tissue. In swine feeding, protein is most frequently the limiting factor in the ration, both from the standpoint of quantity and quality. This is due to the fact that the common farm grains and their by-products—which constitute the chief diet of pigs—are low in protein content, and their proteins are lacking in the essential amino acids. Moreover, the digestive tract of the pig is not adapted to the synthesis of proteins by micro-organisms as is the paunch of ruminants. Also, since protein supplements are the most expensive, there is a temptation to feed too little. The protein in the ration is of special importance for young, growing pigs and for gestating-lactating sows—the critical periods in swine production.

Improvement in the quality of proteins in a ration composed of cereal grains and their by-products can usually be achieved by using combinations of feeds.

Although the protein supplements are higher in price than the carbohydrate feeds, the cash outlay usually yields greater returns in increased rate of gain and better utilization of feed.

Young pigs require a much greater proportion of protein in the ration than do those that are approaching market weight. Accordingly, for most economical results the ration of swine should be changed at different stages. Also, the protein requirements of gestating and lactating sows differ from each other and from those of growing-finishing pigs. The recommended protein levels are given in Table 36-1, and the amino acid needs are given in Table 36-2.

If the pigs are being self-fed, the protein supplements may be provided free choice. Fortunately, pigs show a remarkable ability to balance their own rations when allowed to choose from several feeds cafeteria style. The protein supplements may either be combined as a mixture, or each type of ingredient may be fed in a separate compartment. An exception should be made to the latter method of providing the protein supplement when the grain ration consists of wheat, barley, oats, rye, or kafir. When fed these grains, pigs usually consume more of the protein supplement than necessary, thus reducing the economy of the ration. Likewise, when corn is fed as the grain, sometimes such protein supplements as (1) roasted soybeans, (2) soybean meal, and (3) mixtures of tankage or fish meal and soybean meal are too palatable to be fed separately from the corn.

TABLE 36—1

RECOMMENDED PROTEIN LEVELS, AVERAGE RATE OF GAIN, AND FEED CONSUMPTION FOR SWINE

Description of Animal	Protein Content of Ration	Average Daily Gain		Average Daily Feed Intake		Feed/Pound Gain	
	(%)	(lb.)	(kg)	(lb.)	(kg)	(lb.)	(kg)
Breeding stock							
Gestation:							
Gilts	12-14	.60	.27	4.0	1.81		
Sows	12-14	.50	.23	4.0	1.81		
Lactation:							
Gilts and sows	14-15			12.0	5.44		
Boars	14-15			6.0	2.72		
Growing-finishing pigs:							
Creep feed; *suckling* pigs (5 to 30 lb.)	17-20	.70	.32	.50	.23		
Pig starter; early weaned pigs (10 to 30 lb.)	22	.65	.29	1.1	.50	1.65	.75
Grower (30 to 100 lb.)	14-16	1.4	.64	3.5	1.59	2.50	1.13
Finisher (100 to market weight)							
Full-fed	12-14	1.95	.88	7.0	3.18	3.60	1.63
70% of full-fed (ind. fed)	12-14	1.50	.68	5.0	2.27	3.30	1.50

TABLE 36—2

AMINO ACID NEEDS OF SWINE[1]

Amino Acid	Baby Pig (10 lb. or 4.5 kg)	Weaning Pig[2] (30 lb. or 13.6 kg)			Finishing Pig (100 lb. or 45.38 kg)	Gilts & Sows During Gestation
Protein content of ration (%)	22	14	16	18	12	12
	←– – – – – – – – – – – – –Per cent of diet– – – – – – – – – – – →					
Arginine	.37	.23	.25	.28	.15	unknown
Histidine	.34	.21	.23	.24	.14	.17
Isoleucine	.76	.48	.52	.57	.35	.37
Leucine	.84	.63	.67	.74	.40	unknown
Lysine	.86	.68	.74	.79	.50	.42
Methionine[3]	.73	.45	.50	.53	.30	.30
Phenylalanine[3]	.79	.49	.54	.58	.32	unknown
Threonine	.66	.42	.45	.49	.27	.34
Thryptophan	.18	.11	.12	.13	.07	.07
Valine	.67	.43	.46	.50	.28	.46

[1]From *Balancing Swine Rations*, Ill. Circ. No. 866, 1966, by D. E. Becker, A. H. Jensen, and B. G. Harmon; with permission of the authors.
[2]Calculations based on the premise that the amino acid requirements, expressed as a percentage of the protein, decrease linearly (1.75%/unit increase in % protein) as the dietary protein increases.
[3]Cystine can satisfy 40% of the total need for methionine, and tyrosine can satisfy 30% of the total need for phenylalamine.

Young, lush pastures and early-cut, green, leafy alfalfa are sources of good quality proteins as well as excellent sources of the vitamins and unidentified factors. However, the fiber content of roughages is too great and the stomach of the pig is too small to rely upon pastures or ground alfalfa as the sole source of proteins.

Energy Needs

Energy is the first essential for the necessary life processes of the animal. After these requirements are met, surplus energy may be stored as body fat.

The chief sources of heat and energy in swine rations are the carbohydrates and fats of available feeds. Protein-rich supplements seldom are used for this purpose because of their high cost and inefficiency when so used. Carbohydrates are the most abundant nutrients of all common feeds and are especially abundant in the cereal grains and their by-products. Fats, which are abundant in such common hog feeds as peanuts and soybeans, have an energy value about 2.25 times as great as carbohydrates and proteins. It is to be emphasized, however, that liberal quantities of either soybeans or peanuts will produce soft pork.

Because of the more restricted size of the digestive tract of hogs in comparison with that of ruminants, only limited quantities of roughages are contained in normal swine rations. Roughages (pastures or ground legume hays) are added to the ration because of their vitamins, minerals, and quality proteins, rather than for their energy purposes.

For young pigs, a high energy diet (80 per cent TDN) is recommended.

Mineral Needs[2]

Of all common farm animals, the pig is most likely to suffer from mineral deficiencies. This is due to the following peculiarities of swine husbandry:

1. Hogs are fed principally upon cereal grains and their by-products, all of which are relatively low in mineral matter, particularly in calcium.

2. The skeleton of the pig supports greater weight in proportion to its size than that of any other farm animal.

3. As hogs do not normally consume great amounts of roughage (pasturage or dry forage), it is not always easy to balance mineral deficiencies.

4. Hogs grow more rapidly than other classes of livestock, and they produce young when less mature.

5. Hogs are forced for an early market, before they are mature.

The mineral feeding recommendations for swine are:

1. When supplements of animal or marine origin constitute one-third or more of the source of proteins, allow free access to a two-compartment mineral box with (a) salt (iodized salt in iodine-deficient areas) in one side, and (b) a good commercial mineral mix or a mixture of ⅓ salt (salt added for purposes of palatability) and ⅔ bone meal (or other calcium-phosphorus supplement) in the other side.

2. When supplements of plant origin constitute most of the source of proteins, add a third compartment to the mineral box and place in it a mixture of ⅓ salt and ⅔ ground limestone or oyster shell flour (or other calcium supplement); or provide a suitable commercial mineral mix.

In addition to meeting the calcium and phosphorus needs, iron, copper, and zinc should be provided (see sections on "Iron and Copper" and "Zinc").

Minerals may also be incorporated in swine rations in keeping with the recommendations given in Table 36-3.

SALT

Although swine require less salt than other classes of farm animals, it is generally advantageous to supply them with it, particularly if the protein supplement is not derived from tankage or fish meal (two feeds which supply salt). A lack of salt is marked by poor appetite, unthrifty condition, and failure to grow. Salt may be added to the ration at the rate of ½ pound per 100 pounds of total feed; or it may be provided as salt alone or in a mineral mix in a suitable box or trough to which the animals are allowed free access. When salt is fed free choice, pigs will consume from 0.03 to 0.12 ounce per head daily, the amount depending upon the size of the animal and the type of ration fed. When pigs are salt starved, precaution should be taken to prevent overeating salt.

---

[2] Generally speaking, the recommendations given herein can be followed on a nation-wide basis. However, it is recognized that area differences do exist. Therefore, for more specific recommendations the hogman should always obtain the counsel of his county agricultural agent or state college of agriculture.

TABLE 36—3

RECOMMENDED MINERAL AND VITAMIN LEVELS FOR SWINE RATIONS[1]

Nutrient	Breeder Ration	Creep and Starter Rations	Grower Rations	Finisher Ration
Minerals:[2]				
Salt.............................(%)	.50	.50	.50	.35
Calcium.........................(%)	.75	.90	.75	.50
Phosphorus...................(%)	.50	.60	.50	.35
Zinc...........................(mg/lb.)	30.0	30.0	30.0	20.0
Vitamins:				
Vitamin A.................(I.U./lb.)	2,500.0	1,500.0	1,750.0	1,950.0
(or carotene).............(mg/lb.)	5.0	3.0	3.5	3.90
Vitamin D ....(I.U./lb.)	150.0	300.0	150.0	75.0
Riboflavin...................(mg/lb.)	1.0	1.5	1.0	.80
Nicotinic acid ....(mg/lb.)	8.0	12.0	8.0	6.0
Pantothenic acid ....(mg/lb.)	5.5	7.5	5.5	5.0
Choline ....(mg/lb.)	370.0	600.0	400.0	350.0
Vitamin B$_{12}$ ....(mcg/lb.)	6.0	9.0	6.0	4.0

[1]From *Balancing Swine Rations*, Ill. Circ. No. 866, 1966, by D.E. Becker, A.H. Jensen, and B.G. Harmon; with permission of the authors.
[2]The requirements of swine for other minerals are: 4 mg. of copper, 30 mg. of iron, 0.1 mg. of iodine, and 18 mg. of manganese per pound of diet.

Purdue University[3] studied salt versus no salt in four dry-lot trials in which all plant protein supplements were fed to growing-finishing pigs. It was found that the salt-fed pigs ate 23 per cent more feed and gained at nearly double the rate on 33 per cent less feed. One pound of salt costing less than one cent. saved 185 pounds of feed worth $3.11.

CALCIUM AND PHOSPHORUS

Swine are more likely to suffer from a lack of calcium than from any of the other minerals, except common salt. They are fed largely on cereal grains and their by-products, which are fair or even high in phosphorus. Consequently, a calcium deficiency is more likely in the ration than a phosphorus deficiency.

Calcium and phosphorus make up about three-fourths of the mineral matter of the entire body and over 90 per cent of that in the skeleton. Since they form more than half the minerals in milk, their importance to the lactating sow is not to be overlooked. Liberal amounts of calcium and phosphorus are needed by growing pigs, pregnant sows (especially during the latter third of pregnancy), and by sows when suckling litters. The proportion of calcium to phosphorus is also important, especially when vitamin D is inadequate. From 1½ to 2 parts of calcium are needed to 1 part of phosphorus.

A deficiency of calcium and phosphorus (or a lack of vitamin D) retards normal skeletal development and gain in live weight. The bones become fragile

[3]Vestal, C. M., Purdue University, Agricultural Expt. Sta. Mimeo. Circ. No. 18, 1945: No. 20, 1946; No. 23, 1947; and No. 28, 1947.

and are easily broken, and depraved appetites may be observed. In brood sows, a pronounced lack of these minerals may prevent normal reproduction, and the young may be born weak or even dead. If the deficiency persists with pigs, rickets will develop. This nutritional disease is characterized by a stiffness of the legs and a general unthriftiness; and it may even result in a paralysis of the hind legs.

Steamed bone meal or dicalcium phosphate, which furnishes both calcium and phosphorus, are common supplements when these two minerals are needed for swine. When calcium alone is needed, ground limestone or ground oyster shell flour may be used. When phosphorus alone is needed, monosodium phosphate may be used.

When the swine ration consists of a liberal allowance of cereal grains or their by-products (feeds rich in phosphorus)—along with a protein supplement of animal origin (tankage, fish meal, or milk by-products), feeds rich in calcium— usually no minerals other than salt will be necessary. On the other hand, when protein supplements of plant origin (soybean meal, linseed meal, cull peas, etc.)—feeds poor in calcium—are used, it is very necessary that this mineral be provided.

IODINE

Hogs require a small amount of iodine. A deficiency of this mineral results in poor hair and skin condition, impaired reproduction, dead or weak offspring at birth, and birth of hairless pigs.

Fig. 36-1. Hairlessness in pigs caused by a deficiency of iodine. In iodine-deficient areas, farm animals should receive iodized salt throughout the year. (Courtesy, Dept. of Veterinary Pathology and Hygiene, College of Veterinary Medicine, University of Illinois)

Northwestern United States and the Great Lakes region are iodine deficient areas. In such deficiency areas, stabilized iodized salt containing 0.01 per cent potassium iodide should always be used.

IRON AND COPPER

If suckling pigs are confined to paved pens or lots with no access to soil or forage (a common condition with pigs farrowed in the late winter or early spring months, and standard conditions in confinement rearing) serious losses from anemia (lack of red blood cells) are likely to be encountered. This anemia is due to a deficiency of iron and copper in the milk.

Nutritional anemia in swine, commonly called thumps, is characterized by labored breathing, a swollen condition especially around the head and shoulders, and a general weakened condition.

For the prevention or treatment of anemia in young pigs, either (1) place a little uncontaminated sod (topsoil, and from an area where hogs have not run for years) in the corner of the pen daily, (2) inject a suitable iron preparation at a level of 150 to 200 mg into baby pigs at one to three days of age, (3) swab the sow's udder with iron solution, (4) give an iron-copper pill, or (5) allow access to oral iron preparations. Recommended copper compounds and feeding levels are given in Table 36-4. In addition, the pigs should be encouraged to eat a grain ration as soon as they are old enough.

Fig. 36-2. Anemia or thumps in young pigs can usually be prevented by placing a little clean sod in the pen daily, or by providing iron, orally or by injection. (Courtesy, University of Minnesota)

TABLE 36—4

COPPER COMPOUNDS AND LEVELS IN SWINE RATIONS

Copper Compound	Per Cent of Copper	Amount to Add/Ton of Complete Ration to Furnish Copper at Required Level of 2.7 mg/lb. (6 mg/kg) of Diet[1]
	(%)	(grams)
Cupric carbonate (CuCO₃)	50	10.8
Cupric oxide (CuO)	80	6.75
Cupric sulfate (CuSO₄ . 5H₂O)	25	21.6

[1]For supplements, add copper at 4½ times the rate used for complete rations.

ZINC

Zinc deficiency in swine rations produces parakeratosis or dermatosis, a non-contagious ailment. The dietary level of zinc required to prevent this syndrome is given in Table 36-3; and recommended zinc compounds are given in Table 36-5. However, it is recognized that the zinc requirement is related to the level of calcium (high levels of calcium usually accentuate parakeratosis and increase the dietary zinc requirement), source and level of protein, source of corn, and the phytic acid present in plant proteins.

TABLE 36—5

RECOMMENDED ZINC COMPOUNDS AND LEVELS IN SWINE RATIONS

Zinc Compound	Zinc Content	Add/Ton of Complete Feed to Furnish Zinc at Level of 22.7 mg/lb. (50 mg/kg) of Diet[1]
	(%)	(grams)
Zinc carbonate (ZnCO₃)	56	81.0
Zinc oxide (ZnO)	80	56.8
Zinc sulfate (ZnSO₄ . 7H₂O)	23'	197.3

[1]For protein supplements, add the zinc at 4½ times the rate for complete rations.

OTHER MINERAL NEEDS

Although thought to be essential, under natural conditions, no evidence of deficiencies in swine have been observed of the following mineral elements: manganese, sulfur, potassium, magnesium, and cobalt. There is some evidence that only the ruminants require cobalt.

FEEDS AS A SOURCE OF MINERALS

The most satisfactory source of minerals for hogs is in the feed consumed. It is important to know, however, whether the minerals in the ration are of the right kind and sufficient in amount. Certain general characteristics of feeds in regard to calcium and phosphorus (the two predominating mineral elements of the body) are worth noting:

1. The cereal grains and their by-products and protein supplements of plant origin are low in calcium but fairly high in phosphorus.

2. The protein supplements of animal origin (skim milk, buttermilk, tankage, meat scraps, fish meal), legume forage (pasturage and hay), and rape, all are rich in calcium.

3. Most protein-rich supplements are high in phosphorus.

With the possible exception of common salt, the mineral requirements of swine can often be met through the proper selection of feeds. This may not hold true, however, in feeding young pigs and gestating-lactating sows.

METHOD OF FEEDING THE MINERAL SUPPLEMENT

Hogs may be allowed free access to minerals by providing them in a suitable box or self-feeder, with each mineral in a separate compartment.[4] The particular needs of the animals will guide them in consuming sufficient of the minerals to correct any deficiency of the ration. If the mineral supplement is incorporated in the grain ration, usually 1 to 2 per cent by weight will prove adequate; whereas if it is incorporated in the protein concentrate only, about 5 to 6 pounds of mineral mixture should be added to each 94 to 95 pounds of high-protein feed (see Table 36-6).

TABLE 36—6

RECOMMENDED MINERALS AND ALLOWANCES FOR
INCORPORATION (1) IN ENTIRE RATION, AND (2)
IN PROTEIN SUPPLEMENT ONLY

Kind of Protein Supplement	Kind and Amounts of Minerals Required	
	When Mixed with Ration Containing All Concentrates	When Mixed with Protein Supplement Only
	(lbs./100 lbs. mix)	(lbs./100 lbs. supplement)
1. Tankage, meat meal, fish meal, and/or dried milk constituting ⅓ or more of the source of proteins.	0.25-0.5 salt	1.5 salt
2. Linseed, soybean, cottonseed, and/or peanut meal constituting most of the source of proteins.	0.5 salt 0.75 ground limestone or oyster shell flour	1.5 to 2.0 salt 4.0-5.0 limestone or oyster shell flour

---

[4]Instead of feeding each mineral separately, generally a mixture of 1/3 salt to 2/3 of each mineral is used to provide greater palatability. In addition, salt (or iodized salt in iodine-deficient areas) is provided in a separate compartment or box.

Vitamin Needs

Because of the greater prevalence of dry-lot feeding, swine are more likely to suffer from nutritional deficiencies, especially lack of vitamins, than any other class of farm animals. The vitamin requirements are especially important in young pigs (from birth to 30 pounds) and in gestating-lactating sows.

Recommended vitamin levels for swine rations are given in Table 36-3.

VITAMIN A

Either the plant form (carotene or provitamin A) or the animal form (true vitamin A) can serve as a source of this factor for swine. It must be emphasized, however, that tankage and meat scraps have little vitamin A potency. Fish meal, likewise, is a variable and undependable source. Once the fat has been removed, milk by-products are low in vitamin A. Thus, under practical conditions, the pig is generally limited to plant sources of vitamin A. The best practical plant sources of carotene for swine include green pastures, green hays not over one year old, yellow corn, green or yellow peas, cod-liver oil, and vitamin A feeding oils and concentrates.

The winter period is the most critical time for swine feeding, for over much of the United States this necessitates dry-lot feeding. Green pastures are always an excellent source of carotene.

In the absence of green forages, in periods of drought, and in various parts of the world where pig diets consist of materials low in carotene—such as white corn, barley, wheat, oats, rye, and feeds made from the by-products of these grains—serious vitamin A losses have occurred. Under these conditions, stabilized vitamin A should be added to the ration.

VITAMIN D

A lack of vitamin D (or of calcium or phosphorus) in swine rations will cause rickets in young pigs or osteomalacia in mature hogs. Both conditions result in large joints and weak bones.

In the northern latitudes, a combination of limited and none too effective sunlight, plus limited quantities of sun-cured hay in the ration, cannot always be relied upon to supply ample quantities of vitamin D to hogs. Likewise, this situation applies to hogs kept in confinement. Under these conditions, the addition of vitamin D is cheap and effective protection. It is also to be emphasized that the vitamin-D requirement is less when a proper balance of calcium and phosphorus exists in the ration.

THE B VITAMINS

Young growing pigs and gestating-lactating sows may not secure optimum amounts of certain of these factors, particularly under dry-lot conditions. It is considered good practice, therefore, to include them in swine rations during these critical periods.

Experimental work has indicated that the following B vitamins are required by the pig: thiamine, riboflavin, niacin, pantothenic acid, pyridoxine, choline, B_{12}, and biotin.

Either there is sufficient intestinal synthesis or the pig does not need the following B vitamins: inositol, para-aminobenzoic acid, and folic acid.

UNKNOWN FACTOR OR FACTORS

Optimum results with swine during the critical periods (early growth and gestation-lactation) appear to be dependent upon providing an unidentified factor or factors through feeding one or more of the following: distillers' dried solubles, fish solubles, dried whey, grass juice concentrate, soil, high quality alfalfa meal, brewers' dried yeast, pasture, or liver.

BODY STORAGE

Work at both the Wisconsin and Washington stations has shown that the ration gilts receive during growth influences their performance during reproduction three to five months later. This means that growing gilts, provided that they are fed a well-balanced ration which supplies these factors, store up certain of these factors which are later required in reproduction. This phenomenon is referred to as the residual effects of previous nutrition. This means that the ration of prospective breeding gilts should receive more attention than may be necessary to give to the ration of growing-finishing hogs to be placed on the market.

Work at the Washington Agricultural Experiment Station has also shown a positive relationship between thiamine intake and the deposition of this vitamin in the tissues of hogs. It was found that one pork chop from the pigs consuming the thiamine-enriched ration contained sufficient of this factor to meet the daily requirements of a human. However, it would have required 10 pork chops from the pigs on a low-thiamine ration to meet this same need. This suggests the possibility of increasing the nutritive qualities of pork through the ration.

SUMMARY OF VITAMIN NEEDS OF SWINE

The limiting factor in the use of most vitamin supplements is their price. For economy reasons, therefore, any vitamin fortification of the ration should be in keeping with the nutrient requirements and/or recommended allowances.

Water Needs

The daily water requirements of swine vary from ½ gallon to 1½ gallons per 100 pounds live weight. The higher requirements are for young pigs and lactating sows. Also, the higher the temperature the greater the water consumption. It is preferable that swine have access to automatic waterers, with water available at all times. Otherwise they should be hand watered at least twice daily. During winter, the drinking water should not be permitted to fall below 50° F.

If swine get an abundance of such watery feeds as dairy by-products or slop, there will be less need of furnishing water separately. On the other hand, when self-fed dry feeds, pigs need access to good fresh water at all times. Otherwise feed consumption will be too low for satisfactory performance.

FEEDS FOR SWINE

Throughout the world, swine are raised on a great variety of feeds, including numerous by-products. Except when on pasture or when ground dry forages are incorporated in the ration, they eat relatively little roughage.

In this country, corn and swine production have always been closely associated. Normally, more than one-half of the corn crop is fed to hogs. Yet, the agriculture of the 50 states is very diverse, and the diet of the pig is readily adapted to the feeds produced locally. A similar adaptation in feeding practices is found in other countries. Thus, in most sections of the world, swine are fed predominantly on home-grown feeds. Ireland depends largely upon

Fig. 36-3. Corn is the chief concentrate fed to swine in the United States. Normally, one-half of the corn is fed to hogs. These pigs are being fed ear corn from temporary storage on a Corn Belt farm. (Courtesy, J. C. Allen & Son, West Lafayette, Ind.)

potatoes and dairy by-products; the swine industry of Denmark has been built up to augment the dairy industry, with milk and whey supplementing home-grown and imported cereals (mostly barley); and in Germany the pig is fed on such crops as potatoes, sugar beets, and green forage.

Concentrates for Swine

Because of their simple monogastric stomach, swine consume more concentrates and less roughages than any other class of farm animals. This characteristic gives pigs less opportunity to consume large quantities of calcium and vitamin-rich and better quality protein roughages. Also, swine grow more rapidly than cattle, sheep, or horses, and produce young when less mature. This combination of conditions results in swine suffering more nutritional deficiencies than other large animals. It is probably safe to assume that less than half of the swine in the United States are fed balanced rations; yet, with our present knowledge of nutrition, this need not be so.

Although most concentrate feeds are not suitable as the sole ration for hogs, it must be realized that swine can utilize a larger variety of feeds to greater advantage than any other farm animal. In general, the grain crops—corn, barley, wheat, oats, rye, and the kafirs—constitute the major component of the swine ration. However, sweet potatoes and peanuts are successfully and extensively used in the South, soybeans in the central states, and peas in the Northwest. In those districts where they are grown, potatoes also are usually utilized in considerable quantities in feeding hogs. In addition, in most every section of the country one or more by-product feeds are fed to hogs—including the by-products of the fishing industry, the meat packing industry, the milling industry, and the dairy industry. Human food wastes, such as refuse or garbage, are also fed extensively.

It is estimated that the concentrates—including the grains, root crops, and by-product feeds—make up, on the average, 95.6 per cent of the ration of hogs. Thus, normally, only limited high-quality roughages or superior pastures are included in the ration of the pig.

The protein and vitamin requirements of the monogastric pig differ very greatly from those of the ruminant; for the latter improves the quality of proteins and creates certain vitamins through bacterial synthesis.

Despite all this, it is possible to meet the nutritive needs of the pig on these concentrated feeds by keeping in mind the following factors when balancing the ration:

1. The cereal grains and their by-products are relatively good in phosphorus, but low in calcium and the other minerals.

2. Except for the carotene content of yellow corn and green peas, the grains are very poor sources of the vitamins.

3. Most cereal grains supply proteins of poor quality.

4. Protein supplements of animal origin generally supply proteins of high quality, whereas proteins of plant origin generally supply proteins of low quality.

5. Because of the inadequacies of most concentrates, it is usually necessary to rely on fortifications of minerals and vitamins.

Pastures for Swine

Although swine cannot be grown and finished economically on pasture crops alone, on many farms these crops are an important adjunct to grain rations. Green, succulent pastures are also superior to comparable quality dry roughages for swine. In addition to reducing the cost of the ration, superior pastures, especially if legumes, provide a good source of calcium, serve as an excellent source of

Fig. 36-4. Pigs in alfalfa pasture in Nebraska. (Courtesy, Agricultural Agent, Burlington Lines)

most of the needed vitamins, are higher in protein content than the grains, and carry protein of better quality than is found in grains.

In general, temporary pastures are preferable to permanent pastures for swine, especially from the standpoint of disease and parasite control. But permanent pastures do have a very definite place in the swine program. Although no single pasture crop can be recommended as being best for any and all conditions, there are certain desirable qualities that should be considered in choosing a forage crop for swine. Some of these characteristics are as follows:

1. Adapted to local soil and climatic conditions. Although this is a prime requisite, practical swine producers cannot afford to disregard the grazing qualities.

2. Palatable and succulent.

3. Ability to endure tramping and grazing.

4. Easy to grow, and grown at a nominal cost.

5. Provide tender and succulent growth for a short period or consistent growth over a long period.

6. Highly nutritious; rich in proteins, vitamins, and minerals, and low in fiber.

7. High carrying capacity.

8. Fit satisfactorily into the crop rotation.

9. Uncontaminated with diseases or parasites.

Although it is recognized that no single pasture crop meets all of these characteristics in a faultless manner, the crops of greatest value are those which most nearly meet them. Over much of the country, most of these essential qualities are possessed by alfalfa, the clovers (principally Ladino, red, alsike, and sweet clover), rape, and oat mixtures. Other plants which find use as hog pastures in certain areas and under certain conditions are bluegrass, orchard-grass, lespedeza, carpet grass, rye, wheat, soybeans, cowpeas, field beans, sorghum, and Sudan grass. As there are so many different factors to consider in planning a pasture crop-rotation for hogs, it is recommended that the individual producer consult his local county extension agent or state agricultural college.

Good pastures have definitely established their worth in a successful swine enterprise. In general, the following advantages may be cited in favor of pasture feeding over dry-lot feeding of swine: (1) saves in feed, (2) lessens nutritional deficiencies, (3) saves in labor, (4) conserves manure, (5) favors limited feeding, and (6) improves reproduction.

Dry Roughages for Swine

During the winter months or at other seasons of the year when green, suc-culent pastures cannot be provided, it is desirable that swine rations contain generous quantities of a high-quality ground forage, preferably alfalfa. Well-cured, green, leafy alfalfa will supply the body-building minerals, vitamins, and quality proteins that are lacking in most farm grains.

Nutritionists generally look upon alfalfa as holding a place in animal nutri-tion comparable to that which milk popularly holds in human nutrition. Alfalfa contains proteins of the right quality to balance the amino acid deficiencies of grain proteins; it is a rich source of minerals, especially calcium; and, finally, it is an excellent source of all the vitamins needed by the pig. From the stand-point of vitamins alone, alfalfa is almost indispensable in dry-lot swine rations. If leafy and green, and not over a year old, it is high in carotene (provitamin A), a lack of which results in poor growth and the farrowing of premature, dead, or weak pigs. Sun-cured hay is also a good source of vitamin D, the anti-rachitic vitamin. In the northern latitudes in particular, the pig may have to obtain dietary sources of vitamin D, for the action of the sun's rays on the body of the animal may prove inadequate. Alfalfa is also an excellent source of the long list of B vitamins.

Because of the many virtues of well-cured, green, leafy alfalfa in the swine ration, it is generally recommended that gestating-lactating sow rations contain from 15 to 35 per cent ground alfalfa. Because of the more limited digestive capacity of swine and their inability to utilize fiber, the alfalfa content of the ration for growing pigs must be more restricted. Thus, the alfalfa content of the ration of growing-finishing pigs had best be held to a level of 5 to 10 per cent.

In addition to its beneficial effects in supplying the needed vitamins, min-erals, and proteins, the inclusion of alfalfa in swine rations generally reduces the feed cost, for alfalfa seldom costs as much per pound as the grains.

Silage for Swine

Grass silage has been used successfully in the winter ration of growing-finishing pigs.[5] Silage also appears to be suitable for gestating sows. The Purdue station[6] fed 10 to 12 pounds of silage daily plus supplement to pregnant sows, with one lot receiving grass-legume silage and another lot corn silage. They obtained satisfactory reproduction from each silage-fed lot, and effected a 28 per cent saving in feed cost as a result of using silage. At the Illinois station, an average daily ration of 6.6 pounds of grass-legume silage plus supplement was fed to gestating sows with good results.[7] Silage may also be fed to growing-finishing pigs, but, due to its bulk, it is not as desirable for young stock; and, too, very young pigs frequently suffer digestive disturbances when given silage.

If of good quality, and not frozen or moldy, gilts will eat 7 to 12 pounds and sows 8 to 15 pounds of silage daily; with slightly higher consumption obtained with corn silage than with grass silage. Under proper conditions, the following advantages accrue from feeding silage to brood sows and herd boars:

1. It reduces feed costs.

2. It prevents animals from getting too fat.

3. It provides a close substitute for pasture, from a nutritional standpoint.

4. It provides needed nutritional factors for winter rations which might not otherwise be available unless an exceptionally well balanced ration is fed.

5. It makes possible the use of more home-grown forages in swine rations.

Even though considerable silage may be fed to advantage, it is important that it be of good quality and that it be properly supplemented from a nutritional standpoint.

Hogging Down Crops

The practice of allowing pigs to do their own harvesting is followed quite generally in many sections of the United States. Corn is the principal crop so used, the animals being turned into the field when the grain is in the dent stage. Sometimes small grain crops that have been badly lodged or otherwise damaged are harvested by hogs. Soybeans and field peas also are frequently hogged off. In the South, such crops as peanuts, sweet potatoes, chufas, and other root and tuber crops, are often harvested by hogs.

Space will not permit a full discussion of this method of utilizing the various crops. As corn is the main feed hogged down, comments will be limited to this crop; but the same general principles apply to other crops, when and if they are so utilized.

ADVANTAGES OF HOGGING DOWN CORN

Some of the advantages of this practice are as follows:

1. It saves labor at a busy season of the year.

---

[5] Zeller, John H., *Grass*, Yearbook of Agriculture, 1948, p. 102.
[6] Conrad, J. H. and W. M. Beeson, Mimeo. A. H. 133, Purdue U. Agri. Expt. Sta., 1954.
[7] Terrill, S. W. and N. C. Nesheim, Mimeo. A. S. 326, Ill. Agri. Expt. Sta. 1953.

Fig. 36-5. Hogging down corn. The animals are usually turned into the field when the grain is in the dent stage. (Courtesy, USDA)

2. The maximum fertility value of the manure is conserved.

3. There is less danger of infesting swine with diseases and parasites than in dry-lot finishing.

4. Corn that is down or badly lodged is difficult to harvest, but it may be utilized through hogging down.

DISADVANTAGES OF HOGGING DOWN CORN

Some of the disadvantages of hogging down corn may be enumerated as follows:

1. During wet weather, a considerable amount of corn is lost by being tramped into the ground.

2. During wet weather, the tramping of animals puddles the soil and lowers its tilth. This is especially noticeable in heavy clay soils.

3. It usually requires additional fencing.

4. Early pigs cannot be used in hogging down corn, for they will be too far advanced.

5. Pigs used in hogging down corn are usually finished at a season of the year when prices are low.

6. When corn is hogged down, wheat cannot follow corn in the rotation.

Garbage for Swine

Municipal garbage has long been fed to finishing hogs; but during the past three decades, the practice has declined because of a gradual lowering in the feeding value of garbage and other competition for garbage—notably its manufacture into lawn, greenhouse, and garden fertilizer. By 1960, only 1.85 per cent of the nation's hogs were being fed garbage.

Twenty years ago, the garbage feeder calculated that a ton of city garbage would produce 60 to 100 pounds of pork; whereas, at the present time, it is estimated that a similar quantity will not produce more than 30 pounds of pork.[8] The change in feeding value may be largely attributed to improved refrigeration and the effective use of leftovers. Institutional, hotel, and restaurant garbage are superior to household garbage.

Garbage may be utilized either as a feed for a sow and pig enterprise or for finishing feeder pigs that are obtained from other sources. Usually, the venture seems most successful when a combination of grain and garbage feeding is practiced.

It is also observed that the most successful garbage feeders use concrete feeding floors, practice rigid sanitation, and take every precaution to prevent diseases and parasites. Unless considerable grain is fed to market hogs, especially after weights are over 100 pounds, soft pork and paunchiness will result in garbage-fed hogs.

Raw garbage has a higher feeding value than cooked garbage. Cooking allows for less feed selection on the part of the pig and lowers the digestibility of some of the nutrients, especially the proteins. On the other hand, swine are more likely to become infested with trichinnella and certain other diseases when fed on raw garbage. For this reason, all 48 contiguous states now have laws requiring that commercial garbage be cooked; although compliance with and enforcement of the law leaves something to be desired in some areas.

The claim is frequently made that the greatest number of cases of trichinosis in humans occurs in communities where garbage is fed to hogs. It should be understood, however, that there is little or no danger in transmitting the disease in this way provided the pork and pork products are thoroughly cooked.

Frozen garbage should be thawed before feeding.

Feed Additives

Currently, feed additives, especially antibiotics, are being used extensively in swine rations. Their effects vary according to (1) the levels fed, (2) the particular kind of additive, (3) the health and environment of the animal, (4) the type of ration, (5) the age of animal, etc. Table 36-7 gives the normally used additives and supplementary levels.

CREEP FEEDING PIGS

Young pigs should be creep fed, beginning when they are 7 to 10 days of age and extending to weaning time. Each pig should consume about 25 pounds of

---

[8] Some Canadian authorities consider 4 pounds of heavy garbage to be equivalent to 1 pound of concentrate. (*Feeder's Guide and Formulae for Meal Mixtures,* 13th edition, published by the Quebec Provincial Feed Board, for April 1959-61, p. 46.)

TABLE 36—7

NORMALLY USED ANTIBIOTIC AND ARSENICAL SUPPLEMENTATION
OF SWINE RATIONS[1]

Ration[2]	Supplementary Level, Grams Per Ton of Feed		
	Antibiotic	Arsanilic Acid[3]	3-Nitro-4-Hydroxy-phenylarsonic Acid[3]
	(g)	(g)	(g)
Complete Feed			
Breeder[4]	0 to 20-30		
Creep and starter			
(5 to 30 lb.)	40	90	22
Grower (30 to 100 lb.)	10-20	90	22
Finisher (100 lb. to market			
weight)	0-10	90	22
Supplement (35-40% protein)			
Pig (up to 100 lb.)	50-100	450	100
Hog (100 lb. to market			
weight)	0-50	450	100
Sow[4]	0 to 100 to 150		
Therapeutic	50-250	90	22

[1]Except for "breeder" and "sow" recommendations, from *Balancing Swine Rations*, Ill. Circ. No. 866, 1966, by D. E. Becker, A. H. Jensen, and B. G. Harmon; with permission of the authors.
[2]Feeds containing an arsenical alone, or containing an antibiotic at 50 grams or more per ton, are designated as therapeutic or medicated feeds.
[3]Never use both arsenicals in a single ration at the levels indicated.
[4]The effect of antibiotics on breeding stock is not conclusive, but there is some evidence to indicate that the feeding of antibiotics to pregnant sows may increase the birth weight, livability, and weaning weight of pigs.

feed before reaching the normal weaning age of eight weeks, with about two-thirds of this consumption between the sixth and eighth weeks.

A satisfactory pig creep ration may be either purchased as a commercial feed or home-mixed. In either case, it must contain high quality ingredients, and it must be fresh and palatable.

FEEDING GROWING-FINISHING PIGS

In the practical swine enterprise, growing-finishing generally refers to that period from weaning (about eight weeks of age) to market weight of about 225 pounds. Because hogs are finished at an early age, the process really consists of both growing and finishing. In a general way, there are two methods of finishing hogs for market: (1) full feeding all the time until the animals attain a market weight, and (2) limited feeding early in the period, with full feeding the last 60 to 75 days of the period before marketing. Pasture may be utilized to advantage with both methods. But as would be expected, greater use of forage crops will accompany a system of limited rations. Neither system, full feeding or limited feeding, can be recommended as being best for any and all conditions. The plan to follow should be determined by: (1) market conditions, (2) price of feeds, (3) feeds available on the farm, (4) kind and extent of pastures available, (5) available labor, etc. Self-feeders are well adapted to a system of full feeding, but hand feeding is necessary in any plan for limiting the ration.

For the production of lean (bacon) carcasses, the rate of gain should be restricted to about 1½ pounds daily after a live weight of 100 to 125 pounds. This is easily accomplished by using a lighter, bulkier finishing ration (made by inclusion of 10 to 20 per cent bran, oats, alfalfa, or other suitable bulky feed). Level of protein has no direct effect on carcass excellence, though it does affect the growth of the pig.

When on full feed, finishing pigs will consume 5 to 6 pounds of feed daily per 100 pounds live weight up to 100 pounds in weight. From 100 pounds to a finished weight of 225 pounds, pigs on full feed consume about 4 pounds of feed daily for each 100 pounds of live weight. On the average, about 400 pounds of feed are required to produce 100 pounds of gain during the growing-finishing period, but the amount varies with the inherent ability of the animals, thrift. and the kind and amount of pasture utilized. About 360 pounds of this feed is grain and 40 pounds protein supplement. Of course, the feed consumption of the breeding herd and that of the pigs during the suckling period must be added in order to arrive at the total feed requirements. Cost accounting studies on Corn Belt farms show that approximately 500 pounds of feeds are consumed per 100 pounds of hogs marketed.

The protein requirements of the pig are greatest early in life. For this reason, decreasing percentages of protein supplement should be incorporated in mixed rations as the finishing process progresses. If the ration is self-fed cafeteria style, the pigs generally will automatically balance these needs. In any event, however, ample protein should always be provided in the ration, otherwise growth will be retarded. It is also important that the mineral and vitamin needs of growing-finishing pigs be met.

As previously indicated, pigs can utilize a great variety of concentrates. The chief ingredients of a growing-finishing ration, therefore, are usually, for practical reasons, those most readily available at the lowest possible price. In most cases, only the protein supplement is not home-grown.

FEEDING PROSPECTIVE BREEDING GILTS AND BOARS

For best results, prospective breeding gilts should be fed differently from growing-finishing hogs. The ration fed during growth, from weaning to breeding age, affects the results obtained many months later in conception, reproduction, and lactation. Experimental evidence indicates that there is storage of factors during growth and that later these factors are of considerable importance. The same condition applies to prospective herd boars.

In view of this situation, it is usually important that prospective breeding animals, both gilts and boars, should be fed separately and apart from finishing hogs, beginning at four to five months of age or at 150 to 175 pounds weight. In the first place, it is neither necessary nor desirable that breeding animals become as fat as pigs that are being finished for market. Rather, size, growth-iness, thrift, and good bone are desired. To this end, it is essential that the ration contain sufficient proteins of good quality and that there be an abundance of the essential minerals and vitamins.

Provided that good pastures are available or a generous allowance of a high quality legume is incorporated in the ration, the kind of concentrates (grain and protein supplements) fed to prospective breeding gilts or boars is relatively unimportant. If the animals are inclined to get too fat, which is likely to happen in self-feeding, the ration may well contain considerable bulky feeds, such as ground oats or wheat bran or ground alfalfa meal.

FEEDING HERD BOARS

The feed requirements of the herd boar are about the same as those of a sow of equal weight. He should always be kept in thrifty, vigorous condition and virile. To this end, feed and exercise are important. Year-round succulent pasture is excellent from the standpoint of providing both needed exercise and valuable nutrients. In winter, the boar should still be allowed the run of a lot of sufficient size so that he will get abundant exercise, and 15 to 35 per cent of a high quality ground legume should be incorporated in a well-balanced ration.

In no cases should herd boars be overfat, nor should they be in a thin run-down condition. Except during the breeding season, about 1 pound of concentrates daily per 100 pounds live weight is sufficient for mature boars on good pasture; without pasture, the grain allowance should be about double this amount. A more liberal ration must be provided in the winter time and when the sire is in heavy service. The feed allowance should be varied with the age, development, temperament, breeding demands, and roughage consumed.

FEEDING BROOD SOWS

The gestation-lactation period is a critical one in swine nutrition. It is now known that the feed and care accorded the brood sow materially affect conception, reproduction, and lactation. The basis for successful and practical feeding of the brood sow consists of making the maximum use of pastures and of feeding a generous quantity of ground legumes during those periods when pastures are not available. Such roughages enhance the ration through increasing the quantity and improving the quality of the proteins, providing the necessary vitamins, and improving the mineral content of the ration. Pastures also provide valuable exercise for the sow.

For practical reasons, dry sows are fed considerable roughage—pasture, hay, and/or silage. Generally speaking, they are fed about 2 pounds of concentrate or its equivalent per day for each 100 pounds live weight.

Flushing Sows

The practice of conditioning or having the sows gain in weight just prior to breeding is known as flushing. A great variety of feeds may be used satisfactorily for bringing about the condition of breeding thrift sought at this time. From a practical standpoint, it is usually best to use a home-produced grain ration together with pasture in season or a legume hay during the winter months. For young growing animals or when nonlegume pastures are being used, it is important that a protein supplement be added to the ration. In addition to providing suitable feeds for flushing, it is important that the sows be fed a ration adequate to produce gain in weight at the rate of 1 to 1½ pounds daily, beginning one to three weeks before breeding. The extra feeding of thin sows evidently stimulates the endocrine and reproductive systems to greater activity, with the result that more eggs are produced at breeding time and litter size is increased.

The Gestation Period

The nutrients fed the pregnant sow must first take care of the usual maintenance needs. If the gilt is not fully mature, nutrients are required for maternal growth as well as for growth of the fetus. Quality and quantity of proteins, minerals, and vitamins become particularly important in the ration of young pregnant gilts, for their requirements are much greater and more exacting than those of the mature sow.

Approximately two-thirds of the growth of the fetus is made during the last month of the gestation period. It may be said, therefore, that the demands resulting from pregnancy are particularly accelerated during the latter third of the gestation period. Again, the increased needs are primarily for proteins, vitamins, and minerals.

During gestation, it is also necessary that body reserves be stored for subsequent use during lactation. With a large litter and a sow that is a heavy milker, the demands for milk production are generally greater than can be supplied by the ration fed at the time of lactation. Although desired gains will vary somewhat with the initial condition, mature sows are generally fed to gain 75 to 85 pounds during the pregnancy period, and pregnant growing gilts should gain 100 to 125 pounds. This calls for a feed allowance of 1½ to 2 pounds per day for each 100 pounds live weight, with the upper limit fed to gilts.

There is no better place for pregnant sows than in a leguminous pasture. Luxuriant pasture of this type is particularly valuable in supplementing the grain ration with minerals, vitamins, and quality proteins. Aside from supplying the necessary nutrients at a low cost, this system provides much valuable exercise.

With reference to the quality of proteins, minerals, and vitamins in the winter or dry-lot ration, it is the feeling of most good swine producers that these needs can be met most easily and cheaply through adding 15 to 35 per cent of a high quality ground alfalfa to the ration; or alfalfa hay may be fed in a rack. At least a part of the proteins supplied during the gestation period should be of animal origin (tankage, fish meal, skim milk, etc.). It also is good and cheap protection to allow the sows free access to minerals.

Gestating sows are generally hand-fed to limit feed intake. This avoids (1) excess fatness and (2) unnecessary feed expense. Some breeders cut down on the labor expense of hand-feeding sows by feeding only once a day. However, they may be self-fed if sufficient bulk—at least one-third of the ration to consist of some such suitable bulky feed as oats, alfalfa, wheat bran, and/or corn-and-cob meal—is added to the ration.

Farrowing Time

It is considered good practice to feed lightly and with bulky laxative feeds immediately before and after farrowing. Wheat bran or oats may constitute half of the limited ration, and a small amount of linseed meal may be added. From 10 days to 2 weeks is the usual time suggested in getting the sow back on full feed after farrowing.

The sow may be watered at frequent intervals before or after farrowing, but in no event should she be allowed to gorge. It is also a good plan to take the chill off the water in the wintertime.

The Lactation Period

The nutritive requirements of a lactating sow are more rigorous than those during gestation. They are very similar to those of a milk cow, except they are more exacting relative to quality proteins and the B vitamins because of the absence of rumen synthesis in the pig. A sow will produce from ½ to 1½ gallons of milk daily. A sow's milk is also richer than cow's milk in all nutrients, especially in fat. Thus, sows suckling litters need a liberal allowance of concentrates rich in protein, calcium, phosphorus, and vitamins.

It is essential that suckling pigs receive a generous supply of milk, for at no other stage in life will they make such economical gains. The gains made by pigs from birth to weaning are largely determined by the milk production of the sows; and this in turn is dependent upon the ration fed and the inherent ability to produce milk. The lactating sow should be provided with a liberal feed allowance—ranging from 2½ to 4½ pounds daily for each 100 pounds weight. Generous feeding during lactation, with a small shrinkage in weight, is more economical than a stingy allowance of feed. Lactating sows may be successfully self-fed, because, even when hand-fed, they are practically on full-feed.

When pig scours are encountered, any or all of the following steps should be taken relative to the lactating sow's ration: change and improve the ration, cut down on the feed allowance, and/or remove from succulent pasture.

THE CORN-HOG RATIO

The corn-hog ratio refers to the number of bushels of corn required to equal in value 100 pounds of live hog. Thus, a corn-hog ratio of 13.8 means that price relationships are such that 13.8 bushels of corn equal in value 100 pounds of hogs. Usually, the figures are computed on the basis of some central market, but farm prices may be used. A corn-hog ratio of 13.8 is accepted as normal; this figure is based on the average price relationship for the period 1940 to 1964.

A high corn-hog ratio, one which is above 13.8 means cheap corn and high-priced hogs and likely profit to the producer—conditions that stimulate more

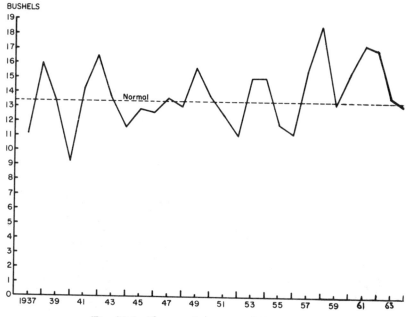

Fig. 36-6. The corn-hog ratio, 1940 to 1964.

breeding and feeding to heavier weights. On the other hand, a low ratio, one which is below 13.8 means high-priced corn and low-priced hogs—conditions that result in less breeding and feeding of swine.

SOFT PORK

Feed fats are laid down in the body without undergoing much change. Thus, when finishing hogs are liberally fed on high-fat content feeds in which the fat is liquid at ordinary temperatures, soft pork results. This condition prevails when hogs are liberally fed such feeds as soybeans, peanuts, mast, or garbage. The fat of the cereal grains is also liquid at ordinary temperatures, but fortunately the fat content in these feeds is relatively low. When such feeds are liberally fed to swine, most of the pork fat is actually formed from the more abundant carbohydrates in these feeds.

Soft pork is undesirable from the standpoint of both the processor and the consumer. It remains flabby and oily even under refrigeration. In soft pork, there is a higher shrinkage in processing; the cuts do not stand up and are unattractive in the show case; it is difficult to slice the bacon; and the cooking losses are higher through loss of fat. For these reasons, hogs that are liberally fed on those feeds known to produce soft pork are heavily discounted on the market.

The firmness of pork carcasses may be judged by: (1) grasping the flank below the ham, (2) lifting one end of the cut while permitting the other end to rest on the table (a firm pork cut will not bend readily), or (3) applying a slight pressure of the thumb (not gouging) on a cut surface. Experimentally, either the iodine number or the refractive index is used in determining the degree of softness; this is a measure of the degree of unsaturation (see Chapter III for a discussion of unsaturation).

Unless the producer is willing to take the normal reduction in price (about $1.00 per hundredweight), it is recommended that feeds which normally pro-

Fig. 36-7. Soft pork. Feed fats do affect body fats. The bacon belly on the left came from a hog liberally fed on soybeans. (Courtesy, University of Illinois)

duce soft pork be liberally fed only to pigs under 85 pounds in weight and to the breeding herd. For growing-finishing pigs over 85 pounds in weight, soybeans and peanuts should not constitute more than 10 per cent of the ration if a serious soft-pork problem is to be averted.

Experimental evidence and practical observation have shown, however, that when a ration producing hard fat is given following a period on feeds rich in unsaturated fats, the body fat gradually becomes harder. It has also been found that this process takes place more rapidly if the animals are first fasted for a period before the change in ration is made. This practice is called "hardening off." Thus, many hogs that are, for practical reasons, finished primarily on such feeds as soybeans, peanuts, or garbage, are hardened off with a ration of corn or some other suitable grain.

FEED ALLOWANCES AND SOME SUGGESTED RATIONS FOR SWINE[9]

Hogs can and do use many different concentrates, which make it possible to choose as chief ingredients those most readily available at the lowest price.

[9] This section and Tables 36-8 through 36-14 were reviewed by the following well-known swine specialists: Dr. R. H. Grummer, Department of Meat and Animal Science, University of Wisconsin, Madison, Wisconsin; Dr. R. F. Wilson, Ohio State University, Columbus, Ohio; and Professor Vaughn Speer, Department of Animal Science, Iowa State University, Ames, Iowa.

Other factors being equal, a variety of feeds is preferable, although the choice of ingredients will and should vary from area to area, and even on adjoining farms. The rations in Table 36-8 to 36-13 will serve as useful guides. As noted, these cover the following classes, ages, and sexes, with proper provision for (1) dry lot, (2) pasture rations, and (3) weight divisions of pigs:

1. Gestating sows (Table 36-8).

2. Lactating sows (Table 36-9).

3. Suckling pigs, 5 to 30 pounds weight (Table 36-10).

4. Early weaned (two to three weeks of age) pigs, 10 to 30 pounds weight (Table 36-11).

5. Growing-finishing pigs from 30 pounds to market weight (Tables 36-12 and 36-13).

TABLE 36—8

HANDY GESTATING-SOW FEEDING GUIDE: FOR ALL AGES
(1) IN DRY LOT AND (2) ON PASTURE[1]
(These rations are equally satisfactory for replacement gilts and herd boars.)[2]

Ingredients (also provide minerals as recommended elsewhere in this section)	For Sows in Dry Lot (12-14% protein)				For Sows on Good Pasture (11-13% protein)	
	Ration No. 1		Ration No. 2		Ration No. 3	
	(lbs.)	(kg)	(lbs.)	(kg)	(lbs.)	(kg)
Ground corn, wheat, barley, oats, and/or sorghum	1,500	680.4	1,200	544.3	1,850	839.1
Alfalfa meal	300	136.1	600	272.1		
Animal protein supplement (tankage, meat meal, meat and bone scrap, fish meal, and/or dried milk)	120	54.4	100	45.4	100[3]	45.4
Plant protein supplement (soybean, cottonseed, linseed, and/or peanut meal)	80	36.3	100	45.4	50[3]	22.7[3]
Total	2,000	907.2	2,000	907.2	2,000	907.2
Proximate analysis: using corn, alfalfa meal (sun-cured), tankage (digester) with bone, and soybean meal						
Protein, crude, %	14.04		14.90		12.20	
Fiber, %	6.12		10.05		2.15	
Fat, %	3.8		3.73		4.60	
Calcium, %	0.91		1.06		0.57	
Phosphorus, %	0.63		0.63		0.60	

[1]Gestating sows are generally hand-fed to limit feed intake. This avoids (1) excess fatness and (2) unnecessary feed expense. However, they may be self-fed if more bulk is added to the ration. Bulk may be provided by (1) using considerable oats or ground ear corn and (2) adding 25 per cent or more of ground alfalfa to the ration.
With mature pregnant sows, it is usually desirable to limit concentrate consumption to about 1½ pounds daily per 100 pounds live weight. With replacement pregnant gilts, concentrate consumption should be at the rate of about 2 pounds or less daily per 100 pounds live weight. Sufficient ground oats and ground alfalfa—two bulky feeds—may be added to the ration to limit feed consumption to these figures.
Ration 1, above, is suitable for hand-feeding. Ration 2 is suitable for self-feeding, provided at least half of the cereal grain consists of oats. Ration 3 is satisfactory for self-feeding on pasture, providing at least half of the grain ration is oats.
[2]The grain ration of replacement gilts may well consist of one-third ground oats. For mature sows, the oats content of the grain ration may be higher.
[3]On lush legume or rape pasture, the protein supplement of Ration 3 may be deleted. However, the quantities of protein supplement indicated are needed when sows are grazing nonlegume or other fair to poor pasture.

The suggested rations given in Tables 36-8 through 36-13 meet the requirements proposed by the National Research Council and provide for reasonable margins of safety.

In addition to the complete rations referred to, Table 36-14 gives suggested formulas for "protein-mineral-vitamin-antibiotic supplements," which may be either purchased commercially or mixed on the farm; and Table 36-15 shows how protein supplements may be combined with grain rations to obtain the desired level of protein.

In formulating the several rations given in Table 36-8 to 36-13, cognizance was taken of the fact that two systems of swine feeding predominate: (1) the use of complete rations, either commercially or home-mixed, versus (2) the grain and the supplement fed separately. Also, both hand-feeding and self-feeding methods are followed, with the latter being most common except for gestating sows.

In recent years, there has been an increasing trend toward the use of complete, mixed rations for all classes and ages of hogs, especially with creep and growing-finishing rations. The use of complete rations has been favored because they afford a more accurate means of controlling the intake of vitamins, trace minerals, and antibiotic and other feed additives. The choice between the systems, or some combination of the two, should be determined by the conditions prevailing on each individual farm, including such factors as (1) the cost of grinding and mixing; (2) the kind, amount, and palatability of available feeds; (3) facilities for handling feeds; (4) the relative cost of proteins and grains; and (5) the results obtained.

Where commercial protein supplements are bought (usually a combined protein-mineral-vitamin-antibiotic supplement) to use with farm-grown grains, they are utilized in any of the following ways:

1. Self-fed in separate self-feeders, with the ground or whole grain also being self-fed in separate self-feeders.

2. Hand-fed; the supplement and the grain each being hand-fed in the proportions recommended (see Table 36-15).

3. Mixed with ground, farm-grown grain in appropriate amounts to make a complete ration. (See Table 36-15. The footnote for this table gives the directions for its use.)

In formulating the suggested rations herein presented, the following facts were also considered.

1. That growth up to 30 pounds in weight and gestation and lactation constitute the most critical periods, nutritionally, in the life of the pig; that the proteins, minerals, and vitamins are especially important during these periods. Accordingly, in the rations suggested in this section, a considerable margin of safety in the most essential nutrients is provided over and above minimum requirements for these periods.

2. That complete mixed rations are much preferable for pigs up to 30 pounds in weight. Because of the difficulty in formulating and home-mixing satisfactory creep or pig-starter rations, the purchase of a good commercial feed usually represents a wise investment.

TABLE 36—9

HANDY LACTATING-SOW FEEDING GUIDE: FOR ALL AGES
(1) IN DRY LOT AND (2) ON PASTURE[1]
(These rations are equally satisfactory for herd boars.)[2]

Ingredients (also provide minerals as recommended elsewhere in this section)	For Sows in Dry Lot (14-15% protein)				For Sows on Good Pasture (13-14% protein)	
	Ration No. 1		Ration No. 2		Ration No. 3	
	(lbs.)	(kg)	(lbs.)	(kg)	(lbs.)	(kg)
Ground corn, wheat, barley, oats,[3] and/or sorghum	1,460	662.3	1,500	680.4	1,820	825.5
Alfalfa meal	300	136.1	300	136.1		
Animal protein supplement (tankage, meat meal, meat and bone scrap, fish meal, and/or dried milk)	120	54.4	120	54.4	80	36.3
Plant protein supplement (soybean, cottonseed, linseed, and/or peanut meal)	120	54.4	80	36.3	100	45.4
Total	2,000	907.2	2,000	907.2	2,000	907.2
Proximate analysis: using corn, alfalfa meal (sun-cured), tankage (digester) with bone, and soybean meal						
Protein, crude, %	14.74		14.05		12.16	
Fiber, %	6.20		6.12		2.24	
Fat, %	4.16		4.23		4.43	
Calcium, %	0.91		0.91		0.47	
Phosphorus, %	0.64		0.63		0.54	

[1]By the time the pigs are 10 days to 2 weeks of age, lactating sows may be self-fed successfully. Lactating sows will consume from 2½ to 4 pounds of concentrates daily per 100 pounds live weight, with mature sows approaching the lower side and gilts the upper side of this range. A good rule of thumb for hand-feeding lactating sows is "one pound daily per pig, plus 2 to 3 lbs."; this allows more feed for the sow suckling a large litter than for one suckling a small litter.
[2]The grain ration for young boars and boars in service may well consist of one-third ground oats. For mature boars not in service, the oats content of the grain ration may be higher.
[3]In general, oats should not constitute more than 15% of the ration, especially for young gilts.

Pointers in Formulating Rations and Feeding Swine

In formulating rations and in feeding swine, the following points are note-worthy:

1. Feeds of similar nutritive properties can be interchanged in the ration as price relationships warrant. Some of these feeds are: (a) *the cereal grains—*corn, barley, wheat, oats, and sorghum; (b) *the animal protein supplements—*tankage, meat meal, meat and bone scrap, fish meal, and dried milk products; and (c) *the plant protein supplements—*soybean, cottonseed, linseed, and pea-nut meal.

2. If wheat, barley, oats, or grain sorghum is used instead of corn as the grain in a ration, the protein supplement may be slightly reduced, because these grains have a higher protein content than corn.

3. Pacific Coast grains are generally lower in protein content than grains produced elsewhere.

TABLE 36—10
HANDY CREEP FEED GUIDE
FOR SUCKLING PIGS, 5 TO 30 POUNDS WEIGHT[1]
(17 to 20% protein)

Ingredient	Dry Lot Ration								Pasture Rations					
	1		2		3		4		5		6		7	
	(lbs.)	(kg)	(lbs.)	(kg)	(lbs.)	(kg)	(lbs.)	(kg)	(lbs.)	(kg)	(lbs.)	(kg)	(lbs.)	(kg)
Cracked yellow corn	1,310	594.2	860	390.1	615	279.0	1,190	539.8	1,400	635.0	1,430	648.6	650	294.8
Ground barley					700	317.5								
Ground or rolled oats														
Oat groats			560	254.0	200	90.7							920	417.3
Cane or beet sugar							200	90.7						
Animal fat (stabilized)													40	18.1
Tankage or meat meal, with bone					125	56.7	100	45.4						
Fish meal (65%)			70	31.8			100	45.4						
Non-fat dry milk			50	22.7	100	45.4	100	45.4			100	45.4	60	27.2
Dried buttermilk			200	90.7			100	45.4					120	54.4
Soybean meal	550	249.5	170	77.1	200	90.7	200	90.7	550	249.5	450	204.1	180	81.7
Alfalfa meal, sun-cured	100	45.4	80	36.3	50	22.7								
Alfalfa leaf meal														
Ground limestone (or equivalent)	10	4.5							20	9.1	10	4.5	10	4.5
Steamed bone meal (or equivalent)	20	9.1							20	9.1	10	4.5	10	4.5
Salt (iodized salt in iodine deficient areas)	10	4.5	10	4.5	10	4.5	10	4.5	10	4.5			10	4.5
Vitamins (Follow Table 36-3)														
Trace minerals (Follow Tables 36-3, 36-4 36-5)														
Antibiotics (Follow Table 36-7)														
Total	2,000	907.2	2,000	907.2	2,000	907.2	2,000	907.3	2,000	907.2	2,000	907.1	2,000	907.0
Proximate analysis:														
Protein, crude, %	18.96		18.62		17.83		18.96		17.63		19.05		18.62	
Fiber, %	4.36		5.17		4.63		1.99		3.05		2.93		2.60	
Fat, %	3.41		3.97		3.36		3.92		3.26		3.87		4.10	
Calcium, %	0.63		0.83		0.89		0.95		0.73		0.78		0.60	
Phosphorus, %	0.40		0.66		0.75		0.75		0.55		0.71		0.57	

[1]Young pigs prefer coarsely cracked or whole corn to finely ground grains. Also, pelleted feeds are more palatable to them than finely ground grains and supplements.

Thrifty pigs should consume about 25 pounds per head of feed before reaching the normal weaning age of 8 weeks, with about two-thirds of this consumption between the sixth and eighth week.

Also, it is well to continue the creep ration slightly beyond weaning.

TABLE 36—11

PIG STARTER RATIONS FOR EARLY WEANED (2 TO 3 WEEKS OF AGE)
PIGS, 10 TO 30 POUNDS WEIGHT[1]

(22% protein)

Ration No. 1			Ration No. 2		
(Ingredient)	(lbs.)	(kg)	(Ingredient)	(lbs.)	(kg)
Sugar (cane or beet)............	15.00	6.80	Yellow corn meal.................	12.60	5.72
Sugar (corn).......................	12.50	5.67	Soybean meal (50%).............	17.50	7.94
Yellow corn (fine ground).....	13.75	6.24	Dried skim milk	40.00	18.14
Dried skim milk..................	40.00	18.14	Dried whey.......................	3.00	1.36
Soybean meal			Fish meal (60%)..................	3.00	1.36
(solvent 44%)	7.00	3.17	Dried brewers' yeast	2.00	.91
Fish meal (70%).................	5.00	2.26	Ground limestone................	0.05	.02
Lard (stabilized)	2.50	1.13	Dicalcium phosphate...........	0.25	.11
Dried brewers' yeast	1.00	.45	Fat (stabilized animal).........	5.00	2.27
Trace minerals....................	0.15	.68	Sucrose............................	10.00	4.54
Dicalcium or bone meal.......	0.35	.15	Cerelose (corn sugar)............	5.00	2.27
Ground limestone...............	0.25	.11	Salt	0.50	.23
Iodized salt	0.50	.22	Trace mineral mix (Tables 36-3		
Vitamin-antibiotic premix[2]...	2.00	.90	36-4, 36-5)......................	0.10	.05
			Vitamin mix (Table 36-3).......	1.00	.45
Total	100.00	45.02	Total..............................	100.00	45.37
Proximate analysis:			Proximate analysis:		
Protein, crude, %	22.06		Protein, crude, %..............	26.60	
Fat, %............................	3.55		Calcium, %.....................	0.80	
Calcium, %......................	0.86		Phosphorus, %.................	0.70	
Phosphorus, %.................	0.65				

[1]Either of these rations is satisfactory for early weaned pigs—pigs weaned at less than three weeks of age. Such feeds are generally fed as a gruel for the first two days, and then as a dry feed thereafter. Beginning with the third week, the creep feed is generally introduced as an additional feed so that during the third week the pigs have access to both the starter and the creep feeds. By the fourth week, the starter is removed and the pigs are fed the creep feed alone. When fed in this manner, each pig will consume about 5 pounds of the starter. See Table 36-10 for creep rations.
[2]Follow Tables 36-3, 36-4, 36-5, 36-7.

4. With good forage (ground alfalfa or pastures), the problem of the supplement is simplified from the standpoint of needed vitamins.

5. A protein supplement including both plant protein and animal protein is considered most satisfactory. However, an all-plant protein supplement of soybean meal may be satisfactory provided vitamins (especially B_{12}), minerals, and antibiotics are added.

6. When proteins of animal origin predominate, adequate mineral protection can be obtained by allowing hogs free access to a two-compartment box or self-feeder with (a) salt (iodized salt in iodine-deficient areas) in one side and (b) a mixture of 1/3 salt (salt added for purposes of palatability) and 2/3 monosodium phosphate or other phosphorus supplement, in the other side. When supplements of plant origin constitute most of the source of proteins, add a third compartment to the mineral box and place in it a mixture of 1/3 salt and 2/3 ground limestone or oyster shell flour.

The mineral supplement may be incorporated in the entire ration. Usually 1 to 2 per cent by weight will prove adequate. If it is incorporated in the protein concentrate only, 5 to 6 pounds of mineral mixture should be added to each 94 to 95 pounds of high-protein feed.

7. Where there is insufficient sunlight or where dehydrated alfalfa meal is fed, vitamin D should be added in keeping with the recommended allowances (see Table 36-3).

TABLE 36—12

HANDY GROWING PIG FEEDING GUIDE;
FOR PIGS IN DRY LOT

Ingredients[1]	30 to 100 Lbs. (14 to 45 kg) Wt. (14-16% protein)[2] Ration No. 1		100 Lbs. (45 kg) to Market Wt. (12-14% protein)[2] Ration No. 2	
	(lbs.)	(kg)	(lbs.)	(kg)
Yellow corn	1,580	716.7	1,670	757.5
Alfalfa meal	100	45.3	100	45.3
Soybean meal	190	86.2	130	59.0
Tankage (digesta) with bone	100	45.4	70	31.8
Salt	10	4.5	10	4.5
Steamed bone meal (or equivalent)	20	9.1	20	9.1
Antibiotics (Follow Table 36-7)				
Total lbs	2,000	907.2	2,000	907.2
Proximate analysis:				
Protein, crude, %	14.79		13.15	
Fiber, %	3.70		3.57	
Fat, %	4.16		4.15	
Calcium, %	0.96		0.78	
Phosphorus, %	0.73		0.65	

[1]Feeds of similar nutritive properties can be interchanged in the ration as price relationships warrant. Among such feeds are: (1) *the cereal grains*—corn, barley, wheat, oats, and sorghum; (2) *the animal protein supplements*—tankage, meat meal, meat and bone scrap, fish meal, and dried milk products; and (3) *the plant protein supplements*—soybean, cottonseed, linseed, and peanut meal. If wheat, barley, oats, and/or sorghum are used instead of corn as the grain in a ration, the protein supplement may be slightly reduced, because these grains have a higher protein content than corn; similar consideration should be given with shifts in protein supplements.

[2]Young pigs require a much greater proportion of protein in the ration than do those approaching market weight. For this reason, less protein supplement is indicated in the above rations as finishing progresses. Of course, as pigs advance in age and weight, they consume a larger daily ration, although the percentage of protein in the mixture is decreased.

8. Where the ration consists chiefly of white corn, barley, wheat, oats, rye, kafir, or by-products of these grains, there may be a deficiency of vitamin A (see Table 36-3 for recommended allowances).

9. Except for gestating sows and boars of breeding age, hogs are generally self-fed. All of the ingredients may be mixed together and placed in the same self-feeder, or the grain may be placed in one self-feeder (or compartment) and the protein supplements (including any ground alfalfa) in another. If the (a) cereal grains and (b) protein supplement (including ground alfalfa) are hand-fed, the grain and supplement should be fed separately, in the proportions indicated in the suggested rations.

10. An exception should be made to the cafeteria-style feeding when the grain ration consists of barley, oats, rye, or kafir. These feeds are higher in protein content than corn and for this reason, are generally fed as a mixed ration. Otherwise, the pigs will often eat more protein supplement than is necessary to balance the ration. Likewise, when corn is fed as the grain, sometimes such protein supplements as (a) roasted soybeans, (b) soybean meal, and (c) peanut meal are too palatable to be fed separately from the corn.

TABLE 36—13

HANDY GROWING-FINISHING PIG FEEDING GUIDE;
FOR PIGS ON GOOD PASTURE

Ingredients[1]	30 to 100 Lbs. (14 to 45 kg) Wt. (14-16% protein)[2] Ration No. 1		100 Lbs. (45 kg) to Market Wt. (12-14% protein)[2] Ration No. 2	
	(lbs.)	(kg)	(lbs.)	(kg)
Yellow corn.................................	1,680	762.0	1,755	796.1
Soybean meal.............................	190	86.2	125	56.7
Tankage (digester) with bone..................	100	45.4	90	40.8
Salt..	10	4.5	10	4.5
Steamed bone meal (or equivalent)..........	20	9.1	20	9.1
Total lbs..................................	2,000	907.2	2,000	907.2
Proximate analysis:				
Protein, crude, %.......................	14.49		13.16	
Fiber, %................................	2.40		2.26	
Fat, %..................................	4.29		4.36	
Calcium, %.............................	0.89		0.82	
Phosphorus, %..........................	0.73		0.70	

[1]Feeds of similar nutritive properties can be interchanged in the ration as price relationships warrant. Among such feeds are (1) *the cereal grains*—corn, barley, wheat, oats, and sorghum; (2) *the animal protein supplements*—tankage, meat meal, meat and bone scrap, fish meal, and dried milk products; and (3) *the plant protein supplements*—soybean, cottonseed, linseed, and peanut meal. If wheat, barley, oats, and/or sorghum are used instead of corn as the grain in a ration, the protein supplements may be slightly reduced, because these grains have a higher protein content than corn. Similar considerations should be given with shifts in protein supplements.
[2]Young pigs require a much greater proportion of protein in the ration than do those approaching market weight. For this reason, less protein supplement is indicated in the above rations as finishing progresses. Of course, as pigs advance in age and weight, they consume a larger daily ration, although the percentage of protein in the mixture is decreased.

11. Full-fed finishing hogs will consume 5 to 6 pounds of feed daily per 100 pounds live weight until they weigh 100 pounds. They will eat 4 to 5 pounds daily per 100 pounds weight from this stage until marketing.

Fitting Rations for Show and Sale Swine[10]

Any of the rations listed in Tables 36-8, 36-9, 36-12, and 36-13 for the respective classes and ages of swine, are suitable for use in fitting show animals of similar classification. In general, however, instead of self-feeding most experienced herdsmen feel that they can get superior bloom and condition by either (1) hand-feeding or (2) using a combination of hand-feeding and self-feeding (hand-feeding twice daily and allowing free access to a self-feeder). When hand-feeding, they also prefer mixing the ration with skim milk, buttermilk, or condensed buttermilk and feeding the entire ration in the form of a slop.

Adding milk to a ration that is already properly balanced does make for a higher protein content than necessary. On the other hand, most experienced herdsmen prefer using rations of higher protein content for fitting purposes.

---

[10]Further information on selecting, fitting and showing swine is presented in *Swine Science,* a book by the same author and publisher as *Animal Science.*

TABLE 36—14

FORMULAS FOR PROTEIN-MINERAL-VITAMIN-ANTIBIOTIC SUPPLEMENTS FOR SWINE[1]

In Dry Lot

Ingredients	1 (lbs.)	1 (kg)	2 (lbs.)	2 (kg)	3 (lbs.)	3 (kg)	4 (lbs.)	4 (kg)	5 (lbs.)	5 (kg)	6 (lbs.)	6 (kg)
Alfalfa meal	615	279.0	780	353.8	725	328.8	415	188.2	420	190.6	450	204.1
Wheat standard middlings												
Pea meal												
Brewers' grains	300	136.0	450	204.1	450	204.1			410	186.0	450	204.1
Tankage (digester) with bone[2]							200	90.7	200	90.7	150	68.2
Meat meal, with bone	100	45.4	200	90.7	100	45.4	300	136.1				
Fish meal (65%)	900	408.2	500	226.9	675	306.2	800	362.9	900	408.2	900	408.2
Soybean meal							200	90.7				
Linseed or cottonseed meal	20	9.1					20	9.1				
Salt	35	16	40	18.1	40	18.1	35	15.9	40	18.1	40	18.1
Steamed bone meal or dical.	20	9	20	9.1			20	9.1	20	9.1		
Ground limestone												
Trace minerals[3]												
Antibiotic supplement[4]	10	4.5	10	4.5	10	4.5	10	4.5	10	4.5	10	4.5
Total lbs.	2,000	907.2	2,000	907.2	2,000	907.2	2,000	907.2	2,000	907.2	2,000	907.2
Proximate analysis:												
Protein, crude %	35.29		34.76		34.93		39.05		39.78		39.39	
Fiber, %	11.80		13.20		12.90		9.46		9.30		9.75	
Fat, %	3.05		4.25		2.94		2.85		3.88		3.98	
Calcium, %	3.31		3.36		3.33		3.10		3.44		3.28	
Phosphorus, %	1.30		1.72		1.63		1.58		1.83		1.73	

On Pasture

Ingredients	1 (lbs.)	1 (kg)	2 (lbs.)	2 (kg)	3 (lbs.)	3 (kg)	4 (lbs.)	4 (kg)	5 (lbs.)	5 (kg)	6 (lbs.)	6 (kg)
Alfalfa meal	600	272.2	400	181.4	260	117.9	220	99.8	470	213.2	450	204.2
Wheat standard middlings			400	181.4	600	272.2			500	226.8	500	226.8
Pea meal					200	90.7	400	181.4				
Brewers' grains			550	249.6								
Tankage (digester) with bone[2]	300	136.1										
Meat meal, with bone	600	272.2			150	68.2						
Fish meal (65%)	400	181.4			700	317.5	1,300	589.7	960	435.5	1,000	453.6
Soybean meal			600	272.2								
Linseed or cottonseed meal	20	9.1					20	9.1				
Salt	30	13.6	40	18.1	40	18.1	30	13.6	40	18.1	40	18.1
Steamed bone meal or dical.	40	18.1			40	18.1	20	9.1	20	9.1		
Ground limestone												
Trace minerals[3]												
Antibiotic supplement[4]	10	4.5	10	4.5	10	4.5	10	4.5	10	4.5	10	4.5
Total lbs.	2,000	907.2	2,000	907.2	2,000	907.2	2,000	907.2	2,000	907.2	2,000	907.2
Proximate analysis:												
Protein, crude %	35.11		34.89		35.28		40.49		39.70		39.56	
Fiber, %	6.30		6.02		8.02		5.38		7.16		5.78	
Fat, %	3.01		4.85		4.47		3.47		4.86		3.85	
Calcium, %	2.02		3.17		2.23		3.14		3.25		2.98	
Phosphorus, %	1.25		1.86		1.49		1.56		1.86		1.69	

[1]Similar supplements may be either purchased commercially or mixed on the farm.
[2]Tankage, meat meal and meat bone scraps are interchangeable.
[3]Follow Tables 36-3, 36-4, 36-5.
[4]The antibiotic activity will vary with the class and age of swine (see Table 36-7).

TABLE 36—15

RATIO OF GRAIN TO PROTEIN SUPPLEMENTS NEEDED TO OBTAIN THE DESIRED LEVEL OF PROTEIN IN A RATION, WITH AND WITHOUT ALFALFA MEAL[1]

% Protein Desired	40% Supplement		35% Supplement		Corn (9.3% crude protein)		Ground Barley (11.6% crude protein)		Ground Oats (11.8% crude protein)		Ground Wheat (12.7% crude protein)		Alfalfa Meal (15.4% crude protein)	
	(lbs.)	(kg)	(lbs.)	(kg)	(lbs.)	(kg)	(lbs.)	(kg)	(lbs.)	(kg)	(lbs.)	(kg)	(lbs.)	(kg)
18	575	261	----	----	1,325	601	----	----	----	----	----	----	100	45
	500	227	----	----	750	340	650	295	----	----	----	----	100	45
	525	238	----	----	1,000	454	----	----	375	170	----	----	100	45
	450	104	----	----	----	----	925	420	----	----	----	----	100	45
	375	170	----	----	----	----	----	----	550	249	975	442	100	45
	----	----	675	306	1,225	556	----	----	----	----	----	----	100	45
	----	----	575	261	675	306	650	295	----	----	----	----	100	45
	----	----	650	295	1,000	454	----	----	----	----	----	----	100	45
	----	----	500	227	----	----	1,000	454	----	----	250	113	100	45
	----	----	500	227	----	----	----	----	500	227	400	181	100	45
	600	272	----	----	1,400	635	----	----	----	----	----	----	----	45
	525	238	----	----	875	397	600	272	----	----	----	----	----	----
	550	249	----	----	1,000	454	----	----	----	----	----	----	----	----
	425	193	----	----	----	----	925	420	450	204	----	----	----	----
	400	181	----	----	----	----	----	----	700	318	650	295	----	----
	----	----	725	329	1,275	578	----	----	----	----	900	408	----	----
	----	----	650	295	750	340	600	272	----	----	----	----	----	----
	----	----	675	306	1,000	454	----	----	325	147	----	----	----	----
	----	----	500	227	----	----	850	386	----	----	650	295	----	----
	----	----	500	227	----	----	----	----	550	249	950	431	----	----
16	450	204	----	----	1,450	658	----	----	----	----	----	----	100	45
	350	159	----	----	850	386	700	318	----	----	----	----	100	45
	300	136	----	----	----	----	950	431	----	----	650	295	100	45
	400	181	----	----	1,150	522	----	----	350	159	----	----	100	45
	275	125	----	----	----	----	----	----	625	283	1,000	454	100	45
	----	----	550	249	1,350	612	----	----	----	----	----	----	100	45
	----	----	425	193	775	352	700	318	----	----	----	----	100	45
	----	----	375	170	----	----	875	397	----	----	650	295	100	45
	----	----	500	227	1,050	476	----	----	350	159	----	----	100	45
	----	----	325	147	----	----	----	----	575	261	1,000	454	100	45
	375	170	----	----	925	420	700	318	----	----	----	----	----	----
	475	215	----	----	1,525	692	----	----	----	----	----	----	----	----
	425	193	----	----	1,225	556	----	----	350	159	----	----	----	----
	250	113	----	----	1,150	522	----	----	----	----	700	318	----	----
	250	113	----	----	----	----	----	----	750	340	1,000	454	----	----
	----	----	450	204	850	386	700	318	----	----	----	----	----	----
	----	----	575	261	1,425	646	----	----	----	----	----	----	----	----
	----	----	525	238	1,125	510	----	----	350	159	----	----	----	----
	----	----	200	91	1,100	499	----	----	----	----	700	318	----	----
	----	----	175	79	----	----	----	----	725	329	1,100	499	----	----
14	325	147	----	----	1,575	714	----	----	----	----	----	----	100	45
	225	102	----	----	875	397	800	363	----	----	----	----	100	45
	275	125	----	----	1,325	601	----	----	----	----	----	----	100	45
	----	----	375	170	1,525	692	----	----	300	136	----	----	100	45
	----	----	250	113	850	386	800	363	----	----	----	----	100	45
	----	----	350	159	1,250	567	----	----	----	----	----	----	100	45
	350	159	----	----	1,650	748	----	----	----	----	----	----	----	----
	250	113	----	----	950	431	800	363	----	----	----	----	----	----
	300	136	----	----	1,300	590	----	----	----	----	----	----	----	----
	----	----	425	193	1,575	714	----	----	400	181	----	----	----	----
	----	----	300	136	900	408	800	363	----	----	----	----	----	----
	----	----	350	159	1,250	567	----	----	----	----	----	----	----	----
12	200	91	----	----	1,700	771	----	----	----	----	----	----	100	45
	150	68	----	----	1,350	612	400	181	----	----	----	----	100	45
	150	68	----	----	1,450	658	----	----	----	----	----	----	100	45
	----	----	250	113	1,650	748	----	----	300	136	----	----	100	45
	----	----	175	79	1,325	601	400	181	----	----	----	----	100	45
	----	----	200	91	1,400	635	----	----	----	----	----	----	100	45
	225	102	----	----	1,775	805	----	----	----	----	----	----	----	----
	150	68	----	----	1,250	567	600	272	----	----	----	----	----	----
	200	91	----	----	1,500	680	----	----	----	----	----	----	----	----
	----	----	275	125	1,725	782	----	----	300	136	----	----	----	----
	----	----	200	91	1,300	590	500	227	----	----	----	----	----	----
	----	----	225	102	1,475	669	----	----	300	136	----	----	----	----

[1]In order to obtain an 18% protein feed, one could mix 575 lbs. of 40% supplement, 1,325 lbs. of corn, and 100 lbs. of alfalfa meal. Likewise, a 14% supplement without alfalfa meal (for use on pasture) could be obtained by mixing 300 lbs. of 35% supplement, 900 lbs. of corn, and 800 lbs. of barley.

They feel they get more bloom that way. In general, however, when skim milk or buttermilk is used in slop feeding, the protein feeds of the ration may be reduced by one-half without harm to the animal.

In fitting show barrows, it may be necessary to decrease or discontinue slop-feeding two to four weeks before the show to avoid paunchiness and lowering the dressing percentage.

When oatmeal (hulled oats) is not too high priced, many successful hog showmen replace up to 50 per cent of the grain (corn, wheat, barley, oats, and/or sorghum) in the ration with oatmeal. They do this especially when fitting hogs—both breeding animals and fat barrows—in the younger age groups. Oatmeal is highly palatable, lighter, and less fattening than corn.

Suitable minerals should always be provided.

QUESTIONS FOR STUDY AND DISCUSSION

1. Why is protein most frequently the limiting factor in the ration of swine, both from the standpoint of quantity and quality?
2. What peculiarities of swine husbandry are conducive to swine suffering from mineral deficiencies?
3. In the feeding of hogs, what primary differences as compared with feeding of ruminants need to be observed?
4. On your home farm (or a farm with which you are familiar), how and why would you (a) utilize pastures for swine and (b) hog off certain crops?
5. Of what significance is the corn-hog ratio?
6. Should we avoid producing soft pork?

SELECTED REFERENCES

Title of Publication	Author(s)	Publisher
Agradata, Vol. 2	Number 12, December, 1958 Baby Pig Nutrition	Chas. Pfizer & Co., Inc., Terre Haute, Indiana.
Creep Feeds for Suckling Pigs	H. S. Teague R. F. Wilson	Research Circular 46, September 1957, Ohio Agricultural Experiment Station, Wooster, Ohio.
Nutrient Requirements for Swine	Publication 1599, Rev. 1968	National Academy of Sciences, National Research Council, 2101 Constitution Ave. N.W., Washington, D. C.
Nutrients, Feeds & Example Rations for Swine	R. J. Meade D. R. Warner M. J. Brinegar	Circular 253, Extension Service, University of Nebraska, Lincoln, Neb.
Nutrition of Pigs and Poultry	J. T. Morgan D. Lewis	Butterworths, London, 1962.
Swine Feeding and Nutrition	T. J. Cunha	Interscience Publishers, New York, N. Y., 1957.
Swine Production	C. E. Bundy R. V. Diggins	Prentice-Hall, Inc., Englewood Cliffs, N. J., 1956.
Swine Production	W. E. Carroll J. L. Krider	McGraw-Hill Book Company, Inc. New York, N. Y., 1962.

Chapter XXXVII

MARKETING AND SLAUGHTERING HOGS

Contents   **Page**

Leading Terminal Hog Markets...888
Market Classes and Grades of Hogs..888
  Factors Determining Market Classes of Hogs..890
    Hogs and Pigs...890
    Use Selection of Hogs and Pigs...890
    The Sex Classes...890
    Weight Divisions 891
  The Federal Grades of Hogs and Their Carcasses.................................891
Other Hog Market Terms and Factors..891
  Roasters 893
  Roughs (or Throw-outs)...893
  Governments 893
  Cripples 893
  Dead Hogs..893
Packer Slaughtering and Dressing of Hogs..893
  Steps in Slaughtering and Dressing Hogs...894
  Packer Versus Shipper Style of Dressing..895
  The Dressing Percentage..896
Disposition of the Pork Carcass...897
The Hog Carcass and Its Wholesale Cuts...897
Lard 898
  Kinds of Lard...898
    Kettle-rendered Leaf Lard..899
    Kettle-rendered Lard 899
    Prime Steam Lard...899
    Neutral Lard...899
    Dry-rendered Lard...899
    New Process Lard (or Deodorized or Hydrogenated Lard)....................899
    Lard Substitutes...899
Questions for Study and Discussion...900
Selected References 900

Hogs are marketed through the several channels open to all classes of live-stock. In comparison with the marketing of cattle and sheep, however, the marketing of hogs differs in the following respects: (1) there has been a greater proportionate increase in country sales, (2) relatively fewer hogs are taken out of the market for further feeding because of parasite and disease problems, and (3) the proportion of hogs slaughtered on farms far exceeds that of cattle or sheep because of the greater ease of slaughtering and the adaptation of pork to home curing.

Hog slaughtering is also unique in that the carcasses are seldom sold, such as is the case with beef, veal, mutton, and lamb. Instead, hogs are reduced to wholesale cuts at the place of slaughter. Also, much more pork is cured than is the case with beef or lamb; and pork fat (lard) is not classed as a by-product, although the surplus fats of beef, veal, mutton, and lamb are in the by-product category.

LEADING TERMINAL HOG MARKETS

As would be expected, the leading hog markets of the United States are located in or near the Corn Belt—the area of densest hog population. With the advent of the motor truck and improved highways, the pork packing plants were moved nearer the areas of hog raising. Thus, during the past two decades, local or interior packers have increased in numbers. In order to meet this added competition, the large packers at more distant points resorted to direct buying and the purchase of interior plants.

The rank of the major hog markets shifts considerably according to feed supplies and general economic conditions. The 10 largest hog markets, by rank, and their receipts are listed in Table 37-1.

TABLE 37—1

TOTAL RECEIPTS OF TEN LEADING TERMINAL HOG MARKETS,
BY RANK, 1966[1]

Market	Average Hog Receipts 1966
Omaha, Nebraska	1,977,047
St. Louis National Stock Yards, Illinois	1,754,793
Sioux City, Iowa	1,747,870
South St. Paul, Minnesota	1,488,955
Chicago, Illinois	1,294,368
St. Joseph, Missouri	1,202,753
Indianapolis, Indiana	1,132,194
Kansas City, Missouri	881,081
Sioux Falls, South Dakota	803,562
Peoria, Illinois	790,280
U.S. total 53 markets	16,270,611

[1]*Livestock and Meat Statistics.* USDA. Supp. for 1966 to Statistical Bul. No. 333, p. 38.

MARKET CLASSES AND GRADES OF HOGS

The market classes and grades of swine were developed in much the same manner as the classifications of cattle were developed and brought into use. They also serve much the same purpose. Swine classes and grades do differ from those used in cattle and sheep in that: (1) there are no age divisions by years (*e.g.,* cattle are classified as yearling and two-year-old and over), (2) only a limited number of hogs are returned to the country as feeders for further growth or finishing, and (3) rarely are hogs of any kind purchased on the market for use as breeding animals. As in the classification of market cattle, the class of market hogs indicates the use to which the animals are best adapted, whereas the grade indicates the degree of perfection within the class.

The market classes and grades of hogs are summarized in Table 37-2.

TABLE 37—2

THE MARKET CLASSES AND GRADES OF HOGS

Hogs or Pigs	Use Selection	Sex Class	Weight Divisions (lbs.)	(kg)	Commonly Used Grades
Hogs	Slaughter hogs	Barrows and Gilts (often called butcher hogs)	120-140 140-160 160-180 180-200 200-220 220-240 240-270 270-300 300-330 330-360 360-400 400 lbs. up	55-64 64-73 73-82 82-91 91-100 100-109 109-123 123-136 136-150 150-163 163-182 182 up	U.S. No. 1, U.S. No. 2, U.S. No. 3, U.S. No. 4, U.S. Utility.
		Sows (or packing sows)	270-300 300-330 330-360 360-400 400-450 450-500 500-600 600 lbs. up	123-136 136-150 150-163 163-182 182-204 204-227 227-272 272 up	U.S. No. 1, U.S. No. 2, U.S. No. 3, U.S. No. 4, U.S. Utility.
		Stags	All weights		Ungraded
		Boars	All weights		Ungraded
	Feeder hogs	Barrows and Gilts	120-140 140-160 160-180	55-64 64-73 73-82	U.S. No. 1, U.S. No. 2, U.S. No. 3, U.S. No. 4, U.S. Utility, Cull.
Pigs	Slaughter pigs	Barrows, Gilts, and Boars	Under 30 30-60	13.6 13.6-27.2	Ungraded
	Slaughter pigs	Barrows and Gilts	60-80 80-100 100-120	27.2-36.3 36.3-45.4 45.4-54.5	Ungraded
	Feeder pigs	Barrows and Gilts	80-100 100-120	36.3-45.4 45.4-54.5	U.S. No. 1, U.S. No. 2, U.S. No. 3, U.S. No. 4, U.S. Utility, Cull.

Factors Determining Market Classes of Hogs

The market class of hogs is determined by the following factors: (1) hogs versus pigs, (2) use selection, (3) sex, and (4) weight.

HOGS AND PIGS

All swine are first divided into two major groups according to age: hogs and pigs. Although actual ages are not observed, the division is made largely by weight in relation to the apparent age of the animal. Young animals weighing under 120 pounds (under about four months of age) are generally known as pigs, whereas those weighing over 120 pounds are called hogs.

USE SELECTION OF HOGS AND PIGS

Hogs and pigs are each further divided into two subdivisions as slaughter animals and feeders. Slaughter swine are hogs and pigs that are suitable for immediate slaughter. The demand for lightweight slaughter pigs is greatest during the holiday season when they are in demand as roasting pigs for hotels, clubs, restaurants, steamships, and other consumers. Such pigs weigh from 15 to 20 pounds, are dressed shipper style (with the head on), and must produce a plump and well-proportioned carcass. Slaughter hogs (the older animals) are in demand throughout the year.

Feeder swine include those animals that show ability to take on additional weight and finish. The feeder group is relatively small. Moreover, because of the greater disease hazard with hogs, this class is under very close federal supervision. Before being released for return to the country, feeder swine must be inspected from a health standpoint, and then either sprayed or dipped as a precautionary measure to prevent the spread of disease germs or parasites.

THE SEX CLASSES

The sex class is used only when it affects the usefulness and selling price of animals. In hogs, this subdivision is of less importance than in cattle. Thus, barrows and gilts are always classed together in the case of both slaughter and feeder hogs. This is done because the sex condition affects their usefulness so little that a price differentiation is not warranted. In addition, because the carcass is not affected, no sex differentiations are made for slaughter pigs under 60 pounds in weight. The terms "barrow," "gilt," "sow," "boar," and "stag" are used to designate the sex classes of hogs. The definition of each of these terms follows:

Barrow.—A castrated male swine animal that was castrated at an early age—before reaching sexual maturity and before developing the physical characteristics peculiar to boars.

Gilt.—A female swine that has not produced pigs and which has not reached an evident stage of pregnancy.

Sow.—A female swine that shows evidence of having produced pigs or which is in an evident stage of pregnancy. Piggy sows are usually docked 40 pounds, but may be docked from 0 to 50 pounds, depending on the market.

Boar.—An uncastrated male swine animal of any age. Mature boars should always be stagged and fed a month longer before being sent to market. The market value of boars is necessarily low, for a considerable number are condemned as unfit for human consumption, primarily because of odor.

Stag.—A stag is a male swine animal that was castrated after developing the physical characteristics of a mature boar. Because of relatively thick skins, coarse hair, and heavy bones, stags are subject to a dockage. They are usually docked 70 pounds, but may be docked from 40 to 80 pounds, depending on the market. When marketed direct, stags are usually not docked in weight but are purchased at a price that reflects their true value from a meat standpoint.

WEIGHT DIVISIONS

Occasionally, the terms "light," "medium," and "heavy" are used to indicate approximate weights, but most generally the actual range in weight in pounds is specified both in trading and in market reporting. Moreover, hogs are usually grouped according to relatively narrow weight ranges because variations in weight affect (1) the dressing percentages, (2) the weight and desirability of the cuts of meat, and (3) the amount of lard produced (heavier weights produce more lard). Boars and stags are not usually subdivided according to weights.

The Federal Grades of Hogs and Their Carcasses

The market grade for swine, as for other kinds of livestock, is a specific indication of the degree of excellence within a given class based upon conformation, finish, and quality. The two chief factors which serve to place a hog in a specific grade are: degree of finish and amount of muscling. While no official grading of live animals is done by the U.S. Department of Agriculture, market grades do form a basis for uniform reporting of livestock marketings. It is intended that the grade of slaughter hogs on foot be correlated with the carcass grade. The federal market grades of slaughter barrows and gilts and pork carcasses are: U.S. No. 1, U.S. No. 2, U.S. No. 3, U.S. No. 4, and U.S. Utility. As will be noted, the market grades of swine differ from the grades of cattle in that: (1) hogs possess five grades instead of the eight common to cattle, (2) the top grade of hogs is U.S. No. 1 instead of Prime, and (3) no Cutter or Canner designations are used in hogs; instead the lowest grade is known as U.S. Utility.

As a rule, slaughter pigs that weigh under 60 pounds are not graded because they have not reached sufficient maturity for variations in their conformation, finish, and quality to affect materially the market value.

OTHER HOG MARKET TERMS AND FACTORS

In addition to the rather general terms used in designating the different market classes and grades of hogs, the following terms and factors are frequently of importance.

SLAUGHTER BARROWS and GILTS
U. S. GRADES

U.S. NO. 1

U.S. NO. 2

U.S. NO. 3

U.S. NO. 4

Fig. 37-1. The four top market grades of slaughter barrows and gilts. (Courtesy, John C. Pierce, Deputy Director, Livestock Division, Consumer and Marketing Service, USDA)

Roasters

Roasters refer to fat, plump, suckling pigs, weighing 15 to 50 pounds on foot. These are dressed shipper style (with the head on). When properly roasted and attractively served with the traditional apple in the mouth, roast pig is considered a great delicacy for the holiday season.

Roughs (or Throw-outs)

The term "roughs" or "throw-outs" is frequently applied to coarse, rough hogs lacking in condition. Carcasses from such hogs are used for the cheaper class of trade, both as cured and fresh pork.

Governments

Governments are suspicious animals that federal inspectors tag at the time of the ante-mortem inspection to indicate that more careful scrutiny is to be given in the post-mortem inspection. If the carcass is deemed unfit for human consumption, it is condemned and sent to the inedible tank.

Cripples

Cripples are hogs that are not able to walk and that must be hauled to the packing plants in cripple carts.

Dead Hogs

Dead hogs are those that arrive dead at the market. These carcasses are sent to the tanks for conversion into inedible grease, fertilizer, etc.

PACKER SLAUGHTERING AND DRESSING OF HOGS

Table 37-3 shows the proportion of hogs slaughtered commercially (meaning slaughtered in federally inspected and other wholesale and retail establish-

TABLE 37—3

PROPORTION OF HOGS SLAUGHTERED COMMERCIALLY
1961 THROUGH 1966[1]

Year	Total Number Slaughtered (commercially and noncommercially)	Number Slaughtered Commercially	Per Cent Slaughtered Commercially
	(1,000 head)	(1,000 head)	
1961	82,050	77,335	94.25
1962	83,543	79,334	94.96
1963	87,252	83,324	95.50
1964	86,420	83,019	96.06
1965	76,394	73,784	96.58
1966	75,324	74,011	98.25

[1]*Livestock and Meat Statistics*, USDA, Supp. for 1966 to Statistical Bul. No. 333, p. 63.

ments) and the proportion slaughtered on farms. The total figure refers to the number dressed in all establishments and on farms.

Although modern equipment may be lacking, the slaughtering procedure on the farm or in a small local plant is much the same as that followed in a large federally inspected plant. Only the procedure used in a modern commercial packing plant will be discussed, however.

After purchase, hogs are driven from the holding pens to the packing plant where they are given a shower and are held temporarily in a small pen while awaiting slaughter.

Steps in Slaughtering and Dressing Hogs

The chain method of slaughtering is used in killing and dressing hogs. In this method, the following steps are carried out in rapid succession:

1. **Rendering insensible.**—The hogs are rendered insensible[1] by use of a captive bolt stunner, gunshot, electric current, or carbon dioxide.

2. **Shackling and hoisting.**—The hogs are shackled just above the hoof on the hind leg and are then hoisted to an overhead rail.

3. **Sticking.**—The sticker sticks the hog just under the point of the breast bone, severing the arteries and veins leading to the heart. The animal is allowed to bleed for a few minutes.

4. **Scalding.**—The animals are next placed in a scalding vat for about four minutes. By means of automatically controlled steam jets, the temperature of the water in the vats is maintained at 142° to 145° F. The scalding process loosens the hair and scurf.

5. **Dehairing.**—After scalding, the animals are elevated into a dehairing machine which scrapes them mechanically. In modern packing plants a single dehairing machine will handle up to 500 hogs per hour. Most large plants are equipped with twin machines which provide a scraping capacity of a thousand hogs per hour.

6. **Returning to overhead tracks.**—As the animals are discharged from the dehairing machine, the gam cords of the hind legs are exposed; and gambrel sticks are inserted in the cords. Then the carcass is again hung from the rail.

7. **Dressing.**—A conveyor then moves the carcass slowly along a prescribed course where attendants perform the following tasks:

    a. Washing and singeing.
    b. Removing the head.
    c. Opening the carcass and eviscerating.
    d. Splitting or halving the carcass with a cleaver or electric saw.
    e. Removing the leaf fat.

---

[1] See footnote under "Steps in Slaughtering and Dressing Cattle," Chapter XV, relative to humane slaughter methods.

f. Exposing the kidneys for inspection and facing the hams (removing the skin and fat from the inside face or cushion of the ham).

g. Washing the carcass and sending it to the coolers where the temperature is held from 31° to 38° F. (Rapid chilling is desirable.)

During the dressing process, federal inspectors carefully examine the head, viscera, and carcass. If the carcass gives no evidence of disease, it is stamped U.S. Inspected and Passed prior to being sent to the coolers. If it shows evidence of a diseased condition and is not considered wholesome, it is stamped U.S. Condemned and is sent to the inedible tank room along with the viscera. There the carcass is cooked under steam pressure in sealed tanks until all the disease germs are destroyed.

Packer Versus Shipper Style of Dressing

The two common styles of dressing hogs in packing plants are: packer style and shipper style. In general, the packer style is followed, and this system is almost exclusively used when carcasses are to be converted into the primal cuts. In packer-style dressing, the backbone is split full length through the center; the head, without the jowl, is removed; and the kidneys and the leaf fat are removed and the hams faced.

The shipper style is ordinarily limited to lightweight slaughter pigs that are sold as entire carcasses to the wholesale trade. In this style of dressing, the carcass is merely opened from the crotch to the tip of the breastbone; the

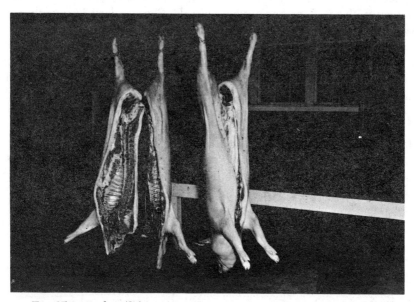

Fig. 37-2. Packer (left) versus shipper (right) style of dressing. Both hogs dressed 75 per cent shipper style, but subsequent removal of the head, leaf fat, and kidneys from the carcass to the left—in preparing it packer style—lowered the dressing per cent of this carcass a further 4 per cent. (Courtesy, Washington State University)

backbone is left intact; the leaf fat is left in; and the entire head is left attached. Roasting pigs are dressed shipper style and prior to cooling are placed in a trough with front legs doubled back from the knee joints and the hind legs extending straight back from the hams.

When dressed packer style, the carcass yields are 4 to 8 per cent less than can be obtained shipper style. The lower yield is due to the removal of the head, leaf fat, kidneys, and ham facings.

The Dressing Percentage

Dressing percentage may be defined as the percentage yield of chilled carcass in relation to the weight of the animal on foot. For example, a hog that weighed 200 pounds on foot and yielded a carcass weighing 140 pounds may be said to have a dressing percentage of 70.

Because hogs have a smaller digestive capacity, fill is less important in determining their dressing percentage than is the case with cattle. The degree of finish and the style of dressing are the important factors affecting dressing percentage in hogs. U.S. No. 1 hogs dressed packer style (with head, leaf fat, and kidneys removed) dress about 70 per cent, whereas hogs dressed shipper style (head left on, and leaf fat and kidneys in) dress 4 to 8 per cent higher.

Table 37-4 gives the approximate dressing percentages that may be expected from the different grades of barrows and gilts. It is generally recognized that fat, lardy-type hogs give a higher dressing percentage than can be obtained with meat- or bacon-type animals. Because lard frequently sells at a lower price than is paid for hogs on foot, an excess yield of lard very obviously represents an economic waste of feed in producing the animals and is undesirable from the standpoint of the processor. Accordingly, attaching great importance to the projected dressing percentage of hogs is outmoded. The more progressive buyers are now focusing their attention on the cut-out value of the carcass, especially on the maximum yield of the more sought primal cuts of high quality.

Hogs have a relatively smaller barrel and chest cavity than cattle and sheep. In addition they are dressed with their skin and shanks on. Consequently, they dress higher than other classes of slaughter animals.

TABLE 37—4

APPROXIMATE DRESSING PER CENT OF BARROWS AND GILTS,
BY GRADE[1]

Grade	Range	Average
U.S. No. 1	67-71	69
U.S. No. 2	68-72	70
U.S. No. 3	69-73	71
U.S. No. 4	65-69	67
Medium (now U.S. Utility)	63-67	65

[1]Provided by J. C. Pierce, Jr., Director, Livestock Division, Consumer and Marketing Service, USDA.

TABLE 37—5

AVERAGE LIVE WEIGHT, CARCASS YIELD, AND DRESSING
PERCENTAGES OF ALL HOGS COMMERCIALLY
SLAUGHTERED IN THE U.S. IN 1966[1]

	Average. Live Weight		Average Dressing Weight[2]		Dressing
	(lbs.)	(kg)	(lbs.)	(kg)	(%)
Hogs	242	110	151	69	62.4

[1]*Livestock and Meat Statistics*, USDA, Supp. for 1966 to Statistical Bul. No. 333, pp. 85, 103.
[2]Carcass weight excluding lard.

The average live weight of hogs, dressed packer style by federally inspected meat packing plants, and their percentage yield in meat for the year
1966 was as shown in Table 37-5.

DISPOSITION OF THE PORK CARCASS

Almost all hog carcasses are cut up at the slaughtering plant and are
sold in the form of wholesale cuts. In most parts of the country not more
than 1 to 2 per cent of the pork in large packing plants is sold in carcass
form. The whole-carcass trade is largely confined to roasting and slaughter
pigs.

The handling of pork differs further from that of beef and lamb in that
only a relatively small percentage, about 30 per cent, of the pork is sold
fresh. The remaining 70 per cent is cured by various methods, is rendered
into lard, or is manufactured into meat products. In general, loins, shoulders,
and spareribs are most likely to be sold as fresh cuts. But it must be remembered
that practically every pork cut may be cured, and, under certain conditions,
is cured. Because pork is well adapted to curing, it has a decided advantage
over beef and mutton, which are sold almost entirely in the fresh state.
The hog market is stabilized to some extent by this factor.

THE HOG CARCASS AND ITS WHOLESALE CUTS

A minimum of 24 hours chilling at temperatures ranging from 31° to
38° F. is necessary to remove properly the animal heat and give the carcasses
sufficient firmness to make possible a neat job of cutting. After chilling,
the carcasses are brought to the cutting floor where they are reduced to the
wholesale cuts.

The method of cutting varies somewhat according to the value of lard
and the relative demand for different cuts. Despite some variation, the most
common wholesale cuts of pork are: ham, bacon, loin, picnic shoulder, Boston
butt, jowl, spareribs, and feet.

Market hogs weighing from 180 to 200 pounds will have about 45.5
per cent of their live weight in the four primal cuts: the ham, shoulder,

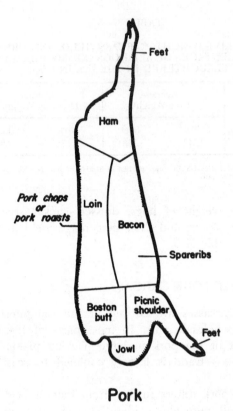

Pork

Fig. 37-3. Wholesale cuts of pork and some of the common retail cuts. (Drawing by R. F. Johnson)

loin, and bacon belly. Yet, because of the relatively higher value per pound of these cuts, they make up three-quarters of the value of the entire carcass.

LARD

Lard is the fat rendered (melted out) from fresh, fatty pork tissue. From 10 to 25 per cent—with an average of 15 per cent—of the hog carcass is made into lard in the large packing houses. The proportion varies with the type, weight, and finish of the hogs, and the relative price of lard and the cuts of meat. Lard is considered a primary product of hog slaughter and not a by-product.

Kinds of Lard

Lard is classified according to the part of the animal from which the fat comes and the method of rendering.

KETTLE-RENDERED LEAF LARD

Kettle-rendered leaf lard is made from leaf fat only. It is rendered in a steam-jacketed open kettle at a temperature of 230° to 250° F. It is very white in color, fine textured, and possesses excellent keeping qualities and a pleasing flavor. It is the highest grade of lard.

KETTLE-RENDERED LARD

Kettle-rendered lard is made from back fat and leaf fat, usually in equal amounts. It is also rendered in a steam-jacketed open kettle but at a temperature of 240° to 260° F. Kettle-rendered lard has good keeping qualities, but it is likely to be somewhat darker than kettle-rendered leaf lard, to which it ranks second in grade.

PRIME STEAM LARD

Probably 85 per cent of packing house lard is of the prime steam type. It is made from killing and cutting fats that are rendered in a closed tank under steam pressure of from 30 to 50 pounds and at a temperature of 285° F. It is somewhat milder in flavor and odor and lighter in color than lard produced by dry rendering.

NEUTRAL LARD

Neutral lard is made entirely from leaf fat that is rendered at a very low temperature of about 120° F. It is used almost entirely in the manufacture of oleomargarine.

DRY-RENDERED LARD

Dry-rendered lard is essentially a kettle-rendered lard, except that the fat is melted in a closed container, usually under reduced pressure. This method of rendering gives a product that has a fine flavor and excellent keeping quality.

NEW PROCESS LARD (OR DEODORIZED OR HYDROGENATED LARD)

New process lard is deodorized lard to which extra atoms of hydrogen and a stabilizing agent (inhibitors of vegetable origin) have been added. Such lard is bland, has a high melting point, and is less subject to rancidity than ordinary lard. New process lard was first placed on the market in 1941.

LARD SUBSTITUTES

Lard substitutes, which are sometimes used in place of lard, are made from: (1) lard and other animal fats mixed with vegetable oils, (2) vegetable

oils alone, and (3) hydrogenated vegetable oils, the most prominent of which
are cottonseed and coconut oil.

QUESTIONS FOR STUDY AND DISCUSSION

1. What primary differences exist between the marketing of hogs and the
   marketing of cattle and sheep?
2. What factors contribute to the making of each of the leading terminal hog
   markets, as listed in Table 37-1?
3. Compare the market classes and grades of hogs with the market classes
   and grades of cattle and sheep.
4. Under what conditions would you recommend each: (a) the packer style?
   (b) the shipper style of dressing?
5. Compare the handling and disposition of pork carcasses, from the standpoints of (a) selling in carcass form vs. wholesale cuts and (b) selling in
   cured vs. fresh form, with the disposition of beef and lamb carcasses.

SELECTED REFERENCES

In addition to the selected references listed in Chapter VI, the following
are recommended for Chapter XXXVII:

Title of Publication	Author(s)	Publisher
Export Market for Pork and Lard, The	A. A. Dowell R. E. Olson O. B. Jesness	Agri. Expt. Sta. Bull. 418, University of Minnesota, St. Paul, Minn., June 1953.
Looking Over the Hog Buyer's Shoulder		Agricultural Research Dept., Swift & Company, Chicago, Ill.
Marketing Hogs in Northeastern Indiana	Agri. Expt. Sta. Bull. 561	Purdue University, Lafayette, Ind.
Marketing Meat-Type Hogs	Marketing Research Report No. 227	AMS, U.S. Department of Agriculture, Washington, D. C.
Pork Marketing Margins and Costs	Misc. Pub. No. 711	AMS, U.S. Department of Agriculture, Washington, D. C., April 1956.
Relationship of Type, Grade, Weight and Price of Market Hogs, The	C. N. Haugse Warren Dekrey V. K. Johnson	Bulletin No. 421, Dept. of Animal Husbandry, North Dakota State University, Fargo, N. D.
Why Not Sell Quality Hogs?	C. R. Harston W. M. Chase	Circ. 219, Montana Agri. Expt. Sta., Montana State University, Bozeman, Mont.

CHAPTER XXXVIII

THE POULTRY INDUSTRY[1]

Contents   Page

Domestication and Early Use of Poultry...901
Importance of the Poultry Industry...902
Transformation of the American Poultry Industry.................................905
Present Status of the Poultry Industry..911
    World Poultry Distribution..911
    U.S. Poultry Distribution..912
    Relative Importance of Different Species of Poultry....................914
Allied Industries 914
Future of the Poultry Industry..915
Questions for Study and Discussion..917
Selected References 918

The term "poultry" covers a rather wide variety of birds of several species, and it refers to them whether alive or dressed. It includes chickens, turkeys, ducks, geese, swans, guineas, pigeons, peafowl, ostriches, pheasants, and other game birds.

The study of birds which are not classed as poultry is known as *ornithology*.

There are about 600,000 species of animals in the world, of which 10,000 species are birds. The most highly developed animals are mammals, which include man and the four-footed farm animals, and which are distinguished by the presence of hair and mammary glands. Birds are distinguished by the covering of feathers.

DOMESTICATION AND EARLY USE OF POULTRY

Ancient man persuaded chickens to live and produce near his abode. It is not known exactly when this happened, but it's obvious that chickens were domesticated at a remote period. The keeping of poultry was probably contemporary with the keeping of sheep by Abel and the tilling of the soil by Cain. Chickens were known in ancient Egypt, and they had already achieved considerable status in the time of the Pharaohs, because artificial incubation was then practiced in crude ovens resembling some still in use in that country.

The use of poultry and eggs as food goes back to very early times in the history of man. Methods of slaughter and preparation for consumption

[1] The author acknowledges with thanks the authoritative review accorded the entire poultry section—Chapters XXXVIII through XLV—by the following persons: Dr. E. L. Stephenson, Head, Department of Animal Sciences, University of Arkansas, Fayetteville, Arkansas; Dr. Eugene B. Patterson, Manager, Developmental Research, Chas. Pfizer & Co., Inc., Terre Haute, Indiana; and Dr. F. M. Hixson, Poultry Department, Fresno State College, Fresno, California.

have varied with succeeding civilizations and cultures. Not until fairly recent times did these operations become a matter of great commercial importance, or of serious concern to consumers, public health officials, and government alike.

IMPORTANCE OF THE POULTRY INDUSTRY

Several criteria may be used to measure or gauge the importance of the poultry industry, among them the following:

1. **As source of farm income.**—U.S. poultry producers sold meat birds and eggs valued at $3.5 billion in 1965, representing 9.1 per cent of the total cash farm income that year (also see Table 1-3, Chapter I, of this book). Actually, the percentage of total farm income derived from poultry has changed only slightly during the past quarter century, through the years accounting for 9 to 10 per cent of the cash farm income. But, this cash income has been received by fewer and fewer poultry producers, because the big have gotten bigger. Further, the production of different kinds of poultry has gradually been concentrated in certain geographic areas where farmers have the greatest comparative advantage in the production of one or more kinds of poultry or poultry products.

2. **As a food.**—Poultry meat and eggs are used chiefly as human food. In 1965, the U.S. per capita consumption of chicken and turkey on a ready-

Fig. 38-1. Roast turkey. Turkeys produce a higher proportion of edible meat to live (on-foot) weight than any other species, and compare favorably with other meats as a source of amino acids. (Courtesy, National Turkey Federation, Mount Morris, Ill.)

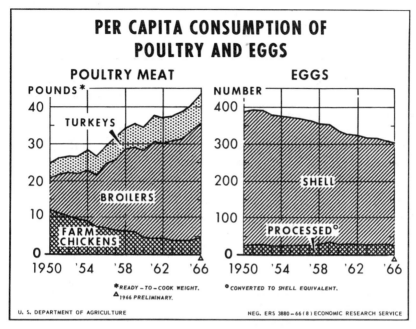

Fig. 38-2. Per capita consumption of poultry and eggs.

to-cook basis totaled 33.3 and 7.4 pounds, respectively. Additionally, in that same year, 308 eggs were consumed per person.

Fig. 38-2 shows the per capita consumption of poultry meat and eggs since 1950. As noted, the consumption of turkeys and broilers, on a per capita basis, has increased very sharply. On the other hand, the per person consumption of eggs has declined, primarily due to a change in eating habits of the average urban dweller.

Eggs contain an abundance of proteins, vitamins, and minerals. Also, they have large amounts of high-quality and easily digestible proteins. Moreover, the proteins are complete proteins; that is, they contain all the essential amino acids to maintain life and promote growth. Additionally, eggs are a rich source of iron; phosphorus; trace minerals; vitamins A, E, K; and all the B vitamins, including vitamin B_{12}. Eggs are second only to fish liver oils as a natural source of vitamin D. Eggs are moderate from the standpoint of calorie content; a medium-size egg containing about 77 calories. Table 38-1 points up the nutritive value of eggs.

Notwithstanding the high nutritive value of eggs, millions of Americans routinely eat eggs for breakfast each morning simply because they like them.

Poultry meat is supplied chiefly by chickens and turkeys, although ducks, geese, guinea and other fowls contribute thereto.

Poultry meat is economical, quick and easy to prepare and serve, and has a number of desirable nutritional properties (Table 38-2).

Nutritionally, people eat meat primarily for its protein content. Turkey and chicken meat is higher in protein than beef and other red meats (Table

TABLE 38—1

SOME OF THE ESSENTIAL NUTRIENTS IN TWO MEDIUM EGGS
(108 grams) WITHOUT SHELL[1]

Nutrient	Function	Percentage of Daily Dietary Recommendations[2]
Protein	To build muscles and body tissues.	16.3%
Iron	To build red blood cells and help promote good health.	17.3%
Vitamin A	To help give normal vision and clear, healthy skin.	22.0%
Thiamine (Vitamin B$_1$)	To promote growth, good appetite, and a healthy nervous system.	8.3%
Riboflavin (Vitamin B$_2$)	To promote growth and good health.	14.8%
Vitamin B$_{12}$	To help prevent and cure pernicious anemia.	1.0% microgram[3]
Vitamin D	To help calcium in building bones and teeth.	25.0%

[1]From the Poultry and Egg National Board, Chicago, Illinois.
[2]Recommendations for girls, ages 16 to 19.
[3]No daily recommendations established.

TABLE 38—2

COMPARISON OF NUTRIENT COMPOSITION OF
COOKED TURKEY, CHICKEN, AND BEEF[1]

Kind of Meat	Protein	Fat	Moisture	Food Energy Calories/lb.
	(%)	(%)	(%)	
Turkey (mature, roasted and boned)				
Breast (white meat)..........	34.2	7.5	58	925
Leg (dark meat)...............	30.5	11.6	56.5	1,029
Chicken (16 weeks old, roasted and boned)				
Breast (white meat)..........	31.5	1.3	66	625
Leg (dark meat)...............	25.4	7.3	67	761
Beef (cooked and boned)				
Round steak....................	27.0	13.0	59	1,056
Rump roast....................	21.0	32.0	46	1,714
Hamburger.....................	22.0	30.0	47	1,650

[1]From Poultry Meat, Ontario Department of Agriculture, Pub. 9, 1964, Table 16, p. 20.

38-2). Additionally, poultry meat contains high quality protein—it's a rich source of all the essential amino acids (Table 38-3). The close resemblance of the amino acid content of poultry meat to the amino acids of milk and eggs (top quality proteins) serves to emphasize the latter point.

3. **In industrial uses.**—Science and technology have teamed up to make for many uses of poultry and eggs, and their by-products. Among such in-

TABLE 38—3

COMPARISON OF AMINO ACID COMPOSITION OF VARIOUS
ANIMAL FOODS[1]

Amino Acid	Turkey[2]	Chicken (5)	Beef (6)	Pork (5)	Milk (7)	Eggs (7)
Arginine	6.5	6.7	6.4	6.7	4.3	6.4
Cystine[3]	1.0	1.8	1.3	0.9	1.0	2.4
Histidine[3]	3.0	2.0	3.3	2.6	2.6	2.1
Isoleucine[3]	5.0	4.1	5.2	3.8	8.5	8.0
Leucine[3]	7.6	6.6	7.8	6.8	11.3	9.2
Lysine[3]	9.0	7.5	8.6	8.0	7.5	7.2
Methionine[3]	2.6	1.8	2.7	1.7	3.4	4.1
Phenylalanine[3]	3.7	4.0	3.9	3.6	5.7	6.3
Threonine[3]	4.0	4.0	4.5	3.6	4.5	4.9
Tryptophan[3]	0.9	0.8	1.0	0.7	1.6	1.5
Tyrosine	1.5	2.5	3.0	2.5	5.3	4.5
Valine[3]	5.1	6.7	5.1	5.5	8.4	7.3

[1]From *Poultry Meat*, Ontario Department of Agriculture, Pub. 9, 1964, Table 15, p. 19.
[2]Average of values for whole turkey (breast and leg).
[3]Essential amino acids.

dustrial uses are: fertile eggs are used in the preparation of vaccines; inedible eggs are used in the preparation of animal feed and fertilizers; egg whites are used in the making of pharmaceuticals, paints, varnishes, adhesives, printer's ink, photography, book binding, wine clarification, leather tanning, and textile dyeing; egg yolks are used in the making of cake mixes, soap, paints, shampoos, leather finishing, and book binding; egg shells are used in making mineral mixes and in fertilizer; feathers are used in animal feed, fertilizer, millinery goods, pillows, cushions, mattresses, dusters, and insulation material; poultry offal is used in animal and mink feeds; and endocrine glands are used in making biological products.

4. **In research.**—The chick is much more sensitive to the lack of several substances in the diet than is the laboratory rat. At first, this great sensitivity was a handicap and made it very hard to keep chicks alive on the kinds of diets which would support a rat fairly well. Eventually, the higher sensitivity of the chick to many dietary factors proved a great advantage in bringing to life new information on vitamins, minerals, and amino acids, and in their more accurate estimation. Also, chicks have the advantages of being cheap and readily available, and large numbers of them can be hatched at the same time so as to provide the accuracy which goes with numbers of animals. Additionally, many scientists feel that the nutritional needs of the human are more like that of the chicken than the rat.

TRANSFORMATION OF THE AMERICAN POULTRY INDUSTRY

The American poultry industry had its humble beginning when chickens were first brought to this continent by the early settlers. Small home flocks were started at the time of the establishment of the first permanent homes at Jamestown in 1607. For many years thereafter, chickens were tenderly cared for by the farmer's wife, who fed them on table scraps and the unaccounted for grain from the crib.

As villages and towns were established, and increased in size, the nearby farm flocks were also increased. Surplus eggs and meat were sold or bartered for groceries and other supplies in the nearby towns. Eventually, grain production to the West, the development of transportation facilities, the use of refrigeration, and artificial incubation further stimulated poultry production in the latter part of the 1800's.

In the past two decades, changes in poultry and egg production and processing have paced the whole field of agriculture. Practices in all phases of poultry production—breeding, feeding, management, housing, marketing and processing—have become very highly specialized. The net result is that more products have been made available to consumers at favorable prices, comparatively speaking, and per capita consumption has increased. This is shown in Fig. 38-3.

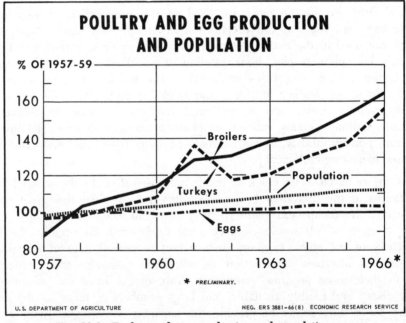

Fig. 38-3. Poultry and egg production and population.

A discussion of each of the most important changes in the poultry industry follows:

1. **Changes in breeding methods.**—Standard-bred chickens decreased as modern breeding methods were applied.

The poultry geneticist discovered that family, as well as individual bird records, are needed to develop high egg production. From this base, breeders created certain strains for high egg production and feed efficiency.

When breeding for broiler production, hybrid vigor is obtained by systematic matings that may involve crossing different breeds, different strains of the same breed, or the crossing of inbred lines. Many of the strains used as sires trace their ancestry to the broad-breasted Cornish breed. The main objective is the improvement of broiler growth rate to eight weeks of age, although improvement in other economic factors is sought.

Breeding for egg production differs from breeding for broiler production in that the individual methods most useful for improving growth rate have little value in selection to improve egg production, because egg production is of low heritability. In breeding for egg production, high producing families are selected. Then, either of two types of crosses are made: (a) crossing of inbred lines or (b) using strains which are not inbred.

2. **Changes in hatcheries.**—In the beginning, hatching was done according to nature's way—by a setting hen hovering over eggs. Then came the first American incubator, patented in 1844, followed by the U.S. Post Office acceptance of chicks for shipment by mail in 1918. Hatcheries became larger in size and fewer in number. In 1934, a half billion chicks were hatched in 11,000 hatcheries. By 1965, 3 billion chicks annually, including broilers, were hatched in 2,365 hatcheries; and 654 of these hatcheries with incubators of 200,000 or more capacity accounted for 71 per cent of the nation's capacity.

3. **Changes in egg production.**—A hundred years ago, a hen produced about 100 eggs per year. Today, the U.S. average is 218 eggs per hen. Formerly, eggs were sold largely on an ungraded basis. Today, most of them are candled for interior quality, weighed, cartoned, and sold according to size and quality. In many modern egg grading plants, efficient, power-operated weighing machines speed grading and move the eggs through the marketing system with dispatch.

Beginning in the early 1930's, three important changes took place in relation to egg production: (a) with the greater emphasis on commercial size flocks, the light breeds and strains of chickens gradually replaced general or dual-purpose breeds for egg production; (b) as the technique for "sexing" chicks became perfected, only the female chicks of egg-type breeds were sold by the hatcheries to layer operations; and (c) feeding, breeding, management, and disease control practices were improved so that more eggs were produced per layer, thereby requiring fewer layers to provide the eggs necessary to supply the market demands.

4. **Changes in chicken meat production.**—Prior to 1930, chicken meat was mainly the by-product of egg production. Birds which were no longer producing eggs at a satisfactory rate were sold for meat purposes, mainly in the fall of the year. Cockerels raised with the pullets were disposed of as fryers or roasters at weights of 3 to 8 pounds.

In 1934, 34 million broilers were produced in the United States. By 1965, 2.3 billion broilers were being produced, or 68 times as many as 31 years earlier. Modern broiler production is so concentrated, and so highly commercialized, that the industry might properly be classed as a poultry meat

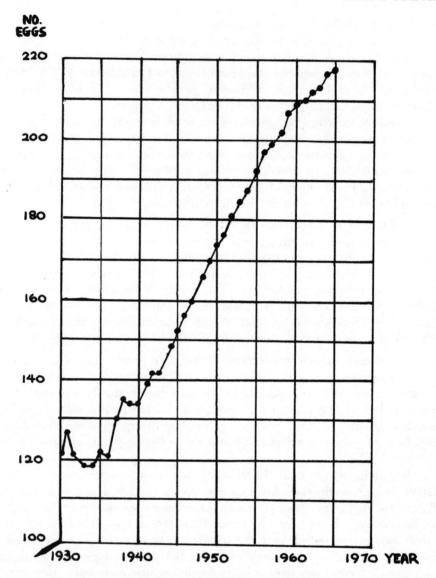

Fig. 38-4. Changes in annual egg production per hen.

factory, rather than a farming operation. Very little land is required beyond the space necessary for a broiler house and a drive-way. Chicks, feed, and other items used in production are purchased, or are obtained from another division of an integrated operation of which the broiler production is a part. The operation is highly specialized, mechanized, and carried on within the limits of the broiler house. Also, the operation is characterized by large numbers.

Similar progress has been made in the processing of poultry. In most areas of the country, poultry processing has become a highly industrialized, large-scale operation using modern mechanical equipment and sanitary methods.

5. **Changes in turkey production.**—Like the situation in chicken production, the production of turkeys was mostly a small side-line enterprise until 1910. At that time, 870,000 farmers raised 3-2/3 million turkeys, or an average of 4 turkeys per farm. In 1965, farmers raised 104.7 million turkeys, and flocks of 5,000 to 50,000 birds were not uncommon.

6. **Changes in number and size of poultry farms.**—In 1910, more than 5-1/2 million farms in the U.S. (88 per cent of the 6.4 million farms in the nation) kept chickens. The average size flock in the U.S. numbered 50 laying hens.

Another indicator of size of poultry farms is the number of chickens or eggs sold per farm (Table 38-4). As noted, from 1929 to 1959, the percentage of farms selling chickens decreased from 50 to 21 per cent, but the average number of chickens sold per farm increased from 91 to 1,950. A similar situation prevailed relative to eggs sold; with the number of farms selling eggs decreasing but the number of eggs sold per farm increasing.

TABLE 38—4

SIZE OF POULTRY FARMS[1]

Year	Percentage of All Farms Reporting Chickens Sold	Average Number Sold per Farm	Percentage of All Farms Reporting Eggs Sold	Dozens Sold per Farm
	(%)	(no.)	(%)	(doz.)
1929	50	91	62	505
1939	41	119	(not reported)	
1949	32	343	45	995
1959	21	1950	29	3040

[1]Latest data available.

7. **Changes in ownership and organization.**—As poultry operations grew in size and efficiency, they vertically integrated (chiefly with feed companies and processors) to secure more credit; and contractual production became commonplace. In 1967, it was estimated that approximately 95 per cent of the broilers, 80 per cent of the turkeys, and 50 per cent of the eggs were produced under some kind of integrated or contract arrangement.

8. **Changes in labor requirements.**—Poultry producers have achieved remarkable efficiency, primarily through increased confinement production and mechanization. In 1935 to 1939, it required 8-1/2 man-hours to produce 100 pounds of broiler; today, it requires only 0.9 man-hour to produce 100 pounds of broiler; and in this same period of time, the labor requirements to produce 100 pounds of turkey was lowered from 23.7 man-hours to 2.9 man-hours (Chapter I, Table 1-8, Fig. 1-18). But no such progress has been made

in lowering the labor requirements for the production of red meats, with the result that the poultry producers have achieved a very real advantage.

9. **Changes in feed efficiency.**—Table 38-5 and Fig. 38-5 show the marked lowering of feed required to produce a unit of eggs, turkeys, and broilers since 1940. In 1930, it required 5 pounds of feed to produce 1 pound of weight gain of broilers; today, it takes less than 3 pounds. But no such

TABLE 38—5

FEED UNITS REQUIRED PER UNIT OF EGGS AND POULTRY
PRODUCED, SELECTED YEARS, 1940-65[1]

Year Ending October	Per Dozen Eggs	Per Pound Liveweight	
		Turkey	Broiler
	(feed units)	(feed units)	(feed units)
1940	7.4	7.2	4.7
1945	7.3	6.3	4.5
1950	7.2	5.6	3.7
1955	6.8	5.7	3.2
1960	6.4	5.4	3.0
1965	6.0	5.2	3.0

[1]Feed units used per dozen eggs or per pound of liveweight turkey or broiler produced. A feed unit is the economic equivalent of one pound of corn. From *Handbook of Agricultural Charts 1965*, Agriculture Handbook No. 300, p. 58, U.S. Department of Agriculture, Oct. 1965.

progress has been made in red meat or milk animals. It requires about 10 pounds of feed to produce 1 pound of beef; and the feed efficiency of beef cattle has changed very little since 1900. Also, it requires more than 5 pounds of feed to produce a pound of gain in hogs, compared to 6-1/2 pounds needed in the early 1900s. Likewise, feed efficiency of dairy cows has changed very little; in 1910, it was 1.2 pounds of feed per pound of milk, today it's still more than a pound of feed per pound of milk.

10. **Changes in geography of production and processing.**—A rising proportion of broilers, turkeys, and eggs are being produced in the Southeast. In 1965, Georgia, Arkansas, Alabama, North Carolina, and Mississippi produced (a) 60 per cent of the nation's broilers—up from 27 per cent in 1950, (b) 12 per cent of the U.S. turkey crop—up from 4 per cent in 1950, and (c) 20 per cent of the nation's eggs—up from 7 per cent in 1950. Processors also shifted to the proximity of production centers.

11. **Changes in marketing.**—In the movement of poultry meat and eggs from the producer to the consumer, fewer agencies are being used and there is more direct marketing.

12. **Changes in proportion of federally inspected slaughter.**—Prior to passage of the Poultry Inspection Act of 1957, relatively little poultry was slaughtered under federal inspection. By 1965, 86.3 per cent of all chickens and 88.5 per cent of all turkeys were slaughtered under federal inspection.

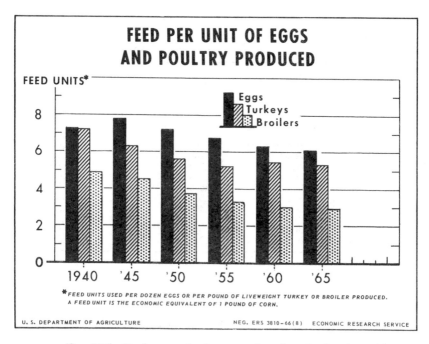

Fig. 38-5. Feed per unit of eggs and poultry produced.

13. **Changes in processing.**—In 1947, New York dressed chicken (only the blood and feathers removed) accounted for 80 per cent of the chickens and 75 per cent of the turkeys marketed. By 1963, only about 11 per cent of the chickens and 5 per cent of the turkeys were marketed that way. By the mid-1960s, 88 per cent of the broilers were ice-packed and ready-to-cook, whereas 86 per cent of the turkeys were marketed frozen. Today, there is a big trend toward ready-to-eat items and TV dinners.

PRESENT STATUS OF THE POULTRY INDUSTRY

As is true in the production of all other commodities, it is important that poultry producers be well informed concerning world-wide poultry production in order to know which countries are potential competitors. Likewise, producers within the country need to know where both their competition and markets are located.

Table 38-6 shows the size and density of the 10 leading poultry producing nations of the world by rank, and world totals.

World Poultry Distribution

The U.S. has about one-fifth of all the chickens in the world, yet it has only about 6 per cent of the world's people. Also, it is noteworthy that the U.S. ranks fifth in chickens per person, yet has the highest per capita egg

TABLE 38—6

SIZE AND DENSITY OF CHICKENS OF TEN LEADING COUNTRIES
OF THE WORLD, BY RANK

Country	Human Population[1]	Chickens 1965[2]	Chickens per Person	Eggs, 1965[2]	Eggs per Person
	(thousands)	(thousands)		(millions)	
United States	194,593[3]	351,975	1.8	64,800	333
Brazil	78,809[4]	233,000	2.9	8,610	109
Mexico	39,643[4]	90,209	2.3	5,000	126
Japan	97,350[4]	88,093	.9	19,192	197
United Kingdom	54,066[4]	76,163	1.4	14,350	265
France	48,492[3]	75,500	1.5	9,600	197
Germany, West	58,290[4]	72,590	1.2	11,930	204
Poland	31,161[4]	67,466	2.2	6,200	198
Canada	19,571[3]	53,942	2.7	5,190	265
Rumania	18,927[4]	39,910	2.1	2,600	137
World totals	3,220,000[4]	1,715,213	.5	233,062	72.4

[1]From *The World Almanac 1966.*
[2]From *Agricultural Statistics 1966,* USDA.
[3]1965 estimate.
[4]1964 estimate.

consumption; clearly showing that the egg production per hen is much higher than in the other countries.

U. S. Poultry Distribution

There are many different ways of measuring the size and the importance of the poultry industry. Numbers alone are important, and they are given in certain tables that follow. However, it is also important to know something about the density of poultry production, as measured in relation to poultry numbers per person and per square mile; hence, the latter figures are given also.

TABLE 38—7

TEN LEADING STATES IN NUMBERS OF EGGS PRODUCED,
1965 AND U.S. TOTAL[1]

State	Produced
California	8,016,000,000
Iowa	3,610,000,000
Georgia	3,546,000,000
Pennsylvania	3,238,000,000
Texas	2,548,000,000
Minnesota	2,494,000,000
Mississippi	2,444,000,000
North Carolina	2,396,000,000
Arkansas	2,362,000,000
Ohio	2,308,000,000
U.S. total	64,588,000,000

[1]From *Agricultural Statistics, 1966,* USDA, U.S. Government Printing Office, Washington, D.C., Table 623, p. 430.

TABLE 38—8

THE LEADING STATES IN EGG PRODUCTION PER PERSON AND
PER SQUARE MILE OF LAND AREA

State	Eggs per Person 1964[1]	State	Eggs per Square Mile 1965[2]
South Dakota	1974	New Jersey	199,000
Iowa	1382	Connecticut	152,000
Arkansas	1157	Rhode Island	75,000
Maine	963	Pennsylvania	72,000
Nebraska	951	Massachusetts	70,000
Mississippi	941	Iowa	64,000
Minnesota	792	Delaware	63,000
Georgia	768	Indiana	62,000
Alabama	635	Georgia	61,000
North Dakota	596	Ohio	56,000
United States	337	United States	17,000

[1]Based on Production Estimates by the U.S. Department of Agriculture and Population Estimates for July 1, 1964 by the Bureau of the Census.
[2]Based on Egg Production by States, 1965, *Agricultural Statistics, 1966*, USDA; and square mile area by states, *The World Almanac*, 1966.

TABLE 38—9

TEN LEADING STATES IN NUMBERS OF COMMERCIAL
BROILERS RAISED, 1965[1]

State	Raised
Georgia	402,770,000
Arkansas	320,135,000
Alabama	285,077,000
North Carolina	234,477,000
Mississippi	167,867,000
Maryland	144,759,000
Texas	142,217,000
Delaware	109,293,000
Maine	68,357,000
California	59,852,000
U.S. total	2,332,589,000

[1]From *Agricultural Statistics, 1966*, USDA, U.S. Government Printing Office, Washington, D.C., Table 604, p. 418.

From Tables 38-7, 38-8, 38-9, 38-10, and 38-11, the following deductions can be made:

1. From an overall standpoint, the Southeast ranks high as a poultry area.

2. Layers are less concentrated geographically than are broilers—broilers center in the Southeast. Yet, on a density basis, as measured by number of birds per person and per square mile, Delaware leads by quite a margin.

3. Minnesota and California hold a sizeable lead on number of turkeys produced. It's difficult to understand why these two states should lead the nation in turkey production, for few states could be more dissimilar in climate, crops grown, and population density.

TABLE 38—10

TEN LEADING STATES IN BROILER PRODUCTION PER PERSON AND
PER SQUARE MILE OF LAND AREA

State	Broilers per Person 1964[1]	State	Broilers per Square Mile 1965[2]
Delaware	221	Delaware	55,254
Arkansas	147	Maryland	14,660
Georgia	87	Georgia	6,911
Alabama	71	Arkansas	6,097
Maine	68	Alabama	5,583
Mississippi	68	North Carolina	4,778
North Carolina	44	Mississippi	3,554
Maryland	38	Connecticut	2,409
Texas	13	Maine	2,204
Virginia	11	Virginia	1,201
United States	11	United States	645

[1]Based on Production Estimates by the U.S. Department of Agriculture and Population Estimates for July 1, 1964 by the Bureau of the Census.
[2]Based on Broiler Production by States, 1965, *Agricultural Statistics, 1966*, USDA; and square mile area by states, *The World Almanac*, 1966.

TABLE 38—11

TEN LEADING STATES IN NUMBERS OF TURKEYS
PRODUCED, 1965[1]

State	Produced[2]
Minnesota	15,813,000
California	15,618,000
Iowa	8,124,000
Missouri	7,577,000
Wisconsin	5,436,000
Texas	5,272,000
North Carolina	5,030,000
Virginia	4,918,000
Arkansas	4,798,000
Ohio	3,489,000
U.S. total	104,501,000

[1]From *Agricultural Statistics, 1966*, USDA, U.S. Government Printing Office, Washington, D.C., Table 615, p. 424.
[2]Turkeys raised less death loss during the year of breeder hens on hand Jan. 1.

Relative Importance of Different Species of Poultry

Table 38-12 shows the relative importance of different species of poultry. This shows that both broiler production and turkey production have gained a higher percentage of the total poultry production in recent years, whereas duck numbers have remained relatively stable.

ALLIED INDUSTRIES

No other livestock industry has spawned so many allied industries as has the poultry business. In addition to the actual breeding, hatching, growing, marketing, processing, and distributing poultry meat and eggs, there are num-

TABLE 38—12

PRODUCTION OF PRINCIPAL SPECIES OF POULTRY
IN THE UNITED STATES[1]

Year	Species of Poultry			
	Chickens	Turkeys	Ducks	Geese
	(millions)	(millions)	(millions)	(millions)
1909				
1919	473			
1929	751	18.5	11.3	4.0
1939	803	33.6	12.1	1.2
1947	1028	34.8		
1953	1048	60.4	11.1	1.7
1958	2086	77.9		
1960	2057	84.5		
1963	2363	93.1	10.3	
1964	2423	99.4	10.7	
1965	2574	104.5	10.4	

[1]From *Agricultural Statistics, 1966,* USDA, 1966. Figures not available in some cases.

erous closely related industries; among them, the commercial feed industry which, in 1964, produced 34.7 million tons of poultry feed, representing 62.12 per cent of all commercially prepared livestock and poultry feeds. Also, there's pullorum testing and vaccinating against certain diseases; the production of drugs; communications; poultry futures market; fertilizer; and numerous items of equipment—incubators, brooders, feeders and waterers, egg cases and cartons, chick boxes, leg bands, time clocks, laying cages, and refrigerators.

FUTURE OF THE POULTRY INDUSTRY

Science and technology have made for great expansion of the poultry industry in recent years. Still further advances will be made, but it is reasonable to expect that the vast majority of these will come among the producers who are less efficient at this time—that a slower advancement will be made among the top 10 per cent.

Some added poultry production will be needed to take care of our rapidly expanding human population. Today, we have over 200 million people to feed; by 1975, we shall have 235 million people.

Per capita consumption increases of poultry meat and eggs will depend largely on how economically they are produced and sold in comparison with other similar foods with which they must compete It also depends on the new uses developed for poultry products and their convenience as food items.

It appears reasonable to expect that the following transitions, most of which are well under way, will continue in the future:

1. **Production units will be larger and more commercial.**—In California, some flocks of layers now number 100,000 or more; and, in the broiler production centers, units of 100,000, or more, bird capacity are not uncommon.

In the future, it appears likely that layers, broilers, and turkeys will be produced in larger units.

2. **More integration will come.**—In particular, it appears that large and well financed commercial feed companies, processors, co-ops, and others will be doing more integrating, through ownership or contract, in the future.

3. **More specialization will evolve.**—An increasing number of poultry producers will specialize in just one kind or phase of production only; for example, in the production of started pullets. Fewer and fewer of them will produce any crop, or diversify in any way whatsoever. Additionally, there will be increased specialization in the feed industry; that is, one local elevator and even some feed manufacturers will produce primarily one kind of feed.

4. **Labor-saving devices and mechanization will increase.**—Higher priced labor, along with more sophisticated equipment, will make for increased mechanization all the way along the line, from production through processing and marketing.

Fig. 38-6. Modern egg handling is highly automated. In the operation pictured above, the worker who sets the eggs in plastic filler-flats on the conveyor to be fed automatically into the egg washer section also brings the eggs on racks from the refrigerated holding room where they have been overnight. As he sets eggs on the conveyor, he also removes obviously defective eggs that should not go through the unit. (Courtesy, FMC Corp.)

5. **Improved housing and environmental control will come.**—Physics, engineering, and physiology will be combined in such a way as to bring about improved houses, brooders, incubators, and labor-saving equipment.

6. **Bird density will increase.**—With improved housing, along with better environmental control and mechanization, bird density will be increased.

7. **Growth rate and feed efficiency of broilers will increase.**—Four pound broilers at eight weeks of age is a reasonable goal. Through the application of improved breeding, feeding, and management this can be achieved. Hand in hand with more rapid growth rate there will be greater feed efficiency. Already, young chickens have been grown on less than a pound of feed per pound of gain by the use of high energy rations. In the future, chemistry, physiology, and nutrition will be combined in the formulation and manufacture of poultry rations that will bring about greater efficiency of feed utilization.

8. **Egg production per layer will increase.**—Some hens among the better strains now lay more than 300 eggs per year. There is increasing evidence that this trait (egg production) may have plateaued in high-producing strains. If this is true, perhaps the time has come when breeders of egg producers should pay more attention to body size and egg size. Without doubt most of the advances in egg production in the future will come in raising the level of the lower producers.

9. **Livability will increase.**—Drugs and vaccines have helped increase livability, and they will be used in the future. However, it is expected that breeding stock will be selected for greater livability.

10. **Quality of products will be improved.**—No other country in the world produces as high-quality poultry meat and eggs as the United States. Yet, further improvements can and will be made.

11. **More specialty meat and egg products will evolve.**—In particular, attention will be focused on improved shelf life, and on convenience foods—the kinds that require a minimum amount of preparation on the part of the housewife.

12. **Improved processing will come.**—Despite the strides already made in poultry processing, more improvements lie ahead. Deboning will be perfected, better methods of extending shelf-life will be developed, and improved by-product utilization will come.

13. **Marketing costs and efficiency will increase.**—The better operations are now very efficient from the standpoint of marketing. However, it is apparent that the less efficient poultry producers can still bring about improvements in this regard.

14. **Production geared to consumption will improve.**—Without doubt, the greatest problem facing the poultry producer today is that of over-producing at intervals. As a result, from time to time, the market is flooded and prices plummet, thereby making for severe losses. Without doubt, some solution—through marketing orders or quotas, or as a result of the controls exerted by fewer and larger owners—will evolve.

QUESTIONS FOR STUDY AND DISCUSSION

1. Why has poultry production changed more rapidly, and more completely, than production in any other class of animals?

2. What factors have caused poultry units to increase in size?

3. What factors have prompted the trend toward more and more specialization in the poultry enterprise, in contrast to diversification?

4. What factors should determine whether the poultryman should raise turkeys, broilers, or layers?

5. In the future, how is poultry production likely to fare in comparison with beef production, sheep production, swine production, and dairy production from the standpoint of (a) increasing or decreasing as our population increases and (b) continuing to use cereal grains as they become scarcer and higher?

6. Is there a hazard of monopolies evolving as poultry production gets into fewer and fewer hands?

7. If the per capita consumption of poultry meats increases in the future, is it likely to be due to increasing total per capita meat consumption or to decreasing the consumption of some of the red meats?

8. How may young men and women train for and get employment in the large poultry units of today?

SELECTED REFERENCES

Title of Publication	Author(s)	Publisher
Changes in the Poultry Industry Effects on the Midwest	Bul. 560	Agricultural Experiment Station, University of Wisconsin, Madison Wisc., April 1963.
Poultry Husbandry	M. A. Jull	McGraw-Hill Book Company, Inc., New York, N. Y., 1951.
Poultry Production	L. E. Card M. C. Nesheim	Lea & Febiger, Philadelphia, Pa., 1966.
Poultry Products Technology	G. J. Mountney	The Avi Publishing Company, Inc., Westport, Conn., 1966.
Poultry Science and Practice	A. R. Winter E. M. Funk	J. B. Lippincott Co., New York. N. Y., 1960.
Practical Poultry Management	J. E. Rice H. E. Botsford	John Wiley & Sons, Inc., New York, N. Y., 1956.

Chapter XXXIX

POULTRY BREEDS AND BREEDING; SELECTING AND CULLING

Contents

	Page
Breeds, and Breeding Chickens	919
Types and Classes	919
Breeds and Varieties	920
Systems of Breeding	923
Business Aspects of Poultry Breeding	926
Foundation Breeders	927
Hatcherymen	927
Random Sampling Performance Test; Multiple Unit Poultry Test	927
Inheritance of Some Characters in Chickens	928
Methods of Mating	933
Selecting and Culling Chickens	935
Methods of Selection	935
Measuring Egg Production	937
Measuring Broiler Production	938
National Poultry Improvement Plan	938
Culling	938
Breeds, and Breeding Turkeys	940
Breeds, and Breeding Ducks	944
Breeds, and Breeding Geese	944
Breeding Other Poultry	945
Questions for Study and Discussion	946
Selected References	946

Breeding of poultry differs from the breeding of four-footed farm animals primarily in that (1) it is more flexible in the hands of man, due to greater numbers and more rapid reproduction; (2) it has passed through the total presently-known cycle of breeding methods more than any other species of animals; and (3) it is concentrated in fewer hands.

BREEDS, AND BREEDING CHICKENS

It is improbable that all of the present-day breeds and varieties of chickens sprang from a common origin. The habits of the varieties in the Asiatic class indicate an ancestry which roosted on the ground and nested on a mound of earth. Such breeds as the Leghorn probably had tree-roosting ancestors.

Authorities generally agree that the red jungle fowl, *Gallus bankiva*, was one of the ancestors of domestic chickens. But more recent investigations suggest that at least four species of jungle fowl may have contributed to the development of domestic fowl.

Types and Classes

Type refers to the general shape and form, without regard to breed. Commercially speaking, chickens are of two types; the egg type, which are bred for egg production, and the meat type, which are bred for meat production.

The term "class" is used to designate groups of breeds which have been developed in certain regions; thus, the class names—American, English, Asiatic, etc.

Breeds and Varieties

The term "breed" refers to an established group of fowls, related by breeding, possessing a distinctive shape and the same general weight.

A "variety" is a subdivision of a breed, distinguished either by color, color and pattern, or comb. Hence, a breed may embrace a number of varieties, distinguished by different color—white, black, buff, etc.; or by color and markings—as Light Brahma, Dark Brahma, etc.; or by different combs—as single comb, rose comb, etc.

The American Standard of Perfection lists nearly 200 varieties of chickens.

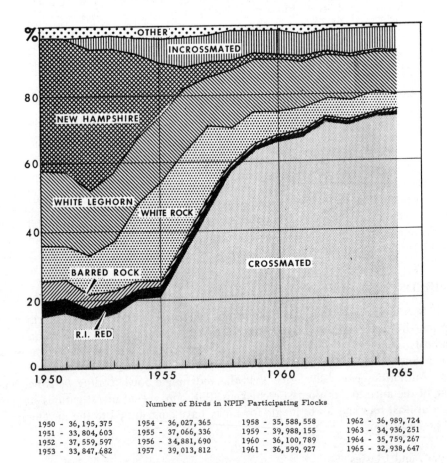

Number of Birds in NPIP Participating Flocks

1950 - 36,195,375	1954 - 36,027,365	1958 - 35,588,558	1962 - 36,989,724
1951 - 33,804,603	1955 - 37,066,336	1959 - 39,988,155	1963 - 34,936,251
1952 - 37,559,597	1956 - 34,881,690	1960 - 36,100,789	1964 - 35,759,267
1953 - 33,847,682	1957 - 39,013,812	1961 - 36,599,927	1965 - 32,938,647

Fig. 39-1. Percentage distribution, by varieties, of National Poultry Improvement Plan flocks, 1950 to 1965. (From ARS 44-2, Rev. April 1966, USDA)

However, only two breeds are really important today, with three other breeds of negligible importance. The passing of the breeds of chickens, and the simultaneous increase of crossmated and incrossmated chickens, is shown in Fig. 39-1 and Table 39-1, taken from the National Poultry Improvement Plan.

TABLE 39—1

U.S. BREED DISTRIBUTION OF NATIONAL POULTRY IMPROVEMENT PLAN
PARTICIPATING FLOCKS, FOR THE YEAR ENDING
JUNE 30, 1965[1]

Total Birds	Percentage Distribution by Varieties							
	New Hampshire	White Leghorn	White Rock	Barred Rock	Rhode Island Red	Cross-mated	Incross-mated	Other
32,938,647	0.4	12.2	5.2	0.7	0.7	73.4	6.8	0.6

[1]From U.S. Department of Agriculture, ARS 44-2, Rev. April 1966.

Table 39-2 lists some representative breeds and varieties of chickens and gives their more important characteristics.

A total of 342 breeds and varieties of domesticated land fowl and water fowl are listed in *The American Standard of Perfection,* 1966 edition, published by the American Poultry Association, Inc. The latter named association was first organized in 1873 by representatives of different sections of the United States and Canada. Its primary objective was to standardize the breeds and varieties of domestic fowl shown in exhibition.

In the poultry industry, there are no breed registry associations like those for four-footed farm animals. Hence, in a sense, *The American Standard of*

Fig. 39-2. Single Comb White Leghorns. (Courtesy, *Poultry Tribune,* Mount Morris, Ill.)

TABLE 39–2

SOME BREEDS AND VARIETIES OF POULTRY AND THEIR CHARACTERISTICS

Breed and Variety	Plumage	Standard Weight, Pounds		Type of Comb	Color of Ear Lobe	Color of Skin	Color of Shank	Shanks Feathered?	Color of Egg
		Cock	Hen						
American:									
White Plymouth Rock	White	9½	7½	Single	Red	Yellow	Yellow	No	Brown
White Wyandotte	White	8½	6½	Rose	Red	Yellow	Yellow	No	Brown
Rhode Island Red	Red	8½	6½	Single and rose	Red	Yellow	Yellow	No	Brown
New Hampshire	Red	8½	6½	Single	Red	Yellow	Yellow	No	Brown
Asiatic:									
Brahma (light)	Columbian pattern	12	9½	Pea	Red	Yellow	Yellow	Yes	Brown
Cochin (buff)	Buff	11	8½	Single	Red	Yellow	Yellow	Yes	Brown
English:									
Australorp	Black	8½	6½	Single	Red	White	Dark slate	No	Brown
White Cornish	White	10½	8	Pea	Red	Yellow	Yellow	No	Brown
Mediterranean:									
White Leghorn	White	6	4½	Single and rose	White	Yellow	Yellow	No	White

Fig. 39-3. White Plymouth Rocks. (Courtesy, *Poultry Tribune*, Mount Morris, Ill.)

Perfection takes the place of such a registry association by recognizing as "purebred" only those individuals that show characteristics conforming to those given in *The American Standard of Perfection.*

Not all commercially important breeds of chickens have been officially recognized by *The American Standard of Perfection.* One such breed is the California Grey, an egg-laying strain which was widely used by hatcherymen for crossing. Without doubt, the California Grey would be eligible for recognition by The American Poultry Association. However, the developers of the strain have not requested such recognition. This is indicative of the lack of interest in purebreds on the part of poultrymen. In fact, the so-called standardbreds are coming to be of less and less importance in the American poultry industry.

Systems of Breeding

The breeding of chickens has passed through the total presently-known systems of breeding; in fact, each method has been, and still is, being used successfully. But the vast majority of chickens in America today are hybrids of one form or another—either strain crosses, breed crosses, or crosses between inbred lines. A discussion of each method of breeding follows:

1. **Standard breed and variety.**—This system of poultry breeding is similar to purebred breeding of four-footed farm animals. It consists in either (a) mass mating of phenotypically selected individuals of the same standard breed and variety, or (b) mating birds based on some measurement of performance, either individual, parental, sib, or progeny. Despite the fact that hybrids produce more eggs than average commerical layers, it is noteworthy that egg-

laying tests show that Single Comb White Leghorns compete on even terms with hybrids under test conditions. Certainly the hybrids can equal, but the point is that they do not excell the best Leghorns.

2. **Pure strains.**—So-called pure strains, which are produced commercially today, are no more pure than the standard breeds and varieties (point 1 above). A purebred strain of chickens generally takes the name of the breeder who developed it. It is called pure strain for the reason that the developer has closed the flock to outside blood for several years. Pure strains are now used extensively as parents of commercial crosses. Generally speaking, such pure strains are not for sale; they are the exclusive property of the developer, who uses them in his business operation.

3. **Strain crosses.**—These are crosses of two or more different strains within the same breed; hence, they are still purebreds. The crossing of two inbred strains may result in some favorable hybrid vigor in egg production, or in other economically valuable characteristics. Thus, this method of breeding has some advantages over pure-line breeding for the production of commercial stock. Most of the chickens produced today for commercial egg production are Leghorn strain crosses.

4. **Breed crosses or crossbreds.**—This consists in crossing different breeds or varieties that combine well, based on the performance of the progeny. Such crossbreds usually show hybrid vigor or heterosis for egg or meat production. Among the more important commercial types of crossbreds are the following:

    a. **Sex-linked cross**—When we speak of sex-linked traits, we refer to those traits that are determined by genes carried (linked) on the x-chromosome, one of the two sex chromosomes (the other is known as the y-chromosome). A common sex-linked cross in chickens consists in the use of either a Rhode Island Red or a New Hampshire male on a Barred Plymouth Rock female. The male progeny from such a cross are barred like their mother, but the females are non-barred like their father. The chicks from such a cross can be easily distinguished at hatching; with the result that the cockerels are raised for meat production, and the pullets are kept as layers.

    It is noteworthy that the reciprocal cross—that is, a Barred Rock male mated to a Rhode Island Red or a New Hampshire female—produces all barred crossbred progeny.

    b. **Leghorn-Red cross**—The offspring of a Leghorn male and a Rhode Island Red female is known as a Leghorn-Red cross. This cross, which was used rather extensively in the Midwest in layer production, results in medium-weight layers which produce eggs of an intermediate color between the chalk white of the Leghorn and the brown of the Rhode Island Red. In addition to being good layers, when the hens are marketed as meat they usually command a better price than Leghorns.

    The reciprocal cross—that is, a Rhode Island Red male mated to a Leghorn female—is quite different; the offspring mature more slowly, and are more inclined to broodiness, but they do have a lower adult mortality rate.

c. **Austra-White**—This cross, which results from mating an Australorp male and a White Leghorn female, has been used somewhat as layers in the Midwest and in southern California. Although they are good layers, they do tend toward excessive broodiness; and sometimes the dark shanks of the pullets and the tinted eggs are discriminated against on the market.

The reciprocal cross—Leghorn male on an Australorp female—results in a cross known as the White-Austra. These crossbreds are less inclined to broodiness than their counterparts, the Austra-White, yet they are apparently quite resistant to respiratory diseases.

5. **Inbred hybrids.**—The use of inbreeding and hybridization to produce commercial hybrids is more or less patterned after the methods of the corn breeder. The actual details of commercially inbred hybrids are trade secrets of the companies producing them. Nevertheless, the general principles used by all are the same—the development and testing of many small inbred lines. Three or more generations of brother-sister matings, or sufficient generations of less intense inbreeding to produce an equivalent degree of inbreeding, may be required to produce a genetically stable stock. Some lines fall by the wayside in the process, due to reduction in hatchability, egg production, and viability under intense inbreeding, with the result that they must be discarded. The more viable and productive lines are mated with one another, and the cross-line progeny tested. Then, if the cross-line progeny is superior, further tests are conducted to find four-line (or more) combinations which will produce outstanding, uniform progeny in commercial volume. Because the inbred populations are, within themselves, not generally outstanding, only sufficient numbers of these inbred lines are maintained to produce the cross-line progeny which are mated to produce four-line combinations for commercial distribution.

In recent years, as a result of performance entries in random sample tests, inbred hybridization has lost some of its popularity, because strain-cross entries frequently prove superior to some of the inbred-hybrid entries. Thus, at this time, there is considerable debate as to the virtues of inbred hybrids. Eventually, the issue will be settled by commercial producers for, over a period of time, they will follow that system of breeding which is most profitable to them.

It is generally recognized that hybrid stocks show quicker recovery from disease outbreaks and greater resistance to unfavorable environment than standardbred stocks. On the other hand, some hybrids have suffered higher mortality than standardbred stocks from the avian leukosis complex. But hybrids with average or better resistance to leukosis have been developed.

6. **Recurrent reciprocal selection.**—The most interesting development in systems of mating since inbred hybrids has been the breeding for cross-line performance by using the system of recurrent reciprocal selection. This system is much like strain crossing but differs from it in the way the pure strains are

Fig. 39-4. H & N "nick chick" Leghorn, produced by recurrent reciprocal selection. (Courtesy, Heisdorf & Nelson, Inc., Kirkland, Wash.)

multiplied by using those individuals which cross best with the other line, rather than on the basis of their own performance.

Business Aspects of Poultry Breeding

Broadly speaking, commercial chicken producers are of two kinds; they're either egg producers or broiler producers. In either event, it's net return that counts. This means that the commercial producer is interested in increasing product output per bird, increasing the efficiency of producing the product, and improving the quality of the product produced. Improvements in fertility, hatchability, growth rate, body conformation, egg yield, meat yield, feed conversion, egg quality, meat quality, and viability (for example, PPLO-free) are all important in that they contribute to the main goal—increased net returns.

No industry has done a better job than the poultry industry in combining science and technology. Literally speaking, these two have upped the ounce to the pound in broiler production, and upped the dozen to the gross in egg production. Hand in hand with the transformation of the poultry industry, there has come a very high degree of specialization. From a breeding standpoint, today's poultry breeding is centered in two types of business enterprises: (1) the foundation breeder and (2) the hatcheryman (or multiplier).

FOUNDATION BREEDERS

Most modern foundation breeders are large, well financed, and well managed. In fact, many of them have the characteristics of any other large business. Generally they are incorporated, departmentalized—breeding and development, sales, advertising, office management, purchases, etc. Many of them have sales representatives abroad, as well as throughout the United States. Most of them recognize the importance of and use copyrighted trade names. The larger ones have well trained geneticists, physiologists, pathologists, and veterinarians on their staff. Also, they make use of computers to handle the thousands of records which they must process.

The foundation breeder furnishes eggs to the hatcheryman.

HATCHERYMEN

The hatcheryman multiplies the stock supplied by the foundation breeder, through hatching eggs. In turn, he sells chicks or poults to the farmer or producer, who then grows them out as commercial egg layers, broilers, or market turkeys.

Until about 1950, the foundation breeder and the hatcheryman operated independently of each other. Today, most of them are associated together through a franchise. A contract, signed by the two parties, specifies that the breeder will provide the hatcheryman with the breeding stock for his hatchery supply flock. Such supply flocks are commonly referred to as parent flocks, because the hatcheryman uses the chickens as parents of the commercial chicks that he sells.

Such franchise arrangements give the breeder virtual control over the stock sold by the associated hatcheries. On the other hand, the hatcheryman finds the franchise agreement desirable because he does not have to spread himself so thinly; he can leave the breeding problems to the foundation breeder and concentrate his efforts on hatching and selling chicks.

RANDOM SAMPLING PERFORMANCE TEST;
MULTIPLE UNIT POULTRY TEST

The idea for random sample testing was first proposed by Hagedoorn, a geneticist of Holland, at the 1927 World's Poultry Congress held in Ottawa, Canada. Twenty years later, the first U.S. random sample laying test was conducted at Pomona, California.

Random sample performance tests are designed to provide information on the performance of commercial chicks and poultry under uniform testing conditions. By 1965, there were 21 egg-laying tests (17 in the U.S. and 4 in Canada), 2 meat production tests for broilers, and 4 turkey performance tests. In these centralized tests, stocks from several growers are hatched at the test. the chicks raised, and the resultant pullets maintained to a fixed age (500 days or older) to determine egg production. Broiler tests, for evaluating growth and quality only, last 9 to 12 weeks.

Theoretically, centralized random performance tests of this kind should give a true comparative evaluation of the stocks tested. However, the following serious criticisms have been leveled at it: (1) that stocks sampled for testing are not truly random—which biases comparisons, (2) that such tests lead to monopolistic tendencies and to a serious reduction of the world's supply of potentially valuable genetic stock by the elimination of small breeders, and (3) that such tests are mainly a tool of breeders used to promote sales.

In order to alleviate some of the disadvantages of the random sample performance test, a new kind of program has recently evolved. It is known as the Multiple Unit Poultry Test. In this program, as implied by the name, more than one type of test is carried out at more than one farm or location.

Even the most vociferous critics of random and multiple testing agree that performance tests of this kind have exerted a powerful influence in developing high genetic merit of commercially sold poultry.

Inheritance of Some Characters in Chickens

There is indication that the fowl has six pairs of chromosomes, including the sex chromosome. Further, the turkey is thought to have nine pairs of chromosomes. But research workers have not yet confirmed, with certainty, the true number of chromosomes in either the chicken or the turkey.

Some of the Mendelian principles were first applied to poultry, following the rediscovery of Mendel's laws about 1900. Fig. 39-5 shows the inheritance of a pair of characters; the result of mating a White Wyandotte hen and a White Plymouth Rock male. Wyandottes have rose combs and Plymouth Rocks have single combs. The gene for rose comb is designated by R, and that for single comb by r. The gametes from the pure Wyandotte will carry only Factor R for rose comb and those from the Plymouth Rock will carry only factor r for single comb (Fig. 39-5). When birds are mated, the offspring, or F_1 generation, will have rose combs. The character (rose comb) is called dominant while the single comb that does not appear is termed recessive.

An example of the inheritance of two pairs of characters may be obtained by crossing a Black Wyandotte with a White Plymouth Rock. In this case, rose comb(R) is dominant to single (r), and black (B) is dominant to white (b). All of the first generation crosses from such a mating will be rose combed and black. However, the F_2 generation will consist of nine rose comb-black, three rose comb-white, three single comb, and one single comb-white, or a nine:three:-three:one ratio.

1. **Plumage color.**—White, or light-colored, feathers have become an important factor in the breeding of broilers because they are easier to pick clean than chickens with dark-colored feathers. Colored chickens often have pigmented pinfeathers at broiler age which have not broken through the skin and, therefore, cannot be readily removed with the result that they detract from the

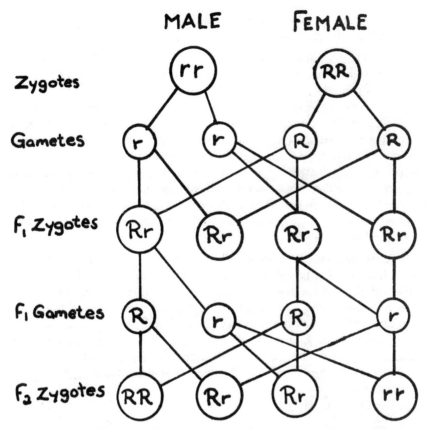

Fig. 39-5. Inheritance of a pair of characters. When a rose comb (R) female is crossed with a single comb (r) male, the first generation birds have rose comb (dominant character). When the F_1 birds are mated among themselves, about 75 per cent of the F_2 generation will have rose combs and the remainder will have single combs.

appearance of the carcass and cut-up parts. Hence, White Rock and specially developed "dominant white" meat-type male lines are preferred for broiler production. Also, white turkeys and white ducks are preferred for the same reason. Bronze turkeys are now being replaced with white turkeys; and most ducks produced commercially are of the White Pekin breed.

The geneticist is well aware of the inheritance of plumage color and makes use of it in the production of broilers. Also, in some cases, he makes use of it where sexing of chicks is desired.

2. **Skin and shank color.**—The several different shank colors found in fowl result from different combinations of pigments in the upper and lower layers of skin. Yellow shanks are due to the presence of carotenoid pigments in the epidermis, and the absence of melanic pigment. Black shanks are due to the presence of melanic pigments in the epidermis. White shanks are the result of complete absence of both types of pigments.

Blue, or slaty blue, shanks occur when melanic pigment is present in the dermis, but neither type of pigment is present in the epidermis. Green shanks occur when there is black in the dermis and yellow in the overlying epidermis.

3. **Rate of feather development.**—Early feathering is essential for minimizing pinfeathers on the dressed carcass. To meet this requisite, all modern broiler strains now carry the sex-linked early-feathering gene. This is a recessive gene. Early feathering chicks can be identified at hatching by the length of the covert feathers of the wing in proportion to the length of the primary feathers. Also, at about 10 days of age, rapid-feathering chicks show well-developed tail feathers, whereas slow-feathering chicks show no tails.

Since the early-feathering gene is sex-linked, it may be used in determining sex at hatching time, thereby alleviating the necessity of vent sexing. An early-feathering male mated to a late-feathering female, produces slow-feathering male progeny and early-feathering pullets. This makes it possible to select pullets at hatching time.

4. **Egg production.**—Perhaps it is fair to say that geneticists have been more successful in increasing broiler (meat) production than they have in egg production. Most of the income from layers is from the sale of eggs for food or for hatching purposes. Thus, the higher the egg production secured, the lower the feed and the total cost per dozen of eggs. Consequently, poultrymen are interested in high egg production. Egg production is affected by feeding. Likewise, management and environment exert considerable influence on egg production; for example, a bird will lay more eggs than it would otherwise if the eggs are removed from the nest daily.

Egg yield is the product of two forces: rate of laying and length of the laying period before molting.

    a. **Sexual maturity** (which has an approximate heritability of 30 per cent).—
       A pullet is said to be sexually mature when she lays her first egg. The earlier a pullet commences laying, the longer will be her laying year, with the result that there is more possibility of her producing more eggs. In turn, this means lower cost per egg.

       Age at maturity is hereditary. On the average, Leghorns become sexually mature at between 170 and 185 days of age; the dual-purpose breeds, such as the White Wyandotte, reach sexual maturity about two weeks later. However, there are differences between strains, and selection can be made accordingly.

       Sexual maturity can also be greatly advanced or delayed by environment, especially by the lighting program followed during rearing. Feeding programs and disease can also delay age at first egg.

       If birds of the light breeds, such as Leghorns, are to lay approximately 250 eggs during the pullet year, they should come into production when about five months old. The general-purpose breeds, such as Rhode Island Reds, should start laying when they are about 5½ to 6 months old.

       In a flock of birds of about the same age, the first 75 per cent to come into production will be the best layers.

b. **Egg size** (which has an approximate heritability of 50 per cent).—
Size of egg is correlated with a number of factors, among them (1)
body size—the larger breeds generally produce larger eggs, (2) age
of pullets—egg size increases from the time pullets start to lay until
somewhere about six months later, (3) weather—the size of eggs declines during the hot summer months, (4) second year—the eggs produced during the second year are larger than those produced the first
year, (5) period of time within the clutch—those laid at the beginning of the clutch are larger than those laid at the end, and (6)
total eggs laid—there is a tendency toward a decline in egg size with
the total number of eggs laid in a year.

Fig. 39-6. Egg shell color can be varied by breeding. (Courtesy, DeKalb
Agricultural Assn., Inc., DeKalb, Ill.)

Shell color is also heritable. As is well known, some breeds produce
white eggs, others produce brown eggs. Varying shades of color may
be expected among brown eggs, but tinted shells should be avoided
among white eggs, as these are not desired by consumers. For
this reason, white eggs that have tinted shells should not be set.

c. **Intensity** (which has an approximate heritability of 10 per cent).—
Intensity, or rate of production, which refers to the number of eggs
laid by a hen during a given period of time, is most important from a
profit standpoint. Thus, if a flock peaks at 85 per cent production, the
average hen in the flock must be laying an egg, on the average, more
than 8 out of every 10 days. Such a flock is said to have a high intensity
of lay.

d. **Hatchability** (which has an approximate heritability of 12 per cent).—Hatchability refers to the percentage of fertile eggs which hatch under artificial incubation. It is largely influenced by feeding and management. Even so, the poultry breeder should select against lethal genes which either reduce or prevent hatching, and against such indirect effects as large and small egg size and poor shell texture.

e. **Broodiness**—When the birds are brooding, they aren't laying. Hence, a minimum of broodiness is desired.

Broodiness is partially determined by a dominant sex-linked character. Breed differences exist; the light breeds, such as the Leghorn, are less broody than general-purpose breeds, such as the White Wyandotte. However, within a given breed or variety, there are strain differences in broodiness.

There is also evidence that broodiness is determined by complimentary effects of genes. For this reason, when certain breeds are crossed, the progeny generally show more broodiness than that shown by either of the parent breeds.

Of course, broodiness was nature's way of aiding propagation. After laying a certain number of eggs, wild birds set on them until they hatched out. But, since this type of behavior is no longer needed in modern poultry production, it has been practically eliminated in today's egg-laying strains.

5. **Body weight and growth rate** (which have an approximate heritability of 60 per cent and 35 per cent, respectively).—It is generally recognized that there are wide differences in body size between breeds—the extremes being illustrated by the difference in body size between bantams and Brahmas. Large body size is of importance to broiler and turkey breeders, chiefly because mature body size is correlated with rate of growth and efficiency of feed utilization.

Because weight of broilers is highly heritable, progress has been excellent through the selection of the larger individuals at broiler age. Further, there is some question whether heterosis, as obtained through hybrid breeding, contributes substantially to broiler weight; for example, the best New Hampshire strains generally equal the most rapid-gaining crosses. Despite the latter fact, cross breeding is usually practiced in broiler production for, among other reasons, more uniformity of growth and fewer runts and culls are found in crossbreds than in standardbred stocks. Also, the crossbreds are generally more viable.

Body conformation is especially important in turkeys, because, in comparison with broilers, turkeys are marketed at higher weights and the carcass is usually marketed whole rather than cut-up. With broiler producers, on the other hand, conformation is of secondary importance because of the increasing practice of marketing broiler meat in cut-up and packaged form. However, the poultry breeder has produced more desirable broiler carcasses through the infusion of broad-breasted, heavily muscled, Cornish breeding.

Body conformation is of little consequence in layers, for the reason that after they have finished their usefulness to produce eggs their carcasses are usually manufactured into chicken soup and other prepared foods.

Growth rate and feed efficiency are highly correlated; hence, growth rate is of great importance in the breeding of both meat chickens and turkeys. Rapid growth makes for a saving in time, labor, feed consumption, and overhead in the production of meat.

6. **Viability.**—Viability, or livability, is influenced greatly by feeding and management practices. Experimental evidence also shows that there are family differences in susceptibility to and resistance against pullorum, fowl typhoid, range paralysis, roundworm infestation, crooked keels, and reproductive troubles. Hence, poultry geneticists have concentrated, and will continue to concentrate, on developing strains of higher livability.

The possibility of developing genetically resistant strains to certain diseases was clearly demonstrated by Cornell University in 1955. In their studies, resistant strains of White Leghorns showed only 2 to 3 per cent mortality from leukosis, whereas susceptible strains showed a mortality of 25 per cent.

As has already been pointed out, crossbreeding generally results in increased vigor and higher livability. On the other hand, inbreeding usually results in reduced vigor and increased mortality.

Methods of Mating

The two most common methods of mating are flock and pen mating, although stud mating and artificial insemination are sometimes used.

Fig. 39-7. Flock mating or mass mating, in which a number of males are allowed to run with an entire flock of hens. (Courtesy, The Cobb Breeding Corporation, Concord, Mass.)

1. **Flock mating.**—Flock or mass mating means that a number of males are allowed to run with the entire flock of hens. Other things being equal, better fertility is obtained from flock mating than from pen mating.

The number of hens per male will vary with the size and age of the birds. With the light breeds, such as Leghorns, it is customary to use one male for 15 to 20 hens. In the case of the general-purpose breeds, such as the White Wyandotte, it is customary to use one male with 10 to 15 hens. With the heavy breeds, one male is placed with each 8 to 12 hens. Also, age is a factor; young males are more active than older ones. Males past three years old are not too satisfactory as breeders.

Fertility can be improved by using cockerels with older hens, and by using older males with pullets.

2. **Pen mating.**—In pen mating, a pen of hens is mated with one male. If the birds are trap-nested and the hen's leg-band number recorded on the egg,

Fig. 39-8. Pen mating, in which a pen of hens is mated to one male. (Photo by J. C. Allen and Son, West Lafayette, Ind.)

this system makes it possible to know the parents of every chick hatched from a pen mating.

About the same number of hens are mated with one male in pen mating as in flock mating. However, fertility is generally not so good in pen mating as in flock mating because (a) there is no opportunity for the birds to mate with the ones they choose and (b) there is no competition between males.

3. **Stud mating.**—Stud mating is comparable to what is called hand mating among four-footed farm animals. In this method, the females are mated individually with a male that is kept by himself in a coop or pen. This system makes it possible to mate more females to a male than can be accomplished in either pen or flock mating. However, stud mating involves more labor than the other two systems because birds should be mated at least once each week in order to maintain good fertility.

Sometimes stud mating is used when a very valuable male is being used as a breeder, and it is desired to use him to the maximum.

4. **Artificial insemination.**—Artificial insemination is frequently used in turkey breeding where poor fertility is encountered. Also, it may be used in experimental work where hens are kept in cages.

Selecting and Culling Chickens

The terms "selection" and "culling" carry opposite connotations. Selection aims at progress; it deals with retaining the best in the flock, seldom more than the top 20 to 25 per cent, and generally not more than 10 to 15 per cent, for carrying forward. On the other hand, culling refers to the removal of the least productive part of the flock. It is aimed at prevention of retrogression rather than making progress.

METHODS OF SELECTION

Except for the poultry fancier, who is interested in breeds and varieties from the standpoint of the *Standard of Perfection*, poultry are seldom exhibited today.

The following methods of selection are used in poultry breeding:

1. **Individual or mass selection.**—In this, selection of individuals is based on physical appearance. Many geneticists and poultrymen maintain that this system has little or no value. Yet, two facts must be recognized: (a) a great deal of the poultry improvement to date has been the result of widely applied mass selection practices, particularly from the standpoint of lessening undesirable individuals that are slow gainers, poor layers, and which detract from the uniformity of the flock; and (b) mass selection may be effective in those cases where the flock is considerably below average in some trait—for example, in a flock where the average egg production is only 150 to 160 during the pullet year.

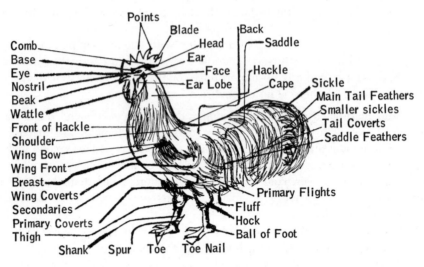

Fig. 39-9. Parts of a chicken. Before attempting to select and cull chickens, it is necessary to master the nomenclature that describes and locates each part, and to know the relative importance of each part. (Drawing by Caren Carney)

On the other hand, where a flock is average or above average in productivity, and for those characters of economic importance which are influenced by many different genes, individual or mass selection is ineffective.

2. **Pedigree selection.**—Pedigree selection is of special importance when production data is not available, or when selection is being made between two males; for example, that are comparable in all other respects. In making use of pedigree selections, however, it must be remembered that ancestors close up in the pedigree are much more important than those many generations removed.

Pedigree selection is of value where one is selecting breeding cockerels; for example, whose dams have very different production records, as between 250 eggs and 175 eggs. It is doubtful, however, that pedigree selection would be of much help in selecting cockerels whose dams produced 175 and 250 eggs, respectively.

3. **Family selection.**—Family selection refers to the performance or appearance of the rest of the members of the family, particularly the bird's sibs (sisters and brothers). Sons of a 250-egg hen which was 1 of 10 sisters laying between 240 and 270 eggs each are more likely to transmit desirable genes for egg production to their daughters than are the sons of a 290-egg hen whose sisters finished the year with records of 180 to 240 eggs. Family testing has been the key to maximizing genetic progress in producing high laying strains of chickens.

Indeed, individuality, pedigree, and family are important, and all should be used as tools in selection, but the only really sure basis concerning the ability of an individual to transmit genes for the desired characters to most of its progeny is based on a breeding test or progeny test.

4. Blood group system.—Research work in genetics and animal breeding has demonstrated that in a population there may be more than two alternative genes that can occupy the loci on chromosomes. Such genes are called multiple alleles. The best known theory of multiple alleles is that which effects blood types in humans. Three different genes are known to be involved in humans, called genes A, B, and O. So far, seven blood group systems have been identified in chickens, and each group is controlled by a group of genes forming an allelic series.

To date, blood typing has not proved to be a simple and quick way for poultry improvement; someday it may. However, blood typing is valuable as a tool for obtaining greater insight concerning genetic mechanisms and for determining parentage.

MEASURING EGG PRODUCTION

With layers, annual egg production is, without doubt, the most important single criterion to invoke when it comes to selection. Yet, it is not the only trait of importance to the poultry breeder; he must select for body size and general appearance, livability, rapid growth and proper feathering, and egg size, shape, color, shell texture, and interior quality. It must be remembered, however, that selection for two or more characters automatically cuts down the effectiveness of selection for any one of them. Also, annual egg production is of low heritability, probably about 20 per cent. All of this means that improvement in egg production through selection is relatively slow, a fact which is confirmed by egg records of the past.

1. Trap-nests.—Trap-nests differ from regular nests in that they are provided with trap doors by which birds shut themselves in when they enter. This was the invention of the late Professor James E. Rice, of Cornell University, about 1895.

There are two primary shortcomings to trap-nesting chickens: (a) the female is in her second year of production before she is used as a breeder, thus, lengthening the time between generations, and (b) the males are themselves untested, usually the sons of phenotypically superior females. Additionally, trap-nesting requires more labor; particularly, if it is done seven days a week, and each week in the year. However, studies have shown that a satisfactory measure of the egg-producing ability of a hen is possible by trap-nesting three days a week. This reduces labor costs.

2. Banding.—Some poultrymen give each pullet a numbered band, or make use of a series of colored bands of different color, in lieu of a complete quantitative trap-nest record. By establishing a "key of colors," and using both the right and the left leg, it is possible to mark the birds so as to indicate such important characteristics as (a) time of starting to lay, (b) winter pause and molt, (c) broodiness, and (d) time of stopping lay in the fall.

3. Examining the birds.—If one cares to do so, the hens may be examined early in the morning, and those which are going to lay on that day can be detected by feeling the egg in the shell gland. By going through this procedure on three successive days each month, a highly accurate record of the relative laying ability of the hens that make up the flock can be obtained, as well as an estimate of the actual number of eggs laid by each hen.

MEASURING BROILER PRODUCTION

Growth rate of broilers to nine weeks of age has an estimated heritability of 35 to 40 per cent. This trait is of major importance in the breeding of meat chickens as well as turkeys, because rapid growth means a saving in time, labor, feed consumption, and overhead in production costs. Also, it is known that feed efficiency is highly correlated with growth rate.

Because of the high heritability of growth rate, progress in breed improvement for weight at broiler age is an excellent way in which to make progress.

Feed efficiency is also highly correlated with growth rate, and it is known that feathering is highly heritable. Because these traits are highly heritable. rapid progress in broiler improvement has been made through mass selection. Also, carcass quality and uniformity have been improved through crossbreeding.

Random sample performance tests of broiler stock are conducted in several states.

NATIONAL POULTRY IMPROVEMENT PLAN

The National Poultry Improvement Plan (established in 1935) and the National Turkey Improvement Plan provide mechanisms for official recognition of breeding improvement under the supervision of official state agencies cooperating with the U.S. Department of Agriculture. Briefly stated, these plans provide standards for grades of chicks and poults based on mass selection of parent stock (U.S. approved), mass-selected female parents mated to males from performance-tested stock (U.S. Certified), and performance tested stocks (U.S. Performance Tested and U.S. Record of Performance). The U.S. Approved stocks may be either standardbred or crossbred.

The stated objectives of the National Poultry Improvement Plan are to improve the production and market qualities of chickens and to reduce losses from hatchery-disseminated diseases. The National Turkey Improvement Plan has similar objectives. Information regarding the plan is available in Miscellaneous Publication No. 739, issued by the U.S. Department of Agriculture.

Proponents of the plan point out that it has been highly effective in increasing egg production and lowering pullorum disease. In 1964-65, of the 33 million birds tested for pullorum disease and fowl typhoid only .004 per cent were reactors; whereas, in 1920, when pullorum testing was first started in the United States, there were 11 per cent pullorum reactors in chicken flocks.

CULLING

The attitude toward culling has changed as American laying flocks have increased in size. Today, extensive culling is no longer practiced in many high-egg-producing commercial flocks. Because only healthy and well-developed birds are placed in commercial laying housing, these flocks normally contain a very small number of poor layers. Hence, it is not considered practical to disturb high producers and reduce egg production merely to identify a few culls. On the other hand, proper culling can increase efficiency of egg production in most farm flocks; and the poorer the flock, the greater the need to cull.

Culling is particularly valuable if the poultryman keeps hens for a second year of egg production. However, it is questionable whether or not it pays to keep a flock longer than the pullet year, since a hen lays 20 to 25 per cent fewer eggs in her second year than in her first year.

Identifying and removing non-laying and low-producing birds from the flock accomplishes the following: (1) keeps the egg production rate of the flock high; (2) saves the cost of feeding unproductive birds (and hens eat about 7 pounds of feed per month whether laying or not); (3) reduces the spread

TABLE 39—3

HANDY CULLING CHART[1]

Separating layers and nonlayers

Character	Layer	Nonlayer
Comb	Large, smooth, bright red, glossy	Dull, dry, shriveled, scaly
Face	Bright red	Yellowish tint
Vent	Large, smooth, moist	Shrunken, puckered, dry
Pubic bones	Thin, pliable, spread apart	Blunt, rigid, close together
Abdomen	Full, soft, pliable	Contracted, hard, fleshy
Skin	Soft, loose	Thick, underlaid with fat

Separating high and low producers

Character	High producer (continuous laying)	Low producer (brief laying)
Vent	Bluish white	Yellow or flesh color
Eye ring	White	Yellow
Ear lobe	White	Yellow
Beak	White	Yellow
Shanks	White, flattened	Yellow, round
Plumage	Worn, soiled	Not much worn
Molting	Late, rapid	Early, slow

Characteristics of desirable producers

Time of maturity..................................	Leghorns begin to lay at 5 to 5½ months; Rhode Island Reds, Plymouth Rocks, and similar breeds, at 5 to 6½ months.
Rate of production.............................	Hens lay at least 220 eggs a year.
Broodiness..	Birds are seldom broody.
Persistence of production......................	Good producers lay consistently for 12 to 15 months.

[1]From *Culling Hens*, USDA Farmers' Bul. No. 2216, p. 10.

of disease from hens to young birds; and (4) provides more space for the remaining birds.

Culling should take place throughout the year. When chicks are started, all obviously weak birds should be culled. As the flock gets older, runty and slow-growing pullets should be eliminated. When the flock is put into the laying house, slow-maturing birds should be removed. During the laying year, flock owners should remove the sick, lame, or injured birds. Generally speaking, heavy culling should not be necessary during the first eight to nine months of lay. However, if egg production slumps badly, it may be desirable to locate the cause and remedy it.

It is possible to secure an indication of a hen's present, past, and future egg production by physical examination of the bird. These characteristics, and their significance, are summarized in Table 39-3, "Handy Culling Chart."

BREEDS, AND BREEDING TURKEYS

Turkeys are native to America. They were found in great numbers by the pioneer settlers, and a limited number of wild turkeys still exist in certain remote areas. Turkeys were also plentiful in Mexico.

It is reported that turkeys were taken from this continent to Spain in 1498, and to England soon thereafter. Later, some of these European stocks were brought back to this country where, along with the native wild turkey, they were used in developing our present varieties

Only one breed of turkeys is recognized by *The American Standard of Perfection;* hence, correctly speaking, we should refer to varieties rather than breeds.

Today, only three varieties of turkeys are important commercially: Bronze, White Holland, and Beltsville Small White. These are listed and described in Table 39-4.

Other varieties of turkeys recognized by *The American Standard of Perfection* are the Narragansett, Black, Slate, and Bourbon Red.

The relative popularity of the different varieties of turkeys, along with changes in numbers of each that have occurred since 1950 are shown in Table 39-5.

Table 39-5 is data from the National Turkey Improvement Plan, administered by the U.S. Department of Agriculture in cooperation with official state agencies, in a program designed to improve the quality of turkeys through selection, pedigree breeding, and disease control. The Large White strain listed in Table 39-5 refers to strains that have been developed since 1950 by first crossing Bronze and White Holland varieties and then backcrossing the second generation white progeny to Bronze males. This procedure is repeated for several generations so that the resulting Large White is essentially a Bronze turkey with white feathering and broad-breasted in conformation. These birds have been developed in recent years in response to processors' objections to the dark pins of the Broad-breasted Bronze. This accounts for the fact that Broad-breasted Bronze turkeys

TABLE 39—4

VARIETIES OF TURKEYS AND THEIR CHARACTERISTICS

Variety	Standard Weights		Plumage	Beak	Color of Throat Wattle	Beard	Shanks & Toes	Comments
	adult tom	adult hen						
Bronze	(lb.) 36	(lb.) 20	Black; with an iridescent sheen of red, green, bronze.	Light horn at tip, dark at base.	Red, changeable to bluish white.	Black	Dull black in young; smoky pink in mature birds.	The Broad-breasted Bronze is a subvariety. Of all meat animals, the Broad-breasted Bronze most uniformly produces a well-fleshed carcass.
White Holland	33	18	Pure white.	Light pinkish horn.	Red, changeable to pinkish white.	Deep black	Pinkish white.	Very similar to Bronze; only white, and slightly higher in fertility.
Beltsville Small White	23	13	Pure white.	Light pinkish horn.	Red, changeable to pinkish white.	Black	Pinkish white.	Developed by the USDA. These small turkeys are good egg producers of high hatchability.

Fig. 39-10. Bronze gobbler. (Courtesy, National Turkey Federation, Mount Morris, Ill.)

have decreased in number since 1950, while the Large White variety has increased. Table 39-5 also brings out the fact that Small White varieties, mostly Beltsville Small White, have decreased in recent years. Many turkey growers do not like the Beltsville Small White, because the tonnage produced is low. One man can take care of about the same number of big turkeys as he can of small turkeys, so labor cost per pound is higher on the smaller varieties.

Most turkeys are bred as standardbreds; that is, bred pure rather than hybridized. Also, individual selections and mass-matings are the usual practices. Color, size, and conformation are highly heritable, with the result that they have responded well to these simple methods

A few breeders have trap-nested their birds and selected for egg production and hatchability.

In the case of turkeys, it appears that the breeding accomplishments in

Fig. 39-11. Beltsville Small White. (Courtesy, USDA)

TABLE 39—5
VARIETY DISTRIBUTION IN THE NATIONAL TURKEY IMPROVEMENT PLAN
HATCHERY SUPPLY FLOCKS 1950-1951 AND 1964-1965[1]

Year	Total Birds	Percentage Distribution by Varieties					
		Broad-breasted Bronze	Other Bronze	Large White	Small White	Crosses	Others
1950-51	2,264,376	76.7	1.5	4.6	16.3	0.1	0.8
1964-65	3,704,423	41.4	0.3	47.9	8.4	1.7	0.3

[1]From ARS 44-11, revised November 1965, USDA.

developing fast-growing, broad-breasted birds has left the breeder with a good market bird but with breeding populations seriously lacking in reproductive qualities. Part of this is attributed to the fact that heavily fleshed males are clumsy in mating. For this reason, many breeders have successfully used artificial insemination.

BREEDS, AND BREEDING DUCKS

The wild mallard duck, *Anas boschas*, is the ancestor of all domestic breeds of ducks. Ducks must have been domesticated a long time, because the Romans referred to them as early as 2,000 years ago. Also, it is believed that commercial duck raising has been practiced longer in China than in any other country.

About 10 million ducks are raised annually in the United States, with approximately 60 per cent of this production on Long Island, New York.

The choice of a breed of ducks should depend upon the market that is to be supplied. White Pekin, Aylesbury, and Muscovy ducks are excellent meat producers. Rouen Cayuga, Swedish, and Call ducks reach market weights that make them valuable as meat producers; but poor egg production, and to some extent colored plumage, make them unsatisfactory for mass commercial production.

Khaki Campbells and Indian Runners are excellent egg laying breeds. Accordingly, where special duck egg markets exist, the choice of either of these breeds would be wise.

Since the vast majority of ducks that are raised commercially in the U.S. are of the White Pekin variety, only it will be described. White Pekins reach market weight (7 pounds) in eight weeks. The breed originated in China and it was introduced in the United States in the late 1870's. White Pekins are large, white-feathered birds, with orange-yellow bills, reddish-yellow shanks and feet, and yellow skin. Their eggs are tinted white. Adult drakes weigh 9 pounds and adult ducks (females) weigh 8 pounds.

White Pekins average approximately 160 eggs per year, but they are not good setters and they seldom bother to raise a brood. They are nervous, with the result that they should be treated gently.

BREEDS, AND BREEDING GEESE

The goose was first domesticated 4,000 years ago in Egypt, where it was regarded as a sacred bird. History also records that the Romans learned to value goose liver as a delicacy, with the result that they placed large numbers of geese in pens and fattened them to increase the size of the liver. We are also told that they learned to use the feathers for filling mattresses, cushions, etc. Geese became well distributed over Europe during the Christian era, and even today goose raising is an important enterprise throughout eastern and western Europe.

In the United States, geese, like ducks, are raised primarily for meat production. However, several varieties of geese are bred by poultry fanciers. Also, a considerable number of geese are used for weeding crops.

The principle meat-producing varieties of geese in the United States are the Toulouse, Emden, and Pilgrim. As is true in chickens, turkeys, and ducks, a white or near-white goose can most easily and attractively be dressed.

Geese differ somewhat from ducks in their mating habits. The large breeds of geese mate best in pairs or trios, although ganders of some lighter breeds will mate satisfactorily with as many as five females. Canada wild geese are largely monogamous and will usually mate that way for life.

BREEDING OTHER POULTRY

There are many other species, breeds, and varieties of poultry; some bred for fancy and show, some bred for game, others bred for racing, and still others bred to fight to the death. A few of these will be discussed:

1. **Guinea fowl.**—Guinea fowl are native to Africa, but they were brought to Europe during the Middle Ages. They are sometimes used as a substitute for game birds. It is thought that they might be more popular were it not for their harsh and seemingly never-ending cry, and their nervous disposition.

There are three domesticated varieties of Guineas: the Pearl, the White, and the Lavender. The Pearl is by far the most popular. It has a purplish-gray plumage, dotted or "pearled" with white.

Like quail and most other wild birds, Guinea fowls have a tendency to mate in pairs. However, one male may be mated with three or four hens.

2. **Pigeons.**—Pigeons are kept in all parts of the United States for squab production, for racing and messengers, and for exhibit.

There is a demand for squabs, especially in large cities, to take the place of game. Pigeons are the most rapid growing of all kinds of poultry. Squabs exceed the normal adult weight at the time they leave the nest, when 30 to 35 days of age. Flight and activity soon slim them down, however.

There are many varieties of pigeon, but the Homer, White King, and Swiss Mondaines are the most popular.

Pigeons mate in pairs and usually remain with their mates throughout life, although the mating may be changed if desired by placing the male and female in a coop together and leaving them there for 6 to 14 days, or until such time as they become settled.

3. **Game birds.**—Game birds are raised by and for those who like to hunt, and those who like to eat them. Among such game birds are pheasants, quail, grouse, chukars (or Chukar partridge), wild ducks, and game birds bred for cockfighting.

4. **Ornamental birds.**—Peafowls and swans are kept chiefly for ornamental purposes.

Peafowls are native to India. They like the habitat of shrubbery or trees. Four or five hens may be mated with one cock bird.

Swans are more common in Europe than in the United States. They live in pairs and remain faithful to each other until death. Swans live to be very old; the females will breed for 30 years, and males have been known to live for more than 60 years.

QUESTIONS FOR STUDY AND DISCUSSION

1. Why is poultry breeding more flexible in the hands of man than the breeding of four-footed animals?

2. Why has crossbreeding been used more extensively in poultry production than in the production of four-footed animals?

3. Records indicate that (a) Single Comb White Leghorns compete on even terms with hybrids, and (b) the best New Hampshire strains generally equal the most rapid-growing crosses in broiler weights. Why crossbreed?

4. Will the standardbred breeds of chickens be completely eliminated in the United States?

5. Why has crossbreeding been used more extensively with chickens than with turkeys, ducks, and geese?

6. Should a poultry breeder who is producing egg-laying strains trap-nest all of his birds?

7. From the standpoint of the commercial poultry producer, is the franchise arrangement between the poultry breeder and the hatcheryman desirable or undesirable?

8. Is it necessary that modern chicken producers, of either layers or broilers, know anything about judging and culling chickens?

9. The modern turkey breeder still makes most of his selections on the basis of physical appearance, whereas the modern chicken producer has largely discarded this basis of selection. Why the difference?

10. Some breeds of ducks are excellent layers. Why haven't they been selected and used for this purpose, in competition with laying flocks of chickens?

SELECTED REFERENCES

Title of Publication	Author(s)	Publisher
Breeds of Chickens for Meat and Egg Production		USDA Farmers' Bulletin 2065, 1954.
Standard of Perfection	M. C. Wallace	The American Poultry Association, Inc., Crete, Nebraska.

Chapter XL

POULTRY NUTRITION AND FEEDING

Contents

	Page
Functions of Feeds	948
Anatomy and Physiology of Digestion	948
Parts of the Digestive Tract	949
Digestion and Metabolism	950
Nutrients	951
Determining Nutrient Requirements and Usefulness of Poultry Feeds	955
Feeds Used in Poultry Rations	962
Non-nutritive Additives	963
Poultry Rations	964
Factors Involved in Formulating Poultry Rations	965
Nutrient Requirements of the Birds	965
Availability, Nutrient Content, and Cost of Feedstuffs	965
Palatability and Physical Condition of Feedstuffs	966
Presence of Substances Harmful to Product Quality	966
Formulating Rations	967
Feed Forms (or Preparation)	969
Feeding Systems	969
Special Feeding Programs; Suggested Rations	970
Feeding Replacement Chicks (Pullets)	970
Feeding Layers and Breeders	973
Phase Feeding Layers	973
Feeding Broilers, Roasters, and Capons	976
Feeding Turkeys	978
Feeding Ducks and Geese	981
Other Feed and Management Guides	983
Questions for Study and Discussion	983
Selected References	984

Poultry feeding has changed more than the feeding of any other class of farm animals. Originally, it was strictly a backyard enterprise; the mother hen did her own incubating and reared her young, and the farmer's wife fed them on table scraps and the unaccounted for grain from the crib. Reproduction was confined to the spring months when green feeds, insects, and sunshine were all available to contribute to the nutrition of the baby chicks. Feeding was largely an art rather than a science, and such commercial feeds as were sold were largely "secret formulas and patented potions." But all this has changed. Today, the vast majority of commercial poultry is produced in large units wherein the maximum of science and technology exist. Confinement production is rather commonplace, and well-balanced rations containing adequate sources of all known nutrient materials are fed for maximum production.

Poultry nutrition is more critical than that of other farm animals with regard to a number of factors. This is so because birds are quite different from four-footed animals; their digestion is more rapid, their respiration and circulation are faster, their body temperature is 8 to 10 degrees higher (about 107° F.), they are more active, they are more sensitive to environmental influences, growth

Fig. 40-1. Good breeding and good feeding make for a good start in life. (Courtesy, Maple Leaf Mills, Ltd., Ontario, Canada)

takes place at a more rapid rate, and birds mature at an earlier age. Also, egg production is an all-or-none process—that is, birds must have enough nutrients to produce an egg, otherwise no egg at all is produced.

The economic importance of poultry feeding becomes apparent when it is realized that 50 to 70 per cent of the total production cost of poultry is from feed. For this reason, the efficient use of feed is extremely important to the poultry producer.

The major objective of poultry feeding is the conversion of feedstuffs into human food. In this respect, the domestic fowl is quite efficient (see Chapter III, Table 3-6).

FUNCTIONS OF FEEDS

In poultry, feeds are used for maintenance, growth, finishing, and reproduction, just as they are for other four-footed animals (see Chapter III for principles of livestock feeding). In mammals, development of a fetus, along with subsequent lactation, constitute the major part of reproduction. With birds, however, the development of the egg is the chief part of reproduction.

ANATOMY AND PHYSIOLOGY OF DIGESTION

An understanding of the principal parts and functions of the digestive system of poultry is requisite to intelligent feeding. Fig. 40-2 shows the organs and structure of the digestive tract as they would appear after being removed from the chicken and arranged in a functional sequence.

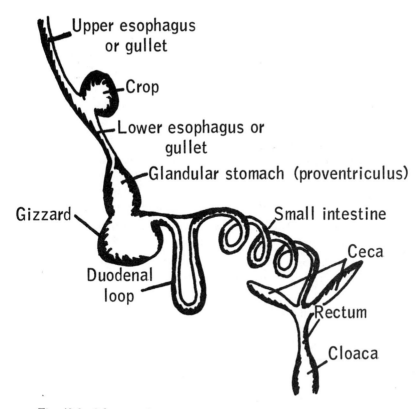

Fig. 40-2. Schematic diagram of the digestive tract of a chicken. (Drawing by Caren Carney)

Parts of the Digestive Tract

A discussion of each of the parts of the digestive tract follows:

1. **The mouth.**—The mouth of most birds does not contain any teeth, so no chewing takes place. The beak is designed to pick up food. The tongue, which has a forked section at the rear, serves to force the feed into the gullet and to aid in drinking water. Very little saliva is secreted, so it plays only a minor part in digestion.

2. **The esophagus.**—The esophagus (gullet) is simply a canal or tube which provides passage of feed and water from the mouth to the crop (upper gullet), and thence to the gizzard (lower gullet). The esophagus of poultry is rather unusual because of its great ability to expand.

3. **The crop.**—The crop is really an enlargement of the gullet. It serves as a place in which food is stored temporarily, for softening and a little predigestion, principally by enzymes (chemical substances) contained in the feed.

4. **The glandular stomach (proventriculus).**—This is the thick-walled organ located immediately in front of the gizzard. As the food passes through it, gastric juice is added from the glands in the thick stomach wall. The gastric juice contains hydrochloric acid and the enzyme pepsin, which acts upon the protein

and reduces it to peptones. The acid acts as a solvent in dissolving mineral matter.

5. **The gizzard (ventriculus).**—This organ serves as the hen's "teeth." It is composed of a horny lining surrounded by a heavy muscular wall. These muscles, through frequent and repeated contractions, exert tremendous pressure upon the food stuffs, breaking them down into small particles and mixing them with the juices from the stomach. The actions of the gastric juice, secreted by the glandular stomach, continue in the gizzard.

6. **The small intestine.**—The small intestine serves three functions: (a) it secretes intestinal juices that contain enzymes, and these enzymes complete the digestion of the protein and split the sugars into more simple form in the duodenal loop; (b) it absorbs the digested food material and transmits it to the blood stream; and (c) it provides the wave-like peristalic action that forces undigested materials through the ceca and the rectum.

7. **The ceca.**—The ceca does not have any important function. Intermittently, it fills up with material from the small intestine, holds it for a time, and then empties it out.

8. **The large intestine.**—The large intestine is that portion of the digestive tract which leads from the junction to the ceca to the opening of the cloaca.

9. **The cloaca.**—The cloaca is the common receptacle of the genital, digestive, and urinary systems.

10. **The accessory organs.**—These structures secrete substances into the alimentary canal to aid digestion, but the food does not pass through them. The important accessory organs are:

    a. **The liver**—The liver consists of two large brown lobes of tissue lying by the gizzard and duodenal loop. It produces a greenish alkaline fluid, the bile, which is stored in the gall bladder, a thin, dark-green sac located under the right lobe of the liver. In addition to secreting bile, the liver serves as a purification plant for digested food before it enters the general circulation, stores glycogen (animal starch), and transforms protein waste products into uric acid and other products suitable for elimination by the kidneys.

    b. **The pancreas**—The pancreas is a narrow strip of pinkish tissue lying between the folds of the duodenal loop. It secretes the enzymes amylase, trypsin, and lipase into the duodenal loop for the digestion of carbohydrates, proteins, and fats. The pancreas also secretes the hormone insulin, which regulates sugar metabolism.

    c. **The spleen**—This is a reddish-brown organ shaped like a buckeye. It lies in a triangle formed by the liver, gizzard, and glandular stomach. The spleen removes broken-down red blood cells and stores iron and blood.

Digestion and Metabolism

"Digestion" refers to all the changes that take place from the time the food is consumed until it is in the proper form and condition for absorption and use by the body tissues, whereas "metabolism" is the term used to describe all the changes which take place in the nutrients after they are absorbed from the digestive tract.

The rate of digestion in the fowl is rapid. It requires only about 2½ hours in the laying hen, and 8 to 12 hours in a non-laying hen, for the feed to pass from the mouth to the cloaca.

The end products of digestion and metabolism are excreted in the feces, the urine, and as carbon dioxide and water eliminated by way of respiration. The mixture of feces and urine voided by birds is known as manure.

On the average, a laying hen excretes about .37 of a pound of water each day through the intestinal waste and kidneys, and about .09 of a pound is lost through the lungs. A hen will produce about 43 pounds (dry weight) of manure each year.

NUTRIENTS

Nutrients are the chemical substances found in feed materials that can be used, and are necessary, for the maintenance, production, and health of animals. The chief classes of nutrient substances are water, carbohydrates, fats, proteins, minerals, and vitamins. These nutrients are needed by the bird in definite amounts, with the quantities varying according to the kind of bird and the purpose for which it is being fed. A deficiency in a nutrient can be, and often is, a limiting factor in egg production or growth. This is clearly illustrated by the "egg story" which follows:

HOW MANY EGGS WILL BE PRODUCED?

If the following nutrients are required for egg production, with each nutrient identified by No. only (for example, No. 1 might be an essential amino acid, No. 2 might be vitamin A., etc., etc):	If to produce 12 (one doz.) eggs, the total units of each nutrient required are:	If the units of each nutrient present in the ration are:	Comments
No. 1	12	9	The ration lacks 3 units of having enough of this nutrient for 12 eggs.
No. 2	20	30	A surplus; ⅓ more of the nutrient than needed.
No. 3	12	13	Barely over.
No. 4	11	11	Even with the board.

Thus, nutrient number one will be the limiting factor; only 9 eggs can be produced.

The nutrient composition of chickens and eggs shown in Table 40-1 gives some idea of the relative importance of these nutrients as body constituents.

TABLE 40—1

NUTRIENT COMPOSITION OF CHICKENS AND EGGS[1]

Nutrient	Chicken	Egg
	(%)	(%)
Water	55-78[2]	66
Protein	21	13[3]
Fat	17	10[4]
Minerals	3.5	11[5]

[1]From *Poultry Nutrition and Feeding,* the Ohio State University, Pub. MM-214, Table 1, p.5.
[2]Depends on age of bird; younger birds have a higher water content.
[3]Chiefly in egg white.
[4]Chiefly in the yolk.
[5]Nearly all is calcium in shell.

A discussion of each of the nutrients follows:

1. **Water.**—Poultry should have free access to clean, fresh water at all times. A mature chicken will consume about ⅓ of a pound of water daily under average conditions. The ratio of water to feed consumption of layers averages about 2.2, with a range from just under 2.0 to more than 3.0 to 1. Of course, water consumption varies according to the kind of feed, temperature, humidity, and activity of the chicken. During hot weather, chickens will consume about twice as much water as they do under conditions of average temperature.

2. **Carbohydrates.**—Carbohydrates, which constitute about 75 per cent of the dry weight of plants and grain, make up a large part of poultry rations. They serve as a source of heat and energy in the animal body. A surplus taken into the body may be transformed into fat and stored as a reserve supply of heat and energy.

In poultry feeds, the term "nitrogen-free extract" (NFE) is often used to refer to the soluble and digestible portion of carbohydrates, whereas the term "fiber" is used to refer to the insoluble and undigestible carbohydrates that are the structural components of plants.

3. **Fats.**—Fats constitute about 17 per cent of the dry weight of the market broiler and about 40 per cent of the dry weight of a whole egg.

Food fat affects body fat. Thus, poultry consuming soft fat, such as most vegetable oils, may accumulate fat that is somewhat soft or oily.

Because the primary function of both carbohydrates and fats is to serve as a source of energy for the body, an insufficient supply of these nutrients results in reduced growth rate or egg production in poultry.

4. **Proteins.**—Typical broiler starter rations contain from 22 to 24 per cent protein, and typical laying rations from about 16 to 17 per cent protein. Grain and millfeeds supply approximately one-half of the protein needs for most poultry rations. Additional protein is supplied from high protein concentrates of either animal or vegetable origin.

From the standpoint of poultry nutrition, the amino acids that make up proteins are really the essential nutrients, rather than the protein molecule itself. Hence, protein content as a measure of the nutritional value of a feed is becoming less important, and each amino acid is being considered individually. The essential amino acid requirements of chickens and turkeys are given in Table 40-6.

In practice, the amino acid requirements of growing chickens and turkeys, and of laying hens, are met by proteins from plant and animal sources. Protein supplements that most nearly supply the essential amino acids of the bird are known as "high-quality" supplements. Usually it is necessary to choose more than one source of dietary protein, then combine them in such a way that the amino acid composition of the mixture meets the requirements of the bird.

In poultry nutrition, special attention needs to be given to supplying the amino acids lysine, methionine and cystine, and tryptophan. These are sometimes referred to as the "critical amino acids" in poultry nutrition.

When formulating poultry rations, they must be so designed as to supply all the essential amino acids in ample amounts. Additionally, there must be sufficient total nitrogen for the chicken to synthesize the other amino acids needed. An amino acid deficiency always results in slow growth or poor egg production. Also, feathering is often poor, and usually the fat content of the carcass of protein deficient birds is higher than that of adequately nourished chicks.

At least 23 different amino acids have been found in plant and animal proteins. These amino acids are present in widely varying amounts in different proteins and feeds, and some of the amino acids are entirely absent from certain proteins and feeds. It has been determined that the chick requires dietary sources of protein to furnish 12 different amino acids. These amino acids are referred to as "essential," since a dietary deficiency of any one of them interferes with body protein formation and affects growth and reproduction. The primary object of protein feeding, therefore, is to furnish the bird with protein which, upon digestion, will yield sufficient quantities of the 12 essential amino acids needed for top performance.

In the laboratory, protein determinations are arrived at by analyzing the feed for nitrogen content, then multiplying this value by a factor of 6.25; the latter step being taken because nitrogen comprises about 16 per cent of the complex protein structure. It is to be noted, however, that from a biological point of view, the quality of a protein is determined by its amino acid composition and digestibility, factors which may not at all be related to nitrogen content.

Any excess protein consumed by the bird can be burned in the body to yield energy in somewhat the same manner as carbohydrates and fats. In practical feeding of poultry, it is seldom wise to use excessive protein because carbohydrates and fats are generally more economical sources of energy.

5. **Minerals.**—The minerals which have been shown to be essential for chickens and turkeys are calcium, phosphorus, magnesium, manganese, zinc, iron, copper, iodine, sodium, chlorine, potassium, sulfur, molybdenum, and selenium. Of these, calcium, phosphorus, manganese, sodium, chlorine, and zinc are considered to be of most practical importance since outside sources of them must be added to practical feed formulation for chickens and turkeys. Most of the pertinent facts relative to poultry minerals are summarized in Table 40-2.

TABLE 40—2

HANDY POULTRY MINERAL CHART

Mineral	Functions of Mineral	Some Deficiency Symptoms	Practical Sources of Mineral	Types of Poultry Rations Usually Requiring Supplementation				Comments
				Starting	Growing	Laying	Breeding	
Calcium	Formation of bone and egg shell. Clotting of blood. Muscular action.	Bones of growing birds become soft and rubbery, called rickets. Thin shelled eggs, drop in egg production, and lowered hatchability.	Oyster shell Limestone	Yes	Yes	Yes	Yes	Most poultry feeds are deficient in Ca and P, thus they must be added.
Phosphorus	Structural part of bone, proteins, and certain fats.	Rickets in growing birds. Reduced egg production.	Dicalcium phosphate. Defluorinated phosphate. Steamed bone meal. Monosodium phosphate.	Yes	Yes	Yes	Yes	Organic phosphorus (present in plants) is poorly utilized by growing birds, but is satisfactory for adult birds.
Sodium and potassium	Maintain balance in tissue fluids; serve as buffers, preventing body from becoming acid or alkaline.	Deficiency of sodium causes poor growth, a nervous condition which usually results in cannibalism and poor feed use. Deficiency of potassium reduces growth and increases nitrogen excretion.	Sodium: Products of animal origin, and common salt. Potassium: Products of plant origin.	Yes	Yes	Yes	Yes	Potassium is not deficient in normal rations, due to large amounts of plant products in poultry feeds.
Magnesium	Regulation of cellular fluids.	Muscular collapse.		Seldom necessary to add				Most poultry rations contain adequate magnesium. Do not use dolemitic (high magnesium) limestones in poultry feeds, as high magnesium interferes with Ca utilization.
Manganese	Necessary for normal bone and tendon development.	Slipped tendon or perosis. Poor egg production, shell quality, and hatchability.	Manganese sulfate or oxide.	Yes	Yes	Yes	Yes	
Iron		Anemia		Yes	Yes	Yes		Iron, iodine, and zinc are sometimes partially deficient in poultry rations unless added.
Iodine		Goiter						
Zinc		Retarded growth and poor feather development.	Zinc oxide or carbonate.	Yes	Yes	Yes	Yes	
Copper, sulphur, cobalt, molybdenum, selenium, fluorine, and chlorine		Anemia		Generally adequate in common poultry feeds.				These trace minerals are essential, but do not have to be added to most poultry rations.

The common calcium and phosphorus supplements used by all animals are listed in Chapter III, Table 3-1, of this book.

The present consensus among poultry nutritionists is that the diet of laying hens should have a minimum allowance of 2.75 per cent to 3.25 per cent calcium, with the higher level used in high energy formulation (950 to 1,000 calories productive energy per pound).

For growing chickens and turkeys, a calcium to phosphorus ratio of 2:1 is considered acceptable, although current thinking is to the effect that a 1:1 ratio is preferable where 0.8 to 0.9 per cent each of calcium and phosphorus are used under commercial conditions.

6. **Vitamins.**—The vitamins required by poultry, along with their deficiency symptoms and dietary sources, are shown in Table 40-3.

The next to last column of Table 40-3 indicates the types of poultry rations in which special attention must be paid to the inclusion of special dietary sources of the vitamins. As shown, vitamins A, D, B_{12}, and riboflavin are commonly low in most poultry rations. It is also to be emphasized that vitamin D_3, the animal form (made by the irradiation of 7-dehydrocholesterol) is more active for poultry, and should, therefore, be used instead of vitamin D_2, the plant form of the vitamin.

The fat-soluble vitamins (A, D, E, and K) can be stored and accumulated in the liver and other parts of the body, while only very limited amounts of the water-soluble vitamins (thiamine, riboflavin, pantothenic acid, nicotinic acid, B_6, choline, biotin, folic acid, and B_{12}) are stored. For this reason, it is important that the water-soluble vitamins be fed regularly in the ration in adequate amounts.

In addition to the vitamins listed in Table 40-3, certain unidentified or unknown factors are important in poultry nutrition. They are referred to as "unidentified" or "unknown" because they have not yet been isolated or synthesized in the laboratory. Nevertheless, rich sources of these factors and their effects have been well established. A diet that supplies the specific levels of all the known nutrients but which does not supply the unidentified factors is inadequate for best performance. There is evidence that the growth factors exist in dried whey, marine and packing house by-products, distillers' solubles, antibiotic fermentation residues, alfalfa meal, and certain green forages. There is also evidence that at least one unkown hatchability factor is in fish solubles and green forage. Most of the unidentified factor sources are added to the diet at a level of 1 to 3 per cent, although antibiotic fermentation residues may be used at levels ranging from 7 to 10 pounds per ton.

DETERMINING NUTRIENT REQUIREMENTS AND USEFULNESS OF POULTRY FEEDS

It is not expected that the poultryman conduct experiments to determine the nutrient requirements of poultry or that he evaluate the different feeds that he uses; that is, unless he is a very large operator. It is important, however, that he

TABLE 40—3

HANDY POULTRY VITAMIN CHART

Vitamin	Some Deficiency Symptoms	Practical Sources of Vitamin	Type of Poultry Ration Usually Requiring Supplementation				Comments
			Starting	Growing	Laying	Breeding	
Vitamin A	**Chicks:** Wobbly gait, uric acid deposits in ureters and kidneys, and general unthriftiness. **Hens:** Reduced egg production and poor hatchability.	Green forage, alfalfa meal, corn gluten meal, yellow corn, fish oils, synthetic vitamin A.	Yes	Yes	Yes	Yes	
Vitamin D₃	**Chicks:** Leg deformities, soft bones (rickets), reduced growth. **Hens:** Poor egg shell formation, reduced egg production, and hatchability.	Irradiated animal sterols, fish liver oils, vitamin A and D feeding oils.	Yes	Yes	Yes	Yes	Vitamin D₃ is more than 30 times as efficient for preventing rickets in chickens as vitamin D₂.
Vitamin E	**Chicks:** Encephalomalacia or "crazy chick disease," edema, or muscular dystrophy. **Hens:** Poor hatchability.	Alfalfa meal, vegetable oils, wheat germ, and pure vitamin concentrates.	Yes	No	No	Yes	
Vitamin K	**Chicks:** Hemorrhages due to failure of blood to clot. **Hens:** Same as for chicks except that condition is rarely seen.	Green pasture, alfalfa meal, synthetic vitamin K (menadione sodium bisulfite).	Yes	No	No	No	
Thiamine (B₁) (Continued)	**Chicks:** Loss of appetite, head retractions, loss in body weight	Grains and grain products, oil seed meals, milk products, and pure vitamin.	No	No	No	No	Special sources of this vitamin are not normally added to poultry rations.

(Continued).

TABLE 40—3 (Continued)

Vitamin	Some Deficiency Symptoms	Practical Sources of Vitamin	Type of Poultry Ration Usually Requiring Supplementation				Comments
			Starting	Growing	Laying	Breeding	
Thiamine B$_1$ (cont.)	**Hens:** Same as for chicks, and egg laying stops.						
Riboflavin (B$_2$)	**Chicks:** Curled toe paralysis and reduced growth. **Hens:** Poor hatchability with many embryo dying during second week of incubation.	Alfalfa meal, milk products, distiller's solubles, fermentation products, and pure vitamin.	Yes	Yes	Yes	Yes	
Pantothenic acid	**Chicks:** Poor growth, ragged feather development, and degeneration of skin around beak, eyes, and vent. **Hens:** Reduced hatchability.	Pure calcium pantothenate, alfalfa meal, dried milk products, and fermentation residues.	Yes	No	No	Yes	
Nicotinic acid or niacin	**Chicks:** Enlargement of hock joints and perosis, retarded growth, and inflammation of mouth and tongue. **Hens:** No symptoms observed in hen except on protein deficient diet.	Chemically synthesized nicotinic acid, liver, yeast, wheat bran and middlings, fermentation products, and most grasses.	Yes	No	No	No	
B$_6$ (Pyridoxine)	**Chicks:** Poor growth, lack of coordination, and convulsions. **Hens:** Reduced body weight, egg production, and hatchability.	Milk products, meat and fish by-products, soybean meal.	No	No	No	No	A deficiency in ordinary rations is not likely.

(Continued)

TABLE 40—3 (Continued)

Vitamin	Some Deficiency Symptoms	Practical Sources of Vitamin	Type of Poultry Ration Usually Requiring Supplementation				Comments
			Starting	Growing	Laying	Breeding	
Choline	**Chicks:** Retarded growth and "slipped tendon." **Hens:** No deficiency known.	Fish products and pure vitamin.	Yes	Yes	No	No	
Biotin	**Chicks:** Cracking and degeneration of skin on feet, around beak, and slipped tendon. **Hens:** Reduced hatchability.	Grains, soybean meal, alfalfa meal, dried yeast, milk products, green pasture.	No	No	No	No	Deficiencies not likely under practical conditions.
Folic acid	**Chicks:** Poor growth, poor feathering, perosis, and anemia. **Hens:** Reduced hatchability.	Alfalfa meal, wheat, soybean meal, and liver preparations.	No	No	No	No	
Vitamin B_{12}	**Chicks:** Reduced growth. **Hens:** Poor hatchability.	Fish meal, fish solubles, meat scrap, liver preparations, fermentation products, and commercial vitamin B_{12} concentrate.	Yes	Yes	No	Yes	

Fig. 40-3. A chick deficient in vitamin D, showing ungainly manner of balancing body. The beak is also soft and rubbery. (Courtesy, Department of Poultry Science, Cornell University)

Fig. 40-4. A chick with nutritional encephalomalacia, due to a lack of vitamin E. Note head retraction and loss of control of legs. (Courtesy, Department of Poultry Science, Cornell University)

Fig. 40-5. Chick in the acute stage of polyneuritis, due to a thiamine deficiency. Note characteristic head retraction. (Courtesy, Dr. H. R. Bird, Department of Poultry Science, University of Wisconsin)

Fig. 40-6. Riboflavin deficiency in a young chick. Note the curled toes and tendency to squat on hocks. (Courtesy, Department of Poultry Science, Cornell University)

Fig. 40-7. An advanced stage of pantothenic acid deficiency. Note the lesions at the corners of the mouth and on the eyelids and feet. (Courtesy, Department of Poultry Science, Cornell University)

Fig. 40-8. Effect of niacin deficiency on chick growth. (Courtesy, Dr. H. R. Bird, Department of Poultry Science, University of Wisconsin)

Fig. 40-9. Biotin deficiency. Note the severe lesions on the bottom of the feet. (Courtesy, Dr. H. R. Bird, Department of Poultry Science, University of Wisconsin)

have a working knowledge of this general area from the standpoint of purchasing and utilizing feeds.

The nutritive requirements for a specific substance are determined by finding the minimum amount of that particular nutrient or substance that will permit maximum development of the physiological function or economic characteristic of concern. In general, the economic characteristics of importance in poultry are growth, efficiency of feed utilization, egg production, and hatchability. For example, if the need of a certain nutrient for growth is being determined, groups of birds must be fed on an experimental ration containing different levels of the nutrient in question until it is known that increasing the quantity of the test nutrient beyond a particular level will not result in further increases in growth. If the test ration is complete in all other respects, then the nutrient requirement will be equal to the minimum supplemental level found to give maximum growth.

Some feeds are more valuable than others; hence, measures of their relative usefulness are important. Among such methods of evaluating the usefulness of poultry feeds are the following:

1. **Chemical analyses of feed.**—While the biological response of animals (feeding trials) is the ultimate indicator of nutritive adequacy in a ration, tests of this type are difficult to perform, require extended periods of time, and are usually expensive. Thus, certain chemical analyses have been developed which are rough indicators of the value of a feedstuff or ration with regard to specific nutrient substances. The usual chemical analysis of feeds includes crude protein, ether extract or crude fat, crude fiber, ash or mineral, and moisture. It is recognized, however, that such proximate analysis of poultry feeds leaves much to be desired because in many cases the protein and nitrogen free extract indicated may not be available to poultry.

In addition to the so-called proximate analysis, specific chemical and microbiological determinations can be made from many of the vitamins and individual mineral elements.

2. **Biological tests.**—Most chemical and microbiological tests for nutrient substances give information about the total amount of nutrient present in a

particular feedstuff or ration. However, these tests do not tell anything about the digestibility and utilization of the feedstuff or ration in the digestive tract of the animal. Hence, biological tests directly involving the bird are required to establish the true usefulness of feed supplying the nutrient needs of the bird. These biological tests are particularly important in evaluating protein and energy yielding nutrients like carbohydrates and fats.

a. **Biological measure of protein utilization**—The amount of protein or nitrogen digested by the bird can be determined by a balance experiment in which a measured intake of protein is compared to the measured undigested protein in the feces of the bird. The biological value of a protein source is defined as the amount of protein retained in the body expressed as a percentage of the digestible protein available. Thus, this expression is a reflection of the kinds and amounts of amino acids available to the bird after digestion. If the amino acids available to the bird closely match those needed for body protein formation, the biological value of the protein is high. If, on the other hand, there are excesses of certain amino acids and deficiencies of other amino acids as a result of digestion, the biological value of the protein is low because of the increased number of amino acids which must be excreted via the kidney.

b. **Biological measure of energy utilization**—The total energy content of a feed can be measured by completely burning the feed in an apparatus known as a bomb calorimeter (see Chapter III, Fig. 3-6). Birds, like other animals, are not able to extract all of the energy present in feeds. Hence, the term "digestible energy" is used to describe the total energy of the feed minus that which remains undigested. Metabolizable energy is the total energy in the feed minus both fecal and urinary energy; it represents all the available energy for any use in the animal. The net energy value of a feed is the metabolizable energy content minus the energy employed in utilizing it; thus, net energy may be used for body storage or the production of heat and muscular activity. Productive energy is the energy content of a feedstuff related to its ability to produce energy storage in the animal. Both productive energy and metabolizable energy values are used to describe the energy content of poultry feedstuffs and rations. The productive energy value, while closely related to economic usefulness of feeds, is very difficult to measure. Metabolizable energy values are easier to measure and affected to a lesser degree by various physiological conditions. The energy terms used in this section, and their relationship to each other, are shown in Fig. 3-7, Chapter III, this book.

3. **Cost factor.**—From the standpoint of a poultryman the most important measurement of a feed's usefulness is in terms of "net returns." Cost per pound or per ton of feed, and pounds of feed required to produce a pound of broiler or a dozen eggs, are important only as they reflect or affect the cost per unit of poultry products produced. For example, if the cost of a broiler ration is

4 cents a pound and 2½ pounds of the ration are required to produce 1 pound body weight, then the feed cost per pound of body weight can be arrived at by multiplying the above figures (4 x 2½), which gives a feed cost of 10 cents per pound. Obviously when rations are compared, the ration that produces a unit of poultry product at the lowest total feed cost is the most desirable from an economic point of view.

FEEDS USED IN POULTRY RATIONS

A wide variety of feedstuffs can be, and are, used in poultry rations. Broadly speaking, these may be classed as energy feedstuffs, protein supplements, mineral supplements, and vitamin supplements.

1. **Energy feedstuffs.**—The major energy sources of poultry feeds are the cereal grains and their by-products and fats. Corn is the most important grain used by poultry, supplying about one-third of the total feed which they consume. Wheat ranks second in importance among the cereal grains used for poultry feeds, and the sorghum grains (milo and kafir) rank third, the latter being particularly important in the southern states.

Animal and vegetable fats are now used extensively in poultry feed. In addition to their high energy value, fats reduce the dustiness of feed mixtures, increase their palatability, and improve the texture and appearance of the feed. However, the use of fats in poultry feeds requires good mixing equipment. Also, it is necessary that the fat be properly stabilized in order to prevent rancidity.

Many other energy feedstuffs, including a great array of milling by-products, are used in poultry feeds.

2. **Protein supplements.**—The usefulness of a protein feedstuff depends upon its ability to furnish the essential amino acids required by the bird, the digestibility of the protein, and the presence or absence of toxic substances. As a general rule, several different sources of protein produce better results than single protein sources. Both animal and vegetable protein supplements are used for poultry. Most of the protein supplements of animal origin contribute minerals and vitamins which significantly affect their value in poultry rations, but they are generally more variable in composition than the vegetable protein supplements.

Among the animal protein supplements commonly used in poultry rations are meat by-products, milk by-products, marine products, and such miscellaneous animal by-products as blood meal, hydrolyzed poultry feathers, and poultry by-product meal.

The common vegetable protein supplements used in poultry feeding include the oil seed meals (soybean meal, cottonseed meal, peanut meal, and occasionally a limited amount of linseed meal), corn gluten meal, and alfalfa meal and other legume meals.

3. **Mineral supplements.**—Mineral supplements are required by poultry for skeletal development in growing birds, for egg shell formation in laying hens, and for certain other regulatory processes in the body.

The common calcium supplements used in poultry feeding are ground limestone, crushed oyster shells or oyster shell flour, bone meal, and calcite, chalk, and marble.

Most of the phosphorus in plant products is in organic form and not well utilized by young chicks or turkey poults. Hence, for poultry, emphasis is placed upon inorganic phosphorus sources in feed formulation. Bone meal, dicalcium phosphate, defluorinated phosphate, colloidal phosphate, and raw rock phosphate are used where both calcium and phosphorus are needed in the ration.

Salt is added to most poultry rations at a 0.5 per cent level. Too much salt will result in increased water consumption and wet droppings.

4. **Vitamin supplements.**—Over the past three decades, a great many vitamins have been discovered that are important in present-day poultry feed formulation. Formerly, a wide variety of crude feedstuffs were added to poultry formulas primarily for their vitamin content. Today, many of these have been replaced by special vitamin supplements, which in many cases are chemically pure sources that need to be used only in very minute amounts. In modern poultry feed formulation and production, premixes often represent the common-sense approach to providing both vitamin and mineral needs for poultry.

NON-NUTRITIVE ADDITIVES

Modern poultry feeds commonly contain one or more non-nutritive additives. These additives are used for a variety of reasons. They are not nutrients, but some of them improve production under certain circumstances, others prevent rancidity in the feed, etc. There is no evidence of a nutritional deficiency when they are omitted from a ration. Among such additives are the following:

1. **Antibiotics.**—The primary reason for using antibiotics in poultry feeds is for their growth stimulating effect, for which purpose they are generally used in both broiler and market turkey rations. The reasons for this still remain obscure, but the best explanation for the growth stimulating activity of antibiotics is the so-called disease level theory. This theory is based on the fact that antibiotics have failed to show any measurable effect on animals maintained under germ-free conditions.

Antibiotics are generally fed to poultry at levels of 5 to 10 grams per ton of feed, depending upon the particular antibiotic used. Higher levels of antibiotics (100 to 400 grams per ton of feed) are used for disease control purposes.

High levels of calcium in a laying mash will inhibit assimilation of certain antibiotics to the blood stream and reduce their effectiveness.

2. **Arsenicals and nitrofurans.**—These products exert much the same effects as the antibiotics; hence, they are often added to poultry feeds to improve performance. It would appear that the action of arsenicals and of antibiotics are very similar, since the effects of the two are not considered to be additive. For broilers, arsanilic acid or sodium arsanilate is used at 45 to 90 grams per ton and "3-nitro" at 22.5 to 45 grams per ton of ration; but, in keeping with

the recommendation made relative to the use of any drug, the manufacturer's directions should be followed.

3. **Drugs.**—Poultry rations frequently contain drugs designed to prevent specific diseases. For example, a wide variety of chemical substances, sold under many trade names, are available for use in the prevention of coccidiosis. These drugs are known as coccidiostats.

Turkey rations are frequently formulated with drugs for the prevention of blackhead. This class of drugs, known as histomonostats, also contain a wide variety of chemical substances sold under various trade names.

4. **Antioxidants.**—Antioxidants are used to prevent rancidity in poultry feeds. The antioxidants which are presently accepted for addition to fat in poultry feeds are butylated hydroxyanisole, butylated hydroxytoluene, and ethoxyquin. These antioxidants may be used to prolong the induction period in fats and to prevent oxidation in mixed feeds. They are used at a level of ¼ pound per ton. Antioxidants are chemical compounds that are capable of temporarily inhibiting the destructive effects of oxygen on sensitive feeding ingredients—the unsaturated fats, fat-soluble vitamins, and other constituents. These chemicals are normally incorporated in the vitamin-trace mineral premix to prevent vitamins A and E from oxidative destruction. Some are added to feed fats to stabilize them against rancidity. BHT (butylated hydroxytuluene) and BHA (butylated hydroxyanisole) are commonly used to stabilize fat. Ethoxyquin is also a common antioxidant in poultry feed.

5. **Grit.**—Grit is a controversial subject. Some research indicates that hens on an all-mash ration do not need grit, but there is growing evidence that as a component of or supplement to all-mash it will improve feed utilization and increase production under some conditions. The purpose of grit is primarily to help the gizzard grind food materials that pass through it. It is definitely needed when birds consume whole grains or coarse, fibrous feedstuffs. Crushed granite or other hard, insoluble material can be used for grit.

POULTRY RATIONS

About 60 million tons of commercially prepared livestock and poultry feeds are produced annually in the U.S., of which 80 per cent are complete feeds and 20 per cent, supplements. The breakdown, percentagewise, by classes of livestock for which commercial feeds were used in 1964 was as follows: poultry, 62.12 per cent; dairy, 21.80 per cent; beef cattle, 6.54 per cent; swine, 6.09 per cent; and other, 3.45 per cent.[1]

As noted, over 60 per cent of the commercial feeds of the U.S. are fed to poultry. Additionally, it is noteworthy that two-thirds of all poultry feeds are mixed commercially.

Actually, the poultryman has the following alternatives for purchasing and preparing feeds:

---

[1] *Feed Situation*, USDA, Fds-212, February 1966, pp. 30 and 33.

1. Purchase of a commercially prepared complete feed.

2. Purchase of a commercially prepared protein supplement, reinforced with vitamins and minerals, which may be blended with local or home-grown grain.

3. Purchase of a commercially prepared vitamin-mineral premix which may be mixed with an oil meal, and then blended with local or home-grown grain.

4. Purchase of individual ingredients (including vitamins and minerals) and mixing the feed from the ground up.

Today's poultrymen are selecting these alternative methods of purchasing and preparing feeds in the order that they are listed.

Factors Involved in Formulating Poultry Rations

Before anyone can intelligently formulate a poultry ration, it is necessary to know (1) the nutrient requirements of the particular birds to be fed; (2) the availability, nutrient content, and cost of feedstuffs; (3) the palatability and physical condition of feedstuffs; and (4) the presence of substances harmful to product quality.

NUTRIENT REQUIREMENTS OF THE BIRDS

Through experimentation, the requirements of most of the nutrients needed by poultry have been established. These requirements differ according to the type and age of poultry being fed, as well as the purpose for which they are kept. The National Research Council compiles and publishes these nutritive requirements, the most recent of which are herewith reproduced in Tables 40-4, 40-5, and 40-6.

AVAILABILITY, NUTRIENT CONTENT, AND COST OF FEEDSTUFFS

Generally speaking, it is most practical to use feedstuffs which are most readily available at the lowest cost—provided they are satisfactory in other respects. Substitutes can be found and used when certain ingredients become scarce or unavailable.

The nutrient content of different feed ingredients can be obtained from feed composition tables. One such table is found in Section II of *The Stockman's Handbook*, 4th edition, a book by the same publisher and the same author as this book. Also, NRC Publication 1684 contains a very complete set of feed composition tables.

The price of feedstuffs must also be taken into consideration. When the price of any one ingredient gets out of line, based on the nutrient that it contributes, substitutions can usually be made. For example, wheat can be used to replace corn, and vice versa. Likewise, soybean meal can be substituted for cottonseed meal or peanut meal when the prices of these protein supplements change.

TABLE 40—4

NUTRIENT REQUIREMENTS OF CHICKENS[1]

(in percentage or amount per kg [2.2046 lb.] of feed)

Nutrient	Starting Chickens 0-8 weeks	Growing Chickens 8-18 weeks	Laying Hens	Breeding Hens
Total protein, %	20	16	15	15
Vitamins				
Vitamin A activity (U.S.P. Units)[2]	2,000	2,000	4,000	4,000
Vitamin D (ICU)[3]	200	200	500	500
Vitamin E				
Vitamin K_1, mg	0.53	?	?	?
Thiamine, mg	1.8	?	?	0.8
Riboflavin, mg	3.6	1.8	2.2	3.8
Pantothenic acid, mg	10	10	2.2	10
Niacin, mg	27	11	?	?
Pyridoxine, mg	3	?	3	4.5
Biotin, mg	0.09	?	?	0.15
Choline, mg [4]	1,300	?	?	?
Folacin, mg	1.2	?	0.25	0.35
Vitamin B_{12}, mg	0.009	?	?	0.003
Minerals				
Calcium, %	1.0	1.0	2.75[5]	2.75[5]
Phosphorus, %[6]	0.7	0.6	0.6	0.6
Sodium, %[7]	0.15	0.15	0.15	0.15
Potassium, %	0.2	0.16	?	?
Manganese, mg	55	?	?	33
Iodine, mg	0.35	0.35	0.30	0.30
Magnesium, mg	500	?	?	?
Iron, mg	40	?	?	?
Copper, mg	4	?	?	?
Zinc, mg	35	?	?	?

[1]From NRC Pub. 1345, p. 3, 1966. These figures are estimates of requirements and include no margins of safety.

[2]May by vitamin A or provitamin A.

[3]One International Chick Unit of vitamin D_3.

[4]Betaine can replace choline in part, but not for certain functions such as perosis prevention.

[5]This amount of calcium need not be incorporated in the mixed feed, inasmuch as calcium supplements fed free-choice are considered as part of the ration.

[6]At least 0.5% of the total feed of starting chickens should be inorganic phosphorus. All the phosphorus of non-plant-feed ingredients is considered to be inorganic. Approximately 30% of the phosphorus of plant products is non-Phytin phosphorus and may be considered as part of the inorganic phosphorus required. A portion of the phosphorus requirement of growing chickens and laying and breeding hens must also be supplied in inorganic form. For birds in these categories the requirement for inorganic phosphorus is lower and not as well defined as for starting chickens.

[7]Equivalent to 0.37% of sodium chloride.

PALATABILITY AND PHYSICAL CONDITION OF FEEDSTUFFS

Some feeds cannot be used in poultry feed formulations because they are not palatable to the birds. Other feed materials may be processed in such a way that their physical condition makes them undesirable for feeding.

Feeds containing milo and rye can be markedly improved by pelleting and spraying hot fat over the exterior of the pellet.

PRESENCE OF SUBSTANCES HARMFUL TO PRODUCT QUALITY

The composition of the feed can affect the product. The color of the skin or shanks of a broiler or of the yolk of an egg is primarily due to the carotenoid pigments consumed in the feed. Corn, alfalfa meal, and corn gluten meal are the main feeds used to contribute these pigments.

TABLE 40—5

NUTRIENT REQUIREMENTS OF TURKEYS[1]
(in percentage or amount per kg [2.2046 lb.] of feed)

Nutrient	Starting Poults 0-8 weeks	Growing Turkeys 8-16 weeks	Breeding Turkeys
Total protein, %[2]	28	20	15
Vitamins			
Vitamin A activity (U.S.P. Units)[3]	4,000	4,000	4,000
Vitamin D (ICU)[4]	900	900	900
Vitamin E			
Vitamin K$_1$, mg	0.7	?	?
Thiamine, mg	2	?	?
Riboflavin, mg	3.6	?	3.8
Pantothenic acid, mg	11	?	16
Niacin, mg	70	?	?
Pyridoxine, mg	3	?	?
Choline, mg	1,900	?	?
Folacin, mg	0.9	?	0.8
Vitamin B$_{12}$, mg	0.003	?	?
Minerals			
Calcium, %	1.2	1.2	2.25[5]
Phosphorus, %[6]	0.8	0.8	0.75
Sodium, %[7]	0.15	0.15	0.15
Potassium, %	0.4	?	?
Manganese, mg	55	?	33
Iron, mg	60	?	?
Copper, mg	6	?	?
Zinc, mg	70	?	?

[1]From NRC Pub. 1345, p. 4, 1966. These figures are estimates of requirements and include no margins of safety.

[2]The protein content of rations for growing turkeys from 16 weeks to market weight may be reduced to 16%.

[3]May be vitamin A or provitamin A.

[4]One International Chick Unit of vitamin D$_3$.

[5]This amount of calcium need not be incorporated in the mixed feed, inasmuch as calcium supplements fed free-choice are considered as part of the ration.

[6]At least 0.5% of the total feed of starting poults should be inorganic phosphorus. All the phosphorus of non-plant-feed ingredients is considered to be inorganic. Approximately 30% of the phosphorus of plant products is non-Phytin phosphorus and may be considered as part of the inorganic phosphorus required. Presumably a portion of the requirement of growing and breeding turkeys must also be furnished in inorganic form.

[7]Equivalent to 0.37% of sodium chloride.

Screw process cottonseed meal, which is high in gossypol, when fed to laying hens may cause egg yolk discoloration in stored eggs. Some fish products may impart fishy flavors to poultry meat or eggs. Thus, certain feedstuffs may be undesirable simply because of the effect they produce on the end product.

Formulating Rations

With the increasing complexity of poultry rations, along with larger and larger enterprises, more commercially mixed feeds for poultry will be used in the future. The poultryman who chooses to mix feed in some manner should be absolutely sure that he will have a nutritionally balanced and adequate ration.

The larger commercial feed companies, and the larger poultry producers who do their own mixing or formulating, generally rely on the services of a nutritionist and the use of a computer in formulating their rations. Even though they are more time-consuming, and fewer factors can be considered simultaneously, a good job can be done in formulating rations by either the (1) trial and

TABLE 40—6

ESSENTIAL AMINO-ACID REQUIREMENTS OF CHICKENS AND TURKEYS[1]

Amino Acid	Starting Chicks Percentage of Diet	Starting Poults Percentage of Diet	Laying Chickens Percentage of Diet
Arginine	1.2	1.6	0.8
Lysine	1.1	1.5	0.5
Histidine	0.4	?	?
Methionine	0.75	0.87	0.53
or			
{ Methionine	0.4	0.52	0.28
{ Cystine	0.35	0.35	0.25
Tryptophan	0.2	0.26	0.15
Glycine[2]	1.0	1.0	?
Phenylalanine	1.3	?	?
or			
{ Phenylalanine	0.7	?	?.
{ Tyrosine	0.6	?	?
Leucine	1.4	?	1.2
Isoleucine	0.75	0.84	0.5
Threonine	0.7	?	0.4
Valine	0.85	?	?
Protein	20.0	28.0	15.0
Metabolizable energy, kcal/kg	2,750	2,450	2,850

[1]From NRC Pub. 1345, p. 6, 1966. These figures are estimates of requirements and include no margins of safety.
[2]The chick can synthesize glycine but the synthesis does not proceed at a rate sufficient for maximum growth.

error method or (2) the square method. The trial and error method of feed formulation is described in Chapter XX of this book, so repetition is unnecessary (although the nutritive requirements of poultry and dairy cattle differ, the principles of ration balancing are similar in both cases).

The "square method" (or the Pearson square method) which follows is the same method that is used in milk plants where it is desired to determine the proportions of milk in cream, the fat percentages of which are known, to mix in order to make cream or milk of a desired percentage fat content. There is nothing complicated about it whatsoever.

The following example will show how to use the square method in formulating a poultry ration: A poultryman has on hand corn containing about 9 per cent protein. He can buy a 36 per cent protein supplement, which is reinforced with minerals and vitamins. A ration containing 16 per cent protein is desired. Step by step, the procedure in balancing this ration is as follows:

1. Draw a square, and place the number 16 in the center thereof.

2. At the upper left-hand corner of the square, write *concentrate* and its protein content (36); at the lower left-hand corner, write *corn* and its protein content (9).

3. Subtract diagonally across the square (the smaller number from the larger number), and write the difference at the corners on the right-hand side (36 — 16 = 20; 16 — 9 = 7). The number at the upper right-hand corner gives the ⁀rts of concentrate by weight, and the number at the lower right-hand corner ⁀he parts of corn by weight to make a ration with 16 per cent protein.

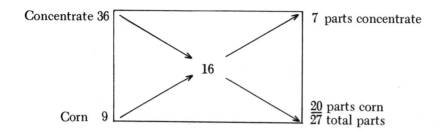

Concentrate 36 — 7 parts concentrate

16

Corn 9 — $\frac{20}{27}$ parts corn / total parts

4. To determine what per cent of the ration would be corn, divide the parts of corn by the total parts; $20 \div 27 = 74\%$ corn. The remainder, 26, would be supplement.

Feed Forms (or Preparation)

The usual end product resulting from mixing of poultry feedstuffs is a ground feed known as mash. While this mash is usually in the form of a ground mixture, it can be processed to produce pellets or crumbles.

Pellets are mash feeds that have been compressed with the aid of live steam to produce small chunks or cylinders of feed. Pellets undergo considerable heating in the process of formation and must be cooled to prevent destruction of certain nutrients. Among the advantages of pelleting are: the feed is less dusty, ingredients will not sift out of the mixture, feed wastage may be decreased, and the density of the ration is improved. Also, birds can generally consume more of a pelleted ration than of the same ration in mash form.

Crumbles are produced by grinding pellets into a coarse, granular form. Crumbles appear to have most of the desirable characteristics of pellets, but they are better adapted to mechanical feeders and they can be used with birds that are too small to consume the pelleted form.

Pellets or crumbles generally cost slightly more than the same ration in mash form.

Feeding Systems

The vast majority of large poultry enterprises feed complete rations, in which all of the nutrients needed by the bird are provided in the quantities necessary. Little or no grain is fed along with this ration because such feeding would destroy the balance of nutrient provided by the complete ration. Even with this system of feeding, laying or breeding hens are usually provided with a supplementary source of calcium, to which they are given free access.

Sometimes poultrymen, expecially farm flock owners, feed whole grain and a fortified protein supplement in separate hoppers. The supplement provides the extra amounts of protein, vitamins, and minerals lacking in the grain. This system enables the farmer to make maximum use of farm-grown or local grains. By estimating the approximate consumption of each the grain and the supplement, and fortifying the supplement accordingly, an overall nutrient intake that is reasonably well balanced is achieved.

SPECIAL FEEDING PROGRAMS; SUGGESTED RATIONS

The nutritive requirements of poultry vary according to species (between chickens, turkeys, ducks, and geese), according to age, and according to the type of production—whether the birds are kept for meat production, layers, or breeders. For this reason, many different rations are required.

To be successful, rations must meet the nutritive requirements of the birds to which they are fed. The National Research Council nutritive requirements are given in Tables 40-4 and 40-5. In using these tables to formulate practical rations, it must be remembered that they are minimum requirements, which means that they do not provide for any margins of safety. Further, the following protein-energy relationships should be observed:

1. **For chickens.**—Protein levels shown in Table 40-4 for chickens will meet the approximate minimum requirements for growth in rations containing 2,750 kcal of metabolizable energy per kg and for egg production in rations containing 2,850 kcal per kg.

2. **For turkeys.**—Protein levels shown in Table 40-5 for turkeys will meet the approximate minimum requirements for early growth in a ration containing 2,450 kcal of metabolizable energy per kg, and for later growth at an energy level of 2,600 kcal per kg.

Also, rations must be reformulated from time to time, in keeping with new developments and changing prices. Moreover, due to the difficulty in formulating and home-mixing poultry rations, an increasing number of poultrymen are coming to the conclusion that the purchase of a commercial feed may be in the nature of good business. Nevertheless, it is hoped that the suggested rations that follow will serve as useful guides.

Feeding Replacement Chicks (Pullets)

Table 40-7 is a yardstick of feed and time required to obtain certain average live weights of chickens. Such a guide is useful in setting up budgets and measuring results.

The objective of feeding young chickens is to produce growth. This requires a liberal supply of nutrient substances in the right proportions. Suggested rations for replacement chicks are given in Table 40-8. These rations meet the NRC requirements given in Tables 40-4 and 40-6, and provide for necessary margins of safety in addition.

These further pointers are pertinent to feeding replacement chicks (pullets):

1. Replacement chicks are usually fed a diet lower in energy than broiler diets. Also, feed and daily light periods may be restricted, so as to permit the pullets to reach larger body size before they start to lay than would be the case were they full-fed, fully lighted pullets.

2. About 20 to 25 pounds of starting and growing ration are required to develop an egg production type pullet to the age of sexual maturity.

TABLE 40—7
FEED REQUIRED AND TIME REQUIRED TO OBTAIN CERTAIN AVERAGE LIVE WEIGHTS WITH COMMON BREEDS OF CHICKENS[1]

Average Live Weight		Kind of Chicken and Quantity of Feed Required per Bird								Kind of Chicken and Age at Which Certain Live Weights Are Reached			
		White Leghorns				Heavy Breed				White Leghorns		Heavy Breeds	
		Females		Males		Females		Males		Females	Males	Females	Males
kg	lb.	kg	lb.	kg	lb.	kg	lb.	kg	lb.	wk.	wk.	wk.	wk.
0.25	.55	0.5	1.10	0.45	.99	0.45	.99	0.4	.88	3.2	2.9	3.0	2.7
0.5	1.1	1.15	2.53	1.0	2.20	0.95	2.09	0.9	1.98	5.8	5.0	4.7	4.3
0.75	1.65	1.85	4.07	1.6	3.52	1.55	3.41	1.45	3.19	8.2	6.8	6.1	5.5
1.0	2.20	2.65	5.84	2.35	5.18	2.25	4.96	2.1	4.63	10.6	8.3	7.5	6.7
1.25	2.75	3.8	8.37	3.15	6.94	3.05	6.72	2.75	6.06	13.3	9.7	8.9	7.8
1.5	3.30	5.3	11.68	4.1	9.04	3.9	8.59	3.45	7.60	16.4	11.3	10.3	8.7
1.75	3.85	8.2	18.08	5.3	11.68	5.0	11.02	4.25	9.37	19.8	13.0	11.6	9.7
2.0	4.41					6.2	13.67	5.1	11.24			13.0	10.6

[1]From NRC Pub. 1345, p. 18, 1966.

TABLE 40—8

ALL-MASH REPLACEMENT CHICK (PULLET) RATIONS[1]

Ingredient		Starter	Grower
		(lbs.)	(lbs.)
Ground yellow corn		1245	1322
Wheat middlings		100	300
Soybean meal (50%)		432	247
Fish meal (60%)		50	--
Stabilized fat		20	20
Alfalfa meal (17%) (100,000 A/lb.)		50	50
Corn distillers' dried grains with solubles		50	--
Dicalcium phosphate		22	32
Ground limestone		24	22
Iodized salt		7	7
Antibiotic supplement		Footnote [2]	--
Antioxidant		Footnote [3]	Footnote [3]
Coccidiostat		Footnote [4]	Footnote [4]
Manganese (grams)		52	52
Vitamin supplements:			
Vitamin A	(U.S.P. units)	1,000,000	1,000,000
Vitamin D3	(I.C.U.)	681,000	681,000
Vitamin B12	(mg)	6	6
Choline chloride	(mg)	227,000	--
Riboflavin	(mg)	1,500	1,000
Calcium pantothenate	(mg)	5,000	5,000
Niacin	(mg)	20,000	10,000
Totals (lbs.)		2,000	2,000

Calculated Analysis of All-Mash Chicken Rations

		Starter	Grower
Metabolizable energy	Cal./lb.	1346	1332
Productive energy	Cal./lb.	973	966
Protein	%	20.03	15.01
Fat	%	4.36	4.50
Fiber	%	3.00	3.41
Calcium	%	1.00	.93
Total phosphorus	%	.61	.67
Readily available phos.[5]	%	.38	.40
Metabolizable energy to protein ratio		67.20	88.74

[1]From *Chicken and Turkey Rations*, prepared cooperatively by the New England Land-Grant Universities, 1967. Wherever substitutions are made in the rations, the total nutrient content should be adjusted to agree with the analyses shown.

[2]An antibiotic may be used in this ration at the level recommended by the manufacturer. For information concerning the use of any additive, consult the supplier of the additive in question.

[3]1, 2-dihydro-6-ethoxy-2, 2, 4-trimethylquinoline (ethoxyquin) or butylated hydroxytoluene (BHT) are antioxidants used in the chick starter ration at the 0.0125% level to help prevent the appearance of encephalomalacia (crazy chick disease), and to help prevent the destruction of the fat soluble vitamins. For information concerning the use of any additive, consult the supplier of the additive in question.

[4]A coccidiosis controlling drug may be used in these rations at the level recommended by the manufacturer. For information concerning the use of any additive, consult the supplier of the additive in question.

[5]Readily available phosphorus has been taken as 30% of total phosphorus from plant sources for chicks, and 75% of total phosphorus from plant sources for adult birds. Phosphorus from other than plant sources are considered to be 100% utilized.

3. Always buy complete starter feeds for chicks, and give chicks starter feeds without grain supplement until they are six weeks old.

4. When chicks are six weeks old, change to growing ration.

5. When pullets are 18 to 20 weeks old, gradually withdraw the growing mash and replace with laying mash over a 2-week period.

6. Range-reared pullets need liberal feeding in addition to whatever green feed they get from the range. Mash or pellets are usually fed in one hopper and grain is fed in another.

Feeding Layers and Breeders

Data showing the approximate quantities of feed required for the production of eggs are presented in Table 40-9.

Rations for layers and breeders are given in Table 40-10.

These further pointers are pertinent to feeding layers and breeders:

1. In the final analysis, the objective of feeding laying hens is to produce a dozen eggs of good quality at the lowest possible feed cost. Thus, the actual cost of the feed that a layer eats in producing a dozen eggs—not the price per pound of feed—determines the economy of the ration.

2. Feed consumption per bird varies primarily with egg production and body size (Table 40-9). It is also influenced by the health of the birds and the environment, especially the temperature.

3. Normally, a mature Leghorn, or other lightweight bird, eats about 90 pounds of feed per year and produces about 17 dozen eggs in that same period of time. Hence, it requires slightly over 6 pounds of feed to produce one dozen eggs. A bird of the heavier breeds eats 95 to 115 pounds of feed per year; hence, they are not as efficient as egg producers. With lightweight layers, the poultryman should aim for a feed efficiency of 4 to 4.5 pounds, or less, of feed per dozen eggs.

4. The nutritive requirements of the breeding flock are more rigorous than those for commercial laying flocks. Breeders require greater amounts of vitamin A, D, E, and B_{12}, riboflavin, pantothenic acid, niacin, and manganese than laying flocks. Rations with these added ingredients in the right proportion give high hatchability and good development of chicks. Such rations cost more than normal layer rations.

5. Birds intended as breeders should be started on breeder rations about one month before hatching eggs are to be saved.

PHASE FEEDING LAYERS

A relatively new term "phase feeding," has become part of the poultrymen's language. As usually used, phase feeding refers to changes in the laying hen's diet (1) to adjust to age and stage of production of the hen, (2) to adjust for season of the year and for temperature and climatic changes, (3) to account for differences in body weight and nutrient requirements of different strains of birds, and (4) to adjust one or more nutrients as other nutrients are changed for economic or availability reasons. Research has shown, for example, that a hen laying at the rate of 60 per cent has different nutritional requirements than one laying at the rate of 80 per cent; hens have different requirements in summer and in winter; a 24-week-old layer has different needs than one 54 weeks old. The main objective, therefore, of phase feeding is to reduce the waste of nutrients caused by feeding more than a bird

TABLE 40—9

FEED REQUIRED BY CHICKENS OF DIFFERENT LIVE WEIGHTS FOR MAINTENANCE AND FOR PRODUCTION OF 0, 100, 200, and 300 EGGS, RESPECTIVELY, PER YEAR[1]

Average Live Weight		Average Total Feed Required per Bird per Year for Maintenance and the Production of the Indicated Number of Eggs							
		0 Eggs per Year		100 Eggs per Year		200 Eggs per Year		300 Eggs per Year	
kg	lb.	kg	lb.	kg	lb.	kg	lb.	kg	lb.
1.36	3.0	21.5	47.4	28.0	61.7	34.0	75.0	40.5	89.3
1.59	3.5	23.5	51.8	30.5	67.2	36.5	80.5	43.0	94.8
1.81	4.0	25.5	56.2	32.5	71.7	38.5	84.9	45.0	99.2
2.04	4.5	27.5	60.6	34.0	75.0	40.5	89.3	47.0	103.6
2.27	5.0	29.5	65.0	36.0	79.4	42.5	93.7	49.0	108.0
2.50	5.5	31.5	69.5	38.0	83.8	44.5	98.1	51.0	112.5
2.73	6.0	33.5	73.9	40.0	88.2	46.5	102.5	52.5	115.8
2.95	6.5	35.5	78.3	42.0	92.6	48.0	105.8	54.5	120.2
3.18	7.0	37.0	81.6	43.5	95.9	50.0	110.2	56.5	124.6

[1]From NRC Pub. 1345, p. 17, 1966.

TABLE 40—10

ALL-MASH LAYER AND BREEDER RATIONS[1]

Ingredient	Layer			Breeder
	Caged birds[2]	Floor birds		
		3½-5 lbs.	5-7 lbs.	
	(lbs.)	(lbs.)	(lbs.)	(lbs.)
Ground yellow corn	1290	1153	1280	1332
Wheat middlings	100	100	100	100
Soybean meal (50%)	280	343	340	100
Fish meal (60%)	40	40	--	230
Stabilized fat	20	87	20	75
Alfalfa meal (17%) (100,000 A/lb.)	50	50	50	20
Corn distillers dried grains with solubles..	50	50	50	50
Dicalcium phosphate	31	35	35	50
Ground limestone	132	135	118	24
Iodized salt	7	7	7	112
Antioxidant	Footnote[3]	Footnote[3]	Footnote[3]	7
Manganese (grams)	52	52	52	Footnote[3]
Zinc (grams)	16	--	--	52
				16
Vitamin supplements:				
Vitamin A ....(U.S.P. units)	4,000,000	3,000,000	3,000,000	4,000,000
Vitamin D₃ .... (I.C.U.)	1,362,000	1,362,000	1,362,000	1,362,000
Vitamin B₁₂ .... (mg)	6	6	6	6
Riboflavin .... (mg)	2,000	2,000	1,000	3,000
Calcium pantothenate . (mg)	5,000	1,500	--	6,000
Niacin.......... (mg)	20,000	20,000	20,000	20,000
Totals (lbs.)	2,000	2,000	2,000	2,000

Calculated Analysis of All-Mash Chicken Rations

		Caged layer	Layer	Layer	Breeder
Metabolizable energy	Cal./lb.	1289	1324	1290	1316
Productive energy	Cal./lb.	934	980	933	953
Protein	%	16.04	17.04	16.29	16.04
Fat	%	4.34	7.45	4.22	4.52
Fiber	%	2.85	2.80	2.90	2.84
Calcium	%	3.13	3.24	2.80	2.75
Total phosphorus	%	.65	.68	.63	.63
Readily available phos.[4]	%	.57	.61	.56	.56
Metabolizable energy to protein ratio		80.36	77.70	79.19	82.04

[1]From *Chicken and Turkey Rations*, prepared cooperatively by the New England Land-Grant Universities, 1967. Wherever substitutions are made in the rations, the total nutrient content should be adjusted to agree with the analyses shown.
[2]For Leghorn-type birds, raise protein to 17% and calcium to 3.25%.
[3]Ethoxyquin is the antioxidant used at the 0.0125% level to help prevent the appearance of encephalomalacia (crazy chick disease), and to help prevent the destruction of the fat soluble vitamins. For information concerning the use of any additive, consult the supplier of the additive in question.
[4]Readily available phosphorus has been taken as 30% of total phosphorus from plant sources for chicks, and 75% of total phosphorus from plant sources for adult birds. Phosphorus from other than plant sources are considered to be 100% utilized.

actually needs under different sets of conditions. In this way, feed efficiency can be improved and the cost of producing a dozen eggs reduced.

A phase-feeding program for laying hens generally calls for use of a rather high protein feed (usually 17 to 18 per cent) from the onset of egg production through the peak production period. Thereafter, a lower level of protein (about 16 per cent) is fed for the next five or six months, followed by still lower levels

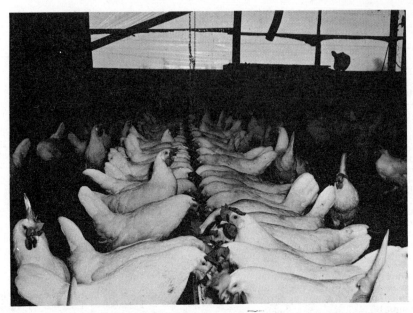

Fig. 40-10. Feeding layers went ultra-modern with the development of the concept of "phase feeding," which is the practice of changing ration formulations to meet changing nutritional requirements due to such factors as rate of lay, environmental temperature, etc. (Courtesy, DeKalb Agricultural Association, Inc., DeKalb, Ill.

(usually 15 per cent) until the laying period is completed. This general plan takes into consideration age, but for greatest benefits other factors will also need to be considered.

Although phase feeding has its advantages, it does present some problems: it is a complicated procedure, it necessitates a knowledgeable poultryman, and it requires more bulk bins, closer check on feed deliveries, etc.

Phase feeding is being practiced, and it is increasing in use. Although it does not promise to bring about large increases in egg production, it can help production reach a higher peak and sustain it longer if other conditions are right. In the latter respect, it is very much like "lead" or "challenge" feeding in dairy cows. Most of all, phase feeding offers a good potential for lowering costs and increasing income. Like many other developments, it favors the larger operator.

Feeding Broilers, Roasters, and Capons

Rations for broilers are given in Table 40-11.

The following pointers on feeding broilers, roasters, and capons are pertinent:

1. Feed is the largest cost item in broiler production, representing 60 to 70 per cent of the total cost.

TABLE 40—11

ALL-MASH BROILER RATIONS[1]

Ingredient	Starter (1st 35 days)	Finisher
	(lbs.)	(lbs.)
Ground yellow corn..	1,075	1,196
Stabilized fat	80	100
Soybean meal (50%)	550	408
Corn gluten meal (40%)	50	100
Fish meal (60%)...	100	40
Corn distillers' dried grains with solubles	50	50
Alfalfa meal (17%) (100,000 A/lb.).......................	50	50
Dicalcium phosphate	18	29
Ground limestone	20	20
Iodized salt..	7	7
Manganese (grams)...	52	52
Antibiotic supplement.......................................	Footnote [4]	Footnote[4]
dl Methionine or equivalent...............................	0.5	0.5
Antioxidant[2]..	.25	.25
Organic arsenical supplement[3]...........................	0.1	0.1
Coccidiostat..	Footnote [5]	Footnote [5]
Vitamin supplements:		
Vitamin A...............................(U.S.P. units)	1,135,000	1,135,000
Vitamin D .... (I.C.U.)	681,000	681,000
Vitamin K.............................. (mg)	500	500
Riboflavin............................. (mg)	3,500	1,500
Calcium pantothenate............. (mg)	5,000	5,000
Choline chloride.................... (mg)	227,000	227,000
Niacin................................. (mg)	21,000	21,000
Vitamin B12 .... (mg)	12	12
Totals (lbs.)	2,000.85	2,000.85

Calculated Analysis of All-Mash Broiler Rations

		Starter	Finisher
Metabolizable energy..............	Cal./lb.	1398	1443
Productive energy....................	Cal./lb.	1022	1054
Protein	%	24.05	20.13
Fat.......................................	%	7.07	8.09
Fiber....................................	%	2.70	2.69
Calcium.................................	%	1.02	.98
Total phosphorus.....................	%	.63	.62
Readily available phos.[6]..........	%	.41	.55
Metabolizable energy to protein ratio........................		58.13	71.68

[1]From *Chicken and Turkey Rations*, prepared cooperatively by the New England Land-Grant Universities, 1967 Wherever substitutions are made in the rations, the total nutrient content should be adjusted to agree with the analyses shown.
[2]1, 2-dihydro-6-ethoxy-2, 2, 4-trimethylquinoline (ethoxyquin) or butylated hydroxytoluene (BHT) are antioxidants used in the broiler rations at the 0.0125% level to help prevent the appearance of encephalomalacia (crazy chick disease), and to help prevent the destruction of the fat soluble vitamins. For information concerning the use of any additive, consult the supplier of the additive in question.
[3]Based on 3-nitro-4-hydroxyphenylarsonic acid at a level of 45 grams (0.1 pounds) per ton. Other compounds that may be used at a level recommended by the manufacturer are sodium arsanilate or arsanilic acid. For information concerning the use of any additive, consult the supplier of the additive in question.
[4]An antibiotic may be used in these rations at the level recommended by the manufacturer. For information concerning the use of any additive, consult the supplier of the additive in question.
[5]A coccidiosis controlling drug may be used in these rations at the level recommended by the manufacturer. For information concerning the use of any additive, consult the supplier of the additive in question.
[6]Readily available phosphorus has been taken as 30% of total phosphorus from plant sources for chicks, and 75% of total phosphorus from plant sources for adult birds. Phosphorus from other than plant sources are considered to be 100% utilized.

2. The starting ration of replacement chicks usually contains about 20 per cent protein, whereas the starting ration of broilers usually contains 20 to 24 per cent protein for the first six weeks. The exact percentage of protein needed depends on the feed's energy content.

3. At about six weeks of age, broilers should be placed on a finishing mash that has an increased energy level and reduced protein level. Pellets often are used for broilers from six weeks until they reach market weight.

4. Give roasters and capons the kind and amount of feed recommended for broilers during the first six weeks. After changing to the finishing mash, supply cracked corn to roasters and capons, in the afternoon. Gradually increase the grain until the birds are getting equal amounts of corn, mash, and pellets at 12 weeks of age.

5. For roasters, increase the corn diet to 50 per cent after the 15th week. Supply grit to birds that receive whole grain.

Feeding Turkeys

The nutritive requirements of turkeys are given in Table 40-5. It must be remembered, however, that these are "requirements" and that no margins of safety have been provided.

Table 40-12 gives the feed requirements and the time required to obtain certain average live weights of two common breeds of turkeys.

Turkey poults and turkeys fed for market purposes should be fed rations that are quite different from those that are fed to turkey breeders. Suggested rations will be given for each, but this does not imply that the turkey grower or breeder should mix his own feed. Rather, the need for specialized equipment and knowledge, skilled labor and managerial assistance, and purchasing and quality control measures involved in mixing feed properly suggests that a turkey producer usually will find it advantageous to purchase a complete ration, or a suitable concentrate, from a feed manufacturer.

Suggested turkey rations are given in Table 40-13.

These further pointers are pertinent to feeding turkeys:

1. Prevent poult "starve-out." Upon arrival, poults should be encouraged to eat feed and water as soon as possible. The use of colored feed, or placing brightly colored marbles in the feed and waterers, may help. It may be necessary to dip the beaks of some of them in feed and water to start them eating and drinking. Some may even have to be force fed.

2. Turkeys grow faster than chickens; hence, they have relatively higher feed and protein requirements.

3. Young turkeys use feed efficiently. Beltsville Small Whites raised to a live weight of 6 to 8 pounds at 14 to 16 weeks of age require 3 pounds of feed per pound of live turkey produced. Broad-breasted turkeys require about 4 pounds of feed to produce one pound of live weight, when grown to a market weight of about 20 pounds and 24 weeks of age.

4. There is a tendency among turkey breeders (egg producers) to provide a high-fiber holding ration, for use beginning at 16 weeks of age. This type of ration retards sexual maturity and may produce some desirable effects upon later reproductive performance. The holding ration limits energy intake, but should not limit protein, vitamins, and minerals. Where a holding ration is

TABLE 40—12

FEED REQUIRED AND TIME REQUIRED TO OBTAIN CERTAIN AVERAGE LIVE WEIGHTS WITH TWO COMMON BREEDS OF TURKEYS[1]

Average Live Weight		Kind of Turkey and Quantity of Feed Required per Bird								Kind of Turkey and Age at Which Certain Live Weights Are Reached			
		Beltsville Small White				Broad-breasted Bronze				Beltsville Small White		Broad-breasted Bronze	
		Females		Males		Females		Males		Females	Males	Females	Males
kg	lb.	kg	lb.	kg	lb.	kg	lb.	kg	lb.	wk.	wk.	wk.	wk.
0.25	.55	0.3	.66	0.3	.66	0.3	.66	0.3	.66	2.7	2.4	2.0	1.8
0.5	1.10	1.0	2.20	0.95	2.09	0.75	1.65	0.75	1.65	4.7	4.2	3.5	3.3
1.0	2.20	2.45	5.40	2.25	4.96	1.75	3.86	1.6	3.53	7.4	6.6	5.6	5.2
1.5	3.30	3.95	8.71	3.55	7.83	3.0	6.61	2.6	5.73	9.6	8.4	7.0	6.9
2.0	4.41	5.45	12.02	4.8	10.58	4.25	9.37	3.9	8.60	11.6	9.8	8.3	7.6
2.5	5.51	7.05	15.55	6.2	13.67	5.6	12.35	5.1	11.25	13.7	11.2	9.7	8.7
3.0	6.61	9.2	20.29	7.55	16.65	7.2	15.88	6.35	14.00	16.4	12.5	11.0	9.6
4.0	8.82			10.8	23.81	10.6	23.37	9.1	20.06	22.5	14.7	13.5	11.2
5.0	11.02			14.75	32.52	15.0	33.07	12.35	27.23		17.9	16.3	13.1
6.0	13.23			20.55	45.31	20.45	45.09	15.8	34.83		21.5	19.2	14.9
7.0	15.43					26.65	58.76	19.25	42.45			23.1	16.8
8.0	17.64							23.15	51.05				18.6
9.0	19.84							27.2	59.98				20.5
10.0	22.05							31.75	70.01				22.3

[1]From NRC Pub. 1345, p. 18, 1966.

TABLE 40—13[1]

ALL-MASH TURKEY RATIONS

Ingredient	Starter (0-8 wks)	Grower (8-16 wks)	Finisher (16-mkt)[3]	Breeder
	(lbs.)	(lbs.)	(lbs.)	(lbs.)
Ground yellow corn	840	1115	1329	1200
Wheat middlings	50	50	50	250
Fish meal (60%)	100	--	--	100
Meat and bone meal (50%)	100	50	--	50
Soybean meal (50%)	720	555	378	170
Stabilized fat	40	50	40	20
Alfalfa meal (17%) (100,000 A/lb.)	60	60	60	60
Corn distillers' dried grains with solubles	50	50	50	50
Dicalcium phosphate	20	40	60	20
Ground limestone	15	20	23	70
Iodized salt	5	10	10	10
Antibiotic supplement	Footnote[4]	--	--	--
Manganese (grams)	30	30	30	30
Zinc (grams)	30	30	30	30
Vitamin supplements:				
Vitamin A (U.S.P. units)	4,086,000	4,086,000	4,086,000	4,086,000
Vitamin D (I.C.U.)	1,700,000	1,700,000	1,700,000	1,700,000
Vitamin E (I.U.)	10,000	10,000	10,000	50,000
Vitamin B12 (mg)	6	6	6	12
Choline chloride (mg)	415,150	80,500	134,550	415,150
Calcium pantothenate (mg)	4,000	4,000	5,000	10,000
Niacin (mg)	45,000	45,600	46,000	50,000
Riboflavin (mg)	4,000	5,000	5,000	5,000
Totals (lbs.)	2,000	2,000	2,000	2,000

Calculated Analysis of All-Mash Turkey Rations

		Starter	Grower	Finisher	Breeder
Metabolizable energy	Cal./lb.	1280	1331	1360	1286
Productive energy	Cal./lb.	936	972	988	940
Protein	%	29.31	21.97	17.16	17.24
Arginine	%	1.91	1.40	1.04	1.00
Lysine	%	1.72	1.14	.80	.86
Methionine	%	.50	.36	.30	.33
Cystine	%	.42	.33	.27	.26
Tryptophane	%	.33	.25	.19	.18
Fat	%	5.07	5.54	5.23	4.81
Fiber	%	3.04	3.01	2.94	3.40
Calcium	%	1.47	1.28	1.35	2.22
Total phosphorus	%	.92	.81	.85	.80
Readily available phos.[5]	%	.69	.58	.77	.72
Manganese	mg/lb.	25.20	23.27	22.16	28.13
Vitamin A activity	U.S.P. units/lb.	6030	6342	6584	6461
Vitamin D	I.C.U./lb.	850	850	850	850
Riboflavin	mg/lb.	3.31	3.61	3.53	3.68
Pantothenic acid	mg/lb.	6.28	5.80	5.91	8.56
Choline	mg/lb.	1059	705.05	590.02	685.52
Niacin	mg/lb.	37.17	35.14	34.58	42.71
Zinc (sup.)	mg/lb.	15.00	15.00	15.00	15.00
Metabolizable energy to protein ratio		43.67	60.58	79.25	74.59

[1]From *Chicken and Turkey Rations*, prepared cooperatively by the New England Land-Grant Universities, 1967. Wherever substitutions are made in the rations, the total nutrient content should be adjusted to agree with the analyses shown.

[2]A coccidiosis controlling drug may be used in this ration at the level recommended by the manufacturer. For information concerning the use of any additive, consult the supplier of the additive in question.

[3]May be fed with grain after 22 weeks.

[4]An antibiotic may be used in this ration at the level recommended by the manufacturer. For information concerning the use of any additive, consult the supplier of the additive in question.

[5]Readily available phosphorus has been taken as 30% of total phosphorus from plant sources for chicks, and 75% of total phosphorus from plant sources for adult birds. Phosphorus from other than plant sources are considered to be 100% utilized.

Fig. 40-11. Feed is the largest single item in the cost of growing turkeys; thus, the selection of a ration greatly influences the opportunity for profit in a turkey enterprise. (Courtesy, Maple Leaf Mills, Ltd., Ontario, Canada)

used, the birds should be switched to the breeder ration one month prior to egg production.

5. Good range provides green feed and tends to reduce feed costs. However, it may make for higher losses from blackhead and other diseases, and predators; and range turkey operations may make the neighbors unhappy because of dust, odors, and noise.

Feeding Ducks and Geese

The suggested crude protein content for duck and goose diets is given in Table 40-14, and suggested feed formulations are given in Tables 40-15 and 40-16.

The following pointers are pertinent to feeding ducks:

1. Ducks should be fed pellets rather than mash; use $\frac{3}{32}$ or $\frac{3}{16}$ inch pellets. Pellets will make for a saving of 15 to 20 per cent in the feed required to produce a market duck.

2. Ducks are nearly as good foragers as geese.

3. Ducks should be ready for market between 7½ and 8 weeks of age.

4. The holding rations are designed to maintain breeding ducks from about eight weeks of age until the breeding season commences, without them getting too fat. It is recommended that birds on holding rations be limited to about ½ pound per bird per day.

5. A breeder diet should be substituted for the holding diet about four weeks before eggs are desired for hatching purposes.

TABLE 40—14

CRUDE PROTEIN CONTENT FOR DUCK AND GOOSE DIETS[1]

Ducks		(% crude protein)
Market ducks	0 to 2 weeks—all mash	18.0
	Grower 2 weeks to market	16.8
Holding diet		(about) 14.0
Breeder diet		(about) 15.3
Geese		
Confined	0 to 3 weeks—all mash	20.0
Grower	3 weeks—market—mash & grain	(about) 15.2
Breeder	mash & grain	(about) 15.3

[1]Ontario (Canada) Department of Agriculture, Pub. 532, p. 72.

TABLE 40—15

DUCK FEED FORMULAS[1]

Ingredient	MARKET DUCKS ALL-MASH FORMULAS		HOLDING and BREEDING FORMULAS			
	No. 1	No. 2	No. 3	No. 4	No. 5	No. 6
	Age in weeks		Holding		Breeding	
	0-2	(2-market)	all-mash	mash:grain	all-mash	mash:grain
	(lbs. per ton)	(lbs. per ton)	(lbs. per ton)	(lbs. per ton)	(lbs. per ton)	(lbs. per ton)
Ground yellow corn	1000	1040	760	700	735	600
Wheat shorts	100	200	200	200	200	100
Wheat middlings	200	150	400	200	200	200
Ground barley	200	200	400	285	400	200
Dehydrated green feed	40	40	80	160	90	180
Meat meal (50% protein)	40	40	—	—	40	40
Fish meal (60% protein)	40	—	—	—	40	80
Dried whey	35	—	—	—	30	50
Soybean meal (50% protein)	285	270	100	360	130	345
Ground limestone	20	20	20	40	100	150
Dicalcium phosphate	20	20	20	30	15	30
Salt (iodized)	5	5	5	10	5	10
Trace mineral premix	5	5	5	5	5	5
Vitamin premix	10	10	10	10	10	10
Total (lbs.)	2,000	2,000	2,000	2,000	2,000	2,000
Trace mineral premix:						
Manganous oxide (56% Mn.) (ozs.).	3.0	3.0	3.0	6.0	3.0	6.0
Zinc oxide (80% Zn.) (ozs.)	2.0	2.0	2.0	4.0	2.0	4.0
Ground limestone (ozs.)	75.0	75.0	75.0	70.0	75.0	70.0
Total (lbs.)	5.0	5.0	5.0	5.0	5.0	5.0
Vitamin premix:						
Vitamin A (millions of U.S.P.U.)	4.0	4.0	2.0	4.0	3.0	6.0
Vitamin D_3 (millions of I.C.U.)	0.6	0.5	0.5	1.0	1.0	2.0
Riboflavin (gms)	4.0	3.0	3.0	6.0	3.0	8.0
D calcium pantothenate (gms)	5.0	4.5	3.0	6.0	5.0	10.0
Vitamin B_{12} (mg)	6.0	6.0	4.0	8.0	4.0	8.0
Niacin (gms)	30.0	25.0	20.0	40.0	10.0	20.0
Menadione sodium bisulfite (gm)	1.0	1.0	1.0	2.0	1.0	2.0
Ethoxyquin (ozs.)	?	?	?	?	?	?
Ground yellow corn to make to 10 lbs.	+	+	+	+	+	+
Total (lbs.)	10.0	10.0	10.0	10.0	10.0	10.0

[1]From *Duck and Goose Raising*, Ontario (Canada) Department of Agriculture, Pub. 532, 1964, p. 73.

TABLE 40—16

GOOSE FEED FORMULAS[1]

Ingredient	ALL-MASH FORMULAS			MASH and GRAIN FORMULAS	
	Age in weeks			Age in weeks	
	0 to 3 (confinement)	3 to market (range)	Breeding (confinement)	3 to market (range)	Breeding (confinement)
	(lbs. per ton)	(lbs. per ton)	(lbs. per ton)	(lbs. per ton)	(lbs. per ton)
Ground yellow corn......................	975	920	835	680	610
Wheat shorts	100	200	100	100	100
Wheat middlings..........................	100	200	200	200	200
Ground barley	200	400	400	400	200
Dehydrated green feed..................	60	20	100	40	140
Meat meal (50% protein)	40	40	40	50	40
Fish meal (60% protein)	40	—	40	—	80
Dried whey	40	—	30	40	50
Soybean meal (50% protein)..........	400	175	150	420	365
Ground limestone........................	10	10	65	20	150
Dicalcium phosphate....................	10	10	15	15	30
Salt (iodized)..............................	10	10	10	20	20
Trace mineral premix....................	5	5	5	5	5
Vitamin premix............................	10	10	10	10	10
Total (lbs.)	2,000	2,000	2,000	2,000	2,000
Trace mineral premix:					
Manganous oxide (56% Mn.) (ozs.)....	3.0	3.0	3.0	6.0	6.0
Zinc oxide (80% Zn.) (ozs.)..............	2.0	2.0	2.0	4.0	4.0
Ground limestone (ozs.)..................	75.0	75.0	75.0	70.0	70.0
Total (lbs.)..............................	5.0	5.0	5.0	5.0	5.0
Vitamin premix:					
Vitamin A (millions of U.S.P.U.)......	3.0	2.0	3.0	4.0	10.0
Vitamin D_3 (millions of I.C.U.)	0.6	0.4	1.0	0.8	2.0
Riboflavin (gms)..........................	4.0	2.0	3.0	4.0	8.0
D calcium pantothenate (gms)	4.0	2.0	5.5	4.0	12.0
Vitamin B_{12} (mg)	6.0	4.0	4.0	8.0	8.0
Niacin (gms)	30.0	15.0	15.0	30.0	25.0
Menadione sodium bisulfite (gms)....	1.0	1.0	1.0	2.0	2.0
Ethoxyquin (ozs.)	2.5	2.0	5.0	4.0	10.0
Ground yellow corn to 10 lbs...........	? +	? +	? +	? +	? +
Total (lbs.)..............................	10.0	10.0	10.0	10.0	10.0

[1]From *Duck and Goose Raising*, Ontario (Canada) Department of Agriculture, Pub. 532, 1964, p. 79.

Pointers on feeding geese follow:

1. As with duck rations, rations for geese should be in pellet form of $\frac{3}{32}$ or $\frac{3}{16}$ inch pellets. Crumbles cause too much feed wastage and should not be used.

2. Geese should be ready for market at around 15 weeks of age.

OTHER FEED AND MANAGEMENT GUIDES

There are innumerable other feed and management pointers of great importance in poultry production. In particular, attention is directed to the feed and water space requirements given in Table 41-2 of Chapter XLI.

QUESTIONS FOR STUDY AND DISCUSSION

1. Why have broiler producers made more marked progress in feed efficiency than beef cattle producers; in 1930, it required 5 pounds feed to produce 1 pound of weight gain of broilers vs. 3 pounds of feed today, whereas during

this same period of time, feed requirements to produce 1 pound of beef have only been lowered by a fraction of a pound?

2. Why is the great bulk of commercially produced feed in the U.S. used for poultry; in 1964, poultry used 62.12 per cent of all commercially produced feeds, whereas swine used only 6.09 per cent commercial feed?

3. Name the parts of the digestive tract of a chicken and describe the functions of each. How does the digestive tract of the chicken differ from that of the ruminant?

4. How do the nutrient requirements of chickens compare with those of cattle, sheep, and swine?

5. How can a poultry farmer, with a relatively small farm flock, determine the nutrient requirements of his birds and the usefulness of available feeds?

6. Should a poultryman use a protein supplement of plant origin, animal origin, or a combination of the two?

7. Using the square method, and corn (9 per cent) and a 44 per cent protein supplement, balance out a ration for six-week-old broilers from the standpoint of protein content.

8. Why do poultrymen use more feed in the form of crumbles than producers of other classes of livestock?

9. Why do the protein requirements of turkeys from one day of age to marketing differ so widely?

10. What is meant by "phase feeding" in poultry, and how does it compare with "challenge" or "lead" feeding in dairy cattle?

11. Could the red-meat producer—the cattle feeder, the sheep feeder, and the hog feeder—use, to his advantage and profit, something similar to "phase feeding in poultry" and "challenge" or "lead" feeding in dairy cattle; that is, could he feed different amounts according to weight gains being made?

12. Is the farm poultry flock completely on the way out; if so, why?

SELECTED REFERENCES

Title of Publication	Author(s)	Publisher
Feed Compositions, Tables of	Pub. 1684	National Academy of Sciences, National Research Council, Washington, D.C., 1964.
Feeding Poultry	G. F. Heuser	John Wiley & Sons, Inc., New York, N. Y., 1955.
Feeds and Feeding, 22nd ed.	F. B. Morrison	Morrison Publishing Company, Ithaca, N. Y., 1956.
Nutrient Requirements of Poultry	Pub. 1345	National Academy of Sciences, National Research Council, Washington, D.C., 1966.
Poultry Nutrition, 5th ed.	W. R. Ewing	The Ray Ewing Company, Pub., 2690 E. Foothill Blvd., Pasadena, Calif., 1963.
Scientific Feeding of Chickens, The	H. W. Titus	The Interstate Printers & Publishers, Inc., Danville, Ill., 1961.
Stockman's Handbook, The	M. E. Ensminger	The Interstate Printers & Publishers, Danville, Ill., 1969.

Chapter XLI

POULTRY HOUSES AND EQUIPMENT

Contents   **Page**

Space Requirements of Buildings and Equipment for Poultry............................ 985
Requisites of Poultry Housing.. 986
Requisites of Poultry Equipment... 988
Specialized Buildings and Equipment for Specialized Purposes...................... 989
Housing and Equipment for Layers... 989
    Houses 989
    Equipment 992
    Care of the House... 993
Brooder Houses and Equipment for Chicks... 993
    Brooder Houses 994
    Brooding Equipment 994
Housing and Equipment for Replacement (Started) Pullets............................... 995
    Housing 995
    Feeders and Waterers.. 995
    Other Equipment 995
Houses and Equipment for Broilers (Fryers).. 996
    Housing 996
    Feeders 997
    Waterers 997
Houses and Equipment for Turkeys.. 997
    Facilities for Breeder Turkeys.. 997
    Facilities for Brooding Turkey Poults... 998
    Facilities for Market Turkeys.. 998
Houses and Equipment for Ducks and Geese... 999
Other Poultry Facilities and Equipment.. 999
    Facilities and Equipment for Handling Manure.. 999
    Emergency Warning Systems..1001
Questions for Study and Discussion..1002
Selected References 1002

Properly designed poultry buildings and equipment should provide for housing, feeding, and handling of poultry in accordance with recommended production practices.

No standard set of poultry buildings and equipment can be expected to be well adapted to such diverse conditions and systems of poultry production as exist in the United States. In presenting the following discussion, therefore, it is intended that it be considered as a guide only. Detailed plans and specifications for buildings and equipment can be obtained from a local architect or through contacting the college of agriculture of the state.

SPACE REQUIREMENTS OF BUILDINGS AND EQUIPMENT FOR POULTRY

One of the first and frequently one of the most difficult problems confronting the poultryman who wishes to construct a building or item of equipment is that of arriving at the proper size or dimension. Table 41-2, at the end of this chapter, contains some conservative figures which it is hoped will prove helpful. In general, less space than indicated may jeopardize the health and well-being of the birds, whereas more space may make the buildings and equipment more expensive than necessary.

REQUISITES OF POULTRY HOUSING

There are certain general requisites of all animal buildings, regardless of the class of livestock, that should always be considered; among them, reasonable construction and maintenance costs, reduced labor, and utility value. These and other general requisites are fully covered in Chapter IV of this book, so repetition at this point is unnecessary. In the case of poultry, however, increased emphasis needs to be placed on the following features of buildings:

1. **Temperature.**—Feathers give some protection against cold. However, the bird's efficiency in egg production, meat production, and feed utilization is greatly lowered when it must endure temperatures appreciably below the zone of comfort.

Birds have a very poor defense against heat, and their cooling system is not very efficient because they do not have sweat glands. They attempt to adjust to heat (a) by panting or breathing rapidly with the mouth open, (b) by eating less and drinking more, (c) by holding their wings away from the body, and (d) by resting against a cool surface such as the damp earth or a concrete floor.

The optimum temperature for layers is 55° to 70° F. and for broilers 75° F. Desirable brooding temperatures for chicks and poults are given in Table 41-2.

Tests conducted by the U.S. Department of Agriculture showed that hens kept at 55° F. laid at a rate of 75 per cent and consumed 3.5 pounds of feed for each pound of eggs, whereas those maintained at 85° F. laid at a rate of only 50 per cent and consumed 4 pounds for each pound of eggs, while those kept at 23° F. laid at a rate of only 26 per cent and ate 12.3 pounds of feed for each pound of eggs. Experiments conducted at the University of Connecticut showed a 12.5 per cent increase in feed efficiency in broilers grown in a 75° F. house compared to those grown at 45° F.

Humidity influences are tied closely to temperature effects. For laying houses, the relative humidity should be within the range of 50 to 75 per cent.

2. **Insulation.**—The term "insulation" refers to materials which have a high resistance to the flow of heat. Such materials are commonly used in the walls and ceiling of poultry houses. Proper insulation makes for a more uniform temperature—cooler houses in the summer and warmer houses in the winter—and makes for a substantial fuel saving in brooder houses.

Heat produced by layers varies with their weight and the environmental temperature. White Leghorn layers will produce 9 Btu/hour of bird weight at a housing temperature of 55° F. This is approximately 40 Btu/hour for a typical 4½-pound White Leghorn hen.

3. **Vapor barrier.**—There is much moisture in poultry houses; it comes from open water fountains, wet litter, the respiration of the birds, and from the droppings. When the amount of water vapor in the house is greater than in the outside air, the vapor will tend to move from inside to outside. Since warm air holds more water vapor than cold air, the movement of vapor is most pronounced during the winter months. The effective way to combat this problem in a poultry house is to use a vapor barrier with the insulation. It should be placed on the warm side or inside of the house.

4. **Ventilation.**—Ventilation refers to the changing of air—the replacement of foul air with fresh air. Poultry houses should be well ventilated, but care must be taken to avoid direct drafts and coldness. Good poultry house ventilation saves feed and helps make for maximum production.

Three factors are essential for good ventilation: (a) fresh air moving into the poultry house, (b) insulation to keep the house temperatures warm, and (c) removal of moist air.

In most poultry houses, easily controlled electric fans do the best job of putting air where it is needed. Gravity flow—or relying on air movement without fans—is suitable only for narrow houses and few birds.

A complete ventilation system has three parts: (a) a fan, or fans, to move fresh air through the house; (b) enough inlets to let plenty of fresh air in; and (c) enough outlets to let stale, moisture-laden air out. All these parts are necessary for success.

Exhaust-type ventilation systems are usually used. Wall fans are generally cheaper and easier to install than ceiling fans. However, ceiling fans provide gravity ventilation if electricity should fail.

The water-holding capacity of air increases with rising temperature (Fig. 41-1).

Fans are rated in cubic feet per minute (cfm) of air they move. To ar-

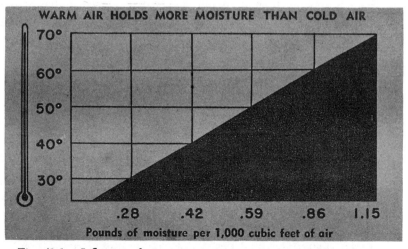

Fig. 41-1. Influence of air temperature on its water holding capacity. (From Washington State University Extension Bulletin No. 529, 1961)

rive at fan capacity, allow (a) 3 cfm per bird for layers of the light breeds, (b) 4 cfm per bird for layers of the medium-weight breeds, and (c) ½ cfm per pound of body weight for broilers and turkeys.

5. **Lighting.**—It has long been known that light stimulates egg production in the domestic fowl and other birds. Records show that the ancient Chinese made their canaries sing more by placing a lighted candle by the cage at night. Much later, early in the 1900's, poultry farmers in the state of Washington found that they could increase winter egg production by placing a lighted lantern in the chicken house for a few hours each evening. At that time, however, it was thought that the role of light was primarily a matter of increasing the "work day" of the bird. Today, the action of light is considered physiological; light enters the eye of the bird and stimulates the pituitary gland. In turn, the pituitary gland releases certain hormones which cause ovulation. Because of this phenomenon, artificial lighting in the poultry house is exceedingly important. For pullets, an increase in the day length during the growing period will stimulate early maturity, whereas a decrease in day length will delay the age of maturity. For mature layers, an increase in day length will stimulate egg production, whereas a decrease in day length will suppress egg production.

Automatic time switches are available at moderate cost and should be installed in poultry houses for pullets or layers. Lighting recommendations are given in Table 41-2.

6. **Manure management.**—The handling of manure is probably the single most important problem confronting commercial poultrymen today. It must be removed for sanitary reasons, and there is a limit how much of it can be left to accumulate in pits or other storage areas. Higher labor costs, and lower priced commercial fertilizers, have made manure of relatively less value as a fertilizer. Also, to the urbanite and city dweller alike, manure odor is taboo. Manure is too costly to burn, too bulky to bury or put in a dump, and, with large operations, there is too much of it to put in lagoons. Hence, it has two primary outlets: (a) as a fertilizer, and (b) for feeding to ruminants (see Chapter 43, section on "Manure").

REQUISITES OF POULTRY EQUIPMENT

The successful poultry producer must have adequate equipment with which to provide feed, water, and care of his birds (see Table 41-2 for feed and water space requirements).

Certain features are desirable in all types of animal equipment, regardless of the species for which it is used. These points are discussed in Chapter IV of this book; hence, repetition is not necessary. But, because poultry are subject to numerous diseases and parasites, equipment for them should be constructed for easy cleaning and disinfection.

There are many types and designs of the various pieces of poultry equipment, and some producers will introduce their own ideas.

SPECIALIZED BUILDINGS AND EQUIPMENT
FOR SPECIALIZED PURPOSES

With the decline in farm flocks, fewer and fewer general-purpose type poultry houses and equipment are seen. The large and highly specialized poultry enterprises have developed buildings and equipment adapted to their highly specialized purposes. Although there is hardly any limit to the number of different styles, sizes, and colors of poultry buildings and equipment, within specialty types of operations certain principles are similar; that is, certain principles are observed in the facilities and equipment for layers, for brooding of chicks, for replacement pullets, for broilers, for turkey poults, for market turkeys, and for breeding turkeys. Building and equipment requisites for each of these specialty areas follow.

HOUSING AND EQUIPMENT FOR LAYERS

The design and construction of houses and equipment for layers should be such as to provide for top performance of the layers, optimum environmental control, functional arrangement of equipment, maximum labor efficiency, satisfactory waste disposal, and minimum housing and care costs per dozen eggs produced.

Houses

Layer houses may be colony houses, multiple-unit houses, or multiple-story houses; some are permanent and others are movable.

The starting point in designing a layer house is the selection of the type of laying system. Presently, layer houses are being arranged in the following ways, or according to the following systems:

1. **Floor or litter-type houses.**—This is the oldest of the systems or arrangements, and at one time it was the exclusive type of layer house. It consists of litter covering the entire floor. Feeders and waterers are located on the litter, and nests usually line one or both sides of the house. This arrangement calls for a minimum amount of equipment. Also, fly control is simple. But it requires a well-insulated house with a good ventilation system.

Litter floor houses may be used in climates where slotted or wire floor houses or cages are unsatisfactory. They are expensive to construct, but maintenance costs are low. Also, they are more flexible; for example, additional brooding facilities are not required since the chicks may be brooded in floor-type laying houses which have been cleared of hens.

2. **Slat or wire floors.**—This means just what the name indicates—the use of slats or wire over the entire floor. Because wire floors rust, and have a high depreciation, slat floors have been replacing them. Slats, usually of wood, are placed on edge. In wire or slat floors, the droppings collect in the space beneath the floor and can be removed with a mechanical cleaner, or a floor section

can be taken out once each year and the droppings removed with tractor-mounted equipment.

The *advantages* of slat floors are: no litter is needed, better control of bacterial diseases, and it is not necessary to clean during the laying year—except to eliminate moisture.

The *disadvantages* of slat floors are: high humidity, no place where the birds can relax, birds appear to be more nervous, feather conditions become rougher, more egg breakage, more feather picking and cannibalism, and lower egg production.

3. **Combination litter and slat or wire floor.**—In this system, built-up litter on the floor is used on about 60 per cent of the area, with raised slats or wire floor over the remaining 40 per cent of the area—usually down the middle of the house. This raised floor provides a place for feed, water, and roosts. About 70 per cent of the droppings collect in the area below the raised floor and can be removed by a mechanical cleaner about twice each week, or as desired. Removal of the droppings also gets rid of considerable moisture, thereby reducing the ventilation problem. The floor litter is easier to manage since it contains fewer droppings and less moisture.

4. **Cage system.**—In this system, small wire cages placed side by side, in long rows, hold the birds. These cages stand in rows on each side of an aisle (usually about 30 to 36 inches wide), placed at a convenient working height for the operator. Some prefer two or three rows of cages, one above the other. The second row of cages may be located directly above the lower row, or it may be placed so that the bottom row projects forward about one-half the cage's depth, giving a stair-step effect.

Originally, one to two hens were kept in individual wire cages. To reduce the cost per bird, however, "colony cages" which will hold up to 20 to 25 hens have been developed.

Cage sizes are not standardized, but Table 41-1 will serve as a useful guide.

While the cage system (a) accommodates more birds in a given floor area than the litter floor system and (b) eliminates many internal parasite troubles,

TABLE 41—1

CAGE SIZES, BIRDS PER CAGE, AND FEED AND WATER SPACE

Cage Size	No. Birds	Total Sq. Inches	Sq. Inches per Bird	Inches Feed and Water Space per Bird
8" x 16"	1	128	128	8
8" x 16"	2	128	64	4
12" x 16"	3	192	64	4
12" x 18"	3	216	72	4
12" x 18"	4	216	53	3
24" x 18"	7	432	62	3.5
24" x 18"	8	432	54	3
12" x 20"	4	240	60	3
2' x 2½'	10	720	72	3
3' x 4'	20	1,728	86	2.4
3' x 4'	25	1,728	69	1.9

Fig. 41-2. Cage system of housing layers, with three decks of cages. (Courtesy, DeKalb Agricultural Association, DeKalb, Ill.)

it does give rise to problems. High initial investment and high labor requirements have been experienced in the hen-per-cage system. With the colony-type cage arrangement, cannibalism and similar social problems have often been encountered. Two hens per cage appears to be the most popular arrangement at the present time.

Controlling flies and removing manure have been particularly difficult with the cage system.

As would be expected, each of these systems has its strong advocates, and the ardent supporters of each system can cite experiences and experiments to substantiate their claims. After studying the overall results obtained in the form of net income per hen or per man by these four main types or systems, the author came to the conclusion that there is no clear-cut advantages for any one type—that among the many factors influencing profit in the egg business, the type or system of housing is not paramount. The most important things are to design the building to fit the local climate; to provide adequate protection, ventilation, and cooling of the birds; and to make for good working conditions for the operator. It is further recommended that anyone planning to construct a layer house should inspect all four types or systems, and confer with those who have used them; then, like the selection of a wife, he will do best with his own choice.

In addition to the layer house, a building for handling, cooling, and holding eggs under refrigeration on the egg farm is essential.

Most poultry feed is purchased in bulk and delivered to bulk tanks from which it is withdrawn as used, by gravity or mechanical conveyors. Where whole grain is used, it may be practical to have sufficient storage facilities to permit purchase of grain at harvest time, when prices are usually more favorable.

A service building for storing supplies and small equipment, and for making repairs, is also needed. It may be a separate building, or it may be a part of the garage or egg room.

Equipment

Good laying-house equipment is essential for satisfactory production. It should be simple in construction, movable, and easily cleaned. The nests, roosts, feeders, and waterers are of particular importance.

1. **Nests.**—Nests should be roomy, movable, easily cleaned, cool and well ventilated, dark, and conveniently located. Nests are usually about 14 inches square, 6 inches deep, and with 15 inches head room. All-metal nests are preferred to wooden nests because of ease of cleaning and less chance of becoming infested by mites.

Nesting material should consist of small particles that are highly moisture absorbent such as shavings, oat hulls, sawdust, and excelsior pads.

Roll-away nests, without nesting material, are becoming more common. They consist of plastic covered wire bottoms, sloped to a covered egg tray.

Trap nests differ from regular nests in that they are provided with trap doors by which the birds shut themselves in when they enter. They are the accepted means of securing accurate individual egg records, and they are essential where pedigree breeding is practiced—that is, where more than one female is continuously mated with one male.

2. **Roosts.**—Where roosts are used, they are commonly made of 2″ x 3″ or 2″ x 4″ lumber, placed sideways, with the edges rounded off.

3. **Feeders.**—Since feed cost is the major item in egg production, it is necessary that there be adequate feeder space and that the feeders be good. They should be easy to fill, easy to clean, built to avoid waste, arranged so that the birds cannot roost on them, high enough so that the birds cannot scratch litter

into them, and so constructed that as long as they contain any feed the birds can reach it. The space requirements for feeders are given in Table 41-2.

4. **Waterers.**—Laying hens drink 2 to 3 pounds of water for each pound of feed they eat. Watering devices should keep the water clean, be easily cleaned, and prevent spillage of water around the vessels or containers. The space requirements for waterers are given in Table 41-2. Also, it is important that the waterers be distributed throughout the laying house so that a hen never has to travel more than 15 feet for a drink.

Care of the House

Good husbandry and housekeeping are essential for optimum production and high egg quality. Also, it is necessary to minimize the spread of diseases. Accordingly, the following practices should be a part of the regular chores of the caretaker: inspect the birds daily, clean waterers daily, keep nests clean, keep light bulbs clean, clean windows regularly, control flies and rodents, and inspect all equipment routinely. Additionally, the following management and environmental factors should receive special attention:

1. **Litter.**—Where litter is used, 6 to 8 inches of it should be provided. Litter absorbs moisture from droppings and then gives this moisture to the air brought in by ventilation. A good litter is highly absorbent and fairly coarse, so as to prevent packing. The litter should be free of mold and contain a minimum amount of dust. Availability and cost will determine the type of litter used. Common litter materials include shredded cane pulp, soft wood shaving, peanut hulls, ground corncobs, rice hulls, and peat moss.

2. **Cooling.**—In warm areas, summer heat may cause retarded egg production and even result in death losses. Well ventilated houses help, but when temperatures become extreme, artificial cooling is necessary. During extremely hot weather, the house can be kept more comfortable by increasing the movement of air, cleaning the fan blades and screens, painting the roof white, and sprinkling the roof. Foggers, controlled by thermostats, may also be used to produce a fine spray. In an emergency, sprinkling water over the hens with a garden hose, using a fine spray, will help cut down death due to heat prostration if enough breeze is available to evaporate the water and cool the birds.

3. **Manure removal.**—A manure removal or holding system should be planned before the operation is started. The importance of this becomes apparent when it is realized that 100,000 layers will produce over 12 tons of manure a day, or well over 4,000 tons a year.

BROODER HOUSES AND EQUIPMENT FOR CHICKS

Wherever chicks are raised—whether for broilers or replacement layers, and whether for continued rearing in confinement or on the range—artificial brooding of some kind is necessary. No phase of the poultry business is so important as brooding—it's the part that makes for a proper start in life.

The recommended space and temperature for brooding are given in Table 41-2. Proper ventilation and dryness are also essential.

Brooder Houses

Until recent years, brooder houses for chicks were, for the most part, either portable or stationary buildings that were used for other purposes the balance of the year—part of the laying house, or the garage, or perhaps one end of the machine shed was used for brooding purposes. Housing arrangements of this type are still common among farm flock owners. However, in large commercial installations, where it is not uncommon to find 30,000 to 50,000 or more chicks being brooded together as a unit, special brooding houses or arrangements are common.

Brooding Equipment

Heating, feeding, and watering equipment are the three main items of equipment needed for the brooding of chicks.

1. **Heating equipment.**—The heat necessary for artificially brooding chicks may be supplied by a wide variety of devices and methods, among them the following:

   a. **Portable brooders**—These units are, as indicated by the name, portable or movable. Although they come in a wide variety of styles and sizes, they generally consist of a central heating unit surrounded by a hover. They may be heated by gas, oil, electricity, coal, or wood. The latter two methods of heating are fast disappearing. Portable brooders cost less to install than central heating systems, but they cost more per chick to operate. Also, they require more attention and labor, and there is more fire hazard from using them than central systems.

   b. **Infrared lamps**—In this method, infrared lamps are suspended 18 to 27 inches above the floor litter. These lamps do not heat the surrounding air, but they warm the chicks in the same manner as direct rays from the sun. One 250-watt infrared bulb will suffice for 60 to 100 chicks.

   c. **Battery brooders**—Commercial battery brooders are becoming hard to get. They may either be (1) unheated brooders made for use in warm rooms, or (2) those equipped with heating units and warm compartments for use in rooms held at 60° to 70° F. Most batteries of today have heating units warmed by electricity and equipped with thermostat regulation.

   d. **Central heating**—Large commercial operations, which handle 5,000 to 25,000 or more chicks per house, need a central heating system. Several different heating systems have been developed for such use. Most of them are highly automated, thermostatically controlled, and fueled by oil, gas, electricity, or coal. Central heating units may provide warmth through either hot water (pipes or radiant heating) or hot air (direct or indirect).

2. **Feeders and waterers.**—The feeding and watering space needs of chicks are given in Table 41-2. Feeding and watering equipment which is suited to six-week-old birds is not satisfactory for day-old chicks. Hence, special feeding and watering equipment must be provided, and the chicks must learn to eat and drink when they are first placed in the brooder.

HOUSING AND EQUIPMENT FOR REPLACEMENT (STARTED) PULLETS

Regular replacement of the laying flock is one of the most important, and most expensive, essentials of egg production. It ranks next to feed in the cost of egg production, and it exceeds labor, housing, equipment, interest, taxes, and other costs.

The poultryman may choose between growing his own pullets or purchasing started pullets. In any event, the building and equipment requirements are the same, whether pullets are raised for sale or raised by the one who will retain them as layers.

Usually it is wise to provide pullets with levels of environment—housing, feed, and general management—considerably above minimum standards, but consistent with realistic cost consideration. This calls for housing that gives reasonable protection from heat and cold and provides good ventilation; and it means adequate feed and water space and facilities.

Housing

Effective isolation of growing stock from older birds is important for disease control, particularly during the early stages. Hence, separate housing should be provided for replacement pullets, completely separated from layers. Housing that is suitable for brooding chicks, or for housing a laying flock, will be satisfactory for rearing pullets. Usually, they are started out in the brooder house, then switched to the layer house.

Feeders and Waterers

Water space is less important than a good distribution of waterers through the house with a constant supply of fresh water. The same principle applies to some degree to feeders. Both feeders and waterers should be located to permit birds in any part of the house to feed or drink conveniently, without having to find their way around barriers or to travel more than 15 feet.

Other Equipment

Hoppers for grit should be provided for replacement pullets throughout the growing period, and, as they near maturity, additional hoppers should be provided for oyster shell or other calcium supplement.

Roosts are not always used where pullets are reared, but they are a desirable addition to the equipment. When used over enclosed pits, roosts aid in sanitation. Also, they add to the comfort of the birds in hot weather and help to establish desirable roosting habits for the laying period that follows. Some poultrymen also feel that flocks with good roosting habits are less likely to present severe problems of floor eggs.

Nesting equipment should be available by the time the pullets begin to lay. Of course, only a few nests are necessary if pullets are moved from rearing quarters to their laying quarters before production becomes heavy.

Except for automatic feeders and waterers, little mechanization exists in the vast majority of pullet rearing facilities, especially when compared to layer facilities.

HOUSES AND EQUIPMENT FOR BROILERS (FRYERS)

No other segment of agriculture is as well suited to assembly-line production techniques as broiler production.

In modern commercial broiler production, the bird spends its entire life in one house; that is, it is not brooded in a special brooder house, then moved to a house for growing, for broiler raising is basically a brooding operation. Instead, brooder houses are thoroughly cleaned and disinfected between flocks, preferably with the quarters left idle one to two weeks before starting a new group.

Today, the vast majority of the nation's broilers are produced in large production units; and it is estimated that 95 per cent of them are grown under some type of vertical integration or contractual arrangement. Hence, in the discussion that follows, only the buildings and equipment common to these larger establishments will be described.

Housing

A broiler house should provide clean, dry, comfortable surroundings for birds throughout the year. The house should be kept warm enough, but not too warm; the litter should be kept reasonably dry; provision should be made to modify the air circulation as broilers grow; and fresh air should be circulated, but the house should be free from drafts. In short, the broiler house should not be too cold, too hot, too wet, or too dry.

Most of the new broiler houses being constructed today are 24 to 40 feet wide, with gable-type roofs. Truss-type (of either wood or steel) construction is replacing pole-type due to lower labor costs in construction and greater ease of cleaning with a tractor. The length varies from 200 to 600 feet, with most of them averaging 300 to 400 feet. Capacity varies, but in the newer houses they generally range from 7,200 to 20,000 broilers. All of the birds may be in one large pen, but the newer trend is to pen units of 1,200 to 2,500 birds.

There is increasing interest in controlled environment housing for broilers. When the broiler house is insulated and environmentally controlled, a centrally heated brooding system may be difficult to justify. However, where broiler houses are not environmentally controlled, a central heating system, of either hot air or hot water, is preferred. Where a chick hover is used, large—1,000 capacity—units are most popular.

Although maintaining adequate temperature is of great importance, constant attention is needed to ventilate the broiler house properly. This calls for a building that is properly insulated and in which there is a forced ventilation system.

Feeders

Baby chicks should be started eating from new, cut-down chick boxes or box lids placed at floor level, allowing one feeder lid per 100 chicks. These feeders allow the chicks to find the feed easily.

Following the "box lid stage," broilers may be fed from trough feeders, hanging tube-type feeders, or from mechanical feeders. Bulk feed bins and mechanical feeders are the most costly of the various types of feeding equipment, but they also make for more saving in labor. As a rule of thumb, installation of a mechanical feeder or feeders is worth-while if the investment is no more than five times the labor saved per year.

Waterers

Clean water at 55° F. should be available at all times. Gallon fountains should be provided for baby chicks, but these should be replaced by automatic, hanging waterers as soon as the chicks have learned to drink from the latter.

All waterers should be cleaned and washed daily.

HOUSES AND EQUIPMENT FOR TURKEYS

Although there are some specie differences between turkeys and chickens, primarily because of a difference in size, the general principles relative to buildings and equipment for turkeys and chickens are very similar.

Facilities for Breeder Turkeys

Breeding turkeys may be kept (1) on restricted range, (2) in confinement housing, or (3) in semi-confinement.

Open range without shelters should not be used unless the flock can be protected from cold winds by trees and/or sloping hillsides. Turkey range should be enclosed by a well-constructed, permanent fence that is at least 5 feet high, preferably with an electric wire around the outside further to discourage predators. A 4-acre area will accommodate about 600 breeders, with provision for some rotation of pens and two night pens. Night pens should be equipped with roosts and lights arranged to insure that the entire area is lighted.

Day pens should be equipped with waterers, feeders, and nests.

Buildings for strict confinement are usually 40 to 50 feet in width and covered with wire on all sides. Most operators enclose three sides of the shelter with plastic to give protection during the winter months. Strict confinement lends itself well to automatic feeding and watering.

Semi-confinement gives the protection advantage of complete confinement during bad weather, with the added yard space for improved sanitation and mating. Buildings for semi-confinement are usually of lower cost construction than those used in strict confinement; generally they consist of an open-front pole-type building, with a fenced yard.

Choice between the systems—restricted range, strict confinement, and semi-confinement—depends to a very large extent upon the physical characteristics of the building site on the farm, the cost involved, and the weather.

Facilities for Brooding Turkey Poults

Turkey poults should be brooded and reared separately from all ages of chickens and adult turkeys. In large commercial turkey operations, they're usually brooded in permanent type houses. Some growers prefer to brood in batteries for the first two or three weeks before placing the poults on the floor. Regardless of the method of brooding employed, at least one square foot of floor space is required to eight weeks of age. More floor space must be provided as the poults grow older.

Any of the types of heating equipment commonly used for baby chicks can be used for brooding poults. To begin with, poults should be maintained at a temperature of 95° to 100° F., with it lessening following the first week. A guard should be placed around the brooder for the first two weeks to prevent crowding and smothering in the corners of the house.

The watering and feeding facilities used by turkey poults are very similar to that used by baby chicks, but generally they are somewhat larger and, of course, more space needs to be provided per bird (see Table 41-2).

Facilities for Market Turkeys

For the first 8 to 10 weeks of life, the brooding of turkey poults is the same regardless of whether they are subsequently to be raised in confinement or moved to the range. Although a large proportion of turkeys are reared on the range, there is an increasing tendency to grow them in confinement in pole-type shelters, or even in environmentally controlled buildings.

Where turkeys are to be range raised under a rotation system, portable range shelters, roosts, feeders, and waterers are necessary. These may be placed on runners or wheels and moved where and when needed.

When confinement reared, turkeys are generally provided with a pole-type shelter, although more costly environmentally controlled units are being used, particularly for turkey-fryer production. When raised in strict confinement, 3 to 5 square feet of floor space should be provided to carry each bird to market age and weight, the amount depending on the size of the strain of turkeys. Automatic waterers and feeders, or bulk feeders, help reduce labor costs.

Care should be taken to provide adequate ventilation and occasional additions to the litter to reduce dampness and dirty litter conditions.

HOUSES AND EQUIPMENT FOR DUCKS AND GEESE

Elaborate and expensive housing facilities are not necessary for ducks or geese. Except during storms, they prefer to be out-of-doors. A fenced-in area, in which there is a colony house or open shed to provide protection during inclement weather, is all that is needed.

Most commercial producers of ducks and geese allow breeders access to water for swimming. However, ducklings and goslings can be reared successfully without swimming facilities, provided they have a constant supply of readily available fresh drinking water.

Commercially produced ducks and geese are brooded much like chicks or poults. Brooding temperatures should be 85° to 90° F. under the hover at the start, but reduced to 80° F. by the end of the first week and 70° F. by the end of the third week.

Many different types of feeders and waterers are used for ducks and geese. The main requisites are that feeders handle pellets without wastage, and that the waterers be of a type which the birds cannot get into and splash.

OTHER POULTRY FACILITIES AND EQUIPMENT

In modern, large-scale poultry operations, three other items of equipment, which for the most part are used in all types of poultry production operations, merit mentioning. These follow.

Facilities and Equipment for Handling Manure

The facilities and equipment for handling poultry manure will vary according to the disposition made of it. Among the common manure disposal systems and equipment are the following:

1. **Dry spreading.**—In most places, the spreading of dry manure on crop land is still the most common and economical way to dispose of it. The major problems or drawbacks to this method are the land acreage required and the odors produced. A manure spreader, a manure pit where storage is planned, and a field constitute the necessary facilities and equipment for this system.

2. **Wet spreading.**—This refers to manure to which water has been added for purposes of facilitating handling. Liquid manure is stored in large water-tight storage pits or tanks (a 30,000 gallon storage facility is required to store manure from 10,000 laying hens for eight weeks), with 90 to 93 per cent water where a sludge pump is used and 80 to 85 per cent water for a vacuum pump. For conveying the manure away from the storage tank or pit, either a water-tight manure spreader or an irrigation pipe must be available.

3. **Lagoons.**—Outdoor lagoons should be between 3 to 5 feet deep, and 1 acre in size for each 1,000 to 2,000 laying hens. Indoor lagoons should have

TABLE 41—2   SPACE REQUIREMENT

	Layers[2]		Pullet Replacements	Broilers
← -- Chickens -- →				
	Light Breeds	Gen.-Purpose Breeds		
Brooding — Space under hover			No. Chicks Size Brooder 500................. 750 750................. 1000	1000-chick Hover Winter, non-insul. house = 750 Insulated house = 850 Environment controlled =1000
Temperature under hover			Degrees F. 2 In. Above Edge of Hover 1st week....................92° Reduce/week............ 5°	Same as pullet replacements.
Room			1st 2 weeks............... 75° F	60-70° F.

Floor space	1.5-2.0 sq. ft./bird.	2.5-3.5 sq. ft./bird.	Period Sq. Ft. Per Bird
			1st 6 weeks............... 0.5
			After 6 wks.—
			  Controlled environ. 1.0
			  Conventional environ. 1.5
				Per Bird In— Marketed At
				(3¾ lbs.) (4 lbs. +)
				Summer................... 1 sq. ft. 1.25
				Rest of yr. & environ-
				ment controlled..... .8 sq. ft. 1.0

Space when range-reared			8-10 wks. & over=400-500/acre.	

Feeder space	3-4 in./bird	4 in./bird	Lin. In. of |No. Hanging
			Mech. Feeder| Feeders/100
			Age /Bird | Birds
			(wks.)
			1-6 1 2
			7-12 2 3
			13-20 3 4
			Also use 1 cut-down chick box/100 chicks 1st 10 days.
				Period Kind of Feeder Units No
				1st 5-10 da. Box lid 1
				1st 3 wks. { Mech. feeder, or 1 lin. ft.
				  15-in., 30-lb. hang- 15
				  ing, or 4-ft. chick 10
				  trough
				After 3 wks. 5-ft. broiler feeder 25

Waterer space	½-1 in./bird		Week Equipment No. Birds
			1st 2 Two 1-gal.
			          fountains 100
			2-12 Two 8-ft. 1000
			          waterers
			12-20 Four 8-ft. 1000
			          waterers
				Per 1000
				Period Type of Waterer No. Units
				1-21 days 1 gal. fountain 10
				10-21 " 8-ft. auto. hanging 3, or ½ li
				Add one extra when temp. 90° F.+ per

Roosts	7-9 in./bird, poles on 14 in. centers		4-5 in. per bird	
Nests	1 for 5 layers or 1 sq. ft. colony nest for ea. 5-7 layers.		Provide before production begins.	
Artificial lights	14-hr. light period/day. One 40-60 watts/200 sq. ft.		Hrs. Light Per Day House with windows 14 max. Windowless house 8	All night. 10 watts/200 sq. in.
Comments	Waterers not more than 10-15 ft. from birds at any time.		Waterers and feeders not more than 15 ft. from birds at any one time.	Waterers not more than 10 ft. from birds.

[1]Linear foot equals one foot of feeding or watering space. For example, a 6-foot feeder open on both sides has 12 linea of feeding space.

Ventilation—Provide adequate ventilation to keep birds comfortable and maintain good litter condition.

a minimum of 3.5 cubic feet of water per bird, proper inlet and outlet mechanisms to control water depth, and provision for supplying oxygen.

4. **Dehydration.**—Drying equipment and marketing require a sizeable investment for this type of operation. Dehydration equipment to handle the manure from 300,000 to 400,000 layers will cost over $120,000. Also, there is an odor problem, which precludes the possibility of locating a manure drying operation near any population center.

...ILDINGS AND EQUIPMENT FOR POULTRY[1]

← --- Turkeys --- →			
Breeders		**Poults**	**Market**
Large Type	**Small Type**		
		Period Sq. Ft. Per Bird 1st 6 weeks.................... 1 6-10 weeks.................... 1.5	
		1st wk.=95-100° F. Decrease 5°/week for 6 weeks.	
		1st 6 weeks=60-70° F.	
...fined=8 sq. ft./bird, ...confined=5 sq. ft. in ...use + same space in ...rd.	Confined=6 sq. ft./bird. Semiconfined=4 sq. ft. in house + same space in yard.	Confined 4-6 sq. ft./bird	
...acre	500/acre		200/acre
...n./bird	4-6 in./bird	Period Per Bird (in.) 8 weeks to market................ 6.5 Poult to maturity................ 4	8 weeks to market 6.5 lin. in. or 4 mechanical feeders
.../bird with automatic waterer, or one station/200 ...250 birds.		One 1-gal. fountain/500 birds. Automatic type=.5 in./poult. Provide added water space in hot weather.	Per Bird Automatic=2½ in. Trough=1 in. Provide added water space in hot weather.
...in./bird	12 in./bird		10-15 in./bird
...e 18-24 in. nest per 5-7 birds, or ...e trap nest per 2-3 hens.			
...hours per day. ...e 60-watt per 100 sq. ft.		7½-10 watts/brooding unit	
...limate-controlled, provide 40% less space.		Limit to 300/brooder and 500/unit.	Large-type turkeys require upper limits of space requirements given above.

[2]More generous space allowances are accorded breeder chickens; for example, breeders of egg-type chicks are generally allowed
.. 2½ sq. ft. of floor space, whereas broiler-supply breeders are allowed 3 ft. per bird.

5. Incinerators.—Incinerators are rather expensive, require the use of considerable fuel to consume manure, and create an odor problem; hence, the use of incinerators for manure disposal does not appear to be the answer.

Emergency Warning Systems

The confinement of large flocks of birds in a mechanically controlled environment entails considerable risk because of the possibility of (1) power or equipment failure or (2) fire or abnormal temperatures. To guard against such troubles, an emergency warning system should be installed. Such a warning system may save its cost during just one power interruption, fire, or undesirable temperature in an incubator, brooder house, layer house, broiler house, egg storage room, or furnace room. The continuation of the poultry enterprise as the result of a timely warning can be far more valuable than any monetary insurance settlement after the operation has failed.

QUESTIONS FOR STUDY AND DISCUSSION

1. Most farm and ranch buildings are depreciated over a period of 20 to 40 years and most equipment over a period of 10 years, for tax purposes. In view of the rapid changes of the past, and the obsolescence, is this fast enough in the case of poultry houses and equipment?

2. On many large commercial establishments, manure has become an unwanted product—an expense rather than a source of income. Do you see any solution to this problem?

3. Discuss the phenomenon of lighting from the standpoint of egg production of birds.

4. Why has there been developed more types of specialized buildings for poultry than for any other class of livestock?

5. What are the advantages and the disadvantages of each of the following systems or arrangements in layer houses: (a) floor or litter-type, (b) slat or wire floors, (c) combination litter and slat or wire floors, and (d) cage system?

6. Will completely controlled environment be a part of more and more poultry house construction?

7. What factors have made for increased confinement rearing of poultry?

8. Why are market turkeys not raised in confinement to the same extent that broilers are raised in confinement?

SELECTED REFERENCES

Title of Publication	Author(s)	Publisher
Commercial Broiler Production Handbook No. 320		U. S. Department of Agriculture, Agricultural Research Service, Washington, D.C., 1967.
Farm Structures	H. J. Barre L. L. Sammet	John Wiley & Sons, Inc., New York, N. Y., 1950.
Management Guide		American Feed Manufacturers Association, 53 West Jackson Blvd., Chicago, Ill.
Stockman's Handbook, The	M. E. Ensminger	The Interstate Printers & Publishers, Inc., Danville, Ill., 1969.

CHAPTER XLII

POULTRY HEALTH, DISEASE PREVENTION, AND PARASITE CONTROL

Contents   Page

A Program of Poultry Health, Disease Prevention, and Parasite Control........1003
   Normal Sickness and Losses..1005
   Diagnostic Laboratory 1005
   Vaccination Program 1006
   Carcass Disposal 1008
   Disinfectants and Their Use...1008
Diseases of Poultry..1009
   Non-nutritional Diseases 1009
   Nutritional Diseases and Ailments..1009
   Other Ailments and Health Problems...1014
Parasites of Poultry..1018
   Internal Parasites of Poultry..1019
   External Parasites of Poultry..1019
Questions for Study and Discussion...1023
Selected References 1023

Healthy birds are a requisite for profit; unhealthy birds cause financial losses. This fact is generally recognized by poultrymen. Yet, diseases and parasites make for monetary losses to the poultry industry totaling more than $450 million per year.[1]

Death and condemnation losses take a tremendous toll. But even greater economic losses result from the decreased growth and egg production, and decreased feed efficiency, among the living.

Not all poultry losses can be prevented, but they can be reduced; and the more knowledgeable poultrymen and those who council with them are, the more successful they will be in instituting and carrying out programs of poultry health, disease prevention, and parasite control. To the latter end, this chapter, along with Chapter V, is presented.

A PROGRAM OF POULTRY HEALTH, DISEASE PREVENTION, AND PARASITE CONTROL

Although the exact program will and should vary according to the specific conditions existing on each individual poultry farm, the basic principles will remain the same. With this in mind, the following program of poultry health, disease prevention, and parasite control is presented. The poultrymen may use it (1) as a yardstick with which to compare his existing program, and (2) as a

---

[1] *Losses in Agriculture*, Agriculture Handbook No. 291, ARS, USDA, pp. 75, 80, and 82, 1965.

Fig. 42-1. When poultry are placed in close confinement, in great numbers, under forced production, and eat and sleep in close contact with their own body discharges, the control of diseases and parasites becomes of paramount importance. (Courtesy, DeKalb Agricultural Association, Inc., DeKalb, Ill.)

guide post so that he and his veterinarian, and other advisors, may develop a similar and more specific program for his enterprise.

1. **Get clean stock.**—Clean stock simplifies the problem of disease control by reducing the number and severity of problems that are present when the flock is established. Disease-free stock is best assured by purchasing stock from breeders who have conscientiously participated in organized disease control programs.

2. **Avoid bringing infection in.**—Visitors should be kept out of poultry houses; such equipment as trucks, shipping crates, and chick boxes should be restricted from the standpoint of area; and rats, mice, and birds should be controlled.

3. **Follow vaccination program.**—Vaccination is cheap insurance against heavy losses from certain diseases. Vaccines are available for the prevention of Newcastle, Bronchitis, Fowl pox, Laryngotracheitis, Epidemic tremor, and for certain other diseases that are of lesser importance in most areas.

4. **Control internal and external parasites; reduce stresses.**—Feed is always too costly to feed to parasites. Also, the control of external and internal parasites,

along with keeping stresses to a minimum, helps maintain the birds in good condition so that they can resist disease organisms.

5. **Recognize disease early.**—The best way in which to recognize the early stages when trouble is about to strike is through record keeping. A slump in feed and water consumption is usually one of the best early indicators. Thus, it pays to keep daily records on feed and water consumption, egg production, and mortality. Any major change from day to day, or over a period of time, may mean that a disease is present in the flock.

Also, the caretaker should set aside a certain time each day for the purpose of observing the flock. At that time, he should note the birds' actions, how they're eating and drinking, and whether there are any unusual sounds—any sneezing or rattling.

6. **Use diagnostic laboratory.**—Modern poultry farms represent a large investment. Thus, heavy losses may accrue if the wrong medication is given. The poultryman should not attempt to identify all diseases on the farm. When in doubt, he should always use the laboratory facilities of his area to get an accurate diagnosis.

7. **Dispose of carcasses properly.**—Sanitary disposal of dead birds is becoming an increasing problem, particularly in large commercial operations. Satisfactory dead bird disposal helps control disease, flies, and odors. The two most commonly accepted methods of dead bird disposal are the use of a disposal pit and incinerator. Both will do the job if properly designed and constructed.

8. **Periodically vacate and clean.**—Periodically, all poultry buildings should be vacated, thoroughly cleaned and disinfected. This is the most effective way in which to prevent the development of disease cycles.

Normal Sickness and Losses

Certain rules of thumb are helpful in evaluating the importance of a developing disease problem; among them, are the following:

1. **More than 1 per cent of the birds sick at one time.**—If the poultryman finds that more than 1 per cent of his flock is sick at any one time, it should be obvious to him that a disease problem is present and that he should give it his immediate attention.

2. **First three weeks losses; 2 per cent chickens, 3 per cent poults.**—During the first three weeks of a chick's life, mortality losses generally average about 2 per cent. For turkey poults, they run about 1 per cent higher. If losses are greater than these figures, there may be cause for alarm.

3. **After three weeks, 1 per cent per month.**—The normal mortality after three weeks of age should not exceed 1 per cent per month. However, a slight rise in mortality can be expected as adult flocks come into egg production.

Diagnostic Laboratory

Most states have one or more poultry pathology laboratories, operated by the state, available to their poultrymen and the state's poultry industry. Additionally, many veterinarians in private practice provide limited laboratory services for areas adjacent to their practice.

Accurate identification of poultry diseases is often difficult for even the best pathologists if they must work without the aid of a properly equipped laboratory. A wrong diagnosis often results in faulty recommendation with improper medication and unsatisfactory results. This can prove to be quite costly due to ineffective medication and a continuance of high mortality and increased diseased birds.

When a disease outbreak is suspected, live birds showing typical symptoms of the sick birds should be immediately submitted to a poultry diagnostic laboratory for examination. Such laboratories are equipped to identify the disease problem and make recommendations for control. Practicing veterinarians, industry service men, and trained extension personnel working with poultrymen and a diagnostic laboratory can bring about a reduction in losses due to disease.

Vaccination Program

In a concentrated poultry area, various diseases are a constant threat to the poultryman's profits. Vaccination is cheap insurance against heavy losses from some of these diseases.

The particular vaccination program and schedule followed should vary according to the area and from flock to flock. Thus, it had best be worked out in consultation with the local veterinarian. For guidance purposes only, a suggested vaccination program and schedule is given in Table 42-1.

TABLE 42—1

SUGGESTED VACCINATION PROGRAM AND SCHEDULE

Vaccines for	Age & Method	First Vaccination	Second Vaccination	Third Vaccination
Chicks for replacement pullets—the laying flock (depending on local conditions):[1]				
Newcastle B₁ type Use if no outbreaks reported in the area during the past months.	Age:	4 weeks.	16 weeks or at housing time.	Every 3 to 4 months or follow manufacturer's recommendations.
	Method:	Water, intranasal, intraocular, intramuscular (dead virus), or method of your choice. Use dead virus for flocks in low exposure areas and SPF flocks.	Water, intranasal, intramuscular (dead virus), or method of your choice. Use dead virus for flocks in low exposure areas and SPF flocks.	Same as for second vaccine. Wing-web Roakin strain may be used prior to onset of lay.
Newcastle B₁ type Use on birds under 4 weeks of age when outbreaks occur in area.	Age:	Up to 4 weeks.	4 to 5 weeks or not earlier than 3 wks. after 1st vaccination.	As above.
	Method:	Water, intranasal, intraocular, intramuscular (dead virus), or method of your choice. Use dead virus for flocks in low exposure areas and SPF flocks.	Same as for 1st vaccination.	
Bronchitis Massachusetts type or polyvalent—Mass.-Conn. type vaccine.	Age:	12 to 16 weeks.	Not necessary unless birds are vaccinated before 12 weeks of age. Follow manufacturer's directions.	Not necessary unless recommended by manufacturer.
	Method:	Water, intranasal, or intraocular.		

Footnote on last page of table.

(Continued)

TABLE 42—1 (Continued)

Vaccines for	Age & Method	First Vaccination	Second Vaccination	Third Vaccination
Avian encephalomyelitis (Epidemic tremors). Use either dead or live virus.	Age: Method:	10 to 18 weeks. (Follow manufacturer's recommendations.) Water or subcutaneous.	Not necessary.	Not necessary.
Fowl cholera Use cholera bacterin	Age: Method:	9 to 12 weeks. Inoculation	At housing. Inoculation	Not necessary.
Approval Required from Division of Animal Industry, Augusta				
Laryngotracheitis Vaccinate all birds on farm at same time. If an outbreak occurs, vaccinate all susceptible birds immediately. Lab diagnosis is required.	Age: Method:	6 to 20 wks or older if necessary. Eye drop vaccine.	If 1st eye-drop vaccination is before 10 wks., apply eye-drop vaccination again at 16 to 20 wks.	Not necessary.
Laryngotracheitis If vaccination becomes necessary before 6 wks. of age.	Age: Method:	2 to 6 weeks. Eye drop vaccine. Variable results before 4 wks. of age.	6 to 8 weeks after 1st vaccination. Eye drop vaccine.	Not necessary.
Fowl pox Where early protection is not necessary.	Age: Method:	8 to 16 weeks. Fowl pox or modified pox vaccine: wing-web stab —2 needles. Pigeon pox vaccine: Brush or spray into 1 in. x 2 in. area of exposed feather follicles on leg or wing-web stab if directed by manufacturer.	Not necessary.	Not necessary.
Fowl pox Where early protection is necessary.	Age: Method:	1 day to 8 weeks. Modified pox vaccine only: wing-web stab. Pigeon pox vaccine: Brush or spray into 1 in. x 2 in. area of exposed feather follicles on leg or wing-web stab if directed by manufacturer.	16 to 20 wks. or before housing. Same as for 1st vaccination. Wing-web stab may be preferred by manufacturer. Follow printed directions.	Not necessary.
Chicks for broiler production (depending on local conditions):				
Newcastle	Age: Method:	7 to 10 days. Intranasal vaccine by drinking water.	4½ to 5 weeks. Intranasal vaccine by drinking water.	
Infectious bronchitis	Age: Method:	2 weeks; give 7-10 days after Newcastle vaccination. Drinking water.		
Turkeys (depending on local conditions):				
Newcastle		Vaccinate in areas where the disease is prevalent in turkeys. Where Newcastle vaccine is used, give it 2 weeks before or after fowl pox vaccine.		
Fowl pox	Age:	8 to 12 weeks.	When breeders are selected.	
Erysipelas	Age:	8 weeks, in areas where erysipelas is present.		
Fowl cholera		Vaccinate with cholera bacterin.		

[1]"Chicks for replacement pullets" portion of this table taken from *Maine Poultry Vaccination Schedule & Record for Laying Flocks,* Cooperative Extension Service, University of Maine, Orono.

Vaccines should always be used according to the instructions of the manufacturer, regarding time and method. Also, they should be kept cool before being opened and used immediately after they are opened.

In no case should the vaccination program be used as a substitute for

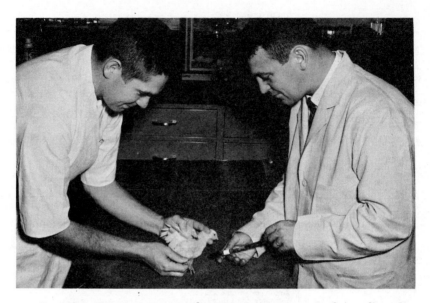

Fig. 42-2. Disease prevention by vaccination is a part of overall poultry management and in the nature of good insurance. This shows a chick being vaccinated. (Courtesy, DeKalb Agricultural Association, Inc., DeKalb, Ill.)

good management. Likewise, no vaccination program is entirely successful without strict management practices to limit possible spread of infection.

Carcass Disposal

Poultrymen find it increasingly important to dispose of dead poultry by methods which are acceptable in an expanding urbanization, as well as economically feasible.

Where there is sufficient concentration of poultry, disposal through a rendering plant is quite satisfactory. Where no such arrangement exists, a disposal pit or an incinerator may be used.

1. **Disposal pit.**—A disposal pit is simply an airtight underground pit covered by boards and earth or concrete, with an opening through which dead birds can be dropped. Disposal pits should not be used where there is a hazard of polluting ground water. With the exception of this precaution, they are entirely satisfactory.

2. **Incinerator.**—Cremation, or burning, is the most satisfactory form of flesh disposal. If done properly, there is no odor, disease, rodent, fly, or water pollution problem. Incinerators may be home-constructed, or a steel-jacketed commercial unit may be purchased. Propane, gas, or oil may be used as the fuel for the incinerator.

Disinfectants and Their Use

The use of disinfectants, substances which have the power to kill micro-

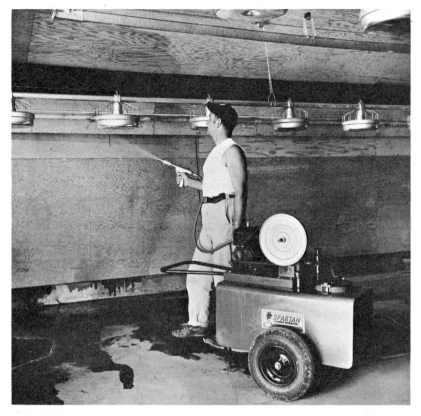

Fig. 42-3. Many disease problems can be avoided by thorough cleaning and disinfecting between broods. (Courtesy, DeKalb Agricultural Association, Inc., DeKalb, Ill.)

organisms, is an important part of disease prevention and control in the poultry establishment. A section on "Disinfectants and Their Use" is given in Chapter V of this book.

DISEASES OF POULTRY

For purposes of convenience and discussion, the diseases of poultry are herein classified as (1) non-nutritional diseases, (2) nutritional diseases and ailments, and (3) other ailments and health problems.

Non-nutritional Diseases

Pertinent facts relative to the most common, and the more devastating, non-nutritional diseases and ailments of poultry are given in Table 42-2.

Nutritional Diseases and Ailments

The vast majority of nutritional deficiency diseases and ailments of poultry are brought about by the deficiency of one or more of the vitamins or minerals.

TABLE 42—2   NON-NUTRITIONAL

Disease	Species Affected	Cause	Symptoms and Signs	Post-Mortem (How they look inside)
Ascites ("Water belly")		Excessive salt intake. Other causes not clearly known.	Abdomen greatly distended, rapid breathing, gasping.	Liquid under skin and in body cavity.
Aspergillosis (Brooder pneumonia)	Almost all birds and animals, including man.	Mold (Aspergillus)	Fever, difficult breathing, nervous symptoms.	Nodules in lungs and air sacs, pus in air sacs.
Blue comb	Chickens Turkeys	Causative agent not definitely identified.	**Chickens:** Increased thirst, loss of appetite, diarrhea, severe drop in egg production, darkening of comb and wattles. **Turkeys:** Poults appear cold and seek heat, stop eating and lose weight.	**Chickens:** Kidneys swollen and pale, mucus in intestines, contents of crop sour, liver may show yellowish pin-point spots. **Turkeys:** Poults show few lesions.
Botulism (Limber-neck; food poisoning)	All domestic fowls and animals, and man. Swine are resistant.	Bacterial toxins from decomposing animal and vegetable matter.	Convulsions, paralysis, and sudden death.	Enteritis
Chronic respiratory disease (C.R.D. or air sac disease)	Chickens	Mycoplasma gallisepticam (PPLO) (E coli causes secondary infection.)	Coughing, gurgling, sneezing, nasal exudate, slow spread, loss in weight.	Mucus in trachea, air sacs thickened and containing yellow pus, thickened membrane over heart.
Coryza (Roup)	All poultry and wild birds.	Bacteria (Hemophilus gallinarium)	Gasping, rattling sound in throat, swollen eyes, nasal discharge, offensive odor.	White to yellow pus in eyes and sinuses.
Epidemic tremor (Avian encephalomyelitis)	Chickens	Virus	Tremors of head and neck, muscular incoordination.	None
Erysipelas	Turkeys primarily, but other fowl affected. Also man and swine.	Bacteria	Sudden losses, swollen snood, discoloration of parts of face, droopy.	Hemorrhages in muscles, mucus in mouth, reddened intestines.
Fowl cholera	Chickens Turkeys Water fowl Other birds	Bacteria (Pasteurella multocida)	Seldom seen in birds under 4 months of age. Fever, purplish head, greenish-yellow droppings, sudden deaths.	Enlarged liver, hemorrhages in heart and in other organs.

Footnote on last page of table.

Distribution and Losses Caused By[1]	Treatment	Prevention	Remarks
	No specific treatment.	Proper amount of salt in ration. Provide proper temperature and ventilation.	
	No treatment.	Avoid musty and moldy feed and litter, provide good ventilation.	
Heaviest losses are in condition and production, but death losses may be high in young turkey poults. Ave. annual losses: Chickens=$1,565,000 Turkeys =$9,285,000	Antibiotics or nitrofurans according to directions.	Sanitation	
	Flush with Epsom salts.	Do not feed spoiled or decomposing feed. Prompt disposal of dead birds and rodents. Avoid wet spots in litter.	
	Antibiotics in feed or water according to directions. In severe outbreaks, inject birds with appropriate antibiotics.	Good management, sanitation, ventilation, and temperature control.	
	Sulfathiazole according to directions.	Keep age groups separate.	
Morbidity in affected flocks averages 5-10%.	None	Vaccination	
Average annual losses: Turkeys=$3,093,000	Use antibiotics according to recommendations. Vaccinate	Keep away from hogs and sheep and from ground used by these animals. Vaccinate	Transmitted via wounds or skin abrasions.
Average annual losses: Chickens=$1,974,000 Turkeys=$2,097,000	Sulfa drugs according to directions. Antibiotics	Sanitation, disposal of sick birds, isolation of new stock. Vaccination	

(Continued)

TABLE 42—2

Disease	Species Affected	Cause	Symptoms and Signs	Post-Mortem (How they look inside)
Fowl pox (Avian pox; avian diptheria; contagious epithelioma; sore head)	Chickens Turkeys Other birds	Virus	Small clear to yellow blisters on comb and wattles that soon scab over; decreased egg production.	May have lesions in throat.
Fowl typhoid	Turkeys Chickens Ducks Pigeons Pheasants	Bacteria (Salmonella gallinarum)	Inactive, fever, greenish-yellow droppings.	Liver and spleen enlarged, bronze or greenish colored liver with some lesions.
Gizzard erosion		Unknown	Unthriftiness, loss of weight, loss of pigment from beak and legs.	Gizzard lining showing patches of shallow fissure, ulcerated, sloughing of portions of the lining.
Hemorrhagic enteritis (Enteritis)	Turkeys	Unknown	Usually the only sign is one or more dead birds.	Severe hemorrhagic inflammation of intestinal lining from gizzard to ceca.
Infectious bronchitis	Chickens only.	Virus	Gasping, wheezing, nasal discharge, sharp and prolonged drop in egg production, soft-shelled eggs.	Yellowish mucus or plugs in lower trachea and air passages in lungs.
Infectious sinusitis	Turkeys	Specific causative agent under investigation.	Nasal discharge, swollen sinuses, labored breathing, coughing.	Exudate in sinuses, cheesy material in air sacs.
Laryngotracheitis (Chicken flu)	Chickens Pheasants	Virus	Gasping, coughing, loss of egg production, soft-shelled eggs, extending of neck outward on inhalation and slumping on exhaling.	Blood-stained mucus in trachea.
Leukosis (Marek's disease) (Big Liver disease; range paralysis)	Chickens Turkeys Other fowls	Viruses	Loss of weight, diarrhea, thickened bones, gray eyes, paralysis of legs or wings.	Enlarged liver and spleen, tumors in various parts of body, enlarged nerve in legs and wings.

Footnote on last page of table.

Distribution and Losses Caused By[1]	Treatment	Prevention	Remarks
Mortality is not high. Economic loss is in reduced feed efficiency and production. Average annual losses: Chickens=$241,000 Turkeys=$515,000	Treatment is of little value.	Vaccination	
Mortality of affected birds ranges from 1 to 40% if treatment not instituted promptly. Average annual losses: Chickens=$1,103,000 Turkeys =$860,000	Nitrofurans or sulfa drugs according to directions.	Get stock from disease-free sources.	Egg and mechanical transmission.
	No specific treatment. Some producers use copper sulfate and feel that this aids.	Good management and feeding balanced ration.	
Average annual losses: Turkeys=$4,916,000	None Changing ration may help.	Good management and prompt removal of dead birds will help.	
When an outbreak occurs, all susceptible chickens get it. Average annual losses: Chickens=$15,581,000	Use of an inhalant to help birds breathe. Keep birds comfortable and eating.	Vaccination	
It may cause significant mortality in poults. Average annual losses: Chickens=$11,004,000 Turkeys=$6,871,000	Injection of antibiotic according to recommendations.	Secure poults from disease-free breeders and keep isolated from chickens.	
Average annual losses: Chickens=$910,000	Keep birds comfortable and stimulate appetite.	Vaccination	
Average annual losses: Chickens and broilers =$58,960,000	None	Buy resistant stock. Raise birds in isolation away from old or adult stock.	Some authorities refer to this as Avian lymphomatosis, or the Avian leucosis complex, of which 5 types are recognized. Big liver disease, or visceral lymphomatosis, is the most common type.

TABLE 42–

Disease	Species Affected	Cause	Symptoms and Signs	Post-Mortem (How they look inside)
Mycosis	Chickens Turkeys Other fowls	Pathogenic fungus (Candida albicans)	Crop distention.	Cheesy scum on crop lining.
Newcastle disease	Chickens Turkeys Other fowls	Virus	Gasping, wheezing, twisting of neck, paralysis, severe drop in egg production, soft-shelled eggs.	Often none. Sometimes mucus in trachea and thickened air sacs containing yellow exudate.
Paratyphoid	Turkeys Other birds	Bacteria (Salmonella group)	Similar to pullorum. Seen mainly in poults.	Enteritis, nodules in wall of intestines.
Pullorum	Chickens Turkeys Other domestic and wild fowl.	Bacteria (Salmonella pullorum)	Highly fatal to young chicks or poults. The symptoms: sleepy, pasted up, inactive. Adults usually do not show recognizable symptoms.	Lesions on lungs, liver and intestines. Unabsorbed egg yolks
Tuberculosis	All poultry	Bacterial (Mycobacterium avium)	Unthriftiness, lowered egg production, and finally death.	Characteristic grayish-white or yellowish tumors of varying sizes in the liver spleen, and intestines.

[1]From: Losses in Agriculture, Handbook No. 291, ARS, USDA, p. 75, 1965. The losses listed are for birds only. In addi there is an average annual loss in poultry products (defective meat and low hatchability) of $147,338,000, or a total annual loss to infectious and non-infectious diseases of $288,224,000.

A summary of these deficiency diseases is given in Tables 40-2 and 40-3, in Chapter XL.

Other Ailments and Health Problems

Although not properly considered diseases, there are several other vices, ailments, or problems which can cause serious problems, and even mortality in a flock. Some of these will be discussed in the section that follows.

1. **Cannibalism.**—Cannibalism may be encountered among birds of all ages. Among baby chicks, the trouble is usually confined to toe and tail picking. With mature birds, the vent, tail, and comb are the regions most frequently picked.

(Continued)

Distribution and Losses Caused By[1]	Treatment		Remarks
Average annual losses: Turkeys=$1,375,000	Copper sulfate in feed.	Sanitation Do not overcrowd.	
Mortality of affected chickens varies from 0 to nearly 100%. Average annual losses: Chickens=$6,580,000	Keep birds comfortable and stimulate appetite.	Vaccination	Symptoms in turkeys are mild; reduction of egg production of turkey breeders is main economic loss.
Mortality in turkey poults usually 1 to 20%. Outbreaks in ducks (keel disease) often run very high. Average annual losses: Chickens=$25,000 Turkeys=$10,664,000	Nitrofurans according to directions. Antibiotics may be used to check mortality.	Buy stock from clean sources.	Egg and mechanical transmission; and through "blow-up" of infected eggs during incubation, and through some feeds.
Mortality in acute outbreaks in birds under 3 weeks of age may approach 90%. Average annual losses: Chickens=$1,575,000 Turkeys=$1,377,000	Nitrofurans or sulfa drugs may be used to check mortality.	Eggs from disease-free breeders, hatched from disease-free incubators.	Primarily egg-transmitted, but transmission may be by other means.
Average annual losses: Chickens=$315,000	None	Sanitation; put new stock in a clean house or on clean ground.	Avian tuberculosis is transmissible to swine, so keep swine and chickens separated.

The cause of cannibalism is not fully understood. It is known that it is more frequent under confined conditions. Without doubt, it may be accentuated by deficiencies in management and nutrition. Also, it may be brought on by just plain boredom.

The best way in which to control cannibalism is by debeaking. Many broiler producers, and some egg producers, have their chicks debeaked at the hatchery. Additionally, layers can be debeaked at the time of housing in the laying house.

2. **Cage fatigue.**—Cage fatigue is a paralytic condition observed in birds held in cages. The disease is most common among high-producing young pullets during the summer. The exact cause is not understood; however, the disorder is considered to be a disturbance in mineral metabolism. Affected birds usually make a spontaneous recovery if placed on the floor or if the cage bottom is covered with newspaper or other such material.

3. **Fatty liver syndrome.**—The "fatty liver disease" continues to be a serious

TABLE 42—

Parasite	Species Affected	Cause	Symptoms	Post-Mortem (How they look inside
Blackhead	Turkeys Chickens, but more resistant than turkeys.	Protozoa *(His-tomonas melea-gridis)*	Droopiness, loss of weight, sulfur-colored diarrhea, and darkened heads.	Lesions in liver and ceca, ceca enlarged, liver enlarged and spotted with dark red or yellow circular areas.
Coccidiosis	Chickens Turkeys	Protozoa *(Eimeria* species)	Bloody droppings (cecal type only), sleepy, pale, ruffled, unthrifty.	Bloody or cheesy plugs in ceca (cecal type). Intestinal wall thickened with small whit or reddish areas (intestinal type).
Hexamitiasis (Infectious catarrhal enteritis)	Turkeys Ducks Quail Partridges Pigeons But not chickens	Turkeys: the one-celled parasite *Hexamita melea-gridis.*	Listlessness, foamy and watery diar-rhea, and convulsions.	Dehydration, emacia tion, thin and water intestinal content and bulbous area in intestines.
Large round-worms	Chickens Turkeys	Ascarid infestation *(Ascaridia galli)*	Pale head and legs, poor flesh.	Roundworms, 1½-3 in long, in intestines
Leucocytozoo-rosis	Turkeys Ducks	Protozoa *(Leucocy-tozoon)*	Symptoms not apparent in older birds. Loss of appetite, droopiness, weakness, increased thirst and rapid, labored breathing, in young turkeys.	
Lice	All poultry, with a separate species of lice for each class of poultry.	Several species of lice.	Frequent picking, pale head and legs, loss of weight.	
Mite infestation (Mites on body only during night)	All poultry.	Common red, or roost, mites *(Der-manyssus galli-nae)*	Droopy, pale condition and listlessness, and reduced egg production.	
Mite infestation (Mites always on body)		Northern fowl mites or feather mites.	Droopy, pale condition and listlessness.	
Tapeworms	Chickens Turkeys Other birds	Several species of tapeworms.	Pale head and legs, poor flesh.	Tapeworms in intes tines.

Footnote on last page of table.

PARASITES OF POULTRY

Distribution and Losses Caused by[1]	Treatment	Prevention	Remarks
Average annual losses: Chickens=$4,795,000 Turkeys=$4,513,000	Drugs in feed or water according to directions.	Sanitation, frequent range rotation. Do not crowd. Preventive medication in feed and water according to directions. Do not keep chickens and turkeys on same premises.	Transmitted by droppings from infected birds.
Average annual losses: Chickens=$34,854,000 Turkeys=$11,866,000	Intermittent medication in feed or soluable form of drugs in water according to directions.	Preventive medication in feed or water according to directions. Vaccination.	Transmitted by droppings of infected birds.
Average annual losses: Turkeys=$1,895,000	Does not respond well to treatment.	Segregation of age groups, and sanitation.	
Average annual losses: Chickens and turkeys= $16,857,000	Deworming preparations according to directions.	Sanitation and rotation of range and yards. Careful use of old litter.	
Average annual losses: Turkeys=$66,000	Sulfaquinoxaline will reduce losses.	Lack of black fly population, and not rearing turkeys near running streams. Brooding in screened houses.	
Average annual losses from lice and mites: Chickens and turkeys =$75,000,000	See Table 42—4, this chapter, for treatment recommendation.	Sanitation. Examine birds periodically for lice infestations.	
(See Lice)	See Table 42—4, this chapter, for treatment recommendation.	Sanitation. Examine birds frequently for signs of mites.	
(See Lice)	See Table 42—4, this chapter, for treatment recommendation.	Examine birds frequently for evidence of mite infestation.	
Average annual losses: Chickens and turkeys= $122,000.	None completely satisfactory.	Control snails, earthworms, beetles, and flies.	

(Continued)

TABLE 42—

Parasite	Species Affected	Cause	Symptoms	Post-Mortem (How they look inside
Trichomoniasis	Turkeys Chickens Pigeons Quail	Protozoa (Trichomonas gallinae)	Loss of appetite, droopiness, loss of weight, and darkened heads.	Lesions—necrotic ulcerations—in the upper digestive tract affecting the crop in particular.

[1]From: *Losses in Agriculture*, Agricultural Handbook No. 291, ARS, USDA, pp. 80 & 82, 1965. Losses from other internal parasites not listed in this column, plus chicken and turkey egg losses of $317,000 due to coccidiosis, make for total annual loss caused by internal parasites of $77,432,000. In addition to the losses from lice and mites, ticks cause an annual loss of $750,000 and mosquitoes of $13,500,000, making for a total annual loss due to external parasites of poultry of $89,250,000.

anomaly in commercial egg operations. It is characterized by deranged fat metabolism resulting in the deposition of excess fat in the liver and body cavities. It is seen most commonly in caged birds, but on occasion it may strike floor birds, particularly in the heavy breeds. The cause is unknown. However, factors which predispose the condition include reduced activity in a cage operation and use of high energy feeds. Although the cause of fatty liver disease is not known, it does appear that higher levels than normally fed of choline, vitamin E, and vitamin B_{12} give favorable responses in preventing the disease.

4. **Aplastic anemia.**—This disease, sometimes referred to as hemorrhagic anemia syndrome, is characterized by hemorrhage and anemia. It is considered to be a disease of chickens only, although there have been reports of its occurrence in turkeys. The condition may affect birds of all ages, but usually those between 4 and 12 weeks of age. The economic losses are in mortality and retarded growth. Little information is available regarding the cause, treatment, and prevention of "aplastic anemia."

5. **Pendulous crop.**—This condition, sometimes known as "baggy crop," or "drop crop," may be found among chickens and among growing poults two to three months of age. The condition may be caused by irregular feeding and by over-consumption of feed or water at any given time. It also seems that there are fewer baggy crops where turkeys are in houses which are not overheated, and when there is adequate shade for poults on the range.

PARASITES OF POULTRY

The prevention and control of parasites is one of the quickest, cheapest, and most dependable methods of increasing meat and egg production with no extra birds, no additional feed, and little more labor. In total, it is estimated that internal parasites of poultry cause an average annual loss of more than $77 million, and external parasites of poultry cause an added loss of nearly $90 million.[2]

---

[2] *Losses in Agriculture*, Agriculture Handbook No. 291, ARS, U. S. Department of Agriculture, pp. 80 and 82, 1965.

(Continued)

Distribution and Losses Caused by[1]	Treatment	Prevention	Remarks
Average annual losses: Chickens=$823,000 Turkeys=$1,186,000	Copper sulfate (bluestone) in drinking water; 1:2,000 dilution for 4-7 days.	Sanitation, clean feed and water.	

Fig. 42-4. Concrete floors may be easily and thoroughly cleaned. Several groups of high quality replacement pullets have been produced in this house in York County, Pennsylvania. (Courtesy, DeKalb Agricultural Association, Inc., DeKalb, Ill.)

Internal Parasites of Poultry

In summary form, the most common internal parasites of poultry, including the treatment and prevention of each, is given in Table 42-3. In using any of the vermifuges, the poultryman should use them according to the manufacturer's directions and in keeping with pure food and drug regulations.

External Parasites of Poultry

External parasites cause birds to look unsightly, reduce weight gains and egg production, and mar the skin. The result is downgrading of quality and lower market value. Heavy infestations cause high mortality among young poults. Studies have shown that poultry lice and mites can sometimes reduce weight gains and egg production from 2 to 25 per cent, or more.

The most common external parasites of poultry, along with recommended control measures, are given in Table 42-4. Any insecticide used on poultry,

TABLE 42—4

HANDY INSECTICIDE CHART FOR THE CONTROL OF EXTERNAL PARASITES OF POULTRY[1]

Insect	Insecticide	Tolerance (p.p.m. in fat unless otherwise indicated)	Min. Days From Last Application To Slaughter	Formulation And Strength	Amount of Formulation per Animal Unless Otherwise Indicated	Where and When to Apply	Safety Restrictions
Lice or mites	Coumaphos	1 meat and fat, 0 eggs	—	WP, 0.25% S	1 gal./1,000 sq. ft. of surface	Thorough coverage.	Do not contaminate feed or water, or water utensils or feed troughs.
				5% D	2 oz./100 sq. ft. of surface or 6.6 oz. per 100 sq. ft. of litter		Do not spray in a confined, non-ventilated area.
				0.5% D	5 lb./100 sq. ft. of litter, 1.4 lbs./100 sq. ft. of interior space.		Do not use coumaphos more often than once a week.
	Malathion	4 meat, 0 eggs	—	WP, 0.25% S	1 gal./100 birds	Direct on birds.	Do not use coumaphos dust or spray on birds within 10 days of vaccination or other stress influence or in conjunction with other organic phosphates. Provide thorough ventilation while dusting.
				0.5% D	1 lb./100 birds		
				3% roost paint	1 pt./150 ft.	Paint roosts thoroughly.	
				EC or WP, 1% S, 4-5% D	1-2 gal./1,000 sq. ft., 1 lb./50-60 sq. ft. of litter	Thorough coverage. Force into cracks.	
				4% D	1 lb./100 birds	Direct on birds. Dip only 3 or 4 inches of the tail.[2]	
				EC or WP, 0.5% S or 0.2% dip	1 gal./100 birds (1 gal./400 birds in dip)		

(Continued)

(Continued)

TABLE 42—4 (Continued)

Insect	Insecticide	Tolerance (p. p. m. in fat unless otherwise indicated)	Min. Days From Last Application To Slaughter	Formulation And Strength	Amount of Formulation per Animal Unless Otherwise Indicated	Where and When to Apply	Safety Restrictions
Lice or mites (cont.)	Naled	—		EC, 0.3% S	1 gal./100 birds	Apply as a light mist to birds, except heads.	Do not apply naled direct on chickens under 6 weeks old or on turkeys under 3 months old.
	Carbaryl	5 meat and fat 0 eggs	7	EC, 0.3% S	2 gal./1,000 sq. ft.	Thorough coverage.	
				5% D	1 lb./100 birds	Dust birds thoroughly. Repeat in 4 weeks if needed, but not more often.	Do not contaminate feed or water, or water utensils or feed troughs.
				5% D	1 lb./40 sq. ft. of litter and roosts	Thorough coverage. Force into cracks.	
				WP, 0.5% S	1-2 gal./1,000 sq. ft.		Do not spray in a confined, non-ventilated area.
				4% water mist spray	1.5 gal./1,000 birds with electric fog machine	Direct on birds, roosts, and walls.	Do not apply carbaryl spray on birds except in a water mist spray. Do not treat nest litter. Ventilate while spraying.
					1 gal./100 birds with cylinder sprayer		
	Nicotine sulfate[3]	—		4.0% nicotine soln.	1 pt./150-200 ft.	Paint on roosts only.	Do not repeat treatment within 4 weeks.
Lice only	Rotenone	—		1% D	1 lb./100 birds	Direct on birds, roosts and nests.	
Depluming mite only (Knemidokoptes gallinae)	Sulfur	Safe	—	100% D 1-2 oz. WP/ gal. water dip	—	Dust or immerse thoroughly.	

Footnotes on last page of table.

(Continued)

TABLE 42-4 (Continued)

Insect	Insecticide	Tolerance (p.p.m. in fat unless otherwise indicated)	Min. Days From Last Application To Slaughter	Formulation And Strength	Amount of Formulation per Animal Unless Otherwise Indicated	Where and When to Apply	Safety Restrictions
Fowl tick (Argas persicus)	Malathion	4 meat 0 eggs	—	EC or WP, 3% S	1-2 gal./1,000 sq. ft.	Thorough coverage of walls, ceilings, and floors.	
	Carbaryl	5 meat and fat 0 eggs	7	WP, 2% S	1-2 gal./1,000 sq. ft.	Force into cracks.	Do not apply naled direct on chickens under 6 weeks old or on turkeys under 3 months old.
	Naled	—	—	EC, 0.3% S	2 gal./1,000 sq. ft.		

[1]From: Agricultural Handbook No. 331, ARS, U.S. Department of Agriculture, Washington, D.C., pp. 178, 179, 1968.
[2]Northern fowl mite (Ornithonyssus sylviarum), chicken body louse (Menacanthus stramineus), and shaft louse (Menopon gallinae).
[3]Not for control of Dermanyssus gallinae.

Use Pesticides Safely—Follow the Label

should be used in keeping with the manufacturer's directions and in accord with Pure Food and Drug regulations.

QUESTIONS FOR STUDY AND DISCUSSION

1. What is the normal temperature, pulse rate, and breathing rate of (a) chickens and (b) turkeys? How would you determine each?
2. Select a specific poultry farm (either your own or one with which you are familiar) and outline (in 1, 2, 3, order) a program of poultry health, disease prevention, and parasite control.
3. Assume that a specific contagious disease (you name it) has broken out in a flock. What steps would you take to meet the situation (list in 1, 2, 3, order; be specific)?
4. Assume that a specific parasite (you name it) has become troublesome in a particular flock. What steps would you recommend taking to meet the situation (list in 1, 2, 3, order; be specific)?
5. Why are diagnostic laboratories more frequently used by poultrymen than by producers of four-footed animals?
6. How do the so-called normal death losses of poultry, as given in this chapter, compare with the mortality of other classes of livestock?

SELECTED REFERENCES

Title of Publication	Author(s)	Publisher
Animal Diseases	Yearbook of Agriculture, 1956	U.S. Department of Agriculture, Washington, D.C.
Animal Sanitation and Disease Control	R. R. Dykstra	The Interstate Printers & Publishers, Inc., Danville, Ill., 1961.
Diseases of Poultry	H. E. Biester L. H. Schwartz	The Iowa State University Press, Ames, Iowa.
Infectious Diseases of Domestic Animals, The	W. A. Hagan D. W. Bruner	Comstock Publishing Associates, Ithaca, N. Y., 1957.
Keeping Livestock Healthy	Yearbook of Agriculture, 1942	U.S. Department of Agriculture, Washington, D.C.
Merck Veterinary Manual, The, 2nd Edition		Merck and Company, Rahway, New Jersey, 1967.
Suggested Guide for the Use of Insecticides to Control Insects Affecting Crops, Livestock, Households, Stored Products, and Forest Products, 1968	Agricultural Handbook No. 313	U.S. Department of Agriculture, Washington, D.C.
Veterinary Medicine	D. C. Blood J. A. Henderson	The Williams and Wilkins Co., Baltimore, Maryland, 1960.

In addition to these selected references, valuable publications on different subjects pertaining to poultry diseases, parasites, disinfectants, and related matters can be obtained from the following sources: Division of Publications, Office of Information, U.S. Department of Agriculture, Washington, D.C.; your state agricultural college; and several biological, pharmaceutical, and chemical companies.

Chapter XLIII

SPECIALIZATION; BUSINESS MANAGEMENT IN POULTRY PRODUCTION

Contents	Page
Chicken Production	1026
Chicken Breeding	1026
Breeding Methods	1027
Breeding for Broiler Production	1027
Breeding for Egg Production	1027
Chicken Breeding Management Practices	1028
Growing Replacement Pullets	1029
Starter Pullet Management	1030
Broiler Production	1030
Current Trends in Broiler Production	1031
Size of Enterprise	1032
Housing and Equipment	1032
Controlled Environment	1032
Selecting Chicks	1033
Management Practices and Guides	1033
Production Goals	1033
Commercial Egg Production	1033
Current Trends in Egg Production	1033
Financing	1034
Size Flock	1034
Housing and Equipment	1035
Breeds	1035
Management Practices and Guides	1035
Production Goals	1036
Turkey Production	1036
Turkey Breeding	1036
Selection	1037
Breeding Systems	1037
Artificial Insemination	1037
Artificial Lighting	1038
Facilities	1038
Management Practices and Guides	1038
Market Turkey Production	1039
Market Contracts	1039
Buildings and Equipment	1040
Management Practices and Guides	1040
Duck Production	1040
Geese Production	1041
Game and Ornamental Bird Production	1042
Hatcheries	1042
Trends in the Hatching Industry	1042
Business and Management Aspects of Poultry Production	1043
Broiler Contracts	1044
Basic Considerations for Contracts	1044
Major Specifications to Be Spelled Out	1044
Type of Contracts	1045
Turkey and Egg Contracts	1045
Manure	1046
Records	1047
Questions for Study and Discussion	1047
Selected References	1048

No phase of American agriculture has undergone such pronounced changes as has the poultry industry during the past 20 years. Broiler and turkey production have skyrocketed in numbers; and poultry has shifted from small farm flocks, often accorded the neglect of a minor enterprise, to large commercial flocks. Hand in hand with this transition has come a high degree of specialization. For example, the commercial egg producer no longer hatches his own replacement stock. Instead, he relies upon highly specialized chicken breeders to produce the foundation stock and on hatcheries to multiply and incubate. More than likely he even relies on another specialized enterprise to raise his replacement pullets.

With the growth of highly specialized enterprises, business methods have also changed. Big enterprises require more financing. In turn, this has spawned vertical integration and contractual arrangements.

The general principles of poultry breeding, feeding, health, buildings and equipment, and marketing are covered elsewhere in this book; hence, repetition at this point is unnecessary. Instead, this chapter is devoted to the practical application of these principles to each of the highly specialized types of poultry production.

CHICKEN PRODUCTION

Modern chicken production embraces the following specialized types of operations: chicken breeding, growing replacement pullets, broiler production, and commercial egg production.

Chicken Breeding

The breeding of chickens has become a highly specialized industry. Today, from a commercial standpoint, the small farm flock poultry breeder is almost a thing of the past. The number of chicken breeding farms has been greatly reduced, and chicken breeders have become very large. Today's chicken breeding industry is a complex, specialized, and highly competitive aspect of poultry production.

Chicken breeding is dominated by the foundation breeder and the hatcheryman, usually joined together under a franchise arrangement. The foundation breeder is concerned with genetic improvement, whereas the hatcheryman multiplies the stock supplied by the foundation breeder, hatches the eggs, and sells the chickens.

Foundation breeders generally employ well-trained geneticists, veterinarians, and physiologists to direct their breeding programs. They recognize the importance of "name lines" or "trade names," which they copyright and promote. These trade names are as identifying as a make of car or a brand of shoes.

Modern foundation chicken breeding farms are organized along the lines of any other big and successful business. They are generally departmentalized— breeding, sales, foreign markets, advertising, business management, purchases, etc.—with specially trained personnel in each division. In their breeding programs, they employ advanced techniques and make use of data-processing equipment.

BREEDING METHODS

Commercial egg and broiler producers are not interested in breed fancy points. No bird meets with their favor unless it efficiently produces meat or eggs, as the case may be. As a result of this thinking, interest has shifted from the *Standard of Perfection,* or so-called Standard breeding, to the breeding of crosses or strains for efficient production of meat and eggs. Individual birds in the flock have no value only insofar as they increase the total egg or meat production of the flock. That is, they have no value as a Standard breed as such. This change of emphasis from the individual bird (Standard breeding) to the flock performance (flock breeding) has greatly changed both breeds and methods of breeding. Each modern breeder produces his own strain and selects only for their value to produce eggs or meat.

BREEDING FOR BROILER PRODUCTION

Most of the effort in broiler breeding in recent years has been directed toward increasing the rate of growth. To this end, chickens used for breeding to improve broiler growth rate are selected at eight weeks of age. Those which weigh the most in each brood are the ones chosen for breeders.

Hybrid vigor is obtained by systematic matings that may involve crossing of different breeds, different strains of the same breed, or the crossing of inbred lines. In addition to hybrid vigor, improvement in economic factors often result from these crosses, provided the mating includes stock having superior qualities of genetic origin.

The end product—modern white, yellow-shanked broiler—is often obtained by crossing the male line from specialized breeders with female lines produced likewise by specialists. Each line may be the result of crossing two or more strains. The male lines usually have dominant white feathers and are selected for rapid growth; meat characteristics such as breast width, body depth, live market grade, and dressing yield; and rapid feathering. The female line also must have outstanding growth rate, high hatchability, and good, but not outstanding, production of eggs of desirable size and texture. In recent years, considerable attention has been given to selection for livability, feed efficiency, skin texture, skin and shank pigmentation, and, in the case of large broilers, roasters, and capons, feathering on the breast or absence of breast blisters.

It is noteworthy that in breeding for broiler production, inbred lines have not been used.

BREEDING FOR EGG PRODUCTION

Breeders for egg production must supply stock that will lay well. In addition, the eggs must be of desirable size and shape, shell texture, and interior quality. Also, the birds must have good livability.

Breeding for egg production differs from breeding for broiler production primarily because egg production as a trait is of low heritability. By contrast, the rate and efficiency of gain of broilers are of high heritability. Hence, in breeding for egg production, family selection rather than individual merit of a particular bird in the flock is considered.

Tests

Public tests are designed to measure the egg or meat production of the multitude of commercial crosses. The most popular of these tests is known as the Random Sample Test. Many states and regions are conducting official Random Sample Tests. The results of all American Official Poultry Tests are summarized each year in bulletin form. This summary bulletin may be obtained from the Agricultural Research Service, U.S. Department of Agriculture, Washington, D.C. Current reports are available directly from each test management.

Stocks which grow or lay better than the average for all entries in each test are the better ones to select for meat or egg production. Any cross which is above the average of its test for several years, or in several tests, is an excellent choice.

In the larger egg or broiler operations, a common practice is to test several stocks on one farm where suitable facilities are available and careful records are kept. Where such studies are made, it is important that the housing, feeding, and management be uniform for all stocks in order to obtain a valid comparison of the factors affecting economic return—egg production, feed consumption, and mortality in layers; rate of growth, pounds of chicken per 100 pounds of feed, mortality, and quality of broilers produced. This information will provide a more reliable basis for the selection of stock if the tests are repeated on a second or third farm. Of course, the farm or farms selected for the tests should follow production practices typical of the area.

CHICKEN BREEDING MANAGEMENT PRACTICES

Every condition for the efficient production of table eggs is required for the production of hatching eggs. In addition, there are certain management practices, and costs, which are peculiar to chicken breeding operations and which do not apply to commercial egg production. Among these, are the following:

1. Cost of production.—Breeders of egg-type chicks are retained for 12 months or more of production, whereas breeders of broiler-type chicks are seldom profitable after 9 to 10 months of laying. The hatching-egg yield of broiler-supply flocks averages between 40 and 60 per cent during this 9- to 10-month period, while egg-type supply flocks average 60 to 70 per cent or even higher for the longer period. Broiler hatching eggs are, therefore, more costly to produce.

The extra cost involved in producing eggs for broiler hatches arises from the greater feed cost per dozen eggs due to larger bodies and lower egg production per hen. Also, more floor space (about 3 square feet per bird) is required than the normal 2 to 2½ square feet of floor space used for the small egg-type hens.

2. **Methods of mating.**—Pedigree matings are used where information is desired on family performance. This consists of 1 male and about 15 females housed in a separate pen. The females are trap-nested so that each egg may be identified for pedigree hatching. When the eggs are transferred to the hatching trays on the eighteenth day of incubation, each hen's eggs are placed in a separate basket. Following hatching, the chicks in each basket are wing banded to identify their parentage.

Flock matings are more common. The females are housed in large flocks varying from 100 to 1,000 or more per pen. In broiler-type stock, about 8 males per 100 females are placed together; in egg-type chickens, fewer males are used—usually about 6 per 100 females.

3. **Selecting and handling hatching eggs.**—Certain physical characteristics of eggs are related to hatchability. For best results, hatching eggs should be neither too large nor too small. They should be of normal shape with strong clean shells.

Usually a reasonably high percentage of fertile eggs can be expected a week after the males are put in the flock, but maximum fertility will not be reached until approximately two weeks after adding males.

Eggs are suitable for hatching any time after the flock has been laying longer than six weeks, or about a month after the flock has reached 50 eggs per 100 hens. Pullets are about seven months of age at this time.

Improper care of hatching eggs can greatly reduce their hatchability (see Chapter XLIV, section on "Handling Hatching Eggs").

Growing Replacement Pullets

A recent trend in poultry production involves specialization within a specialization. For example, some commercial egg producers are only concerned with producing market eggs—leaving the rearing of replacement pullets to other specialists. This means that the commercial chicken producer has two alternatives of specializing—raising replacement pullets or producing eggs. Likewise, the commercial egg producer has two alternatives in procuring replacement stock: (1) growing his own baby chicks or (2) buying started pullets. The majority of large commercial egg producers today prefer to buy started pullets rather than raise their own. In the final analysis, the choice of the system should be based on the cost of pullets of the desired quality, with added consideration given to available facilities and labor.

Many factors influence the cost of pullets, whether they are grown by the layer operator or purchased; and these vary from area to area, year to year, and farm to farm. Approximate percentages of the different items are: feed, 60 per cent; chick, 15 per cent; labor, 15 per cent; and all other costs, 10 per cent.

The grower of started pullets should be a specialist—one whose business is raising pullets to sell. He should not have any adult birds on his farm unless he is large enough to keep the two operations well separated.

STARTER PULLET MANAGEMENT

Well bred and well grown, healthy, vigorous started pullets are requisite to success in the laying house. Proper feeding, care, and management during the pullet starting period can develop the potential productive egg capacity of the birds, whereas poor practices and management may reduce or obliterate the genetic potential that has been bred into them. The following management pointers in raising started pullets are recommended:

1. **Sanitation.**—A strict sanitation program is a must in raising started pullets. Recommended rules are: (a) do not mix ages or strains of birds in the same house; (b) do not allow visitors in the house; (c) screen out birds and control rats, mice, and other rodents; (d) do not permit contaminated equipment to come on the farm; (e) use incinerator or disposal pit for dead birds; (f) keep birds free from external and internal parasites; and (g) post all dead birds.

2. **Vaccination.**—The vaccination program should be in keeping with the needs of the area. Also, it should be completed far enough ahead of moving the pullets so that they will not be going through a vaccination reaction during or soon after moving.

3. **Debeaking and dubbing.**—Pullets should be debeaked at 9 to 16 weeks of age, perhaps at the same time that they are vaccinated for fowl pox. This will make for a permanent job.

Dubbing (removal of the comb) should be done when the birds are a day old. Dubbing alleviates a source of injury, especially to caged birds, and results in 2 to 4 per cent more eggs.

4. **Lights.**—The lighting system used will depend on the type of building and the season of the hatch. It should be designed to avoid an increasing photoperiod during the last half to three-fourths of the growing period.

5. **Moving the pullets.**—The pullets should be moved in such manner that there will be a minimum of stress. This calls for clean (preferably steamed) coops and truck, not moving in inclement weather, providing fresh air but avoiding drafts during the move, and gentle handling.

Broiler Production

Commercial broiler production is a highly specialized and complex business enterprise. During the past two decades, it has been the fastest growing segment of the poultry industry. The total output increased from 34,000,000 broilers in 1934 to 2,568,338,000 in 1966. Broilers now account for over $1.3 billion of the $3.5 billion total annual income from poultry and poultry products in the U.S.

No other segment of agriculture is as well suited to assembly-line production techniques as broiler production.

Fig. 43-1. Broilers produced by Fred Armitage, Salinas, California. (Courtesy, James Mfg. Co., Fort Atkinson, Wisc.)

CURRENT TRENDS IN BROILER PRODUCTION

The broiler industry has been characterized by rapid changes. Many of the recommendations of 10 years ago no longer hold good. Among the pertinent trends affecting broiler production are the following:

1. **Shift in production centers.**—In recent years, the center of broiler production has moved from the Eastern Seaboard—the Delmarva Peninsula, Maine, and Connecticut—to the southeastern states of Georgia and North Carolina and the south central states of Arkansas, Alabama, Mississippi, and Texas. In 1964, the 10 leading states in broiler production produced 1,800 million birds, or 84 per cent of all the broilers in this nation. Area competition is primarily dependent on production and transportation costs of processed broilers.

2. **Integration.**—Probably 95 per cent of the broilers of the U.S. are grown under some type of vertical integration or contractual arrangement.

In the beginning, most commercial broiler production was by independent growers. They paid cash for everything and took all the profit. However, as margins became smaller, and flocks became larger, there was need for more credit. At first, the local feed dealer was the source of credit. As the industry grew, feed dealers began to depend on feed manufacturers as a source of funds. Then, to spread their risks, both feed dealers and feed manufacturers integrated vertically with hatcheries and processors.

Integration may include one or more phases, such as financing, feed, hatching, breeding stock, production, processing, and retail marketing. In most cases, the production of breeding stock and retailing have not been included.

3. **Financing.**—Today, banks and the production credit associations largely finance the broiler industry through credit extended to feed manufacturers, dressing plants processors, hatcherymen, and integrated operations. Much of this money is loaned at the local level to growers with mortgages as collateral.

One of the principal reasons for the rapid expansion of the poultry industry in the South has been that financing is easier in that area, poultry house construction is cheaper, labor is cheaper, and more capital is available to invest in poultry enterprises.

4. **Contracts.**—A contract is a legal agreement between the grower and the integrated operator. The numerous types of broiler contracts now being used indicate the need for those involved to have a clear understanding of the various specifications and their possible impact on any present or future method of operation.

SIZE OF ENTERPRISE

A competent man on a full-time basis, with mechanical feeders and waterers, can care for 36,000 to 45,000 broilers at a time. However, not all broiler operations are mechanized. Further, not all operators devote full time to the enterprise. As a result, there are many small operations. But even most part-time operators will not undertake a broiler enterprise unless it will provide at least a quarter of the income. This means that most of them will have at least 5,000 broilers per lot. There is also an increasing number of very large broiler establishments, with 60 to over 100,000 capacity at any one time.

HOUSING AND EQUIPMENT

The space requirements for broiler housing and equipment are given in Table 41-2. There are, of course, many different styles and designs of houses, and even more variations in equipment. The important thing is that broiler houses and equipment provide comfortable conditions, including adequate feed and water, so that the birds can perform at the highest level of which they are genetically capable. A satisfactory broiler house must protect against heat and cold, high winds, and inclement weather. Generally speaking, a 10,000 to 12,000 bird house is considered ideal for efficient broiler production. Most houses are 24 to 40 feet wide and as long as necessary to accommodate a minimum of 10,000 to 12,000 birds.

CONTROLLED ENVIRONMENT

There is a tendency for the larger and better financed broiler operators to construct environmentally controlled housing. These are windowless, fan-ventilated, and insulated. With this type of arrangement, it is possible to provide a more uniform temperature, along with a proper supply of clean fresh air without drafts. The final result is an improved market quality of bird and higher income.

SELECTING CHICKS

The selection of commercial broiler stock can make the difference between profit and loss. Accordingly, it is most important that the broiler producer select stock which, from a genetic standpoint, is capable of producing a high quality product as efficiently as possible.

Very little convincing data are available showing that the advantages of separating the sexes, if any, offset the cost involved. Thus, straight-run chicks are generally used for raising broilers. Also, since the demand has been for only white-feathered broilers, there has been very little interest in sex-linked crosses, which facilitate separating the sexes at hatching time.

MANAGEMENT PRACTICES AND GUIDES

The management practices and guides followed by most successful broiler producers include the following:

1. Only one age on the farm at any one time.
2. Debeak chicks when necessary.
3. Use all-night lights.
4. Adapt vaccination schedule (Table 42-1) to local needs.
5. Keep visitors out of houses; lock doors.
6. With automatic feeders, not more than 18 minutes labor should be required per 1,000 broilers per day; without automatic equipment, labor should not exceed 31 minutes.
7. Use 2 to 4 inches of litter—less in hot weather.

PRODUCTION GOALS

Broiler producers should aim for broilers with an average weight production of over 3 pounds at eight weeks of age. Feed conversion should be less than 2.15, and mortality should be under 1 per cent.

Commercial Egg Production

Specialization and business are the key words in modern egg production. The industry is changing rapidly and providing new opportunities for those who can meet its requirements.

The time has passed when egg production can be considered a small side-line operation, worthy only of the leftovers of the producer's time and money. Current commercial egg production units represent major enterprises in which success or failure depends largely on good production and business management practices. Of course, an important tool in business management is the maintenance and use of accurate records.

CURRENT TRENDS IN EGG PRODUCTION

In recent years, the number of laying flocks has become fewer and the size of the flocks larger. Where this will stabilize, no one knows. In California, flocks

Fig. 43-2. Layers in individual cages on the poultry farm of Kenneth Bishop, Edwardsburg, Mich. (Courtesy, James Mfg. Co., Fort Atkinson, Wisc.)

of 75,000 to over 100,000 are not uncommon. These have been described as "egg factories," where inputs of housing, equipment, pullets, feed, supplies, and labor are combined to produce eggs—hopefully for a profit.

Eastern flocks are somewhat smaller than those in California. In the Midwest, commercial layer flocks vary from 5,000 to 30,000, although many of these operations are increasing in size today.

In the West and East, the layer flock usually constitutes the only enterprise. It is expected that this type of operation will increase in the Midwest.

FINANCING

Unlike the situation in broiler production, most egg-laying operations are owner-financed. It is noteworthy, however, that leasing of buildings and equipment and contract egg production are on the increase.

Most egg contracts require that the operator furnish housing, equipment, and labor, with the contractor supplying the pullets, feed, medication, and some supervision. For his facilities and services, the owner usually receives 4 to 6 cents per dozen eggs sold plus a bonus for superior egg production and feed conversion.

SIZE FLOCK

The size of flocks has been increasing steadily over the years. The determining factors in size of flock are: (1) amount of income which the owner wishes to derive from the business, (2) how the egg-producing business fits in with the other farm enterprises or other employment, (3) method of marketing eggs, and (4) available finances and labor.

Generally speaking, a flock of 5,000 or more hens is more efficient than one of smaller size.

HOUSING AND EQUIPMENT

Layer houses and equipment come in many styles and sizes. The space requirements are given in Table 41-2, Chapter XLI, so repetition is not necessary at this point. Likewise, the types of layer houses along with management systems are covered in Chapter XLI.

BREEDS

Unless there is a premium market for brown eggs, it is recommended that either White Leghorns, or Leghorn crosses, be used for commercial production. Hens require about eight pounds of feed per year per pound of body weight just for maintenance. Heavy breeds average from 1 to 1½ pounds more body weight than Leghorns and require 8 to 12 pounds more feed per year. If feed costs 4 cents per pound, this means that it will cost 30 to 50 cents more to keep a heavy hen for a year than a Leghorn. Of course, the heavy hen brings more as a cull, but the difference does not compensate for the extra feed consumed. Egg production is about the same, or perhaps even a little lower for the heavy hen.

It is more important to get a high-producing strain than to get a particular breed or cross. It pays to make a careful check on the stock before purchasing, possibly by inquiring how well it performed in laying tests.

MANAGEMENT PRACTICES AND GUIDES

Bigness alone does not assure success of profit in commercial egg production. Rather, it makes it imperative that there be superior management. Among the management practices and guides followed by successful commercial egg producers are the following:

1. An average of 20 eggs per bird per month is a good standard for high producing strains.

2. Mortality of about 1 per cent per month for layers is normal.

3. Lights should be provided so as to make for about a 14-hour working day for the hens. Lights may also be used to help bring slow-maturing pullets into lay.

4. Culling should be done to remove diseased or low vitality birds. With high producing strains, little, if any, culling may be required. Accurate records should be kept on percentage of lay, feed intake, mortality, and other pertinent facts.

5. Eggs should be gathered three to five times daily, cleaned immediately, and stored at 55°F. and 75 to 80 per cent relative humidity.

6. Where the cage system is followed, it is important that there be a regular spray schedule, along with proper dropping management to control flies, that birds be debeaked if multiple caging is used, and that cages and waterers be cleaned once each week.

7. Ventilation should provide fresh air and remove moisture, without producing drafts. The condition of the litter and the amount of fumes (ammonia fumes) are good indicators of the adequacy of ventilation.

PRODUCTION GOALS

The producer of commercial eggs strives for the maximum of egg production at a minimum cost—yet, bearing in mind that net returns are more important than costs as such

The largest item of cost in the production of eggs is feed. It normally constitutes 50 to 60 per cent of the total cost, though, in exceptional cases, it may run as low as 45 per cent, or as high as 65 per cent. Labor costs and cost of replacement pullets are the other two major cost items in production.

Generally speaking, higher egg production means lower costs per dozen eggs. This is so because the feed required for maintenance is constant for hens of any given weight and bears no relation to the number of eggs laid. Hence, it is important that the commercial producer strive for high egg production.

The following production goals are suggested for the commercial egg producer:

1. Production of 240 eggs per hen per year.
2. Feed conversion of less than 4½ pounds of feed per dozen eggs.
3. A laying house mortality of less than 10 per cent.
4. Seventy-five per cent or more extra large and large Grade A eggs.
5. Ninety-five per cent or more marketable eggs.
6. On-farm egg breakage under 2 per cent.
7. No layers over 19 months old.
8. Mortality of less than 5 per cent from day old to five months.

TURKEY PRODUCTION

Turkey production has long been an important phase of agriculture in the U.S. During the last two decades, it has greatly expanded. In 1946, 39,746,000 turkeys were produced in this country, while the total production sold in 1966 was in excess of 114,000,000 birds.

Turkey Breeding

The breeding of turkeys is the most specialized phase of turkey production. The breeder must have a good knowledge of genetics in order to develop a sound breeding program. Further, all traits of economic importance must be taken into consideration at selection time.

SELECTION

Most turkeys for breeding are selected from flocks being raised for market. However, there is much merit in raising turkeys especially for breeding purposes, and selecting the birds intended for breeding purposes therefrom.

The initial selection of future breeding stock should be made at 12 to 16 weeks of age. An additional and final selection should be made at 22 to 26 weeks of age, or before the remainder of the flock is sent to market. Among the many traits of economic importance for which the breeder should make selection are body type and conformation, livability, health and vigor, early market finish, and rapid feathering. Additionally, selection for reproductive traits—egg production, fertility, and hatchability—is most important. In the case of the reproductive traits, it is necessary to select on a family basis in order to achieve the maximum rate of improvement, while for the physical traits selection of the outstanding individuals is sufficient.

The selection of a variety is largely determined by intended market, along with any preference that the producer may have. In general, the family-size turkey most preferred weighs about 15 pounds or less. Until recently, large-size turkeys were used primarily for the hotel and restaurant trade. However, the further processing of large turkeys is increasing rapidly and turkey is now available in many different forms—canned, cut-up, rolled, and pies.

Breeding Systems

The two most used breeding systems followed in turkeys are (1) pure line and (2) strain crossing. A pure line refers to a flock that has been closed mated (no stock brought in from an outside source) for at least five years. Strain crossing consists in crossing two lines of the same variety—for example, two different lines of Broad-breasted Bronze turkeys.

Crossbreeding was used in the development of the Broad White variety. However, even within this variety, no further crossbreeding was followed after establishing the foundation. To date, therefore, crossbreeding has been little used in turkey breeding.

As has been previously pointed out, chicken breeders have made extensive use of the inbreeding and hybridization techniques of the corn breeder. To date, hybridization breeding in turkeys has been confined largely to the experimental stage.

Male: Female Ratio

One tom to 10 hens of the large varieties, and 1 tom to 15 hens of the small-type strains of turkeys, is recommended.

Artificial Insemination

Artificial insemination in turkeys is considered practical in flocks where natural fertility is below 80 per cent during the early season or below 70 per cent late in the season. In some flocks, a combination of artificial insemination and natural mating is used, with each supplementing the other.

Generally speaking, inseminating the hens every two weeks is considered sufficient. On the other hand, fertility in Broad-breasted Bronze may be improved slightly by inseminating at weekly intervals.

ARTIFICIAL LIGHTING

During the short-day, winter months, artificial lights should be used to stimulate turkeys to lay eggs. A 13- to 15-hour day should be provided about one month before hatching eggs are wanted. A 60-watt lamp with reflectors 6 feet above the floor, every 10 feet in the house, will provide adequate light to stimulate turkeys into egg production. Males should be lighted two to three weeks before the hens to insure maximum fertility.

FACILITIES

Except in the more moderate sections of the country, housing is recommended for turkey breeders. In the North, housing makes it possible to produce hatching eggs out-of-season during the cold winter months. In the warmer sections of the country, turkey breeders can be maintained outside on ranges or in semi-confined lots. Semi-confinement refers to that type of operation where there is a shelter, but with yards or restricted range in connection therewith. Further details relative to the space requirements of buildings and equipment for turkeys is given in Table 41-2.

MANAGEMENT PRACTICES AND GUIDES

Among the pertinent management practices and guides peculiar to, or of particular importance in, the breeding of turkeys are the following:

1. **Saddles.**—These are just what the name implies—canvas saddles fitted over the hens that are to be mated by natural service, prior to the onset of the mating. This prevents much of the loss from hens being torn or cut by the toe nails or spurs of the toms during mating.

2. **Care of broodies.**—Broodiness is responsible for much of the poor egg production in turkeys. Broody hens will produce 20 to 30 fewer eggs than non-broody hens. Consequently, it is very important to remove the broody hens from the rest of the flock as soon as they exhibit such behavior. A good practice is to remove all the hens that are on the nest at dark; then, place them in other quarters, but give them the same care and feed as the other hens in the flock in order to get them back into production as soon as possible. It also helps to move the nests to various locations to discourage broodiness in turkeys.

3. **Debeaking and wing clipping.**—Debeaking of turkeys is commonly done to prevent cannibalism, just as it is with chickens. With turkeys, it is usually done at two to three weeks of age, with at least one-half of the upper beak removed with an electric debeaker.

Wing clipping is done to prevent flight. When practiced, it is done during the first three weeks of life. Poults are wing-clipped by cutting off the tip of one wing just outside the last joint. It can be done with an electric debeaker, which cauterizes the cut and prevents excessive bleeding.

Market Turkey Production

The marketing of turkeys is big business. In 1965, a total of 1.88 billion pounds of turkeys was marketed in the U.S. Another noteworthy statistic is that, in 1966, the per capita consumption of turkeys in the United States was 7.4 pounds, exceeding both lamb (3.7 pounds) and veal (5.2 pounds). These figures clearly indicate that the production and marketing of turkeys are no longer confined to providing a bird for Thanksgiving. Instead, turkey meat is used throughout the year.

Fig. 43-3. Market turkeys at self-feeder. (Photo J. C. Allen and Son, West Lafayette, Ind.)

MARKET CONTRACTS

An estimated 80 to 85 per cent of the nation's turkey crop is handled on a contract basis, in comparison with 95 per cent of the national broiler crop so handled. In general, the types of contracts used in turkey production are very similar to those used in broiler production.

BUILDINGS AND EQUIPMENT

Poults are usually brooded in permanent-type houses. Some growers prefer to brood in batteries for the first two to three weeks before placing the poults on the floor. After 8 to 10 weeks of age, heat is no longer needed. At that time, the poults may be either moved to the range or placed in their confinement quarters for further growing. If properly managed, either system of rearing is satisfactory, although there is an increasing tendency to grow market turkeys in confinement in pole-type shelters. Some market turkey producers do not use range shelters. However, they might be ahead, year after year, were they to provide shelters as they make it possible to use the range forage better and to distribute the manure more evenly over the land.

Turkeys are good foragers. Hence, production costs may be lowered by providing good pasture or such crops as milo.

MANAGEMENT PRACTICES AND GUIDES

The following management practices and guides are pertinent to the raising of market turkeys:

1. **Sexed and unsexed poults.**—Some producers buy day-old sexed poults. Others buy straight-run poults, then separate the sexes at 12 to 14 weeks of age. In any event, most producers raise the sexes apart because (a) slightly better weight gains can be obtained by separating the sexes, either on the range or in confinement, and (b) more efficient gains can be obtained by designing a feed especially for male or female birds after they are 12 weeks old.

2. **Desnooding.**—Desnooding, or the cutting off of the snood of the young poults, is practiced by some growers to prevent injury among mature males. It is believed that this practice helps prevent the spread of erysipelas in the flock. Most hatcherymen will desnood poults for a small fee upon request.

DUCK PRODUCTION

Ducks have for ages been popular with connoisseurs of good food. In spite of this, annual production of ducks in the U.S. has remained in the neighborhood of 10 million, with little change over the past decade; 10.1 million ducks were produced in 1960 and 10.5 million in 1966.

Approximately 60 per cent of the nation's ducks are raised on Long Island, New York. Although climatic conditions on Long Island are ideal for duck production, it is recognized that major production could shift to other areas where feed and labor costs are lower and real estate values and property taxation are more advantageous to the grower.

Most meat ducks are marketed as ducklings, at seven to eight weeks of age. They are generally frozen and ready to cook after thawing.

There is little demand for duck eggs in the United States.

Fig. 43-4. White Pekin ducks. The commercial duck industry of the U.S. relies solely on this breed. (Photo by J. C. Allen and Son, West Lafayette, Ind.)

GEESE PRODUCTION

The production of geese for meat purposes has never enjoyed the popularity in the U.S. that it has in some European countries. In recent years, considerable attention has been focused on raising geese for weeding purposes.

Fig. 43-5. Commercial geese on the range. (Photo by J. C. Allen and Son, West Lafayette, Ind.)

Weeder geese are used with great success to control and eradicate trouble-some grass and certain weeds in a great variety of crops and plantings, including cotton, hops, onions, garlic, strawberries, nurseries, corn, orchards, groves, and vineyards. The geese eat grass and young weeds as quickly as they appear, but they do not touch certain cultivated plants. They will work continuously from daylight to dark, seven days a week (even on bright moonlight nights) nipping off the grass and weeds as promptly as new growth appears.

At the end of the weeding season, geese are generally brought from the field and placed in pens for fattening for three or four weeks, until they weigh 10 to 12 pounds or more. Markets are highest during the four to six weeks prior to Thanksgiving and Christmas.

The carrying of geese over from one season to the next for weeding purposes is not recommended, because older geese are less active in hot weather than young birds.

GAME AND ORNAMENTAL BIRD PRODUCTION

Game and ornamental birds are sometimes raised for pleasure. A limited number of producers also raise them for profit, on a full-time or part-time basis. Game birds are raised for sale to game preserves or for shooting preserves. For these outlets, there is a limited, but satisfactory, market. Also, there is a limited market for the sale of ornamental birds.

HATCHERIES

Few phases of the poultry industry have undergone more changes than has the hatchery business. In the early 1900's, the "old cluck" was forced to yield her pleasant job of spending three weeks on the nest "expecting." The incubator in the small hatchery gradually took over the job. As hatcheries developed, they grew in size and improved in efficiency, and the old setting hen was practically eliminated. Today, more than 96 per cent of all chicks raised, either farm chickens or commercial broilers, are bought from hatcheries as baby chicks.

Perhaps it is fair to say that hatcheries have exerted more influence on improving the general level of the poultry industry than any other segment of the business. This has been achieved through their own breeding programs or through the breeding programs of the poultry breeders with whom they have a franchise arrangement.

Trends in the Hatching Industry

The major changes or trends in the hatching industry in recent years are:

1. **Fewer and larger hatcheries.**—Back in 1934, there were 11,405 hatcheries in the United States; today, there are 2,365, or only 1/5 as many. But, in this same period of time, the average size of hatchery increased by nearly nine fold, so that there was a substantial excess of capacity in the hatchery industry. The following figures from the U.S. Department of Agriculture point up the trend toward fewer and larger hatcheries:

Year	Number of Hatcheries	Total Egg Capacity	Average Egg Capacity
1934	11,405	276,287,000	24,000
1953	8,233	616,976,000	80,000
1965	2,365	471,318,000	199,000

The bigness of hatcheries becomes obvious when it is realized that on January 1, 1965, 654 U.S. hatcheries with incubators capable of holding 200,000 or more eggs accounted for 71 per cent of the nation's capacity. A similar trend has occurred in turkey poult hatchery capacity. On January 1, 1965, some 158 of the 453 hatcheries had 78 per cent of poult hatching capacity.

2. **Year-round business.**—Formerly, most hatcheries operated in the spring of the year only. In 1937-38, slightly under two hatches of chicks were taken off per year. Today, more than four hatches per year are produced. The primary reasons for extending the hatching season to more nearly a year-round business are (a) less seasonality in the production of eggs and turkeys, and (b) the development of a year-round commercial broiler industry.

3. **Franchise agreements have come in.**—In 1937-38, franchising was practically unknown in the hatchery business. Today, many hatcheries have franchise arrangements with breeders who use advanced methods to produce superior strains of birds. Under these agreements, the breeders furnish the eggs and the hatcheries agree to sell breeder's strain of birds in specified areas.

4. **Less custom-hatching.**—Today, very little custom-hatching is done. Most of that which is done is for the hatching of turkey poults.

5. **More integration.**—Many hatcheries have become a part of broader businesses which involve poultry growing and processing, or sale of supplies. This may involve the selling of poultry feeds, medicines, equipment, farm supplies, and farm products.

6. **Fewer started chicks sold.**—With the growth of larger and more specialized poultry farms and their improved brooding technology, fewer and fewer started chicks (chicks two to four weeks of age) are being sold.

7. **Geographical shift.**—With the shift of the broiler industry to the South and South Atlantic states, the total output of hatcheries has also increased in this area, which means that hatcheries have followed broiler production, geographically speaking.

BUSINESS AND MANAGEMENT ASPECTS OF POULTRY PRODUCTION

With the increase in specialization and size of enterprises, the business and management aspects of poultry production have become more important. More capital is required, competent management is in demand, records are essential, computers have come in, futures trading has increased, and such things as tax management, estate planning, and liability have taken on a new look. The general principles of many of these business aspects are similar for all types of animal production. These are covered in Chapter VIII of this book; hence, they will not be repeated. Instead, those business and management aspects that are peculiar to and/or particularly important to the poultry industry will be covered in the sections that follow.

Broiler Contracts

Broilers were one of the first animal industry commodities to shift from the conventional merchant-producer credit arrangement to a contractual type program.

For maximum protection and minimum misunderstanding, all contracts should be in writing. Also, those involved should know and understand what constitutes a good contract.

BASIC CONSIDERATIONS FOR CONTRACTS

All contracts should make provision for the following:

1. **Tenure.**—The contract should be specific as to starting and ending dates per brood or time basis. A time contract usually specifies three to four broods per year.

2. **Renewal.**—Each party should retain the same right for continuing or closing the program. This could minimize hardships for growers who have used credit in providing housing and equipment.

3. **Cancellation.**—This should be specific and clearly understood, with equal rights and privileges.

4. **Management.**—The contract should make known who is responsible for decisions; and details of the management program should be spelled out.

5. **Production and credit resources.**—Detail as to who is to furnish what, when, amount (under what provisions), and security for credit should be given.

6. **Payment or settlement.**—The contract should be clear as to method of computing rate, time, incentives, penalties, and losses including condemnation.

7. **Assignment of interest.**—There should be mutual agreement as to assignment privileges as dictated by the situation.

8. **Arbitration.**—There should be procedures providing for binding settlement to avoid court proceedings.

9. **Legal relationship of contracting parties.**—It should be clearly stated whether or not the contract is a partnership, employer-employee situation, or arranged on an independent basis. This is important for social security and income tax purposes.

MAJOR SPECIFICATIONS TO BE SPELLED OUT

In most broiler contracts, the following matters are spelled out: number and size of broods; disease, parasite, and cannibalism control; ownership, facilities, and labor; technical assistance and supervision; taxes and insurance; marketing method, price, age, weight, loading, weighing, and transportation; feeding program and its control; records and accounting; changing or adjusting contract; responsibility and division of losses; credit arrangements, notes, and chattels; other poultry on premises and visitors; method of figuring costs; and method of settlement and payment for broilers at time of marketing, leftover supplies, and division of interest.

TYPES OF CONTRACTS

There are numerous types of contracts. But most of them fall into one of the following seven categories:

1. **Conventional-type credit plan or "open account" agreement.**—The producer-owner retains title, makes all decisions, assumes all risks, takes any profit and/or loss (except where dealer provides a "no-loss" clause), and pays credit account at time of sale of birds. Credit may be secured by note or chattel.

2. **Share.**—Under this type of contract, the producer furnishes the house, equipment, labor, and may or may not furnish litter and fuel; shares in the proceeds above costs as designated by terms of the contract; and shares in condemnation losses.

The contractor retains title, provides all production supplies, medication, supervision, makes necessary decisions, and usually assumes losses.

3. **Flat fee.**—The grower receives a guaranteed fixed amount on a per bird or on a per pound basis. Some contracts include other incentives and provisions on feed conversion, gains, market price, etc.

4. **Feed conversion.**—The grower is paid on specific rates based on feed conversion. Variations of incentives in addition to feed conversion are: share, market price and share, and production cost and share.

5. **Market price.**—Payment to the grower is calculated on a specific schedule of rates based on the various market prices.

6. **Guaranteed price.**—The dealer guarantees the grower a specific (prearranged) market price per pound for the broilers sold. The dealer may provide a "no-loss" clause as further protection for the grower.

7. **Salary.**—Payment is made to the grower on a regular wage scale, paid on a weekly or monthly basis. If the grower owns buildings and equipment, he may increase income through rental or lease to contractors.

Turkey and Egg Contracts

Turkey contracts are very similar to broiler contracts.

Contracts are relatively new in the egg industry, but the principles are much the same. The usual contract provisions for egg production cover the following: management of laying house (feeding, space, etc.); strain and number of birds; months of lay (production and quality); egg gathering and delivery; egg cleaning (who does it, methods used); cooling (temperature, humidity, and time); oiling specifications, if used; disease, parasite, and cannibalism control; quantity and quality of eggs to be delivered; restriction of other poultry and visitors; record keeping and maintenance; pullet replacement program; sale and removal of fowl at end of lay period; provision for disposal of manure; provision for use of eggs and fowl; obligation of assets to insure the contract; credit (amount and repayment); labor (present and future); incurring additional expense; share of fixed cost during the down period.

The main kinds of egg contracts are:

1. Shell and/or breaker egg.
2. Hatching egg.
3. Hatching egg foundation stock, lease basis.
4. Pullet growing contracts for laying flock.

Many adaptations of methods and techniques are used in the various kinds of egg contracts.

Manure

Most poultry manure is utilized as a fertilizer. However, a limited amount of it is being fed to beef cattle.

1. **Fertilizer.**—In pure form, without added litter, poultry manure is produced in about the quantities shown in Table 43-1.

TABLE 43—1

QUANTITY AND VALUE OF PURE MANURE FROM VARIOUS FLOCKS[1]

Birds	Types of Flock	Average Bird Wt.	Quantity Manure Produced (dry basis)	Time Period	Estimated Value of Manure[2]
100	Laying hens	4.5 lbs.	2,400 lbs.	12 mos.	$ 22.80
1,000	Broilers (chickens)	4.0 lbs.	2,700 lbs.	9 wks.	25.65
1,000	Broilers (turkeys)	8.0 lbs.	4,320 lbs.	16 wks.	41.04
1,000	Heavy turkeys	20.0 lbs.	35,000 lbs.	24 wks.	332.50

[1]From University of Maryland Extension Service, Fact Sheet 39.
[2]Assuming the value of N, P_2O_5, and K_2O to be 15, 10, and 5 cents per pound, respectively.

Pure poultry manure (dry basis) contains an average of 4 per cent nitrogen (N), 2½ per cent phosphate (P_2O_5), and 2 per cent potash (K_2O)—or 80 pounds nitrogen, 50 pounds phosphate, and 40 pounds potash per ton—assuming no leaching or loss of ammonia to the air occurs. Arbitrarily assuming that the value per pound of nitrogen in mixed fertilizer is 15 cents, phosphate, 10 cents, and potash, 5 cents, pure poultry manure would have a value of $19 per ton. Of course, these values are based on pure dry manure only (droppings as they are cleaned from cage houses) with no litter added and no allowance for loss of nutrients through leaching, heating, addition of dry agents, or evaporating changes.

Where litter is used, the value of the manure for fertilizer varies according to the chemical composition of the litter, and the amount of litter used.

2. **Feeding manure.**—There are a number of reports of U.S. beef cattle operations using poultry manure as a feed. Also, several experiment stations have conducted, or are conducting, experimental work on the feeding value of this product. Of course, the nutritive content of manure varies appreciably, according to the type of rations fed, and more particularly according to the type of litter used. But, in general, the economic efficiencies of feeding poultry manure, in properly balanced rations, in the wintering ration of cows, or in the finishing ration of cattle appears to be worth-while.

It should be pointed out, however, that there are certain possible hazards to the feeding of poultry manure. For example, much remains to be known about the transmission of diseases from poultry to other species. Also, it is not generally known whether certain drugs administered to poultry are toxic to cattle when consumed at the levels found in litter. Neither is the effect of certain molds common in litter known. Finally, there is the esthetic angle, but this does not appear insurmountable within itself.

Cattle fed poultry manure are, in common with all other slaughtered animals, subject to the Pure Food and Drug Administration regulations governing the amount of residue in the meat. It is conceivable, therefore, that high carcass residues might result from litter containing a high percentage of medicated poultry feeds.

Records

The key to good business and management is records. The historian, Santayana, put it this way, "Those who are ignorant of the past are condemned to repeat it." Also, good records help the poultry producer to overcome the banker's traditional fear of feathers.

The record forms will differ somewhat according to the type of enterprise. For example, with layers, cost per dozen eggs is the important thing, whereas in broiler and market turkey production, it's cost per pound of bird. Net returns are important, but it is also necessary that records show all the items of cost and income—egg production, feed consumption, and mortality of layers; rate of growth, pounds of chicken per 100 pounds of feed, mortality, and quality of broilers produced. Good records, properly analyzed and used, will increase net earnings and serve as a basis for sound management and husbandry.

QUESTIONS FOR STUDY AND DISCUSSION

1. What factors have caused the development of such a high degree of specialization in the poultry industry; for example, in the chicken business, there are breeders, growers of replacement pullets, broiler producers, and commercial egg producers?

2. Are poultry breeders any more highly specialized than breeeders of four-footed animals? Bear in mind, for example, that in the beef cattle industry there are specialized purebred breeders, commercial cow-calf operators, feeders

of grower-type rations (those who background cattle), and cattle finishers or feeders.

3. What future do you foresee for the grower of replacement pullets?

4. Today, chicken breeders—those who produce hatchery eggs for broilers or layers—are few in number and very large. Is this good or bad; that is, the concentration of chicken breeding in so few hands?

5. What economic factors have caused the recent shifts in broiler production to the southeastern part of the United States?

6. It is estimated that 95 per cent of the nation's broilers and 80 per cent of the turkeys are raised under contract. What are the advantages and disadvantages of contract production of broilers and turkeys in comparison with the non-contract basis?

7. How do you account for the fact that hybrid breeding has been more extensively used in broiler production than in layer production; and that hybrid production in chickens has been more prevalent than in turkeys?

8. The production of both broilers and market turkeys has been subject to frequent overproduction and low prices. How may producers alleviate this situation?

9. Most large hatcheries now have franchise agreements with poultry breeders. Is this a desirable development?

10. What is the best use of manure?

SELECTED REFERENCES

Title of Publication	Author(s)	Publisher
Commercial Broiler Production, Agriculture Handbook No. 320	R. T. Parkhurst	U.S. Department of Agriculture, ARS, Washington, D.C., 1967.
Hatchery Industry, The Marketing Research No. 483	E. H. Rinear	U.S. Department of Agriculture, Agricultural Marketing Service, Washington, D.C.

CHAPTER XLIV

THE EGG

Contents   **Page**

Parts of an Egg..1049
Composition of an Egg..1049
Formation of the Egg..1050
   Ovary 1050
   Oviduct 1051
Egg Quality, and Factors Affecting It..1051
   Producing Quality Eggs...1052
   Handling Table Eggs..1053
   Handling Hatching Eggs...1055
Fertilization of the Egg..1055
Incubation 1055
   Embryonic Development...1057
Questions for Study and Discussion..1059
Selected References 1060

The bird egg is a marvel of nature. It's one of the most complete foods known to man, as evidenced by the perfect balance of proteins, fats, carbohydrates, minerals, and vitamins which it provides during that 20-day in-the-shell period when it serves as the developing chick's only source of food. Also, the egg is one of the few foods that is produced in pre-packaged form. Not only that, it is the reproductive cell (ovum) of the hen. Upon fertilization by the male's reproductive cell (sperm), the egg will develop into a chick when incubated properly.

PARTS OF AN EGG

A schematic side-view of an egg is shown in Fig. 44-1, with the various parts labeled in their normal position.

The protective covering, known as the shell, is composed primarily of calcium carbonate, with 6,000 to 8,000 microscopic pores permitting transfer of volatile components. The air cell, located in the large end of the egg, is formed when the cooling egg contracts and pulls the inner and outer shell membranes apart. The cord-like chalaza holds the yolk in position in the center of the egg. As shown, the yolk is surrounded by membrane, known as the vitelline membrane. The germinal disc, a normal part of every egg, is located on the surface of the yolk. Embryo formation begins here only in fertilized eggs.

COMPOSITION OF AN EGG

The chemical composition of the egg is given in Table 44-1.

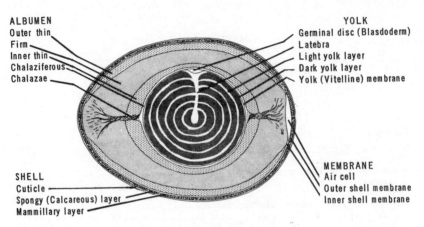

ALBUMEN
Outer thin
Firm
Inner thin
Chalaziferous
Chalazae

YOLK
Germinal disc (Blasdoderm)
Latebra
Light yolk layer
Dark yolk layer
Yolk (Vitelline) membrane

SHELL
Cuticle
Spongy (Calcareous) layer
Mammillary layer

MEMBRANE
Air cell
Outer shell membrane
Inner shell membrane

Fig. 44-1. Parts of an egg.

TABLE 44—1

CHEMICAL COMPOSITION OF THE EGG

	Per Cent	Water	Protein	Fat	Ash
		(%)	(%)	(%)	(%)
Whole egg	100	65.5	11.8	11.0	11.7
White	58	88.0	11.0	0.2	0.8
Yolk	31	48.0	17.5	32.5	2.0
Shell	11	——	——	——	96.0

FORMATION OF THE EGG

The "egg making" machinery of the hen consists of two main parts: the ovary and the oviduct. These are shown in Fig. 44-2.

Ovary

Females of most animals have two functional ovaries—a right one and a left one. But the hen has only one functional ovary, the left one, which is situated in the body cavity near the backbone. At the time of hatching, the female chick's left ovary contains up to approximately 3,600 to 4,000 tiny ova from which full-sized yolks may develop when the hen matures.

Each yolk (ovum) is enclosed in a thin-walled sac (follicle) which is attached to the ovary by a stalk. This sac contains the vast network of blood vessels which supply the yolk materials.

When a pullet reaches sexual maturity, or comes into egg production, some of the ova develop to mature yolks. When mature, the yolk is released from the follicle by rupture of the follicle wall along a line called the stigma. Soon after its release, the yolk is picked up, or engulfed, by the funnel of the oviduct.

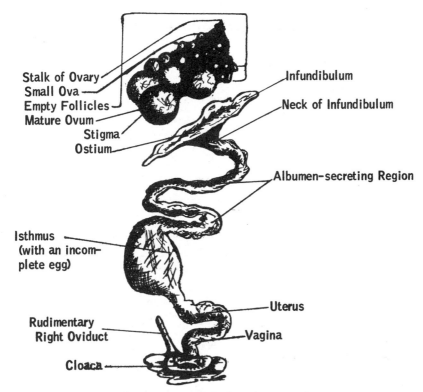

Stalk of Ovary
Small Ova
Empty Follicles
Mature Ovum
Stigma
Ostium

Infundibulum

Neck of Infundibulum

Albumen-secreting Region

Isthmus
(with an incom-
plete egg)

Rudimentary
Right Oviduct

Uterus

Vagina

Cloaca

Fig. 44-2. Reproductive organs of the hen. (Drawing by Caren Carney)

Oviduct

The oviduct is a coiled, folded tube about 20 to 30 inches long occupying a large part of the left side of the abdominal cavity. The oviduct is divided into five rather clearly defined regions, each of which plays a specific role in the completion of the whole egg. A normal hen requires slightly over 24 hours to complete an egg. Within 30 minutes after the egg is laid, another yolk will be released from the ovary for laying the following day. The functions of each of the five parts of the oviduct are set forth in Table 44-2.

EGG QUALITY, AND FACTORS AFFECTING IT

The quality of eggs produced by today's commercial egg-laying flocks is becoming increasingly superior through improved breeding, feeding, management, and marketing. However, eggs are a perishable product, and they should be handled as such. It is of utmost importance, therefore, that producers, jobbers, and retailers maintain superior quality.

Consumers want eggs with fresh-laid appearance, good flavor, and high nutritive value. The shells should be strong, regular, and clean; the white (or albumen) should be thick, clear, and firm; the yolk should be light-colored,

TABLE 44—2

FUNCTIONS OF THE OVIDUCT

Part	Approximate Time Egg Spends In Section	Functions
Infundibilum (Funnel)	15 min.	Picks up yolk from the body cavity after it is released from the follicle. If live sperm are present, fertilization occurs in this section.
Magnum (Albumen-secreting region)	3 hrs.	Thick white (albumen) is deposited around the yolk. This layer later forms the chalaziferous layer, the chalaza, and inner thin and thick white.
Isthmus	1¼ hrs.	Inner and outer shell membranes are added and some water and mineral salts. These membranes give some protection to the egg contents from outside contamination.
Shell Gland (Uterus)	21 hrs.	During the first part of the egg's stay in the shell gland, water and minerals pass through the shell membranes into the white, inflating the egg and giving rise to the outer layer of thin white. Soon after the egg is inflated, the shell gland starts to add calcium over the shell membranes, continuing this process until just prior to laying. If the shell is going to be colored, pigment is added in this section.
Vagina	Entire time from ovulation to laying is slightly more than 24 hours.	The egg passes into this section just prior to laying. Its function is not known. Some believe it adds a protein sealer to the shell to seal the pores which then functions as a protective layer.

well-centered, and free from blood and meat spots. The factors which determine final grade are summarized in Chapter XLV, Table 45-2.

Producing Quality Eggs

Contrary to popular belief, not all eggs gathered from the nest are necessarily of first-rate quality. However, a large percentage of top quality eggs can be produced by adopting the following practices:

1. **Select a strain of birds noted for its abilities to lay eggs of high quality.**—Inherent capacity for producing high initial egg quality is important. Egg shape, shell color, shell strength, albumen quality, and incidence of blood and meat spots are quality factors which can be improved through selective breeding. Most breeders are giving considerable attention to this possibility. Data from random sample tests are highly useful for this purpose.

2. **Feed well-balanced rations.**—Deficiencies of calcium, phosphorus, manganese, and vitamin D_3 lead to poor shell quality. Yolk color is almost entirely

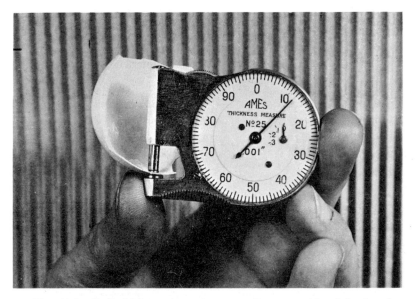

Fig. 44-3. Shell thickness is an important factor considered by breeders. Thickness is correlated with shell strength. (Courtesy, DeKalb Agricultural Association, Inc., DeKalb, Ill.)

dependent on the bird's diet. Low vitamin A levels may increase the incidence of blood spots.

3. **Keep the flock disease-free.**—Certain diseases, especially Newcastle and infectious bronchitis, often cause birds returning to production to lay eggs of poor shape, poor shell quality, and low interior quality.

4. **Replace birds in the laying flock when they are 18 to 20 months old.**— The finest quality eggs are laid by pullets. Older hens lay eggs lacking in acceptable shell quality and albumen firmness.

5. **Produce infertile market eggs.**—Keep males out of the laying flock.

Handling Table Eggs

Observance of the following rules will aid in maintaining top quality all the way to the consumer:

1. **Gather eggs frequently.**—Eggs should be gathered in well-ventilated baskets or filler-flats three to four times daily. Frequent gatherings reduce the amount of body heat to which eggs are exposed. Also, the number of broken and cracked eggs will be reduced.

2. **Produce clean eggs.**—Eggs are usually cleanest when they are laid. If plenty of non-staining, dry, nesting material is provided and changed when needed, and eggs are gathered three times a day, very few eggs will become dirty or stained.

3. **Clean soiled eggs.**—To avoid excessive handling, clean all eggs rather

than take time to separate the dirty eggs. The essential items for properly cleaning shells include water, detergent-sanitizer, and an egg washing machine. Use clean water for washing eggs and maintain the water temperature between 110° and 120° F. Add detergent-sanitizer to water according to manufacturers directions.

4. **Coat shell.**—To preserve the high initial quality, coat the egg shell with a thin, odorless, colorless, and tasteless mineral oil to prevent the egg's carbon dioxide from escaping into the surrounding atmosphere. Apply oil, either automatically with in-line egg processing facilities or with a hand-type aerosol spray.

5. **Cool eggs properly.**—Cooling eggs immediately after gathering removes the animal heat and retards any reaction which might be conducive to deterioration of quality. The egg cooler should be large enough to accommodate the daily production plus eggs held until they are marketed. An egg cooler operating at 55° F. or lower, with a relative humidity of 70 to 80 per cent, is considered adequate.

Eggs cooled prior to packing will sweat if removed from the cooler for candling or sizing. Therefore, eggs should be processed in coolers or in an adjoining air conditioned room.

6. **Candle eggs.**—Candling is the most practical way to determine interior quality of shell eggs. The object of candling is to discover and cull out eggs with blood spots and checks.

The shell should be sound and free from checks or cracks, and it should be of good texture.

7. **Separate eggs into weight classes.**—After candling, eggs should be separated into weight classes. In large commercial operations, this is done by conveying the eggs over a series of scales to obtain uniform weight for a given pack. When so classified, eggs have eye appeal. Weight classes of eggs based on minimum net weight per dozen are given in Chapter 45, Table 45-4.

8. **Pack eggs properly.**—Eggs should be packed with small ends down. It is possible for the air cell to break loose and move to the small end when the large end of the egg is packed down.

It is also important that cartons and cases be kept clean. This prevents the possibility of mold formation which may pass off-flavors to the eggs.

9. **Make frequent deliveries.**—Eggs should be moved to market as quickly as possible—at least twice a week. Also, it is essential to keep all eggs cool en route to market.

After eggs are delivered to the jobber or retailer, maintenance of quality is the responsibility of the middle-man. Generally speaking, he has adequate facilities to protect the high quality product that the producer has delivered to him.

Refrigeration is a must for both short-time holding and displaying of eggs.

Handling Hatching Eggs

The fertile egg is usually in a fairly advanced stage of development from an early embryological standpoint at the time of laying. Accordingly, ideal handling would consist of setting the egg at once, so that development could proceed without being checked. Obviously, this isn't practical under most conditions, for hatching eggs must be held for varying lengths of time. The practical problem, therefore, is to hold these eggs in a suspended state of development without destroying the developing embryo. To this end, the following handling practices are recommended:

1. **Gather frequently.**—Generally, hatching eggs are gathered more frequently than eggs intended for table use. When temperatures are normal, three to four gatherings a day will suffice. However, when temperatures are extremely hot or cold, hatching eggs should be gathered every hour.

2. **Length of holding.**—Hatchery eggs should be held for as short a period of time as possible, for hatchability decreases as the time of holding is increased. At the most, they should not be held longer than 10 days. Commercial hatcheries usually set twice a week.

3. **Holding temperature.**—As soon as possible, hatching eggs should be cooled to a temperature between 50° and 60° F., with a relative humidity of about 70 to 80 per cent.

When it is necessary to hold hatching eggs more than seven days, it is recommended that they be warmed to 100° F. for one to five hours early in the holding period.

4. **Position and turning.**—Hatching eggs are usually packed with the large end up, just as is the situation with market eggs. However, they may be placed in trays in a horizontal position.

If it is necessary to hold hatching eggs for more than five days, they should be turned. This prevents the yolk from sticking to the shell. Turning can be done by tipping the egg cases sharply. It is recommended that the cases be turned in this manner twice daily.

FERTILIZATION OF THE EGG

The hen can produce an egg without mating with a male bird. But such an egg will not hatch.

Each male chicken has two testes, located within the body, about midway of the back. These testes discharge sperm.

If the rooster mates with and fertilizes the hen, the male sperm unites with the ova, which is found on the yolk. Such an egg will hatch.

INCUBATION

Eggs have been incubated by artificial means for thousands of years. Both the Chinese and the Egyptians are credited with having originated artificial incubation procedures. The Chinese developed a method in which they burned charcoal to supply the heat. They also used the hot-bed method in which decomposing manure furnished the heat. The Egyptians constructed large brick incubators which they heated with fires right in the rooms where the eggs were incubated. These ancient methods were crude when compared to our present-day mammoth incubators which hold from a few thousand up to 100,000 or more eggs, and in which the temperature, humidity, ventilation, and turning are automatically controlled.

There are four factors of major importance in incubating eggs artificially: temperature, humidity, oxygen and turning. Of these, temperature is the most critical. In natural conditions, heat is furnished by the body of the setting hen. This temperature is usually slightly lower than that of the non-broody hen's average temperature of 106° F.

1. **Temperature.**—Maintenance of the proper temperature is of prime importance for good hatchability of fertile eggs. Depending on the type of incubation, optimum temperatures range from 99° to 103° F. In the usual forced-air machine, the temperature should be maintained at about 99.5° F.

Overheating is much more critical than underheating; it will speed up rate of development, cause abnormal embryos in the early stages, and lower the percentage of hatchability. Fig. 44-4 shows the effect of temperature on the percentage of fertile eggs.

2. **Humidity.**—Humidity is of great importance for normal development of

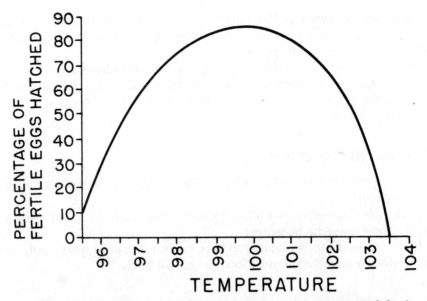

Fig. 44-4. The effect of incubation temperature on percentages of fertile eggs hatched. Relative humidity 60 per cent, oxygen 21 per cent, carbon dioxide below 0.5 per cent. (From The University of Connecticut College of Agriculture Extension Service publication entitled "Incubation and Embryology of the Chick," page 3.)

the chicken embryo. Although a variation of 5 to 10 per cent is acceptable, the relative humidity of the air within an incubator for the first 18 days should be about 60 per cent. During the last three days, or the hatching period, it should be nearer 70 per cent. Lower humidity causes excess evaporation of water, while high humidity prevents the evaporation of sufficient amounts of water from the egg. In both cases, hatchability is reduced.

3. **Egg turning.**—The embryo head must occupy a position in the large end of the egg for proper hatching. Thus, the egg must be incubated large end up as gravity orients the embryo with its head uppermost. Somewhere between the fifteenth and sixteenth day, the head of the embryo is near the air cell.

Eggs should be turned from three to five times a day between the second and the eighteenth day. The purpose of this turning is to prevent the germ spot from migrating through the albumen and becoming fastened to the shell membrane. That is, turning the eggs prevents an adhesion between the chorion and the shell membrane.

Proper turning consists of rotating the egg back and forth, not in one direction (a 30- to 45-degree angle is best).

4. **Oxygen utilization.**—As the embryo develops, it uses oxygen and gives off carbon dioxide. Thus, sufficient ventilation within the incubator is required to assure an adequate supply of oxygen and the proper removal of carbon dioxide.

The best hatching results are obtained with 21 per cent oxygen in the air—the normal oxygen level in the atmosphere. The embryo will tolerate a carbon dioxide level of .5 per cent, but it will die if this level reaches 5 per cent.

5. **Incubation time**—The normal incubation periods for several species of birds follow:

Common Name	Incubation Period (in days)
Chicken	21
Turkey	28
Duck	28
Muscovy duck	33-35
Goose	28-32
Guinea	26-28
Pigeon	18
Pheasant	24
Quail	24
Peafowl	28
Ostrich	42
Swan	35-40

Embryonic Development

The development which takes place in the egg from the time of fertilization to the time of hatching is one of the wonders of nature. Our knowledge of this phenomenon has been gained largely through the use of the microscope. The complexity of the development cannot be understood without some thorough training in embryology. In this book, we shall confine further discussion to outlining the highlights of development. (The student who is interested in more detailed discussion of the complexities of embryology should consult some of the references listed at the end of this chapter.)

Since the fertilized germinal disc, or blastoderm, spends about 24 hours in the warmth of the hen's body (at about 107° F.) while the egg is being completed, certain stages of embryonic development occur during that time. About three hours after fertilization, the newly formed single cell divides and makes two cells. Then there are four, eight, sixteen, and more. Cell division continues until there are many cells grouped in a small, whitish spot visible on the upper surface of the egg yolk.

TABLE 44—3

IMPORTANT EVENTS IN EMBRYONIC DEVELOPMENT

Stage or Period	What Takes Place
Before Egg Laying	Fertilization, division, and growth of living cells, segregation of cells into groups of special function.
Between Laying and Incubation	No growth; stage of inactive embryonic life.
During Incubation	
First day:	
16 hours	First sign of resemblance to a chick embryo
18 hours	Appearance of alimentary tract
20 hours	Appearance of vertebral column
21 hours	Beginning of formation of nervous system
22 hours	Beginning of formation of head
23 hours	Appearance of blood islands—vitelline circulation
24 hours	Beginning of formation of eye
Second day:	
25 hours	Beginning of formation of heart
35 hours	Beginning of formation of ear
42 hours	Heart begins to beat
Third day:	
50 hours	Beginning of formation of amnion
60 hours	Beginning of formation of nasal structure
62 hours	Beginning of formation of legs
64 hours	Beginning of formation of wings
70 hours	Beginning of formation of allantois
Fourth day	Beginning of formation of tongue
Fifth day	Beginning of formation of reproductive organs and differentiation of sex
Sixth day	Beginning of formation of beak and egg-tooth
Eighth day	Beginning of formation of feathers
Tenth day	Beginning of hardening of beak
Thirteenth day	Appearance of scales and claws
Fourteenth day	Embryo turns its head toward the blunt end of egg
Sixteenth day	Scales, claws, and beak becoming firm and horny
Seventeenth day	Beak turns toward air cell
Nineteenth day	Yolk sac begins to enter body cavity
Twentieth day	Yolk sac completely drawn into body cavity; embryo occupies practically all the space within the egg except the air cell
Twenty-first day	Hatching of chick

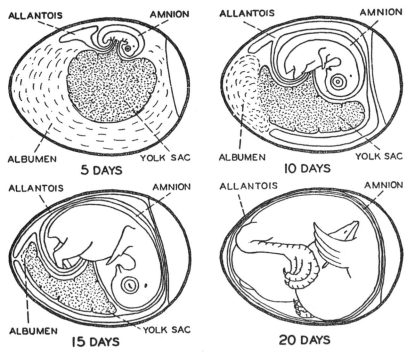

Fig. 44-5. Successive changes in the position of the chick embryo and its embryonic membranes. (From A. L. Romanoff, Cornell Rural School Leaflet, September 1939).

When the egg is laid and its temperature drops below about 80° F., shell development ceases. Cooling at ordinary temperatures will not kill the embryo, and it will begin to develop again when the egg is placed in the incubator. Keeping eggs at temperatures above about 80° F. prior to incubation will cause a slow growth which leads to a weakening and eventual death of the embryo.

During incubation, various processes occur. They are mainly respiration, excretion, nutrition, and protection.

The stages of embryonic development are listed in summary form in Table 44-3, and the important events are pictured in Fig. 44-5.

Newly-hatched chicks can be shipped long distances (up to 17 hours of travel time) without food or water. The yolk is largely unused by the embryo and is drawn into the body of the chick on the nineteenth day, just before it hatches. The yolk is highly nourishing and provides proteins, fats, vitamins, minerals, and water for the first several hours of the chick's life. The yolk is gradually used up during the first 10 days of life of the chick.

QUESTIONS FOR STUDY AND DISCUSSION

1. Nutritionally, or chemically, how do two eggs compare with one glass of milk or eight ounces of beef?

2. Sketch the reproductive system of the hen, name each part, and trace the formation of an egg.

3. In what ways do the handling of table eggs and hatching eggs differ?

4. Why shouldn't eggs intended for table use be fertilized?

5. How do you account for the ancient Chinese and Egyptians originating artificial incubation procedures, rather than relying on nature's method—the setting hen?

6. For proper incubation, what is considered desirable temperature, humidity, egg turning, and oxygen utilization; and what is the function of each of these environmental factors?

7. Outline the occurrence of the most prominent landmarks in the development of the chick.

SELECTED REFERENCES

Title of Publication	Author(s)	Publisher
Avian Egg, The	A. L. Romanoff A. J. Romanoff	John Wiley & Sons, Inc., New York, N. Y., 1963.
Avian Embryo, The	A. L. Romanoff	The Macmillan Co., New York, N. Y., 1960.
Early Embryology of the Chick	D. M. Patten	The Blakiston Co., New York, N. Y., 1952.
Fertility and Hatchability of Chicken and Turkey Eggs	L. W. Taylor	John Wiley & Sons, Inc., New York, N. Y., 1949.
Hatchery Operation and Management	E. M. Funk M. R. Irwin	John Wiley & Sons, Inc., New York, N. Y., 1955.
Lillie's Development of the Chick	H. L. Hamilton	Henry Holt and Co., New York, N. Y., 1952.

Chapter XLV

MARKETING POULTRY AND EGGS

Contents   **Page**

Market Value of Poultry and Eggs..1061
Poultry and Egg Consumption..1061
Market Changes, and the Forces Back of Them...1062
Market Classes and Grades..1065
    Poultry (Chickens) 1066
    Eggs 1067
Federal Inspection 1067
Market Channels and Selling Arrangements..1069
    Pricing Broilers...1070
    Pricing Turkeys...1070
    Pricing Eggs 1070
Financial Aspects 1071
    Broiler Grower Returns..1071
    Profitability of Poultry Processing Firms...1071
    Poultryman's Share of the Consumer's Dollar.......................................1072
Foreign Trade in Poultry..1073
Trends in Marketing Ahead...1074
Questions for Study and Discussion...1074
Selected References 1075

Marketing is selling. Practically everything that is done to poultry and eggs is done with the hope of improving salability.

The changes in the marketing of poultry and eggs have been particularly marked in recent years. These changes encompass processing and distribution as well as farm production. Technological advances in poultry breeding, nutrition, housing, disease control, and other phases of production have brought with them organizational changes which have lowered production costs and transformed traditional poultry farming into a factory-type operation. The transformation of the industry structure has advanced furthest for broilers, but turkeys and eggs are now closing the gap.

MARKET VALUE OF POULTRY AND EGGS

U.S. poultrymen sold poultry and eggs valued at a total of $3.5 billion in 1965. This represented 9.1 per cent of the total cash farm income. Eggs accounted for about half of the value of farm poultry sales, broilers about one-third, turkeys around 12 per cent, and other poultry products, mainly non-broiler chickens, the remainder.

POULTRY AND EGG CONSUMPTION

Since World War II, chicken and turkey consumption, on a per capita basis, has gone up, while egg consumption per person has dropped (see Table 45-1).

TABLE 45—1

CONSUMPTION PER PERSON—EGGS, CHICKEN, TURKEY
1947-1965[1]

	Annual Consumption per Person			
	1947-49	1957-59	1964	1965
Eggs (farm basis), number	385	356	313	308
Chicken, ready-to-cook pounds	18.7	27.5	31.2	33.3
Turkey, ready-to-cook pounds	3.3	6.0	7.2	7.4

[1]From *Organization and Competition in the Poultry and Egg Industries*, Technical Study No. 2, National Commission on Food Marketing, p. 1, 1966.

Consumers have been willing to increase their consumption of chicken and turkey meat as advances in production and marketing technology make for lower prices (see Fig. 45-1). But technological advances and lower prices in eggs have brought no such consumption increases in eggs. Even at lower prices, the average person uses one-fourth fewer eggs than early after the war. The reasons for eggs not faring so well as poultry meat are not fully understood.

RETAIL FOOD PRICES

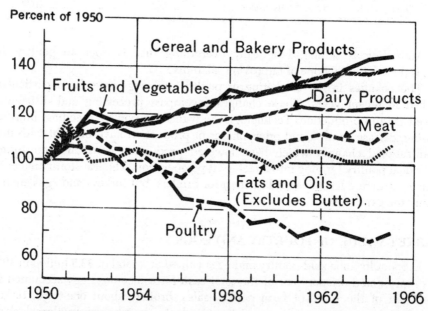

Fig. 45-1. Retail food prices. From *Food from Farmer to Consumer,* Report of the National Commission on Food Marketing, June 1966, Fig. 3, p. 9.

MARKET CHANGES, AND THE FORCES BACK OF THEM

Changes in marketing poultry and eggs have extended all the way from the producer to the consumer, and they have involved technology, organization, and location. It is impossible to separate the changes from the forces back of them. Among the pertinent changes affecting the marketing of poultry and eggs are the following:

1. **Fewer and larger producers.**—All poultry producing units—layers, broilers, and turkeys—have become fewer in number and larger in size in recent years. There are laying and broiler units of 100,000 or more capacity, and there are market turkey operations with 20,000 to 40,000 birds. These operations are large enough (a) to command competent farm management know-how, (b) to justify labor and cost-saving facilities such as automatic watering and feeding equipment, and (c) to warrant the cooling facilities and other equipment necessary to maintain quality.

2. **Increased production efficiency.**—This is best measured on the basis of pounds of feed required to produce a unit of product (see Table 38-5). In 1940, it required 4.7 pounds of feed to produce a pound of broiler; in 1965, 3.0 pounds of feed produced a pound of broiler. The ratio for turkeys was 7.2 in 1940 and 5.2 in 1965. In this same period of time, from 1940 to 1965, the pounds of feed required to produce one dozen eggs decreased from 7.4 to an estimated 6.0 pounds.

3. **Shifts in production areas.**—Hand in hand with changes in efficiency and industry organization, there have been shifts in the principal production areas. From 1950 to 1965, for example, the five top broiler producing states—Georgia, Arkansas, Alabama, North Carolina, and Mississippi—increased their dominance from 27 per cent to 60 per cent of the commercial production. During the same 15-year period, the two major turkey producing states of California and Minnesota increased their proportionate share of U.S. turkey production from 25 to 30 per cent. And from 1950 to 1965, the 10 leading layer producing states increased their proportion of the U.S. egg production from 46 to 50 per cent.

4. **More vertical integration, contracts, and direct marketing.**—Rapid technical advances in poultry production following World War II made it possible for a pound of poultry meat or a dozen eggs to be produced with decreasing amounts of feed and other production costs. The incentive was strong to achieve these new efficiencies as quickly as possible. But capital was necessary. Feed manufacturers stepped in, providing capital in order to have a market for their feeds without generally involving added feed selling costs. This set off a whole chain of events involving vertical integration all the way from the producer to the consumer. Also, contractual arrangement and direct marketing followed; and all three developments—integration, contracts, and direct marketing—became commonplace among broiler, turkey, and egg producers.

   a. **Broiler integration.**—Initially, feed manufacturers served as the integrators in broiler production. To protect their interests, processors followed—integrating both with feed companies and producers. Integration spread quickly to all stages of broiler production and distribution except two: (1) development of the basic breeding stock, and (2) distribution to consumers.

In order to protect their financial investment, and to exercise certain controls over management phases, contracts evolved. These contracts proved particularly attractive to those who had land and/or facilities and a surplus of labor, but who were unable to finance the purchase of birds and feed. From the standpoint of the integrator—the feed manufacturer and the processor—they were also attractive because they involved no social security, workmen's compensation, or other similar employee fringe benefits. Likewise, the integrator could use his capital to earn higher returns in other ways.

By 1964, only 20.7 per cent of the broilers produced in the U.S. were purchased after grown. Stated differently, this means that four-fifths of the broilers were sold prior to being grown.

b. **Turkey integration.**—Vertical coordination and control have not advanced as far in turkey as in broiler production. This is attributed to the fact that turkeys need a longer growing period, the market is seasonal, and capital and management requirements have been greater and disease risk higher than in broiler production. Also, cooperatives have played a more important role in turkey than in broiler production.

In 1964, 59.8 per cent of the nation's market turkeys were purchased after grown—that is, they were not under contract arrangement prior to market time. As noted, this is much higher than the 28.7 per cent purchased after grown in the case of broilers. This means that over twice as many turkeys as broilers were not market contracted ahead of growing. Of course, "purchased after grown" does not necessarily imply that there was no contractual arrangement or integration from the standpoint of feeding the birds, or even supplying them. As pointed out in Chapter XLIII, an estimated 95 per cent or more of the broilers produced in the U.S. are under some form of integration or contract, and more than 80 per cent of the turkeys are under a similar arrangement.

c. **Egg integration.**—Eggs have been produced under a variety of conditions and arrangements, but fewer commercial egg production enterprises are integrated or under contract than is the case with broilers. It should be added, however, that these developments are increasing in egg production. More integration and contracts among egg producers have been prompted because of the formation of more large-scale specialized egg producing units, resembling factory production systems. These require more capital.

In 1959, 90.9 per cent of the nation's eggs were purchased after they were produced—with no contract or prior arrangement. By 1964, five years later, this figure had been lowered to 67.5 per cent. It seems very obvious, therefore, that as laying operations get larger there will be increasing integration and contractual arrangements.

Hand in hand with increased vertical integration and contracts, there has been more direct marketing of broilers, turkeys, and eggs. As a result, wholesale markets have declined in volume and relative importance.

5. **Fewer and larger processors.**—In recent years, there has been a marked shift to larger processors and they have shifted their location near the production rather than the consumption area. In 1964, 55 chicken processors and 35 turkey processors slaughtered 70 per cent of the nation's broilers and turkeys, respectively.

Because commercial egg production is more widely dispersed over the U.S., the concentration of egg handling and processing isn't as great in the market egg business as in poultry meat processing. Processing is higher in liquid and frozen egg processing than in the handling of fresh eggs.

6. **More new products.**—Finally, throughout the poultry and egg industry, renewed attention has been given to developing new poultry and egg products. In particular, more convenience foods have been developed.

In 1947, New York style dressed chickens and turkeys (only the blood and feathers removed) accounted for 80 per cent of the chickens and 75 per cent of turkeys marketed. By 1963, only about 11 per cent of chickens and 5 per cent of turkeys were marketed that way. This transition was facilitated by new processing and transportation technology which favored location of slaughtering and eviscerating plants in production areas.

Today, most broilers are sold by processors as eviscerated, ice-packed, ready-to-cook, whole birds. Only 11.8 per cent of them are frozen. On the other hand, most mature chickens and turkeys are marketed frozen. In 1964, 34 per cent of the mature chickens and 86 per cent of the turkeys processed under federal inspection were frozen.

The second significant development in the marketing of poultry meats is the increase in cut-up and packaged poultry meat and the use of poultry in canned and other processed foods, such as soups, cooked and frozen dinners, and turkey rolls and roasts. By 1965, cut-up and packaged young chickens (broilers) amounted to 19.3 per cent of the quantity processed under federal inspection. Additionally, retailers cut up substantial volumes of whole birds bought from processors.

In the marketing of eggs, the most important product development has been the improvement in quality and freshness.

First the processor took the feathers off the birds, then they cleaned them out for the housewife. All these changes were designed to add variety to the housewife's menus while subtracting labor from her kitchen duties, and all were designed to increase sales.

The most important items, listed by the amount of poultry meat used, are: rolls, roasts, and breasts; soups, broth, consommés; pot pies; canned boned meat; cooked chicken parts; turkey dinners; fried chicken dinners; and canned whole birds.

MARKET CLASSES AND GRADES

The U.S. Department of Agriculture has established specifications for different kinds, classes, and grades of poultry. They define kind as referring to the different species of poultry, such as chickens, turkeys, ducks, geese, guineas, and pigeons. "Class" refers to kinds of poultry by groups which are essentially of the same physical characteristics, such as fryers or hens. These physical characteristics are associated with age and sex. The kinds and classes of live, dressed, and ready-to-cook poultry listed in the U.S. classes, standards, and grades are in general use in all segments of the poultry industry.

Poultry (Chickens)

The commonly used classes of chickens are:

1. **Rock Cornish game hen or Cornish game hen.**—A Rock Cornish game hen or Cornish game hen is a young immature chicken (usually five to seven weeks of age) weighing not more than 2 pounds ready-to-cook weight, which was prepared from a Cornish chicken or the progeny of a Cornish chicken crossed with another breed of chicken.

2. **Broiler or fryer.**—A broiler or fryer is a young chicken (usually 9 to 12 weeks of age), of either sex, that is tender-meated with soft, pliable, smooth-textured skin and flexible breastbone cartilage.

3. **Roaster.**—A roaster is a young chicken (usually three to five months of age), of either sex ,that is tender-meated with solf, pliable, smooth-textured skin and breastbone cartilage that may be somewhat less flexible than that of a broiler or fryer.

4. **Capon.**—A capon is a surgically unsexed male chicken (usually under eight months of age) that is tender-meated with soft, pliable, smooth-textured skin.

5. **Stag.**—A stag is a male chicken (usually under 10 months of age) with coarse skin, somewhat toughened and darkened flesh, and considerable hardening of the breastbone cartilage. Stags show a condition of fleshing and a degree of maturity intermediate between that of a roaster and a cock or rooster.

6. **Hen or stewing chicken or fowl.**—A hen or stewing chicken or fowl is a mature female chicken (usually more than 10 months of age) with meat less tender than that of a roaster, and nonflexible breastbone tip.

7. **Cock or rooster.**—A cock or rooster is a mature male chicken with coarse skin, toughened and darkened meat, and hardened breastbone tip.

Classes are also provided for turkeys, ducks, geese, guineas, and pigeons.

The grades of individual live birds are: A or No. 1 Quality, B or No. 2 Quality, and C or No. 3 Quality. The criteria used in determining grade are health and vigor, feathering, conformation, fleshing, fat covering, and defects.

Dressed and ready-to-cook poultry are graded for class, condition, and quality. These are most important since they are the grades used at the retail level. These grades are: U.S. Grade A, U.S. Grade B, and U.S. Grade C. These grades apply to dressed and ready-to-cook chickens, turkeys, ducks, geese, guineas, and pigeons.

Additionally, there are U.S. Procurement Grades, which are designed primarily for institutional use. These grades are: U.S. Procurement Grade 1 and U.S. Procurement Grade 2. In procurement grades, more emphasis is placed on meat yield than on appearance.

The factors determining the grade of carcasses or ready-to-cook poultry parts therefrom are: conformation, fleshing, fat covering, pinfeathers, exposed flesh, discoloration, disjointed bones, broken bones, missing parts, and freezing defects.

Eggs

The grading of eggs involves their sorting according to quality, size, weight, and other factors that determine their relative value. U.S. standards for quality of individual shell eggs have been developed on the basis of such interior quality factors as condition of the white and yolk, the size and condition of the air cell, and the exterior quality factors of cleanliness and soundness of the shell. These standards cover the entire range of edible eggs.

Eggs are also classified according to weight (or size), expressed in ounces per dozen.

Egg grading, then, is the grouping of eggs into lots according to similar characteristics as to quality and weight. Although color is not a factor in the U.S. standards of grades, eggs are sometimes sorted for color and sold for either "white" or "browns."

Three sets of grades, based on the quality standards for individual shell eggs, are used in this country: (1) consumer grades—used in the sale of eggs to individual consumers, (2) wholesale grades—used in the wholesale channels of trade; and (3) U.S. Procurement Grades—used for institutional buying and Armed Forces purchases.

The U.S. standards for quality of individual shell eggs are applicable only to eggs of the domesticated chicken that are in the shell. These are given in Table 45-2.

The basis for the egg grades given in Table 45-2 is resemblance to normal new-laid eggs.

Consumer grades are those used for lots of eggs that have been carefully candled and graded for retail trade. These are given in Table 45-3.

Wholesale grades differ from consumer grades in the tolerance of lower quality eggs permitted and in possible inclusion of some "loss" or inedible eggs. The grade designations of wholesale grades are U.S. Specials, U.S. Extras, U.S. Standards, U.S. Trades, U.S. Dirties, and U.S. Checks.

In the marketing of eggs, weight classes are also provided. These are given in table 45-4.

It is to be emphasized that weight is separate and distinct from egg quality.

FEDERAL INSPECTION

The Poultry Products Inspection Act, Public Law 85-175, was enacted on August 28, 1957, and became fully effective January 1, 1959. The Poultry Division of the Consumer and Marketing Service in the USDA is charged with the

TABLE 45—2

SUMMARY OF UNITED STATES STANDARDS FOR QUALITY OF INDIVIDUAL
SHELL EGGS[1]

Quality Factor	Specifications for Each Quality Factor			
	AA Quality	A Quality	B Quality	C Quality
Shell	Clean Unbroken Practically normal	Clean Unbroken Practically normal	Clean; to very slightly stained. Unbroken. May be slightly abnormal.	Clean; to moderately stained. Unbroken. May be abnormal.
Air cell	1/8 inch or less in depth. Practically regular.	3/16 inch or less in depth. Practically regular.	3/8 inch or less in depth. May be free or bubbly.	May be over 3/8 inch in depth. May be free or bubbly.
White	Clear Firm (72 Haugh units or higher).	Clear May be reasonably firm (60 to 72 Haugh units).	Clear May be slightly weak (31 to 60 Haugh units).	May be weak and watery. Small blood clots or spots may be present. (less than 31 Haugh units).*
Yolk	Outline slightly defined. Practically free from defects.	Outline may be fairly well defined. Practically free from defects.	Outline may be well defined. May be slightly enlarged and flattened. May show definite but not serious defects.	Outline may be plainly visible. May be enlarged and flattened. May show clearly visible germ development but no blood. May show other serious defects.

*If they are small (aggregating not more than 1/8 inch in diameter)

For eggs with dirty or broken shells, the standards of quality provide three additional qualities. These are:

Dirty	Check	Leaker
Unbroken. May be dirty.	Checked or cracked but not leaking.	Broken so contents are leaking.

[1]From *Egg Grading Manual*, Agriculture Handbook No. 75, USDA, Agricultural Marketing Service, Table 2, p. 24.

responsibility of administering this Act. The law requires inspection for wholesomeness of all poultry processing plants shipping any of their products in interstate or foreign commerce. Personnel and supervisory cost of the service required by the Act except for necessary overtime are borne by appropriated federal funds.

Under the provisions of this Act, the USDA has four major responsibilities: (1) to determine that the poultry being processed is fit for human food—as determined by ante-mortem and post-mortem inspection, (2) to make sure that the processing is done in a sanitary manner, (3) to protect poultry and poultry products from adulteration, and (4) to require that poultry and poultry products are properly labeled in compliance with the requirements of the law.

TABLE 45—3

SUMMARY OF U.S. CONSUMER GRADES FOR SHELL EGGS[1]

U.S. Consumer Grade	At Least 80 Per Cent (lot average[2]) must be—	Tolerance Permitted[3]	
		Per Cent	Quality
Grade AA or Fresh Fancy Quality	AA quality	15 to 20 Not over 5[4]	A B, C, or Check
Grade A	A Quality or better	15 to 20 Not over 5[4]	B, C, or Check
Grade B	B Quality or better	10 to 20 Not over 10[4]	C, Dirty or Check

[1]From *Egg Grading Manual*, Agriculture Handbook No. 75, USDA, Agricultural Marketing Service, Table 3, p. 25.
[2]In lots of two or more cases or cartons.
[3]Within tolerance permitted, an allowance will be made at receiving points or shipping destination for ½ per cent leakers in Grades AA, A, and B.
[4]Substitution of higher qualities for the lower qualities specified is permitted.

TABLE 45—4

U.S. WEIGHT CLASSES FOR CONSUMER GRADES FOR SHELL EGGS[1]

Size or Weight Class	Minimum Net Weight per Dozen	Minimum Net Weight per 30 Dozen	Minimum Weight for Individual Eggs at Rate per Dozen
	(ounces)	(pounds)	(ounces)
Jumbo	30	56	29
Extra large	27	50½	26
Large	24	45	23
Medium	21	39½	20
Small	18	34	17
Peewee	15	28	——

[1]From *Egg Grading Manual*, Agriculture Handbook No. 75, USDA, Agricultural Marketing Service, Table 5, p. 25.

The grading services for both poultry meat and eggs are on a voluntary basis, with charges made for those requesting the service. However, inspection of poultry and egg products is mandatory in those poultry plants processing and shipping any of their products in interstate or foreign commerce.

MARKET CHANNELS AND SELLING ARRANGEMENTS

Most poultry and eggs are marketed through retail food stores. The institutional markets, government purchases, and exports account for the remainder. In all cases, market channels have become more direct.

Until the mid-1940's, most eggs moved from producers to country buying stations, or to hucksters and peddlers, thence to central assembling plants and shippers, thence to city wholesalers and jobbers, and finally to store warehouses or retail stores. In recent years, the desire to sell to premium outlets has had a major impact on the channels used in areas close to markets, with the result that a substantial proportion of eggs are moving from producers either directly to consumers or to retail stores. As a result, some of the middle-men—country buying stations and city wholesalers—are being eliminated. In those surplus-egg-producing states that are located long distances from markets, so-called assembling plants take over the function of assembling eggs and shipping them to wholesalers in distant cities, or direct to chain store warehouses, or direct to retail stores.

The marketing of poultry meat has also changed, largely as a result of a substantial increase in commercial broiler production and a shift from New York dressed (blood and feathers removed only) to ready-to-cook birds or parts. In the heavy producing broiler areas, birds are moved directly from producers to the processing plants, thence to chain store warehouses or direct to retail stores. In the less populous poultry areas, the buying station type of agency assembles small quantities of poultry from individual producers, then sells them in larger quantities to city or country processing plants.

In summary, it may be said that, in both egg and broiler production, larger operations have resulted in processors locating near production and the elimination of some of the middle-men who formerly performed a needed service where many small producers were involved.

Pricing Broilers

For each commodity—broilers, turkeys, and eggs—there is a great deal of formula pricing. Originally, the typical broiler formula was based on live price divided by 73 per cent (the approximate yield of ready-to-cook from live weight) plus 5 to 7 cents to cover processing costs. However, as more and more broilers were produced under contract, fewer and fewer live broilers changed hands. As a result, the trend is away from farm base calculations to ready-to-cook prices.

Pricing Turkeys

Since most turkeys are sold frozen, there is less urgency in either selling or buying them than in the case of broilers or fresh meat. The Urner Barry daily report of wholesale turkey prices in the New York area is widely used as a guide in price negotiations. In the Chicago area, for example, the typical rule of thumb for turkey transactions is to apply the Urner Barry New York quotation, 5-day average for the week in which delivery was made, less 1¼ cents per pound.

Pricing Eggs

Pricing of eggs is both complex and confusing. East of the Rocky Mountains, egg prices were formerly tied by formula to the Urner Barry quotation from the New York Mercantile Exchange spot market. Finally, in 1953, producer dissatisfaction with pricing on the New York market led to the formation of an egg marketing cooperative.

On the West Coast, particularly in the Los Angeles area, egg pricing formulas have been tied to prices reported by the USDA Market News Service.

As integration and various forms of vertical coordination continue to spread within the poultry industries, fewer actual purchases and sales of products occur and fewer genuine negotiated prices are generated. Also, formula pricing reduces further the fraction of total supply entering into market price formation. Consequently, it is increasingly difficult for a poultry producer to determine what is the "going market," and markets are more vulnerable from the standpoint of manipulation.

FINANCIAL ASPECTS

Most people are in business to make money, and poultrymen are people; hence, they are no exception in this regard, nor should they be. The following sections reveal, to the extent that the facts and figures are available, how well or how poorly the named segments of the poultry industry are doing from the standpoint of profits.

Broiler Grower Returns

Broiler growers who produce birds under contract usually receive 5 to 7 cents per bird. Their income less operating expenses, depreciation, taxes, and return on capital invested has been estimated at between 25 cents and $2 per hour, the amount depending on efficiencies achieved in producing the birds and how fully grower's labor and capital can be kept employed.

Profitability of Poultry Processing Firms

There are two ways of gauging the profitability of poultry processing firms: (1) net return per dollar of sales, and (2) return on net worth. Figures computed on both bases, and averages for the six-year period 1959 to 1964, for chicken processors, turkey processors, and egg handlers or processors are given in Table 45-5. Admittedly, profits as a per cent of sales are not necessarily indicative of return on owner's investment, for the reason that companies that process and

TABLE 45—5

PROFITABILITY OF POULTRY PROCESSING FIRMS, 6 YEAR AVERAGE, 1959-64[1]

Processor	No. of Firms	Net Profits After Taxes as Per Cent of Sales	Net Profit as Per Cent of Share- holders Equity
Chicken	17	0.65	7.7
Turkey	11	1.34	17.8
Egg	17	0.81	12.8

[1]*Organization and Competition in the Poultry and Egg Industries*, Tech. Study No. 2, National Commission of Food Marketing, June 1966, Table 7-2, p. 59.

distribute products with a rapid turnover often have profits as a per cent of sales below those of companies processing and distributing products with a slow turnover. However, the return on net worth, or net profit as a per cent of shareholders' equity, is reasonably comparable for all types of businesses. In studying Table 45-5, it can be understood why the net profit after taxes as a per cent of sales of chickens is smaller than that of turkeys, simply because of the more rapid turnover of broilers. However, the net profit as a per cent of shareholders equity clearly shows that chicken processing has been less profitable over the period of the six years reported. By comparison, it is noteworthy that the net profit after taxes as a per cent of sales of 14 major companies processing and manufacturing dairy products in 1964 was 3 per cent, and their per cent of shareholders equity was 12.2 per cent.

Poultryman's Share of the Consumer's Dollar

The poultryman's share of the consumer's dollar is shown in Table 45-6. Beef has been added for comparative purposes.

TABLE 45—6

DISTRIBUTION OF THE CONSUMER'S DOLLAR ACCORDING TO MARKETING FUNCTION, POULTRY PRODUCTS AND BEEF, 1964[1]

Item	Broiler (pound)	Turkey (pound)	Eggs, Grade A or Better, All Sizes (dozen)	Beef, Choice (pound)[2]
	cents	cents	cents	cents
Retail price	36.3	40.6	51.5	70.8
Retailing[3]	7.9	4.0	8.8	17.0
Wholesaling, transportation, other distribution	4.5	3.0	6.2	2.3
Processing	3.6	7.0	6.0	5.3
Assembly	.6	.6	1.4	3.8
Farm value	19.7	26.0	29.1	42.4
Per cent of retail price: Farm share	54	64	57	60

[1] *Food from Farmer to Consumer*, Report of the National Commission on Food Marketing, June 1966, pp. 14 and 15.
[2] More than half of all beef is choice grade, but the exact proportion is unknown.
[3] In-store costs only. Warehousing, delivery, etc., included in wholesaling.

Without doubt, the smaller retail mark-up shown in Table 45-6 for broilers and turkeys in comparison with beef can be attributed largely to the practice of many retail outlets using poultry as a "loss-leader." This refers to the practice of selling poultry during special sale periods at a relatively low price, and on a small mark-up basis. Table 45-6 also brings out the fact that "assembly" costs for poultry products are much lower than they are for beef. This is due to the fact that poultry units have tended to become more concentrated in certain areas, and that flocks have become larger, with the result that the cost of assembling the products has lessened.

FOREIGN TRADE IN POULTRY

Prior to 1950, exports of poultry products amounted to no more than one per cent of domestic production. However, beginning in the late 1950's, exports of broilers increased rapidly, and by 1962 they accounted for 3.4 per cent of domestic production. Beginning in 1962, however, the European Economic Community (EEC) imposed high levies on chickens and turkeys. As a result, chicken exports to these countries have declined. But exports to other countries have expanded, with the result that, in 1964, chicken exports represented 2 per cent of domestic production.

Turkey exports have continued to grow, accounting for 2.8 per cent of turkey production in 1962 and 3 per cent in 1964.

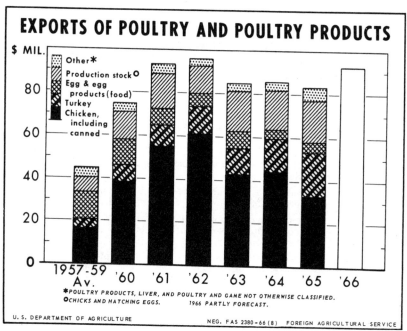

Fig. 45-2. Exports of poultry and poultry products, 1957 to 1966.

In 1965, the major U.S. markets for poultry meat exports, by rank, were: West Germany, Netherlands, Japan, Hong Kong, Canada, Switzerland, and Austria; with West Germany taking 84.5 million pounds out of a total export of 198.3 million pounds.

U.S. imports of poultry products, mainly eggs (in the shell) from Canada have been small compared with exports of poultry products. Total poultry and egg imports amounted to $2 million in 1964, slightly over 2 per cent of the value of U.S. exports of poultry products.

In 1966, the U.S. had an import duty of 3½ cents per dozen on shell chicken eggs, 5 cents per dozen on other shell eggs, and 3 cents per pound on chicken meat imports.

TRENDS IN MARKETING AHEAD

There is every indication that broiler, turkey, and egg production will each become more highly specialized, larger, and concentrated in fewer farms, and more vertically integrated. The motivating forces back of this increasing "bigness" are the advantages in management, marketing, and distribution. Also, with increasing mechanization and smaller labor requirements, it is quite likely that an increasing number of the production units will be owned by the integrator, rather than controlled on a contract basis.

With it all, it appears that market reporting and bases for establishing the going market price of broilers, turkeys, and eggs will become increasingly difficult. Perhaps the ultimate solution lies in the "giants" in the poultry industry taking a page out of the book of the automobile manufacturers; learning to live together in competition, but cutting back or closing down production at such intervals as necessary to avoid over-production and ruinous prices. Of course, there remain two great differences between poultry producers and automobile manufacturers: (1) consumers don't eat cars, and (2) biologically controlled animals cannot be turned on and off as can the manufacture of a car.

QUESTIONS FOR STUDY AND DISCUSSION

1. How does the market value of poultry and eggs compare with the market value of dairy products?
2. How does poultry rank in terms of farm and ranch income in comparison with the income from beef cattle, sheep, swine, and dairy cattle?
3. As a further means of alleviating middle-men—particularly the processor and the retailer—why do not more housewives buy broilers and process them themselves?
4. In most areas of the U.S., it is possible to enter into an integrated enterprise in either broiler, turkey, or egg production. Select one of these enterprises, decide on the size operation desired, then determine how much capital you would have to have to get into the business, and how much borrowed money you might be able to obtain.
5. To date, turkey processing appears to have been more profitable than the processing of eggs or the processing of broilers. Why has this been so?
6. The Meat Inspection Act which applies to the slaughter of beef cattle, sheep, and swine was passed on June 30, 1906; and since that time, animals of these species intended for interstate commerce have been inspected. With poultry, on the other hand, inspection did not come into effect until January 1, 1959. Why this difference?
7. Do most housewives make use of federal grades of poultry and eggs when they purchase these products at a retail store?
8. Who determines, and how do they determine, prices for broilers, turkeys, and eggs?
9. Does the poultry producer get a fair share of the consumer's dollar?
10. What is the possibility of exporting more poultry in the years ahead?
11. Is there a place for a family operated broiler, turkey, or egg farm now and in the years ahead?

SELECTED REFERENCES

Title of Publication	Author(s)	Publisher
Egg Grading Manual	Agriculture Handbook No. 75	USDA, Agricultural Marketing Service, Washington, D.C., 1964.
Food from Farmer to Consumer	Report of June 1966	National Commission on Food Marketing, Washington, D.C., 1966.
Marketing Poultry Products	E. W. Benjamin J. M. Gwin F. L. Faber W. D. Dermohlen	John Wiley & Sons, Inc., New York, N. Y., 1960.
Organization and Competition In the Poultry and Egg Industries	Technical Study No. 2	National Commission on Food Marketing, Washington, D.C., 1966.
Poultry Grading Manual	Agriculture Handbook No. 31	USDA, Consumer and Marketing Service, Washington, D.C., 1965.
Poultry Products Technology	G. J. Mountney	The Avi Publishing Co., Inc., Westport, Conn., 1966.

Chapter XLVI

THE HORSE INDUSTRY

Contents

	Page
Evolution of the Horse	
Origin and Domestication of the Horse	1077
Origin and Domestication of the Donkey	1081
Position of the Horse in the Zoological Scheme	1084
Man's Use of the Horse	1085
Introduction of Horses and Mules to and Early History in the United States	1086
Growth and Decline of the U.S. Horse and Mule Production	1087
World Distribution of Horses and Mules	1089
U.S. Horse Population	1092
The Cow Pony of the West	1093
Present Status and Future of the Horse Industry	1096
Questions for Study and Discussion	1099
Selected References	1099
	1100

The evolution and transformation of the horse from the early-day wild forms, its subsequent domestication, and the overlapping uses made of it in both war and peace is a fascinating story.

EVOLUTION OF THE HORSE

Fossil remains prove that members of the horse family roamed the plains of America (especially what is now the Great Plains area of the United States) during most of Tertiary time, beginning about 58 million years ago. Yet no horses were present on this continent when Columbus discovered America in 1492. Why they perished, only a few thousand years before, is still one of the unexplained mysteries of evolution. As the disappearance was so complete and so sudden, many scientists believe that it must have been caused by some contagious disease or some fatal parasite. Others feel that perhaps it was due to multiple causes; including (1) climatic changes, (2) competition, and/or (3) failure to adapt. Regardless of why horses disappeared, it is known that conditions in America were favorable for them at the time of their re-establishment by the Spanish Conquistadors less than 500 years ago.

Through fossil remains, it is possible to reconstruct the evolution of the horse (see Table 46-1), beginning with the ancient four-toed ancestor, the *Eohippus* (meaning "dawn horse"). This was a small animal, scarcely more than a foot high, with four toes on the front feet and three toes on the hind feet, and with slender legs, a short neck, and even teeth. It was well adapted to travelling in and feeding on the herbage of swamp lands. Gradually, the descendants of *Eohippus* grew in size and changed in form, evolving into a three-toed animal known as *Mesohippus,* which was about 24 inches in height, or about the size of a collie dog. Further changes continued, transforming the animal from a deni-

TABLE 46—1—EVOLUTION OF THE HORSE AS

Eras	Periods	Epochs	Approximate Duration In Years	Approximate Number of Years Since Beginning	General Characteristics
Cenozoic (Recent life) Age of mammals and Angiosperms	Quaternary	Recent	12,000+	12,000+	Post Glacial Age. Rise of Modern Man *Homo sapiens.* Development of complex cultures and civilizations. Domestication of animals.
		Pleistocene (Gr. *pleistos,* most + *kainos,* recent)	1,000,000	1,000,000	Ice Age: Four major advances. Evolution of primitive man, Neanderthal, Heidelberg, Peking, Java, etc. Mammoth, mastodon, great sloth, saber-tooth tiger, etc. 90-100% modern species. Rise of Alps and Himalayas.
	Tertiary	Pliocene (Gr. *pleion,* more + *kainos*)	11,000,000	12,000,000	Mammals increase in size. 50-90% modern species.
		Miocene (Gr. *meion,* less *kainos*)	16,000,000	28,000,000	The Golden Age of mammals. Luxuriant grasses; culmination of plains-dwelling mammals. 20-40% modern species.
		Oligocene (Gr. *oligos,* little + *kainos*)	10,000,000	38,000,000	Modern mammals predominate over primitive ones. 10-15% modern species.
		Eocene (Gr. *eos,* dawn + *kainos*)	20,000,000	58,000,000	Archaic mammals, the advent of the horse. 1-5% modern species.
		Paleocene	17,000,000	75,000,000	The beginning of the age of mammals. Great development of the angiosperms. 1% modern species.

[1]Grateful acknowledgement is made to the following eminent authorities for their help in the preparation of this table: Dr. Frank Scott, Department of Geology, Washington State University, and Mr. Karl P. Schmidt, formerly, Chief Curator, Department of Zoology, Chicago Natural History Museum, Chicago, Illinois. (Drawings by R.F. Johnson.)

DECIPHERED FROM THE FOSSIL RECORD[1]

The Horse[2]

Equus (Modern Horse. *Equus* is the Latin for horse). Beginning about 25,000 years ago, during the Paleolithic (Old Stone Age), man hunted horses and used them as a source of food. They were probably the last of the common domestic animals to be domesticated. This domestication is thought to have occurred toward the end of the Neolithic (New Stone Age) about 5,000 years ago. The horse was returned to the New World by the Spanish Conquistadors less than 500 years ago.

Equus (Modern Horse). One large functional toe on each foot with the two side toes reduced to mere splint bones and entirely non-functional. The horse reached the climax of his evolutionary development with *Equus*. Several known species in North America. Most of these were the size of small ponies but one fully equaled the greatest of modern draft horses. However, in the Americas he died out toward the end of the Pleistocene Epoch; perhaps due to multiple causes, including: (1) climatic changes, (2) competition, (3) epidemic, and/or (4) failure to adapt. Fortunately, however, horses had found a land bridge (probably via Alaska and Siberia) into the Old World, where they survived to become a servant and friend to man. They had entered the Old World by this same route at other times in the Tertiary past.

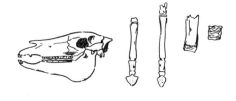

Pliohippus (Gr. *pleion*, more + *hippos*, horse). First one-toed horse, the side toes being reduced to splints. High-crowned grazing type teeth. Pony size. This was the immediate and virtually fullgrown forerunner of *Equus*. Also *Hipparion* (Gr. dim. of *hippos*; a pony), a three-toed grazer, and several other genera.

Merychippus (Rudimentary horse. Gr. *Meryx*, ruminant + *hippos*, horse). Three toes on each foot with the middle much heavier than the others which failed to touch the ground. A slim, graceful animal about the size of a Shetland pony. His teeth were high-crowned and hard-surfaced, suitable for eating grass. Thus *Merychippus* was thoroughly adapted to life on the prairie. Also *Protohippus* (Gr. *Protos*, first, primordial + *hippos*) generally similar to *Merychippus*; *miohippus* (Gr. *meion*, less + *hippos*) with foot structure like *Merychippus* but with short-crowned, browsing, teeth: *Parahippus* (Almost, nearly *hippos*) and others.

Mesohippus (Gr. *meso*, in the middle, intermediate—*hippos*). Three toes on each foot with the middle toe distinctly larger and a fourth toe on the front foot reduced to a splint, all touched the ground and shared in carrying the animal's weight. Teeth low-crowned, probably for browsing. *Mesohippus* was about the size of a collie dog with longer legs and a straighter back than his tiny Eocene forerunner. Also his intelligence and agility increased.

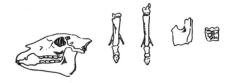

Eohippus (Gr. *eos*, dawn—*hippos*). Four functional toes on the front foot, one larger than the others, with a fifth reduced to a splint; the hind foot had three functional toes and a splint. *Eohippus* was a small graceful animal, scarcely more than a foot high with a slender face, an arched back, short neck, slender legs and a long tail. He was adapted for living in swamps. Also *Orohippus* (Gr. *oros*, mountain—*hippos*), having foot structure like *Eohippus* but without vestigial splints, and *Epihippus* (Gr. *epi*, upon, among—*hippos*).

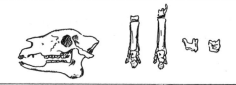

Pre-horse. The five toes (one a splint) on the forefeet of *Eohippus* indicate that its ancester probably had five toes all around, but no five toed horse has yet been found. The ancestors of the horse were probably primitive five toed ungulates, perhaps similar to some primitive Condylarth.

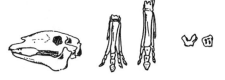

[2]In some cases, other genera might well be listed, but the leading ones of the respective epochs are here given.

zen of the swamp to a creature capable of surviving in the forest and finally to one adapted to the prairie. In terms of conformation, the animal grew taller. The teeth grew longer, stronger, and more roughened to suit the gradual changes to grazing on the prairie. The cannon bones (metacarpals and meta-tarsals) lengthened; the middle toe (or third toe) grew longer and stronger, forming a hoof; and the other toes (second and fourth toes) gradually disappeared except for vestiges, the slender bones known as splints under the skin. The transformation in length and structure of foot made for greater speed over prairie type of terrain, thus enabling the animal to feed farther and farther from water, and providing for greater safety in its struggle to survive. The horse is an excellent example, therefore, of the slow adaptation of animal life to changing conditions in environment, climate, food, and soil. The animal was transformed from one adapted to a swamp type of environment to one adapted to the prairie.

Fig. 46-1. Przewalsky's horse. This is the only surviving species of original wild horses—not feral or escaped from domestication—known to exist at the present time. Note that the animal is small and stockily built, with an erect mane and no forelock. (Courtesy, New York Zoological Society, New York)

Though all horses eventually perished in the New World and none were present on the continent when America was discovered, fortunately some of these animals had long before emigrated to Asia and Europe at a time when there was a land bridge connecting Alaska and Siberia (now the Bering Strait). These emigrants formed the sturdy wild European stock from which the horse family of today has descended, and this stock also populated Africa with its asses and zebras.

From Table 46-1, it can be seen that the evolution of the horse covered a period of approximately 58,000,000 years, but that man hunted him as recently as 25,000 years ago and domesticated him a mere 5,000 years ago, and that the Spanish Conquistadors returned him to the New World less than 500 years ago.

ORIGIN AND DOMESTICATION OF THE HORSE

The horse was probably the last of present-day farm animals to be domesticated by man. According to early records, after subduing the ox, the sheep and

Fig. 46-2. Joseph using horses in his move to Egypt (about 1500 B.C.), from a miniature painting in the Bible of the Counts of Toggenburg, 16th century. (Courtesy, The Bettmann Archive)

the goat, man domesticated the ass and then the camel; and, finally, the horse became his servant.

Horses appear to have been domesticated first in Central Asia or Persia more than 3,000 years B.C., for they spread westward through southern Europe in the time of the Lake Dwellers. They were reported in Babylonia as early as 2000 B.C., perhaps coming into the country via neighboring Persia.

Although the Egyptians—the most advanced civilization of the day—had domesticated and used the ass from the earliest times, horses were wholly unknown to them until the dynasty of the Shepherd Kings, who entered Egypt from Asia in 1680 B.C. It is reported that, thereafter, the horse was much favored in Egypt.

Presence of the horse seems to have prompted the invention of the chariot, a type of vehicle drawn by horses that the Egyptians used in war and other pursuits. The Bible also relates that when Joseph took his father's remains from Egypt back to Canaan "there went up with him both chariots and horsemen."[1]

Fig. 46-3. Distinguished young Greek in fashionable riding habit. Bowl painting, 500 B.C. Though the Greeks were accomplished horsemen, at this time the use of the saddle and stirrups appears to have been unknown. (Courtesy, The Bettmann Archive)

---

[1] Genesis 50:9.

It is probable that the Egyptians were largely responsible for the spread of domesticated horses to other countries.

Certainly, Greece was not even peopled, and there were no horses in Arabia during the early period when they were flourishing in Egypt. But horses and chariots were in use in Greece at least a thousand years before Christ, to judge from the account of their use in the siege of Troy. It is also interesting to note that the first and most expert horsemen of Greece, the Thessalians, were colonists from Egypt. As evidence that the Greeks were accomplished horsemen, it might be pointed out that they developed the snaffle bit at an early period. One of their number is also said to have originated the axiom: "No foot, no horse." Yet the use of the saddle and stirrups appears to have been unknown at this time.

From Greece, the horse was later taken to Rome and from there to other parts of Europe. The Romans proved to be master horsemen. It was they who invented the curb bit. According to historians, when Caesar invaded Britain, about 55 B.C., he took horses with him. Although there were other horses in

Fig. 46-4. Horses vary in size and use. The Shetland pony foal (left) is thought to have descended from the small, shaggy wild stock of northern Europe, whereas the draft horse (right) is thought to have descended primarily from the ponderous wild black horse of Flanders. (Courtesy, Iowa State University)

Britain at the time of the Roman occupation, eastern breeding was probably greatly infused at this time—thus laying the foundation for the Blood Horse of today.

The Arabs, strangely enough, did not use horses to any extent until after the time of Mohammed (570 to 632 A.D.), depending on camels before that time. As evidence of this fact, it is noted that in the seventh century after Christ, when Mohammed attacked the Koreish near Mecca, he had but two horses in his whole army; and, at the close of his murderous campaign, although he drove off 24,000 camels and 40,000 sheep and carried away 24,000 ounces of silver, not one horse appeared in his list of plunder. This would seem to indicate rather conclusively that Arabia, the country whose horses have done so much to improve the horses of the world, was not the native home of the horse and that the Arabs did not use horses until after the time of Christ.

Of course, it seems incredible that all the various breeds, colors, and types of draft, light, and pony horses should have descended from a common wild ancestor. Rather, there were probably many different wild stocks giving descent to domestic horses.

ORIGIN AND DOMESTICATION OF THE DONKEY

The two species of the horse family that have been tamed by man are *Equus caballus*, the horse, and *Equus asinus*, the ass or donkey. The history of the domestic donkey is as clear as that of the horse is obscure. Donkeys were first domesticated in Egypt, where they served man from earliest times. Good figures of them appear on slates of the First Dynasty, about 3400 B.C. Domestic donkeys are descended from the wild donkey (the Nubian wild ass) of North Africa, a species which is now almost extinct. Because of the frequent tendency

Fig. 46-5. A Mongolian wild ass in the Gobi desert in Asia (Courtesy, American Museum of Natural History, New York)

to stripes on the legs, however, some zoologists also think that the domestic donkey is related to the Somali wild ass of Africa.

From Egypt, the use of the domestic donkey spread into southwestern Asia sometime prior to the year 1000 B.C. The Bible first refers to the ass in relating how Abraham, the patriarch of the Old Testament, rode one of these animals from Beersheba to Mount Mordah. Every child is familiar with the fact that Jesus rode into Jerusalem on an ass. This mode of transportation was not unusual at the time of Christ, for donkeys were then the common saddle animals throughout the Near East.

As is generally known, the donkey is commonly used in this country in the production of mules.[2] Mules have been known from very ancient times, as we learn from accounts of the Trojan War.

Fig. 46-6. Chariot driven through Pompeii. The horse-drawn chariot was used by the sports-loving Greeks in chariot races, as well as in war and other pursuits. (Courtesy, The Bettmann Archive)

POSITION OF THE HORSE IN THE ZOOLOGICAL SCHEME

The following outline shows the basic position of the domesticated horse in the zoological scheme:

Kingdom *Animalia:* Animals collectively; the Animal Kingdom.

Phylum *Chordata:* One of the approximately 21 phyla of the animal kingdom, in which there is either a backbone (in the vertebrates) or the rudiment of a backbone, the chorda.

Class *Mammalia:* Mammals, or warm-blooded, hairy animals that produce

---

[2] In recent years, some miniature donkeys are being used as children's pets in the U.S.

their young alive and suckle them for a variable period on a secretion from the mammary glands.

Order *Perissodactyla:* Nonruminant hoofed mammals, usually with an odd number of toes, the third digit the largest and in line with the axis of the limb. This suborder includes the horse, tapir, and rhinoceros.

Family *Equidae:* The members of the horse family may be distinguished from the other existing perissodactyla (rhinoceros and tapir) by their comparatively more slender and agile build.

Genus *Equus:* Includes horses, asses, and zebras.

Species *Equus caballus:* The horse is distinguished from asses and zebras by the longer hair of the mane and tail, the presence of the "chestnut" on the inside of the hind leg, and by other less constant characteristics such as larger size, larger hoofs, more arched neck, smaller head, and shorter ears.

MAN'S USE OF THE HORSE

The name "horse" is derived from the Anglo-Saxon *hors,* meaning swiftness; and the word "horseman" comes from the Hebrew root "to prick or spur."[3] These

Fig. 46-7. Pack mules and "mule skinners" in service during World War II. Horses and mules dramatically proved their worth again and again on the field of battle and on our farms during World War II. (U.S. Army photo)

---

[3] The Jews were forbidden to use horses by divine authority. In fact, they were required to hamstring horses captured in war.

early characterizations of the horse, within themselves, tell somewhat of a story. Perhaps the very survival of the wild species was somewhat dependent upon its swiftness, which provided escape from both beast and man. The Hebrew description of a horseman was obviously assigned after the horse had been domesticated and ridden by man.

The various uses that man has made of the horse down through the ages, in order of period of time, follow: (1) as a source of food, (2) for military purposes, (3) in the pastimes and sports of the nations, (4) in agricultural and commercial pursuits, and (5) for recreation and sport.

INTRODUCTION OF HORSES AND MULES TO AND EARLY HISTORY IN THE UNITED STATES

It has been established that most of the evolution of the horse took place in the Americas, but this animal was extinct in the Western World at the time of Columbus' discovery, and apparently extinct even before the arrival of the Red Man, some thousands of years earlier.

Columbus first brought horses to the West Indies on his second voyage in 1493. Cortez brought Spanish horses with him to the New World in 1519 when he landed in Mexico (16 animals were in the initial contingent, but approximately 1,000 head more were subsequently imported during the two-year conquest of Mexico). Horses were first brought directly to what is now the United States by DeSoto in the year 1539. Upon his vessels, he had 237 horses. These animals traveled with the army of the explorer in the hazardous journey from the Everglades of Florida to the Ozarks of Missouri. Following DeSoto's death and burial in the upper Mississippi three years later, his followers returned by boats down the Mississippi, abandoning many of their horses.

One year following DeSoto's landing in what is now Florida, in 1540, another Spanish explorer, Coronado, started an expedition with an armed band of horsemen from Mexico, penetrating to a point near the boundary of Kansas and Nebraska.

Beginning about 1600, the Spaniards established a chain of Christian missions among the Indians in the New World. This chain of missions extended from the eastern coast of Mexico up the Rio Grande, thence across the mountains to the Pacific Coast. Each mission brought animals from the mother country, including horses.

There are two schools of thought relative to the source of the foundation stock of the first horses of the American Indians, and the hardy bands of mustangs —the feral horses of the Great Plains. Most historians agree that both groups were descended from animals of Spanish (Arabian) extraction. However, some contend that their foundation stock came from the abandoned and stray horses of the expeditions of DeSoto and Coronado, whereas others claim that they were obtained chiefly from Santa Fe, ancient Spanish mission founded in 1606. It is noteworthy that Santa Fe and other early Spanish missions were the source of Spanish Longhorn cattle, thus lending credence to the theory that the missions were the source of foundation horses for the Indian and the wild bands of mustangs.

Much romance and adventure is connected with the mustang, and each band of wild horses was credited with leadership by the most wonderful stallion ever beheld by man. Many were captured, but the real leaders were always alleged to have escaped by reason of speed, such as not possessed by a domesticated horse. The mustang multiplied at a prodigious rate. In one high luxuriant bunchgrass region in the state of Washington, wild horses thrived so well that the region became known as "horse heaven," a name it bears today.

The coming of the horse among the Indians increased the strife and wars between tribes. Following the buffalo on horseback led to greater infringement upon each other's hunting grounds, which had ever been a cause for war. From the time the Indians came into possession of horses until the country was taken over by the white man, there was no peace among the tribes.

Later, animals of both light- and draft-horse breeding were introduced from Europe by the colonist. For many years, however, sturdy oxen continued to draw the plows for turning the sod on many a rugged New England hillside. Horses were largely used as pack animals, for riding, and later for pulling wagons and stagecoaches. It was not until about 1840 that the buggy first made its appearance.

Six mares and two stallions were brought to Jamestown in 1609, these being the first European importations. Some of these animals may have been eaten during the period of near starvation at Jamestown, but importations continued; and it was reported in 1611 that a total of 17 horses and mares had been brought to this colony.

The horse seems to have been much neglected in early New England, as compared with cattle and sheep. This is not surprising, inasmuch as oxen were universally used for draft purposes. Roads were few in number; speed was not essential; and the horse had no meat value like that of cattle. Because of the great difficulty in herding horses on the commons, they were usually hobbled. Despite the limited early-day use of the horse, the colonists must have loved them, because, very early, the indiscriminate running of stallions among the mares upon the commons was recognized as undesirable. Massachusetts, before 1700, excluded from town commons all stallions "under fourteen hands high and not of comely proportion."[4]

Even before horses found much use in New England, they became valuable for export purposes to the West Indies for work in the sugar mills. In fact, this business became so lucrative that horse stealing became a common offense in New England in the eighteenth century. Confiscation of property, public whippings, and banishment from the colony constituted the common punishments for a horse thief.

As plantations materialized in Virginia, the need for easy-riding saddle horses developed, so that the owners might survey their broad estates. Racing also became a popular sport among the Cavaliers in Virginia, Maryland, and the Carolinas—with the heat races up to four miles being common events. The

[4] Thompson, James Westfall, *History of Livestock Raising in the United States, 1607-1860*, USDA, Agricultural History Series No. 5, Nov. 1942.

plantation owners took considerable pride in having animals worthy of wearing their colors. So great was the desire to win that by 1730 the importation of English race horses began.

George Washington maintained an extensive horse- and mule-breeding establishment at Mount Vernon. The President was also an ardent race fan, and riding to hounds was a favorite sport with him. As soon as Washington's views on the subject of mules became known, he received some valuable breeding stock through gifts. In 1787, the Marquis de Lafayette presented him with a jack and some jennets of the Maltese breed. The jack, named Knight of Malta, was described as a superb animal, of a black color, with the form of a stag and the ferocity of a tiger. In 1795, the King of Spain gave Washington a jack and two jennets that were selected from the royal stud at Madrid. The Spanish jack, known as Royal Gift, was 16 hands high, of a gray color, heavily made, and of a sluggish disposition. It was said that Washington was able to combine the best qualities of the two gift jacks, especially through one of the descendants named Compound. General Washington was the first to produce mules of quality in this country, and soon the fame of these hardy hybrids spread throughout the South.

The Dutch, Puritan, and Quaker colonists to the north adhered strictly to agricultural pursuits, frowning upon horse races. They imported heavier types of horses. In Pennsylvania, under the guidance of William Penn, the farmers prospered. Soon their horses began to improve, even as the appearance and fertility of their farms had done. Eventually, these large horses were hitched to enormous wagons and used to transport freight overland to and from river flatboats and barges along the Ohio, Cumberland, Tennessee, and Mississippi Rivers. Both horses and wagons were given the name Conestoga,[5] after the Conestoga Valley, a German settlement in Pennsylvania. The Conestoga wagon was the forerunner of the prairie schooner and before the advent of the railroad it was the freight vehicle of the time. It was usually drawn by a team of six magnificent Conestoga horses, which were well groomed and expensively harnessed. At one time, the Conestoga horses bid to become a new breed—a truly American creation. However, the railroads replaced them, eventually driving them into permanent oblivion. Other breeds were developed later, but this is another story.

GROWTH AND DECLINE OF THE U.S. HORSE AND MULE PRODUCTION

The golden age of the horse extended from the Gay Nineties to the mechani-

---

[5] It is noteworthy that the American custom of driving to the right on the road, instead of to the left as the practice in most of the world, is said to have originated among the Conestoga wagon drivers of the 1750's. The drivers of these four- and six-horse teams either sat on the left wheel horse or on the left side of the seat, the better to wield their whip hand (the right hand) over the other horses in the team. Also, when two Conestoga drivers met, they pulled over to the right so that, sitting on the left wheel horse or on the left side of the seat, they could see that the left wheels of their wagons cleared each other. Lighter vehicles naturally followed the tracks of the big Conestoga wagons.

Fig. 46-8. Conestoga freight wagon drawn by six Conestoga horses, in front of a country inn. These improved horses and large wagons were both given the name Conestoga, after the Conestoga Valley, a German settlement in Pennsylvania. The advent of the railroads drove the Conestoga horses into oblivion, and the Conestoga wagon was succeeded by the prairie schooner. (Courtesy, The Bettmann Archive)

zation of agriculture; to the advent of the automobile, truck, and tractor. During this era, everybody loved the horse. The town livery stable, watering trough, and hitching post were trademarks of each town and village. People wept when the horse fell down on the icy street, and jailed men who beat or mistreated him. The oat-bag, carriage, wagon, buggy-whip, axle grease, horseshoe, and horseshoe-nail industries were thriving and essential parts of the national economy. Every school boy knew and respected the village blacksmith.

Bob-tailed hackneys attached to high-seated rigs made a dashing picture as they pranced down the avenue; they were a mark of social prestige. A few memorable dinner parties of the era were even staged on horseback; with the guests lining up in exclusive restaurants astride their favorite mounts, and drinking and eating to the merriment of music, while their steeds munched oats and costumed lackeys cleaned up behind them.

In 1900, the automobile was still the plutocrat's plaything, and the truck and tractor were unknown. Most of the expensive 8,000 cars in the country at the time were either imported or custom built. Tires cost about $40.00 each, and lasted only 2,000 miles. Few really loved the auto. People complained of the noise that they made, enacted laws against them going through the city parks, and split their sides with laughter when they had to be pushed uphill or got stuck in the mud.

Then, in 1908, Henry Ford produced a car to sell at $825. The truck, the tractor, and improved highways followed closely in period of time. Old Dob-

U.S. Farm and Ranch: (1) Horse and
Mule Population (2) Tractor Numbers (3) Truck Numbers and
(4) Automobile Numbers

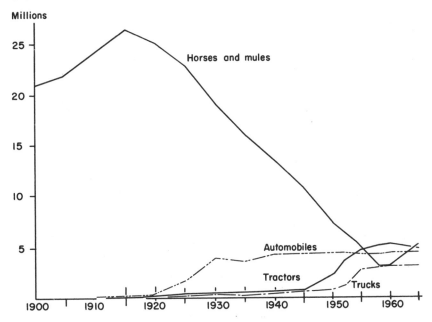

Fig. 46-9. Growth and decline of U.S. horse and mule production. Horse numbers reached a peak in 1915, whereas mule numbers reached a peak in 1925. The period of decline in horse and mule numbers coincided closely with the advent of mechanized power, especially the tractor, truck, and automobile. (Drawing by R. F. Johnson)

bin did not know it at the time, but his days were numbered. As shown in Figure 46-9, the passing of the horse age and the coming of the machine age went hand in hand; as automobile, truck, and tractor numbers increased, horse and mule numbers declined.

The number of horses in the United States increased up to 1915, at which time there was a record number of 21,431,000 head. Horse production expanded with the growth and development of farms.

On the other hand, mules on farms slowly but steadily increased in numbers for 10 years after horses began their decline, reaching a peak in 1925, at 5,918,000 head. Mule numbers have decreased proportionately less than horses because of their great use in the deep South where labor was cheaper and more abundant and the farms smaller in size.

On January 1, 1968, there were an estimated 6,675,000 head of horses in the United States.[6]

---

[6] Ensminger, M. E., *Fact Sheet Relative to U.S. Horse Population*, April, 1968.

WORLD DISTRIBUTION OF HORSES AND MULES

Since prehistoric times, there has been nearly world-wide distribution of the horse. Moreover, man's effective use of the horse has constantly progressed, especially from the standpoint of improvement in the equipment to which he was attached for the purpose of drawing loads. The past has been good, but even ardent horsemen recognize the passing of the horse as a source of power. For the most part, his brightest future lies in the fields of recreation and sport and as the cow pony of the West.

After the horse was domesticated and no longer hunted down and killed for meat, he was used to carry riders and support goods upon his strong back. In an effort to provide transportation for a longer load than could be fastened directly to the back of the horse, ingenious man devised a basket-like arrangement which was fitted between two long poles. One end of these poles rested on the back of the horse and the other end dragged on the ground to the rear. In an effort to reduce the resistance of this vehicle and permit the carrying of still heavier loads, man supported the poles on a wooden axle and two wheels made of wood, thus inventing a two-wheeled cart. Next, leather harness was developed transferring the pull from the back of the horse to the better-adapted shoulders.

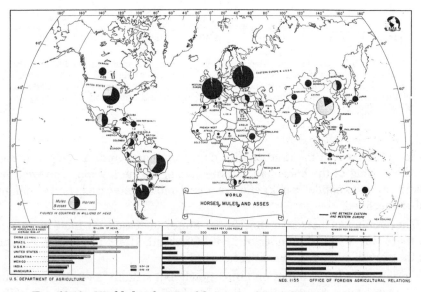

Fig. 46-10. World distribution of horses, mules, and asses.

Finally, man developed the four-wheeled, self-supporting vehicle with improved axles made of iron instead of wood; and eventually he replaced steel wheels with pneumatic tires mounted on ball bearings.

At a very early date and throughout the world, the versatility and adaptation of the horse were recognized. He was unexcelled in carrying a rider comfortably and swiftly on a long journey; he possessed a long life of usefulness; and, above all, he was intelligent. Despite all these virtues, in some areas the horse has been unable to replace the patient roughage-burning ox, and to this day oxen and water buffaloes are the chief source of power in many sections of the world. In the more isolated portions of the New England states, many oxen are still used, and stone boat pulling contests are a great attraction at the New England fairs.

Members of the ass family, mules and donkeys, are distributed in the warmer regions of the world. Like the horse and the ox, they are used for both pack and draft purposes.

Table 46-2 shows the size and density of horse population of the important horse countries of the world. According to the best available data, world horse numbers in 1961-62 totaled 64.7 million head.[7] This was far below the 1934-38 pre-war average of 96.4 million head. The decline in horse numbers since 1938 can be attributed chiefly to mechanization of agriculture in certain areas. For example, the number of tractors in use in agriculture in the world (exclusive of the U.S.S.R. and mainland China) in early 1954 was estimated at 6.7 million units, compared with fewer than 2 million in 1939.[8]

U. S. HORSE POPULATION

The sharp decrease in the number of horses and mules in the United States during the last four decades has had a serious and far-reaching effect upon American agriculture—and indirectly upon all industry. In 1920, there were 25,199,552 horses and mules on farms and ranches in the United States and about an additional 2,000,000 head in cities, but by January 1, 1960, there were only 3,089,000 head on the nation's farms and ranches (not counting suburban-owned horses and those kept on parcels under 10 acres in size). Thus, despite expansion in light horse numbers since World War II, until recent years there has been a steady decrease in the total number of horses and mules since the 1920s. Naturally, the explanation of this marked decrease is the invasion of the automobile, tractor, truck, and improved heavy farm machinery; and in point of time, the decrease in horses has closely followed the introduction of such machinery.

This decrease in the work stock of the country was a considerable factor in the overproduction problem which confronted American agriculture, except during and immediately following World War II. It has been estimated that about 100,000,000 acres of land that formerly produced feed for draft horses and mules was released for other purposes. This surplus production represents an area two and one-half times the size of the state of Illinois.

Today, there is much disagreement relative to the U.S. horse population. Part of the confusion stems from the fact that the Census Bureau figures of horses have always been limited to those on farms (and ranches), with no consideration

---

[7] In addition, there are approximately 50 million mules and asses and 78 million water buffaloes in the world, many of which are used for draft purposes. (From: *Foreign Agriculture Circular*, June 1955, p. 7.)

[8] *Foreign Agriculture Circular*, June 1955, p. 6.

TABLE 46—2

SIZE AND DENSITY OF HORSE POPULATION OF TEN LEADING HORSE-PRODUCING COUNTRIES OF THE WORLD, BY RANK

Country	Horses[1] Number	Horses[1] When Estimated	Human Population[2] Number	Human Population[2] When Estimated	Size of Country (sq. mi.)	Size of Country (sq. km.)	Horses per Capita[3]	Horses per (sq. mi.)	Horses per (sq. km.)
U.S.S.R.	9,400,000	61/62	229,100,000	1964	8,655,890	22,418,755	.027	1.09	.41
Brazil	8,374,000	61/62	78,809,000	1964	3,286,270	8,511,439	.11	2.55	.98
China	7,411,000	55/56	686,400,000	1960	2,279,134	5,902,957	.01	3.25	1.25
United States	6,675,000[4]	1968	200,000,000	1968	3,548,974	9,191,843	.03	1.88	.73
Mexico	4,169,000	61/62	39,643,000	1964	758,259	1,963,891	.11	5.50	2.12
Argentina	3,930,000	61/62	22,045,000	1964	1,072,700	2,778,293	.18	3.66	1.41
Poland	2,657,000	61/62	31,161,000	1964	120,359	311,730	.09	22.08	8.52
France	1,617,000	61/62	48,492,000	1965	212,659	550,787	.03	7.60	2.93
India	1,351,000	60/61	471,627,000	1964	1,261,597	3,267,536	.003	1.07	.41
Turkey	1,305,000	61/62	31,118,000	1964	296,500	767,935	.04	4.40	1.69
World Total	64,700,000	61/62	3,220,000,000	1965	52,403,746	135,725,702	.02	1.23	.47

[1] *Production Yearbook*, Food and Agriculture Organization, Volume 17, Table 71, 1963.
[2] *World Almanac*, 1966, New York World-Telegram.
[3] Horses per capita computed from most recent horse and human census figures reported; in some cases necessitated using data for different years.
[4] Ensminger, M.E., *Fact Sheet Relative To U.S. Horse Population*, April, 1968.

Fig. 46-11. The way it used to be done.

given to those owned by suburbanites. Most population figures fail to reflect the shift in the horse population from farm to town.

To complicate matters still further, there is little unanimity of opinion on the definition of a farm; on the dividing line between farm and non-farm. Then the coup de grâce was administered when the census takers discontinued counting horses in 1960; they counted Old Dobbin out with the passing of the draft horse. But they failed to recognize that the light horse was coming up fast; indeed, that the horse was rising to a new and more important position in the fields of recreation and sport.

Some definitions are necessary if horse population figures are to be meaningful:

1. **Farm.**—The definition of a farm varies from source to source, and from time to time. Webster defines a farm as "any tract devoted to agricultural purposes." The U.S. Census Bureau has changed its definition from time to time. As recently as 1954, it drew the line at 3 acres; units under 3 acres being classed as non-farm, and over 3 acres as farm. In 1960, the figure was changed to 10 acres. In addition to acreage, the Census Bureau has certain stipulations relative to income. Using their definitions, there were 3.2 million farms in 1967. By common usage, a farm is a parcel of land used for agricultural purposes from which the operator derives most of his income.

2. **Rural population.**—The words "rural" and "farm" are frequently, but erroneously, used interchangeably. At one time, this was essentially correct, for most rural residents lived on farms. But with the rise of "rural living," this was no longer true. Today, there are about 54 million rural residents,[9] with a distribution between "farm" and "other rural, but non-farm," living as follows:

---

[9] *The World Almanac, 1966*, p. 324 (from Bureau of the Census—1960 census).

a. **Farm living**—11.5 million people (using the Census Bureau definition of a farm).[10]

b. **Other rural, but non-farm, living**—42.5 million people live in the open country, but not on farms[11]; they live in small, unincorporated places, along highways and streams, and in suburban areas. They're craftsmen, foremen, and operators; white-collar workers; manufacturers; and other commuters. They moved to the country to recapture a romantic ideal, to escape the hustle and bustle of city life, to cut the cost of living, or to find a better place for their children. Others moved to the country to acquire a status symbol, for prestige, or for gracious living. Many of them have rural backgrounds or are only a generation or two removed from the land. Among these non-farm rural people are many ardent horsemen.

3. **U.S. horse population.**—Using as guideposts (a) the census figures of horses on farms in 1960 and (b) Cornell's survey estimate of total U.S. horses in 1964,[12] and by making certain arbitrary assumptions and computations, the author arrived at the following estimates of U.S. horse population:

	1968 horse numbers
Farm horses (using the Census Bureau definition of a farm)	2,605,000
Non-farm horses	4,070,000
Total U.S. horses	6,675,000

The computations out of which the 6,675,000 figure evolved are shown in Table 46-3.

THE COW PONY OF THE WEST

The 500,000 horses in the 17 western range states are nearly holding their own. Even the Jeep does not appear sufficiently versatile for use in roping a steer on the range. It is reasonable to assume, therefore, that the cow pony will continue to furnish needed assistance to man in the Far West.

---

[10] *Agricultural Statistics 1967*, p. 526, Table 649.

[11] 54 million (rural) — 11.5 million (farm) = 42.5 million "other rural, but non-farm," residents.

[12] *New York Equine Survey*, by Prof. Harold A. Willman, Department of Animal Husbandry, Cornell University, Ithaca, New York, February 15, 1965; with national estimate of "over six million horses" projected therefrom by Dr. David L. Call, Graduate School of Nutrition, Cornell University, in a paper entitled "Looking Ahead at the Pet Food Market." Latter paper was given at 1964 Cornell Nutrition Conference for Feed Manufacturers, Buffalo, New York.

TABLE 46—3

U.S. HORSE POPULATION

Year	Estimated No. Mares Bred[1]	Estimated No. Foals Produced[1]	Estimated Death Losses[1]	Horses on Farms	Horses on Non-farms	Total U.S. Horses
1960	275,000	137,500	50,000	2,125,000[2]	3,400,000	5,525,000
1961	300,000	150,000	50,000			5,625,000
1962	325,000	162,500	50,000			5,737,500
1963	350,000	175,000	50,000			5,862,500
1964	375,000	187,500	50,000			6,000,000 (Cornell survey estimate)
1965	400,000	200,000	50,000	2,400,000	3,750,000	6,150,000
1966	425,000	212,500	50,000	2,470,000	3,850,500	6,312,000
1967	450,000	225,000	50,000	2,530,000	3,957,500	6,487,500
1968	475,000	237,500	50,000	2,605,000	4,070,000	6,675,000

[1]Estimates by M.E. Ensminger.
[2]*Horses and Horsemanship*, 3rd ed., 1963, p. 33, by M.E. Ensminger. The 2,125,000 figure was for 1958-59, which is arbitrarily estimated by M.E.E. to be the same for 1960.

Fig. 46-12. The cow pony of the West will continue to furnish needed assistance in handling the range herds. Shown is Poco Bueno, Quarter Horse stallion. (Courtesy, *The Quarter Horse Journal*)

Fig. 46-13. White Lipizzan stallion literally flying through the air with per-fectly-seated stirrupless rider. The horse is decorated with gold trappings and the rider is smartly dressed in an old-time Napoleonic military uniform. The stallion is pictured doing the Capriole, one of the several intricate movements resembling the leaping, twisting, fighting, and frolicking of high-spirited horses in pasture.

The Lipizzan breed—named after the town of Lipizza, one-time site of the old Hapsburg stud farm—was founded back in 1565 by Emperor Maximilian of Austria. The emperor assembled white animals of Arabian and Spanish breeding and estab-lished the Spanish Riding School in Vienna, Austria. Foals of the Lipizzan breed are brown or gray at birth, but turn completely white at four to six years of age.

Toward the close of World War II, the Spanish Riding School and the Lipizzan breed were threatened with extinction by both the German and Russian armies. In desperation, the school heads appealed to ex-cavalryman George S. Patton, whose tanks were dashing across Austria in the spring of 1945. After observing a special exhibition of the historic white horses, the horse fancier General agreed to preserve and protect the entire herd as a part of European culture. To this end, the Spanish Riding School and its horses were moved to Wels, Austria, near Salzburg. (Courtesy, Colonel Alois Podhajsky, Spanish Riding School, Wels, Austria)

PRESENT STATUS AND FUTURE OF THE HORSE INDUSTRY

Horse numbers alone do not tell the whole story. Horse racing continues to be America's leading spectator sport. In 1967, 68,231,089 people went to horse races[13]—28 million more than went to automobile racing,[14] the second-ranking spectator sport; 32.3 million more than went to football (pro and college),[14] the third-ranking sport; and 33.5 million more than witnessed baseball (including both major and minor leagues).[14] As further evidence of the magnitude of horse racing, the following figures for 1967 are noteworthy: (1) $4,921,518,485 was wagered through the mutuel windows,[15] (2) $167,087,846 in purses was collected by horsemen,[15] and (3) $393,873,251 in revenue[15] was turned into the treasuries of the 30 states having legalized pari-mutuel wagering and used to build and operate schools, hospitals, fairs, and other things of benefit to old and young alike.

In 1966, for the first time in history, 4-H Club horse and pony projects took the lead over 4-H beef cattle projects, 165,510 to 157,949, respectively. In 1967, this lead was widened further—there were 187,369 horse and pony projects to 152,273 beef projects.

This generation has more money to spend and more leisure time in which to spend it than any population in history. People are spending approximately 10 per cent of their disposable income on leisure time activities—this made for a sum of $47 billion in 1968. A shorter work week, increased automation, more suburban and rural living, and the continued recreation and sports surge, with emphasis on physical fitness and the out-of-doors, will require more horses and support more race tracks, shows, and other horse events.

QUESTIONS FOR STUDY AND DISCUSSION

1. Trace the evolution of the horse from the standpoints of (a) the body changes which transformed him from a denizen of the swamp to a creature capable of surviving in the forest and finally to one adapted to the prairie, and (b) the period of years covering each; evolution, domestication, and return to America.

2. Trace the domestication and use of the horse prior to the time of Christ.

3. Discuss the rise and fall of the horse population of the U.S. from the standpoints of (a) the forces which caused such shifts and (b) the economic effects thereof.

4. What is your prediction as to the future of the horse industry (a) in the U.S. and (b) throughout the world?

5. Discuss the various uses that man has made of the horse down through the ages: (a) as a source of food, (b) for military purposes, (c) in the pastimes and sports of nations, (d) in agricultural and commercial pursuits, and (e) for recreation and sport.

6. To which school of thought do you subscribe relative to the source of the foundation stock of the first horses of the American Indians: (a) that they came from the abandoned and stray horses of DeSoto and Coronado, or (b) that they

---

[13] 38,526,589 to Thoroughbred races (personal communication from The National Association of State Racing Commissioners); 27,201,833 to harness races (personal communication from The United States Trotting Association); and 2,502,667 to Quarter Horse races and fairs (personal communication from The National Association of State Racing Commissioners).

[14] Triangle Publications, Inc. reported the following attendance figures for 1967: Automobile racing, 40,177,800; football, 35,955,219; baseball, 34,699,590.

[15] Personal communication from The National Association of State Racing Commissioners.

were obtained chiefly from Santa Fe, an ancient Spanish mission? Justify your answer.

SELECTED REFERENCES

Title of Publication	Author(s)	Publisher
Appaloosa Horse, The	Francis Haines G. B. Hatley Robert Peckinpah	R. G. Bailey Printing Company, Lewiston, Ida.
Changes in Horse Numbers as Related to Farm Mechanization, Recreation, and Sport	B. G. Stark	Thesis, Washington State University, Pullman, Wash., 1960.
Encyclopaedia Britannica		Encyclopaedia Britannica, Inc., Chicago, Ill.
Evolution of the Horse	W. D. Matthew S. H. Chubb	American Museum of Natural History, New York, N. Y., 1921.
Horse, The	D. J. Kays	Rinehart & Company, New York, N. Y., 1953.
Horses	G. G. Simpson	Oxford University Press, New York, N. Y., 1951.
Horses and Americans	P. D. Strong	Frederick A. Stokes, Co., New York, N. Y., 1939.
Horses and Horsemanship	M. E. Ensminger	The Interstate Printers & Publishers, Danville, Ill., 1969.
Horses of Today	H. H. Reese	Wood & Jones, Pasadena, Calif., 1956.
Light Horses	M. E. Ensminger	Farmers' Bul. No. 2127, U.S. Department of Agriculture, Washington, D.C.
Our Friendly Animals and Whence They Came	K. P. Schmidt	M. A. Donohue & Co., Chicago, Ill., 1938.
Power to Produce	Yearbook of Agriculture, 1960	U.S. Department of Agriculture, Washington, D.C., 1960.
Principles of Classification of Mammals, The	G. G. Simpson	Bulletin of the American Museum of Natural History, Vol. 85, New York, N. Y., 1945.
Thoroughbred Racing Stock	Lady Wentworth	Charles Scribner's Sons, New York, N. Y., 1938.
Use of Horses and Mules on Farms, The	J. J. Csorba	ARS 43-94, March 1959, U.S. Department of Agriculture, Washington, D.C.

Chapter XLVII

TYPES; AND MARKET AND SHOW CLASSES OF HORSES

Contents   Page

Types; and Market and Show Classes of Light Horses....................1101
  Riding Horses 1103
    Three- and Five-gaited Saddle Horses....................1103
    Walking Horses....................1105
    Stock Horses....................1106
    Polo Mounts 1107
    Hunters and Jumpers....................1108
    Ponies for Riding....................1109
  Race Horses....................1109
    Running Race Horses....................1110
    Harness Race Horses (Trotters and Pacers)....................1112
    Quarter Race Horses....................1113
  Driving Horses 1114
    Heavy Harness Horses....................1114
    Fine Harness Horses....................1115
    Roadsters 1116
    Ponies for Driving....................1117
Types; and Market and Show Classes of Work Horses and Mules....................1118
  Work Horses....................1118
  Mules 1119
Questions for Study and Discussion....................1121
Selected References 1122

In no class of animals have so many diverse and distinct types been developed as in the horse. The descendants of the Oriental light-legged horse have, for generations, been bred and used for riding and driving purposes—first as the chariot and riding horses of Egypt, Greece, and Arabia; later as the running horse of England; and finally for purposes of recreation and sport in the United States and throughout the world. In due time, further refinements in breeding light horses were made, and these animals were adapted for more specific purposes.

As with light horses, similar distinct types—though smaller in number—evolved in the draft horse. From the ponderous beast of Flanders, used as foundation stock, the Great War Horse of the Middle Ages was developed; the Great War Horse, in turn, served as the forerunner of the draft horse of commerce and agriculture. Further and eventual refinement through breeding and selection adapted draft animals to many and diverse uses, some of which have subsequently passed into oblivion with mechanization.

TYPES; AND MARKET AND SHOW CLASSES
OF LIGHT HORSES

In attempting to produce animals to meet specific purposes, new breeds of

TABLE 47—1

LIGHT HORSE SUMMARY

Type	Use	Breeds	Height (hands)	Weight (pounds)	(kilograms)	Place of Origin
Riding horses	Three-gaited saddle horses	American Albino Horse	14-2 to 17	900-1,400	409-636	United States
		American Saddle Horse				United States
		Arabian				Arabia
		Appaloosa				United States
		Missouri Fox Trotting				United States
		Morgan				United States
		Palomino				United States
		Thoroughbred				England
	Five-gaited saddle horses	American Saddle Horse	14-2 to 17	900-1,400	409-636	United States
	Walking horses	Tennessee Walking Horse	15 to 16	1,000-1,200	454-545	United States
	Stock horses	Grades, cross-breds, or following pure-breds:				
		American Paint	15 to 15-1	1,000-1,100	454-499	United States
		Appaloosa				United States
		Arabian				Arabia
		Buckskin				United States
		Hungarian Horse				Hungary
		Morgan				United States
		Palomino				United States
		Pinto				United States
		Quarter Horse				United States
		Spanish Mustang				United States
		Thoroughbred				England
	Polo mounts	Grades, cross-breds, and pure-breds of all breeds but predominantly of Thoroughbred breeding.	14-2 to 15-2	1,000-1,250	454-568	
	Hunters and jumpers		15-2 to 16-2	1,000-1,250	454-568	
	Ponies for riding	American Gotland	9 to 14-2	500-900	227-409	Sweden
		Connemera Pony				Ireland
		Pony of the Americas				United States
		Shetland				Shetland Isles
		Welsh				England
Race horses[1]	Running race horses	Thoroughbred	15-1 to 16-2	900-1,150	409-522	England
	Harness race horses (trotters and pacers)	Standardbred	14-2 to 15-2	900-1,150	409-545	United States
	Quarter race horses	Quarter Horse	14-2 to 15-2	1,000-1,200	454-545	United States
Driving horses	Heavy harness horses	Cleveland Bay	14-2 to 16-1	900-1,300	409-590	England
		Hackney				England
	Fine harness horses	American Saddle Horses (predominantly, although other breeds are so used.)	14-2 to 17	900-1,400	409-636	United States
	Roadsters	Morgan	14-2 to 15-2	900-1,200	409-545	United States
		Standardbred				United States
	Ponies for driving Harness show ponies	Hackney	9 to 14-2	500-900	227-409	England
		Shetland				Shetland Isles
	Heavy harness ponies	Welsh				England

[1]On a limited basis, and in a few states, Appaloosa and Arabian horses are also being raced under saddle.

light horses were developed. In certain cases, however, the particular use or performance is so exacting that only one breed appears to be sufficiently specialized; for example, harness races are now synonymous with the Standardbred breed. The several types and breeds of light horses are summarized in Table 47-1.

Riding Horses

Riding horses have many and varied uses, but, as the name indicates, they are all ridden. They may have a very definite utility value, as is true of stock horses, or they may be used chiefly for purposes of recreation and sport. For the latter use, training, manners, and style are of paramount importance, although durability and efficiency are not to be overlooked in any horse.

THREE- AND FIVE-GAITED SADDLE HORSES

Long after the development of the New England town, the opening up of roads along the eastern seaboard, and the development of the buggy and the popularity of the roadster type of horse, the states of Virginia, West Virginia, Kentucky, Tennessee, and Missouri still consisted of large plantations under the ownership of southern gentlemen. Roads were few and far between, and travel was largely on horseback over the most natural paths that could be found. Thus, there was need for a horse that would carry the plantation owners with dignity befitting their station in life and with the least distress possible to both rider and horse. As the plantation owners rode over their broad estates, easy gaits were a necessity. Such was the need, and out of this need arose the beautiful American Saddle Horse.

Animals qualifying as either three- or five-gaited saddle horses in the leading American horse shows are generally of American Saddle Horse breeding, a truly American creation.[1] Occasionally, however, animals of the other light horse breeds are trained to execute the five gaits. It must also be remembered that the vast majority of American horses of all breeds are of the three-gaited variety and that only a relatively small proportion of these animals are ever exhibited. Instead, most of the three-gaited horses are used for utility purposes and pleasure riding.

The gaits of three-gaited horses are: the walk, the trot, and the canter. In addition to performing these same gaits, the five-gaited horse must possess a slow gait and the rack or single-foot. The slow gait may be either the running-walk, fox trot, or stepping pace (slow pace), with the latter slow gait preferred. In the show ring, generally the judge requests that five-gaited horses execute the gaits in the following order: the walk, the trot, the slow gait, the rack, and the canter.

Whether an animal is three-gaited or five-gaited is primarily a matter of training. Custom decrees that three-gaited horses be shown with their manes roached or clipped short and their tails clipped or shaved for a short distance

---

[1] Herein reference is made to the Saddle Horse Division as described by the American Horse Shows Assn., and not to the several performance classes in which three-gaited horses of various breeds compete.

Fig. 47-1. Wing Commander, among whose notable winnings were: (1) World's Grand Champion five-gaited saddle horse at the Kentucky State Fair and (2) eight-time winner of the World's Championship Stake at the Chicago International. Owned and bred by Mrs. Frederick L. Van Lennep, Dodge Stables, Castleton Farm, Lexington, Kentucky. Wing Commander, presented here in the trot, was 15-2 hands in height and weighed 1,100 pounds. Note his superb style and type. True to custom for five-gaited horses, Wing Commander is shown with flowing mane and full-length tail. (Courtesy, Earl Teater, Mgr., Dodge Stables Division, Castleton Farm)

from the base; whereas five-gaited horses are shown with flowing mane and full-length tails. Also, because of the speed at which five-gaited horses are expected to perform at the trot and the rack, they are permitted to wear quarter boots to protect the heels of the front feet; a practice which is forbidden in three-gaited classes.

Both three- and five-gaited horses are shown under saddle; and each may be shown in combination classes, in which they must perform both in harness and under saddle. Also, five-gaited horses (but not three-gaited horses) may be shown in a third division; namely, in fine harness classes.

In combination classes, the entries enter the ring hitched to an appropriate four-wheeled vehicle, with the saddle and bridle hidden in the back of the rig (or the groom may carry in the saddle and bridle). The judge works the class both ways of the ring, then lines them up in the center for inspection and backs each horse in order to test his manners. Next the judge orders that the entries be unhitched, unharnessed, saddled, bridled, and worked under saddle both

Fig. 47-2. Steppin On, champion three-gaited mare; bred, trained, and exhibited by Sunnyslope Farm, Scott City, Kansas. Note the roached mane and tail, which custom decrees in a three-gaited American Saddler. (Courtesy, Miss Irene Zane, American Saddlebred Pleasure Horse Assn., Inc., Scott City, Kansas)

ways of the ring. Finally, the horses are again lined up in the center of the ring, and each animal is backed under saddle.

WALKING HORSES

This particular class of horses is largely comprised of one breed: the Tennessee Walking Horse.[2]

Horses of this type were first introduced into Tennessee by the early settlers from Virginia and the Carolinas. For many years, the plantation owners of middle Tennessee—men who spent long hours daily in supervising labor from the saddle—selected and bred animals for their easy, springy gaits, good dispositions, and intelligence. Particular stress was placed upon the natural gait known as the running-walk and upon the elimination of the trot. Thus, the three gaits that evolved in the walking horse (also called plantation walking horses) were: the walk, the running-walk, and the canter.

In animals of this type, the head is somewhat low in carriage, and at the running-walk there is a characteristic nodding of the head. Sometimes there is also a flopping of the ears and a snapping of the teeth while the animal is in this rhythmic movement. Walking horses are also noted for their wonderful dispo-

---

[2] A more detailed description of this and other breeds may be found in Chapter XLVIII.

Fig. 47-3. A Tennessee Walking Horse in action and well ridden. Son's Shadow, stallion, shown by Sam Paschal; owned by Mr. and Mrs. E. Carl Hengen, Lawn Vale Farm, Gainsville, Va. (Courtesy, *The National Horseman* and Mr. Paschal)

sitions. Their easy gaits and a superb disposition make them an ideal type of horse for the amateur rider or the professional or society person who rides infrequently.

STOCK HORSES

Stock horses constitute the largest single class of light horses in this country; there are approximately 500,000 of them in use in the seventeen range states. They are the cow ponies of the West.

Usually, stock horses are of mixed breeding. Most generally they are descended from the Mustang—the feral horse of the United States. Subsequently, Mustang mares were mated to sires of practically every known light horse breed—especially Thoroughbreds and Quarter Horses. Stallions of the Palomino, Morgan, Arabian, and other breeds have also been used. Such grading-up has improved the size, speed, and perhaps the appearance of the cow pony, but most horsemen will concede that no amount of improved breeding will ever produce a gamier, hardier, and more durable animal than the Mustang. In addition to being game and hardy, the stock horse must be agile, sure-footed, fast, short coupled, deep, powerfully muscled, durable, and must possess good feet and legs. Above all, the cowboy insists that his pony be a good companion and that he possess "cow sense."

Fig. 47-4. Clipper, champion cutting horse (an Appaloosa stallion), owned by Capay Rancho, Orland, California; trained and shown by Jim Mathews. (Courtesy, Jim Mathews)

POLO MOUNTS

As the name would indicate, polo mounts include that type and class of

Fig. 47-5. An excellent polo mount. Note the pronounced Thoroughbred type. (Courtesy, United States Polo Assn., New York, N. Y.)

horses particularly adapted for use in playing the game of polo. This game, which was first introduced into this country in 1876, is played by four mounted men on each team. The object is to drive a wooden ball between goal posts at either end of a playing field 300 yards long and 120 to 150 yards wide. Long-handled regulation mallets are used to drive the ball.

At the time the game was first introduced into the United States, there was a decided preference for ponies under 13-2 hands in height. Later, horses up to 14-2 hands were accepted, and more recently horses up to 15-2 and over, have been used.

Although very similar to the hunter in type, the polo mount is smaller in size. He must be quick and clever in turning, and he must be able to dodge, swerve, or wheel while on a dead run. He must like the game and be able to follow the ball.

The polo mount is trained to respond to the pressure of the reins on the neck, so that the rider may be free to guide him with only one hand. Up to five or six years is required to complete the schooling of a polo horse, and as many as four to six mounts may be used by each player in a single game—all of which contribute to the expensiveness of the sport.

Polo ponies are usually of mixed breeding, but most of them are predominantly Thoroughbred. Type and training, together with native ability and intelligence, are the primary requisites.

The American Horse Show Association has developed show classifications for polo ponies. For information relative to same, the reader is referred to the *AHSA Rule Book*.

HUNTERS AND JUMPERS

The hunter is that type of horse used in following hounds in fox hunting. The sport is traditional in England, and each year it is sharing its glamour with greater numbers in the United States.

Again the hunter is not necessarily of any particular breeding, but Thoroughbred blood predominates. The infusion of some cold blood (draft breeding) is often relied upon in order to secure greater size and a more tractable disposition.

Hunters are classified as *small* (those under 15-2½ hands in height); *light-weight* (those expected to carry a rider weighing under 165 pounds); *middle-weight* (those expected to carry weights ranging from 165 to 185 pounds), and *heavyweight* (those expected to carry over 185 pounds but under 205 pounds).

As many folks who ride to hounds do so in order to keep down their weight, their need for a sizeable mount can be fully appreciated. It must also be realized that a 5-foot object is 4 inches lower for a 16-hand horse than for one only 15 hands in height. Hunters are further classified as green or qualified, the latter having hunted one season with a pack recognized by the United Hunts and Steeple Chase Association.

In addition to being of ample size and height, the hunter must possess the necessary stamina and conformation to keep up with the pack. He must be able to hurdle with safety such common field obstacles as fences and ditches. The

Fig. 47-6. A hunter in action, and well ridden. (Courtesy, A. Mackay-Smith, Editor, *The Chronicle*)

good hunter, therefore, is rugged, short coupled, and heavily muscled throughout.

All hunters are jumpers to some degree, but a high jumper is not necessarily a good hunter. To qualify as a hunter, the horse must do more. He must execute many and varied jumps over a long period of time.

Jumpers are a nondescript group; consisting of all breeds and types. The only requisite is that they can jump.

PONIES FOR RIDING

These are children's mounts. In addition to their miniature size, they should possess the following characteristics: (1) gentleness, (2) sound feet and legs, (3) symmetry, (4) good eyes, (5) endurance, (6) intelligence, (7) patience, (8) faithfulness, and (9) hardiness. Above all, they must be kind and gentle in disposition.

Race Horses

According to some historians, the Greeks introduced horse racing in the Olympic games in 1450 B.C. Also, it is reported that a planned horse race of consequence was run in 1377 between animals owned by Richard II and the Earl

Fig. 47-7. Miss Betty MacLane up on Wampus Kitty, champion jumper in the Open Horse Show at Washington State University. (Courtesy, Washington State University)

of Arundel. The sporting instinct of man being what it is, it is reasonable to surmise, however, that a bit of a contest was staged the first time that two proud mounted horsemen chanced to meet.

Today, three types of horse races are run: (1) running races, (2) harness races, and (3) quarter races. For the most part, each type of race is dominated by one breed. Thus, in running races, it's Thoroughbreds; in harness races, it's Standardbreds; and in quarter races, it's Quarter Horses. However, on a limited basis, and in a few states, Appaloosa and Arabian horses are now being raced under saddle.

RUNNING RACE HORSES

Race horses, used for running (an extended gallop) under the saddle, are now confined almost exclusively to one breed, the Thoroughbred.[3] On the other hand, the Thoroughbred breed (including both purebreds and crossbreds) has been used widely for other purposes; especially as a stock horse, polo mount, hunter, and cavalry horse.

―――――――

[3] The exception being Quarter Horse races.

Fig. 47-8. An eight-year-old on a Welsh Pony mare.

Fig. 47-9. Citation, sensational Thoroughbred, bred and owned by Calumet Farm, shown as a two-year-old. Citation was the first million dollar winner, with total turf earnings of $1,085,760. (Courtesy, The Jockey Club)

Although trials of speed had taken place between horses from the earliest recorded history, the true and unmistakable foundation of the Thoroughbred breed as such traces back only to the reign of Charles II, known as the "father of the British turf."

Although the length of race, weight carried, and type of track have undergone considerable variation in recent years, the running horse always has been selected for speed and more speed at the run.

More people go to Thoroughbred races than to other kinds of horse races. In 1967, 38,526,589 people went to Thoroughbred races, compared with 27,201,833 who went to harness races, and 2,502,667 who went to Quarter Horse races.[4]

HARNESS RACE HORSES (TROTTERS AND PACERS)

Prior to the advent of improved roads and the automobile, but following the invention of the buggy, there was need for a fast, light-harness type of horse. This horse was used to draw vehicles varying in type from the light roadster of the young gallant to the dignified family carriage. In the process of meeting this need, two truly American breeds of horses evolved: the Morgan and the Standardbred. The first breed traces to the foundation sire, Justin Morgan; and the latter to Hambletonian 10, an animal which was line-bred to imported Messenger.

As horse and buggy travel passed into permanent oblivion, except for recreation and sport, the Standardbred breeders wisely placed greater emphasis upon the sport of racing; whereas the Morgan enthusiasts directed their breeding programs toward transforming their animals into a saddle breed.

The early descendants of Messenger were sent over the track, trotting (not galloping) under the saddle; but eventually the jockey races in this country came to be restricted to a running type of race in which the Thoroughbred was used.

The pneumatic-tire racing vehicles, known as sulkies, were first introduced in 1892. With their use that year, the time was reduced nearly four seconds below the record of the previous year. Thus was developed harness racing and the Standardbred breed of horses, which today is the exclusive breed used for this purpose.

Trotters and pacers are of similar breeding and type, the particular gaits being largely a matter of training. In fact, many individuals show speed at both the trot and the pace. It is generally recognized, however, that pacers are handicapped in the mud, in the sand, or over a rough surface.

The Standardbred breed—like the Thoroughbred—also finds other uses—as driving horses in roadster classes, delivery horses, and general utility farm

---

[4]Personal communications to the author from The National Association of State Racing Commissioners (for Thoroughbred races), The United States Trotting Association (for harness races), and The National Association of State Racing Commissioners (for Quarter Horse races).

Fig. 47-10. The fabulous Dan Patch, flawless early-day performer and great attraction on tracks throughout the U.S. He was foaled in 1896, and in 1903 was sold at private treaty for $60,000. The official record for the great horse was 1:55¼, which stood as a world record until 1938 when Billy Direct paced the mile in 1:55 (unofficially, Dan Patch ran the mile in 1:55) with the aid of a windshield; but this form of assistance had been ruled out previously, with the result that this record was not accepted. Dan Patch lived to the age of twenty. (Courtesy, United States Trotting Association, Columbus, Ohio)

horses. By way of comparison with the Thoroughbred, the Standardbred possesses a more tractable disposition and is smaller, longer bodied, closer to the ground, heavier-limbed, and sturdier in build. The latter characteristic is very necessary because harness races are usually heat races—for example, the best two out of three races.

Horses of this type now find their principal use in harness races at county and state fairs, although pari-mutuel harness racing has been established at certain tracks. Today, harness race horses are almost exclusively of the Standardbred breed.

QUARTER RACE HORSES

Quarter racing has become an increasingly popular sport in the West. For the most part, races of this type are confined to animals of the Quarter Horse breed, which animals derived their name and initial fame for their extraordinary speed at distances up to a quarter of a mile. Although the great majority of Quarter Horses are used to work cattle and never appear on the race track, the proponents of quarter racing advocate the race track as a means of proving animals. Performance, so they argue, is the proof of whether or not a horse can do the job for which he is bred. Thus, quarter racing is used as a breed proving ground for the Quarter Horse, for in this racing the fundamental quality of speed can be measured accurately and recorded in such a way that the performance of horses in all parts of the country can be compared.

Fig. 47-11. A rare—triple-dead heat—of Quarter Horses, which occurred at the Alameda County Fairgrounds, Pleasanton, Calif. (Photo by Photo-Patrol, Inc., San Mateo, Calif. Courtesy, American Quarter Racing Association, Tucson, Arizona)

Driving Horses

At the present time, driving horses are used chiefly for purposes of recreation. According to the specific use made of them, driving horses are classified as heavy harness horses, fine harness horses, roadsters, or ponies.

HEAVY HARNESS HORSES

These are also known as carriage horses. At the present time, this type of horse has very little place in the utility field, its use being largely confined to the show ring. As the name implies, the heavy harness horse of the show ring wears heavier leather than the fine harness horse or the roadster, though it in no way approaches draft harness. The heavy leather used on these animals was first decreed by fashion in England; the idea being that to drive handsomely one must drive heavily. The vehicles drawn were of heavy construction and elegant design, and logically and artistically the harness had to be in proportion thereto.

Heavy harness horses were especially popular during the Victorian era, and the ownership of a handsome pair was an indication of social prestige. In this country during the gay nineties, bob-tailed hackneys attached to high-seated rigs made a dashing picture as they pranced down the avenue.

At one time, there were several heavy harness breeds, but at present all except the Hackney have practically ceased to exist in America. In this country, therefore, the Hackney is now the heavy harness breed; and the American Horse Shows Association officially refers to show classifications as Hackneys rather than as Heavy Harness Horses.

Animals of this type are bred for high hock and knee action, but skilled training, bitting, and shoeing are necessary for their development. In the show ring, heavy harness horses must be able to fold their knees, flex their hocks, and set their chins. "Wooden-legged" horses cannot take competition.

Fig. 47-12. Star Shot, Hackney pony, owned and exhibited by Mr. and Mrs. Dean Briggs, Garden Plains, Kansas. Note the characteristic smooth, gracefully-curved form. (Courtesy, the Briggs)

FINE HARNESS HORSES

A fine harness horse is exactly what the name implies—a fine horse presented in fine harness. The entire ensemble is elegant, and represents the ultimate in grace and charm.

Fig. 47-13. The Lemon Drop Kid, four-times Champion Fine Harness Horse; shown by Sunnyslope Farms, Scott City, Kansas. (Courtesy, Miss Irene Zane, American Saddlebred Pleasure Horse Assn., Inc., Scott City, Kansas)

In the show ring, fine harness horses are, according to the rules of the American Horse Shows Association, limited to the American Saddle Horse breed. In some shows, however, other breeds are exhibited in fine harness classes. Fashion decrees that fine harness horses shall be shown wearing long mane and tail, and drawing a four-wheeled road show wagon without top, or with top drawn. Light harness with a snaffle bit is required. Fine harness horses are shown at an animated park trot and at an animated walk.

ROADSTERS

The sport of showing a roadster originated in the horse and buggy era. It was founded upon the desire to own an attractive horse that possessed the necessary speed to pass any of his rivals encountered upon the city or country thoroughfares.

In the show ring, roadsters are generally shown in either or both (1) roadster to bike or (2) roadster to buggy classes. The latter are hitched singly or in pairs. Some shows also provide a class or classes for roadsters under saddle. In all divisions—whether shown to bike or buggy, or under saddle—entries must trot; pacing is barred.

Fig. 47-14. Saint Nick, Standardbred shown here as a roadster to buggy. (Courtesy, *Saddle and Bridle*)

Custom decrees that roadsters shall enter the ring at a jog, and work the wrong way (clockwise) of the track first. After the roadsters jog for a brief time, the judge usually asks that they perform at the road gait, then jog again (all clock wise of the ring). Then, in succession, the judge asks them to reverse, jog, road gait, and turn on or trot at speed. Lastly, they are called to the center of the ring for inspection in a standing position; at which time the judge usually tests their manners by asking each driver to back his horse.

Originally, roadster classes included animals of both Standardbred and Morgan extraction. In recent years, however, the Morgan has developed more in the direction of a saddler, leaving the roadster classification almost exclusively to the Standardbred.

In addition to possessing the usual Standardbred characteristics, particular stress is placed in roadster show classes upon the manners, style, and beauty of conformation, combined with speed. In striking contrast to heavy-harness classes, the roadster is shown hitched to very light vehicles permitting fast travel.

PONIES FOR DRIVING

Ponies for driving are of two kinds: (1) harness show ponies, and (2) heavy harness ponies.

The best harness show ponies are vest-pocket editions of fine harness horses; that is, they possess the same desirable characteristics, except that they are in miniature. According to the rules of The American Horse Shows Association, harness show ponies may be of any breed or combination of breeds; the only requisite is that they must be under 12-2 hands in height. Three breeds produce animals that qualify under this category; namely, the Shetland, Welsh, and Hackney breeds.

Heavy harness ponies are, as the name indicates, miniature heavy harness horses. Generally they are either purebred Hackneys or predominantly of Hackney breeding.

Fig. 47-15. Star Shot and Sure Shot, Wm. Pinch driving. (Courtesy, Mrs. Dean J. Briggs)

Three breeds produce animals that qualify as ponies; namely, the Hackney, Welsh, and Shetland breeds. The Hackney is generally exclusively of the harness type, but the Welsh and Shetland breeds are used either under the saddle or in harness. In the major horse shows of the land, the latter two breeds may be exhibited in harness, but in practical use they are children's mounts.

TYPES; AND MARKET AND SHOW CLASSES OF WORK HORSES AND MULES

Although the types and classes of work horses and mules listed in Tables 47-2 and 47-3 still prevail, today horse and mule markets are of negligible importance, and the market terms are primarily of historical interest. Some of the uses have even passed into oblivion with mechanization; for example, expressers—fast-stepping, delivery-type horses in great demand during the early part of the present century—are now almost unknown.

Work Horses

Work horses are classified according to use as: (1) draft horses, (2) wagon horses, (3) farm chunks, and (4) southerners. Originally, classes for loggers and artillery horses were included, but these have been pretty much the victims of mechanization.

Fig. 47-16. The magnificent eight-horse hitch of champion Clydesdale horses exhibited by Anheuser-Busch, Inc. (Courtesy, Anheuser-Busch, Inc., St. Louis, Mo.)

Although marked differences in size and weight exist between these various classes, all possess a deep, broad, compact, muscular form suited to the pulling of a heavy load at the walk.

The market classification of work horses according to the use to which they are put and their range in height and weight is shown in Table 47-2.

TABLE 47—2

MARKET CLASSIFICATION OF WORK HORSES

Class	Range in Height	Range in Weight	
	(hands)	(pounds)	(kilograms)
Draft horses......................	16 to 17—2	1600 upward	726 upward
Wagon horses...................	15—2 to 16—2	1300—1600	590—726
Farm chunks....................	15 to 16	1300—1400	590—635
Southerners......................	14—2 to 15—2	600—1100	272—499

Mules

It has been correctly said that the mule is without pride of ancestry or hope of posterity. He is a hybrid, being a cross between two species of the family *Equidae*—the *caballus* or horse and the *asinus* or ass.[5] Like most hybrids, the mule is seldom fertile.

---

[5] The cross between a jennet and a stallion is known as a hinny. The mule and the hinny are indistinguishable, but the hinny is seldom seen because of the greater value of jennets in producing jacks and jennets.

The use of the mule in the United States was first popularized by two early American statesmen, George Washington and Henry Clay. The first jack to enter this country, of which there is authentic record, was presented by the King of Spain to General Washington in 1787, shortly after the close of the Revolutionary War. Other importations followed; and from that time until mechanization, the hardy mule furnished the main source of animal power for the South. In comparison with the horse, the mule can: (1) withstand higher temperatures; (2) endure less experienced labor; (3) better adapt his eating habits to either irregularity or self-feeding with little danger of founder or digestive disturbances; (4) work or stable in lower areas without head injury (the mule lowers his head when his ears touch an object, whereas a horse will throw his head upward under similar conditions); (5) encounter less foot trouble, wire cuts, etc.; and (6) generally maneuver about without harm to himself.

Although the mule resembles his sire, the jack, more than the mare, the desired conformation is identical to that described for the horse; perhaps the one exception is that more stress is placed upon the size, set, and quality of the ear. The most desirable mules must be of good size and draftiness, compact, and heavily muscled; must show evidence of plenty of quality; must stand on correct feet and legs; and must be sound. As the natural tendency of the mule is to be lazy and obstinate, an active, energetic disposition is sought.

In the South and Southeast, where there are still a limited number of mules, certain distinct types are bred. The type of mule desired is largely controlled through the selection of certain types of mares for breeding purposes.

The market classification of mules according to the use to which they are put, including range in height and weight, is shown in Table 47-3.

TABLE 47—3

MARKET CLASSIFICATION OF MULES

Class	Range in Height	Range in Weight	
	(hands)	(pounds)	(kilograms)
Draft	16 to 17—2	1200—1600	545—726
Sugar	16 to 17	1150—1300	522—590
Farm	15—2 to 16	900—1250	409—568
Cotton	13—2 to 15—2	750—1100	341—499
Pack and mining	12 to 16	600—1350	272—613

Naturally, there is considerable spread in value between the animals within each class—depending upon weight, conformation, quality, temperament, condition, action, age, and soundness. Mare mules usually outsell horse mules. The most desirable age is between four and eight years, and well-matched spans of black or sorrel mules are most popular.

Fig. 47-17. A mare mule of excellent type; as a three-year-old when she was Grand Champion at the Missouri State Fair. (Courtesy, the owner, E. D. Frazier, Drexel, Mo.)

QUESTIONS FOR STUDY AND DISCUSSION

1. Compare horses from the standpoint of the diverse and distinct types that have been developed with each: beef cattle, sheep, and swine.
2. What one breed of light horses do you consider to be best adapted to each of the specific uses?
3. Is there need to develop one or more new breeds of light horses for certain specific uses? If so, to what uses does this apply?
4. What specific uses of light horses have no utility use; that is, they are for show only?
5. What breeding is used to produce the different market classes of work horses?
6. What breeding is used to produce the different market classes of mules?
7. What use, if any, is currently made of the different market classes of work horses and mules?

SELECTED REFERENCES

Title of Publication	Author(s)	Publisher
Horse, The	D. J. Kays	Rinehart & Company, New York, N. Y., 1953.
Horses and Horse-manship	M. E. Ensminger	The Interstate Printers & Publishers, Danville, Ill., 1969.
Light Horse Breeds, The	J. W. Patten	A. S. Barnes & Co., Inc., New York, N. Y., 1960.
Light Horses	M. E. Ensminger	Farmers' Bul. No. 2127, U.S. Department of Agriculture, Washington, D.C.
Western Horse, The	J. A. Gorman	The Interstate Printers & Publishers, Danville, Ill., 1967.

Chapter XLVIII

TYPES AND BREEDS OF HORSES[1]

	Page
Classes of Horses	1123
Popularity of Breeds	1123
Characteristics of Breeds	1124
Questions for Study and Discussion	1136
Selected References	1136

It is noteworthy that most of the breeds of light horses common to this country are American creations. There are two primary reasons for this: (1) the diverse needs and uses for which light horses have been produced, and (2) the fact that many men of wealth have bred light horses.

CLASSES OF HORSES

Horses may be classified as light horses, ponies, or draft horses, according to size, build, and use.

Light horses stand 14-2 to 17 hands high, weigh 900 to 1,400 pounds, and are used primarily for riding, driving, or racing, or for utility purposes on the farm. Light horses generally are more rangy and are capable of more action and greater speed than draft horses.

Ponies stand under 14-2 hands high and weigh 500 to 900 pounds.

Draft horses stand 14-2 to 17-2 hands high, weigh 1,400 pounds or more, and are used primarily for drawing loads and for other heavy work.

POPULARITY OF BREEDS

Table 48-1 shows the 1966 and total registrations to date of the various breeds of light horses.

---

[1] Sometimes folks construe the write-up of a breed of livestock in a book or in a U.S. Department of Agriculture bulletin as an official recognition of the breed. Nothing could be further from the truth, for no person or office has the authority to approve a breed. The only legal basis for recognizing a breed is contained in the Tariff Act of 1930, which provides for the duty free admission of purebred breeding stock provided they are registered in the country of origin. But the latter stipulation applies to imported animals only.

In this book, no *official* recognition of any breed is intended or implied. Rather, the author has tried earnestly, and without favoritism, to present the factual story of the breeds in narrative and picture. In particular, such information relative to new and/or less widely distributed breeds is needed, and often difficult to come by.

TABLE 48—1

1966 AND TOTAL REGISTRATIONS OF LIGHT HORSES IN
UNITED STATES' BREED ASSOCIATIONS

Breed	1966 Registrations	Total Registrations (since Breed Registry started)
Quarter Horse	56,457	444,721
Thoroughbred	19,836	500,000
Half-Breds[4]	383[2]	39,791[2]
Appaloosa	12,700	80,508
Standardbred	9,448	312,100
Tennessee Walking Horse	6,800	91,000
Arabian		
Purebreds	5,340	40,525
Half Arabians and Anglo Arabs[1]	7,200	45,200
Shetland Pony	3,986	119,543
American Saddle Horse	3,386	122,593
American Paint Horse	1,915	6,452
Morgan	1,909	33,366
Welsh Pony	1,824	17,800
Pinto	1,526[2]	5,602[2]
Palomino	1,157[3]	31,035[3]
Pony of the Americas	1,124	6,883
Hackney	836[2]	14,177[2]
Missouri Fox Trotting Horse	386[2]	2,101[2]
American Buckskin	200	736
Galiceno	147	1,217
Connemara Pony	109	887
American Albino	43	2,429
Spanish Barb Mustang	23	151
Gotland Horse	14[2]	115[2]

[1]Registered in the International Arabian Horse Association, 224 East Olive Avenue, Burbank, California 91503.
[2]1965 figures.
[3]Includes registrations in both the Palomino Horse Association, Inc. and the Palomino Horse Breeders of America.
[4]Registered in the American Remount Assn., Colorado Springs, Colo.

CHARACTERISTICS OF BREEDS

There is scarcely a breed of horses that does not possess one or more distinctive breed characteristics in which it excels all others. Moreover, any one of several breeds is often well adapted to the same use. To the amateur, this is most confusing, and he is prone to inquire as to the best breed. Certainly, if any strong preference exists, it should be an important factor, though it is recognized that certain breeds are better adapted to specific purposes.

TABLE 48—2

BREEDS OF LIGHT HORSES, PONIES, AND DRAFT HORSES;
AND THEIR CHARACTERISTICS

Breed	Place of Origin	Color	Other Distinguishing Characteristics	Primary Uses	Disqualifications
Light Horses and Ponies:					
American Albino Horse (or American White Horses and Ponies)	United States; on White Horse Ranch, Naper, Nebraska.	Snow-white hair; pink skin; and light blue, dark blue (near black), brown, or hazel eyes.	The breed ranges from 32 in. to 17 hands high; thus, it includes both ponies and horses.	Riding and utility; exhibition purposes; parade horses; and flag bearer horses.	Pale cream or off white
American Buckskin	United States	Buckskin, red dun, gruella.	Dorsal stripe, and usually zebra type stripes on the legs and transverse stripe over the withers and shoulders.	Stock horses. Pleasure horses. Show purposes.	White markings above knees and hocks. White spots on body.
American Gotland Horse	Baltic Island of Gotland, a part of Sweden.	Bay, brown, black, dun, chestnut, palomino, roan, and some leopard and blanket markings.	Average about 48'' high, with a range of 11 to 13 hands.	Harness trot racing, pleasure horses, and junpers; for children and moderate sized adults.	Pintos and animals with large markings are dis qualified.
American Paint Horse[1]	United States	White plus any other color. Must be a recognizable paint.	No discrimination is made against glass, blue, or light-colored eyes.	Stock horses. Pleasure horses. Show purposes. Racing.	Lack of natural white markings above the knees or hocks except on the face; horses with Appaloosa color or blood; adult horses under 14 hands; 5-gaited horses.
American Paso Fino[2]	In the Caribbean. May have been registered in Puerto Rico, Cuba, and Colombia.	All colors. Bays, chestnuts, and blacks with white markings are most common. Occasionally, palominos and pintos.	Paso fino gait, which is a broken pace.	Pleasure horses. Cutting horses. Endurance rides. Parade horses. Drill team work.	Not possessing paso fino gait or tracing to Paso Fino ancestry.
American Saddlebred Horse	United States; in Fayette County, Kentucky.	Bay, brown, chestnut, gray, or black. Gaudy white markings are frowned upon.	Ability to furnish an easy ride with great style and animation. Long, graceful neck and proud action	Three- and five-gaited saddle horses. Fine harness horses. Pleasure horses. Stock horses.	
Appaloosa	United States; in Oregon, Washington, and Idaho; from animals originating in Fergana, Central Asia.	Variable, but usually white over the loin and hips, with dark round, or egg-shaped spots thereon.	The eye is encircled by white, the skin is mottled, and the hoofs are striped vertically black and white.	Stock horses. Pleasure horses. Parade horses. Race horses.	Animals not having Appaloosa characteristics and animals of draft horse or pony, Albino, or Pinto breeding; cryptorchids; and animals under 14 hands at maturity (5 years or older).
Arabian	Arabia	Bay, gray, and chestnut with an occasional white or black. White marks on the head and legs are common. The skin is always dark.	A beautiful head, short coupling, docility, great endurance, and a gay way of going.	Saddle horses. Show horses. Pleasure horses. Stock horses. Racing.	

Footnotes on last page of table.

(Continued)

TABLE 48—2 (Continued)

Breed	Place of Origin	Color	Other Distinguishing Characteristics	Primary Uses	Disqualifications
Cleveland Bay	England; in the Cleveland district of Yorkshire.	Always solid bay with black legs.	Larger than most light horse breeds; weigh from 1,150 to 1,400 pounds.	General utility horse; for riding, driving, and all kinds of farm work. Also, used in crossbreeding to produce heavyweight hunters.	Any color other than bay, although a few white hairs on the forehead are permissible.
Connemara Pony	Ireland; along the west coast.	Gray, black, bay, brown, dun, cream, with occasional roans and chestnuts.	Av. height of 14 hands.	Jumpers, showing under saddle and in harness; for both adults and children.	Piebalds and skewbalds not accepted.
Galiceno	Galicia, a province in northwestern Spain.	Solid colors prevail. Bay, black, chestnut, dun, gray, brown, and palomino are most common.	Intermediate in size; at maturity they stand 12 to 13 hands and weigh 625 to 700 pounds.	Riding horses.	Albinos, pintos, and paints are ineligible for registry. Cryptorchids or monorchids.
Hackney	England; on the eastern coast, in Norfolk and adjoining counties.	Chestnut, bay, and brown most common; roans and blacks are seen. White marks are common and are desired.	In the show ring, custom decrees that Hackney horses and ponies be docked and have their manes pulled. High natural action.	Heavy harness or carriage horses and ponies. For crossbreeding purposes to produce hunters and jumpers.	
Hungarian Horse	Hungary	All colors; either solid or broken.	Unique combination of style and beauty with ruggedness.	Stock horses; cutting horses, pleasure horses, trail riding, hunters and jumpers.	Cryptorchids; glass-eyed.
Missouri Fox Trotting Horse	U.S.; in the Ozark Hills of Missouri and Arkansas.	Sorrels predominate, but any color is accepted.	The fox trot gait.	Pleasure horses. Stock horses. Trail riding.	If animal cannot fox trot.
Morgan	United States; in the New England states.	Bay, brown, black and chestnut; extensive white markings are uncommon.	Easy keeping qualities, endurance, and docility.	Saddle horses. Stock horses.	Wall-eye (lack of pigmentation of the iris), or natural white markings above the knee or hock except on the face.
Palomino	United States; from animals of Spanish extraction.	Golden (the color of a newly minted gold coin or 3 shades lighter or darker), with a light colored mane and tail (white, silver, or ivory, with not more than 15% dark or chestnut hair in either). White markings on the face or below the knees are acceptable.		Stock horses Parade horses Pleasure horses. Saddle horses. Fine harness horses.	Animals of drafthorses or pony breeding and offspring of piebald or albino breeding not eligible for registration.
Peruvian Paso[2]	Peru	Any color, although solid colors are preferred.	Naturally five-gaited; walk, paso, trot, huachano, and canter.	Pleasure horses. Parade horses. Endurance horses.	Light fore-quarters, coarseness, extreme height.

Footnotes on last page of table.

(Continued)

TABLE 48—2 (Continued)

Breed	Place of Origin	Color	Other Distinguishing Characteristics	Primary Uses	Disqualifications
Pinto[1]	United States; from horses brought in by the Spanish Conquistadores.	Preferably half color or colors and half white, with many spots well placed. The two distinct pattern markings are: Overo and Tobiano.	Glass eyes are not discounted. Assn. has separate registry for ponies and/or horses under 14 hands.	Any light horse purpose, but especially for show, parade, novice, pleasure purposes, stock horses.	
Pony of the Americas	United States; Mason City, Iowa.	Similar to Appaloosa; white over the loin and hips, with dark, round or egg-shaped spots.	Happy medium of Arabian and Quarter Horse in miniature, ranging in height from 46 to 54 inches, with appaloosa color.	Children's western type using pony.	Ponies not within the height range, or not having the Appaloosa color, including mottled skin and much exposed sclera of the eye. Pinto markings and loud-colored roans.
Quarter Horse	United States	Chestnut, sorrel, bay and dun are most common although they may be palomino, black, brown, roan, or copper-colored.	Well-muscled and powerfully built. Small, alert ears; sometimes heavily muscled cheeks and jaw.	Stock horses. Racing. Pleasure horses.	Pinto, Appaloosa, and albino colors are ineligible for registry; also white markings on the underline.
Shetland Pony	Shetland Isles	All colors, either solid or broken.	Small size. Two class sizes recognized by breed registry: (1) 43" and under, and (2) 43" to 46". Good disposition.	Children's mounts. Harness. Roadster. Racing.	Over 46" in height.
Spanish Mustang	United States	They run the gamut of equine colors, including all the solid colors, and all the broken colors except tobiano.	Only 5 lumbar vertebrae. Short ears, low-set tail, and round leg bones.	Cow ponies. Trail riding.	
Standardbred	United States	Bay, brown, chestnut, and black are most common, but grays, roans and duns are found.	Smaller and less leggy and with more substance and ruggedness than the Thoroughbred.	Harness racing, either trotting or pacing. Harness horses in horse shows.	
Tennessee Walking Horse	United States; in the Middle Basin of Tennessee.	Sorrel, chestnut, black, roan, white, bay, brown, gray, and golden. White markings on the face and legs are common.	The running walk gait.	Plantation Walking Horses. Pleasure horses. Show horses.	
Thoroughbred	England	Bay, brown, chestnut, and black; less frequently, roan and gray. White markings on the face and legs are common.	Fineness of conformation. Long, straight and well-muscled legs.	Running races. Stock horses. Saddle horses. Polo mounts. Hunters.	

Footnotes on last page of table.　　　　　　　　　　　　　　　　　　　　(Continued)

TABLE 48—2 (Continued)

Breed	Place of Origin	Color	Other Distinguishing Characteristics	Primary Uses	Disqualifications
Welsh Pony	Wales	Any color except piebald and skewbald. Gaudy white markings are not popular.	Small size; intermediate between Shetland ponies and other light horse breeds. The American Welsh Stud Book height stipulations are: "A" Div.—cannot exceed 12-2 hands. "B" Div.—over 12-2 and not more than 14 hands.	Mounts for children and small adults. Racing. Roadsters. Trail riding. Parade. Stock cutting. Hunting.	Piebald or skewbald.
Draft Horses:					
American Cream Horse	United States	Cream, with white mane and tail and pink skin. Some white markings.	Medium size. Good disposition.	Farm work horses. Exhibition purposes.	
Belgian	Belgium	Bay, chestnut, and roan are most common, but browns, grays, and blacks are occasionally seen. Many Belgians have a flaxen mane and tail and a white-blazed face.	Lowest set and most massive of all draft breeds.	Farm work horses. Exhibition purposes.	
Clydesdale	Scotland; along the River Clyde.	Bay and brown with white markings are most common, but blacks, grays, chestnuts, and roans are occasionally seen.	Superior style and action. Feather or hair on the legs.	Farm work horses. Exhibition purposes.	
Percheron	France; in the northwestern district of La Perche.	Mostly black or gray, but bays, browns, chestnuts, and roans are seen.	In comparison with other draft breeds, noted for its handsome clean-cut head.	Farm work horses. Exhibition purposes	
Shire	England; primarily in the east central counties of Lincolnshire and Cambridgeshire.	Common colors are bay, brown, and black with white markings; although grays, chestnuts, and roans are occasionally seen.	Taller than any other draft breed. Feather or hair on the legs.	Farm work horses. Exhibition purposes.	
Suffolk	England; in the eastern county of Suffolk.	Chestnut only.	They are the smallest of the draft breeds. Close-to-the-ground and chunky build.	Farm work horses. Exhibition purposes	Any color other than chestnut.

Footnotes on last page of table.

(Continued)

TABLE 48—2 (Continued)

Breed	Place of Origin	Color	Other Distinguishing Characteristics	Primary Uses	Disqualifications
Donkeys:					
Miniature Mediterranean Donkeys	Sardinia and Sicily.	Mouse color to almost black.	Dorsal stripe, forming a cross with stripe over withers and down shoulders.	Children's pet.	Over 38″ high. Without cross.

[1]Two different associations have evolved for the registration of these vari-colored horses. In the Pinto Horse Association of America, Inc. the breed is known as Pinto, whereas in the American Paint Horse Association, it is known as the American Paint Horse. Both groups of horses are of similar background and color.

[2]Two U.S. breed associations have evolved for the registration and promotion of horses of Paso Fino background—the American Paso Fino Pleasure Horse Assn., Inc. and the American Assn. of Owners & Breeders of Peruvian Paso Horses. But each of the registries has slightly different standards.

Fig. 48-1. White Wings, American Albino Horse stallion; owned by White Horse Ranch, Naper, Nebraska. Top show horse with the famous White Horse Troupe. (Courtesy, Ruth E. White)

Fig. 48-2. Gulldson 40, imported American Gotland Horse stallion, at age five. He's a blood bay and is 12-1 hands. Senior herd sire at Krona Farms, Columbia, Missouri. (Courtesy, American Gotland Horse Assn.)

Fig. 48-3. American Paint Horse stallion, Dual Image, an AAA rated race horse; owned by J. R. Archer, Corpus Christi, Texas; Grand Champion at the 1966 Ft. Worth Show. (Courtesy, American Paint Horse Assn.)

Fig. 48-4. American Saddle Horse. Beau Fortune. Winner of numerous five-gaited stakes. Highest priced stallion ($50,000) in history of breed. Note the beautiful head carried on a long, graceful neck, the short back, well-turned croup, high-set tail, and stylish appearance. (Courtesy, Warrick 4-H American Saddle Horse Breeders' Club, Newburgh, Ind.)

Fig. 48-5. Appaloosa mare, Sugar High Spot, owned by Circle Double A Ranch, St. Jo, Texas; Grand Champion at the Appaloosa Show, Dallas, Texas, 1965. (Courtesy, Appaloosa Horse Club, Inc.)

Fig. 48-6. Cassandra, Grand Champion Arabian mare at many shows, including the All Arab Show at San Francisco. Bred by Mr. and Mrs. R. B. Field, Leavenworth, Washington. Note her beautiful head, neck, and shoulders; qualities characteristic of the breed. (Courtesy, the Fields)

Fig. 48-7. Cleveland Bay stallion, Cleveland Farnley 1788. Owned by A. Mackay-Smith, White Post, Virginia. (Courtesy, Mr. Smith)

Fig. 48-8. Connemara Pony mare, Miss Murvey. Owned by Robert P. Gibb, Oldwick, New Jersey. (Courtesy, Mrs. Bruce Read, Secretary, American Connemara Pony Society)

Fig. 48-10. Missouri Fox Trotting foal, owned by Ralph Hodges, Foil, Missouri. (Courtesy, Missouri Fox Trotting Horse Breed Assn., Inc.)

Fig. 48-9. Hackney stallion, Creation's King. All-American Hackney stallion, 1951-56. Note the characteristic smooth, gracefully-curved form. (Courtesy, Heyl-Pony Farm, Washington, Ill.)

Fig. 48-11. Morgan stallion, Rex's Major Monte. (Courtesy, Morgan Horse Club, Inc.)

Fig. 48-12. Desert Dawn, Palomino stallion shown by Bent Arrow Ranch, Broken Arrow, Oklahoma. Grand Champion at many shows, including the Tulsa State Fair, 1954-58. (Courtesy, Palomino Horse Breeders of America)

Fig. 48-13. Baby Doll, Pinto chestnut and white (Tobiano) mare of the parade horse type; owned by Bonnie and Bill Bailey, Kent, Ohio. (Courtesy, Pinto Horse Assn. of America, Inc.)

Fig. 48-14. Lady of Paint, International POAC Award Winner in Halter and Performance, 1964 and 1965. (Courtesy, Pony of the Americas Club, Inc.)

Fig. 48-15. Pokey Bar, racing type Quarter Horse; consistent winner in 1961 and 1962, with winnings totaling $162,543.81; owned by Hugh Huntley, Madera, California. (Courtesy, Hugh Huntley)

Fig. 48-16. A racing Shetland Pony in action. (Courtesy, The United States Pony Trotting Assn.)

Fig. 48-17. Cochise, Spanish Mustang stallion. (Courtesy, Robert E. Brislawn, Sr., Oshoto, Wyo.)

Fig. 48-18. Bret Hanover, Standardbred stallion. World's champion pacer, with a record mile of 1:53⅗, set at Lexington, Kentucky, in 1966. After winning more than $900,000, Bret Hanover, a bay four-year-old son of Adios, was sold for $2,000,000 to Castleton Farm, Lexington, Kentucky, and retired to stud service in 1967. (Courtesy, Larry Evans, Publicity Director, The United States Trotting Assn.)

Fig. 48-19. Greyhound, Standardbred harness race horse in action. He still holds the world's trotting record of 1:55¼ for the mile (the record was made in 1938). With a stride exceeding 27 feet, Greyhound was often referred to as the "Silver Groomed Flyer." Trotters and pacers are of similar breeding and type, the particular gait being largely a matter of training. Today, harness race horses are almost exclusively of the Standardbred breed. (Courtesy, The United States Trotting Assn.)

Fig. 48-20. Tennessee Walking Horse stallion, Go Boy's Shadow. Grand Championship Stake winner Walking Horse National Celebration. (Courtesy, Wiser's Walking Horse Stables, Shelbyville, Tenn.)

Fig. 48-21. Thoroughbred stallion, Swaps. Kentucky Derby winner; won $848,900 in racing purses; set six world's records. Note the long body, deep chest, rather long legs, and high degree of quality and refinement—characteristics of the breed. (Courtesy, Mr. Olin Gentry, Mgr., Darby Dan Farm, Lexington, Ky.)

Fig. 48-22. Liseter Bright Light, Welsh Pony stallion; a champion and fine breed representative; owned by Mrs. J. Austin duPont, Liseter Hall Farm, Newton Square, Pennsylvania. (Courtesy, Mrs. duPont)

Fig. 48-23. Two-year-old Belgian stallion, Conceur; bred, owned, and shown by Meadow Brook Farm, Howell, Michigan. Grand champion at the Ohio, Illinois, and Indiana state fairs, and at the National Belgian Show, Davenport, Iowa, in 1965. (Courtesy, Belgian Draft Horse Corp. of America)

Fig. 48-24. Benefactor, Clydesdale stallion purchased by Messrs. T. and M. Templeton at the Netherhall Dispersion of A. & W. Montgomery, Castle Douglas, Scotland, in 1925, for 4400 guineas (approximately $13,000). (Courtesy, Clydesdale Breeders' Assn. of the U.S.)

Fig. 48-25. Lynwood Dixiana, champion Percheron mare owned by Lynwood Farm, Carmel, Indiana. The Percheron is noted for its handsome, clean-cut head, good action, excellent temperament, and longevity. (Courtesy, Percheron Horse Assn. of America)

Fig. 48-26. A champion Shire stallion. The Shire is taller than any other draft breed.

Fig. 48-27. Typical Suffolk stallion, imported from England. Suffolk horses are distinguished by their chestnut color and chunky build. (Courtesy, American Suffolk Horse Assn.)

Fig. 48-28. Miniature Mediterranean Donkeys. (Courtesy, Daniel Langfeld, Sr., Pres., Miniature Donkey Registry of the U.S., Inc., Omaha, Nebr.)

QUESTIONS FOR STUDY AND DISCUSSION

1. What accounts for the fact that so many light horse breeds were American creations, but that only one draft breed originated in this country?

2. In outline form, list the (a) place of origin, (b) distinguishing characteristics, and (c) disqualifications of each breed of light and draft horses; then discuss the importance of each of these listings.

3. Obtain breed registry association literature and a sample copy of a magazine of your favorite breed of horses. Evaluate the soundness and value of the material that you receive.

4. Justify any preference that you may have for one particular breed of horses.

SELECTED REFERENCES

Title of Publication	Author(s)	Publisher
Appaloosa Horse, The	Francis Haines G. B. Hatley Robert Peckinpah	R. G. Bailey Printing Company, Lewiston, Idaho.
Breeds of Livestock, The	C. W. Gay	The Macmillan Company, New York, N. Y., 1918.
Breeds of Livestock in America	H. W. Vaughan	R. G. Adams and Company, Columbus, Ohio, 1937.
Horse, The	D. J. Kays	Rinehart & Company, New York, N. Y., 1953.
Horse America Made, The	Louis Taylor	American Saddle Horse Breeders Assoc., Urban Building, Louisville, Ky., 1944.
Horse Science Handbook	M. E. Ensminger (editor)	Agriservices Foundation, 3699 E. Sierra Ave., Clovis, Calif.
Horses: Their Selection, Care and Handling	M. C. Self	A. S. Barnes and Company, New York, N. Y., 1943.
Horses of Today, Their History, Breeds and Qualifications	H. H. Reese	Wood & Jones, Pasadena, Calif., 1956.
Kellogg Arabians, The	H. H. Reese G. B. Edwards	Borden Publishing Company, Los Angeles, Calif., 1958.
Light Horse Breeds, The	J. W. Patten	A. S. Barnes & Co., New York, N. Y., 1960.
Light Horses	M. E. Ensminger	Farmers' Bul. No. 2127, U.S. Department of Agriculture.
Modern Breeds of Livestock	H. M. Briggs	The Macmillan Company, New York, N. Y., 1958.
Shetland Pony, The	L. Frank Bedell	The Iowa State University Press, Ames, Iowa, 1959.

Titles of Publication	Author(s)	Publisher
Stockman's Handbook, The	M. E. Ensminger	The Interstate Printers & Publishers, Danville, Ill., 1969.
Stud Managers' Handbook	M. E. Ensminger (editor)	Agriservices Foundation, 3699 E. Sierra Ave., Clovis, Calif.
Study of Breeds, The	Thomas Shaw	Orange Judd Company, New York, N. Y., 1912.
Types and Breeds of Farm Animals	C. S. Plumb	Ginn and Company, Boston, 1920.
World Dictionary of Breeds Types and Varieties of Livestock, A	I. L. Mason	Commonwealth Agricultural Bureaux, Farnham House, Farnham Royal, Slough, Bucks., England, 1951.

Also, breed literature pertaining to each breed may be secured by writing to the respective breed registry associations. (See Sec. VI, Appendix, for the name and address of each association.)

CHAPTER XLIX

SELECTING AND JUDGING HORSES

Contents   Page

Selection Based on Individuality..1140
Selection Based on Pedigree..1140
Selection Based on Show-Ring Winnings...1141
Selection Based on Performance Testing..1141
Judging Horses 1141
  Parts of a Horse...1142
  Desirable Characteristics According to Type and Breed.......................1142
    Good Head, Neck, and Shoulders...1143
    Strong, Heavily Muscled Topline; Short Back and Loin; Long, Level
      Croup 1143
    Ample Chest and Middle...1143
    Well-muscled Arm, Forearm, and Gaskin..1143
    Correct Legs, Feet, and Pasterns...1144
    Good Action 1145
      The Gaits...1146
      Common Defects in Way of Going...1148
    Sound 1149
  How to Determine the Age by the Teeth..1150
  How to Measure a Horse..1152
  Other Considerations in Buying a Horse..1152
    Style and Beauty...1152
    Balance and Symmetry..1152
    Quality 1153
    Energetic Yet Manageable Disposition...1153
    Freedom from Vices...1153
    Good Wind 1153
    Freedom from Diseases..1153
    Condition 1153
    Misrepresentations 1154
  Method of Examining...1154
  Questions for Study and Discussion..1154
  Selected References 1154

The great horse shows throughout the land have exerted a powerful influence in molding the types of certain breeds of light horses. Other breeds have been affected primarily through selections based on performance, such as the race track. It is realized, however, that only comparatively few animals are subjected annually to the scrutiny of experienced judges or to trial on the race track. Rather, the vast majority of them are evaluated by horse users; by those who take pride in owning a good horse and who conduct their own buying and selling operations.

Before buying a horse, the amateur should enlist the help of a competent horseman.

As with other classes of farm animals, any one or a combination of all four of the following methods may serve as bases for selecting horses: (1) individuality, (2) pedigree, (3) show-ring winnings, and/or (4) performance testing. One must also be aware of the fact that environment, including feeding and training, plays a tremendously important part in the individuality and performance of a horse.

SELECTION BASED ON INDIVIDUALITY

As is well known, the type or individuality of the horse varies according to the specific functions that the animal is supposed to fulfill—whether it be racing, saddle, heavy harness, polo, etc. In considering individuality or type, one usually more or less automatically examines the performance of the individual at the type of work for which he is bred, adapted, and selected. That is, in addition to studying the individual excellence in body conformation, the animal is observed in action. Thus, the saddle horse is studied while executing the gaits, and, if old enough, the running horse is actually timed on the track.

Selection followed by mating of the best to the best, which is merely selection based on individuality, has long been the principal tool through which man has brought about the improvement of the horse. Following domestication, certain animals were chosen for breeding purposes while others were slaughtered and eaten. In no case has this method of improvement achieved more success than with this particular class of livestock.

That selection based on individuality has been effective over a long period of time in developing distinct types of horses well adapted for specific purposes is self-evident. Thus, from one or a few wild types of horses—by selecting individuals for their ability to perform certain types of work while giving consideration in some instances to their style and beauty—man has developed distinct types of horses; horses that are best adapted to draft, riding, driving, and race purposes. Thus, the Great War Horse and his descendant, the draft horse, were selected for their ability to carry and draw heavy loads—a characteristic requiring heavy, compact, low-set, heavily-muscled, and heavy-boned animals with a relatively docile and quiet type of temperament. By way of contrast, the horses developed by the Bedouins of the desert—a warring tribe whose safety often depended upon the speed of their escape—and later used as foundation animals for the race horse, were selected for a lithe, lean, relatively long-muscled, and light-boned animal with a quick, nervous disposition. Still other qualities, especially beauty and high action, were sought in the heavy harness horse; and the saddle horse was selected primarily because of the ease with which he carried the rider.

Selection on the basis of individuality and performance alone is still the best single method for obtaining suitable utility horses, whether they be used for draft, heavy-harness, light-harness, saddle, or pony purposes. In other words, the individuality of the horse, its phenotype, is closely correlated with its performance. However, if the animals are selected for breeding purposes, additional criteria should be considered.

SELECTION BASED ON PEDIGREE

The Arabians were the first livestock breeders to trace the lineage of their animals, often memorizing many generations of the pedigree. Moreover, they accorded particular importance to the dam's side of the heritage, a condition that still prevails in certain breeds of livestock today as evidenced by the family names tracing to certain great females many generations removed.

If the pedigree is relatively complete in terms of records of performance (speed, show winnings, etc.) of the ancestors, particularly those close up, it can be of very great usefulness in providing a safer basis for selection. A pedigree of this type is of value in predicting (1) the usefulness of the individual (whether it be for racing under the saddle or jumping, etc.), and (2) the probable prepotency as a breeding animal.

SELECTION BASED ON SHOW-RING WINNINGS

Breeders of horses have long used show-ring records as a basis of selection. Because training plays such an important part in the performance and show-ring winnings of pleasure horses, however, it is likely that this basis of selection is less valuable from a breeding standpoint than with any other class of farm animals. At the same time, the show record may be a most valuable criterion in indicating the utility value of the horse.

SELECTION BASED ON PERFORMANCE TESTING

Although selection based on progeny testing is the most infallible tool available to the horse breeder, it must be pointed out that, fine as it is, the following limitations exist:

1. Because of relatively few offspring, it is difficult to apply it to females.

2. Even with males, a progeny testing rating cannot be obtained until late in life, after sufficient offspring have been born and have reached an age when they can be tested.

3. There is the hazard that the stallion being tested will only be bred to a few select mares and that only the top offspring will be tested.

4. Training and feeding play such a major part in horses that it is always difficult to separate out environmental from hereditary influences.

Performance testing is easier to apply than progeny testing because it is an individual matter. In fact, most race horses used for breeding purposes are first performance tested on the track.

Perhaps it might be added that the progressive breeder will continue to use all four methods of selection: individuality, pedigree, show-ring winnings, and performance testing, but with increasing emphasis upon the latter method.

JUDGING HORSES

The general requisites in judging, which are similar for all classes of livestock, are fully covered in Chapter XI and will not be repeated here.

Accomplished stockmen generally agree that horses are the most difficult to judge of all classes of farm animals. In addition to considering conformation—which is the main criterion in judging other farm animals—action and numerous unsoundnesses are of paramount importance.

Parts of a Horse

Before being able to arrive accurately at an ideal or standard of perfection, the amateur horseman must first master the language that describes the parts of an animal. Figure 49-1 sets forth this information.

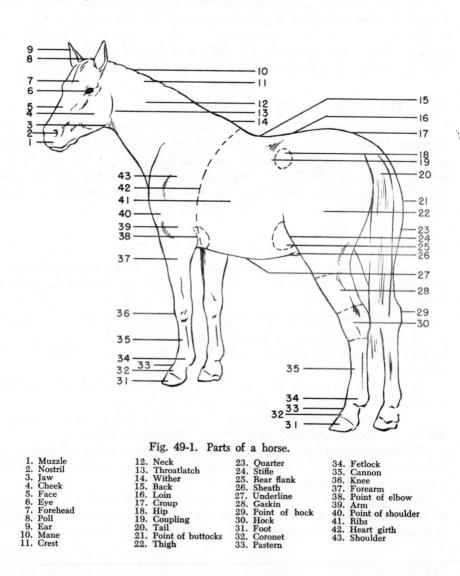

Fig. 49-1. Parts of a horse.

1. Muzzle	12. Neck	23. Quarter	34. Fetlock
2. Nostril	13. Throatlatch	24. Stifle	35. Cannon
3. Jaw	14. Wither	25. Rear flank	36. Knee
4. Cheek	15. Back	26. Sheath	37. Forearm
5. Face	16. Loin	27. Underline	38. Point of elbow
6. Eye	17. Croup	28. Gaskin	39. Arm
7. Forehead	18. Hip	29. Point of hock	40. Point of shoulder
8. Poll	19. Coupling	30. Hock	41. Ribs
9. Ear	20. Tail	31. Foot	42. Heart girth
10. Mane	21. Point of buttocks	32. Coronet	43. Shoulder
11. Crest	22. Thigh	33. Pastern	

Desirable Characteristics According to Type and Breed

A horse must first conform to the specific type which fits him for the function he is to perform. Secondly, he should be true to the characteristics of the breed that he represents. Regardless of type or breed, however, the following desirable characteristics should be present in all horses.

GOOD HEAD, NECK, AND SHOULDERS

The head should be well proportioned to the rest of the body, refined and clean-cut, with a chiseled appearance. A broad, full forehead with great width between the eyes indicates intelligence. A straight face is usually preferable to a concave or convex profile (Roman nose), the former suggesting a timid disposition and the latter strong will power. The jaw should be broad and strongly muscled. There should be great width between large, clear eyes; and the ears should be of medium size, well carried, and active. The neck should be fairly long. It should be carried high, slightly arched, lean and muscular, and clean-cut about the throatlatch, with the head well set on. Also, the neck should neatly join long, oblique, smooth shoulders. The head and neck of the animal should show sex character—boldness and masculinity in the stallion and refinement and femininity in the brood mare.

STRONG, HEAVILY MUSCLED TOPLINE, SHORT BACK AND LOIN; LONG, LEVEL CROUP

The topline should include a short, strong back and loin, with a long, nicely turned and heavily muscled croup, and a high, well-set tail. The withers should be rather clearly defined and of the same height as the hips. Good withers and oblique shoulders make for a better seat in riding horses. Moreover, a sloping shoulder is usually associated with sloping pasterns and more springy, elastic action. The back and loin muscles help sustain the weight of the rider, lift the forequarters of the horse, and strengthen the arch of the back of the horse in motion. A desirable short coupling is obtained when the last rib is close to the hip.

AMPLE CHEST AND MIDDLE

Ample chest and middle due to long, well-sprung ribs are to be desired. A deep, wide chest and large, full heart-girth—together with a good middle—provide needed space for the vital organs and indicate a strong constitution and good feeding and staying qualities. All horses should be fairly well let-down in the hind flank, though race horses in training may show much less depth at this point than other types of horses. Even with race horses, however, the extremely high-cut, so-called wasp-waisted ones will not endure heavy racing. Moreover, race horses usually deepen materially in the rear flank with age or higher condition.

WELL-MUSCLED ARM, FOREARM, AND GASKIN

The muscles of the arm, forearm, and gaskin should be well developed. Since little or no fat can be placed upon the forearm and gaskin, these areas are a good indication of the muscular development of the entire animal, even when horses are in high condition. The powerful muscles of the croup, thigh, and gaskin give the animal ability to pull, jump, or run.

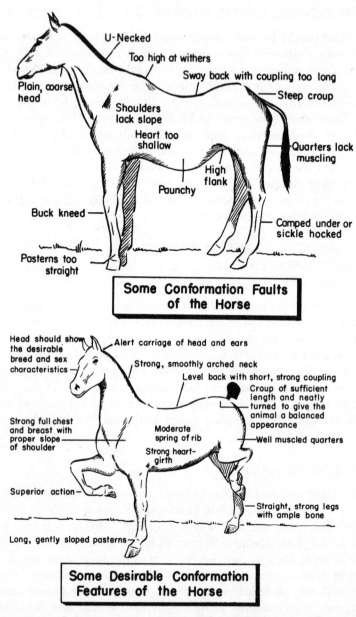

Some Conformation Faults of the Horse

Some Desirable Conformation Features of the Horse

Fig. 49-2. Ideal type versus common faults. Regardless of type or breed, certain desirable characteristics should be present in all horses. The successful horse judge must be able to recognize both the desirable characteristics and the common faults, and the relative importance of each. (Drawing by R. F. Johnson)

CORRECT LEGS, FEET, AND PASTERNS

There has long been a saying "no foot, no horse." After all, the value of a horse lies chiefly in his ability to move, hence the necessity of good underpinning. The legs should be straight, true, and squarely set; the bone should be well placed and clearly defined. The pasterns should be sloping; the feet large and wide at the heels and tough in conformation.

The hock should be large, clean, wide from front to back, deep, clean-cut, and correctly set. The knee should be deep from front to rear, wide when viewed from the front, straight, and, taper gradually into the leg. Since the hock and knee joints of the horse are subject to great wear and are the seat of many unsoundnesses, they should receive every attention.

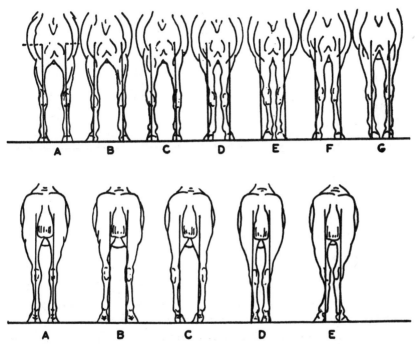

Fig. 49-3. The proper and faulty conformation of the forelegs (top) when viewed from the front, and the hind legs (bottom) when viewed from the rear. The forelegs: A represents correct conformation; B, splay-footed or base-narrow forefeet, toe cut out, heels in; C, bowed legs; D, knock-kneed, set close together with toes pointing outward; E, conformation predisposing to interfering; F, knees set close together; G, pigeon-toed or toe narrow—a conformation which will cause the animal to wing or throw out the feet as they are elevated. The hind legs: A represents correct conformation; B, hind legs set too far apart; C, bandy-legged—wide at the hocks and hind feet toe in; D, hind legs set too close together; E, cow-hocked. The direction of the leg and the form of the foot are very important in the horse. (Courtesy, USDA)

GOOD ACTION

Although the degree of action of the horse will vary somewhat with the type (draft, speed, show, and saddle), the usefulness of all horses is dependent upon their action and their ability to move in various types of racing, driving, hunting, riding, polo, etc. In all types and breeds, the motion should be straight and true with a long, swift, and elastic stride.

The Gaits

A gait is a particular natural or acquired way of going, characterized by a distinctive rhythmic movement of feet and legs.

In proper show-ring procedure, horses are brought back to a walk each time before they are called upon to execute a different gait. An exception sometimes is made in five-gaited classes—the rack may be executed from the slow gait. The gaits are:

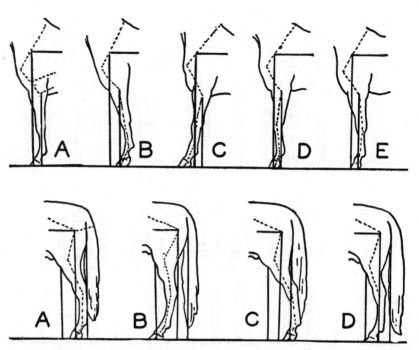

Fig. 49-4. The proper and faulty conformation of the forelegs (top) when viewed from the side, and the hind legs (bottom) when viewed from the side. The forelegs: A, correct conformation; B, forelegs too far under the body; C, forelegs too far advanced; D, knee-sprung or buck kneed—over in the knees; E, calf-kneed—standing with knees too far back. The hind legs: A, correct conformation; B, sickle hocked—hind legs too far under the body; C, legs set too far back; D, hock joint is too straight. The direction of the legs and the form of the foot are very important in the horse. (Courtesy, USDA)

Walk.—A natural, slow gait of four beats in which each foot leaves and strikes the ground at separate intervals. The walk should be springy, regular, and true.

Trot.—A natural, rapid, two-beat diagonal gait in which the front foot and the opposite hind foot take off together and strike the ground simultaneously.

All four feet are off the ground at the same time for a brief moment; the trotting horse thus seems to float through the air.

This gait varies considerably with different breeds. The trot of the Standardbred is characterized by length and rapidity of individual strides; the trot of the Hackney shows extreme flexion of the knees and hocks that produces a high-stepping show gait.

Run or *gallop.*—A fast, three-beat gait during which two diagonal legs are paired and strike the ground together between the successive beats of the other two unpaired legs. All four feet are off the ground for a brief interval. The two unpaired legs that act independently—the forefoot with which the horse leads and the diagonal hindfoot—naturally bear more weight and are subject to more fatigue than the paired legs that act jointly.

In the gallop, propulsion is chiefly in the hindquarters, although the forequarters sustain a tremendous jar as the horse lands. The gallop is the fast natural gait of horses.

Canter.—A slow, restrained gallop or run. Like the gallop, it is a three-beat gait, and it puts unusual wear on the leading forefoot and its diagonal hindfoot. It is important frequently to change the lead. A well-trained horse will do this easily at the will of the rider.

In the show-ring, the lead should be toward the inside of the ring, and the lead is changed by reversing direction of travel (when the ringmaster calls for "reverse and canter"). This gait should be executed in such a slow collected manner that the animal may perform in a relatively small circle.

Pace.—A fast, two-beat gait in which the front and hind feet on the same side start and stop simultaneously. The feet rise just above the ground level. All four feet are off the ground for a split second and the horse appears to float forward.

The pace is faster than the trot but slower than the run or gallop. It allows for a quick getaway, but it produces an objectional side or rolling type of motion. This gate is not suited to travel in mud or snow; a smooth, hard footing and easy draft are necessary for its best execution.

The pace once was popular in England but lost in favor soon after the development of the Thoroughbred early in the eighteenth century.

Stepping pace (or *slow pace*).—A modified pace in which the objectionable side or rolling motion is eliminated because the two feet on each side do not move exactly together. Instead, it is a four-beat gait with each of the four feet striking the ground separately. The hind and front feet start almost together in the take off, but the hind foot touches the ground slightly ahead of the front foot on the same side. This is the preferred slow gait for five-gaited show horses.

Fox trot.—A slow, short, broken type of trot in which the head usually nods. In executing the fox trot, the horse brings each hind foot to the ground an instant before the diagonal forefoot. This gait is accepted as a slow gait, but it is not as popular as the stepping pace.

Running walk.—A slow, four-beat gait, intermediate between the walk and rack. The hind foot oversteps the front foot from 2 or 3 to as many as 18 inches, giving the motion a smooth, gliding effect. This gait is characterized by a bobbing or nodding of the head, a flopping of the ears, and a snapping of the teeth in rhythm with the movement of the legs.

The running walk is easy on both horse and rider; it is the all-day working gait of the South, executed at a speed of six to eight miles per hour. It is a necessary gait for Tennessee Walking Horses.

Rack.—A fast, brilliant, flashy, unnatural, four-beat gait in which each foot strikes the ground separately at equal intervals; known originally as the "single foot." The rack is easy on the rider, hard on the horse. It is, undoubtedly, the most popular gait in the American show-ring. On the tanbark, greater speed at the rack is requested with the command "rack on."

Traverse or *side step.*—The traverse or side step is simply a lateral movement of the animal without forward or backward movement. This step often helps the rider in opening and closing gates, lining up horses in the show-ring, and taking position in a mounted drill or posse.

COMMON DEFECTS IN WAY OF GOING

The feet of a horse should move straight ahead parallel to an imaginary center line drawn in the direction of travel. Any deviation from this way of going constitutes a defect.

Some defects are:

Cross-firing.—A scuffing on the inside of the diagonal forefeet and hindfeet; generally confined to pacers.

Dwelling.—A noticeable pause in the flight of the foot, as though the stride were completed before the foot reaches the ground; most noticeable in trick-trained horses.

Forging.—Striking forefoot with toe of hindfoot.

Interfering.—Striking fetlock or cannon with the opposite foot; most often done by base-narrow, toe-wide, or splay-footed horses.

Lameness.—A defect detected when the animal favors the affected foot when standing. The load on the ailing foot in action is eased and a characteristic bobbing of the head occurs as the affected foot strikes the ground.

Paddling.—Throwing the front feet outward as they are picked up; most common in tow-narrow or pigeon-toed horses.

Pointing.—Perceptible extension of the stride with little flexion; likely to occur in the long-strided Thoroughbred and Standardbred breeds—animals bred and trained for great speed.

Pounding.—Heavy contact with ground instead of desired light, springy movement.

Rolling.—Excessive lateral shoulder motion; characteristic of horses with protruding shoulders.

Scalping.—The hairline at the top of the hindfoot hits the tow of the forefoot as it breaks over.

Speedy Cutting.—The inside of diagonal fore and hind pastern makes contact; sometimes seen in fast-trotting horses.

Stringhalt.—Excessive flexing of hind legs; most easily detected when a horse is backed.

Trappy.—A short, quick, choppy stride; a tendency of horses with short, straight pasterns and straight shoulders.

Winding or *rope-walking.*—A twisting of the striding leg around in front of supporting leg, which results in contact like that of a rope-walking artist; often occurs in horses with very wide fronts.

Winging.—An exaggerated paddling particularly noticeable in high-going horses.

SOUND

An integral part of selecting a horse lies in ability to recognize common blemishes and unsoundness and to rate the importance of each.

A thorough knowledge of normal, sound structure makes it easy to recognize imperfections.

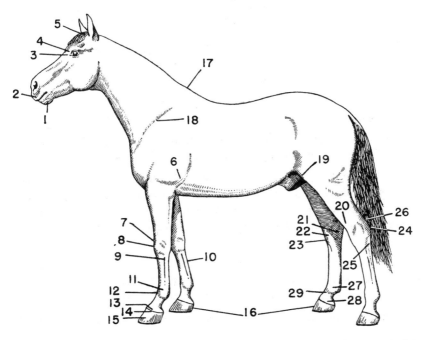

Fig. 49-5. Location of points of common unsoundnesses in horses. Head: undershot jaw (1); parrot mouth (2); moon blindness (3); blindness (4); poll evil (5). Front limbs: shoe boil (6); calf kneed (7); knee sprung (8); splints (9); bowed tendons (10); wind puffs (11); cocked ankles (12); ring bone (13); quittor (14); navicular disease (15). Feet (16): contracted feet; corns; founder; side bones; thrush; quarter or sand crack; scratches or grease heel. Withers and shoulders; fistulous withers (17); sweeny (18). Rear limbs: stifled (19); string-halt (20); blood spavin (21); bog spavin (22); bone spavin or jack (23); capped hock (24); curb (25); thoroughpin (26); wind puffs (27); ring bone (28); cocked angles (29). General: heaves; hernia; roaring; thick wind.

Any abnormal deviation in the structure or function of a horse constitutes an unsoundness. From a practical standpoint, however, a differentiation is made between abnormalities that do and those that do not affect serviceability.

Blemishes include abnormalities that do not affect serviceability—such as wire cuts, rope burns, nail punctures, shoe boils, or capped hocks.

Unsoundnesses include more serious abnormalities that affect serviceability.

Figure 49-5 shows the location of common blemishes and unsoundnesses.

One should consider the use to which it is intended to put the animal before buying a blemished or unsound horse.

How to Determine the Age by the Teeth

The life span of horses averages 20 to 25 years—about one-third that of man. Horses generally are at their best between 3 and 12 years of age. This may vary because of individual differences in animals or because of differences in the kind of work they do.

The age of horses is, therefore, important to the breeder, seller, and buyer.

The approximate age of a horse can be determined by noting the time of appearance, shape, and degree of wear of temporary and permanent teeth. Temporary, or milk, teeth are easily distinguishable from permanent ones because they are smaller and whiter.

The best way to learn to determine age in horses is by examining teeth of individual horses of known ages.

A mature male horse has 40[1] teeth. A mature female has 36[1]. A foal of either sex has 24. The mare does not have tushes as a rule (Table 49-1).

Table 49-1 may be used as a guide to determining age of horses by their teeth. The gradual wearing and disappearance of the cups (the inside or center of the tooth) according to a rather definite pattern in period of time enables the experienced horseman to judge the age of an animal with a fair degree of accuracy up to 12 years.

Even experienced horsemen cannot determine the age of an animal accurately after it is 12 years old. After this age, the teeth change from oval to triangular, and they project or slant forward more and more as the horse becomes older.

Side views of the mouths of 5-, 7-, and 20-year-old horses are shown in Fig. 49-6.

An animal's environment can affect wear on teeth materially. Teeth of horses raised in dry sandy areas, for example, will show more than normal wear;

---

[1] Quite commonly, a small, pointed tooth, known as a "wolf tooth", may appear in front of each first molar tooth in the upper jaw, thus increasing the total number of teeth to 42 in the male and 38 in the female. Less frequently, two more "wolf teeth" in the lower jaw increase the total number of teeth in the male and female to 44 and 40, respectively.

TABLE 49—1

A SUMMARY OF THE CHANGES OF THE TEETH OF HORSES

Age	Condition of Teeth	
At birth or before ten days of age......	First or central upper and lower incisors appear.	Appearance of temporary teeth
4 to 6 weeks of age....	Second or intermediate upper and lower incisors appear.	
6 to 10 months..........	Third or corner upper and lower incisors appear.	
1 year of age.............	Crowns of central incisors show wear.	Wear of temporary teeth
1½ years of age.........	Intermediate incisors show wear.	
2 years of age...........	All temporary incisors show wear.	
2½ years of age.........	First or central incisors appear.	Appearance of permanent teeth
3½ years of age.........	Second or intermediate incisors appear.	
4½ years of age.........	Third or corner incisors appear.	
4 to 5 years of age (in male)...............	Canines appear.	Wear of permanent teeth
5 years of age...........	Cups in all incisors.	
6 years of age...........	Cups worn out of lower central incisors.	
7 years of age...........	Cups also worn out of lower intermediate incisors.	
8 years of age...........	Cups worn out of all lower incisors, and dental "star" appears on lower central and intermediate pairs.	
9 years of age...........	Cups also worn out of upper central incisors, and dental "star" appears on upper central and intermediate pairs.	
10 years of age.........	Cups also worn out of upper intermediate incisors, and dental "star" is present on all incisors, both upper and lower.	
11 years of age.........	Cups worn out of all upper and lower incisors, and dental "star" approaches center of cups.	
12 years of age.........	No cups. "Smooth mouthed."	

a five-year-old western horse may have teeth that would be normal in a six- to eight-year-old horse raised elsewhere. The teeth of cribbers also show more than normal wear. It is hard to determine the age of such animals. The age of a horse with a parrot mouth, or undershot jaw, also is difficult to estimate.

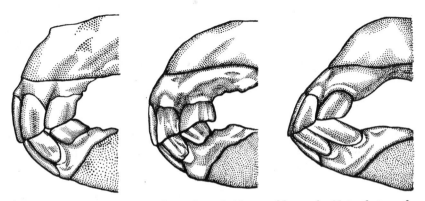

Fig. 49-6. Side view of 5-, 7-, and 20-year-old mouth. Note that as the horse advances in age the teeth change from nearly perpendicular to slanting sharply toward the front.

How to Measure a Horse

Normal pertinent measurements are height, weight, girth, and bone.

Height.—The height of a horse is the vertical distance from the highest point of its withers to the ground when the animal is standing squarely on a level area. The unit of measurement used in expressing height is the "hand," which is 4 inches. A horse measuring 62 inches is said to be 15-2 hands high (15 hands and 2 inches).

A person can estimate a horse's height if he knows the exact number of inches from the level of his eyes to the ground. Knowing this, all he need do is stand beside the animal's front limbs and look at the highest point of the withers; he can then estimate the horse's height rather closely.

Weight.—Although weight may be estimated by means of a tape measure, it is best to use scales.

Girth.—Girth is a measure of the circumference of the chest behind the withers and in front of the back.

Bone.—Size of bone usually is determined by placing a tape measure around the cannon bone halfway between the knee and fetlock joints. This measurement is in inches.

Other Considerations in Buying a Horse

In addition to the desirable qualities in conformation already enumerated, there should be style and beauty, balance and symmetry, an abundance of quality, an energetic yet manageable disposition, freedom from vices, good wind, suitable age, freedom from disease, and proper condition. The buyer should also be on the alert for possible misrepresentations. As each of these factors should receive careful consideration when buying a horse, they will be discussed separately.

STYLE AND BEAUTY

This has reference to the attractiveness with which the horse displays himself at all times. Good carriage of the head, active ears, an alert active disposition, and beauty of conformation are factors contributing to the style of the horse. This quality is especially important in heavy harness, fine harness, and saddle horses.

BALANCE AND SYMMETRY

Balance and symmetry refer to the harmonious development of all parts. With the full development of all important parts which are nicely blended together, the horse will present an attractive appearance.

QUALITY

Quality is denoted by clean, flat bone, well-defined joints and tendons, refined head and ears, and fine skin and hair. Good quality in the horse indicates easy keeping and good endurance.

ENERGETIC YET MANAGEABLE DISPOSITION

Both sexes and all types of horses should at all times display energetic yet manageable dispositions. The disposition of a horse, whether good or bad, is usually considered as being a product of both inheritance and environment. Regardless of the cause of a nasty disposition, one should avoid purchasing such an animal. Superb manners and disposition are especially important in all types of pleasure horses.

FREEDOM FROM VICES

Although not considered as unsoundnesses, such stable vices as cribbing, weaving, tail-rubbing, kicking, stall-walking and stall-trotting, and halter-pulling do detract from the value of a horse. But vices are not confined to actions in the stall. Some horses object to taking a bit in their mouths; others are touchy about the ears; still others jump when an attempt is made to place a saddle or harness on their backs. Any of these traits are objectionable.

GOOD WIND

Good wind is imperative. Defects of wind may be easily detected by first moving the animal at a rapid gait for some distance, then suddenly bringing him to a stop and listening in near proximity to the head. Unsound animals are usually noisy in breathing.

FREEDOM FROM DISEASES

In transporting a horse, there is always a possible exposure to the many ills to which he is subject. Sometimes these prove to be of sufficiently serious nature as to make working impossible at a time when the animal is most needed; and occasionally they even prove fatal. It must also be remembered that such diseases as contracted may very likely spread to the other horses on the farm and even in the community, thus exposing them to the same risk.

CONDITION

Both productive ability and endurance are lowered by either a thin, run-down condition or an overfat and highly fitted condition. A good vigorous, thrifty condition is conducive to the best work and breeding ability, and horses so fitted attract the eye of the prospective buyer. However, extremes in feeding and lack of exercise are to be avoided in purchasing a horse for either work or breeding. It must be remembered that fat will cover up a multitude of defects. In buying valuable mares or stallions, the purchaser should insist on having a health certificate signed by a licensed veterinarian. Such examination should also show that the reproductive organs are normal and healthy.

MISREPRESENTATIONS

Especially is the inexperienced man likely to encounter misrepresentations as to age, soundness, vices, and the training and working ability of the horse. Perhaps knowing the seller as well as the horse is the best preventive of this sort of thing.

Method of Examining

Custom decrees somewhat different procedure in examining or judging horses. Halter classes usually are first examined while lined up side by side, and later inspected while moved one at a time; whereas performance classes are first examined with the entire class in action, and later lined up for close inspection.

After a judge has inspected a light horse performance class, both in action and when lined up, it is considered entirely proper for him to request that certain animals be pulled out and again put through their gaits.

QUESTIONS FOR STUDY AND DISCUSSION

1. Discuss each of the four bases of selection of horses and compare the relative importance of each with their importance in selecting beef cattle, sheep, or swine.

2. In judging horses, what primary differences exist in comparison with beef cattle, sheep and hogs?

3. Classify horse gaits as (a) two-beat gaits, (b) three-beat gaits, and (c) four-beat gaits.

4. Prepare a list of common horse blemishes and describe each of them.

5. Rank in order of their severity the common horse unsoundnesses and describe each of them.

6. Rank in order of their severity the common horse vices and describe each of them.

7. What is involved in determining the age of horses by the teeth (a) up to 5 years of age, (b) from 6 to 12 years of age, (c) beyond 12 years of age?

8. Of what importance are the following measurements: (a) height, (b) weight, (c) girth, and (d) bone?

9. Generally speaking, trainers consider breeding to be more important than training in determining the performance of a horse, whereas owners consider training more important than breeding. Why?

10. Custom decrees somewhat different show-ring procedure in judging horses than is followed with beef cattle, sheep, and swine. Explain.

SELECTED REFERENCES

Title of Publication	Author(s)	Publisher
Breeding Better Live-stock	V. A. Rice F. N. Andrews E. J. Warwick	McGraw-Hill Book Co., New York, N. Y., 1953.
Determining the Age of Farm Animals by Their Teeth	Farmer's Bul. 1721	U.S. Department of Agriculture, Washington, D.C.
Elements of Livestock Judging, The	W. W. Smith	J. B. Lippincott Co., Philadelphia, Pa., 1930.

Titles of Publication	Author(s)	Publisher
Horse, The	D. J. Kays	Rinehart & Co., New York, N. Y., 1953.
Horse Science Handbooks	M. E. Ensminger (editor)	Agriservices Foundation, 3699 E. Sierra Ave., Clovis, Calif.
Horses	M. C. Self	A. S. Barnes and Company, New York, N. Y., 1953.
Horses and Horse-manship	M. E. Ensminger	The Interstate Printers & Publishers, Danville, Ill., 1969.
Lameness in Horses	O. R. Adams	Lea & Febiger, Philadelphia, Pa., 1967.
Light Horses	M. E. Ensminger	Farmers' Bulletin No. 2127, U.S. Department of Agriculture, Washington, D.C.
Livestock Judging Handbook	J. E. Nordby W. M. Beeson D. L. Fourt	The Interstate Printers & Publishers, Danville, Ill., 1962.
Selecting, Fitting and Showing Horses	J. E. Nordby H. E. Lattig	The Interstate Printers & Publishers, Danville, Ill., 1963.
Soundness and Nutrition in Stable and Kennel		Radiol Chemicals Limited, 78 Upper Richmond Road, London S. W. 15 England.
Stockman's Handbook The	M. E. Ensminger	The Interstate Printers & Publishers, Danville, Ill., 1969.
Stud Managers' Handbooks	M. E. Ensminger (editor)	Agriservices Foundation, 3699 E. Sierra Ave., Clovis, Calif.

CHAPTER L

BREEDING HORSES

Contents

	Page
Normal Breeding Habits of Mares	1158
Age of Puberty	1158
Age to Breed Mares	1158
Heat Periods	1158
Signs of Estrus	1159
Fertilization	1159
Gestation Period	1159
Breeding After Foaling	1160
Per Cent of Mares Bred Producing Foals	1160
Sterility or Barrenness in Mares	1161
Temporary Sterility	1162
Permanent Sterility	1162
Fertility of the Stallion	1163
Conditioning the Mare for Breeding	1163
The Breeding Operations	1163
Hand Breeding, Corral Breeding, and Pasture Breeding	1163
Examination of the Mare	1164
Signs and Tests of Pregnancy	1164
Care and Management of the Stallion	1165
Quarters for the Stallion	1165
Feeding the Stallion	1166
Exercise for the Stallion	1166
Grooming the Stallion	1168
Age and Service of the Stallion	1168
Care of the Pregnant Mare	1169
Quarters for the Mare	1169
Feeding the Pregnant Mare	1169
Exercise for the Pregnant Mare	1170
Care at Foaling Time	1170
Work and Exercise	1170
Signs of Approaching Parturition	1170
Preparation for Foaling	1171
Feed at Foaling Time	1172
The Attendant	1172
Parturition	1172
The Afterbirth	1173
Cleaning the Stall	1174
Feed and Water After Foaling	1174
Be Observant	1174
Handling the Newborn Foal	1174
Normal Breeding Season and the Time of Foaling	1180
How to Lower the Cost of Raising Horses	1180
Buying Horses or Raising Foals	1181
Experience of the Horseman	1182
Comparative Cost	1182
Risks Surrounding the Introduction of Horses	1183
Registration of Foals Produced Through Artificial Insemination	1183
Stallion Enrollment Laws	1183
Hybrids with the Horse as One Parent	1185
Lethals in Horses	1186
Performance Testing Horses	1187
Questions for Study and Discussion	1187
Selected References	1187

Horses will continue to be bred so long as they (1) serve the livestock industry of the West, and (2) provide recreation and sport. It is important, therefore, that both the student and the progressive animal husbandman be familiar with the breeding of them.

NORMAL BREEDING HABITS OF MARES

Perhaps at the outset it should be emphasized that strictly normal breeding habits of the horse do not exist under domestication. In the wild state, each band of 30 to 40 mares was headed by a stallion leader who sired all of the colts in that band. With plenty of outdoor exercise on natural footing, superior nutrition derived from plants grown on unleached soils, regular production beginning at an early age, little possibility of disease or infection, and frequent services during the heat period, 90 per cent or higher foaling rates were commonplace. Under domestication, the average conception rate is less than 50 per cent, and only the better establishment exceeds 70 per cent. Thus, the low fertility usually encountered under domestication must be caused to a large extent by the relatively artificial conditions under which horses are mated.

Age of Puberty
Mares generally start coming in heat when 12 to 15 months of age.

Age to Breed Mares

Only exceptionally well-grown fillies should be bred as late two-year-olds, so as to foal at three years of age. Under a system of early breeding, the fillies must be fed exceptionally well in order to provide growth for their own immature bodies as well as for the developing fetus. Furthermore, they usually should not be bred the following year. Generally speaking, it is best to breed the mare as a three-year-old so that she will foal when four. Not only will the three-year-old be better grown, but there will not be the handicap of training her while she is heavy in foal.

If they are properly cared for, it is not uncommon for brood mares to produce regularly up to 14 to 16 years of age; and, of course, in the more exceptional cases they may produce up to 25 years of age.

In selecting a brood mare, it is usually advisable either to obtain a young three- or four-year-old or to make certain of the sure and regular breeding habits of any old mares.

Heat Periods

The heat periods recur approximately at 21-day intervals, with a spread of from 10 to 37 days. The duration of heat varies from 1 to 37 days and averages 4 to 6 days, although some mares (especially maiden mares) will remain in heat up to 50 to 60 days in the early spring. Maiden mares that show "in heat" signs practically every day for many weeks should not be bred, as it is a waste of time and effort. In the vast majority of such cases, patience is rewarded by the mare subsequently settling into a normal cycle.

SIGNS OF ESTRUS

The experienced horseman who is familiar with a band of mares can usually detect those that are in season by observing (1) the relaxation of the external genitals, (2) more frequent urination, (3) the teasing of other mares, (4) the apparent desire for company, and (5) a slight mucus discharge from the vagina. In shy breeders or when there is any question about the mare being in season, she should be tried. When possible, it is usually good business to present mares regularly to the teaser every day or every other day as the breeding season approaches. A systematic plan of this sort will save much time and trouble.

Above all, precaution should be taken against false heats of mares in foal, the breeding of which may result in abortion. Such precaution is obtained by properly teasing the mare under the watchful eye of an experienced horseman who is familiar with the peculiarities of the individual animal.

Fertilization

Generally, the egg is liberated during the period of one day before to one day after the end of heat. Unfortunately, there is no reliable way of predicting the length of heat nor the time of ovulation.

The sperm (or male germ cells) are deposited in the uterus at the time of service and from there ascend the reproductive tract. Under favorable conditions, they meet the egg, and one of them fertilizes it in the upper part of the oviduct near the ovary.

A series of delicate time relationships must be met, however, or the egg will never be fertilized. The sperm cells live only 24 to 30 hours in the reproductive tract of the female, and it probably requires 4 to 6 hours for them to ascend the female reproductive tract. Moreover, the egg is viable for an even shorter period of time than the sperm, probably for not more than four to six hours after ovulation. For conception, therefore, breeding must take place within 20 to 24 hours before ovulation.

As mares usually stay in heat from five to eight days, perhaps the highest rate of conception may be obtained by serving the mare daily or every other day during the heat period, beginning with the third day. When many mares are being bred and heavy demands are being made upon a given stallion, this condition may be obtained by reinforcing a natural service with subsequent daily artificial inseminations as long as heat lasts. In no case should the mare be bred twice the same day.

Gestation Period

The average gestation period of mares is 336 days, or a little over 11 months. This will vary, however, with individual mares and may range from 310 to 370 days.

A handy rule-of-thumb method which may be used to figure the approximate date of foaling is to subtract one month and add one day to the date the mare was bred. Hence, a mare bred May 20 should foal April 21 the following year.

Breeding After Foaling

Mares usually come in heat 7 to 11 days after foaling, with individual mares varying from 3 to 13 days after foaling. Provided that foaling has been entirely normal and there is no discharge or evidence of infection at this time, many good horsemen plan to rebreed the mare during this first recurrence of heat after foaling or on about the ninth day. They believe that mares so handled are more likely to conceive than if bred at a later period. Mares suffering from an infection of the genital tract are seldom settled in service; and, even if they do conceive, there is danger of the foal being undersized and poorly developed. Also, the infection may be needlessly spread to the stallion and other mares by allowing such a practice. Mares not bred at this time or not conceiving will come in heat between the 25th and 30th day from foaling.

The usual reasons advanced in favor of rebreeding at the first heat period following foaling are:

1. It gives an added chance to rebreed the mare in an effort to get her in foal.

2. Occasionally a mare will not again show signs of heat during the breeding season.

3. If the mare conceives, she will foal about 20 days earlier the following year. This may be important where an early foal is desired.

Some arguments against rebreeding on the ninth day following foaling are:

1. If only one service is given on the ninth day following foaling, it is estimated that not more than 25 per cent of the mares conceive.

2. During the period extending up to two weeks following foaling, the brood mare is more susceptible to genital infection than during any other period of her life.

3. Older mares that have been raising foals regularly each year may require a longer period of rest between pregnancies.

4. If the chances of conception are not too great, it may be unwise to overwork the stallion deliberately.

It is noteworthy that more and more of the good horsemen of Kentucky prefer not to breed mares on the ninth day following foaling.

PER CENT OF MARES BRED PRODUCING FOALS

Without question, more difficulty is experienced in breeding mares than any other kind of livestock. The percentage of mares bred that actually conceive each year will vary from 40 per cent to a high of 85 per cent, with an average probably running less than 50 percent; and some of this number will fail to produce living foals.

This means that, on the average, two mares are kept a whole year in order to produce one foal. By contrast, nationally, 86 per cent of all beef cows that are bred calve; 90 to 94 per cent of all ewes lamb; and 80 to 85 per cent of all sows bred farrow. The lower percentage conception in mares than in other classes of livestock is due primarily to the following: (1) research in the field has lagged, (2) we try to get mares bred in about 4 months instead of 12, and (3) we have arbitrarily limited our breeding season (late winter and early spring) to a period that at its best is only about 50 per cent in agreement with nature.

In the Bluegrass Region of Kentucky, where there are both good horsemen and as desirable conditions for breeding as can be secured under domestication, 66 per cent foaling is considered as average for the area.

Recognition of the following facts may help to increase the percentage of foals produced:

1. Mares bred in the late spring of the year are more likely to conceive. If mares are bred out of season, spring conditions should be duplicated as nearly as possible.

2. Mares bred as three- and four-year-olds and kept in regular production thereafter are more likely to conceive and produce living foals.

3. Infections or other unhealthy conditions of either the mare or the stallion are not favorable for production.

4. More conceptions will occur if the mare is bred at the proper time within the heat periods. Usually mares bred just before going out of heat are more likely to conceive.

5. Returning the mares to the stallion for retrial or rebreeding is important.

6. Mares in foal should be fed and cared for properly so as to develop the young. Balance of proteins, minerals, and vitamins is important.

7. It must also be remembered that old mares, overfat mares, or mares in a thin, run-down condition are less likely to be good breeders. Unfortunately, these conditions frequently apply to mares that are bred following retirement from the race track or the show ring.

A shift of the date of birth (the January 1 birthday, for purposes of racing and showing) to somewhere between March 1 and May 1 would improve conception rate and foaling percentage, simply because mares would be bred under more natural and ideal spring conditions. Thus, it would have considerable virtue from the standpoint of the horse producer. On the other side of the ledger, however, it would create problems in racing and in registrations, both here and abroad. Also, such a deep-rooted tradition would be difficult to change; in fact, much consideration has been given to this matter from time to time. In the final analysis, therefore, stepping up breeding research is the primary avenue through which the deplorably low percentage foal crop may be improved.

STERILITY OR BARRENNESS IN MARES

Sterility is a condition of infertility. Whatever the cause, there are no cure-alls for the condition. Rather, each individual case requires careful diagnosis and specific treatment for what is wrong. Also, it should be recognized that there are two types of sterility—temporary and permanent—although no sharp line can be drawn between them.

Regardless of the cause of sterility, it is well to give a word of caution against the so-called "opening up" of mares, which is the practice of inserting the hand and arm into the genital organs for the purpose of rearranging the organs in order to insure conception. Few laymen, no matter how expert they may classify themselves, have either sufficient knowledge of the anatomy of the mare or appreciation of the absolutely sterile methods necessary in such procedure to be probing about. Moreover, it is only rarely that the reproductive organs are out of place. Unless the "opening up" is recommended and conducted by a competent veterinarian, it should not be permitted. When performed by an amateur, or even most would-be experts, it is a dangerous practice that is to be condemned.

Temporary Sterility

Some common causes of temporary sterility are:

1. Lack of exercise, irregular work, and overfeeding accompanied by extremely high condition.

2. Overwork, underfeeding, and an extremely thin and run-down condition.

3. Nutritional deficiencies.

4. Infections of various kinds.

5. Some types of physiological imbalance characterized by such things as cystic ovaries or failure to ovulate at the proper time.

Temporary sterility can be reduced by removing the cause and correcting the difficulty, whatever it may be.

Permanent Sterility

Naturally, permanent sterility is much more serious to the horse breeder. Perhaps the most common causes of permanent sterility are:

1. Old age, which is usually accompanied by irregular breeding and eventual total sterility.

2. Infections in the reproductive tract, usually in the cervix, uterus, or fallopian tubes.

3. Some types of physiological imbalances characterized by such things as cystic ovaries or failure to ovulate at the proper time.

4. Closure of the female genital organs.

Sometimes a veterinarian is able to correct the latter two conditions; and on an extremely valuable breeding mare, it may be worth while to obtain such professional service in an effort to bring about conception.

Retained afterbirth or other difficulties encountered in foaling may cause inflammation and infection that will prevent conception as long as the condition exists. There is real danger of spreading the infection if the mare is bred while in such a condition.

FERTILITY OF THE STALLION

Any stallion of breeding age that is purchased should be a guaranteed breeder; this is usually understood among reputable breeders.

The most reliable and obvious indication of potency is a large number of healthy, vigorous foals from a season's service. As an added protection, or in order to follow the horse during the midst of a heavy breeding program, a microscopic examination of the semen may be made by an experienced person. As the stallion dismounts from service, some of the semen is collected in a sterilized funnel by holding the penis over the plugged funnel. A sample of the semen is then strained through sterile gauze, and a small amount is placed on a slide for examination. A great number of active sperm cells is an indication, although not definite assurance, that the stallion is fertile. Some establishments make a regular practice of making such a microscopic examination twice each week during the breeding season. If it is desired to examine a stallion's semen after the breeding season or when a mare is not in season, an artificial vagina may be used. When an entire ejaculate is available for study, the four main criteria of quality are: (1) semen volume, (2) spermatozoan count, (3) progressive movement, and (4) morphology.

If the stallion is a shy breeder or lacks fertility although one is certain that the feed and exercise have been up to standard, masturbation should be suspected.

CONDITIONING THE MARE FOR BREEDING

Proper conditioning of the mare prior to breeding is just as important as in the stallion. Such conditioning depends primarily upon adequate and proper feed and the right amount of exercise.

For the highest rate of conception, mares should neither be too thin nor too fat; a happy medium in condition makes for best results. It is especially important that one avoid the natural tendency of barren or maiden mares to get too fat.

Time permitting, mares of the light-horse breeds may best be exercised and conditioned by riding under the saddle or driving in harness. When these methods are not practical or feasible, permitting a band of mares to run in a large pasture will usually provide a satisfactory amount of exercise.

THE BREEDING OPERATIONS

No phase of horse production has become more unnatural or more complicated with domestication than the actual breeding operations.

Hand Breeding, Corral Breeding, and Pasture Breeding

Hand mating is undoubtedly the best way in which to breed mares; it is the accepted practice in the better breeding establishments throughout the world. It guards against injury to both the stallion and the mare.

Although leaving much to be desired, corral breeding is next best to hand breeding. In this system, after first ascertaining that the mare is in heat, she and the stallion are turned loose together in a small, well-fenced corral. The attendants should remain out of the corral, where they can see but not be seen by the animals, until service is completed, following which the stallion and the mare are returned to their respective quarters.

Pasture breeding simply consists of turning the stallion into a pasture with the band of mares which it is intended that he serve. Except on the ranges of the Far West, this method of breeding is seldom practiced with domestic horses. With valuable animals, both corral and pasture breeding are too likely to cause injury, and the practices should be condemned. In pasture breeding, a stallion will handle fewer mares because of the repeated services of a mare, and he may even become sterile toward the end of the breeding season. Moreover, in pasture breeding, accurate breeding records are impossible.

Examination of the Mare

Before accepting a mare for service, the stallion owner should check every possible condition with care. The stallioner should examine the mare closely and question the owner concerning her health, last foaling date, breeding record, and similar matters. He should be well acquainted with the symptoms of dourine and other venereal diseases. Even though these diseases are not common in this country, there is always danger of finding them in imported stallions and mares.

When mares have been barren over an extended period or when there is the slightest suspicion of infection, it is good protection to require a veterinarian's certificate to the effect that the mare is in a healthy breeding condition.

SIGNS AND TESTS OF PREGNANCY

Some mares will continue to exhibit the characteristic heat symptoms even when in foal. Sometimes in-foal mares will show such pronounced signs of heat that they will be given the service of the stallion. This often results in abortion. Only the horseman knowing individual mares is capable of passing the best judgment on this question.

In order to produce as high a percentage of foals as possible and to have them arrive at the time desired, the good horseman will be familiar with the signs of and tests for pregnancy. This is doubly important when it is recognized that a great many mares may either be shy breeders or show signs of heat even when well advanced in gestation. The signs and tests of pregnancy may be listed as follows:

1. *The cessation of the heat period*—recognizing that this may be hard to determine and even misleading.

2. *The movement of the living fetus.* This movement can be seen or felt through the abdominal walls. It will not be possible, however, to use this test until about the seventh month of gestation. Movement of the fetus is most evident the first thing in the morning. This method is not so certain with young maiden mares, as the foal is carried nearer the backbone.

3. *A rectal examination,* made 40 to 60 days after the last service in which

the uterus is felt through the rectum. This should be done only by an experienced horseman or veterinarian.

4. *The blood serum test,* which may be used on mares any time after 45 to 50 days following breeding and up to three months.[1]

5. *The urine test,* which is used on mares from three months after breeding until termination.

6. *The male toad (Bufo) test,* which may be used in mares that have been bred between 45 and 120 days.[2]

CARE AND MANAGEMENT OF THE STALLION

Although certain general recommendations can be made, it should be remembered that each stallion should be studied as an individual, and his care, feeding, exercise, and handling should be varied accordingly.

Quarters for the Stallion

The most convenient arrangement for the stallion is a roomy box stall which opens directly into a two- or three-acre pasture paddock, preferably separated

Fig. 50-1. Stallion barn at Washington State University, with each box stall opening directly into large pasture paddocks separated by a double fence. (Courtesy, Washington State University)

---

[1] For details pertaining to this biological test for pregnancy, see *Horses and Horsemanship;* a book by the same author and publisher as *Animal Science.*

[2] See footnote 1.

from the other horses by a double fence. A paddock fence made of heavy lumber is safest. The stall door opening into such a paddock may be left open except during extremely cold weather; this will give the stallion plenty of fresh air, sunshine, and additional exercise.

Feeding the Stallion

The feed and water requirements of the stallion are adequately discussed in Chapter LI. In addition to this, it may be well to re-emphasize that, in season, clean, lush pastures produced on fertile soils are excellent for the stallion. Grass is the horse's most natural feed, and it is a rich source of vitamins that are so necessary for vigor and reproduction. Perhaps the ideal arrangement in providing pasture for the stallion is to give him access to a well-sodded paddock.

Exercise for the Stallion

Regular exercise daily for the stallion is important. It is one of the best means of keeping the horse in a thrifty, natural condition and virile.

Stallions of the light-horse breeds are most generally exercised under the saddle or hitched to a cart. Thus, Standardbred stallions are usually jogged three to five miles daily while drawing a cart. Thoroughbred stallions and saddle stock stallions of all other breeds are best exercised under the saddle for from 30 minutes to 1 hour daily, especially during the breeding season.

Exercise should not be hurried or hard; the walk and the trot are the best gaits to use for this purpose. After the stallion is exercised, he should be rubbed down and cooled off before he is put up, especially if he is hot. Better yet, the ride should be so regulated at the end that the horse will be brought in cool, in which case he can be brushed off and turned into his corral.

Frequently, in light horses, bad feet exclude exercise on roads, and faulty tendons exclude exercise under the saddle. Under such condition, one may have to depend upon: (1) exercise taken voluntarily by the stallion in a large paddock, (2) longeing or exercising on a 30- to 40-foot rope, or (3) leading.

Longeing should be limited to a walk and a trot; and, if possible, the stallion should be worked on both hands; that is, made to circle both to the right and to the left. It is also best that this type of exercise be administered within an enclosure. Two precautions in longeing are: (1) Do not longe a horse when the footing is slippery, and (2) do not pull the animal in such manner as to make him pivot too sharply with the hazard of breaking a leg.

Leading is a satisfactory form of exercise for some stallions if it is not practical to ride them. In leading, a bridle should always be used—never a halter—and one should keep away from other horses and be careful that the horse being ridden is not a kicker.

The objection to relying upon paddock exercise alone is that the exercise cannot be regulated, especially during inclement weather. Some animals may take too much exercise and others too little. Moreover, merely running in the paddock will seldom, if ever, properly condition any stallion.

Fig. 50-2. The Thoroughbred stallion Nashua, winner of $1,288,565 and syndicated at $1,251,200, in breeding condition. (Courtesy, Mr. Leslie Combs II, Spendthrift Farm, Lexington, Ky.)

A two- or three-acre grassy paddock should always be provided, even for horses that are regularly exercised. Stallions that are worked should be turned out at night and on idle days. While the pasture paddock is much superior to close confinement and no exercise in a stall, the stallion not being used regularly at useful work will be benefited by any additional forced exercise, even though it does become somewhat monotonous.

Grooming the Stallion

Proper grooming of the stallion is necessary, not only to make the horse more attractive in appearance, but to assist in maintaining the best of health and condition. Grooming serves to keep the functions of the skin active. It should be thorough, with special care taken to keep all parts of the body clean and free from any foulness, but not so rough nor severe as to cause irritation either of the skin or temper.

AGE AND SERVICE OF THE STALLION

It should be remembered that the number and kind of foals that a stallion sires in a given season is more important than the total number of services. The number of services allowed during a season will vary with the age, development, temperament, health, and breeding condition of the animals and the distribution of services. Therefore, no definite best number of services can be recommended for any and all conditions, and yet the practices followed by good horsemen are not far different. All are agreed that excessive service of the stallion may reduce his fertility.

Table 50-1 contains recommendations relative to the number of services for stallions of different ages, with consideration given to age and type of mating.

Because of their more naturally nervous temperaments, stallions of the light-horse breeds are usually more restricted in services than stallions of the draft-horse breeds. Also, there is a difference between breeds.

The most satisfactory arrangement for the well being of the stallion is to allow not more than one service each day. With proper handling, however, the mature, vigorous stallion may with certainty and apparently without harm serve two mares in a single day. During the heavy spring breeding season, this may

TABLE 50—1

HANDY STALLION MATING GUIDE[1]

Age	No. of Matings/yr.		Comments
	Hand-mating	Pasture-mating	
2-year-old......................	10—15	Preferably no pasture-mating	Limit the 2-year-old to 2 to 3 services/week; the 3-year-old to 1 service/day; and the 4-year-old or over to 2 services/day.
3-year-old......................	20—40		
4-year-old......................	30—60		
Mature horse.................	80—100		A stallion should remain a vigorous and reliable breeder up to 20 to 25 years of age.
Over 18 years old...........	20—40		

[1]There are breed differences. Thus, when first entering stud duty, the average three-year-old Thoroughbred should be limited to 20 to 25 mares per season, whereas a Standardbred of the same age may breed 25 to 30 mares; and the four- or five-year-old Thoroughbred should be limited to 30 to 40 mares, whereas a Standardbred of the same age may breed 40 to 50 mares. Mature stallions of the draft breeds may and do breed up to 100 mares in a season.

often be necessary. It is a good plan to allow a stallion to rest at least one day a week. In the program of the U.S. Remount Service, now dissolved, three-year-old stallions were usually limited to 15 mares; and stallions from 4 to 18 inclusive were limited to a book of 40 mares. However, even mature stallions within the latter age group were usually limited to 25 mares when standing their first season.

In order to secure higher conception of the mares and yet avoid overwork of the stallion with an excessive number of natural services, most Thoroughbred breeders now reinforce each natural service with one artificial insemination.

Stallions often remain virile and valuable breeders until 20 to 25 years of age, especially if they have been properly handled. However, it is usually best to limit the number of services on a valuable old sire in order to preserve his usefulness and extend his longevity as long as possible.

Occasionally, Thoroughbred and Standardbred stallions are used to a limited extent before retirement to the stud, although many good horsemen seem to feel that it is not best to use them until it is time for them to be retired. Saddle horses may be bred to a few mares and still be used in the show ring. However, sometimes it makes them more difficult to handle.

It frequently happens that a wonderful horse is injured in the midst of his racing career, and, while awaiting the next racing season, he is bred to a few mares.

If two services a day are planned with the mature stallion, one should be rather early in the morning and the other late in the afternoon. It is also best not to permit teasing or services immediately before or soon after feeding the stallion; for this may result in a digestive disturbance, particularly in the nervous, fretful individuals.

CARE OF THE PREGNANT MARE

Barren and foaling mares are usually kept separately because pregnant mares are sedate; whereas barren mares are more likely to run, tease, and kick. Precautions in handling the pregnant mare will be covered in the discussion that follows.

Quarters for the Mare

If mares are worked under the saddle or in harness, they may be given quarters like those accorded to the rest of the horses used similarly, at least until near parturition time. Idle mares may best be turned to pasture. Even in the winter time, a simple shelter is adequate. In some sections of the country, an open shed is satisfactory.

Feeding the Pregnant Mare

The feed and water requirements for the pregnant mare are adequately discussed in Chapter LI, so repetition is unnecessary.

Exercise for the Pregnant Mare

The pregnant mare should have plenty of exercise. This may be obtained by allowing a band of brood mares to roam over large pastures in which shade, water, and minerals are available. Mares of the light-horse breeds may be exercised for an hour daily under the saddle or hitched to a cart. When handled carefully, the brood mare may be so exercised to within a day or two of foaling. Above all, when not receiving forced exercise or on idle days, she should not be confined to a stable or a small dry lot.

CARE AT FOALING TIME

A breeding record should be kept on each mare so that it will be known when she is due to foal. As has been previously indicated, the period of gestation of a mare is about 336 days, but it may vary as much as a month in either direction. Therefore, the careful and observant horseman will be ever alert and make certain definite preparations in ample time.

The period of parturition is one of the most critical stages in the life of the mare. Through carelessness or ignorance, all of the advantages gained in selecting genetically desirable and healthy parent stock and in providing the very best of environmental and nutritional conditions through gestation can be quickly dissipated at this time. Generally speaking, less difficulty at parturition was encountered in the wild state, when the females of all species brought forth their young in the fields and glens.

Work and Exercise

Saddle or light-harness mares should be exercised moderately in the accustomed manner. If they are not used one or two days prior to foaling, other gentle exercise, such as leading, should be provided. This is especially important if she has not been accustomed to being on pasture and if it is desired to avoid any abrupt changes in feeding at this time.

Signs of Approaching Parturition

Perhaps the first sign of approaching parturition is a distended udder, which may be observed two to six weeks before foaling time. About 7 to 10 days before the arrival, there will generally be a marked shrinking or falling away of the muscular parts of the top of the buttocks near the tailhead and a falling of the abdomen. Although the udder may have filled out previously, the teats seldom fill out to the ends more than four to six days before foaling; and the wax on the ends of the nipples generally is not present until within two to four days before parturition. About this time, the vulva becomes full and loose. As foaling time draws nearer, milk will drop from the teats; and the mare will show restlessness, break into a sweat, urinate frequently, lie down and get up, etc. It should be remembered, however, that there are times when all signs fail and a foal may be dropped when least expected. Therefore, it is well to be prepared as much as 30 days in advance of the expected foaling date.

Preparation for Foaling

When signs of approaching parturition seem to indicate that the foal may be expected within a week or 10 days, arrangements for the place of foaling should be completed. Thus, the mare will become accustomed to the new surroundings before the time arrives.

During the spring, summer, and fall months when the weather is warm, the most natural and ideal place for foaling is a clean, open pasture away from other livestock. Under these conditions, there is decidedly less danger of either infection or mechanical injury to the mare and foal. Of course, in following this practice, it is important that the ground be dry and warm. Small paddocks or lots that are unclean and foul with droppings are unsatisfactory and may cause such infectious troubles as navel-ill.

Fig. 50-3. A mare and her newborn foal on pasture. (Courtesy, National Cottonseed Products Association, Inc.)

During inclement weather, the mare should be placed in a roomy, well-lighted, well-ventilated, comfortable, quiet box stall which should first be carefully cleaned, disinfected, and bedded for the occasion. It is best that the mare be stabled therein at nights a week or 10 days before foaling so that she may become accustomed to the new surroundings. The foaling stall should be at least 12 feet square and free from any low mangers, hayracks, or other obstructions that might cause injury either to the mare or the foal. After the foaling stall has been thoroughly cleaned, it should be disinfected to reduce possible infection. This may be done by scrubbing with boiling-hot lye water, made by using 8 ounces of lye to 20 gallons of water (one-half this strength of solution should be used in scrubbing mangers and grain boxes). The floors should then be sprinkled with air-slaked lime. Plenty of clean, fresh bedding should be provided at all times.

A foaling stall somewhat away from other horses and with a smooth, well-packed clay floor is to be preferred. The clay floor may be slightly more difficult to keep smooth and sanitary than concrete or other such surface materials, but there is less danger to the mare and the newborn foal from slipping and falling; and it is decidely better for the hoofs.

Feed at Foaling Time

Shortly before foaling, it is usually best to decrease the grain allowance slightly and to make more liberal use of light and laxative feeds, especially wheat bran. If there are any signs of constipation, a wet bran mash should be provided.

The Attendant

A good rule for the attendant is to *be near but not in sight*. Some mares seem to resent the presence of an attendant at this time, and they will delay foaling as long as possible under such circumstances. Mares that have foaled previously and which have been properly fed and exercised will usually not experience any difficulty. However, young mares foaling for the first time, old mares, or mares that are either overfat or in a thin, run-down condition may experience considerable difficulty. The presence of the attendant may prevent possible injury to the mare and foal; and, when necessary, he may aid the mare or call a competent veterinarian.

Parturition

The immediate indications that the mare is about to foal are extreme nervousness and uneasiness, lying down and getting up, biting of the sides and flanks, switching of the tail, sweating in the flanks, and frequent urination.

The first actual indication of foaling is the rupture of the outer fetal membrane, followed by the escape of a large amount of fluid. This is commonly referred to as the rupture of the water bag. The inner membrane surrounding the foal appears next, and labor then becomes more marked.

With normal presentation, a mare foals rapidly, usually not taking more than 15 to 30 minutes. Usually, when the labor pains are at their height, the mare will be down; and it is in this position that the foal is generally born, while the mare is lying on her side with all legs stretched out.

In normal presentation, the front feet, with heels down, come first, followed by the nose which is resting on them, then the shoulders, the middle (with the back up), the hips, and then the hind legs and feet. If the presentation is other than normal, a veterinarian should be summoned at once, for there is great danger that the foal will smother if its birth is delayed. If the feet are presented with the bottoms up, it is a good indication that they are the hind ones, and there is likely to be difficulty.

If, after reasonable time and effort have been expended, a mare appears to be making no progress in parturition, it is advisable that an examination be made and assistance be rendered before the animal has completely exhausted her strength in futile efforts at expulsion. In rendering any such assistance, the following cardinal features should exist:

1. Cleanliness.
2. Quietness.
3. Gentleness.
4. Perseverance.
5. Knowledge, skill, and experience.

When parturition is unduly delayed or retarded, the fetus often dies from twists or knots in the umbilical cord, or from remaining too long in the passage. In either case, there may be stoppage of fetal circulation or lack of oxygen for the fetus, or both.

If foaling has been normal, the attendant should enter the stable to make certain that the foal is breathing and that the membrane has been removed from its mouth and nostrils. If the foal fails to breathe immediately, artificial respiration should be applied. This may be done by blowing into the mouth of the foal, working the ribs, rubbing the body vigorously and permitting the foal to fall around. Then after the navel has been treated, the mare and foal should be left to lie and rest quietly as long as possible so that they may gain strength.

The Afterbirth

If the afterbirth is not expelled as soon as the mare gets up, it should either be tied up in a knot or tied to the tail of the mare. This should be done so that the foal or mare will not step on the afterbirth and thereby increase the danger of inflammation of the uterus and foal founder in the mare. Usually the afterbirth will be expelled within one to six hours after foaling.

If it is retained for a longer period or if lameness is evident, the mare should be blanketed, and an experienced veterinarian should be called. Retained afterbirth often causes laminitis, which is recognized by lameness in the mare. This is usually treated by feeding easily digested feed for a period of 36 hours and by applying cold applications to the mare's feet until the condition is relieved.

To prevent development of bacteria and foul odors, the afterbirth should be removed from the stall and burned or buried in lime as soon as possible.

Cleaning the Stall

Once the foal and mare are up, the stall should be cleaned. Wet, stained, or soiled bedding should be removed. The floor should be sprinkled with lime; and clean, fresh bedding should be provided. Such sanitary measures will be of great help in preventing the most common type of joint-ill.

If the weather is extremely cold and the mare hot and sweaty, she should be rubbed down, dried, and blanketed soon after getting on her feet.

Feed and Water After Foaling

Following foaling, the mare usually is somewhat hot and feverish. She should be given small quantities of lukewarm water at intervals but should never be allowed to gorge. It is also well to feed lightly and with laxative feeds for the first few days. The very first feed might well be a wet bran mash with a few oats or a little oatmeal soaked in warm water. About one-half the usual amount should be fed. Usually, for the first week, no better grain ration can be provided than bran and oats. The quantity of feed given should be governed by the milk flow, the demands of the foal, and the appetite and condition of the mare. Usually the mare can be back on full feed within a week or 10 days after foaling.

Be Observant

The good horseman will be ever alert to discover difficulties before it is too late. If the mare has much temperature (normal for the horse is about 100.5° F.) something is wrong, and the veterinarian should be called. As a precautionary measure, many good horsemen take the mare's temperature a day or two after foaling. Any discharge from the vulva should also be regarded with suspicion.

Handling the Newborn Foal

Immediately after the foal has arrived and breathing has started, it should be thoroughly rubbed and dried with warm towels. Then it should be placed in one corner of the stall on clean, fresh straw. Usually the mare will be less restless if this corner is in the direction of her head. The eyes of a newborn foal should be protected from a bright light.

THE NAVEL CORD

At the time the umbilical cord is ruptured, there is a direct communication from without to some of the vital organs and the blood of the foal. Usually this opening is soon closed by the ensuing swelling and final drying and sloughing-off process. Under natural conditions, in the wild state, there was little danger of navel infection, but domestication and foaling under confined conditions have changed all this.

To reduce the danger of navel infection (which causes a disease known as joint-ill or navel-ill) the navel cord of the newborn foal should be treated at once with tincture of iodine (metaphin or methiolate may be used). This may be done by placing the end of the cord in a widemouthed bottle nearly full of tincture of iodine while pressing the bottle firmly against the abdomen. This, of course, is best done with a foal lying down. The cord should then be dusted with a good antiseptic powder. Dusting with the powder should be continued daily until the stump dries up and drops off and the scar heals, usually in three or four days. If an antiseptic powder is not available, air-slaked lime may be used. Any foreign matter that accumulates on the navel should be pressed out, and a disinfectant should be applied.

If left alone, the navel cord of the newborn foal usually breaks within 2 to 4 inches from the belly. Under such conditions, no cutting is necessary. However, if it does not break it should be severed about 2 inches from the belly with clean, dull shears, or it may be scraped in two with a knife. Never cut diagonally across. A torn or broken blood vessel will bleed very little; whereas, one that is cut directly across may bleed excessively. If severing of the cord is resorted to, it should be immediately treated with iodine.

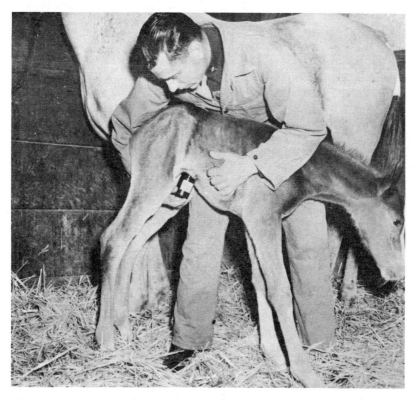

Fig. 50-4. Treating the navel cord of the newborn foal with iodine. (Courtesy, Col. F. W. Koester)

NAVEL INFECTION (JOINT-ILL OR NAVEL-ILL)

Although most newborn foal infections are referred to as navel infection—implying that the infection is postnatal, with entrance to the body gained through the umbilical cord after birth—many such troubles are of prenatal origin. In the latter type, infection of the foal takes place in the uterus (womb) of the

Fig. 50-5. Foal with navel infection (joint-ill or navel-ill). The disease is fatal in about 50 per cent of the cases. Also, a large proportion of the animals that survive are left with deformed joints like the foal shown above. (Courtesy, College of Veterinary Medicine, University of Illinois)

dam before the foal is born. The infection may either be present in the dam before she is bred, or it may be introduced by the stallion, if he is infected or if he has previously bred other infected mares. If prenatal infection does not result in abortion and the mare carries the fetus the normal term, the foal is often born weak or develops navel-ill within a few days and dies; or if it does not die, it becomes a hopeless cripple that must be destroyed.

Under unsanitary conditions, there is also great danger from germs that may enter the blood stream through the opening of the navel cord prior to the time that it has dried up and the scar has healed over. When weather conditions permit foaling on a clean pasture in the fresh air and sunshine, danger of such infection is held to a minimum. On the other hand, foaling in a filthy paddock or stall and with no precautions taken is very likely to result in infection and navel-ill. For this reason, when it is necessary to have mares foal in the stall, every precaution should be taken. The stall should be thoroughly cleaned, disinfected, and bedded; and the navel should be treated with iodine immediately after the foal arrives and then dusted with a good antiseptic powder several times daily.

Navel infection (joint-ill or navel-ill) may be recognized by a loss of appetite, soreness and stiffness in the joints, and a general listlessness of the foal. If this is recognized in the early stages and a veterinarian is called at once, the infected foal may be treated and may recover. If, however, the disease has reached the pus-forming stage, very likely it will be fatal. Blood tranfusions from the dam to foal have been given in all types of foal infections, usually with good results. With certain specific types of infections, antibiotics, sulfanilamide, serums, or bacterins may be used successfully; but these should always be administered by a veterinarian. Prevention is decidedly the best protection.

In summary, it may be stated that the practice of sanitation and hygiene, starting with the stallion and brood mare at the time of mating and continuing with the brood mare and young foal at foaling time, usually prevents the most common type of joint-ill. In certain areas, particularly those known to be goiterous or semi-goiterous, such as the Pacific Northwest, the feeding of stabilized iodized salt to in-foal mares has seemed to reduce losses from joint-ill.

THE COLOSTRUM

The colostrum is the milk that is secreted by the dam for the first few days following parturition. It differs from ordinary milk in the following aspects:

1. It is more concentrated.
2. It is higher in protein content, especially globulins.
3. It is richer in vitamin A.
4. It contains more antibodies.
5. It has a more stimulating effect on the alimentary tract.

Because of these many beneficial qualities of colostrum, the horseman should make very certain that the newborn foal secures this first milk.

The strong, healthy foal will usually be up on its feet and ready to nurse within 30 minutes to 2 hours after birth. Occasionally, however, a big awkward foal will need a little assistance and guidance during its first time to nurse. The stubborn foal should be coaxed to the mare's teats (forcing is useless). This may be done by backing the mare up on additional bedding in one corner of the stall and coaxing the foal with a bottle and nipple. The attendant may hold the bottle while standing on the opposite side of the mare from the foal. The very weak foal should be given the mare's first milk even if it must be drawn in a bottle and fed by nipple for a time or two. Sometimes these weak individuals will nurse the mare if steadied by the attendant.

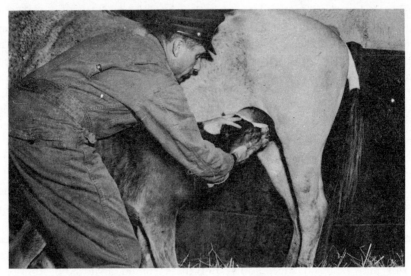

Fig. 50-6. Assisting newborn foal to nurse. (Courtesy, Col. F. W. Koester, General Manager, Calif. Thoroughbred Breeders Assn., Arcadia, Calif.)

Aside from the difference in chemical composition, the colostrum (the milk yielded by the mother for a short period following the birth of the young) seems to have the following functions:

1. It contains anti-bodies that temporarily protect the foal against certain infections, especially those of the digestive tract.

2. It serves as a natural purgative, removing fecal matter that has accumulated in the digestive tract.

This, therefore, explains why mares should not be milked out prior to foaling and why colostrum is important to the newborn foal.

Before allowing the foal to nurse for the first time, it is usually good practice to wash the mare's udder with a mild disinfectant and to rinse it with clean, warm water.

BOWEL MOVEMENT OF THE FOAL

The regulation of the bowel movement in the foal is very important. Two common abnormalities are constipation and diarrhea or scours.

Impaction in the bowels of the excrement accumulated during the development prior to birth—material called meconium—may prove fatal if not handled promptly. Usually a good feed of colostrum will cause elimination, but not always—especially when foals are from stall-fed mares.

Bowel movement of the foal should be observed within 4 to 12 hours after birth. If by this time there has been no discharge and the foal seems rather sluggish and fails to nurse, it should be given an enema. This may be made by using one to two quarts of water at blood heat, to which a little glycerin has been added; or warm soapy water is quite satisfactory. The solution may be injected with a baby syringe (one having about a 3-inch nipple) or a tube and can. This treatment may be repeated as often as necessary until the normal yellow feces appear.

If the foal is scouring, the ration of the mare should be reduced, and a part of her milk should be taken away by milking her out at intervals.

Diarrhea or scours in foals may be associated with infectious diseases or may be caused by unclean surroundings. Any of the following conditions may bring on diarrhea: contaminated udder or teats; nonremoval of fecal matter from the digestive tract; fretfulness or temperature above normal in the mare; an excess of feed affecting the quality of the mare's milk; cold, damp bed; or continued exposure to cold rains. As treatment is not always successful, the best practice is to avoid the undesirable conditions.

Diarrhea is caused by an irritant in the digestive tract that should be removed if recovery is to be expected. Only in exceptional cases should an astringent be given with the idea of checking the diarrhea; and such treatment should be prescribed by the veterinarian.

RAISING THE ORPHAN FOAL

Occasionally a mare dies during or immediately after parturition, leaving an orphan foal to be raised. Also, there are times when mares fail to give a sufficient quantity of milk for the newborn foal. Sometimes there are twins. In such cases, it is necessary to resort to other milk supplies. The problem will be simplified if the foal has at least received the colostrum from the dam, for it does play a very important part in the well being of the newborn young.

If at all possible, the foal should be shifted to another mare. Some breeding establishments regularly follow the plan of breeding a mare that is a good milk producer but whose foal is expected to be of little value. Her own foal is either destroyed or raised on a bottle, and the mare is used as a foster mother or nurse mare.

The larger nurseries usually keep a supply of colostrum on hand. They remove colostrum from mares that (1) have had dead foals or (2) produce excess milk, then store it in a freezer for future use for foals that do not receive colostrum from their dams. When needed, it can be removed from the freezer, heated, and fed. This is an excellent practice.

If no colostrum is available, the foal should be placed on either (1) cow's milk made as nearly as possible of the same composition of mare's milk, or (2) a synthetic milk replacer.

A comparison of cow's milk and mare's milk is given in Table 50-2.

As can be observed, mare's milk is higher in percentage of water and sugar than cow's milk and is lower in other components.

For best results in raising the orphan foal, milk from a fresh cow, low in butterfat, should be used. To about a pint of milk, add a tablespoon of sugar and from 3 to 5 tablespoonsful of lime water. Warm to body temperature and for the first few days feed about ¼ pint every hour. After three or four weeks the sugar can be stopped, and at five or six weeks skimmed milk can be used entirely.

TABLE 50—2

COMPOSITION OF MILK FROM COWS AND MARES[1]

Source	Water (%)	Protein (%)	Fat (%)	Sugar (%)	Ash (%)
Cow	87.18	3.55	3.69	4.88	0.75
Mare	90.78	1.99	1.21	5.67	0.35

[1]USDA, Farmers' Bulletin No. 803.

Orphan foals may also be raised on milk replacer, fed according to the directions of the manufacturer. Here again the situation is simplified if the foal has first received colostrum.

For the first few days, the milk (either cow's milk or milk replacer) may be fed by using a bottle and a rubber nipple. The foal then should be taught to drink from a pail. It is important that all receptacles be kept absolutely clean and sanitary (clean and scald each time) and that feeding be at regular intervals. Grain feeding should be started at the earliest possible time with the orphan foal.

NORMAL BREEDING SEASON AND THE TIME OF FOALING

The most natural breeding season for the mare is in the spring of the year. Usually mares are gaining flesh at this time; the heat period is more evident; and they are more likely to conceive. Furthermore, the springborn foal may be dropped on pasture—with less danger of infection and with an abundance of exercise, fresh air, and sunshine to aid in his development. Also there will be good, green, succulent pasture for the mare. Such conditions are ideal.

However, when the demands for using the mares are such that spring foaling interferes and fall or perhaps late-winter foals are desired, plans may be changed accordingly. Under such circumstances, spring conditions should be duplicated at the breeding season. That is, the mare should be fed to gain in flesh and, if necessary, should be blanketed for comfort.

Also, it must be remembered that the showman will want to give consideration to having the foals dropped at such time that they may be exhibited to the best advantage. The same applies to the person who desires to sell well-developed yearlings of the light-horse breeds or to race two-year-olds. It is noteworthy, however, that the percentage of barren mares that conceive at an early breeding is markedly lower than is obtained later in the season. Nevertheless, some mares do conceive early in the year, and even a small percentage is advantageous to some breeders.

HOW TO LOWER THE COST OF RAISING HORSES

Some management principles that should receive consideration in lowering the cost of raising horses are:

1. Attain higher fertility in both mares and stallions; secure a higher per cent foal crop. With a 50 per cent foal crop, two mares are kept a whole year to raise one foal.

2. Eliminate unnecessary concoctions, including drugs, vitamins, and minerals if they are not needed.

3. Begin using horses moderately at two years of age, at which time their use should more than compensate for the feed cost.

4. Keep all horses of usable age earning their way. Animals that are not necessary or that do not increase in value at a profitable rate are a needless expense.

5. Utilize pastures to the maximum. Such a practice will supply nutritious feeds at a low cost, save time in feeding, reduce man labor in caring for the horses, and do away with bedding the stalls and cleaning the barn.

Fig. 50-7. Thoroughbred mares and foals on pasture. The cost of raising horses can be materially lessened by utilizing pastures to the maximum. (Courtesy, The Thoroughbred of California)

6. Utilize the less salable roughage as much as possible, particularly during the second and third years.

7. Do not construct or maintain costly quarters for the young, growing horse.

8. Keep animals free from parasites, both internal and external. Feeding parasites is always too costly.

9. Provide balanced ration, including a balance of proteins, necessary minerals, and vitamins. Plenty of good, clean water should be available at all times.

BUYING HORSES OR RAISING FOALS

Where horses are needed, either they must be purchased or foals must be raised. The primary factors to consider in determining whether horses will be

Fig. 50-8. Yearling Thoroughbred colt being sold at public auction at Keeneland Race Course under the auspices of the Breeders' Sales Company, Lexington, Ky.

Shown is a bay colt by Bimelech out of Durazna, consigned by Mr. Leslie Combs II, Spendthrift Farm, Lexington, Ky., and sold for $40,000. (Courtesy, Breeders' Sales Company, Lexington, Kentucky)

bought or foals raised are: (1) the experience of the individual, (2) comparative cost, and (3) risks surrounding the introduction of horses.

Experience of the Horseman

Certainly it must be recognized that the man who would attempt to raise replacements must have more knowledge of horse production than the person buying mature horses. In addition to knowing the regular care and management aspects of horse production, the man who raises his replacements must be somewhat familiar with the breeding of horses and the rearing of foals.

Comparative Cost

In determining whether horses will be bought or foals raised, the comparative cost of the two methods should be computed. In arriving at such comparative cost figures, the following factors should be remembered:

1. Such figures should be on the basis of animals of equal merit and usefulness for the purpose desired. Consideration should also be given to age and future depreciation.

2. Computing the purchase price on horses should be on the basis of price delivered to the farm. Commission, freight or trucking, and insurance charges should not be overlooked.

3. In computing the cost of raising a foal to usable age, feed price should be figured on the basis of farm values rather than on actual grain market values. Also consideration should be given to the fact that cheap and somewhat unsalable roughages may often be used. Further, such items as service fees, manure produced, and handling charges should be considered.

Risks Surrounding the Introduction of Horses

After giving full consideration to the experience of the horseman and the comparative cost of the two methods, there are still some rather perplexing problems encountered in introducing horses. These difficulties may be summarized as follows:

1. **Misrepresentations.**—The inexperienced man, especially, is likely to encounter misrepresentations as to age, soundness, vices, and the training and usefulness of the horse.

2. **Diseases.**—In moving a horse, there is always a possible exposure to the many ills. Sometimes these are of sufficiently serious nature as to make the use of the animal impossible at a time when it is most needed; occasionally, they even prove fatal. Also, it must be remembered that such diseases as are contracted very likely may spread to the other horses on the farm and even to those in the community, thus exposing them to the same risk.

3. **Acclimating.**—Horses coming from a distance usually need time to become acclimated before being most useful.

4. **Condition.**—In all too many instances, horses brought in for sale and speculative purposes have been made fat for the occasion. Usually such liberal feeding has been made even more harmful through accompanying lack of work and confinement to a stall. Such horses are soft and require a period of gradual fitting for work. Also, it must be remembered that fat will cover up a multitude of defects.

REGISTRATION OF FOALS PRODUCED THROUGH ARTIFICIAL INSEMINATION

Ironically enough, although artificial insemination was first practiced in horses, many American horse registry associations now frown upon the practice. Moreover, there is little unanimity of opinion among them so far as their rules and regulations apply to the practice. By breeds, their rules and attitudes are given in Table 50-3.

STALLION ENROLLMENT LAWS

At one time, 22 states had stallion enrollment laws, enacted to bring about the improvement of horses and mules through the control of the public service stallions and jacks. With the decline in horse and mule numbers, some states repealed these laws; others have been lax in enforcing them. Also, the National Stallion Board was legally liquidated several years ago.

TABLE 50—3

HORSE ASSOCIATION RULES RELATIVE TO REGISTERING
YOUNG PRODUCED ARTIFICIALLY

Breed	Pertinent Rules or Attitudes
Light Horses:	
American Albino Horse	Will accept.
American Gotland Horse	No provisions.
American Saddle Horse	Will accept if A. I. is on premises where stallion is standing.
Appaloosa	Must be accompanied by natural service.
Arabian	Not eligible.
Half-Arabian Anglo-Arabian	Not eligible.
Cleveland Bay	Accepted provided adequate evidence is furnished.
Hackney	Not eligible.
Missouri Fox Trotting Horse	No rules at present, but Association is favorable.
Morgan	Not eligible.
Palomino	Accepted.
Quarter Horse	Limited to (1) use on the owner's ranch and (2) fresh (non-frozen) semen.
Spanish Mustang	Accepted.
Standardbred	Accepted provided semen is not transported off the premises where it is produced.
Tennessee Walking Horse	Not eligible.
Thoroughbred	Not eligible for registry unless begotten by natural service, although it is permissible to reinforce at once the natural service by A. I.
Ponies:	
Pony of the Americas	Artificial insemination may be done on the farm, but semen cannot be mailed.
Shetland Pony	Accepted if breeder owns both mare and stallion.
Welsh Pony	Not eligible.
Draft Horses:	
American Cream Horse	No rules on the registry of foals produced artificially.
Belgian	Eligible if stallion and mare were on the same farm at the time the semen was taken and mare impregnated.
Clydesdale	No rules on A. I.
Percheron	Eligible if stallion and mare were on the same farm at time semen was taken and mare impregnated.
Shire	Accepted.
Suffolk	Accepted.
Jacks and Jennets:	Eligible for registration. No stipulations.

The first stallion law was passed by the legislature of Wisconsin in 1906. In 1907, Minnesota and Iowa enacted similar laws. Other states soon followed suit. Although the laws vary considerably among states, all had similar objectives. They were designed to accomplish one or more of the following things:

1. To prevent false representation as to breeding.
2. To bar heritably unsound and diseased horses.
3. To label unsound horses and jacks.
4. To eliminate the inferior sire, whether he be scrub, grade, or purebred.

At the time these stallion laws were enacted, there was much controversy among horse breeders concerning the heritability of certain unsoundnesses and diseases; consequently, many were listed that now are not considered transmissible from parent to offspring. Even now, there is no unanimity of opinion relative to the inheritance of certain unsoundnesses, and new information is constantly revising past thinking.

The majority of stallion enrollment laws bar from public service stallions that are affected with any of the following unsoundnesses or diseases: bone spavin, ringbone, sidebone, heaves, stringhalt, roaring, blindness, glanders (farcy), dourine, and urethral gleet.

Most horsemen agree that much improvement in the horse population came about through stallion legislation, but that the time has come when existing laws should be either modified or repealed. If the laws are amended, consideration should be given to incorporating the following provisions:

1. Include privately used stallions as well as those stood for public service.
2. License only purebred registered stallions of approved type.
3. Revise the list of hereditary unsoundnesses and transmissible diseases, and license only stallions that are free from these afflictions.
4. Scrutinize the qualifications of the veterinarians who inspect the stallions.
5. Classify stallions relative to: (1) conformation, (2) performance (track record, show record, etc.), (3) breeding, and (4) progeny performance (the record of the get).
6. "Put teeth into the law" by providing for enforceable penalties for violations.
7. Provide simple lien laws for protection of the stallion owner.

HYBRIDS WITH THE HORSE AS ONE PARENT

The mule, representing a cross between the jack (male of the ass family) and the mare (female of the horse family) is the best known hybrid in the United States. The resulting offspring of the reciprocal cross of the stallion mated to a jennet is known as the hinny.

Rarely have mules proved fertile; only five authentic cases of mare mules producing foals have been reported in the United States. This infertility of the mule is probably due to the fact that the chromosomes will not pair and divide equally in the reduction division.

Fig. 50-9. It has been said that the mule has no pride of ancestry and no hope of posterity, but "Old Beck"—a bay "cotton-type" mule owned by Texas A & M University—was an exception. Shown above is Old Beck and her second living foal, a "horse-like" offspring sired by a stallion and foaled 9/26/23. The colt was fertile and sired a number of living foals. (Courtesy, Texas A & M University)

The offspring of fertile mules are generally horse-like in appearance,[3] showing none of the characteristics of the mule's sire (or ass). For the most part, therefore, the eggs (ova) which produce them do not carry chromosomes from the ass; they are pure horse eggs without any inheritance from their maternal grandfathers. This indicates that in the production of eggs in mare mules the reduction division is such that all of the horse chromosomes go to the egg and none to the polar bodies.

The zebroid, a zebra X horse hybrid, is rather popular in certain areas of the tropics because of its docility and resistance to disease and heat.

LETHALS IN HORSES

The term lethal refers to a genetic factor that causes death of the young, either during prenatal life or at birth. Lethals which have been reported in horses include the following: abnormal sex ratio, atresia coli, lethal white, and stiff forelegs. Breeding animals carrying these or other lethal factors should be culled.

------

[3] Not all are horse-like, however. Thus, one of Old Beck's (fertile mule owned by Texas A & M University) three offspring were mule-like in appearance.

PERFORMANCE TESTING HORSES

The breeders of race horses have always followed a program of mating animals of proved performance on the track. For example, it is interesting to note that the first breed register which appeared in 1791—known as "An Introduction to the General Stud Book,"—recorded the pedigrees of all the Thoroughbred horses winning important races. In a similar way, the Standardbred horse—which is an American creation—takes its name from the fact that, in its early history, animals were required to trot a mile in 2 minutes and 30 seconds, or to pace a mile in 2 minutes and 25 seconds, before they could be considered as eligible for registry. The chief aim, therefore, of the early-day breeders of race horses was to record the pedigree of outstanding performers rather than all members of the breed.

The simplest type of progeny testing in horses consists of the average record of merit of an individual stallion's or mare's offspring. Thus, the offspring of Thoroughbred or Standardbred animals bred for racing may be tested by timing on the track. Less satisfactory tests for saddle horses and harness horses have been devised. However, it is conceivable that actual exhibiting on the tanbark in the great horse shows of the country may be an acceptable criterion for saddle and harness-bred animals. Also, the dynamometer might conceivably be used for testing animals of draft-horse breeding, although it has not been so used in the past.

QUESTIONS FOR STUDY AND DISCUSSION

1. How do you account for the fact that less applied knowledge of genetics is available in the equine field than with other classes of livestock?
2. Since black is dominant to chestnut, show what happens when a pure black stallion is crossed on a chestnut mare. Then project the progeny of this cross into the F_2 generation.
3. Explain how sex is determined in horses.
4. Why is closebreeding rarely practiced among present-day horsemen (especially breeders of race horses), though it was common in the foundation animals of most breeds?
5. What management techniques at breeding and parturition time are unique to horses and are not applied to cattle, sheep, and hog breeding?
6. List the things that may be done to increase the percentage of foals produced.
7. List the signs and tests of pregnancy of mares.
8. How can you explain the facts (a) that rarely have mules proved fertile and (b) that the offspring of mules are generally horse-like in appearance?
9. How would you go about performance testing the breed of horses of your choice? List and discuss each step.

SELECTED REFERENCES

In addition to the selected references listed in Chapter II, the following are recommended for Chapter L:

Title of Publication	Author(s)	Publisher
Arabian Horse Breeding	H. H. Reese	Borden Publishing Company, Los Angeles, Calif., 1953.

Titles of Publication	Author(s)	Publisher
Breeding Thorough-breds	Col. J. F. Wall	Charles Scribner's Sons, New York, N. Y., 1946.
Horse, The	D. J. Kays	Rinehart & Company, New York, N. Y., 1953.
Horse Science Handbooks	M. E. Ensminger (editor)	Agriservices Foundation, 3699 E. Sierra Ave., Clovis, Calif.
Horseman's Handbook on Practical Breeding, A	Col. J. F. Wall	Washington Planograph Company, Inc., Washington, D.C., 1950.
Light Horses	M. E. Ensminger	Farmers' Bul. No. 2127, U.S. Department of Agriculture, Washington, D.C.
Practical Light Horse Breeding	J. F. Wall	Monumental Printing Company, Baltimore, Md., 1936.
Robert Bakewell: Pioneer Livestock Breeder	H. C. Ramson	Crosby Lockwood & Son, Ltd., 26 Old Brompton Road, London, S.W. 7, England.
Stud Managers' Handbooks	M. E. Ensminger (editor)	Agriservices Foundation, 3699 E. Sierra Ave., Clovis, Calif.
Study on the Breeding and Racing of Thoroughbred Horses Given Large Doses of Alpha Tocopherol, A	F. G. Darlington J. B. Chassels, D.V.M.	Reprint from The Summary, Vol. 8, No. 1, Feb., 1956 (London, Canada).
Veterinary Notebook	W. R. McGee, D.V.M.	The Blood Horse, Lexington, Ky., 1958.
Veterinary Notes for the Standardbred Breeder	W. R. McGee, D.V.M.	The United States Trotting Association, 1349 East Broad Street, Columbus, Ohio.
Your Shetland Pony	J. M. Kays	The American Shetland Pony Club, Lafayette, Ind.

Chapter LI

FEEDING HORSES

Contents   **Page**

Specific Nutritive Needs of Horses..1190
  Protein Needs 1191
  Energy Needs 1191
  Mineral Needs 1192
    Salt 1192
    Iodine 1193
    Calcium and Phosphorus...1193
    Other Minerals 1193
  Vitamin Needs..1194
    Vitamin A 1195
    Vitamin D 1195
    Vitamin E 1195
    B Vitamins..1196
  Water Needs...1196
Horse Feeds and Their Preparation..1197
  Pasture for the Horse..1197
  Hay for the Horse...1198
  Commercial Horse Feeds..1199
  Processing Grains 1199
  Pelleting 1200
Amount to Feed..1201
A Feed for Every Need...1202
  Feeding the Brood Mare..1203
  Feeding the Stallion..1204
  Feeding the Young Horse..1205
    Feeding Foals Before Weaning..1205
    The Weanling 1206
    The Yearling 1207
    The Two- and Three-year-old...1207
  Fitting for Show or Sale..1207
  Feeding Race and Show Horses...1208
Some Suggested Rations...1210
Questions for Study and Discussion...1213
Selected References 1213

Feed is the most important influence in the environment of the horse. Unless they are fed properly, their maximum potential in reproduction, growth, body form, speed, endurance, style, and attractiveness cannot be achieved.

The following conditions make it imperative that the nutrition of horses be the best that science and technology can devise:

1. **Confinement.**—Many horses are kept in stables or corrals.

2. **Fitting yearlings.**—When forcing young equines, it is important to their development and soundness that the ration be nutritionally balanced.

3. **Racing two-year-olds.**—In the United States, we race more two-year-olds than any other nation in the world; our richest races are for them. If the nutrient content of the ration is not adequate, there is bound to be more breakdown on the track—this is costly.

4. **Stress.**—Stress is affected by excitement, temperament, fatigue, number of horses together, previous nutrition, breed, age, and management. Race and show horses are always under stress; and the more tired they are and the greater the speed, the greater the stress. Thus, the ration for race and show horses should be scientifically formulated, rather than based on fads, foibles, and trade secrets. The greater the stress the more exacting the nutritive requirements.

5. **Horses are unique.**—They differ from other farm animals from the standpoint of use and should not be fed the same feeds. They have greater value; are kept for recreation, sport, and work; are fed for a longer life of usefulness; have a smaller digestive tract; should not carry surplus weight; and are fed for nerve, mettle, animation, and character of muscle.

Relative Capacities of Digestive Tracts

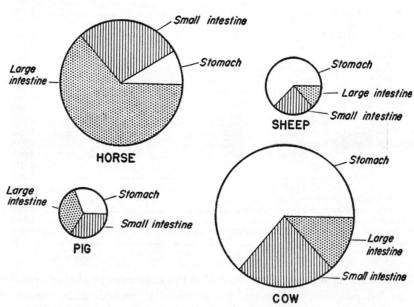

Fig. 51-1. Diagram showing comparative capacities of digestive tracts of different classes of farm animals. Note that the horse has a relatively small stomach. (Drawing by R. F. Johnson)

SPECIFIC NUTRITIVE NEEDS OF HORSES

The proper nutrition of horses is a major factor in determining their efficiency and years of service.

The various nutritive needs of the horse will be discussed under the following headings: (1) protein needs, (2) energy needs, (3) mineral needs, (4) vitamin needs, and (5) water needs.

Protein Needs

Horses of all ages and kinds require adequate amounts of protein of suitable quality for maintenance, growth, finishing, reproduction, and work. Of course, the protein requirements for growth and reproduction are the greatest and most critical.

A deficiency of proteins in the horse may result in the following deficiency symptoms: depressed appetite, poor growth, loss of weight, reduced milk production, irregular estrus, lowered foal crops, loss of condition, and lack of stamina.

Since the vast majority of protein requirements given in feeding standards meet minimum needs only, the allowances for race, show, breeding, and young animals should be higher.

In the case of ruminants (cattle and sheep), there is tremendous bacterial action in the paunch. These bacteria build body proteins of high quality from sources of inorganic nitrogen that nonruminants (humans, rats, chickens, swine, poultry, and dogs) cannot. Farther on in the digestive tract, the ruminant digests the bacteria and obtains good proteins therefrom. Although the horse is not a ruminant, apparently the same bacterial process occurs to a more limited extent in the cecum (caecum), that greatly enlarged blind pouch of the large intestine of the horse. However, it is much more limited than in ruminants, and the cecum is located beyond the small intestine, the main area for digestion and absorption of nutrients. This points up the fallacy of relying on cecum synthesis in the horse; above all, it must be remembered that little cecum synthesis exists in young equines.

In recognition of the more limited bacterial action in the horse, most state laws forbid the use of such non-protein nitrogen sources as urea in horse rations. For such an animal, high quality proteins in the diet are requisite to normal development.

The limited protein synthesis in the horse (limited when compared with ruminants) and the lack of efficiency of absorption due to the cecum being on the lower end of the gut (thereby not giving the small intestine a chance at the ingesta after it leaves the cecum), clearly indicate that horse rations should contain high quality proteins, adequate in amino acids. This is especially important for young equines, because cecum synthesis is very limited early in life. In practical horse feeding, foals should be provided with some protein feeds of animal origin in order to supplement the protein found in grains and forages. In feeding mature horses, a safe plan to follow is to provide plant protein from several sources.

Grass hays and farm grains are low in quality and quantity proteins. Hence, they should be supplemented with other sources of protein.

Energy Needs

The energy needs of horses vary with the individuality and size of animals and the kind, amount, and severity of work performed. In racing, horses may use up to 100 times the energy utilized at rest.

A lack of energy may cause slow and stunted growth in foals and loss of weight, poor condition, and excessive fatigue in mature horses.

It is common knowledge that a ration must contain proteins, fats, and carbohydrates. Although each of these has specific functions in maintaining a normal body, they can all be used to provide energy for maintenance, for work, or for finishing. From the standpoint of supplying the normal energy needs of horses, however, the carbohydrates are by far the most important, more of them being consumed than any other compound, whereas the fats are next in importance for energy purposes. Carbohydrates are usually more abundant and cheaper, and they are very easily digested, absorbed, and transformed into body fat. Also, carbohydrate feeds may be more easily stored in warm weather and for longer periods of time. Feeds high in fat content are likely to become rancid, and rancid feed is unpalatable, if not actually injurious in some instances. Also, fats are utilized very poorly by horses.

Generally, increased energy for horses is met by increasing the grain and decreasing the roughage.

The fiber of growing pasture grass, fresh or dried, is more digestible than the fiber of most hay. Likewise, the fiber of early cut hay is more digestible than that of hay cut in the late-bloom or seed stages. The difference is due to both chemical and physical structure, especially in the presence of certain encrusting substances (notably lignin) which are deposited in the cell wall with age. This is understandable when it is recognized that lignin is the principal constituent of wood; for no one would think of feeding wood to horses.

Young equines and working (or running) horses must have rations in which a large part of the carbohydrate content of the ration is low in fiber, and in the form of nitrogen-free extract.

Mineral Needs[1]

When we think of minerals for the horse, we instinctively think of bones.

A horse's skeleton is large and heavy, weighing 100 pounds or more in a full grown horse, of which more than half consists of inorganic matter or minerals.

The proper development of the bone is particularly important in the horse, as evidenced by the stress and strain on the skeletal structure of the race horse, especially when racing the two-year-old.

The classical horse ration of grass hay and farm grains is usually deficient in calcium, but adequate in phosphorus. Also, salt is almost always deficient, and usually iodine.

SALT

Salt, in either granulated or block form (preferably the former), should always be available in the stall, paddock, or pasture. When salt is fed free-choice, only

---

[1] Generally speaking, the mineral recommendations given herein can be followed on a nation-wide basis. However, it is recognized that area differences do exist. Therefore, for more specific recommendations, the horseman should always secure the counsel of his county agricultural agent or state agricultural college.

enough to meet the body requirements will be consumed. But with irregular use, an abnormal appetite develops for salt, and this is often followed by an excessive consumption and digestive troubles if unlimited access is allowed.

On the average, a horse will consume about 3 ounces of salt daily, or 1⅓ pounds per week; although the salt requirements vary with work and temperature. When at hard work during warm weather—conditions accompanied by profuse perspiration and consequent loss of salt in the sweat—even greater quantities may be required. The white, encrusted sides of a horse after work are evidence of the large amount of salt drawn from the body through sweat (2 gms. of salt/lb. of sweat). Horses at moderate work may lose 50 to 60 grams of salt in the sweat and 35 grams in the urine daily. Unless this salt is replaced, the animal will soon exhibit signs of excessive fatigue. Overheating of horses seldom occurs if the animals are allowed free access to salt at all times and are given water at frequent intervals.

IODINE

In some sections of the country, such as the northwestern part of the United States and in the Great Lakes region, iodine deficiencies are prevalent. In these areas, unless iodine is provided to the pregnant mare, foals often are born either dead or very weak, and appear to be more subject to navel-ill. There may even be beneficial results in such deficient areas from supplying horses other than pregnant mares with iodine. It is sound protection always to feed *stabilized iodized salt*, containing 0.01 per cent potassium iodide, in areas known or suspected to be deficient in iodine.

CALCIUM AND PHOSPHORUS

Young equines, breeding animals, and animals being forced for race or show are most likely to be affected by deficiences of calcium and/or phosphorus because of their greater needs for these minerals.

The Ca/P ratio of horse rations should be maintained close to 1:1. Osteomalacia may develop in mature horses when rations with a calcium-phosphorus ratio of 0.8:1 are fed for 6 to 12 months and will progress rapidly when the ratio is 0.6:1. The disease may be arrested by adding calcium to increase the ratio to 1.4:1. If the concentration of calcium in a ration is below 0.15 per cent or if feedstuffs unusually rich in phosphorus are fed, some calcium supplement will be needed. It is recommended that the total ration contain at least 0.5 per cent calcium and 0.45 per cent phosphorus. Because phosphorus is more expensive than calcium, there is a tendency to be long on calcium and short on phosphorus.

OTHER MINERALS

Other minerals (in addition to salt, calcium, phosphorus, and iodine) required by horses include iron, copper, and cobalt; but little information is available as to the amounts needed.

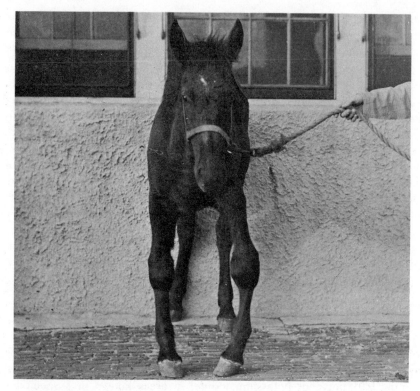

Fig. 51-2. Foal with severe rickets. Note the enlarged joints and crooked legs. (Courtesy, Dept. of Veterinary Pathology and Hygiene, College of Veterinary Medicine, University of Illinois)

The needed minerals for horses may be incorporated in the ration in keeping with recommended allowances. Additionally, horses should have free access to a good mineral supplement.

Vitamin Needs

The lack of vitamins in a horse ration may, under certain conditions, be more serious than a short supply of feed. Deficiencies may lead to failure in growth or reproduction, poor health, and even to characteristic disorders known as deficiency diseases.

Unfortunately, there are no warning signals to tell a caretaker when a horse is not getting enough of certain vitamins. But a continuing inadequate supply of any one of several vitamins can produce illness which is very hard to diagnose until it becomes severe; at which time it is difficult and expensive—if not too late— to treat. The important thing, therefore, is to insure against such deficiencies occurring. But horsemen should not shower a horse with mistaken kindness through using "shotgun type" vitamin preparations. Instead, the quantity of each vitamin should be based on available scientific knowledge.

Deficiencies may occur during periods (1) of extended drought or in other conditions of restriction in diet; (2) when production is being forced, or during stress; (3) when large quantities of highly refined feeds are being fed; or (4) when low-quality forages are utilized.

Although the occasional deficiency symptoms are the most striking result of vitamin deficiencies, it must be emphasized that in practice mild deficiencies probably cause higher total economic losses than do severe deficiencies. It is relatively uncommon for a ration, or diet, to contain so little of a vitamin that obvious symptoms of a deficiency occur. When one such case does appear, it is reasonable to suppose that there must be several cases that are too mild to produce characteristic symptoms, but which are sufficiently severe to lower the state of health and the efficiency of production.

It has long been known that the vitamin content of feeds varies considerably according to soil, climatic conditions, and curing and storing.

Certain vitamins are necessary in horse rations in order to permit proper growth, development, health, and reproduction. Although the particular role played by vitamins in the nutrition of the horse has not been explored extensively, there is reason to suppose that the vitamin requirements of the horse are similar to those of the pig. Also, they may be accentuated during stress and strain, to which modern horses are subjected. Certainly deficiencies of vitamins A and D are encountered. Although very little information is available, indications are that vitamin E and some of the B group of vitamins, especially riboflavin and perhaps thiamine, pantothenic acid, and B_{12}, are required by the horse. Further, it is recognized that single, uncomplicated vitamin deficiencies are the exception rather than the rule.

VITAMIN A

A severe deficiency of vitamin A may cause night blindness, reproduction difficulties, uneven and poor hoof development, respiratory symptoms, incoordination, and fanciful appetite. There is also evidence which indicates that a lack of vitamin A may cause or contribute to certain leg bone weaknesses. At the first sign of a vitamin A deficiency symptom, the horseman should add a therapeutic amount of a stabilized vitamin A product to the ration.

VITAMIN D

Foals sometimes develop rickets, caused by lack of vitamin D, or of calcium or phosphorus. This condition may be prevented by exposing the animal to direct sunlight as much as possible, by allowing access to a suitable mineral mixture, and/or providing good quality sun-cured hay or luxuriant pasture grown on well-fertilized soils. In areas lacking in sunshine, horsemen should provide the foal with a vitamin D supplement.

VITAMIN E

Horses seem to require vitamin E, but most practical rations contain liberal quantities of it—perhaps enough except under conditions of stress or where there is interference with its utilization. Rather than buy and use costly vitamin E concentrates indiscriminately, therefore, add them to the ration only on the advice of a nutritionist or veterinarian.

B VITAMINS

A deficiency of riboflavin may cause periodic ophthalmia (moon blindness), but it is known that lack of this vitamin is not the only factor in producing this condition (sometimes moon blindness follows Leptospirosis in horses). Periodic ophthalmia may be lessened by feeding green hays and green pastures—feeds high in riboflavin—or by adding crystalline riboflavin at the rate of 40 mg. per horse per day.

A thiamine deficiency has been observed in horses fed on poor quality hay and grain.

Although some of the B vitamins and unidentified factors are synthesized in the cecum of the horse, it is doubtful that this microbial activity is sufficient to meet the needs during the critical periods—growth, reproduction, and when animals are subjected to great stress as in showing or racing. Also, there is reason to question the efficacy of absorption this far down the digestive tract. It is known that horses fed thiamine-deficient rations lose weight, become nervous, and show incoordination in the hind quarters; then when thiamine is added to the ration, this condition is cured. For these reasons, in valuable horses it is not wise to rely solely on bacterial synthesis. The B vitamins, along with unidentified factors, may be provided by adding to the ration such ingredients as distillers' dried solubles, dried brewers' yeast, dried fish solubles, or animal liver meal; usually through a reputable commercial feed.

The author subscribes to the view that most light horses are under stress and that the more exacting the performance, the greater the stress; hence, that the vitamin requirements of most light horses are higher than for draft horses.

Water Needs

Water is one of the most vital of all nutrients. In fact, horses can survive for a longer period without feed than they can without water. Yet, comparatively little discussion will be given to this nutrient simply because, under ordinary conditions, it can be readily provided in abundance and at little cost.

Water is one of the largest single constituents of the animal body, varying in amount with condition and age. The younger the animal, the more water it contains. Also, the fatter the animal, the lower the water content. Thus, as an animal matures, it requires proportionately less water on a weight basis, because it consumes less feed per unit of weight and the water content of the body is being replaced by fat.

Water performs the following important functions in horses:

1. It is necessary to the life and shape of every cell and is a constituent of every body fluid.

2. It acts as a carrier for various substances, serving as a medium in which nourishment is carried to the cells and waste products are removed therefrom.

3. It assists with temperature regulation in the body, cooling the animal by evaporation from the skin as perspiration.

4. It is necessary for many important chemical reactions of digestion and metabolism.

5. As a constituent of the synovial fluid, it lubricates the joints; in the cerebrospinal fluid, it acts as a water cushion for the nervous system; in the perilymph in the ear, it transports sound; and in the eye, it is concerned with sight and provides a lubricant for the eye.

Surplus water is excreted from the body, principally in the urine, and to a slight extent in the perspiration, feces, and water vapor from the lungs.

The average mature horse will consume about 12 gallons of water daily; the amount varying according to the type and severity of work (sweating), weather conditions, and the kind of feed consumed. It is recommended that the horse be watered (1) regularly and frequently and (2) lightly when very warm or thirsty. Water may be given before, during, or after feeding.

Automatic waterers are the modern way to provide clean, fresh water at all times—as nature intended. Also, frequent, but small waterings avoid gorging. All waterers should have drains for easy cleaning, and should be heated to 40° to 45° F. in cold regions.

Waterers should be available in both stalls and corrals.

HORSE FEEDS AND THEIR PREPARATION

During the past 25 years, remarkable progress has been made in feeding meat animals; as a result of which (1) feed required per pound of gain has been reduced 14 per cent, and (2) rate of gain has been increased by 21 per cent. But no such progress has been made in horses; altogether too many of them are being fed the same old oats and the same old timothy hay. In fact, many horses of today are being fed about the same as they were a century ago. How many meat animal producers could survive were they to turn back the pages of time and feed as their great, great grandfathers did 100 years ago?

Pasture for the Horse

The great horse breeding centers of the world are characterized by good pastures. Thus, the bluegrass area of Kentucky is known for its lush pastures produced on residual limestone soils. In short, good horsemen, good pastures, and good horses go hand in hand—good pasture is the cornerstone of successful horse production. Yet, it is becoming increasingly difficult to provide good pastures for many horses, especially those in suburban areas. Also, it is recognized that many folks are prone to overrate the quality of their grass.

In season, there is no finer forage for horses than superior pastures—pastures that are much more than gymnasiums. This is especially true of idle horses, brood mares, and young stock. In fact, pastures have a very definite place for all horses, with the possible exception of animals at heavy work or in training. Even with the latter groups, pastures may be used with discretion. Work horses may be

Fig. 51-3. Mares and foals on lush pastures. (Courtesy, Col. F. W. Koester, General Manager, Calif. Thoroughbred Breeders Assn., Arcadia, Calif.)

turned to pasture at nights or over the weekend. Certainly, the total benefits derived from pasture are to the good, although pasturing may have some laxative effects and produce a greater tendency to sweat.

In addition to the nutritive value of the grass, pasture provides invaluable exercise on natural footing—with plenty of sunshine, fresh air, and lowered feed costs as added benefits. Feeding on pasture is the ideal existence for young stock and breeding animals.

The use of a temporary pasture (grown on a regular crop rotation), instead of a parasite-infected permanent pasture, is recommended. Legume pastures are excellent for horses, as equines are less subject to bloat than cattle or sheep. The specific grass or grass-legume mixture will vary from area to area, according to differences in soil, temperature, and rainfall. The county agricultural agent or state agricultural college can furnish recommendations for the area that they serve.

Horse pastures should be well drained and not too rough or stony. All dangerous places—such as pits, stumps, poles, and tanks—should be guarded. Shade, water, and suitable minerals should be available in all pastures.

Most horse pastures can be improved by seeding new and better varieties of grasses and legumes, and by fertilizing and management. Also, horsemen need to give attention to balancing pastures. Early-in-the-season pastures are of high-water content and lack energy. Mature, weathered grass is almost always deficient in protein (being as low as 3 per cent or less) and low in carotene (the precursor of vitamin A). But these deficiencies can be corrected by proper supplemental feeding.

Hay for the Horse

Through mistaken kindness or carelessness, horses are often fed too much hay or other roughage, with labored breathing and quick tiring the result. With cattle and sheep, on the other hand, it is usually well to feed all the roughage they will eat. This difference between horses and ruminants is due primarily to the relatively small size of the simple stomach of the horse in comparison with the four-fold stomach of the ruminant.

When limiting the allowance of roughage, it is sometimes necessary to muzzle greedy horses (gluttons) to prevent them from eating the bedding.

Usually, young horses and idle horses can be provided with an unlimited allowance of hay. But one should gradually increase the grain and decrease the hay as work or training begins.

Much good will result from feeding young and idle horses more roughage and less grain.

The hay should be early cut, leafy, green, well cured, and free from dust and mold. Hay native to the locality is usually fed. However, horsemen everywhere prefer good quality timothy. With young stock and breeding animals especially, it is desirable that a grass-legume mixture or alfalfa hay be fed. The legume provides a source of high quality proteins and certain minerals and vitamins.

Horses like variety. Therefore, if at all possible, it is wise to have more than one kind of hay in the stable. For example, timothy may be provided at one feeding and a grass-legume mixed hay at the other feeding. Good horsemen often vary the amount of alfalfa fed, for increased amounts of alfalfa in the ration will increase urination and give a softer consistency to the bowel movements. This means that elimination from kidneys and bowels can be carefully regulated by the amount and frequency of alfalfa feedings. Naturally, such regulation becomes more necessary with irregular use and idleness. On the other hand, in some areas alfalfa is fed as the sole roughage with good results.

Commercial Horse Feeds

Commercial feeds are just what the name implies—mixed by manufacturers who specialize in the feed business, rather than farm mixed. Today, about 60 million tons of commercial feeds are marketed each year. It's big and important business, and it will get bigger.

The commercial feed manufacturer has the distinct advantages of (1) purchase of feed in quantity lots, making possible price advantages; (2) economical and controlled mixing; (3) the hiring of scientifically trained personnel for use in determining the rations; and (4) quality control. Most horsemen have neither the know-how nor the quantity of business to provide these services on their own. In fact, due to (1) the small quantities of feed usually involved and (2) the complexities of horse rations, horsemen have more reason to rely on good commercial feeds than do owners of other classes of farm animals and poultry.

Also, it is to the everlasting credit of reputable feed dealers that they have been good teachers; often getting horsemen started in the feeding of balanced rations.

Processing Grains

If properly done, steam rolling of grains is preferred to grinding for horses, because the ration is lighter and fluffier and fewer digestive disturbances are encountered. However, there is great variation in steam rolling. Altogether too much steam rolling consists of exposing the grain to steam for three to five minutes, using a temperature of about 180° F., and adding an unknown amount of moisture. Such processing is little better than dry rolling.

Recent experimental studies at the University of Arizona, with cattle, showed that proper steam rolling is achieved as follows: Subject the grain to 20 pounds of steam pressure, for 20 minutes, at approximately 205° F.; then at this temperature and 18 to 20 per cent moisture content, run the grain through large rollers operated at one-third to one-half capacity and roll to thin flakes. Of course, excess moisture must be removed prior to storage.

Dry rolling, crimping, and grinding can be, and are, used in preparing horse feeds. The important thing is to keep the grain as coarse as possible and to avoid fines.

A very attractive and palatable concentrate can be prepared by flaking the grains and pelleting the fines. However, feeds prepared in this manner are very subject to mustiness; hence, it is important that they not contain excess moisture, and that they be stored properly.

Pelleting

Currently, horsemen are much interested in pelleted feeds, a development which has gone hand in hand with mechanization and automation.

This type of feed preparation may be, and is, applied to (1) concentrates alone, (2) forage alone, and (3) concentrates and roughage combined in a complete ration. The practice of pelleting feed for horses will increase for the following reasons:

1. Pelleted feeds are less bulky (pelleted roughage requires one-fifth to one-third as much space as in loose or chopped form) and easier to store and handle—thus lessening transportation, storage, and labor costs. For these reasons, it is particularly advantageous to use pelleted feeds where storage space is limited and feed must be transported considerable distances, conditions which frequently characterize small enterprises and the suburban horse owner.

2. Pelleting prevents horses from selectively refusing ingredients likely to be high in certain dietary essentials; each bite is a balanced feed.

3. Pelleting practically eliminates wastage. Since horses may waste up to 20 per cent of long hay, less pelleted feed is required. Wastage of conventional feed is highest where low quality hay is fed and/or feed containers are poorly designed.

4. Pelleting eliminates dustiness and lessens heaves.

5. Pellet-fed horses are trimmer in the middle and more attractive, due to consuming less bulk.

Those who have tried all-pelleted (grain and hay combined) rations, are very enthusiastic about them. Based on experiments and observations, the following comments are pertinent:

1. One-half-inch pellets are recommended for mature horses, and ¼-inch

pellets for weanlings and short yearlings. Also, very hard pellets should be avoided; if horses cannot chew them, they will spit them out.

2. It is recommended that the ratio of roughage to concentrate be higher in all-pelleted rations than when long hay is fed. For most horses, 60.5 to 69 per cent roughage, which means, 39.5 to 31 per cent concentrate is about right.

3. Because of eliminating waste, less all-pelleted feed is required than of conventional rations. For a horse at light work, feed 14 to 18 pounds daily of a 53 to 56 per cent TDN pellet per 1,000 pounds of live weight. Increase the feed allowance with the severity of the work.

4. As with any change in feed, the switch to an all-pelleted ration should be made gradually. Continue to offer all the long hay the horse wants, and slowly replace the grain portion of the conventional ration with the complete pelleted feed. Increase the pelleted feed by one to two pounds daily while gradually lessening the hay. After a few days, the horse will usually stop eating the hay on his own accord, following which it can be completely eliminated.

The biggest deterrent to increased pelleting at the present time is difficulty in processing chopped forage which is coarse enough so that it will not cause digestive disturbances. A minimum of ¼-inch chop is recommended. One highly successful horseman, who has fed pelleted feed for several years, puts his roughage through a ⅜-inch screen and steam rolls the grain.

AMOUNT TO FEED

The main qualities desired in horses are trimness, action, spirit, and endurance. These qualities cannot be obtained with large, paunchy stomachs or lack of energy, which may result from excessive use of roughage. Moreover, a healthy condition is desired, but excess fat is to be avoided. The latter is especially true with horses used for racing, where the carrying of every pound of surplus body weight must be avoided.

The quantity of grain and hay required by horses depends primarily upon the following:

1. The individuality; horses vary in keeping qualities, just as people do. Some horses simply utilize their feed more efficiently than others. A hard keeper will require considerably more feed than an easy keeper when doing the same amount of work.

2. The age, size, and condition of the animal.

3. The kind, regularity, amount, and speed of work performed. With greater speed, the horse requires proportionately greater energy; hence, considerably more concentrate is required when performing work at a trot than at a walk.

4. The weather; for example, under ideal October weather conditions in Missouri, a horse may require 14 pounds of 60 per cent TDN feed daily, whereas in the same area, the same horse may require 16 pounds daily of the same feed in July and August, and 20 pounds in the winter.

5. The kind, quality, and amount of feed.

6. The system of management.

7. The health, condition, and temperament of the animal.

Because the horse has a rather limited digestive capacity, the amount of concentrates must be increased and the roughages decreased when the energy needs rise with the greater amount, severity, or speed of work. The following are general guides for the daily ration of horses under usual conditions.

1. For horses at light work (1 to 3 hours/day of riding or driving).—Allow ⅖ to ½ pound of grain and 1¼ to 1½ pounds of hay per day per 100 pounds of live weight.

2. For horses at medium work (3 to 5 hours/day of riding or driving).—Allow about ¾ pound of grain to 1 to 1¼ pounds of hay per 100 pounds of live weight.

3. For horses at hard work (5 to 8 hours/day of riding or driving).—Allow about 1¼ to 1⅓ pounds of grain and 1 to 1¼ pounds of hay per 100 pounds of live weight.

As will be noted from these recommendations, the total allowance of concentrates and hay should be within the range of 2.0 to 2.5 pounds daily per 100 pounds of live weight. No grain should be left from one feeding to the next, and all edible forage should be cleaned up at the end of each day.

About 6 to 12 pounds of grain daily is an average grain ration for a light horse at medium or light work. Race horses in training usually consume 10 to 16 pounds of grain per day—the exact amount varying with the individual requirements and the amount of work. The hay allowance averages about 1 to 1¼ pounds daily per 100 pounds of live weight, but it is restricted as the grain allowance is increased. Light feeders should not be overworked.

It is to be emphasized that the quantities of feeds recommended above are intended as guides only. The feeder will increase the allowance, especially the concentrates, when the horse is too thin and decrease the feed when the horse is too fat.

The regular practice of turning horses on pasture at night and on idle days is good for the health and well being of the animals and decreases the quantity of grain and hay required. If the horse must be confined to the stall on idle days, the grain ration should be reduced by 50 per cent in order to avoid azoturia or other digestive disturbances. When idle, it is also advisable to add some wheat bran to the ration. A mixture of two-thirds grain and one-third bran is quite satisfactory. Many good horsemen regularly give a feeding of bran, either dry or as a wet mash, on Saturday night.

During off-work seasons, pastures may be used to advantage for idle horses —with or without grain, depending upon the individuality and condition of the horse.

A FEED FOR EVERY NEED

The nutritive requirements of all farm animals vary according to age, weight, use or demands, growth, state of gestation or lactation, and environment. Horses are no exception.

Feeding the Brood Mare

Brood mares need a ration that will meet their own body needs plus (1) those of the fetus and (2) furnish the nutrients required for milk production. If work is also being performed, additional energy feeds must be provided. In the young, growing mare, additional protein, minerals, and vitamins, above the ordinary requirements, must be provided; otherwise, the fetus will not develop normally, or milk will be produced at the expense of the tissues of the dam. Protein deficiency may affect undesirably the fertility of the mare.

Most of the growth of the fetus occurs during the last third of pregnancy, thus the reproductive requirements are greatest during this period. In this connection, it is noteworthy that the cannon bones (the lower leg bones extending from the knees and hocks to the fetlocks) are as long at the time of birth as they will ever be and that in an amazingly short time after birth a foal can run almost as fast as its mother. This points up the importance of bone-building minerals and vitamins for the brood mare.

As with the females of all species, the nutritive requirements for milk production in the mare are much more rigorous than the pregnancy requirements. It is estimated that, two months following foaling, mares of mature weights of 600, 800, 1,000, and 1,200 pounds may produce 36, 42, 44, and 49 pounds of milk daily. Thus, it can be appreciated that a mare's feed requirements during the suckling period are not far different from those of a high-producing dairy cow. In general, it is important that the ration of the gestating-lactating mare should supply sufficient energy; ample protein, calcium, and phosphorus; and vitamins A and D (the D being provided through the feed if the animal is not exposed to sunlight) and riboflavin.

Brood mares should be kept in thrifty condition, but they should neither be allowed to become too fat nor too thin.

The correct feeding of a brood mare that is worked is often simpler than the feeding of an idle one, for the condition of the animal can be regulated more carefully under working conditions. In addition to a ration that will meet the maintenance and work requirements largely through high-energy feeds, the working brood mare needs ample protein, calcium, and phosphorus with which to take care of the growth of the fetus and/or milk production.

The brood mare should be fed and watered with care immediately before and after foaling. For the first 24 hours after parturition, she may have a little hay and a limited amount of water from which the chill has been taken.

A light feed of bran or a wet-bran mash is suitable for the first feed and the following meal may consist of oats or a mixture of oats and bran. A reasonably generous allowance of good quality hay is permissible after the first day. If confined to the stable, as may be necessary in inclement weather, the mare should be kept on a limited and light grain and hay ration for about 10 days after foaling. Feeding too much grain at this time is likely to produce digestive disturbances in the mare; and, even more hazardous, it may produce too much milk, which may cause indigestion in the foal. If weather conditions are favorable and it is possible to allow the mare to foal on a clean, lush pasture, she will regulate her own feed needs most admirably.

In comparison with geldings or unbred mares, the following differences in feeding gestating-lactating brood mares should be observed:

1. A greater quantity of feed is necessary—usually about 20 to 50 per cent more—the highest requirement being during lactation.

2. Dusty or moldy feed and frozen silage should be avoided in feeding all horses, but especially so in feeding the brood mare, for such feed may produce complications and possible abortion.

3. More proteins are necessary for the brood mare.

4. More attention must be given to supplying the necessary minerals and vitamins.

5. The bowels should be carefully regulated through providing regular exercise and feeding such laxative feeds as bran, linseed meal, and alfalfa hay.

6. A few days before and after foaling, the ration should be decreased and lightened by using wheat bran.

7. Regular and ample exercise is a necessary adjunct to proper feeding of the brood mare.

Feeding the Stallion

"Reduce the ration and increase the exercise when the stallion is not a sure breeder" has been the advice given to many worried stallion owners. In all too many instances, little thought is given to the feeding and care of the stallion, other than during the breeding season. The program throughout the entire year should be such as to keep the stallion in a vigorous, thrifty condition at all times. Immediately before the breeding season, the feed might very well be increased in quantity so that the stallion will gain in weight. The quantity of grain fed will vary with the individual temperament and feeding ability of the stallion, the work and exercise provided, services allowed, available pastures, and quality of roughage. Usually this will be between ¾ and 1½ pounds daily of the grain mixture per 100 pounds weight, together with a quantity of hay within the same range.

During the breeding season, the stallion's ration should contain more protein and additional minerals and vitamins than are given in rations fed work horses or stallions not in service. During the balance of the year (when not in service), the ration for the stallion may be like that of other horses similarly handled.

In addition to the grain and roughage, there should be free access to a mineral supplement and salt. These should be placed in separate compartments of a suitable box. During the winter months or when little work or exercise is provided, the stallion should receive a succulent feed such as carrots or silage (carrots or silage should be neither moldy nor frozen). Also, laxative feeds, such as wheat bran or linseed meal, should be supplied at these times. Plenty of fresh, clean water should be provided at all times. Drugs or stock tonics should not be fed in an attempt to increase virility.

Overfitted, heavy stallions should be regarded with suspicion, for they may be uncertain breeders. On the other hand, a poor, thin, run-down condition is also to be avoided.

Feeding the Young Horse

As with all young mammals, milk from the dam gives the foal a good start in life. Within 30 minutes to 2 hours after birth, the foal should be up on its feet and getting the colostrum.

But milk is not the perfect food, as once claimed. It is deficient in iron and copper, with the result that suckling young may suffer from anemia. This may be prevented, and increased growth, durability, and soundness may be obtained by creep feeding foals.

FEEDING FOALS BEFORE WEANING

When the foal is between 10 days and 3 weeks of age, it will begin to nibble on grain and hay. In order to promote thrift and early development and to avoid setback at weaning time, it is important to encourage the foal to eat supplementary feed as early as possible. For this purpose, a low-built grain box should be provided especially for the foal; or, if on pasture, the foal may be creep-fed.

The choice between creep and individual feeding can be left to the horseman; the important thing is that foals receive supplemental feed.

A "creep" is an enclosure for feeding purposes, made accessible to the foal(s), but through which the dam cannot pass. For best results, the creep should be built at a spot where the mares are inclined to loiter. The ideal location is on high ground, well drained, in the shade, and near the place of watering. Keeping the salt supply nearby will be helpful in holding mares near the creep.

It is important that foals be started on feed carefully and at an early age. At first only a small amount of feed should be placed in the trough each day, any

Fig. 51-4. A foal creep built around a hay rack. With this arrangement, the foal can be fed separately from the dam. (Courtesy, Col. F. W. Koester)

surplus being removed and given to other horses. In this manner, the feed will be kept clean and fresh, and the foals will not be consuming any moldy or sour feed.

When foals are on luxuriant pasture and their mothers are milking well, difficulty may be experienced in getting them to eat. Thus, patience on the part of the caretaker is extremely important. However, foals are curious. Usually, they'll examine a creep. But it may be necessary to start them on the creep ration by first letting them nibble a little feed from the hand.

At four to five weeks of age, the normal healthy foal should be consuming ½ pound of grain daily per 100 pounds of live weight. By weaning time, this should be increased to about ¾ pound or more per 100 pounds live weight (or 6 to 8 pounds of feed/head/day); the exact amount varying with the individual and the development desired.

Because of the difficulty in formulating and home-mixing a foal ration, the purchase of a good commercial feed usually represents a wise investment.

In addition to his grain ration, the foal should be given good quality hay (preferably a legume) or pasture.

Free access to salt and a suitable mineral mixture should be provided. The mineral will be consumed to best advantage if placed in a convenient place and under shelter; or it may be incorporated in the ration. Plenty of fresh water must be available at all times.

Under such a system of care and management, the foal will become less dependent upon its dam, and the weaning process will be facilitated. If properly cared for, foals will normally attain one-half of their mature weight during the first year. Most Thoroughbred and Standardbred breeders plan to have the animals attain full weight by the time they are two years of age. However, such results require liberal feeding from the beginning.

It is well recognized that the forced development of race, show, and sale horses must be done expertly if the animals are to remain durable and sound. Also, and equally important, a foal stunted in the first year by insufficient feeding cannot be developed properly later in life.

THE WEANLING

Perhaps the most critical period in the entire life of a horse is that interval from weaning time (about six months of age) until one year of age. Foals suckling their dams and receiving no grain may develop very satisfactorily up to weaning time. However, lack of preparation prior to weaning and neglect following the separation from the dam may prevent the animal from gaining proper size and shape. The primary objective in the breeding of horses is the economical production of a well-developed, sound individual at maturity. To achieve this result requires good care and management of weanlings.

As previously indicated, no great setback or disturbances will be encountered at weaning time provided that the foals have developed a certain independence from proper grain feeding during the suckling period. Generally, weanlings should receive 1 to 1½ pounds of grain and 1½ to 2 pounds of hay daily per each 100 pounds live weight. The amount of feed will vary somewhat with the individuality of the animal, the quality of roughage, available pastures, and whether the weanling is being developed for race, show, or sale. Naturally, animals being developed for early use or sale should be fed more liberally, although it is equally important to retain clean, sound joints, legs, and feet—conditions which cannot be obtained so easily in heavily fitted animals.

Because of the rapid development of bone and muscle in weanlings, it is important that, in addition to ample quantity of feed, the ration also provide quality proteins and adequate minerals and vitamins.

THE YEARLING

If foals have been fed and cared for so that they are well grown and thrifty as yearlings, usually little difficulty will be experienced at any later date.

Yearlings that are being grown for show or sale should be fed while on pasture. They should be kept up in the daytime during the hot days and turned out at night (because of not being exposed to sunshine, adequate vitamin D must be provided). This point needs to be emphasized when forced development is desired, for, good as pastures may be, they are roughages rather than concentrates.

The winter feeding program for the rising two-year-olds should be such as to produce plenty of bone and muscle rather than fat. From ½ to 1 pound of grain and 1 to 1½ pounds of hay should be fed for each 100 pounds of live weight. The quantity will vary with the quality of the roughage, the individuality of the animal, and the use for which the animal is produced. In producing for sale, more liberal feeding may be economical. Access to salt and to a mineral mixture should be provided at all times, or the minerals should be incorporated in the ration. An abundance of fresh, pure water must be available.

THE TWO- AND THREE-YEAR-OLD

Except for the fact that the two- and three-year-olds will be larger and, therefore, will require more feed, their proper care and management are merely a repetition of the principles that have already been discussed for the yearling.

With the two-year-old that is to be raced, however, the care and feeding at this time become matters of extreme importance. Once the young horse is placed in training, the ration should be adequate enough to allow for continued development and to provide necessary maintenance and additional energy for work. This means that special attention must be given to providing adequate proteins, minerals, and vitamins in the ration. Over-exertion must be avoided, the animal must be properly groomed, and the feet must be cared for properly. In brief, every precaution must be taken if the animal is to remain sound—a most difficult task when animals are raced at an early age, even though the right genetic make-up and the proper environment are present.

Fitting for Show or Sale

Each year, many horses are fitted for shows or sales. In both cases, a finishing process is involved, but exercise is doubly essential.

For horses that are being fitted for shows, the conditioning process is also a matter of hardening, and the horses are used daily in harness or under saddle. Regardless of whether the show or sale is the major objective, fleshing should be obtained without sacrificing action or soundness or without causing filling of the legs and hocks.

In finishing horses, the animals should be brought to full feed rather gradually, until the ration reaches a maximum of about 2 pounds of grain daily for each 100 pounds of live weight. When on full feed, horses make surprising gains. Daily weight gains of 4 to 5 pounds are not uncommon. Such animals soon become fat, sleek, and attractive. This is probably the basis for the statement that "fat will cover up a multitude of sins in a horse."

Although exercise is desirable from the standpoint of keeping the animals sound, it is estimated that such activity decreases the daily rate of gains by as much as 20 per cent. Because of the greater cost of gains and the expense involved in bringing about forced exercise, most feeders of sale horses limit the exercise to that obtained naturally from running in a paddock.

In comparison with finishing cattle or sheep, there is more risk in finishing horses. Heavily fed horses kept in idleness are likely to become blemished and injured through playfulness, and there are more sicknesses among liberally fed horses than in other classes of stock handled in a similar manner.

In fitting show horses, the finish must remain firm and hard, the action superb, and the soundness unquestioned. Thus, they must be carefully fed, groomed, and exercised to bring them to proper bloom. Training is also extremely important in preparing for the show ring. Horsemen who fit and sell yearlings or younger animals may feed a palatable milk replacer or commercial feed to advantage.

Feeding Race and Show Horses

In a study made by the author,[2] it was found that, on the average, it costs $5,099 to produce and raise a Thoroughbred to two years of age, plus an added cost of $3,410 to keep him in training the first year. Thus, when a Thoroughbred breaks down permanently at the end of the third year, following one year in training and on the track, an investment of $8,509 is involved. Obviously, the stakes are high to keep him sound and running.

It is recognized that some unsoundnesses may be inherited, others may be due to accident and injury, and still others may be due to subjecting horses to stress and strain far beyond the capability of even the best structure and tissue. However, nutritional deficiencies appear to be the major cause of unsoundnesses.

Race and show horses are equine athletes whose nutritive requirements are the most exacting, but the most poorly met, of all animals. This statement may be shocking to some, but it's true for the following reasons.

Race and show horses are commonly:

---

[2] M. E. Ensminger, *Horses and Horsemanship*, 3rd ed., pp. 568-73.

1. Started in training very shortly past 12 months of age, which is comparable to an adolescent boy or girl doing sweatshop labor.

2. Moved from track to track, or show to show, under all sorts of conditions.

3. Trained the year round, raced or shown innumerable times each year, and forced to perform when fatigued.

4. Outdoors only a short time each day—usually before sun-up, with the result that the sun's rays have little chance to produce vitamin D from the cholesterol in the skin.

5. Without opportunity for even a few mouthfuls of grass—a rich, natural source of the B vitamins and unidentified factors.

6. Fed oats, grass hay, and possibly bran—produced in unknown areas, and on soils of unknown composition. Such an oats-grass hay-bran ration is almost always deficient in vitamins A and D and the B vitamins, and lopsided and low in calcium and phosphorus.

7. Given a potion of some concoction of questionable value—if not downright harmful.

By contrast, human athletes—college football teams and participants in the Olympics, for example—are usually required to eat at a special training table, supervised by nutrition experts. They are fed the best diet that science can formulate and technology can prepare. It's high in protein, rich in readily available energy, and fortified and balanced in vitamins and minerals.

It's small wonder, therefore, that so many equine athletes go unsound, whereas most human athletes compete year after year until overtaken by age.

Indeed, high strung and highly stressed race and show horses need special rations just as human athletes do—and for the same reasons; and, the younger the age, the more acute the need. This calls for rations high in protein, rich in readily available energy, fortified with vitamins, minerals, and unidentified factors—and with all nutrients in proper balance.

A race or show horse is asked to develop a large amount of horsepower in a period of a few minutes. The oxidations that occur in a race or show horse's body are at a higher pitch than in a draft horse, and, therefore, more vitamins are required.

Also, race and show horses are the *prima donnas* of the equine world; most of them are temperamental, and no two of them can be fed alike. They vary in rapidity of eating, in the quantity of feed that they will consume, in the proportion of concentrate to roughage that they will take, and in response to different caretakers. Thus, for best results, they must be fed as individuals.

Most race and show horse rations are deplorably deficient in protein, simply because they are based on the minimum requirements of little stressed, slow, plodding draft horses.

During the race and show season, the hay should be limited to 7 or 8 pounds, whereas the concentrate allowance may range up to 16 pounds. Heavy roughage eaters may have to be muzzled to keep them from eating their bedding. A bran mash is commonly fed once a week.

SOME SUGGESTED RATIONS[3]

Oats, corn, and barley—all farm-grown concentrates—are the grains most commonly used for horses; whereas, wheat bran, linseed meal, soybean meal, and cottonseed meal are the favored supplements to the grains. Alfalfa, clover, soybean, timothy, prairie grass, Johnson grass, lespedeza, cereal hays, and dried corn and sorghum fodder constitute the chief forages fed to horses. To be sure, the concentrate and roughage combination used varies in different sections of the United States. Horses of the West, for example, are largely fed on barley and alfalfa or cereal hay; in the northern Mississippi Valley, the ration consists of oats and corn with timothy or mixed hay for roughage; whereas in the deep South, corn is the leading grain and Johnson grass, lespedeza, and corn fodder the chief roughages.

The addition of a few sliced carrots to the ration and an occasional bran mash, or a small amount of linseed meal, are particularly desirable during the wintering period. Such feeds may also be used in regulating the bowels at other times as required. Such cooling feeds should also be given to horses whose legs must undergo blistering or firing, for they reduce the tendency toward feverish, inflammatory symptoms. Care must be taken to prevent the animal from getting flabby or washy from too much soft feed while undergoing treatment. Whether working or idle, the trainer must never relax his vigilant observation nor let his judgment sleep.

The horse feeder should give consideration to the (1) quality and availability of feeds, (2) the character and severity of the work, (3) the age and individuality of the animal, and (4) the results obtained. With horses, more than with any other class of animals, results are more important than cost per bag.

Table 51-1 is a "Handy Light Horse Feeding Guide."

------

[3] Where possible, these rations were computed from the requirements as reported by the National Research Council and adapted by the author.

TABLE 51—1

HANDY LIGHT HORSE FEEDING GUIDE[1]
(Horses for Recreation and Sport)

Age, Sex, and Use	Daily Allowance	Kind of Hay[1] (More than one kind of hay makes for variety and appetite appeal. In season, any good pasture can replace part or all of the hay except for horses at work or in training.)	Suggested Grain Rations[1] — Ration No. 1 (lbs.) (kg)	Ration No. 2 (lbs.) (kg)	Ration No. 3 (lbs.) (kg)
Stallions in breeding season (weighing 900 to 1,400 lbs. or 409 to 636 kg)	¾ to 1½ lbs. (.3 to .7 kg) grain per 100 lbs. (45 kg) live wt. with a quantity of hay within same range	Grass-legume mixed (or 1/3 to ½ legume hay, with balance grass hay).	Oats —55 (25); Wheat —20 (9); Wheat bran —20 (9); Linseed meal — 5 (2)	Corn —35 (16); Oats —35 (16); Wheat —15 (7); Wheat bran —15 (7)	Oats (alone)
Pregnant mares (weighing 900 to 1,400 lbs. or 409 to 636 kg)	¾ to 1½ lbs. (.3 to .7 kg) grain per 100 lbs. (45 kg) live wt., together with a quantity of hay within same range	Grass-legume mixed or 1/3 to ½ legume hay, with balance grass hay (straight grass hay may be used first half of pregnancy).	Oats —80 (36); Wheat bran —20 (9)	Barley —45 (20); Oats —45 (20); Wheat bran —10 (5)	Oats —95 (43); Linseed meal — 5 (2)
Foals before weaning (weighing 100 to 350 lbs. or 45 to 159 kg with projected mature wts. of 900 to 1,400 lbs. or 409 to 636 kg)	½ to ¾ lb. (.2 to .3 kg) grain per 100 lbs. (45 kg) live wt., together with a quantity of hay within same range	Legume hay.	Oats —50 (23); Wheat bran —40 (18); Linseed meal —10 (5)	Oats —30 (14); Barley —30 (14); Wheat bran —30 (14); Linseed meal —10 (5)	Oats —80 (36); Wheat bran —20 (9)
			(Rations balanced basis of following assumptions: (1) Mares of lighter breeds (about 900 lbs. mature wt.) will give foals about 3 gals. milk daily and (2) mares of heavier breeds (about 1,400 lbs. mature wt.) will give foals about 3½ to 4½ gals. milk daily.)		
The weanlings (weighing 350 to 450 lbs. or 159 to 204 kg)	1 to 1½ lbs. (.5 to .7 kg) grain and 1½ to 2 lbs. (.7 to .9 kg) hay per 100 lbs. (45 kg) live wt.	Grass-legume mixed (or 1/3 to ½ legume hay, with balance grass hay).	Oats —30 (14); Barley —30 (14); Wheat bran —30 (14); Linseed meal —10 (5)	Oats —70 (32); Wheat bran —15 (7); Linseed meal —15 (7)	Oats —80 (36); Linseed meal —20 (9)

Footnote on following page.

(Continued)

TABLE 51—1 (Continued)

Age, Sex, and Use	Daily Allowance	Kind of Hay[1] (More than one kind of hay makes for variety and appetite appeal. In season, any good pasture can replace part or all of the hay except for horses at work or in training.)	Suggested Grain Ration[1]		
			Ration No. 1 (lbs.) (kg)	Ration No. 2 (lbs.) (kg)	Ration No. 3 (lbs.) (kg)
The yearlings: 2nd summer (weighing 450 to 700 lbs. or 317 kg)	Good luxuriant pastures (if in training or for other reasons without access to pastures, the ration should be intermediate between the adjacent upper and lower groups).				
The yearling or rising 2-yr-old; 2nd winter (weighing 700 to 1,000 lbs. or 317 to 454 kg)	½ to 1 lb. (.2 to .5 kg) of grain and 1 to 1½ lbs. (.5 to .7 kg) hay per 100 lbs. (45 kg) live wt.	Grass hay.	Oats —80 36 / Wheat bran —20 9	Barley —35 16 / Oats —35 16 / Bran —15 7 / Linseed meal —15 7	Oats (alone)
Light horses at work, in riding, driving, and racing (weighing 900 to 1,400 lbs. or 409 to 637 kg)	**Hard Use**—1¼ to 1 1/3 lbs. (.57 to .6 kg) grain and 1 to 1¼ lbs. (.5 to .57 kg) hay per 100 lbs. (45 kg) live wt **Med. Use**—¾ to 1 lb. (.1 to .5 kg) grain and 1 to 1¼ lbs. (.5 to .6 kg) hay per 100 lbs. (45 kg) live wt. **Light Use**—2/5 to ½ lb. (.18 to .2 kg) grain and 1¼ to 1½ lbs. (.57 to .7 kg) hay per 100 lbs. (45 kg) live wt.	Grass hay.	Oats —(alone)	Oats —70 32 / Corn —30 18	Oats —70 32 / Barley —30 18
Mature idle horses; stallions, mares and geldings (weighing 900 to 1,400 lbs. or 409 to 637 kg)	1½ to 1¾ lbs. (.7 to .8 kg) of hay per 100 lbs. (45 kg) live wt.	Pasture in season; or grass-legume mixed hay.	(With grass hay, add ¾ lb. (.34 kg) daily of a high protein supplement)		

Note: With all rations and for all classes and ages of horses, provide free access to separate containers of (1) salt (iodized salt in iodine-deficient areas) and (2) a mixture of one part salt and two parts steamed bone meal or other suitable calcium-phosphorus supplement.
[1]Good quality oats and timothy hay have always been considered the standard feeds for light horses. However, feeds of similar nutritive properties can be interchanged in the ration as price relationships warrant. This makes it possible at all times to obtain a balanced ration at the lowest cost. Some of these feeds are: (1) the grains (oats, corn, barley, wheat, and sorghum); (2) the protein supplements (linseed meal, soybean meal, and cottonseed meal); and (3) hays of many varieties.

QUESTIONS FOR STUDY AND DISCUSSION

1. Write down the ration that is fed to a certain horse (your horse or a friend's horse). Then, evaluate the ration from the standpoints of (a) rate of feeding, (b) protein content, (c) content of vitamins A, D, and riboflavin, and (d) content of salt, iodine, calcium, and phosphorus.
2. List all of the ways in which the nutritive requirements and the feeding of horses are different from beef cattle, sheep, and swine.

SELECTED REFERENCES

In addition to the selected references listed in Chapter III, the following are recommended for Chapter LI.

Title of Publication	Author(s)	Publisher
Horse, The	D. J. Kays	Rinehart & Company, Inc., New York, N. Y., 1953.
Horse Science Handbooks	M. E. Ensminger (editor)	Agriservices Foundation, 3699 E. Sierra Ave., Clovis, Calif.
Horseman's Handbook on Practical Breeding, A	J. F. Wall	Thoroughbred Bloodlines, Myrtle Beach, S. C., 1939.
Horses and Horsemanship	M. E. Ensminger	The Interstate Printers & Publishers, Danville, Ill., 1969.
Light Horses	M. E. Ensminger	Farmers' Bull. No. 2127, U.S. Department of Agriculture, Washington, D.C.
Merck Veterinary Manual, The		Merck & Co., Inc., Rahway, N. J., 1967.
Recommended Nutrient Allowances for Horses		National Research Council, 2101 Constitution Ave., N. W., Washington, D.C., 1961.
Stud Managers' Handbooks	M. E. Ensminger (editor)	Agriservices Foundation, 3699 E. Sierra Ave., Clovis, Calif.
Study on the Breeding and Racing of Thoroughbred Horses Given Large Doses of Alpha Tocopherol, A	F. G. Carlington J. B. Chassels	Reprint from The Summary, Vol. 8, No. 1—February, 1956, London, Canada.
Your Shetland Pony	J. M. Kays	The American Shetland Pony Club, West Lafayette, Ind.

APPENDIX

Section		Page
I	Animal Units	1215
II	Weights and Measures	1216
III	Storage Space Requirements for Feed and Bedding	1223
IV	Estimating Steer Weights from Heart Girth Measurements	1224
V	Gestation Table	1225
VI	Breed Registry Associations	1226
VII	Breed Magazines	1231
VIII	State Colleges of Agriculture	1234

SECTION I.—ANIMAL UNITS

An animal unit is a common animal denominator, based on feed consumption. It is assumed that one mature cow or one mature horse represents an animal unit. The comparative (to a mature cow or a mature horse) feed consumption of other age groups or classes of animals determines the proportion of an animal unit which they represent. For example, it is generally estimated that the ration of one mature cow or one mature horse will feed five hogs raised to 200 pounds. For this reason, the animal unit/head on this class and age of animals is 0.2. Table I-1 gives the animal units for different classes and ages of livestock.

TABLE I—1

ANIMAL UNITS

Type of Livestock	Animal Unit per Head
Horse	1
Cow	1
Bull	1
Young cattle, one year old	0.5
Calf	0.25
Colt	0.5
Brood sow or boar	0.4
Hogs raised to 200 pounds	0.2
Ewe or ram	0.14
Lamb	0.07
Poultry (per 100)	1
Chickens raised (per 200)	1

SECTION II.—WEIGHTS AND MEASURES

HANDY WEIGHTS AND MEASURES[1]

From time to time, stockmen and those who counsel with stockmen have need to refer to such weights and measures as follow.

Length

Unit	Is Equal To	
Metric System		
1 millimicron (mu)	.000000001 meter	(U.S.) .000000039 in.
1 micron (u)	.000001 meter	.000039 in.
1 millimeter (mm)	.001 meter	.0394 in.
1 centimeter (cm)	.01 meter	.3937 in.
1 decimeter (dm)	.1 meter	3.937 in.
1 meter (m)	1 meter	39.37 in.; 3.281 ft.; 1.094 yds.
1 hectometer (hm)	100 meters	328 ft.; 1 in., 19.8838 rods
1 kilometer (km)	1000 meters	3280 ft.; 10 in.; 0.621 mi.
U.S. System		
1 inch (in.		(metric) 2.54 centimeters
1 hand*	4 in.	
1 foot (ft.)	12 in.	30.48 cm; .305 meter
1 yard (yd.)	3 feet	.914 meter
1 fathom**	6.08 feet	1.829 meters
1 rod (rd.), pole, or perch	16½ ft.; 5½ yds.	5.029 meters
1 furlong	220 yds.; 40 rods	201.168 meters
1 mile	5280 ft.; 1760 yds.; 320 rods; 8 furlongs	1609.35 meters 1.609 kilometers
1 knot or nautical mile	6080 ft.; 1.15 land miles	
1 league (land)	3 miles (land)	
1 league (nautical)	3 miles (nautical)	

*Used in measuring height of horses.
**Used in measuring depth at sea.

CONVERSIONS

To Change	To	Multiply By
inches	centimeters	2.54
feet	meters	.305
meters	inches	39.37
miles	kilometers	1.609
kilometers	miles	.621

---

[1]For additional conversion factors, or for greater accuracy, see *Misc. Publ. 233*, the National Bureau of Standards.

Surface or Area

Unit	Is Equal To	
Metric System		(U.S.)
1 sq. millimeter (mm²)	.000001 m²	.00155 sq. in.
1 sq. centimeter (cm²)	.001 m²	.155 sq. in.
1 sq. decimeter (dm²)	.01 m²	15.50 sq. in.
1 sq. meter (m²)	1 centare (ca)	1550 sq. in.; 10.76 sq. ft 1.196 sq. yd.
1 are (a)	100 m²	119.6 sq. yds.
1 hectare (ha)	10000 m²	2.47 acres
1 sq. kilometer (km²)	1,000,000 m²	247.1 acres; .386 sq. mi
U.S. System		(metric)
1 sq. inch (sq. in.)	1 inch x 1 inch	6.452 cm²
1 sq. foot (sq. ft.)	144 sq. in.	.093 m²
1 sq. yard (sq. yd.)	1296 sq. in.; 9 sq. ft.	.836 m²
1 sq. rod (sq. rd.)	272.25 sq. ft.; 30.25 sq. yds.	25.29 m²
1 rood	40 sq. rods	10.117 ares
1 acre (a)	43,560 sq. ft.; 4,840 sq. yds. 160 sq. rds.; 4 roods	4,046.87 m² 259 hectares
1 sq. mile (sq. mi.)	640 acres	2.59 sq. km. or 259.0 ha
1 township	36 sections; 6 miles square	

CONVERSIONS

To Change	To	Multiply By
square inches	square centimeters	6.452
square centimeters	square inches	.155
square yards	square meters	.836
square meters	square yards	1.196

(Continued)

Volume

Unit	Is Equal To		
Liquid and Dry:		(U.S.)	
Metric System		(liquid)	(dry)
1 milliliter (ml)	.001 liter	.271 dram (fl.)	.061 cu. in.
1 centiliter (cl)	.01 liter	.338 oz. (fl.)	.610 cu. in.
1 deciliter (dl)	.1 liter	3.38 ozs. (fl.)	
1 liter (l)	1000 cc.	1.057 qts. (fl.)	.908 qt.
1 hectoliter (hl)	100 liter	26.418 gals.	2.838 bu.
1 kiloliter (kl)	1000 liter	264.18 gals.	1308 cu. yds.
U.S. System		(ounces)	(cu. in.)	(metric)
Liquid:				
1 teaspoon (t.)	60 drops	1/6		
1 dessert spoon	2 t.			
1 tablespoon (T.)	3 t.	½		
1 sill (si.)	½ c.	4	7.22	118.29 ml
1 cup (c.)	16 T	8	14.44	236.58 ml
1 pint (pt.)	2 c.	16	28.88	.47 liter
1 quart (qt.)	2 pts.	32	57.75	.95 liter
1 gallon (gal.)	4 qts.	8.34 lbs.	231	3.79 liter
1 barrel	31½ gals.			
1 hogshead	2 barrels			
Dry:				
1 pint (pt.)	½ qt.		33.6	.55 liter
1 quart (qt.)	2 pts.		67.20	1.10 liter
1 peck (pk.)	8 qts.		537.61	8.81 liter
1 bushel (bu.)	4 pecks		2150.42	35.24 liter
Solid:				
Metric System				
1 cu. millimeter (mm³)	.001 cc			
1 cu. centimeter (cc)	1000 mm		.061	
1 cu. decimeter (dm³)	1000 cc		61.023	
1 cu. meter (m³)	1000 dm³		35.315 cu. ft. 1.308 cu. yd.	

(Continued)

Volume (Continued)

Unit	Is Equal To	
U.S. System		(metric)
1 cubic inch (cu. in.)		16.387 cc
1 board foot (bd. ft.)	144 cu. in.	2359.8 cc
1 cubic foot (cu. ft.)	1728 cu. in.	.028 m³
1 cubic yard (cu. yd.)	27 cu. ft.	.765 m³
1 cord	128 cu. ft.	3.625 m³

CONVERSIONS

To Change	To	Multiply By
ounces (fluid)	cubic centimeters	29.57
cu. centimeters	ounces (fluid)	.034
quarts	liters	.946
liters	quarts	1.057
cu. inches	cu. centimeters	16.387
cu. centimeters	cu. inches	.061
cu. yards	cu. meters	.765
cu. meters	cu. yards	1.308

(Continued)

Weight

Unit	Is Equal To	
Metric System 1 microgram (mcg)	.001 mg	(U.S.)
1 milligram (mg)	.001 gram	.015432356 grain
1 centigram (cg)	.01 gram	.15432356 grain
1 decigram (dg)	.1 gram	1.5432 grains
1 gram (g)	1000 mg	.03527396 oz.
1 dekagram (dkg)	10 grams	5.643833 drams
1 hectogram (hg)	100 grams	3.527396 oz.
1 kilogram (kg)	1000 grams	35.274 oz. 2.2046223 lbs.
1 ton	1000 kg	2204.6 lb. 1.102 tons (short) or 0.984 ton (long)
U.S. System 1 grain (gr.)	.037 dram	(metric) 64.798918 mg; .064798918 g
1 dram	.063 oz.	1.771845 g
1 ounce (oz.)	16 drams	28.349527 g
1 pound (lb.)	16 oz.	453.5924 g or 0.4536 kg
1 hundredweight (cwt.)	100 lbs.	
1 ton (tn.) (short)	2000 lbs.	907.18486 kg or 0.907 (metric) ton
1 ton (long)	2200 lbs.	1016.05 kg or 1.016 (metric) ton
1 part per million (ppm)	1 microgram/gran 1 mg/l 1 mg/kg	.4535924 mg/lb .907 g/ton .0001% .013 oz./gal.
1 percent (%) (1 part in 100 parts)	10,000 ppm 10 g/l	1.28 oz./gal. 8 lbs./100 gal.

CONVERSIONS

To Change	To	Multiply By
grains	milligrams	64.799
ounces (dry)	grams	28.35
pounds (dry)	kilograms	.4535924
kilograms	pounds	2.2046223
mg/lb.	ppm	2.2046223
ppm	grams/ton	.90718486
grams/ton	ppm	1.1
mgm/lb.	grams/ton	2
grams/ton	mgm/lb.	.5
grams/lb.	grams/ton	2000
grams/ton	grams/lb.	.0005
grams/ton	lbs./ton	.0022
lbs./ton	grams/ton	453.5924
grams/ton	%	.00011
%	grams/ton	9072

Weights and Measures per Unit

Unit	Is Equal To
Volume per unit area:	
1 liter/hectare	0.107 gals./acre
1 gal./acre	9.354 liters/hectare
Weight per unit area:	
1 kilogram/cz^2	14.22 lbs./sq. inch
1 kilogram/hectare	0.892 lb./acre
1 lb./sq. in.	0.0703 kilogram/cm^2
1 lb./acre	1.121 kilograms/hectare
Area per unit weight:	
1 cm^2/kg	0.0703 sq. in./lb.
1 sq. in./lb.	14.22 cm^2/kg

(Continued)

Temperature

One Centigrade (C) degree is 1/100 the difference between the temperature of melting ice and that of water boiling at standard atmospheric pressure.

One Fahrenheit (F) degree is 1/180 of the difference between the temperature of melting ice and that of water boiling at standard atmospheric pressure.

To Change	To	Do This
Degrees Centigrade	Degrees Fahrenheit	Multiply by 9/5 and add 32
Degrees Fahrenheit	Degrees Centigrade	Subtract 32, then multiply by 5/9

Weights and Measures of Common Feeds

In calculating rations and mixing concentrates, it is usually necessary to use weights rather than measures. However, in practical feeding operations it is often more convenient for the farmer or rancher to measure the concentrates. Table II-1 will serve as a guide in feeding by measure.

TABLE II—1

WEIGHTS AND MEASURES OF COMMON FEEDS

Feed	Approximate Weight	
	(lbs. per quart)	(lbs. per bushel)
Alfalfa meal	0.6	19
Barley	1.5	48
Beet pulp (dried)	0.6	19
Brewers' grain (dried)	0.6	19
Buckwheat	1.6	50
Buckwheat bran	1.0	29
Corn, husked ear	—	70
Corn, cracked	1.6	50
Corn, shelled	1.8	56
Corn meal	1.6	50
Corn-and-cob meal	1.4	45
Cottonseed meal	1.5	48
Cowpeas	1.9	60
Distillers' grain (dried)	0.6	19
Fish meal	1.0	35
Gluten feed	1.3	42
Linseed meal (old process)	1.1	35
Linseed meal (new process)	0.9	29
Meat scrap	1.3	42
Molasses feed	0.8	26
Oats	1.0	32
Oats, ground	0.7	22
Oat middlings	1.5	48
Peanut meal	1.0	32
Rice bran	0.8	26
Rye	1.7	56
Soybeans	1.8	60
Tankage	1.6	51
Velvet beans, shelled	1.8	60
Wheat	1.9	60
Wheat bran	0.5	16
Wheat middlings, standard	0.8	26
Wheat screenings	1.0	32

SECTION III.–STORAGE SPACE REQUIREMENTS
FOR FEED AND BEDDING

Table III-1 gives the storage space requirements for feed and bedding. This information may be helpful to the individual operator who desires to compute the barn space required for a specific livestock enterprise. Also, it provides a convenient means of estimating the amount of feed and bedding in storage.

TABLE III—1

STORAGE SPACE REQUIREMENTS FOR FEED AND BEDDING

Kind of Feed or Bedding	Pounds per Cubic Feet (approx.)	Cubic Feet per Ton (approx.)	Pounds per Bushel of Grain	Cubic Feet per Bushel
Hay[1]............Timothy, loose	3	625-640		
Wild hay, loose	3-4	450-600		
Alfalfa, loose	4	470-485		
Clover, loose	4	500-512		
Chopped hay	10	210-225		
Baled hay (closely stacked)	10	150-200		
Straw and Shavings......Straw, baled[1]	10	200		
Straw, loose[1]	2-3	600-1000		
Shavings, baled	20	100		
Silage............Corn or sorghum silage in tower silos	40	50		
Corn or sorghum silage in trench silos	35	57		
Mill feed.........Bran	13	154		
Middlings	25	80		
Linseed or soybean meal	35			
Grain ....Corn—shelled	45	45	56	1.25
Corn—ear	28	72	70	2.50
Corn—snapped	25	81	80	3.25
Oats	26	77	32	1.25
Barley	39	51	48	1.25
Wheat	48	42	60	1.25
Rye	45	44	56	1.25
Grain sorghum	45	44	56	1.25

[1]From Doane Agricultural Digest, Table 1, p. 532 (Courtesy, Mr. Howard Doane). Under hay and loose straw, a range is given under the columns for pounds per cu. ft. and cubic feet per ton; the higher figures being for hay and loose straw settled one to two months, and the lower figure for hay or loose straw settled over three months.

SECTION IV.—ESTIMATING STEER WEIGHTS FROM
HEART GIRTH MEASUREMENTS[1]

It is highly desirable to know the weight of steers at various stages during the finishing process so that (1) rations can be evaluated, (2) rate of gain can be calculated, and (3) show-ring classification can be determined.

Frequently suitable scales on which to weigh animals are not available. Under such conditions, a simple but reasonably accurate method of estimating body weight is very useful.

Based on heart girth measurements made on a number of steers exhibited at the Ogden and Salt Lake Junior Livestock shows, Professor James A. Bennett, Head, Department of Animal Science, Utah State University, developed the following ingenious formula for estimating steer weights:

Live Wt. = 1.04 [27.5758 (heart girth in inches)—1049.67].

Based on this formula, the calculated live weight values of *steers grading Prime and Choice* and with heart girth measurements within the range of 63 to 80 inches are shown in Table IV-1.

Thus, if a steer (grading Prime or Choice) has a heart girth measurement of 63 inches, his calculated weight may be determined by (1) multiplying 27.5758 by 63, (2) subtracting 1049.67 from the product, and (3) multiplying the remainder by 1.04; or read directly from Table IV-1.

TABLE IV—1

ESTIMATING STEER WEIGHTS FROM HEART GIRTH
MEASUREMENTS

Heart Girth	Calculated Live Weight	Heart Girth	Calculated Live Weight
(inches)	(pounds)	(inches)	(pounds)
63	715	72	973
64	744	73	1002
65	773	74	1031
66	801	75	1060
67	830	76	1088
68	859	77	1117
69	887	78	1145
70	916	79	1174
71	945	80	1203

In taking heart girth measurement, it is important (1) that the steer be kept off feed and water for a minimum of 12 hours (an overnight shrink will be satisfactory and will avoid throwing the animal off feed), (2) that the animal stand with all four legs squarely under the body and with the head up in a normal position, and (3) that the tape be passed around the body just back of the shoulders at the smallest circumference and pulled up snugly.

---

[1] Formulae used in estimating weights of dairy cattle from heart girth measurements are not applicable to market steers, beef animals being lighter than dairy animals of the same heart girth measurement.

SECTION V.—GESTATION TABLE

The stockman who has information relative to breeding dates can easily estimate parturition dates from Table V-1.

TABLE V—1

GESTATION TABLE

Date Bred	Cow 283 Days (date due)	Ewe 148 Days (date due)	Sow 114 Days (date due)	Mare 336 Days (date due)
Jan. 1	Oct. 11	May 29	April 25	Dec. 3
Jan. 6	Oct. 16	June 3	April 30	Dec. 8
Jan. 11	Oct. 21	June 8	May 5	Dec. 13
Jan. 16	Oct. 26	June 13	May 10	Dec. 18
Jan. 21	Oct. 31	June 18	May 15	Dec. 23
Jan. 26	Nov. 5	June 23	May 20	Dec. 28
Jan. 31	Nov. 10	June 28	May 25	Jan. 2
Feb. 5	Nov. 15	July 3	May 30	Jan. 7
Feb. 10	Nov. 20	July 8	June 4	Jan. 12
Feb. 15	Nov. 25	July 13	June 9	Jan. 17
Feb. 20	Nov. 30	July 18	June 14	Jan. 22
Feb. 25	Dec. 5	July 23	June 19	Jan. 27
Mar. 2	Dec. 10	July 28	June 24	Feb. 1
Mar. 7	Dec. 15	Aug. 2	June 29	Feb. 6
Mar. 12	Dec. 20	Aug. 7	July 4	Feb. 11
Mar. 17	Dec. 25	Aug. 12	July 9	Feb. 16
Mar. 22	Dec. 30	Aug. 17	July 14	Feb. 21
Mar. 27	Jan. 4	Aug. 22	July 19	Feb. 26
April 1	Jan. 9	Aug. 27	July 24	Mar. 3
April 6	Jan. 14	Sept. 1	July 29	Mar. 8
April 11	Jan. 19	Sept. 6	Aug. 3	Mar. 13
April 16	Jan. 24	Sept. 11	Aug. 8	Mar. 18
April 21	Jan. 29	Sept. 14	Aug. 13	Mar. 23
April 26	Feb. 3	Sept. 21	Aug. 18	Mar. 28
May 1	Feb. 8	Sept. 26	Aug. 23	April 2
May 6	Feb. 13	Oct. 1	Aug. 28	April 7
May 11	Feb. 18	Oct. 6	Sept. 2	April 12
May 16	Feb. 23	Oct. 11	Sept. 7	April 17
May 21	Feb. 28	Oct. 16	Sept. 12	April 22
May 26	Mar. 5	Oct. 21	Sept. 17	April 27
May 31	Mar. 10	Oct. 26	Sept. 22	May 2
June 5	Mar. 15	Oct. 31	Sept. 27	May 7
June 10	Mar. 20	Nov. 5	Oct. 2	May 12
June 15	Mar. 25	Nov. 10	Oct. 7	May 17
June 20	Mar. 30	Nov. 15	Oct. 12	May 22
June 25	April 4	Nov. 20	Oct. 17	May 27
June 30	April 9	Nov. 25	Oct. 22	June 1
July 5	April 14	Nov. 30	Oct. 27	June 6
July 10	April 19	Dec. 5	Nov. 1	June 11
July 15	April 24	Dec. 10	Nov. 6	June 16
July 20	April 29	Dec. 15	Nov. 11	June 21
July 25	May 4	Dec. 20	Nov. 16	June 26
July 30	May 9	Dec. 25	Nov. 21	July 1
Aug. 4	May 14	Dec. 30	Nov. 26	July 6
Aug. 9	May 19	Jan. 4	Nov. 31	July 11
Aug. 14	May 24	Jan. 9	Dec. 6	July 16
Aug. 19	May 29	Jan. 14	Dec. 11	July 21
Aug. 24	June 3	Jan. 19	Dec. 16	July 26
Aug. 29	June 8	Jan. 24	Dec. 21	July 31
Sept. 3	June 13	Jan. 29	Dec. 26	Aug. 5
Sept. 8	June 18	Feb. 3	Dec. 31	Aug. 10
Sept. 13	June 23	Feb. 8	Jan. 5	Aug. 15
Sept. 18	June 28	Feb. 13	Jan. 10	Aug. 20
Sept. 23	July 3	Feb. 18	Jan. 15	Aug. 25
Sept. 28	July 8	Feb. 23	Jan. 20	Aug. 30
Oct. 3	July 13	Feb. 28	Jan. 25	Sept. 4
Oct. 8	July 18	Mar. 5	Jan. 30	Sept. 9
Oct. 13	July 23	Mar. 10	Feb. 4	Sept. 14
Oct. 18	July 28	Mar. 15	Feb. 9	Sept. 19
Oct. 23	Aug. 2	Mar. 20	Feb. 14	Sept. 24
Oct. 28	Aug. 7	Mar. 25	Feb. 19	Sept. 29
Nov. 2	Aug. 12	Mar. 30	Feb. 24	Oct. 4
Nov. 7	Aug. 17	April 4	Mar. 1	Oct. 9
Nov. 12	Aug. 22	April 9	Mar. 6	Oct. 14
Nov. 17	Aug. 27	April 14	Mar. 11	Oct. 19
Nov. 22	Sept. 1	April 19	Mar. 16	Oct. 24
Nov. 27	Sept. 6	April 24	Mar. 21	Oct. 29
Dec. 2	Sept. 11	April 29	Mar. 26	Nov. 3
Dec. 7	Sept. 16	May 4	Mar. 31	Nov. 8
Dec. 12	Sept. 21	May 9	April 5	Nov. 13
Dec. 17	Sept. 26	May 14	April 10	Nov. 18
Dec. 22	Oct. 1	May 19	April 15	Nov. 23
Dec. 27	Oct. 6	May 24	April 20	Nov. 28

SECTION VI.—BREED REGISTRY ASSOCIATIONS

A breed registry association consists of a group of breeders banded together for the purposes of: (1) recording the lineage of their animals, (2) protecting the purity of the breed, (3) encouraging further improvement of the breed, and (4) promoting the interest of the breed. A list of the breed registry associations is given in Table VI-1.

TABLE VI-1
BREED REGISTRY ASSOCIATIONS

Class of Animal	Breed	Association	Secretary and Address
Beef and Dual-Purpose Cattle:	Angus	American Angus Assn.	Lloyd D. Miller, 3201 Frederick Blvd., St. Joseph, Mo. 64506
	Beefmaster	Beefmaster Breeders Universal	Mrs. Richard E. Brown, Gunter Hotel, San Antonio, Texas 78206
	Belted Galloway	American Belted Galloway Cattle Breeders' Assn.	Charles C. Wells, South Fork Station, West Plains, Texas 65775
	Brahman[1]	American Brahman Breeders' Assn.	Harry P. Gayden, 4815 Gulf Freeway, Houston, Texas 77023
	Brangus	International Brangus Breeders' Assn.	Roy Lilley, 908 Livestock Exchange Bldg., Kansas City, Mo. 64102
	Charolais	American International Charolais Assn.	J. Scott Henderson, 923 Lincoln Liberty Life Bldg., Houston, Texas 77002
	Devon	American Devon Cattle Club, Inc.	Kenneth Hinshaw, 32 Gunn-Geary Lane, Agawam, Mass. 01001
	Dexter	American Dexter Cattle Assn.	Mrs. Daisy Moore, 707 W. Water St., Decorah, Ia. 52101
	Galloway	American Galloway Breeders' Assn.	Harold E. Gerke, P.O. Box 1424, Billings, Mont. 59103
	Hereford	American Hereford Assn.	Dr. W. T. Berry, Hereford Drive, Kansas City, Mo. 64105
	Milking Shorthorn	American Milking Shorthorn Society	Harry Clampitt, 313 S. Glenstone, Springfield, Mo. 65802
	Polled Hereford	American Polled Hereford Assn.	Orville Sweet, 4700 E. 63rd St., Kansas City, Mo. 64130
	Polled Shorthorn	American Polled Shorthorn Society	C. D. "Pete" Swaffar, 8288 Hascall St., Omaha, Nebr. 68124
	Red Angus	Red Angus Assn. of America	Mrs. Sybil Parker, Box 776, Denton, Texas 76201
	Red Brangus	American Red Brangus Assn.	Mike Levi, Paleface Ranch, Spicewood, Texas 78669
	Red Poll	Red Poll Cattle Club of America	Wendell H. Severin, 3275 Holdrege St., Lincoln, Nebr. 68503
	Santa Gertrudis	Santa Gertrudis Breeders' International	R. P. Marshall, Box 1257, Kingsville, Texas 78363
	Scotch Highland	American Scotch Highland Breeders' Assn.	Margaret Manke, Edgemont, S. D. 57735
	Shorthorn	American Shorthorn Breeders' Assn.	C. D. "Pete" Swaffar, 8288 Hascall St., Omaha, Nebr. 68124
	Simmental	American Simmental Assn.	Dale J. Lynch, 270 Country Commons Rd., Cary, Ill. 60013
Dairy Cattle:	Ayrshire	Ayrshire Breeders Assn.	David Gibson, Jr., Brandon, Vt. 05733
	Brown Swiss	Brown Swiss Cattle Breeders Assn.	Marvin L. Kruse, 800 Pleasant St., Beloit, Wisc. 53511
	Guernsey	American Guernsey Cattle Club	Francis X. Chapman, 70 Main St., Peterborough, N. H. 03458
	Holstein-Friesian	Holstein-Friesian Assn. of America	Robert H. Rumler, Box 808, Brattleboro, Vt. 05301

(Continued)

Footnotes on last page of table.

(Continued)

TABLE VI-1 (Cont.)

Class of Animal	Breed	Association	Secretary and Address
Dairy Cattle: (Continued)	Jersey	American Jersey Cattle Club	J. F. Cavanaugh, Secretary, 1521 E. Broad St., Columbus, Ohio 43205
Sheep:	Cheviot	American Cheviot Sheep Society, Inc.	S. R. Gates, P.O. Box 5051, Lafayette Hill, Pa. 19444
	Columbia	Columbia Sheep Breeders' Assn. of America	Richard L. Gerber, P.O. Box 272, Upper Sandusky, Ohio 43351
	Corriedale	American Corriedale Assn., Inc.	Russell E. Jackson, Box 92C, Seneca, Ill. 61360
	Cotswold	American Cotswold Record Assn.	Peter W. Hintz, 217 Penn Ave., Fremont, Ohio 43420
	Debouillet	Debouillet Sheep Breeders' Assn.	Mrs. A. D. Jones, 300 S. Kentucky Ave., Roswell, N. M. 88201
	Delaine-Merino	American & Delaine-Merino Record Assn.	Harold E. Simms, Aleppo, Pa. 15310
		Black Top and Delaine-Merino Sheep Breeders' Assn.	Emerson F. Richards, 416 W. Maple, Byron, Mich. 48418
		Texas Delaine-Merino Record Assn.	Mrs. G. A. Glimp, Route 1, Burnet, Texas 78611
	Dorset and Polled Dorset	Continental Dorset Club	J. R. Henderson, P.O. Box 97, Hickory, Pa. 15340
	Hampshire	American Hampshire Sheep Assn.	Roy A. Gilman, Stuart, Ia. 50250
	Lincoln	National Lincoln Sheep Breeders' Assn.	R. O. Shaffer, 5284 S. Albaugh Rd., West Milton, Ohio 45383
	Montadale	Montadale Sheep Bredeers' Assn., Inc.	E. H. Mattingly, 4103 N. Broadway, St. Louis, Mo. 63147
	North Country Cheviot	American North Country Cheviot Sheep Assn.	John C. Goater, Hitchner Hall, Univ. of Maine, Orono, Me. 04473
	Oxford	American Oxford Down Record Assn.	C. E. Puffenberger, Eaton Rapids, Mich. 48827
	Panama	American Panama Registry Assn.	W. G. Priest, Rt. 2, Jerome, Ida. 83338
	Rambouillet	American Rambouillet Sheep Breeders' Assn.	Mrs. Russell G. Harlow, 2709 Sherwood Way, San Angelo, Texas 76901
	Romney	American Romney Breeders' Assn.	John H. Landers, Jr., 214 Withycombe Hall, Oregon State Univ. Dept. of Animal Science, Corvallis, Ore. 97330
	Shropshire	American Shropshire Registry Assn.	Mrs. Jessie Ritenour, Box 678, Lafayette, Ind. 47902
	Southdown	American Southdown Breeders' Assn.	W. L. Henning, 212 S. Allen St., State College, Pa. 16801
	Suffolk	American Suffolk Sheep Society	Allan Jenkins, 206 Livestock Exchange Bldg., Ogden, Utah 88401
		National Suffolk Sheep Assn.	Mrs. Betty Biellier, Box 324, Columbia, Mo. 65201
	Targhee	U. S. Targhee Sheep Assn.	Gene Coombs, P.O. Box 2513, Billings, Mont. 59101
	Tunis	National Tunis Sheep Registry, Inc.	Eloise S. Spraker, Bath, N. Y. 14810
Goats:	Angora	American Angora Goat Breeders' Assn.	Mrs. Thomas L. Taylor, Rocksprings, Texas 78880
Milk Goats:		American Goat Society, Inc.	J. Willett Taylor, 1606 Colorado St., Manhattan, Kansas 66502
		American Dairy Goat Assn.	Don Wilson, P.O. Box 186, Spindale, N. C. 28160
Swine:	American Landrace	American Landrace Assn., Inc.	Eugene G. Benedict, Box 111, Culver, Ind. 46511
	Berkshire	American Berkshire Assn.	Gene Mason, 601 W. Monroe St., Springfield, Ill. 62704

Footnotes on last page of table.

(Continued)

TABLE VI-1 (Cont.)

Class of Animal	Breed	Association	Secretary and Address
Swine (Continued)	Chester White	Chester White Swine Record Assn.	Larry L. Rus, 116 E. 8th St., Rochester, Ind. 46975
	Duroc	United Duroc Swine Registry	Bruce Henderson, 237-9 N.E. Monroe, Peoria, Ill. 61603
	English Large Black	National Large Black Swine Breeders' Assn.	R. L. Teeter, Route 1, Midland, N. C. 28107
	Hampshire	Hampshire Swine Registry	Harold Boucher, 1111 Main St., Peoria, Ill. 61606
	Hereford	National Hereford Hog Record Assn.	Mrs. Sylvia Schulte, Norway, Ia. 52318
	Inbred Breeds	Inbred Livestock Registry Assn.	George W. Slater, Pres., Rt. 4, Box 207, Noblesville, Ind. 46060
	OIC (Ohio Improved Chester)	OIC Swine Breeders' Assn., Inc.	Thomas R. Hendricks, Box 111, Greencastle, Ind. 46135
	Poland China	Poland China Record Assn.	C. W. Mitchell, 501 E. Losey St., Galesburg, Ill. 61401
	Red Berkshire	Kentucky Red Berkshire Swine Record Assn.	Hogan Teater, Lancaster, Ky. 40444
	Spotted	National Spotted Swine Record, Inc.	Duane Fort, West Main St., Bainbridge, Ind. 46105
	Tamworth	Tamworth Swine Assn.	Erwin Mahrenholz, 4705 Middle Mt. Vernon, Rd., Evansville, Ind. 47712
	Wessex Saddleback	Wessex Saddleback Swine Assn.	A. M. McCracken, 4100 Clinton Ave., Des Moines, Ia. 50310
	Yorkshire	American Yorkshire Club, Inc.	Wilbur L. Plager, Box 878, Lafayette, Ind. 47902
Light Horses:	American Albino Horse	American Albino Assn., Inc.	Ruth White, Box 79, Crabtree, Ore. 97335
	American Paint Horse	The American Paint Horse Assn.	Ralph Dye, P.O. Box 12487, Ft. Worth, Texas 76116
	American Saddle Horse	American Saddle Horse Breeders' Assn.	Chas. J. Cronan, Jr., 929 S. Fourth St., Louisville, Ky. 40203
	Appaloosa	Appaloosa Horse Club, Inc.	George B. Hatley, Box 403, Moscow, Ida. 83843
	Arabian	Arabian Horse Club Registry of America	Ward B. Howland, 332 S. Michigan Ave., Chicago, Ill. 60604
	Buckskin	American Buckskin Registry Assn.	Bonnie Trent, P.O. Box 772, Anderson, Calif. 96007
	Cleveland Bay	Cleveland Bay Assn. of America	A. Mackay-Smith, White Post, Va. 22663
	Galiceno	Galiceno Horse Breeders' Assn., Inc.	D. L. Adkins, 708 Peoples Bank Bldg., Tyler, Texas 75701
	Hackney	American Hackney Horse Society	Paul E. Bolton, Jr., 527 Madison Ave., New York, N. Y. 10022
	Half-Arabian & Anglo-Arabian	International Arabian Horse Assn.	Ralph E. Goodall, Jr., 224 E. Olive Ave., Burbank, Calif. 91503
	Half-Thoroughbred	American Remount Assn.	George Havens, Box 1171, Colorado Springs, Colo. 80901
	Hungarian Horse	Hungarian Horse Assn.	Mrs. Margit Sigray Bessenyey, Bitterroot Stock Farm, Hamilton, Mont. 59840
	Missouri Fox Trotting Horse	Missouri Fox Trotting Horse Breed Assn., Inc.	Homer Harley, Box 637, Ava, Mo. 65608
	Morgan	Morgan Horse Club, Inc.	Seth P. Holcombe, Box 2157, West Hartford, Conn. 06117
	Palomino	Palomino Horse Assn.	Mrs. Edna Fagan, Box 446, Chatsworth, Calif. 91311
		Palomino Horse Breeders' of America	Melba Lee Spivey, Box 249, Mineral Wells, Texas 76067
	Paso Fino	American Paso Fino Pleasure Horse Assn., Inc.	Mrs. Rosalie MacWilliam, Arrott Bldg., 401 Wood St., Pittsburgh, Pa. 15222
	Peruvian Paso	American Assn. of Owners & Breeders of Peruvian Paso Horses	Dr. Marguerite Rogers, P.O. Box 371, Calabasas, Calif. 91302
	Pinto	Pinto Horse Assn. of America, Inc.	Mrs. Helen H. Smith, 8245 Hillside Ave., Alta Loma, Calif. 91701

Footnotes on last page of table.

(Continued)

TABLE VI-1 (Cont.)

Class of Animal	Breed	Association	Secretary and Address
Light Horses: (Continued)	Quarter Horse	American Quarter Horse Assn.	Don Jones, Box 200, Amarillo, Texas 79105
	Spanish Mustang	Spanish Mustang Registry, Inc.	Bob Racicot, Box 398, Thompson Falls, Mont. 59873
	Standardbred	U. S. Trotting Assn. (Standardbred)	Edward Hackett, 750 Michigan Ave., Columbus, Ohio 43215
	Tennessee Walking Horse	Tennessee Walking Horse Breeders & Exhibitors Assn. of America	Mrs. Sharon Brandon, Box 286, Lewisburg, Tenn. 37091
	Thoroughbred	The Jockey Club (Thoroughbred)	John F. Kennedy, 300 Park Ave., New York, N. Y. 10022
Ponies:	American Gotland Horse	American Gotland Horse Assn.	Mrs. John C. Murdock, 110 E. Parkway, Columbia, Mo. 65201
	Connemara Pony	American Connemara Pony Society	Al Mavis, Rt. 2, Rochester, Ill. 62563
	Pony of the Americas	Pony of the Americas Club, Inc.	L. L. Boomhower, P.O. Box 1447, Mason City, Ia. 50401
	Shetland Pony	American Shetland Pony Club	Burton J. Zuege, P.O. Box 2339, W. Lafayette, Ind. 47906
	Welsh Pony	Welsh Pony Society of America, Inc.	Mrs. Sydney S. Swett, 1770 Lancaster Ave., Paoli, Pa. 19301
Draft Horses: Jacks: Donkeys:	American Cream Horse	American Cream Horse Assn.	Mrs. K. B. Topp, Hubbard, Ia. 50122
	Belgian	Belgian Draft Horse Corporation of America	B. A. Schmalzried, 282 S. Wabash St., Wabash, Ind. 46992
	Clydesdale	Clydesdale Breeders' Assn. of the United States	Chas. W. Willhoit, Batavia, Ia. 52533
	Percheron	Percheron Horse Assn. of America	Dale Gossett, Route 1, Belmont, Ohio 43718
	Shire	American Shire Horse Assn.	Edwin R. Henken, P.O. Box 88, Lynden, Wash. 98264
	Suffolk	American Suffolk Horse Assn., Inc.	Edwin R. Henken, P.O. Box 88, Lynden, Wash. 98264
	Jacks and Jennets	Standard Jack and Jennet Registry of America	Mrs. F. G. Johns, Rt. 7, Todds Rd., Lexington, Ky. 40502
All Horses and Half-Breeds:	Any and all colors and types (including animals not eligible for registry, eligible to but not registered, or registered in existing associations) including both light and draft horses.	National Recording Office	Ruth E. White, Box 79, Crabtree, Ore. 97335
	Half-bred Thoroughbreds: Foals with one registered Thoroughbred parent.	American Remount Association (Half-Thoroughbred Registry)2	George Havens, Box 1171, Colorado Springs, Colo. 80901
	Half-Arabian: In the Half-Arabian Registry: Foals by registered Arabian stallions and out of mares that are not registered in either the American (Jockey Club) Stud Book or The Arabian Stud Book.	International Arabian Horse Assn.	Ralph E. Goodall, Jr., 224 E. Olive Ave., Burbank, Calif. 91502

Footnotes on last page of table. (Continued)

TABLE VI-1 (Cont.)

Class of Animal	Breed	Association	Secretary and Address
All Horses and Half-Breeds (Continued)	In the Anglo-Arab Registry: (1) Foals by registered3 Thoroughbred stallions and out of registered Arabian mares; (2) Foals by registered Arabian stallions and out of registered Thoroughbred or registered Anglo-Arab mares.		

[1] Includes three breeds of *Bos indicus* cattle that have and are contributing to beef production in the U.S.; namely, American Brahman, Indu-Brazil, and Africander.

[2] Formerly the Half-Bred Stud Book operated by The American Remount Association (U.S. Army Remount), but now a privately owned registry. It records only foals sired by registered Thoroughbred stallions and out of mares not registered in The American (Jockey Club) Stud Book, or in the Arabian Stud Book.

[3] Thoroughbred stallions registered in either The American (Jockey Club) Stud Book, the General Stud Book (English), or the French Stud Book are accepted.

SECTION VII.—BREED MAGAZINES

The livestock magazines publish news items and informative articles of special interest to stockmen. Also, many of them employ field representatives whose chief duty it is to assist in the buying and selling of animals.

In the compilation of the list herewith presented (see Table VII-1) no attempt was made to list the general livestock magazines of which there are numerous outstanding ones. Only those magazines which are devoted to a specific class or breed of animal are included.

TABLE VII-1
BREED MAGAZINES

Class of Animal	Breed	Publication	Address
Beef and Dual-Purpose Cattle:	General [1]	American Cattle Producer	801 E. 17th Ave., Denver, Colo. 80218
		Calf News	Suite 303, 18345 Ventura Blvd., Tarzana, Calif. 91356
		Canadian Cattleman	Rm. 251, Calgary Centre, 1632 14th Ave. N.W., Calgary, Alberta, Canada
		Cattleman, The	410 E. Weatherford St., Fort Worth, Texas 76102
		Feedlot	Box 67, Minneapolis, Minn. 55440
	Angus	Aberdeen-Angus Journal	P.O. Box 238, Webster City, Ia. 50595
	Brahman	International Brahman Review	P.O. Box 1030 Kissimmee, Fla. 32741
	Brangus	Brangus Journal	908 Livestock Exchange Bldg., Kansas City, Mo. 64102
	Charolais	Charolais Banner	P.O. Box 16050, Kansas City, Mo. 64112
	Devon	Devon Cattle Quarterly	Agawam, Mass. 01001
	Galloway	American Galloway Journal	South Fork, Mo. 65776
	Hereford	American Hereford Journal	700 W. 12th St., Kansas City, Mo. 64105
		Canadian Hereford Digest	512 4th Ave. S.W., Calgary, Alberta, Canada
		Texas Hereford	1207 Burk Burnett Bldg., Fort Worth, Texas 76102
	Milking Shorthorn	Milking Shorthorn Journal	313 S. Glenstone, Springfield, Mo. 65802
	Polled Hereford	Polled Hereford World, Inc.	300 Southwest Blvd., Kansas City, Mo. 66103
	Red Poll	Red Poll News	3275 Holdrege St., Lincoln, Nebr. 68503
	Santa Gertrudis	Santa Gertrudis Journal	P.O. Box 2386, Ft. Worth, Tex., 76101
	Shorthorn	The Shorthorn World	16 S. Locust St., Aurora, Ill. 60506
Sheep:	General [2]	Montana Wool Grower	Livestock Bldg., Helena, Mont. 59601
		National Wool Grower	600 Crandall Bldg., Salt Lake City, Utah 84101
		Sheep Breeder and Sheepman	Box 769, Columbia, Mo. 65201
		Sheep and Goat Raiser	Cactus Hotel Annex, San Angelo, Texas 76901
		Shepherd, The	Sheffield, Mass. 01257
Goats:	General [3]	Better Goat Keeping	Harvard, Mass. 01451
		Bleat, The [4]	Box 350, Port Coquitlam, British Columbia, Canada
		Dairy Goat Journal	8th & Broadway, Columbia, Mo. 65201

Footnotes on last page of table.   (Continued)

TABLE VII-1 (Cont.)

Class of Animal	Breed	Publication	Address
Swine:	General[5]	National Hog Farmer	1999 Shepard Rd., St. Paul, Minn. 55116
	American Landrace	American Landrace, The	313 S. Glenstone, Springfield, Mo. 65802
	Berkshire	Berkshire News	601 W. Monroe St., Springfield, Ill. 62704
	Chester White	Chester White Journal	Rochester, Ind. 46975
	Duroc	Duroc News	237-9 N.E. Monroe St., Peoria, Ill. 61603
	Hampshire	American Hampshire Herdsman	1111 Main St., Peoria, Ill. 61606
	OIC	OIC News	Box 111, Greencastle, Ind. 46135
	Poland China	Poland China World	501 E. Losey St., Galesburg, Ill. 61401
	Spotted	Spotted News	Alamo Bldg., Greencastle, Ind. 46135
	Tamworth	Tamworth News	Lacona, Ia. 50139
	Yorkshire	Yorkshire Journal	1001 South St., Lafayette, Ind. 47902
Dairy Cattle:	General[6]	Dairy Herd Management	The Miller Publishing Co., 2501 Wayzata Blvd., Minneapolis, Minn. 55440
		Hoard's Dairyman	W. D. Hoard & Sons Co., 28 Milwaukee Ave. W., Ft. Atkinson, Wis. 53538
		Western Dairy Journal	Nelson R. Crow Publications, Inc., 1730 So. Clementine St., Anaheim, Calif. 92802
	Ayrshire	Ayrshire Digest	Ayrshire Breeders Assn., 1 Union St., Brandon, Vt. 05733
		Canadian Ayrshire Review	Ayshire Breeders' Assoc. of Canada, 1160 Carling Ave., Ottawa, Canada
	Brown Swiss	The Brown Swiss Bulletin	Brown Swiss Cattle Breeders Assn., Box 1019, Beloit, Wisc. 53511
	Guernsey	Guernsey Breeders Journal	American Guernsey Cattle Club, 70 Main St., Peterborough, N. H. 03458
	Holstein-Friesian	Holstein-Friesian Journal	Donovan Ltd., 129 Adelaide St. W., Toronto 1, Canada
		Holstein-Friesian World	The Holstein-Friesian World, Inc., Lacona, N. Y. 13083
	Jersey	Canadian Jersey Breeder	290 Lawrence Ave. W., Toronto 20, Ontario, Canada
		The Jersey Journal	American Jersey Cattle Club, 1521 E Broad St., Columbus, Ohio 43205
Horses:	General[6]	Chronicle of the Horse, The	Middleburg, Va. 22117
		Florida Horse	Box 699, Ocala, Fla. 32670
		Horse & Rider	116 E. Badillo, Covina, Calif. 91722
		Horse and Show Journal, The	20614 Aurora Rd., Bedford, Ohio 44146
		Horse Lover, The	Box 914, El Cerrito, Calif. 94530
		Horseman	5314 Bingle Rd., Houston, Texas 77018
		Horsemen's Advisor, The	624 Payton Ave., Des Moines, Ia. 50315
		Horse Show	527 Madison Ave., New York, N. Y. 10022
		Horse World	P. O. Box 588, Lexington, Ky. 40501
		Lariat, The	Rt. 5, 14239 N.E. Salmon Creek Ave., Vancouver, Wash. 98665

Footnotes on last page of table.

(Continued)

Class of Animal	Breed	Publication	Address
Horses: (Continued)		Maryland Horse	P. O. Box 4, Timonium, Md. 21093
		National Horseman	933 Baxter Ave., Louisville, Ky. 40204
		Northeast Horseman	Box 47, Summer St., Hampden Highlands, Me. 04445
		Saddle and Bridle	8011 Clayton Rd., St. Louis, Mo. 63117
		Southern Horseman, The	P. O. Box 5735, Meridian, Miss. 39301
		Turf and Sport Digest	511-513 Oakland Ave., Baltimore, Md. 21212
		Western Horseman	3850 N. Nevada Ave., Colorado Springs, Colo. 80901
		Your Pony	1040 W. James St., Columbus, Wisc. 53925
	Appaloosa	Appaloosa News	Box 403, Moscow, Ida. 83843
	Arabian	Arabian Horse News	Box 1009, Boulder, Colo. 80302
		Arabian Horse World	23 E. Main St., Springville, N. Y. 14141
	Hackney	Hackney Journal	Box 29, Columbus, Wisc. 53925
	Morgan	Morgan Horse Magazine	P.O. Box 149, Leominster, Mass. 01453
	Palomino	Palomino Horses	Box 249, Mineral Wells, Texas 76067
	Pinto	Pinto Horse, The	4315 Hilldale Rd., San Diego, Calif. 92116
	Pony of the Americas	Pony of the Americas Club Official Magazine	1452 N. Federal, P. O. Box 1447, Mason City, Ia. 50401
	Quarter Horse	Quarter Horse Digest	Gann Valley, S. D. 57341
		Quarter Horse Journal	Box 9105, Amarillo, Texas 79105
	Shetland Pony	American Shetland Pony Journal	Box 2339, West Lafayette, Ind. 47906
	Standardbred	Harness Horse, The	Telegraph Press Bldg., Harrisburg, Pa. 17101
		Hoof Beats (U. S. Trotting)	740 Michigan Ave., Columbus, Ohio 43215
		Standardbred Horse Review	21-300 Kennedy, Desert Hot Springs, Calif. 92240
	Tennessee Walking Horse	Voice of the Tennessee Walking Horse	Voice Pub. Co., P. O. Box 6009, Chattanooga, Tenn. 37401
	Thoroughbred	B. C. Thoroughbred, The	4023 E. Hastings St., North Burnaby, B. C., Canada
		Blood Horse, The	Box 4038, Lexington, Ky. 40504
		Mountains & Plains Thoroughbred	Box 766, Littleton, Colo. 80121
		Thoroughbred of California, The	Box 750, 201 Colorado Place, Arcadia, Calif. 91006
		Thoroughbred Record, The	Box 850, Lexington, Ky. 40501
		Washington Horse, The	13470 Empire Way, Seattle, Wash. 98178
	Welsh Pony	Welsh News	1427 Hampshire St., Quincy, Ill. 62301
Poultry:	General	American Poultry Journal	Pacific Edition, 749 Foothill Blvd., La Canada, Calif. 91011
		Broiler Growing	Mount Morris, Ill. 61054
		Pacific Poultryman	Watt Publishing Co., Mount Morris, Ill. 61054
		Poultry Digest	Sea Isle City, N. J. 08243
		Poultry Tribune	Mount Morris, Ill. 61054

[1] Covers all breeds
[2] Covers all breeds.
[3] Covers all breeds of milk goats.
[4] Mimeographed bulletin of B. C. Milk Goat Breeders Assn.
[5] Covers all breeds of swine.
[6] Covers several breeds.

SECTION VIII.–STATE COLLEGES OF AGRICULTURE

The stockman can obtain a list of available bulletins and circulars, and other information regarding livestock, by writing to his state agricultural college. A list of the state agricultural colleges follows. Land-grant institutions are designated by an asterisk (*).

State	Address
Alabama	*School of Agriculture, Auburn University, Auburn. Tuskegee Institute, Tuskegee.
Alaska	*Division of Agriculture, University of Alaska, College.
Arizona	*College of Agriculture, University of Arizona, Tucson. Arizona State University, Tempe.
Arkansas	*College of Agriculture, University of Arkansas, Fayetteville.
California	*College of Agricultural and Environmental Sciences, University of California, Davis. Division of Agriculture, Chico State College, Chico. Division of Agriculture, Fresno State College, Fresno. Department of Agriculture, California State Polytechnic College, San Luis Obispo.
Colorado	*College of Agriculture, Colorado State University, Fort Collins.
Connecticut	*College of Agriculture, University of Connecticut, Storrs.
Delaware	*School of Agriculture, University of Delaware, Newark.
Florida	*College of Agriculture, University of Florida, Gainesville. Florida A & M University, Tallahassee.
Georgia	*College of Agriculture, University of Georgia, Athens.
Hawaii	*Department of Agriculture, University of Hawaii, Honolulu.
Idaho	*College of Agriculture, University of Idaho, Moscow.
Illinois	*The College of Agriculture, University of Illinois, Urbana. School of Agriculture, Southern Illinois University, Carbondale. Illinois State University, Normal. Western Illinois University, Macomb.
Indiana	*School of Agriculture, Purdue University, Lafayette.
Iowa	*The College of Agriculture, Iowa State University, Ames.
Kansas	*College of Agriculture, Kansas State University, Manhattan.
Kentucky	*College of Agriculture, University of Kentucky, Lexington. Berea College, Berea. Eastern Kentucky University, Richmond. Morehead State University, Morehead. Murray State University, Murray. Western Kentucky State University, Bowling Green.
Louisiana	*The Louisiana State University, University Station, Baton Rouge. Frances T. Nicholls State College, Thibodaux. Grambling College, Grambling. Louisiana Polytechnic Institute, Ruston. McNeese State College, Lake Charles. Northeast Louisiana State College, Monroe. Northwestern State College of Louisiana, Natchitoches. Southeastern Louisiana State College, Hammond. Southern University and A & M College, Baton Rouge. University of Southwestern Louisiana, Lafayette.
Maine	*College of Agriculture, University of Maine, Orono.
Maryland	*College of Agriculture, University of Maryland, College Park.
Massachusetts	*School of Agriculture, University of Massachusetts, Amherst.
Michigan	*College of Agriculture, Michigan State University, East Lansing. Michigan Emmanuel Missionary College, Berrien Springs.

Minnesota	*Department of Agriculture, University of Minnesota, University Farm, St. Paul.
Mississippi	*School of Agriculture, Mississippi State University, State College.
Missouri	*Division of Agricultural Science, University of Missouri, Columbia.
Montana	*Department of Agriculture, Montana State University, Bozeman.
Nebraska	*College of Agriculture, University of Nebraska, Lincoln.
Nevada	*College of Agriculture, University of Nevada, Reno.
New Hampshire	*College of Agriculture, University of New Hampshire, Durham.
New Jersey	*State College of Agriculture, Rutgers University, New Brunswick.
New Mexico	*College of Agriculture and Home Economics, New Mexico State University of Agriculture, Engineering, and Science, University Park.
New York	*New York State College of Agriculture, Cornell University, Ithaca.
North Carolina	*North Carolina State College of Agriculture, University of North Carolina, Raleigh. Agricultural and Technical College of N. C., Greensboro. Pembroke State College, Pembroke.
North Dakota	*North Dakota State University, State University Station, Fargo.
Ohio	*The College of Agriculture, Ohio State University, Columbus.
Oklahoma	*School of Agriculture, Oklahoma State University, Stillwater. Panhandle A & M College, Goodwell.
Oregon	*School of Agriculture, Oregon State University, Corvallis.
Pennsylvania	*School of Agriculture, Pennsylvania State University, State College. Delaware Valley Col. Sci. & Agr., Doylestown.
Puerto Rico	*College of Agriculture, University of Puerto Rico, Rio Piedras.
Rhode Island	*School of Agriculture, University of Rhode Island, Kingston.
South Carolina	*Clemson University, Clemson.
South Dakota	*South Dakota State University, Brookings.
Tennessee	*College of Agriculture, University of Tennessee, Knoxville. Middle Tennessee State University, Murfreesboro. Tennessee A & I State University, Nashville. Tennessee Polytech Institute, Cooksville.
Texas	*Department of Agriculture, Texas A & M University, College Station. Abilene Christian College, Abilene. Prairie View A & M College, Prairie View. Sul Ross State College, Alpine. Texas A & I University, Kingsville. Texas Technological College, Lubbock.
Utah	Brigham Young University, Provo. *Utah State University, Logan.
Vermont	*College of Agriculture, University of Vermont, Burlington.
Virginia	*School of Agriculture, Virginia Polytechnic Institute, Blacksburg. Virginia State College, Petersburg.
Washington	*College of Agriculture, Washington State University, Pullman.
West Virginia	*College of Agriculture, West Virginia University, Morgantown.

Wisconsin	*College of Agriculture, University of Wisconsin, Madison. Wisconsin State University, River Falls.
Wyoming	*College of Agriculture, University of Wyoming, Laramie.

IN CANADA

Alberta	University of Alberta, Edmonton, Alberta
British Columbia	University of British Columbia, Vancouver, B. C.
Manitoba	University of Manitoba, Winnipeg, Manitoba
Nova Scotia	University of Nova Scotia, Truro, Nova Scotia
Ontario	Ontario Agricultural College, Guelph, Ontario
Saskatchewan	University of Saskatchewan, Saskatoon, Saskatchewan
Quebec	MacDonald College, St. Anne de Bellevue, Quebec

INDEX

Page

Abilene, Kansas, shipping point 343
Accounts, farm 326
Acetonemia 144
Aging beef 481
Aging lamb and mutton 742
Ailments, nutritional 143
Alcohol, disinfectant 211
Alkali disease (selenium poisoning) 154
Allergy 216
Alpine goat 788
American
    Albino Horses 1125
    Cream Horse 1128
    Buckskin 1125
    Gotland 1125
    Landrace hogs 802
    Meat Institute 264
        grading system of 284
    Paint Horse 1125
    Paso Fino 1125
    Saddle Horses 1125
Anemia, nutritional 144, 858
Angora goat (see also Goat) 779
Angus 363, 365
Animal
    agriculture 4
    breeding, principles 31
    clothing 15
    companion of grain production 22
    convert inedible feeds 18
    disease 194
    Disease Eradication Division 214
    diversification 22
    efficiency 160
    erosion control 20
    fats, feeding of 97
    food 15
    functions 15
    health 201
    imports 304
    labor requirements 27
    power 15
    production 33
    recreation 15
    science 2
        birth of 2
        definition of 1
    soil fertility 21
    unit month 578
    units 1215
    vs. cereal diet 6
Animals
    distribution of 4
    early American importations 4
Ante-mortem inspection 254
Anthelmintic 216
Antibiotics 131, 216
    medium-spectrum 217
Antibody 216
Antigen 216
Antiseptic 216
Aphosphorosis 144
Appalachian and Great Lakes region, cattle in.... 353
Appaloosa horses 1125
Arabian horses 1125
Arthropods 198
    insects 198
    ticks 198
Artificial insemination 74, 1183
    dairy 537

Page

Asiatic Urial sheep 622
Associations, breed registry 1226
Auctions
    community or local 238
    purebred 243
Australia
    beef production in 350
    sheep raising in 633
Autopsy 216
Ayrshire cattle 500
Azoturia (blackwater of horses) 144

Baby beef
    definition 477
    production 393
Baby pig shakes 144
Bacon type of swine 807
Bacteria 195, 216
Bacterins 205
Bacteriostat 216
Bakewell, Robert 339, 626
Balanced ration 88
Barn roofs 178
Barn, size to build 1223
Bates boom 52
Bedding
    storage space, requirements for 1223
Beef
    aging 481
    carcass, disposition of 482
    cuts 482
    dairy (dairy beef) 574
    duties, import 358
Beef cattle (see also Cattle)
    adaptation 382
    age and longevity 378
    breeding 399
        breeding season and time of calving.... 410
        bull, age and service of 405
        bull, care and management of 403
        calf crop, % 33, 379
        calving 407
        dwarfism 413
        estrus, signs of 402
        fertility in 402
        freemartin 412
        gestation period 402
        heat periods 401
        heifers, age to breed 400
        lethals 413
        mating, hand 403
        mating, pasture 403
        pregnancy, signs and tests of 403
        pregnant cow, care of 406
        Production Testing 416
        puberty, age of 399
        purebreds 392
        two-year-olds 400
    breeds 363
        Angus 365
        Beefmasters 365
        Belted Galloway 365
        Brahman 366
        Brangus 366
        Charbray 366
        Charolais 366
        Devon 366
        Dexter 367
        Galloway 367
        Hereford 367

Page

Indu Brazil (Zebu) 368
Milking Shorthorn 370
Polled Hereford 368
Polled Shorthorn 368
popularity of breeds 363
Red Angus 369
Red Brangus 369
Red Poll 370
Santa Gertrudis 369
Scotch Highland 369
Shorthorn 369
buildings and equipment
for finishing cattle 456
bulls (see Bulls)
establishing the herd 376
fattening (see Cattle finishing)
feeding
antibiotics 131
concentrates for 436
contract 458
custom 458
energy need 425
hay and roughage for 433
mineral needs 426
pastures for 432
protein needs 424
rations, suggested 459
roots for 434
salt requirements of 426
self-feeding salt-feed mixtures 437
silage for 434
vitamin needs 429
water needs 431
future of industry in U.S.A. 357
growth of industry 344
herd size 377
history
Abilene, Kansas, shipping point 343
ancient use of 336
Bakewell's improvements 339
Bos indicus 337
Bos taurus 336
breeding in America 341
domestication 336
industry, growth in U.S.A. 344
origin 336
oxen 338
westward expansion 343
world distribution 345
zoological classification of 338
judging 385
ideal type and conformation 386
method of examining 388
parts of a cow 386
production
Australia, in 350
breeding purebreds 392
Canada, in 349
cow-and-calf 392
factors favorable to 355
factors unfavorable to 356
Mexico, in 350
South America, in 346
systems 391
U.S.A., in 351
production areas in U.S.A.
Appalachian 353
Corn Belt 353
Cotton Belt 354
Great Lakes 353
leading states 355
western range 352
purebreds or grades 376
record forms 417-419
reproductive ability 379
selection bases 382
improvement through 384
pedigree 383

Page

show-ring winnings 384
type or individuality 383
selection of breed 377
size in 380
types of 361
Beefmasters cattle 365
Beef type 361
Belgian horses 361, 386
Belted Galloway 1128
Beltsville No. 1 hogs 365
Berkshire hogs 809
Bichloride of mercury, disinfectant 809
Biologic standardizing 211
Biological test 215
Biologics 960
bacterins 203
other protectives 205
serums 205
toxoids (anatoxins) 205
vaccines 205
Births, multiple 204
Black-faced Highland sheep 45
Blackwater of horses (azoturia) 653
Blindness 144
moon 150
night 154
Bloat, prevention 144, 571
Boars
age and service of 833
care and management of 831
feeding 872
Bologna bulls 477
Bomb calorimeter 99
Boric acid, disinfectant 211
Bos indicus 337
Bos taurus 336
Brahman cattle 366
Brands, inspection of 246, 257
Brangus cattle 326
Break-joint of sheep 740
Breathing rate, normal 193
Breed magazines 1231
Breed registry associations
history of 78
list of 1226
recognition of 361
Breeding
new frontiers in 79
systems of 55
Breeding purebreds 392
Breeds
cattle 363
horses 1102, 1123
recognition of 645
sheep 645
swine 805
Broad-spectrum antibiotic 216
Broadtail fur 649
Brown Swiss cattle 500
Brucellosis 521
Brucellosis test 206
Bruises and crippling 247
prevention of 247
Budgets 327
Buildings and equipment for finishing cattle 456
Buildings for livestock
attractiveness 170
convenient 172
cost, reasonable 169
dryness 170
durability 170
fire prevention 173
floors 178
headquarters location 166
insulation 174
lighting 171
maintenance costs reasonable 169
manure disposal and pit 171

Page

passages 177
protect newborn animals from elements 170
requisites 169
rodent control 173
roofs 178
safety 173
sanitation 171
scales 188
space adequate 172
storage 172
sunlight 171
use, multiple 172
utility value 170
ventilation 171
water facilities 173
Bulls
age and service of 405
bologna 477
care of 403
feeding 438
grading 415
management of 403
Business aspects 318
dairy 494
poultry 926
Butcher stock 477
By-products from slaughter 310

Calcium 103, 427, 708, 856
calcium-phosphorus ratio 105
deficiencies 106
supplements 107
vitamin D relationship 105
Calf crop, % 33, 379
Calf, leading markets 467
Calf scours 571
Calorie system 98, 579
Calorimeter, bomb 99
Calves
creep feeding 441
death losses 33
feeding grain 441
weaning age 33
weaning weight 33
Canada, beef production in 349
Canning meat 306
Capital needs 320
Caracul fur 649
Carbohydrates 92
N.F.E. and fiber 92
Carcass, disposal of dead animals 209
Carcass grade as selling basis 241
Carotene 122
Cationic bactericides, disinfectant 211
Cattle (see also Beef cattle)
domestication of 336
dressing percentage of 479
dual-purpose breeds of 363
Milking Shorthorn 370
Red Poll 370
duties, import 358
finishing 394, 450
age as a factor in 452
breeding, value of 451
buildings for 456
confinement feeding 456
dry-lot 443
equipment for 456
excess 457
heifers vs. steers 454
hogs following cattle 457
margin in 447
market grades to select for 450
pasture 446
slotted floors 456
type, value of 451
leading markets 466
market classes and grades of 469

factors determining 469
quality grades 470
yield grades 470
markets, leading 466
market terms of cattle
baby beef 477
bologna bulls 477
butcher stock 477
fed cattle 476
grassers 476
native cattle 476
western cattle 476
origin 336
quotas 357
slaughtering and dressing 477
tariffs 358
type changes 272
westward expansion 343
world distribution 345
zoological classification of 338
Challenge feeding 560, 594
Characters, relative emphasis on each 71
Charbray cattle 366
Charolais cattle 366
Chemical analyses of feed 960
Chester White hogs 809
Cheviot sheep 651
Chevon (goat meat) 743
Chlorine, disinfectant 212
Chromosomes 35
number 36
Chicken
hen, eggs laid 33
Classes and grades of livestock........... 257
definition of 259
factors determining 259
use made of 258
Cleveland Bay horses 1126
Closebreeding 57
Clydesdale horses 1128
Cobalt 113, 428, 709
Colic in horses 146
Colleges 1234
Colostrum of
cattle 410
dairy cattle 582
horses 1177
Columbia sheep 653
Commercial feeds 142
Community auctions 238
Computers 327
Concentrates for
cattle 436
dairy cattle 551
per cent fed 20
sheep 714
swine 863
Concrete lots (paved lots) 181
Confinement, animal 174
feeding cattle 456
Connemara Pony 1126
Consumer, food $ 294
Contract feeding 458
Copper 109, 858
deficiencies 109
supplements 110
Corn Belt 25
cattle in 353
swine in 800
Corned beef 306
Corn-hog ratio 874
Correction factors, dairy 530-532
Corriedale sheep 653
Corrosive sublimate, disinfectant 211
Cotswold sheep 652
Cotton Belt 25
cattle in 354
Country selling 240

Page

Cow-and-calf system 392
Cows
  beef, feeding
    feeding at calving time 439
    feeding dry cows 438
    feeding pregnant cows 438
    feeding the lactating cow 440
  beef production 33
  breeding habits 399
    estrus signs 402
    gestation period 402
    heat periods 401
    heifer, age to breed 400
  dairy production 33
  pregnant
    afterbirth 410
    assistance 409
    calf, newborn 409
    calving time 407
    care of 406
    feeding 438
    parturition, signs of 407
    presentation of calf 408
    puberty, age of 399
Credit 320
  rating 321
  types 321
Creep feeding 138
  calves 441
  foals 1205
  lambs 719
  pigs 869
Cresols, disinfectant 211
Crippling, losses in marketing 247
Crooked calf disease 146
Crossbreeding 63
  sheep 697
  swine 843
Culture 216
Custom feeding 458
Cycles
  cyclical trends 261
  longtime trends 260
  seasonal changes 261
  short-time changes 262

Dairy cattle
  artificial insemination 537
  breeding 515
    daughter average 524
    daughter-dam 528
    delayed 518
    program 536
    records 523-528
    systems 535
  breed(s) 499
    Ayrshire 500
    Brown Swiss 500
    characteristics of 499
    Guernsey 500
    Holstein 500
    Jersey 500
    milk and butterfat production of 501
    popularity of 499
    type 510
  bulls, feeding of 569
  business aspects of 494
  calf scours 571
  calves 565-577
  calving time 564
  commercial feeds 553
  correction factors 530
    age of cow 531
    days milked 531
    fat-corrected milk 532
    times milked/day 531
  cows, selecting 534
  culling 508

Page

dairy beef 574
DHIA 569
DHIR 502
digestive system 540
diseases, reproductive 520, 521
dry cows 563
drying off cows 598
environment effect 528, 592
establishing herd 505
farms, kinds and sizes 492
feeding 539
  balanced rations 556
  bulls 569
  calving time 564
  challenge 560, 594
  dairy calves 565
  dry cows 563
  energy 543
  heifers 567
  lead 560
  minerals 545
  nutritive requirements 543
  pasture 563
  protein 545
  rations 557
  show and sale, for 564
  vitamins 546
  water 547
    facilities 576
feed(s)
  antibiotics 552
  commercial 553
  concentrates 551, 554, 560
  facilities 576
  green chop 550
  haylage 550
  irradiated yeast 553
  palatability 547
  pasture 550
  preparation 547
  propylene glycol 553
  rations 557
  roughage 548
    consumption of 550
  silage 549
  sodium propionate 553
  thyroprotein 552
  urea 551
future of 496
genetics 521
  heritability 522
gestation period 520
heat period 519, 520
heifers, growth of 568
herdmate-daughter 528
heritability 522
housing 575
infertility causes 520
judging 509
lactating ration 555
leading countries 490
leading states 491
magnitude of industry 490
management 575
mastitis 596
mature equivalent 592
milk fever 571
milk records 569
numbers 491
nutritive requirements 543, 544
parts of a cow 510
production of 489
  factors favorable 494
  factors unfavorable 495
  per cow 491
  testing 502
purebred business 507
rations 557

Page

recognition awards 503
records 523
    environmental affect 528
    milk 569
region of U.S..... 490
replacements 507, 534, 567, 577
    marketing 574
score card 510
selecting
    bases 533
    cows 534
    methods 533
    replacement heifers 534
    sires 534
sire(s)
    selection records 524
    selecting 534
sterility 518
stomach 541, 543
testing programs 569
type 361, 510
    classification 502
udder 582
water 547
world distribution 489
Dairy Herd Improvement Registry...................... 502
Dam, importance of.................. 49
Death losses
    birth to weaning.............................. 33
    in marketing 247
    prevention of 247
Debilitating 217
Debouillet sheep 651
Decentralization of meat packing............ 232
Devon cattle 366
Dexter cattle 367
Diagnostic agents 206
Digestible energy 100
Digestion 950
Digestive system 540
Direct marketing 240
Disease 194
    causes 195
        arthropods (insects and ticks)............ 198
        bacteria 195
        flukes 197
        helminths 197
        nutritional 143
        parasites 196
        protozoa 196
        roundworms 197
        tapeworms 197
        thorny-headed worms 198
        viruses 196
    control regulations 214
    definition of 194
    losses caused by 192
    nutritional 143
    prevention of 206
Disinfectants 210, 217
    alcohol 211
    bichloride of mercury.................... 211
    boric acid 211
    cationic bactericides 211
    chlorine 212
    cresols 211
    heat 212
    hypochlorites 212
    iodine 212
    iodofor 212
    lime 212
    lye 213
    phenolic germicides 213
    quicklime 212
    salsoda 213
    soap 213
    soda ash 213

Page

Disposable income
    food 294
    meat 294
Diversification by animals.................... 22
Dominant factors 40
Donkey 1129
    domestication 1084
    origin 1084
Dorset sheep 651
Draft horses 1101, 1118
Draft-type cattle 362
Dressing (see also Packer slaughtering),
  percentage of
    cattle 479
    hogs 896
    sheep 741
Driving horses 1114
Droving 226
Drugs 206
Dual-purpose cattle 362
    breeds 363
    production 395
    U.S.A., in 364
Ducks (see Poultry)
Duroc hogs 809
Duties, cattle 358
Dwarfs, in cattle.... 413

East Indian pig.... 793
Efficiency, animal 160
Egg(s) 1049
    composition 1049
    consumption 903, 1061
    contracts 1045
    embryonic development 1057
    fertilization 1055
    formation 1050
    grades 1067
    handling 1053
    hatchability 932
    incubation 1055
    intensity of lay.............................. 931
    marketing 1061
    nutrients in 904
    parts of 1049
    pricing 1070
    production 930
        breeding for 1027
        breeds 1035
        commercial 1033
        financing 1034
        goals 1036
        measuring 937
        size flock 1034
    quality 1051
    sex cell 36
    size 931
Emaciated 217
Energy
    calorie system 98
    digestible 100
    gross 100
    measuring of 97
    metabolizable 100
    needs for in 91
        cattle 425
        horses 1191
        sheep 707
        swine 854
    net 100
    TDN system 97
Environmental control 174
Environment, influence of..................52, 528
Enzootic 217
Equipment requisites for stock............ 175
Estate planning 331
Estrus, signs of in
    cows 402

Page

ewes 685
mares 1159
sows 828
European wild boar................................ 792
Ewes
    breeding habits
        age to breed.......................... 685
        gestation period 685
    heat periods 685
        puberty, age of........................ 684
    feeding 715
        flushing 715
        lactating 717
        lambing time 717
        pregnant 715
Excreta 217
Exports, meat 301-303
Exudate 217

Family names 51
Farm
    accounts 326
    assets 320
    debt 320
    herd 395
    number of 319
    records 326
    size 319
    worker productivity 8, 319-320
Farming regions
    Corn Belt 25
    Cotton Belt 25
    dairy 25
    western range 25
Farmstead, arrangement of 167
Fat-corrected milk 532, 578
Fats
    animal vs. vegetable...................... 95
    feed fats affect body fats.............. 94
    feeding, animal fats...................... 96
    melting point of............................ 94
    rancidity 94
    some fats desirable........................ 95
    unsaturation, degree of................ 94
Federal meat grades.............................. 280
Feed
    additives 130, 715, 869
    biological test 960
    chemical analysis 960
    concentrate, % 20
    cost 961
    efficiency 160
    functions 85
        finishing and show-ring fitting......... 86
        growth 85
        maintenance 85
        reproduction and lactation................. 86
        wool 87
        work or running...................... 87
    in transit 246
    preparation 139
        cooking 139
        cutting 139
        grinding 139
        pelleting 141
        rolling 139
        shredding 139
        slopping 139
        soaking 139
    roughage, % 20
    storage space requirements for.................. 1223
    weights and measures....................1216
Feeder-cattle markets 467
Feeder's margin 447
Feeding 83
    abrupt changes to be avoided.................. 136
    amount 135
    animal fats 95

Page

art of 134
balanced ration 88
beef cattle 423, 431
floors 181
frequency 136
hand-feeding vs. self-feeding 137
horses 1189
minerals 115
order of feeding.............................. 136
regularity 136
selection of feeds............................ 136
sheep 705
starting on feed.............................. 134
swine 851
Feeds
    commercial 142
    relative importance of principal feeds.......... 84
    storage space 1223
    terms 578
    weights and measures of................1216, 1222
Feeds, suggested rations for
    beef cattle 459
    dairy cattle 556
    horses 1210
    poultry 964, 970
    sheep 724
    swine 876
Fences 189
Fertility in
    beef cattle 402
    horses 1163
    sheep 685
    swine 829
Fertilization, dairy 518
Fiber in feeds.. 92
Fill in marketing animals..................... 251
Filterable virus 217
Fine harness horses................................ 1115
Finishing
    cattle 394, 442
    sheep 718
    swine 870
Fitting, suggested rations for
    beef cattle 459
    horses 1210
    sheep 727
    swine 883
Fleece characteristics 754
Floors
    slotted 179
    stalls, types 178
Flukes 197
Fluorine poisoning (fluorosis)............ 146
Flushing of
    ewes 686
    swine 830, 872
Foals
    crop, % 33
    death losses 33
    feeding before weaning.................. 1205
    newborn, handling of..................... 1174
    orphan 1179
    weaning age 33
    weaning weight 33
Food
    disposable income for..................... 294
    dollar 294
    efficiency 160
Founder 146
Freemartins 412
Freezing meat 306
French Alpine goat.................................. 788
Fungi 217
Futures trading 329

Gaits of horses 1146
Galiceno horses 1126
Galloway cattle 367

Page

Garbage for swine 868
Geese (see Poultry)
Genes 35, 44
Genetics, principles of................................. 31
Germ cells 36
Gestation, period of in
    beef cattle 402
    dairy cattle 520
    horses 1159
    sheep 685
    swine 829, 873
Gestation table 1225
Gilts (see also Sows)
    feeding 871
Goats
    adaptation 780
    Angora 779
    breeds 787
    characteristics 781
    chevon (goat meat)................................. 786
    distribution 780
    domestication 623
    feeding 787
    kidding 784
    leading states in..................................... 780
    management of 783
    meat 786
    milk 787
    mohair 786
    origin 623
    registration of 782
Goiter (iodine deficiency) 146
Grade
    quality 259
    yield 259
Grades, market
    of cattle 469
    of hogs 888, 891
    of sheep 733
Grades, meat 281
Grading up 61
    Sni-A-Bar experiment 62
Gram
    negative bacteria 217
    positive bacteria 217
Grassers 476
Grass tetany (staggers)................................. 146
Green chop 550
Gross energy 100
Growth 85
Guernsey cattle 500

Hackney horses 1126
Hampshire hogs 809
Hampshire sheep 651
Hand-feeding 137
Harness racehorses 1112
Hay, equivalent 578
Hay for
    cattle 433
    horses 1198
    sheep 712
Haylage 550
Health
    certificates 246
    signs of 192
Health-control officials 257
Heat, a disinfectant.. 212
Heat, periods of
    beef cattle 401
    dairy cattle 519, 520
    horses 1158
    sheep 685
    swine 828
Heat tolerance, evaluating............................. 28
Heaves 146
Heavy harness horses.......................................1114
Heifers vs. steers... 454

Page

Helminths (worm parasites)............................ 197
Heredity and environment.............................. 52
Heredity, fundamentals of.............................. 35
Hereford cattle 367
Hereford hogs 809
Hermaphrodites 413
Heterozygosity 41
Hides 311
Hinny 1185
Hog
    breeds
        American Landrace 809
        Beltsville No. 1................................... 809
        Berkshire 809
        Chester White 809
        CPF No. 1 809
        CPF No. 2 809
        Duroc 809
        Hampshire 809
        Hereford 809
        Kentucky Red Berkshire.................... 810
        Lacombe 810
        Maryland No. 1................................... 810
        Minnesota No. 1.................................. 810
        Minnesota No. 2.................................. 810
        Minnesota No. 3.................................. 810
        Montana No. 1.................................... 810
        OIC 810
        Palouse 810
        Poland China 810
        Spotted 810
        Tamworth 811
        Wessex Saddleback 811
        Yorkshire 811
    carcass
        cuts of 897
        disposition of 897
    classes, market 888
    dressing percentage 896
    grades, market 888, 891
    lard
        kinds of 898
        substitutes for 899
    markets, leading 888
    market terms and factors...................... 891
    packer slaughtering and dressing........... 893
    packer vs. shipper dressing.................... 895
    roaster 893
Hogging down crops... 867
Hogs following cattle.. 457
Holidays, Jewish 263
Holstein dairy cattle.. 500
Hom ·gosity 50
Hormones 132
Horse
    action in 1145
        defects in 1148
    age, determination of.............................1150
    artificial insemination of.............74, 1183, 1184
    blemishes 1150
    breeding 1158
        artificial insemination, registration.......1183
        barrenness 1161
        breeding after foaling.......................1160
        breeding season and time of foaling....1180
        conditioning the mare.......................1163
        estrus, signs of...................................1159
        fertility in stallion...........................1163
        fertilization in 1159
        foal 1174
        foaling 1170
        foaling percentage 1160
        gestation period 1159
        heat period 1158
        hybrids 1185
        lethals 1186
        mare, examination of.......................1164
        mares, age to breed...........................1158

Page

mating, corral 1163
mating, hand 1163
mating, pasture 1163
performance testing 1187
pregnancy, signs and test of.................1164
pregnant mare, care of.....................1169
puberty, age of.................................1158
stallion, age and service of........ 1168
stallion, care and management of........1165
stallion enrollment laws.....................1183
sterility 1161
breeds
  draft
    American Cream Horse.................1128
    Belgian 1128
    Clydesdale 1128
    Percheron 1128
    relative popularity of.................1123
    Shire 1128
    Suffolk 1128
  light
    American Albino Horse.................1125
    American Buckskin 1125
    American Gotland 1125
    American Paint Horse.................1125
    American Paso Fino.................1125
    American Saddle Horse.................1125
    Appaloosa 1125
    Arabian 1125
    Cleveland Bay 1126
    Connemara Pony 1126
    Galiceno 1126
    Hackney 1126
    Hungarian Horse 1126
    Lipizzan 1098
    Missouri Fox Trotting.................1126
    Morgan 1126
    Palomino 1126
    Peruvian Paso 1126
    Pinto 1127
    Pony of the Americas.................1127
    Quarter Horse 1127
    relative popularity of.................1123
    Shetland Pony 1127
    Spanish Mustang 1127
    Standardbred 1127
    Tennessee Walking Horse.........1127
    Thoroughbred 1127
    Welsh Pony 1128
buying or raising foals.................1181
cost of raising; how to lower.................1180
cow pony 1096
domestication of 1081
donkeys 1129
evolution of 1077
feeding
  antibiotics 131
  brood mare 1203
  energy needs 1191
  feeds 1197
    allowances 1201
    commercial 1199
    pelleting 1200
    preparation 1197, 1199
  fitting for shows.................................1207
  hay for 1198
  market feeding 1207
  mineral needs 100, 1192
  pastures for 1197
  protein needs 1191
  racehorses 1208
  rate of 1201
  rations, suggested 1210
  show horses 1208
  stallion 1204
  two- and three-year-old.................1207
  vitamin E 1195

Page

  vitamin needs 1194
  water needs 1196
  weanling 1206
  yearling 1207
  young horse, feeding of.................1205
fitting 1207
foals 1174, 1205
  orphan foal 1179
future of industry in U.S.A.................1099
gaits 1146
growth and decline of industry.................1089
history
  domestication 1081
  evolution 1077
  industry, growth and decline of........1089
  introduction to U.S.A.................1087
  origin 1081
  production in U.S.A.................1089
  Przewalsky's horse 1080
  world distribution 1092
  zoological classification of.................1085
judging 1141
  method of examining 1154
  parts of horse.................................1142
  type and breed characteristics.................1142
mares (see Mares)
measuring 1152
  bone 1152
  girth 1152
  height 1152
  weight 1152
moon blindness 150
navel infection 1176
origin 1081
population
  U. S. 1093
  world 1094
racing attendance and revenue.................1099
recreation and sport.................................1099
riding 1103
selection bases
  individuality 1140
  pedigree **1140**
  Performance Testing 1141
  show-ring winnings 1141
stallion (see also Stallion).................1163
teeth 1150
types and classes
  draft 1118
  light 1101
    driving horses 1114
      fine harness 1115
      heavy harness 1114
      ponies 1117
      roadsters 1116
    racing horses 1109
      harness race 1112
      quarter race 1113
      running race 1110
    riding horses 1103
      five-gaited 1103
      hunters and jumpers.................1108
      plantation walking horses....1105
      polo mounts 1107
      ponies 1109
      stock horses 1106
      three-gaited 1103
unsoundnesses 1150
uses 1086
weanling 1206
world distribution 1092
yearling 1207
zoological classification of.................................1085
Hothouse lambs 696, 736
Housing of animals, purposes and requisites........169
Humane slaughter 478, 740, 894
Hungarian Horse 1126

	Page
Hunters	1108
Hybrids	1185
Hydroponics	552
Hypersensitivity	217
Hypoglycemia	148
Immunity	202
Imports	
animal	304
meat	301-303
tariff duties, cattle	358
Inbreds	56
Inbreeding	56
Incentive bases	323-326
Incentives, indirect	325
Incomplete dominance	44
Indemnity payments	216
Index, selection	73
Individual Merit Testing	
(see also Performance Testing)	66
Indu Brazil (Zebu)	368
Infertility causes	520
Ingestion	217
Inheritance (estate planning)	331
Inheritance	
multiple gene	44
simple gene	39
Insects (arthropods)	198
losses	192
Insemination, artificial	74
advantages of	75
limitations of	76
practical considerations of	78
Inspection	
ante-mortem	254
brands	257
meat	215
post-mortem	254
stockyards	215
Intradermal	217
Intramuscular	217
Intraperitoneal	217
Intrauterine	217
In vitro	217
In vivo	217
Iodine	111
deficiencies	112, 148
disinfectant	212
supplements	113
Iron	109, 858
deficiencies	109
supplements	110
Jersey cattle	500
Jewish holidays	263
Job description	323
Joint-ill	1176
Judging	
cattle	385
dairy cattle	509
horses	1141
sheep	661, 668
swine	817, 821
Karakul sheep	653
Kentucky Red Berkshire hogs	810
Ketosis (acetonemia)	148
Kidding, goats	784
Kidney stones	154
Kosher meats	286
Kosher slaughter	479
Labor requirements, animal	27
Lacombe hogs	810
Lactation and reproduction	86

	Page
Lamb	
consumption of	640
crop, %	33
death losses	33
feeding	694, 719
areas	720
creep	719
dry-lot	722
field finishing	720
finishing considerations	723
types of	720
imports of	641
raising methods	
Easter	696
grass	697
hothouse	696
spring	696
weaning age	33
weaning weight	33
Landrace hogs	809
Land use and ownership	9, 12
Lard	802, 898
kinds of	898
substitutes	899
Leicester sheep	652
Leptospirosis	521
Lethals	47
cattle, in	413
genetic abnormalities	47
horses, in	1186
sheep, in	699
swine, in	845
Liability	332
Light horses	1101
Lime	212
Lincoln sheep	652
Line breeding	58
Lipizzan horses	1098
Livestock	
budgets in	327
building requisites	169
business, credit in	320
computers in	327
Conservation, Inc.	264
enterprise	
factors in establishing	23
kind and adaptation of livestock	26
leading livestock states	24
quality of livestock	27
requisites of a stockman	26
systems of farming	23
equipment requisites	175
industry	
cash income from	11
land area devoted to	9
magnitude of	9
number and value of animals	14
number of farms and ranches	9
pasture and grazing land devoted to	11
size of packing industry	15
transformation in	4
losses	192
marketing	
methods	232
prices determined by	260
Local (community) auctions	238
Losses, livestock	192
Lye, disinfectant	213
Magazines, breed	1231
Maintenance requirements of animals	85
Manager	322
check list	323
traits of	322
Manganese deficiency	146, 148
Manure	
disposal of	171, 208

Page

feeding of 1047
handling 187
value of 21
Mares
  age to breed..............................1158
  breeding after foaling...............1160
  breeding habits 1158
  breeding operations 1163
  breeding season and time of foaling.....1180
  colostrum of 1177
  conditioning for breeding..........1163
  feeding 1203
  fertilization 1159
  foaling percentage 1160
  foaling time care...................1170
  gestation period 1159
  heat periods 1158
  pregnancy, signs and tests of........1164
  pregnant, care of..................1169
  puberty, age of.......................1158
  quarters for 1169
  sterility or barrenness............1161
Market (see also Central markets)
  basket 294
  calf, leading 467
  cattle, leading 466
  central 233
  channels, % 233
  classes and grades
    cattle 469
    definition of 259
    development of 257
    factors determining 259
    hogs 888
    sheep 733
    use of 258
  development of 257
  feeder cattle, leading............467
  feeder sheep, leading............732
  hog, leading 888
  prices, factors influencing............260
  sheep, leading 732
Marketing 221
  direct 240
  future of 263
  methods of livestock 232, 245
    auctions, community 238
    auctions, purebred 243
    carcass grade and weight selling.....241
    country selling 240
    direct marketing 240
    importance of 222
    terminal 233
  prices determined by...........260
  supply and demand..............260
Marketing wool 767
Market news service, kinds............252
  commission company information............253
Maryland No. 1 hogs.....................810
Mating methods in
  cattle 403
  horses 1163
  sheep 687
  swine 830
McLean County system of swine sanitation.......837
Measures of feeds 1216
Meat
  consumption per capita............298-300
  cookery methods 307
  exports 301, 303
  freezing 306
  grades 281
  grading
    American Meat Institute system............284
    federal grades 280
    federal grading 278
    need for 276

Page

  packer brand names....................285
historical record 270
imports 302, 303
inspection 215
  ante-mortem 254
  federal 253
  post-mortem 254
  state 256
kosher 286
markets, number of....................273
nutritive qualities 287
origin of names....279....................271
packing
  decentralization of 232
  development of 227
  efficiency 229
  eras in 228
  geography of consumption........230
  geography of production........230
  modern packing 228
  national packers 231
  number of establishments........229
  services of packers............229
preservation 305
prices, determined by............260
promotion 315
qualities desired 274
salting 306
sausage 306
smoking 306
U.S.A. production 297
world production 297
Meat Certification program............821
Medicines from animals...............310
Mendel, Gregor Johann...............34
Mendelism 35
Merino sheep 651
Metabolic 217
Metabolism 217, 950
Metabolizable energy 100
Metric system 1216
Mexico, beef production in............350
Microorganism 217
Milk
  All-Jersey 611
  certified 611
  composition 581, 590, 592
  consumption/capita 606
  exports 615
  Federal milk marketing orders............607
  flavor 573, 597
  goats 787
  Golden Guernsey 611
  handling 589, 602
  importance of 488
  imports 615
  leading states 491
  manufactured milk products............612
  manufacturing plants 612
  marketing 601
    channels 606
    cooperatives 608
    Federal orders 607
    grades 609
    importance 601
    sanitary regulations 608
    state
      control 607
      trade laws 609
  outlook 616
  pesticide residues 572
  pricing of 607, 609
    support program 611
  processing firms 612
  quality 589, 602
  records 523, 569
  regulatory programs 608

	Page
sanitary regulations	608
secretion	581, 584
selling	602
solid-not-fat	610
testing programs	569
DHIA	569
owner-sampler records	569
wadam	570
uses of	488, 603, 606, 613
Milk fever	148, 571
Milking	586
ejection of	586
equipment	589
holdup of	586
letdown of	586
managed	586
prepartum	596
Milking Shorthorn cattle	370
Minerals	
bone meal	107
calcium	103
cobalt	113
commercial	115
complex mixtures	115
copper	109
essential	101
function of	101
iodine	111
iron	109
limestone	107
methods of feeding	115
mixtures	115
needs for, in	100
cattle	101, 426
horses	101, 1192
sheep	101, 708
swine	101, 855
oyster-shell flour	107
phosphorus	103
salt	102
trace	114
Minnesota No. 1 hogs	810
Minnesota No. 2 hogs	810
Minnesota No. 3 hogs	810
Missouri Fox Trotting horse	1126
Mohair	
characteristics of	772
classes of	773
grades of	773
handling of	773
marketing of	773
production of	773
U.S.A. consumption	771
U.S.A. production	771
uses for	775
world production	770
Molybdenum	111
toxicity	148, 429
Montadale sheep	652
Montana No. 1 hogs	810
Moon blindness (periodic ophthalmia)	150
Morbidity	217
Morgan horses	1126
Mortality	217
Moufflon sheep	621
Mules	
feeding (see Horse feeding)	
growth and decline	1089
introduction in U.S.A.	1087
production in U.S.A.	1089
types and classes of	1118
Mutations	38
Names, family	51
Narrow-spectrum antibiotic	217
National Livestock and Meat Board	264
National Wool Act	775
Native cattle	476
	Page
Navel-ill	1176
Necrosis	218
Net energy	100, 578
New York Mills Auction of 1873	52
New Zealand, sheep raising in	635
Nicking	50
Night blindness	154
Nitrate (nitrite) poisoning	150, 572
Nitrogen free extract	92
Nubian goat	788
Nutrition, future research in	143
Nutritional anemia	144
Nutritional diseases and ailments	143, 144-157
Nutritive needs of	
beef cattle	424
dairy cattle	543, 544
horses	1190
poultry	955
sheep	706
swine	852
Oat hay poisoning	150
OIC hogs	810
Oleomargarine	311
Oral	218
Organization chart	323, 324
Orphan	
foals	1179
lambs	694
pigs	836
Osteomalacia	150
Outcrossing	60
Overeating disease	723
Oxford sheep	652
Packer brand names	285
Packer slaughtering and dressing	
cattle	477
dressing percentage	479
kosher	479
steps in	478
veal calves differ	479
hogs	893
dressing percentage	896
packer vs. shipper style	895
steps in	894
sheep	739
dressing percentage	741
steps in	740
Packers and Stockyards Act	256
Packing (see Meat packing)	
Packing house by-products	308
Paint horses	189
Palomino horses	1126
Palouse hogs	810
Panama sheep	653
Parakeratosis	152, 859
Parasites	196
losses	192
Partial dominance	44
Partnerships	331
Pasture rotation	209
Pasturing of	
cattle	432
horses	1197
sheep	711
swine	864
Pathogenic	218
Pathological	218
Paved lots (concrete)	181
Pelleting feeds	141
Percheron horses	1128
Performance Testing	66
Periodic ophthalmia	152
Perosis	114
Persian lamb fur	649
Pesticide residues	572
Phosphorus	103, 427, 709, 856

Page

calcium-phosphorus ratio 105
deficiencies 106
defluorinated phosphates 107
supplements 107
vitamin D relationship............... 105
Physiology of reproduction.............. 516
Pig crop, % 33
Pigs
death losses 33
weaning age 33
weaning weight 33
Pine needle abortion............... 152
Pinto horses 1127
Plantation walking horses...........1105
Plants, poisonous 198
Poisoning
fluorine 146
plants 199
selenium (alkali disease)........... 154
Poland China hogs............... 810
Polled character 41
Polled Hereford cattle............... 368
Polled Shorthorn cattle............... 368
Polo mounts 1107
Ponies 1109
Connemara 1126
driving 1117
Pony of the Americas..............1127
riding 1109
Shetland 1127
Welsh 1128
Population trends
animal 5
human 5
farm 8
non-farm 8
Pork (see also Swine)
soft 875
Post-mortem inspection 218, 254
Poultry 90
anatomy 948
breeders, foundation 927, 973
breeding
changes in 906
chickens 1026
hatching eggs 1029
inheritance of characters............ 928
mating methods 1029
multiple unit test................ 927
random sampling test............ 927
systems of 923
tests 1028
turkeys 1036
breeds 919, 922
broilers
breeding for 1027
contracts 1032, 1044
equipment 996
feeding 976
financing 1032
grower returns 1071
houses 996, 1032
management 1033
pricing 1070
production 938, 1030
brooder
equipment 994
houses 994
business aspects 926, 1025, 1043
cages 990
cannibalism 1014
capons 976
carcass disposal 1008
chickens, breeding 1026
classes 919, 1066
consumption/capita 903, 1061
contracts 1044

Page

culling 938
digestive tract 949
diseases 1003, 1009
distribution
U.S.A. 912
world 911
domestication 901
ducks 944, 981
equipment 999
houses 999
production 1040
equipment 985
ducks 999
geese 999
layers 992
requisites of 988
space requirements 1000
turkeys 997
exports 1073
feeding 947
breeders 973, 975
broilers 976
ducks 981
geese 981
layers 973, 975
phase 973
rations 964-967, 970
formulation of 967
replacement chicks 970
systems 969
feed(s) 962, 965
amino acids 968
amount required 971
antibiotics 963
antioxidants 964
arsenicals 963
carbohydrates 952
digestion of 948
drugs 964
fats 952
functions of 948
grit 964
minerals 953
nitrofurans 963
nutrients 951
palatability 956
preparation 969
proteins 952
vitamins 954
water 952
game birds 945, 1042
geese 944, 981
equipment 999
houses 999
production 1041
guinea fowl 945
hatcheries 1042
changes in 907
eggs 1055
hatchery men 927
health 1003
houses 985
brooder 994
care of 993
ducks 999
geese 999
layer 989
lighting 988
replacement pullet 995
requisites of 986
space requirements 1000
temperature 986
turkeys 997
ventilation 987
importance of industry 902
imports 1073
industry 905
future of 915

Page

present status 911
inspection, federal 1067
layers 973
    houses 989
    management 1035
losses 1005
manure 988, 999, 1046
marketing 1061
    changes 1062
    channels 1069
    classes 1065
    foreign trade 1073
    grades 1065
    inspection 1067
    pricing 1070
mating, methods of 933
meat, composition of 904
metabolism 950
multiple unit test 927
National Poultry Improvement Plan 938
nutrients 951
    requirements 955
ornamental birds 945, 1042
parasites 1003
phase feeding layers 973
pigeons 945
products 1065
processing firms 1071
random sampling test 927
rations 964, 972
records 1047
replacement chicks 970, 972
    equipment 995
    growing of 1029
    houses 995
    management 1030
roasters 976
selection methods 935
sex-linked cross 924
species, importance 914, 915
trap-nest 937
turkeys
    artificial insemination 1037
    breeding 940, 1036
        systems 1037
    breeds 940
    changes in 909
    contracts 1039, 1045
    equipment 997
    facilities 1038
    feeding 978
        amino acids 968
    feeds required 979
    houses 997
    management 1038
    market production 1039
    National Turkey Improvement Plan .. 938
    nutritive requirements 967
    poults 1040
    pricing 1070
    production 1036
    rations 970, 980
    selection 1037
    types 919
    vaccination 1006
    varieties 920
Pregnancy disease in sheep 152
Pregnancy signs and tests in
    beef cattle 403
    horses 1164
Preparation of feeds
    cooking 139
    cutting 139
    grinding 139
    pelleting 141
    rolling 139
    shredding 139
    slopping 139
    soaking 139

Page

Prepotency 50
Price, determination of market 260
Production per animal 33
Production Registry 821, 849
Production Testing 66
    cattle 416
    dairy 502
    Danish system 69
    horses 1187
    sheep 699
    swine 845
Prophylaxis 218
Promotional and research organizations 264
Protein
    digestible 579
    need of
        cattle 424
        general 88
        horses 1191
        sheep 706
        swine 852
    quality 89
    rumen synthesis 90
    sources 91
Protozoa 196, 218
Przewalsky's horse 1080
Puberty, age of in
    cattle 399
    horses 1158
    sheep 684
    swine 828
Pulse rate, normal 193
Purebred auctions 243
Purebreds 392
Purebreeding 55

Qualitative traits 39
Quality grade 259
Quantitative traits 44
Quarantine 214
Quarter Horse 1127
Quarter racehorses 1113
Quicklime, disinfectant 212

Racehorses 1109
Racing
    attendance and revenue.................1099
    magnitude of 1110
    Thoroughbred 1112
Rail transportation 226
    number of animals per car..................... 250
    refrigerator car 225
Ram
    age and service of 689
    care of 689
    feeding of 718
    management of 689
    mating preparation of..................... 687
Rambouillet sheep 651
Ranch headquarters, location of..................... 166
Range (see Western range)
Range cattle method 396
Range sheep states 637, 679
Ration(s)
    balanced 88
    definition 424
    essentials of 88
    suggestions for
        beef cattle 459
        dairy cattle 557
        horses 1210
    how to balance....................556, 967
    poultry 964, 972
    sheep 724
    swine 876
Recessive factors 40
Records, farm 326
Red Angus cattle 43, 369
Red Brangus cattle 369

Page

Red Poll cattle 370
Refractive index 94
Refrigerator car 225
Registry associations 1226
Reproduction
    physiology of 516
    statistics 33
Reproduction and lactation 86
Reproductive
    diseases 520, 521
    organs 517
Research 28
    organizations 264
        American Meat Institute 264
        National Livestock and Meat Board .. 264
Rickets 152
Rigor mortis 218
Roadster 1116
Roaster pig 893
Roofs for barns, types of 178
Roots for
    cattle 434
    sheep 713
Romney sheep 653
Roughages
    bacterial action in rumen 90, 92
    for
        cattle 433
        horses 1198
        sheep 712
        swine 866
    per cent fed 20
    preparation of 139
Roundworms 197
Rumen
    bacterial action in 92
    synthesis 90
Ruminant stomach 541
Running racehorses 1110

Saanen goat 788
Salt 102, 426, 708, 855
    deficiency 102, 152
    feeding precautions 103
    iodized 113
    poisoning 103, 152
    sick 152
Sanitation and disease prevention 206
Santa Gertrudis cattle 369
Sausage 306
Scales 188
Score card, dairy 510
Scotch Highland 369
Secondary invaders 218
Selection of 64
    bases for 64
        individuality 65
        pedigree 65
        Production Testing 66
        show-ring winnings 65
        type 65
    cattle 382
    horses 1140
    sheep 665
    swine 820
    systems of 72
        minimum culling levels 73
        selection index 73
        tandem selection 72
Selenium poisoning (alkali disease) 154
Self-feeding 137
Self-feeding salt-feed mixtures 437
Selling
    country 240
    grade and weight 241
Serum, blood 218
Serums 205

Page

Service passages, width 177
Sex control 537
Sex determination 46
Sex development, abnormal, in cattle 412
Sex-linked cross 924
Sheep (see also Wool)
    Asiatic Urial 622
    break-joint 740
    breeding 683
        crossbreeding 697
        ewes, age to breed 685
        fertility and prolificacy in 685
        flushing 686
        gestation period 685
        heat periods 685
        hormonal control 703
        lambing 691
        lethals 699
        mating, preparation of ewes for 687
        mating, preparation of rams for 687
        pregnant ewe, care of 690
        Production Testing 699
        puberty, age of 684
        ram, age and service of 689
        ram, care and management of 689
        systems of lamb raising 695
    breeds 645
        American Merino 651
        Black-faced Highland 653
        Cheviot 651
        Columbia 653
        Corriedale 653
        Cotswold 652
        Debouillet 651
        Delaine Merino 651
        Dorset 651
        Hampshire 651
        Karakul 653
            fur wools 648
                broadtail 649
                caracul 649
                Persian lamb 649
        Leicester 652
        Lincoln 652
        Montadale 652
        North Country Cheviot 652
        Oxford 652
        Panama 653
        Rambouillet 651
        Romney 653
        Shropshire 652
        Southdown 652
        Suffolk 652
        Tailless 653
        Targhee 653
        Tunis 652
    domestication of 620
    dressing percentage of 741
    feeding 705
        additives 715
        antibiotics 131
        concentrates for 714
        energy needs 707
        ewes, feeding of 715
        hay and roughage for 712
        lamb feeding 719
        mineral needs 91, 708
        pastures for 711
        protein needs 706
        ram feeding 718
        ration, suggested 724
        roots for 713
        silage for 713
        urea 707
        vitamin needs 709
        water needs 711
    fleece characteristics 754
    flock establishing, factors to consider 661

Page

history
Asiatic Urial 622
Bakewell's improvement of 626
domestication of 620
England, in 626
importation in U.S.A. 626
improvement in U.S.A. 626
Moufflon 621
origin of 620
Spain, in 625
westward movement 628
world distribution 630
zoological classification of 623
industry
Australia, in 633
future of American 640
growth and decline in U.S.A. 629
New Zealand, in 635
production areas in U.S.A. 637
South Africa, in 636
South America, in 635
U.S.A., in 636
judging 668
age determination 672
catching 672
fleece, type and conformation 670
handling 672
method of examining 670
mutton, type and conformation 668
parts of a sheep 668
lamb raising systems 695
Easter 696
grass 697
hothouse 696, 736
spring 696
lambs, disowned 693
lambs, orphan 694
marketing and slaughtering
aging lamb and mutton 742
classes 733
cuts of lamb and mutton 743
disposition of carcasses 742
dressing percentage 741
feeder sheep 732
grades 733
quality 734
yield 734
market terms 737
markets, leading sheep 732
packer slaughtering 739
Moufflon 621
origin of 620
pelts 312
production
areas
farm flock sheep states 638
range sheep states 637
factors favorable to 640
factors unfavorable to 640
per ewe 33
states, leading 639
systems
farm flock 677
lamb feeding 680
purebred flock 678
range-band 679
ram (see also Ram)
age and service of 689
care and management of 689
selection bases for flock 665
flock improvement by selection 667
individuality 666
pedigree 666
Production Testing 667
show-ring winnings 667
type 666
shearing (see also Wool) 757
Soay sheep 622

Page

tagging 687
westward movement 628
world distribution 630
zoological classification of 623
Shetland Pony 1127
Shipping livestock, preparation for 244
Shire horses 1128
Shorthorn cattle 369
Bates boom 52
color inheritance 39
New York Mills Auction of 1873 52
Shrinkage in marketing animals, effects of 250
age 251
fill 251
rail transportation 251
season 251
time of transit 251
truck transportation 251
weight 251
Shropshire sheep 652
Silage for
cattle 434
sheep 713
swine 866
Silos
carbon dioxide danger 184
types 182
Sire, importance of 49
Slaughter
by-products 308
Slaughtering
cattle 477
hogs 894
humane 478, 740, 894
sheep and lambs 740
Slotted floors 179
cattle 456
Sni-A-Bar Farms, grading up work 61
Soap, disinfectant 213
Soay sheep 622
Soda ash 213
Sodium chloride (salt) 102
Soils, good, essential for livestock 132
South Africa, sheep raising in 636
South America
beef production in 346
sheep raising in 635
Southdown sheep 652
Sow
farrowing time, care of 834
feeding 872
flushing 830
gilts vs. older sows 843
litter, care of 837
pregnant, care of 833
two litters vs. one litter yearly 841
Space requirements for
bedding 1223
feed 1223
Spain, sheep raising in 625
Sperm 36
Sports 38
Spotted hogs 810
Sprouted grain 552
Staggers (grass tetany) 146
Stallion
age and service of 1168
care of 1165
enrollment laws 1183
exercise for 1166
feeding 1166, 1204
grooming of 1168
management of 1165
quarters for 1165
Stalls, floor types 178
Standardbred horse 1127
State colleges 1234
State veterinarians 214

	Page
Steers vs. heifers	454
Steer, weights estimating	1224
Sterility, dairy	518
Stiff lamb (white muscle) disease	154
Stocker and feeder cattle	
feeding	442
growing	393
production	393
Stock horses	1106
Stockman, requisites for	26
Stockyard inspection	215
Stones (urinary calculi)	154
Storage space requirements	178, 1223
Subcutaneous	218
Suffolk horses	1128
Suffolk sheep	652
Sulfa drug	218
Supportive treatment	218
Sweet clover disease	154
Swine	
bacon-type	817
boar (see also Boars)	
age and service of	833
care and management of	831
clipping tusks	832
feeding	831
ranting	832
breeding and management	828
breeding after farrowing	829
breeding season and time of	
farrowing	840
castration	840
crossbreeding	843
ear-notching	838
farrowing	834
fertility and prolificacy in	829
flushing	830
gestation period	829
gilts, age to breed	828
gilts vs. older sows	843
heat periods	828
lethals	845
mating, hand	830
McLean County system	837
needle teeth removal	837
pregnant sow, care of	833
Production Testing	845
puberty, age of	828
two litters vs. one litter per year	841
breeding crate	830
breeds (see also Hog breeds)	805
corn-hog ratio	874
domestication of	791
ear-notching	838
East Indian pig	793
European wild boar	792
farrowing, multiple	842
farrowing time	834, 874
feeding	851
antibiotics	131
breeding gilts	871
brood sow	872
concentrates for	863
creep	869
energy needs	854
farrowing time	874
fitting rations	883
garbage for	868
gestation period	873
growing-finishing pigs	870
herd boar	872
hogging down crops	867
lactating sows	874
mineral needs	100, 855
pastures for	864
protein needs	852
rations suggested	876
roughages, dry for	866
silage	866
vitamin needs	861
water needs	862
future of industry in U.S.A.	802
growth of industry	796
guard rail	835
herd establishing	817
crossbreds	818
grades	818
purebreds	818
selection of breed	819
history	
American breeds	795
domestication	791
East Indian pig	793
European wild boar	792
industry, growth in U.S.A.	796
introduction to America	794
origin of	791
production in U.S.A.	799
world distribution	797
zoological classification of	794
improvement	821
judging	821
conformation	822
hog parts	822
method of examining	824
type	822
lard	802, 898
lard type	806
leading states	800
lethals	845
marketing (see Hog markets, leading)	
McLean County system	837
meat type	808
needle teeth	837
origin of	791
orphan pigs	836
pork, soft	875
production	
areas in U.S.A.	800
factors favorable to	800
factors unfavorable to	802
Production Testing	845
prolificacy	829
quarters	835
selection bases	
individuality	820
Meat Certification	821, 849
pedigree	820
Production Registry	821, 849
Production Testing	845
show-ring winnings	820
type	820
sow	
farrowing	834
pregnant	833
production of	33
types of	806, 817
world distribution	797
zoological classification of	794
Swiss Alpine goat	788
Synthetic fibers	640
Tagging ewes	687
Tailless (no-tail) sheep	653
Tamworth hogs	811
Tandem selection	72
Tapeworms	197
Targhee sheep	653
Tariff duties, cattle	358
Tax	
management	330
reporting	330
TDN system	97, 579
computation of	98
Temperature, animal	1222
normal	193

Page

Tennessee Walking Horse 1127
Terminal markets 233
Tetany (grass staggers) 146
Therapy 218
Therm 579
Thorny-headed worms 198
Thoroughbred horse 1127
Thyroprotein 552, 596
Ticks (arthropods) 198
Toggenburg goat 788
Toxemia 218
Toxoids (anatoxins) 205
Trace minerals 114
Tractors, number of 1091
Trading futures 329
Trailing (droving) 226
Transportation 225
    rail 226
    trailing (droving) 225
    truck 227
    water 225
Transporting livestock, preparation for 244
Trichomoniasis 521
Trucks 1091
Truck transportation 227
    number of animals in truck 250
Tunis sheep 652
Turkeys (see Poultry)
Twenty-eight hour law 246, 256

Udder 582
Urinary calculi (stones) 154
Urea 551

Vaccination 202
Vaccines 204
Veal carcass 483
    cuts of 483
Ventilation of buildings 171, 207
Veterinarians, state 214
Vibriosis 521
Viruses 196, 218
Vitamins
    chart for animals 119
    need of for 116
        cattle 429
        horses 1194
        sheep 709
        swine 861
    vitamin A 122, 861
    vitamin A deficiency 154
    vitamin B 119, 126, 861
    vitamin B_{12} 121
    vitamin C 119, 126
    vitamin D 119, 124, 861
    vitamin E 119, 125
    vitamin K 119, 125

Water 129
    belly 154
    functions 130
    need of 130
        cattle 431
        horses 1196

Page

    poultry 952
    sheep 711
    swine 862
Weaning
    age 33
    weight 33
Weights
    estimating steer 1224
    feeds, of 1216
Welsh Pony 1128
Wessex Saddleback hogs 811
Western cattle 476
Western range 25
    cattle in 352
    sheep in 637
White muscle (stiff lamb) disease 156
Wool
    carpet 761
    chemical composition 754
    classes 760
    clothing 761
    combing 760
    consumption, per capita 641
    duty on 768
    fiber 753
    fleece, characteristics 754, 770
    French combing 761
    grades 763
    grading 762
    grease 755
    handling of clip 756
    imports 641
    industry, U.S. wool and textile 750
    leading countries 633
    manufacturing process 769
    marketing 767
    National Wool Act 775
    natural clothing of sheep 748
    nutritive requirements 87
    production 756
        U.S.A. 750
        world 632
    requisites of 760
    shearing 757
    shrinkage 755, 760
    synthetics 641
    uses of 750
    virtues of 749
    worsted spinning count 766
Work, feeding for 87
World distribution of
    beef cattle 345
    dairy cattle 489
    horses 1092
    poultry 911
    sheep 630
    swine 797
    wool 632
Worm parasites (helminths).................. 197

Xerophthalmia 154

Yield grade 259
Yorkshire hogs 811